STATISTICAL ANALYSIS FOR BUSINESS AND ECONOMICS

STATISTICAL ANALYSIS FOR BUSINESS AND ECONOMICS

Ya-lun Chou

St. John's University
New York, New York

UCT Library

Elsevier
New York · Amsterdam · London

Elsevier Science Publishing Co., Inc.
655 Avenue of the Americas, New York, New York 10010

Sole distributors outside the United States and Canada:
Elsevier Science Publishers, B.V.
P.O. Box 211, 1000 AE Amsterdam, the Netherlands

Library of Congress Cataloging-in-Publication Data

Chou, Ya-lun, 1922–
    Statistical analysis for business and economics.

    Includes index.
    1. Economics—Statistical methods.   2. Commercial
statistics.   I. Title
HB137.C485   1988   001.4′22   88–10958
ISBN 0-444-01301-6

Current printing
10 9 8 7 6 5 4 3 2 1

This book is dedicated

To my wife, Pauline, and my grandsons, Daniel and Justin Allan

And to those colleagues of mine who love statistics, who love to teach statistics,
and who, above all, love the students they teach

Contents

Preface

This is a new version of my *Statistical Analysis with Business and Economic Applications,* published by Holt, Rinehart and Winston in 1969 and 1975. Both editions of this text enjoyed worldwide adoptions, and their warm receptions by users would warm any author's heart.

Shortly after the second edition of my *Statistical Analysis* went out of print in 1984, I received scores of letters from past users urging me to write a new edition of the book. I received correspondence not only from this country but also from many others, including England, West Germany, and the Middle East. It was suggested that I have the old version reprinted for their use until a revised edition could be written. Because of such requests, I had the 2nd edition of my *Statistical Analysis* reprinted in Great Britain by the Pitman Press in 1984. The reprints and the Spanish translation of the text still command a respectable showing in Europe and South America. For those loyal and friendly users of my book, I can only hope this new text fills the need and becomes even more useful than the earlier one.

In response to the urging of many of my colleagues, I started to work on this new book entitled *Statistical Analysis for Business and Economics* in 1985. Happily, I can report that it is finally completed. This new version, as was its predecessor, is mainly designed as a full-year introductory text for either undergraduate or graduate use by business and economics majors. Inasmuch as economics and business subjects often constitute a major portion of programs in public administration, political science, and sociology, this volume can perhaps also be used by students in these areas of concentration.

Anyone who is familiar with the predecessor would detect that this volume is indeed a new book, not just a revised version. Nearly 90% of my old *Statistical Analysis* has been rewritten with some old topics dropped and new ones added. However, I still hold my main objectives as before and believe that the original objectives have been achieved much more effectively by this new volume.

Students in business and economics are required to take at least one course in statistics. Most of them seem to realize that such a course would be of help to them in the study of other business and economic subjects, as well as in their jobs after graduation. However, they generally do not look forward to such a course with great anticipation, because, correctly or incorrectly, they feel that the study of statistics is often excruciatingly dull and difficult. The answer to this problem is to present the material in an interesting and easily understood manner, so that it not only clarifies but also intrigues. Thus, my main objective is to create an interest in statistical methods as well as to convince students of the usefulness of these tools in economic analysis and the control function of management.

Moreover, most students of business and economics do not continue to study statistics after the completion of their first course. Since it is not possible to teach one in a single course, using a textbook even as comprehensive as the present volume, all one should know about statistics, an introductory course should do no more than to train students to become intelligent consumers rather than competent producers of statistics. This, then, is my second objective. To this end, I have attempted to obtain a proper balance between the underlying principles of statistics and their applications. This reflects my feeling that theory is practical and that practice that is often too far removed from theory leads one astray. My intention is to introduce to the reader a correct way of thinking as he is led through the basic field of statistics. Such an approach will help the reader to properly use and interpret statistical results produced by others, which in turn will guide him to venture into advanced courses in statistical analysis and actual application of what has been learned with minimum difficulty and maximum understanding.

My third objective is to introduce theories, concepts, and procedures that exist in modern statistics at a minimum level of mathematical requirement. Any student who is familiar with college freshman mathematics, or indeed with simple high school algebra, with no experience in calculus and matrix algebra, will be quite prepared to follow this text with ease. Because of this practice, all statistical methods have been developed verbally or by numerical demonstrations. It has been my experience over the years that regardless of the students' mathematical preparation, few of them are willing or able to work through a terse statistics text where material is presented as a series of formulas or proofs. On this score, I have made an effort to make up what has been omitted in mathematics through written explanation. My intention here is to enhance readability without sacrifice of precision and rigor. The mathematically inclined readers will also benefit from this approach, since they may gain additional insights into mathematical derivations with which they are already familiar, along with clearer intuitive interpretation of the derived results.

There is something else that can be said in favor of a non-mathematical approach. With the ready availability of moderately priced pocket calculators, and even home computers, a student can, as the content of this volume indicates, go very far in applied statistics without the need of knowledge in higher mathematics. For example, in the study of multivariate analysis, formulas would become very involved and lengthy without the use of linear algebra notations when more than three variables are involved. However, whether ordinary algebra or linear algebra is employed, computations by hand are equally difficult and time-consuming and may often be impossible. Fortunately, as we all know, if one has mastered trivariate analysis with, say, only a background of high school algebra, one should encounter no more difficulty in understanding and using the results of computer printouts when the association analysis involves more than three variables, since the underlying logic, the various measures, and the interpretations of numerical results are exactly the same in a multivariate analysis, irrespective of the number of variables used in the study. Thus, we can easily introduce the general theory of multivariate analysis, but confine our numerical examples to the special simple case of three variables, and resort to the computer to do all the computations for more comprehensive problems. As a matter of fact, without the availability of computers, many of the more advanced topics in this text could never have been introduced with the same flavor and depth as have been presented. In this connection, it must also be mentioned that I have, for convenience, used the integral sign in a few places for defining the cumulative distribution functions for continuous random variables. Such a sign is thoroughly explained when it is first introduced. Furthermore, no operations on integrals are introduced or required in the main discussions.

Finally, realizing that repetition is the only route to learning, I have covered important theorems, concepts, and procedures in each chapter at least four times: once in the main body of the text with examples, once in the glossary of formulas, once in the review questions, and once in the problems. This may be a chore for the student, but he should thoroughly understand each chapter when he has finished it.

In order to help the student acquire a "feel" for the usefulness of statistics, hypothetical but realistic economic and business examples are used to illustrate the application of statistical procedures, and a great variety of problems with real-world counterparts in economic and business decision situations are used. Problem material has been carefully chosen to provide a maximum coverage of basic principles and interpretations of concepts and statistical results. Computational labor for most of the problems has been confined to a minimum in order to avoid the danger of losing the great ideas of statistics in a sea of arithmetic operations. I hope the student will attempt to solve some of the problems with regularity even if the material presented in the text or in lectures seems absolutely clear. Statistics is a discipline in which better understanding and deeper appreciation of principles and methods can come only from actual solution of problems.

Compared with other texts currently in use, this volume is

relatively strong in descriptive techniques. In addition to a more thorough discussion of measures for describing the various characteristics of cross-section univariate data, a complete chapter is devoted to tabular presentation of data and graphic displays. I have done so because descriptive statistics, though relatively simple, is quite important from the viewpoint of frequency of use. The extended coverage of descriptive measures is by no means achieved at the expense of analytical methods. As a matter of fact, my presentation of probability theory, random variables, probability models, and sampling distributions is quite detailed in order to provide a firm foundation for inferential statistics. In these cases where instruction time is critical, instructors should find that sufficient explanations have been given in the chapters on descriptive statistics for most students to learn these techniques on their own or with a minimum of lecture time.

In order to prepare the student more adequately for later couses in operation research, simulation, forecasting, marketing research, econometrics, and so on, in addition to a rather comprehensive introduction to probability models three chapters have been devoted to the study of bivariate and multivariate analyses. These chapters, I believe, cover all the important and basic aspects of regression and correlation studies.

As to the presentations of index numbers and time series, I have confined myself purely to the classical approach. There is no discussion beyond a brief mention of the new and interesting as well as promising work being done in time series by Box and Jenkins or by Nelson. My position of this is twofold: first, these techniques have not yet been fully developed and introduced; and, second, they are extremely difficult, if not impossible, to reduce to elementary or simple forms so as to be useful in application.

Three chapters have been devoted to Bayesian statistics, reflecting the growing acceptance of Bayesian decision procedures as an indispensable part of a regular course in business and economic statistics. In this connection, I have treated the classical theories of estimation and testing as decision procedures. Then Bayesian inferential methods are considered as an extension of the classical inductive statistics. Finally, Bayesian decision theory is taken as yet another extension of Bayesian inference. I have, in short, presented classical and Bayesian analyses as complementary methods rather than as substitutes for each other.

Finally, a chapter on nonparametric statistics is given as a supplement to classical and Bayesian methods. In this chapter, an effort has been made to select those nonparametric methods that have as their counterparts classical tests introduced earlier, in addition to the usual but quite useful nonparametric tests.

Overall, this text is more analytical in approach and broader in scope for an introductory course than many other texts of the same type currently in use. Also, the organization and presentation of the various topics have been quite flexible; hence, this book can be used in different ways. As it now stands, all the nonstarred chapters would constitute a complete standard undergraduate course. If one is pressed for time, the starred sections in some of these chapters can be considered as optional material. If used as a graduate text, the entire volume can be utilized. If one is pressed for time, Chapters 14, 19, and 25 can be eliminated from classroom discussion. In general, the starred chapters are optional; some or all of them can be eliminated without loss of continuity. The actual coverage, of course, depends upon the student's need and the instructor's judgment.

In writing this book, I have resisted the current popular practice of incorporating computer printouts in the main text. My position is that they occupy too much valuable space without adding much to the students' understanding of the principles and methods of statistics. Furthermore, computer printouts tend to break up the continuity of the main discussion. This practice does not mean that I have ignored the contribution of computers to the study of statistics. It only reflects my judgment on the role of computers should play in the study of statistics.

The availability of electronic computers is to assist in the study of statistics by eliminating most of the tedious and time-consuming computations. The modern large-scale digital computer, properly instructed, can perform arithmetic chores and a multitude of complex algebraic manipulations with greater accuracy, facility, and rapidity than can any human brain. In addition, the computer's memory is capable of storing and accurately recalling vast amounts of information. The computer, with such capabilities, naturally has great impact on the field of statistics, as it has had on any study where quantitative methods are applied. First, it gives the student of statistics more time to learn basic principles and methods, since he no longer needs to be concerned with learning short-cut methods of doing computations. Next, it enables statisticians to solve problems never before practical to undertake—for example, in multiple regression analysis when a large number of variables are involved; in the analysis of variance when more than two factors are employed or when a large number of observations are used in the simpler experimental designs; in simulation when many alternative models for a given problem are to be evaluated. Finally, the use of computers, which under some circumstances forces the user to make explicit assumptions at each stage and to make comprehensive tests of results, may actually produce new knowledge, which, in turn, may lead to improvements in existing theory or method.

Meanwhile, it must be recognized that a digital computer has the unfortunate limitation of doing only what it is told to do. Thus, despite its amazing powers, the user must understand the underlying principles and computational mechanics of any quantitative technique to which the computer's skill is applied. This is to say, that computer technology cannot replace one's learning in statistical (or any other quantitative) theories and methods. Our dependence upon the computer to solve problems stems from the fact that most practical problems are so vast in scale that, in the absence of the computer's amazingly alacritous computational capacity, their solutions by hand would certainly be impractical. We use the computer to solve problems that we have neither the time nor the patience to solve on our own.

It is important to note that we can benefit from the computer's talents without knowing how it works; we need only to know what it does. We can do this by relying on standardized coding and computer programs. Every computer installation has a library of proven routines. For each routine, a prepared "problem description" is available. This literature explains in general terms what calculations the program is designed to perform, which of these are optional or otherwise, what restrictions must be observed, and what input and output formats are prescribed or allowed.

A computing system is either "batch" or "interactive". In a *batch system,* such as SAS or SPSS, all data and calculating instructions are typed up at the very start and run through the computer; then all the output emerges for the user to sort out. With an *interactive system,* the computer carries on a running conversation with the operator, who gives one instruction at a time. Depending on the computer's answer, the operator can then select the next instruction. When a mistake is made, it can be corrected easily. An interactive system is so forgiving that it is indeed the best friend of amateurs. One of the most popular interactive systems was written by Ryan, Joiner, and Rayan (1976) and is called MINITAB.

I claim no originality for the material in this book. All ideas contained in it are now common property of all statisticians. A considerable amount of material in this book has come through the work of others—from my teachers, my colleagues, original thinkers of the past and present, and scholars who have written textbooks in statistics. The coverage, organization, and presentation of this volume have also been influenced to a great extent by comments, suggestions, and criticisms I have received from the users of my previous books in many parts of the world. To them all, I express my deep gratitude.

There are, however, a number of people whose names must receive special mention for various tasks they have performed in the making of this book. First of all, Dr. Chipei Tseng, Professor of Business System Analysis at Northern Illinois University, who served as one of the readers for the publisher initially, did such an excellent job in reviewing the first draft of this book that I asked him later, with my publisher's consent, to serve as the technical editor of this text. The final version of this book has been greatly influenced and improved by his valuable service. Next, Professor F. Victor Lu of St. John's University has read parts of the manuscript and has made a number of suggestions for the clarification of quite a few rough spots. Third, the late Dr. John Alexion, Dean of the College of Business Administration; Dr. Bruce Bosworth, Chairman of the Department of Quantitative Analysis; and Mr. James Rafferty, Assistant Dean of the College of Business Administration, all of St. John's University, as administrators, have given me a great deal of assistance in order to expedite the successful completion of this project. Ms. Betsy N. Brown, editor at Elsevier Science Publishing Co., Inc., has been a delightful person to work with. Her help and advice have certainly been appreciated. I am also thankful to Mr. Seibert G. Adams, Vice President of Random House, Inc., the publisher of a one-semester statistics text of which I am the senior coauthor, who has given me a blanket permission to publish with any publisher of my choice a full-year text in business statistics, without any problem of copyright violation or violation of my contract with Random House. Finally, I am indebted to the Literary Executor of the late Sir Ronald A. Fisher, F.R.S., to Dr. Frank Yates, F.R.S., and to Longman Group Ltd., London, for permission to reprint Tables II and XXXIII from their book *Statistical Tables for Biological, Agricultural and Medical Research*.

GREEK ALPHABET

A	α	Alpha	N	ν	Nu
B	β	Beta	Ξ	ξ	Xi
Γ	γ	Gamma	O	o	Omicron
Δ	δ	Delta	Π	π	Pi
E	ε	Epsilon	P	ρ	Rho
Z	ζ	Zeta	Σ	σ	Sigma
H	η	Eta	T	τ	Tau
θ	θ	Theta	Y	υ	Upsilon
I	ι	Iota	Φ	ϕ	Phi
K	κ	Kappa	X	χ	Chi
Λ	λ	Lambda	Ψ	ψ	Psi
M	μ	Mu	Ω	ω	Omega

1 The Significance and Scope of Statistics

1.1 WHY IS STATISTICS IMPORTANT?

Before we formally define "statistics," let us briefly discuss its significance. All knowledgeable persons know something about statistics, even about its importance as a subject of study. However, unless they have studied statistics, they may not know exactly why it is important. The truth of the matter is that statistical methods are used today in nearly all fields of scientific investigation, since they enable us to find the answers to a vast number of important, complicated, and exciting questions, some of which are listed below.

1. How do scientists evaluate the validity of new theories?

2. How do medical researchers test the effectiveness of new drugs?

3. How do military commanders determine the frequency of bombing missions on selected enemy targets?

4. How do sociologists forecast the size of the population of the world at any future time?

5. How can one differentiate between an atomic explosion and a small earthquake from a distance of thousands of miles?

6. How many rounds of ammunition should be fired in order to ascertain the quality of new types of machine guns?

7. How can an economist ascertain whether the current change in the Consumer Price Index is a continuation of a secular trend, a seasonal fluctuation, or simply a random deviation?

8. Is high salt intake a cause of high blood pressure, or is high blood pressure a cause of high salt intake?

9. How is it possible for one to predict the outcome of an election by interviewing just a few hundred voters?

10. Does cigarette smoking increase the chance of lung cancer?

11. How can one distinguish between the natural noise in a Geiger counter and regular cosmic radiation?

12. How can both employment and unemployment be increasing during the same period of time?

These are but a few examples in which the application of statistics is necessary in order to obtain the answer.

In fact, statistics encompasses many other aspects of numerous types of research projects and of operations and control of management functions, other than those indicated by the questions posed above. The reader may presume that mathematics is the Queen of Sciences because it provides the theoretical framework for nearly all other sciences. If you have already had a basic course in physics, you may even be familiar with some of the mathematical laws governing subjects as diversified as gravity, energy, light, electricity, satellites, etc. You may not be aware, however, of the fact that mathematical theories are being developed every day in many areas by theoretical statisticians—people trained in statistical theory and probability. To cite just a few illustrative cases, they are developed for theories of space flights in physics; for theories of learning of animal and human behavior in psychology, of genetics, of intelligence, and of mutation in biology; for theories of migration and of race differentials in sociology; for theories of epidemics in public health; for theories of premiums and of distribution of claims in insurance.

The contributions to society made by statisticians were perhaps best summarized by Lord Wilson of Rivaux, the former Prime Minister of Great Britain. For the opening of the 37th Session of the International Statistical Institute in London, September 4, 1969, Lord Wilson said:

> The list of papers for the Session reflects the ever-widening range of application of statistical methods. When I joined the Royal Statistical Society, the papers read were still mainly on economic and social statistics. Nowadays, the papers read before a society like those for your session of the Institute cover many more topics relating to many disciplines. It means, I am afraid, that as statisticians today you help so many people in so many diverse subject fields that none of your clients can see the overall contribution which you as statisticians make together as a whole. As a result, your value is not perhaps sufficiently recognized by

any one group of the people with whom you deal, nor are your great services fully realized by the general public.

Indeed, statistics has become an everyday tool of all types of professional people who come into contact with quantitative data or draw conclusions from them. Such people need some familiarity with statistical principles in order to evaluate numerical reports and to avoid the common misuses of statistics and fallacies in statistical reasoning. Students in many fields must have a working knowledge of statistical methods.

This book is concerned with the development of statistical principles and methods and their application to economic and business problems. Students of business or economics who are required to take at least one such course in statistics may wonder why. The answer is perhaps best given through a sampling of questions they may encounter:

1. What do we mean by such terms as "seasonally adjusted sales of department stores for any given month", "real per capita income," "escalator clause in a labor contract," and so on?

2. How is the rate of growth of a nation's GNP measured?

3. How can one determine, with sufficient speed and desired accuracy, the inventory of materials in process for a manufacturing firm's financial statements?

4. How and why can we estimate the unemployment rate of the entire labor force by observing the unemployment rate among only 25 000 households selected from throughout the nation? How reliable is such an estimate?

5. How and why can we determine whether a manufacturing process is under control by examining a small number of products produced by such a process?

6. How and why is it possible to forecast consumption expenditures for the following quarter using disposable income for the current quarter?

7. Given a variable demand for a firm's sales, how does one go about selecting from among a number of alternative inventory plans the one that will maximize total profits or minimize total losses?

8. Should a new product be commercialized or abandoned? Why?

9. Should a marketing survey for the potential demand for a new product be conducted at one, two, or even more stages of the development of the product?

10. If two or more types of repair facilities differ greatly in prices and efficiencies, which should a firm install in order to minimize its overall repair costs?

11. Suppose there are several methods of performing a given task; which should one adopt with respect to a specific objective?

12. Which opportunity should one select if a number of investment opportunities require the same amount of capital but yield different gains under different economic conditions (inflation, prosperity, recession, or depression)?

If you have an interest in answering these and many, many more questions of a similar nature, you will need a course in business and economic statistics.

1.2 WHAT IS STATISTICS?

Having pointed out the significance and some possible applications of statistics, let us turn our attention to the nature and scope of this discipline. The notion of "statistics" was originally derived from the same root as the word "state", since it has been the traditional function of central governments to keep records of population, births, deaths, vocations, crop yields, taxes, and many other kinds of information and activities. The counting and measuring of these quantities and events generates all types of numerical data that are useful for performing many types of governmental functions and formulating various kinds of public policies. The average person today conceives of "statistics" as columns of figures or zig-zag graphs in the daily newspapers, associated with batting averages, divorce and crime rates, stock prices, exports and imports, and the like.

Numerical data are indeed a part of statistics, but they are only the raw material, which must be fed into "statistical methods" for further analysis. Statistics, as a scientific method, is concerned with the design of experiments, describing and interpreting observations that are made, and the use of results thus derived as the rational basis to make reasonable decisions for practical actions. The purpose of statistics, in other words, is to develop principles that will aid us in making decisions. From the modern viewpoint, *statistics* is often defined as a method of decision making in the face of uncertainty. In dealing with many physical, economic, social, industrial, business, or psychic phenomena, one is called upon to generalize or to take action in the face of uncertainty as to the way things are—"the state of nature." Statistics becomes a valuable tool in decision making whenever one is uncertain about the state of nature.

While the definition given above may appear to be a bit narrow, it does define the central and ultimate function of statistical methods. In a broader and more comprehensive perspective, the vast scope of statistics may be thought to encompass three different branches of studies: (1) descriptive statistics, (2) inductive statistics, and (3) statistical decision theory.

Descriptive Statistics

Descriptive statistics refers to the body of methods that has been developed to collect, organize, present, and describe numerical data. This branch of statistics is concerned with the following tasks:

1. To find an appropriate method to collect numerical data efficiently and accurately for the given problem at hand.

2. To determine an efficient format, such as a tabular presentation, for organizing the data gathered in a systematic and orderly manner, so that information provided by the data can be observed with greater ease, accuracy, and precision.

3. To present numerical data, whether organized or not, in ways such that characteristics and behavior of the data are clearly and easily revealed. Such presentations are made by means of graphic displays.

4. To summarize or describe each characteristic or property of the data by a single number, such as an average, a percentage, or some other appropriate measure, which is computed from the data on hand by means of a formula derived from some valid principle.

Inductive Statistics

Inductive statistics, which is also often called *inferential statistics* or *statistical inference,* in contrast to descriptive statistics, is analytical in nature. It consists of a collection of principles or theorems that enable us to generalize about some characteristic of a "population" from the observed characteristic of a "sample." In this definition, a *population* is the collection of all the items, objects, things, or people about which information is desired for the solution of a problem. A *sample* is a group of items selected by some carefully designed method from a population. As we shall see, there are various kinds of samples, owing to the different methods of selection available. In this text, we will be almost exclusively concerned with what are called simple random samples. A *simple random sample,* roughly speaking, is one that is drawn in such a way that each and every item in the population has the *same chance* of being included in the sample at each and every selection.

Now, we may take notice that if a descriptive measure is computed from population data, it is called a *population parameter,* or simply a *parameter*; if it is computed from sample data, it is called a *sample statistic,* or simply a *statistic.* With these notions now in mind, we can now redefine *inductive statistics* to be the process of generalizing about the value of a parameter from the value of a statistic.

There are two different, but related, inferential procedures: estimation and testing. *Estimation* is the process of using the value of a sample statistic to estimate or guess about the corresponding value of a parameter that is unknown, but a constant. As an example, suppose that we have a population consisting of 100,000 marbles in a bag, all of which are alike except for color, and that we cannot see them though we do know that some of them are white and the rest are black. Suppose that we wish to ascertain the proportion of, say, white marbles in this population. To find this out, suppose we select 1,000 marbles at random from the bag and find that 350 are white. This means that our sample proportion of white marbles is 35%. From this we can conclude that the population proportion of white marbles is also 35%. Having done this, we have made what is called a *point estimate*. We can also state that the odds are, say, 95 to 5 that our sample showing a certain proportion of white marbles is within three percentage points of what a complete count of the 100,000 marbles would show. When such a statement is made, we have made what is called an *interval estimate*. As we shall see, when the sample is properly drawn or when it is truly a simple random sample, statistical theory not only aids us to estimate a special population parameter, but also helps us to determine how accurate our estimate is likely to be.

The second aspect of statistical inference, *testing,* is also referred to as *tests* of *statistical hypotheses*. A *hypothesis* is an assumption made about the value of a parameter. The procedure here, simply stated, is to use the value of a sample statistic to judge whether the assumed value of the parameter is attainable or reasonable. Intuitively, you may understand that there is nearly always a difference between such an assumed value and the value observed from the sample. The point here is that statistical theory will again be able to tell us whether such a difference is small enough to be nonsignificant and, hence, whether the hypothesis cannot be rejected; that is, whether the hypothetical value is attainable. Alternatively it will tell us whether such a difference is large enough to be significant and, hence, whether the hypothesis should be rejected; that is, whether the hypothetical value is unattainable.

This very brief sketch of inductive statistics clearly indicates that inferential procedures are very useful and exciting methods, since they enable us to say a great deal about a whole population with judged accuracy from information provided by a sample that usually consists of only a small fraction of the corresponding population.

Statistical Decision Theory

Broadly speaking, *statistical decision theory,* the third branch of statistics, refers to the process of selecting the optimal (best) act by some decision rule, established to achieve some specific objective, from a set of two or more acts, given the states of nature and payoffs or losses. Here, the payoffs or losses (measured in terms of money or "utility"), are the consequences produced jointly by each and every combination of the available courses of action and the possible states of nature in a given decision situation. Our discussion of this branch of statistics will be confined to Bayesian statistics only. Bayesian statistics embraces both inferential procedures and decision theory. *Bayesian inferences,* just as the classical theories mentioned before, consist of estimation and testing, though there exist differences that will be noted later in both conceptual orientations and interpretations between these two schools of thought. *Bayesian decision theory* is more typical of Bayesian analysis. It is defined exactly as statistical decision theory in general, except that, within the Bayesian framework, only the *"Bayes" measure* is used as *the* decision rule. The *Bayes' measure* is an average value of the payoffs or losses of an act for all the possible stated values. The optimal act, in this context, is the Bayes' measure that has either the greatest average payoff or the smallest average loss. This brief explanation of Bayesian decision theory merely attempts to impress upon the reader that this theory is especially useful in business operations, since many business decisions involve the selection of an act that can either maximize the payoffs or minimize the losses.

1.3 HOW TO CONDUCT A STATISTICAL INVESTIGATION

Thus, we see that statistical methods are useful in a very wide variety of fields. The statistical methods used in business and economic problems are similar to those used in other areas. The differences one finds in statistics when going from one area to another are differences in detailed techniques, not in basic approach. That is, some statistical concepts and formulas are used much more frequently in some areas than in others, but the basic aim of getting information for decisions under uncertainty is always there.

At this point it is convenient to organize our discussion of the basic statistical approach to solving a problem under five headings. As previous questions suggest, statistical investigations can be quite complicated, and the five headings are an orderly way of attacking these complications.

1. State the Problem

Research questions typically start out as very short and vague questions. They need to be sharpened before it becomes practical to answer them. A precise, detailed question should be written. The context in which the research question needs answering should also be written down. This context should briefly indicate the various decisions that might be made. The population about which data are desired should be described in great detail. Frequently, words used in research questions, decision contexts, and population description have to be defined in great and almost painful detail.

A precise, detailed description of the problem serves many purposes. Sometimes the attempt to write such a description indicates that the problem does not really exist. Sometimes it is clear that the problem exists, but that enough information is already at hand to solve it. In the remaining cases, the statement of the problem is an indispensable guide to the kinds and quantities of data that must be gathered.

2. Design the Experiment

This amounts to the distinction between the population and the frame. In general, a *population* is a group of items about which information is desired and, thus, it is sometimes called the *target population*. In contrast, a *frame* is a list of the items in the population; thus, a frame is sometimes called the *sampled population*. Listing items of a target population is often prohibitively expensive for a specific problem. Fortunately, there are many published frames that may correspond, or roughly correspond, to populations of interest. Typical lists are city directories, telephone directories, real estate tax lists, income tax reports, car registration lists, business directories, subscription lists for magazines or newspapers, organization memberships lists, and so on.

In using readily available lists or lists of one's own, the distinction between a population and a frame is of great importance. This is because they are never exactly the same. Almost always, one has to select observations from a group that is a little different from the group one really wants to study. Worse yet, the frame can be greatly different from the population, in which case the results of the study apply only to the frame and do not apply to the population. The frame should be described in detail so that it can be compared with the population. Then a judgment is made whether the frame is close enough to the population to justify going ahead with the study, or whether the frame is so different from the population that the study should be modified or abandoned.

Some of the knowledge about the differences between frames and populations is the fruit of bitter experience. A famous example is the *Literary Digest* presidential election poll of 1936, which predicted that Landon would win the U.S. presidential election by a landslide. In fact, Roosevelt won the election. The *Literary Digest* mailed 10,000,000 questionnaires to voters and received 2,300,000 completed question- naires back. About 60% of the 2,300,000 returned questionnaires favored Landon, so it certainly appeared that Landon would win by a large margin. Of course, this election forecast was disastrously wrong. Statisticians are not in agreement on what went wrong. One explana- tion is that the *Digest*'s frame was imperfect because the mailing list for the 10,000,000 questionnaires was taken from such sources as telephone directories and automobile registrations, which overrepresented upper- class and middle-class people at that time. The *Digest*'s poll, according to this explanation, predicted the voting behavior of these people quite well, but this frame excluded most of the "ill-housed, ill-clad, ill- nourished" people who overwhelmingly favored Roosevelt because they were to be the main beneficiaries of his "New Deal" policies. Another, very different explanation, stresses the fact that the 2,300,000 people who returned their questionnaires selected themselves into the sample. True, the *Digest* sent out 10,000,000 questionnaires, but the people sending them back volunteered their cooperation with the poll. After all, 7,700,000 people receiving the questionnaires decided not to return them. The assumption that those volunteering to return a questionnaire are truly representative of the whole population is highly suspect.

After describing the frame in detail, the next step in designing the experiment is deciding whether to take a complete census or merely a sample. If a sample is to be taken, it is necessary to decide how to select the items for the sample, how many items to select, and what data to collect from each of the items being observed. For example, suppose you are trying out the productivity of a new machine by having a worker produce a day's output on it and you find that using the new machine cuts costs by 10% comparing to the old. Should you then scrap the old machines and convert entirely to the new ones? Common sense suggests that such a move is a very rash one indeed, because the better results could have been due to factors other than the new machine. Furthermore, before such a decision is made, many important questions on data observations must be raised and answered. Should only total production be observed, or production classified by degrees of quality, or what? Should daily totals be observed, or hourly totals, or what? Should some of the data be ignored, such as those generated either by an unusually good worker or by a worker who has no experience at all with the new machine? Also, perhaps a trial run of, say, ten days would be more appropriate, since then results would show greater variations, with some days' results being worse than those from the old machine. The question here is to how to design a trial run to get the information you need and how to interpret the results of the trial.

3. Collect the Data

Frequently, data that already exist will satisfactory answer the research question. If so, fine, although such data should never be accepted at face value, but should instead be examined to see that they are appropriate and accurate. In the absence of suitable existing data, the investigator must gather his or her own data. Gathering data is likely to be expensive, time-consuming, and subject to many clerical errors. Administering the collection of data is a demanding task. As will be noted in the next chapter, several problems usually arise when new data are collected. One of them is that new data cannot be accepted at face value, but must be edited. Another problem that must be faced is that of nonrespondents. At some point too, a decision must be made to stop collecting data, even though all of the desired data have not been gathered. Later, when the study results are being interpreted, a judgment must be made about the seriousness of any flaws in the data-collection phase of the study. There are almost always some flaws. It is usually possible, in a well-conducted study, to ensure that the flaws are minimal and relatively unimportant.

When we must collect data ourselves, we must decide the way in which they will be gathered. Again as we shall see in the next chapter, direct observation, or direct counting, can be used, as in traffic studies. Questionnaires are used in many studies. These can be administered by mail, telephone, or personal interviews. All of the decisions about how to conduct the research should be regarded as tentative until the methods have been tested by actually gathering a small amount of data. This "dry run" or *pre-test* usually uncovers some problems that require revision of the research methods. It may then be necessary to further pre-test the revised methods to see if they actually work. When the research has been designed in detail and the last pre-test fails to uncover any more major problems, the next phase starts.

4. Summarize the Data

Imagine a report listing every item of information obtained from the *Literary Digest*'s 2,300,000 returned questionnaires. If the data from 10 questionnaires could be presented on one page, the complete report would be 230,000 pages in length: this is mind-boggling. Since we desire a conclusion instead of a boggled mind from a statistical study, something has to be done with the raw data.

The solution is to summarize the data. Individual data are classified and report by class, either in tables or by graphs. Summary statistics, such as proportions or averages, are computed and reported.

5. Interpret the Data

At last, the research question can be answered. Sometimes only a partial answer can be given, in which case it is important to spell this fact out. Sometimes questions that were not raised can be answered because, in the process of answering the research question, other interesting and useful facts surfaced. These by-products of an investigation should not be overlooked when judging the worth of a research proposal, since they are often very valuable. When sampling is involved, inferences are made to the entire population (or, more correctly, the entire frame) from the sample data. Suggestions for further research are made.

At this point, the reader should be informed that for a variety of reasons, as we shall explain in due time, nearly all statistical investigations today are conducted through sampling, rather than by census (or complete enumeration). This practice makes the study of statistics more demanding as well as more exciting.

Perhaps this description of a statistical investigation is a bit overwhelming. What the reader should understand is that statistics is a complete set of procedures for making decisions under uncertainty, rather than being merely a set of numerical facts. The details of this section are less important than a general appreciation of the scope of statistics such as we have taken up in the previous sections and as we shall introduce throughout the entire text.

REVIEW QUESTIONS

1.1 More than three decades ago, a well-known historian commented that very soon a basic knowledge of statistics would become as important as the ability to read and write in order to assume effective citizenship in a democracy. Do you think that such a day has already arrived? Explain as fully as you can.

1.2 Cite a few situations in your major field of study where statistics is useful. Explain why they are useful.

1.3 Would you agree that it is adequate to define statistics as a body of methods for the study of numerical data. Why or why not?

1.4 What are the three branches of statistical studies? Define and illustrate each in your own words.

1.5 Differentiate the following pairs of concepts:
   a. Population *vs* sample
   b. Population *vs* frame
   c. Parameter *vs* statistic

1.6 What is a simple random sample?

1.7 In the definition of modern statistics, the term "uncertainty" was implicitly explained, but not formally defined. Can you define "uncertainty" according to your understanding with reference to our discussion of it? If not, check the Index at the back of the book to locate a formal definition of this term.

1.8 What are the five stages common to all statistical investigations? Can you think of a problem of your own that can be solved by the statistical method by going through the five stages as fully as possible?

1.9 It has been mentioned, but not explained in this chapter, that statistical investigations today are usually conducted by sampling rather than by complete enumeration. Can you think of some of the reasons for this practice with your knowledge of statistics at this time?

1.10 What is the most important function digital computers can perform, as far as the study of statistics is concerned?

PROBLEMS

Note. Terms used in some of the problems below may not have been defined explicitly in the text. If so, whenever you have doubt, check the Index in the back of the book, you can always find proper definitions for these terms at various places in this book. Also, do not be disappointed if you find that you cannot answer some of the questions here, since the main objective of this set of problems is to indicate to you what statistics can do; not to test your ability to understand the subject matter presented in them. As you proceed with this text, though, you will find that these problems are not only quite interesting but also quite easy to solve.

1.1 Find a recent newspaper article that reports the results of a sample study. Summarize the article or include a clipping with your homework. Comment on any major problems the investigators had to overcome in order to answer the research question posed in this study.

1.2 Keep a log for a week, recording every television program you watch. After the week is over, review your log and discuss how accurate it is. Did you have any trouble deciding whether you "watched" a particular program? If so, what was the problem?

1.3 Keep a log for a week, recording every payment you made in currency and coins. (Exclude payments made by check or credit card.) After the week is over, review your log and discuss how accurate it is. Did you set up a checking system so that you could tell whether you recorded every payment? If so, what was it? Did it work? Did you have any trouble deciding which payments to include and which to exclude? If so, what was the problem?

1.4 Using the *Statistical Abstract of the United States,* find out how many people in the United States are illiterate by whatever definition the *Statistical Abstract* uses. Is this really the number of people in the United States who are illiterate? Why or why not?

1.5 Suppose you manufacture sporting goods. You would like to expand your sales of football equipment, and you ask for some statistics on the popularity of football in the United States, Canada, Mexico, and Great Britain. What difficulties are you likely to find with the definition of "football"?

1.6 Using the *Encyclopaedia Britannica* or another suitable source, find out how accurately a person's weight can be measured. Do not expect to get a precise answer, such as "to the nearest 0.000000774 pound." A rough order of magnitude is sufficient. Briefly describe the equipment needed to make the most accurate determination of a person's weight.

1.7 Point out some differences between the population and the frame in each of the following situations.
   a. A new product intended for distribution throughout the United States is test-marketed by giving away small samples of the product to hundreds of consumers in Jamestown, N.Y., Troy, N.Y., and Utica, N.Y.
   b. An organization interested in voters' opinions on banning pistols and revolvers uses "random-digit dialing" to select its sample. That is, random digits are used to select a random sample of telephone numbers, and then these telephone numbers are called. Compare this method with that of random selection from telephone directories. Is random-digit dialing the best method for this organization? Discuss briefly.
   c. A psychologist interested in whether humor improves learning tries out two versions of the same college textbook material, one spiced with some jokes and the other not, on the first 10 student volunteers at the college where she teaches.

1.8 A linguist is interested in whether a computer can be programmed to write English sentences through random selection from a predetermined vocabulary. He starts with five words in the vocabulary: cat, eats, loves, rat, tulip. He has the computer write three-word sentences by selecting words at random from this list. List the population, one sample that might be drawn, and the sample space. The sample space is rather long, so it is enough to list 10 items in it and then state how many items would be in the sample space if it were completely listed. Classify each sentence in your sample space according to whether it makes any sense at all, is true or false, and is serious or humorous, but don't spend much time on these classifications. What hope do you see for computerized English composition?

1.9 To get a simple random sample of parents of the students attending an elementary school, the Principal assigns a serial number to each pupil and then uses a table of random digits to select pupils. The sample consists of the parents of the selected pupils. Did the Principal get a simple random sample of parents? Why or why not?

1.10 It is known from census data that, in a particular city, approximately 50% of those employed hold white-collar jobs and 50% hold blue-collar jobs. As part of a survey, an interviewer is told to stand at a particular corner in the downtown area of the city, select five people wearing suits and interview them, and then select five people wearing work clothes and interview them. The interviewer is told nothing else. Is this a good way to select respondents? Discuss.

2 Measuring, Collecting, and Presenting Statistical Data

2.1 *A PRIORI* PLANNING OF A STATISTICAL INVESTIGATION

As has been mentioned in our introductory chapter, in a statistical investigation, sampling is the rule rather than the exception. However, in order to obtain maximum efficiency, we must, before the selection of a sample, ask many important questions. What type of information is needed? How should we proceed to solve a problem if and when complete information can be made available? How much information is needed for a particular problem? How are decisions to be related to available information? Answers to all these questions, and more, are associated with the first step of a statistical investigation: statistical definition of the decision problem.

Thus, whenever there is a decision problem and it is recognized that the uncertainty attached to it can be removed by numerical data, the very first step in the decision probedure is to translate the problem into statistical terms. Statistical definition of a problem involves two distinct, but closely related steps: defining the statistical population, and describing the characteristic(s) of the elements of the defined population.

The concentration on statistical definition of a problem at the initial stage of a survey is a very rewarding effort, even if the decision will ultimately be made on the basis of a sample. First of all, a precise definition of the population is indispensable in the selection of the sample, since this will avoid the frequent mistake of drawing the sample from the wrong population. Second, thinking in terms of complete information at the beginning will enable us to concentrate on the design of decision—the design of a survey that goes beyond the mere collection or presentation of numerical facts—that can lead directly to decisions. Third, too much initial stress on data gathering often leads to converting a decision problem into a data-collection problem. Little attention is paid to the problem of how to use the data when they are obtained. Consequently, numerical information gathered often proves to be of no use for the decision problem in question.

In short, the stress on statistical definition of the problem is the stress on *a priori* planning in attacking the decision problem. Modern statistics demands that decisions be related to observations before observations are made. This demand calls for a decision maker to specify the possible decisions *a priori* that are conditional upon the actual observations. Suppose you are faced with a decision problem of jumping from the window or running out the door through the smoke when your house is on fire. You may make the decision *a priori,* relating the action to be taken to an observation that is to be made, say, with the toss of a coin. The rule may be this: if the head turns up, jump from the window; if the tail appears, run to the door through the smoke. This illustration may strike you as absurd. Nevertheless, it does bring out the necessary condition of a good decision rule: relate decisions to observations before observations are made. Throughout this book, you will learn many methods of constructing statistical decision rules. Now, we may turn our attention to a discussion of the various aspects of defining decision problems statistically.

2.2 POPULATIONS, ELEMENTARY UNITS, AND CHARACTERISTICS

In statistics, the term *population* is used to mean an aggregate of individual items, whether composed of people or things, that are to be observed in a given problem situation. The individual items in a population are called *elementary units*. To define a population is in a sense to limit the scope of the elementary units. Elementary units possess certain characteristics, sometimes referred to as traits or properties. For instance, a decision problem may involve observing the effectiveness of a shipment of certain drugs. Here the population includes all the individual units of drugs—the elementary units—in the shipment, and the characteristic of the elementary unit to be observed is its quality—its ability to cure some disease. Another problem may require observing the family income in a given state. Here the population includes all the households in that state, and the trait to be observed is the quantity of family income of the elementary units, the households. The result of observing an elementary unit is called an observation. Since an observation is made on each elementary unit in the process of an investigation, we may consider *a population* as the totality of all pertinent observations that may be made in a given decision problem.

Note that both the definition of a population and the characteristics of its elementary units to be observed depend upon the nature of the decision problem at hand. If the following list of examples is studied thoughtfully the importance of this concept will be evident.

Example 1 Male Adults' Hats

Decision problem: To decide the appropriate quantities of hat production for male adults in accordance with varying sizes.

Population: All American male adults.

Characteristic: Circumference of each male adult's head.

Example 2 Housing Supply

Decision problem: To determine the effective supply of apartment units in New York City.

Population: All apartments in New York City.

Characteristic: Availability.

Example 3 Acceptance of An Order

Decision problem: To decide whether to accept or reject a shipment of television tubes.

Population: All television tubes in the shipment.

Characteristic: Time to failure.

Example 4 Tax Policy

Decision problem: For the government to determine a reasonable corporate profits tax.

Population: All corporations in America.

Characteristic: Net corporate incomes.

Example 5 Corporation Policy

Decision problem: For a firm to set up a pension plan.

Population: All employees in the firm.

Characteristic: Length of service of employees.

Example 6 Quality of A Production Process

Decision problem: To determine the quality of steel rods produced by a certain process.

Population: All steel rods that could have been produced by that process.

Characteristic: Tensile strength, or diameter, or weight, or all three traits.

Example 7 Sales Forecast

Decision problem: To estimate future consumers' demand.

Population: All retail stores and mail-order houses.

Characteristic: Volume of sales.

Example 8 Testing Economic Theory

Decision problem: To test whether marginal propensity to consume decreases with an increase in income.

Population: All American families.

Characteristic: Family income and consumption expenditures.

Example 9 Personal Investment

Decision problem: To decide on investment in U.S. common stocks.

Population: All common stock listed on the New York Stock Exchange, American Stock Exchange, and over the counter.

Characteristic: Dividend rates.

From the preceding list it can be found that populations can be classified into two types: infinite and finite. *An infinite population* is one that includes an infinitely large number of elementary units. For instance, the sixth example in the list is such a population, since in this case the population is associated with the process of producing steel rods. Theoretically, such a population includes all the possible steel rods that could be produced if the manufacturing process continued to operate indefinitely under given operating conditions. Another illustration of infinite population is all the possible outcomes when a die is rolled continuously and for an indefinitely long time. A population that is not indefinitely large or that contains only a finite number of items is said to be *a finite population*. There are a number of examples of finite populations in the above list. The student can easily think of many others.

It is also important to note that an aggregate of elementary units that is considered as the population in a given problem situation may also be considered as a sample in a different problem situation. For instance, in the third example, where the problem is to determine whether to accept or reject a shipment of television tubes, the population is defined to include all the tubes in the shipment. This very shipment, however, can also be considered as a sample drawn from an infinite population of television tubes if the problem is to make a decision on the process of production itself. In other words, the first problem is to determine the quality of the tubes in the shipment, and the second is to make a decision on the quality of the production process.

Another point to be noted is that for a given problem the population may be defined in different ways. For instance, to estimate future consumers' demand we may also define the population as all family units in the United States, and the characteristic to be observed becomes family income. For the same problem (the seventh example), the population includes all retail stores and mail-order houses, and the characteristic to be observed is the volume of sales. The first definition is based on the theory that consumers' demand, among other things, may be considered as a function of income. The second definition is founded on the knowledge that past sales can be considered as a reliable estimate of future purchases. Clearly, both sets of data are useful in solving the same problem. However, which definition would yield better results depends upon the investigator's personal judgment. The important implication here is that in any statistical survey the investigator must have a thorough knowledge of the field of investigation in addition to his skill in statistical techniques. This is true not only in defining statistical populations, but also at all stages of the statistical procedure. A statistician who does not have the theoretical knowledge in a given field should form a partnership with one who does, in order to do research in that field fruitfully. Indeed, in many business and economic decision-making research projects, teamwork is the rule rather than the exception.

At this stage, the student may ask: "Can the same population be used for decision making in different problem situations?" This is an important, but relatively simple question to answer. A moment's reflection will reveal that the same population and the characteristic of its elementary units, say, all American families and family incomes, can be used as a basis for decisions concerning the future consumers' demand, the formulation of an individual income tax policy, the standard of living of American people, the pattern of distribution of income, and so forth. Actually, it is the possibility of using the same population to solve different problems that makes it advisable, once the nature of the decision problem is known, to check whether there exist data collected by others, for other purposes, that can be used to advantage in solving our own problem.

2.3 SCALES—LEVELS OF MEASUREMENT

Statistics deals with numerical data obtained from measurement or enumeration of elementary units of a population or a sample. Regardless of how numerical data are obtained, we must have some rule for assigning numbers to the elementary units. Such a rule is called a *scale*, or *level* of *measurement*. Proper selection of statistical methods for the analysis of numerical data depends, among other things, upon the type of scale on which numerical data are expressed. Namely, the particular mathematical operations that may be performed on data depend upon the scale by which the observations are made. There are four different types of scales of measurement. Given in advancing levels in terms of information content and precision, they are nominal, ordinal, interval, and ratio scales.

The Nominal Scale

The nominal scale is the lowest level of measurement. With the *nominal scale,* numbers are used to classify observations into mutually exclusive categories or classes. It is thus merely a naming device; that is, numbers are assigned solely for the purpose of identifying the attribute categories to which the individual observations belong. This scale is usually employed for measuring qualitative data. For example, employees of a firm may be classified according to levels of education, and numbers such as 1, 2, and 3 can be assigned to represent high-school graduates, college graduates, and employees with graduate degrees, respectively. An important application of nominal scales is found in encoding qualitative data for computer processing. For example, an analyst who is studying price movements of stock listed on the New York Stock Exchange may adopt a coding rule for identifying each industry group by using, say, 1 to indicate the chemical industry, 2 for the auto industry, 3 for the energy industry, and so on.

When a nominal scale is used, the resulting data are called *nominal data*. It is important to remember that numbers on a nominal scale are names only; they do not in any way indicate quantitative magnitudes. Thus, no basic arithmetical operation such as addition or subtraction can be performed with nominal data. As a matter of fact, even the less precise mathematical expressions such as $3 > 2$ or $5 < 7$ are meaningless for numbers on a nominal scale.

The Ordinal Scale

The ordinal scale is one level above the nominal scale in measurements. With *ordinal scale* there is an "order relationship" among the numbers assigned to the observations. In other words, numbers on an ordinal scale indicate the ranks of different categories that have some relationship in terms of a definite order. For example, in studying the performances of a given type of assembly line workers, an investigator may assign a numeral 1 as unsatisfactory, a numeral 2 as poor, a numeral 3 as average, and numeral 4 as good, and a numeral 5 as excellent. These numbers, 1, 2, 3, 4, and 5, constitute a set of *ordinal data*. Since these numbers stand for an ordered relationship, with reference to our specific example we can definitely say that 5 is better than 4 which, in turn, is better than 3, and so on. In some situations, we can also imagine that $10 > 9$, $3 < 5$, and similar inequalities are meaningful expressions with ordinal data. It may be noted that although we can now say that $2 > 1$, we cannot assume that 2 is twice as large as 1. In other words, for numbers on an ordinal scale the intervals between units are nearly always unequal. Owing to this inequality of intervals between units, basic arithmetic operations, just as in the case of nominal scale, cannot be applied to ordinal data. However, different numbers on an ordinal scale do represent different quantities or preferences of the characteristic being measured. This type of scale is quite useful as a ranking device for workers' productivities, quality of raw materials from different sources, consumers' brand preferences, and so forth.

The Interval Scale

The interval scale is a more advanced level of measurement than the ordinal scale. *The interval scale,* in addition to the property of "order relationship" possessed by the ordinal scale, has the "stronger" property of "equal intervals." Namely, on an interval scale, equal intervals anywhere along the scale represent an equal amount of difference in the characteristic being measured. Temperature is measured on an interval scale. Thus, when we measure temperature change on the Celsius scale, for example, a decrease from 50°C to 45°C measures the amount of temperature decrease as from 60°C to 55°C.

The property of equal intervals possessed by the interval scale makes it permissible to apply operations of addition and subtraction on *interval data.* However, the zero point on the interval scale is arbitrary (as, when measuring temperature either by the Celsius or Fahrenheit scale, "0" does not mean the absolute zero of temperature), it is therefore not meaningful to compute a ratio between two numbers. This implies that the arithmetic operation of division and its related operation of multiplication are not permissible for interval data.

The Ratio Scale

The *ratio scale* is the most advanced scale of measurement, and may be defined as an interval scale with an absolute zero point. By an *absolute zero point* we mean the number 0 represents complete absence of the characteristic being measured. With this property, the ratio between any two numbers on the scale is independent of the units in which the characteristic is being measured. For example, the monetary value of any commodity can be measured in terms of dollars, pounds, pesos, yuans, or any other monetary system, and the origin of each system is the same; the number 0 in each case here means the commodity has no value at all. With an absolute zero point, all arithmetic operations are now permissible with *ratio data.*

The ratio scale is the level of measurement used most frequently by laymen as well as by statisticians. The scale is used in counting or enumerating objects of all kinds. The monetary scale is used to measure monetary value of anything. The kilogram scale is used to measure weight. The centimeter scale is used to measure length. The miles-per-gallon scale is used to measure consumption of gasoline by cars. The miles-per-hour scale is used to measure speed. All these cases are examples of commonly used ratio scales.

2.4 VARIABLES AND STATISTICAL DATA

A collection of measurements of the elementary units, either of a population or of a sample, is called a *data set.* The measurements contained in a data set are called *data points,* or *variates.* All the data points or variates of each data set constitute a *variable.* A "variable" is very important in statistical analysis and is related to statistical data—the raw material of statistics. We shall take a close look at these two related concepts in this section.

When we make observations or measurements on a set of elementary units, we usually find differences among observed units with respect to the characteristic being observed. Because of the variability that exists among the observations, *characteristics of obsevations* are generally referred to as *variables*. In statistics, the definition of a variable is quite broad. Formally speaking, a *variable* is any observable characteristic with respect to which the elementary units in a population or a sample may differ and may be described. As presented below, there are two important ways to classify different kinds of variables.

Quantitative and Qualitative Variables

First, since a characteristic of observation may be either a *quantity,* such as the age of a person, or a *quality,* such as the sex of a person, statistical variables may be either quantitative or qualitative. A *quantitative variable* results when the data points differ from each other in magnitudes or amounts of some characteristic. A *qualitative variable* arises when the data points differ in kind from each other with respect to the characteristic being observed. Wages of U.S. Steel workers, ages of undergraduates, prices of a given commodity charged by different sellers, annual incomes of families, and so on, are examples of quantitative variables. Examples of qualitative variables include the quality (by some criterion) of items in a shipment of cargo, voters' registration according to party affiliations, ratings such as excellent, good, average, and poor for the performance of workers on a given job, and the like.

Quantitative characteristics of elementary units are sometimes called *traits*. Traits can be transformed into numerical data simply by direct measurement in units, such as inches, pounds, dollars, calories. The results of measuring the quantities of the elementary units form the totality of observations that are expressed numerically in terms of the units of measurement used.

When the characteristics are qualitative, the elementary units can be classified only as having or not having a certain quality or property. Nevertheless, the qualitative observations of elementary units, which are called *attributes,* may often be expressed numerically. We do this by counting the elementary units that have a certain attribute, such as males in a human population, or satisfactory or nondefective items in a population of some industrial products. In the process of enumerating, we score "one" for an element that has the attribute and "zero" for one that lacks it. We are in effect assigning the qualitative observations numerical values, 0 or 1. With the completion of counting we can get the total by adding the 1's together, obtaining a numerical result. In general, we convert qualitative data into numerical terms through the method of *enumeration.* By this method, the observations are sorted into categories or classes on the basis of the various attributes of the variable, then we count the number of elements possessing each attribute. This quantitative expression of qualitative data opens up to statistical treatment many areas beyond the reach of direct measurement.

Often, quantitative data can also be treated qualitatively if the nature of the problem demands it. As an example, the age of a person in a community is quantitative, but it can also be treated as an attribute if we are interested in, say, estimating the eligible voters in that community. In this decision problem, each person may be characterized by either of the two attributes: being of voting age or being of nonvoting age. Treating a quantitative trait as a qualitative attribute is quite common in statistical work.

Continuous and Discrete Variables

The second way to classify variables is in terms of the difference between continuous and discrete scales of measurement. On a *continuous scale,* an observation may have any conceivable value within a particular range. Characteristics that are measurable on continuous scales are referred to as *continuous variables*. Scales of time, weight, and length, for example, are continuous. Thus, time, weight, and length are all continuous variables. On the other hand, a *discrete scale* is one on which there are breaks or gaps between any two possible values that an observation may have. A characteristic that can only be measured on a discrete scale is called a *discrete variable*. For instance, a family may have 1, 2, 3, or 8 children; but to have 2.5 or 5.72 children or any other fractional unit is clearly an impossibility. Again, the highest degree of precision in measuring family income is to the nearest cent. The variable cannot take any value ending in a fraction of one cent. Hence, number of children and family income are discrete variables.

Although the theoretical distinction between continuous and discrete variables is clear and precise, in practical statistical work it is only an approximation. The reason is that even the most precise instruments of measurement can be used only to a finite number of numerical places. Thus, no theoretically continuous variable can ever be expected to flow continuously with one measurement touching another without any break in actual observations. However, this practical drawback should not invalidate the simplifying assumption of the continuity of quantitative observations in statistical theory. Moreover, as will be explained elsewhere in this text, in the application of statistical methods it is often helpful to treat discrete series as if they were continuous. What should be kept in mind is that, in interpreting and using statistical results, the investigator should always pay attention to the logical distinction between the continuous and the discrete variables.

We have mentioned many times that statistics is concerned with numerical data. From our discussion on scales, we note that, depending on the scale of measurement, we have the four-way classification of data: nominal, ordinal, interval, and ratio data. Via our presentation of variables, we have made the distinction between qualitative, quantitative, discrete, and continuous data.

It may now be noted that there are still two other ways to classify statistical data. The first is that numerical data may be classified as cross-section or time series. *Cross-section data* are those gathered at a given point of time, such as the number of defective items in a lot of radios, or tensile strengths of steel wires of a certain make, or the wage rates of auto workers in a given year. A *time series* consists of a collection of observations recorded over a period of time, such as annual production figures of General Motors since 1945 or the changes in population in the United States every ten years since 1800.

The second important way of classifying data is in terms of the number of characteristics of the same set of elementary units being observed. In this connection, data may be univariate, bivariate, or multivariate. *Univariate data* refer to a single variable, such as the IQ's of a group of children of the same age, or the grades of students in an economics class. Alternatively, we see that univariate data result from observing a specific characteristic of each element in a population or sample. Sometimes, we may wish to observe two distinct traits of each element under consideration, such as weights and heights of adult men. Then our observations would produce two distinct variables, the weight and the height, which are appropriately called *bivariate data*. Similarly, three or more distinct properties may be observed simultaneously about each element, such as the family income, family food consumption expenditure, and the size of family, so that *multivariate data* are obtained.

So far our discussions of statistical data and their classifications have concentrated on the differences of nature among different data sets. We shall now turn our attention to the types of statistical data in terms of sources from which data are generated. Such a discussion will directly lead us to the presentation of various sources of data and methods of their collection.

2.5 STATISTICAL DATA CLASSIFIED BY SOURCES

From the point of view of origins, statistical data can be classified into two categories. First, there are those obtained firsthand in connection with a specific decision problem. Such information is called *primary data,* and a study made from it is referred to as a *primary study*. Second, there are those data useful for a given decision problem, but collected for other purposes and already published in books, magazines, newspapers, government publications, corporate reports, and the like. This type of numerical information is called *secondary data* and a survey based upon it is referred to as a *secondary study*.

Secondary data can be further classified as internal or external. *Internal data* come from the internal records related to operations of a business firm: records of shipments, personnel files, production figures, the accounting system, and so forth. *External data* are collected and published by agencies external to the enterprise.

Moreover, external data are of two distinct sources: primary and secondary. The *source* of external data is referred to as *primary* when the data are released or published by the organization that collected them. When the data are released or published by an organization other than the one that collected them, they are said to be from a *secondary source*.

In the solution of a problem, primary data will be the most reliable, provided, of course, that the investigator is not biased and has the appropriate skills and training. Internal data are also highly useful for many types of decision problems. For this reason, management should have its internal records in such form as to facilitate their use for statistical decisions.

However, the use of either primary or internal data for decision making has great limitations. Primary data may prove too expensive and time-consuming to collect, and internal data may be either insufficient or inappropriate for the problem to be solved. In a highly interdependent economy, many managerial decisions of a firm require information about the industry to which it belongs and about economic conditions throughout the whole nation. Thus, decision making often demands data external to the enterprise being studied.

When external data are used, a primary source is often preferred to a secondary source. The superiority of the former over the latter is twofold. In the first place, the primary source shows, as a rule, more information concerning the collection procedure, the sampling design, definitions of terms and units, and so on; thus, it often gives us more adequate information with which to evaluate the appropriateness of the data for our own problem. In the second place, a secondary source may contain additional errors of transcription, because of faulty reproduction or inept or prejudiced manipulation of the primary source. The distinct advantage of secondary sources is their convenience. An example is the *Statistical Abstract of the United States,* which reproduces data from a large number of diverse primary sources, and enables us to find in a single volume many of the facts we want.

In using external data, either from primary or secondary sources, we must exercise extreme caution. Here, we are dealing with data we did not see for ourselves. They have been seen through the eyes of others and analyzed by other minds. We must therefore constantly ask ourselves many qustions about external data: Does the collecting agency have skilled observers of this particular type of material? Were the data obtained by a reliable procedure? Do the data contain complete or sample information? If it is a sample, how was it selected? Is the collecting agency open-minded or biased? Were the facts compiled honestly or were they presented in order to propagandize a particular position or claim? All this is not to say that external data may not be valid, but that we must carefully investigate each existing source in regard to these questions so that we may have confidence in the applicability of external data to the problem at hand. In the Appendix to this chapter, the sources of external data for business and economic studies are given.

2.6 METHODS OF COLLECTING EXTERNAL DATA

The existence of vast and rich sources of external data enables us to solve many business and economic problems without collecting original data ourselves. Nevertheless, an understanding of the procedures of data collection is of immense value to any student of statistics. In the first place, we may sometimes find that adequate secondary data are not available for the problem at hand. Moreover, such an understanding will enable us to evaluate data taken from the existing sources. A full discussion of data collection is, however, beyond the scope of this textbook. What we intend to do in the following pages is to give the reader a working knowledge of the proper procedures by introducing some of the basic features on this topic.

The collection of data refers to the methods of obtaining pertinent information from the elementary units under study. It may be noted at the outset that the method of collecting data from nonhuman populations is, for some problems, often simple and direct. For instance, if we are interested in studying the length of steel wires, we need only to measure them. Or if we want to determine whether certain textiles are of the right color, we need only to look at them. For other problems, the procedures of observing elementary units of nonhuman populations are highly complicated and technical. For example, to discover whether flaws exist in aluminum castings, fluoroscope or X-ray inspection is usually required. In a case like this, the choice of method is often beyond the ability of the statistician; it is therefore made by the expert in the field—say, the chemist or the engineer. For these reasons, we shall concentrate our attention on the basic methods of data collection that are useful in surveys dealing with human populations.

Data on human populations can be collected by making direct observations or by asking questions. In either method, appropriate recording is made of the results. These records of the observations or of the answers, constitute the original data from which the statistician prepares his tables and graphs for further analysis.

Direct Observation

The method of direct observation, which is also referred to as direct counting, is quite appropriate and highly efficient for collecting some types of statistical data. For example, traffic studies, which provide useful information for planning streets, highways, bridges, and so on, regularly use this method. Observers are stationed to count and record the number of vehicles that pass a given point. This method may also be used to collect data on the number of people passing a prospective location for a store in a business district. A hand-held counter that records a cumulative total as it is clicked is highly useful for on-the-spot counting. Recently, automatic devices have been introduced to facilitate direct counting. For example, in deciding on parking fees to charge and on maximum allowable parking time, the photoelectric cell has been used in big cities to record the number of cars using municipal parking facilities at various hours of the day. Again, a recording device such as the audimeter used by the A.C. Nielsen Company is employed to record the number of television sets that are turned on as well as the stations being tuned in. The most up-to-date generation of this system uses the Storage Instantaneous Audimeter. This device automatically stores, in electronic memory, data on television stations tuned in. Nielsen has a central computer that dials these memories on the telephone twice a day and collects the information from them. The psychogalvanometer is another automatic device for making observations. This machine measures minute emotional reactions through changes in the rate of perspiration, much like a lie detector. Advertisements can be tested for relative impact by showing them to respondents and measuring the emotional response of the respondent on the galvanometer.

The great value of direct observation is that it usually gives more accurate information than do questionnaires. The audimeter, for example, generally yields more accurate data on the TV program preferences of the audience than would be yielded by asking them what programs they are watching. However, the amount and type of data that can be collected by direct counting is often limited. Furthermore, this method is frequently very expensive and often cannot be adapted to the sampling procedures desired. Consequently, information on human populations is largely obtained by asking questions of those who possess it.

Questioning People

Needed information can be secured by several methods of communication. The most frequently employed devices are personal interviews, mail questionnaires, and telephone interviews. Advantages and disadvantages of different methods vary with circumstances. In general, a method is considered the best in a given survey if it will obtain the needed information with the highest degree of accuracy, with the lowest costs, and in the shortest time.

When the personal interview technique is employed, a relatively high proportion of usable returns may be obtained from persons approached. By explaining the purpose and importance of the survey, the interviewer arouses interest in it. With a planned approach, the interviewer can get the respondent talking and thereby improve the chance of a successful completion of the interview. In addition to its having a high degree of accuracy, the information can be obtained directly from the source and can be verified at that time.

The physical presence of the interviewer, which is the main advantage of the personal interview, is also a major disadvantage. Subjective factors are involved in recording by interview. By the inflections of the voice, by the motions of the eyebrows—in fact, by facial expression—and by the way the interviewer may word questions, the interviewer can considerably influence or bias the answers of the respondent. It is most important, therefore, that the interviewer does not let personal judgment influence the respondent. Also, this method is not efficient when many people, scattered over a wide area, are to be included in the survey, since the time and expense involved necessarily mean a limited field coverage.

The main advantage of mail surveys is that a wide area may be covered easily and quickly at relatively low cost. Using mail questionnaires, there is no need to train interviewers, but, instead, it is necessary to prepare a standardized set of questions. This method has another advantage in that it encourages the respondent to answer questions frankly in the privacy of the home, and without the subjective influence of the interviewer.

Low response rate is the major shortcoming of mail questionnaires. Only 10–20 percent respond in ordinary mail surveys, a fact that suggests that those who respond are highly motivated, and so are not typical of the whole group to which the questionnaire was mailed. Clearly, to ensure the success of mail questionnaires, the cooperation of the respondents must be solicited. Thus, the Bureau of Labor Statistics receives mailed forms from thousands of business firms throughout the country each month; and many marketing research agencies receive mailed reports from respondents who have agreed to serve on a consumer panel. Moreover, to avoid serious bias in the results, nonresponse must be investigated. This is usually done by supplementary mail questionnaires with follow-up letters. Then, if necessary and not too expensive, personal interviews of the nonrespondents may be undertaken. The combination of mail survey and personal interview is the best and most economical method of collecting data. No wonder it has become most widely used in survey work.

Telephone interviews stand between personal interviews and mail questionnaires in terms of costs as well as reliability. Although telephone interviews are slightly more expensive than mail surveys, they have a much lower refusal rate.

The telephone interview finds its main application in determining the size of television and radio audiences. This method requires that the questions be simple and short. In a typical telephone interview, for instance, the following set of questions may be used.

1. Do you have a television set?

2. Were you watching television just now?

3. What program were you watching?

4. Over which channel is the program coming?

5. What is the name of the sponsor of the program?

6. Please tell me how many people were watching television when the telephone rang?

Whatever the method used to seek information by questioning people, the first thing to do is to plan the questionnaire carefully. The best way to ensure that the queries are stated properly is to pretest them on a small pilot sample and make the necessary improvements on the basis of the response before they are used on a large scale.

Some general principles of good questioning technique must be kept in mind. First, questions must be stated simply and clearly so that there may be no doubt in the mind of the respondent as to their meaning. Second, only questions that the respondent will and can answer correctly may be asked. Incorrect information and erroneous results often arise when questions concerning individual prestige (income, social status, job responsibilities), questions concerning emotional issues (sexual behavior, for example), or questions concerning personal bias or prejudice (religious or political affiliations, race, personal ethics) are asked. Whenever information on those topics is needed the questions should be formulated in such a way that emotional response and embarrassment may be reduced. It would also be helpful to assure the respondent that information will remain completely confidential. Third, if possible, questions should be short and answers should require the least amount of effort. To this end, questions are preferred whose answers consist of a "yes" or a "no," a check or a blank space, or a numerical indication. Fourth, each question should require only one response. Finally, questions must be logically constructed and so arranged as to facilitate the tabulation of the answers.

From a mechanical point of view, there are four main types of questions. First, there are the *forced-choice questions*. A question of this type requires the respondent to answer with a simple choice between "yes" or "no," "right" or "wrong," "for" or "against," or "true" or "false." The simple alternative question is an excellent device, but it is limited to a situation in which a clear-cut alternative exists. For example, it is appropriate to prepare a question such as this:

Do you have a washing machine at your home?
    Yes( )   No( )

However, it would be misleading and confusing to ask:

Are you in favor of the policies of the Democratic party?
    Yes( )   No( )

Clearly, to the latter question a single "yes" or "no" cannot be the answer: A political party stands for many policies and only the most partisan individual may oppose or favor them all.

Second, there are the *multiple-choice questions*. In this type of question several possible answers are prepared for the respondent to select. Multiple-choice questions are appropriate when several factual responses exist, or when varying degrees of opinion are expected. For example:

1. Where did you buy your new television set?
    ( ) A department store
    ( ) A store selling radios and television sets exclusively
    ( ) An electrical appliance store
    ( ) A mail-order house
    ( ) Other ____ (Please specify)

2. How would you describe your feelings toward the use of a high interest rate as an anti-inflation policy?
    ( ) Strongly in favor of it
    ( ) In favour of it

( ) Strongly opposed to it
( ) Opposed to it
( ) Uncertain

Third, there are the *specific information questions*. A question of this type seeks information on a specific item: "What is your age?" "When did you graduate from high school?" "What kind of television do you own?" Although this type of question is simple and direct, we must be careful to use it only when the respondent can and will answer it correctly. For instance, it would be impossible for most drivers to answer a question such as "What is the acceleration in feet per second of your car?" Again, a question concerning premarital sexual behavior may either cause nonresponse due to embarrassment or receive a lurid embellished reply due to pride in erotic conquests.

Finally, there are the *open-ended questions*. An open-ended question calls for a reply in the respondent's own words. An example would be: "What is your opinion as to why our auto industry is in trouble today?" The merit of this type of question is that the respondent is not influenced by someone else's prepared answers. It is believed that the respondent's own statement could be more meaningful than one suggested by the investigator. One limitation of the open question is the difficulty of tabulating the results. Since a great variety of answers will be given to an open question, not only are numerous classifications required but the classifications themselves may fail to be exclusive of each other.

2.7 EDITING AND TABULATING RESULTS

When data have been collected, they must be edited and then tabulated. In editing the questionnaires or schedules, the investigator tries to discover omissions of responses and computational errors, and detect inconsistency and lack of uniformity in answers. All this must be carefully edited before tabulation is performed.

Data are tabulated from questionnaires in accordance with some predesignated classifications that follow logically from the nature and number of questions. Thus, answers to a forced-choice question will be distributed into "yes" and "no" categories. Similarly, results of multiple-choice questions will be classified in accordance with the prepared answers, each being a separate class. If necessary and convenient, answers to two or more questions may be cross-classified—classified in terms of two or more categories.

Tabulation can be performed manually or by machines. Automated machinery is frequently used when relatively large surveys are made. The data are transferred from the questionnaires or schedules to the computer, thus creating a data bank. Once these data have been stored in computer memory, computer programs can summarize the data and give printouts of the responses to each question that are the same, the number of people who have answered the question the same way, and so forth.

2.8 DATA PRESENTATION: STATISTICAL TABLES

After data have been collected and tabulated, they are usually presented in the form of tables or charts. Statistical tables and charts may serve as preparation for further analysis, or as the final product of a survey presented to management or the public. To serve this dual purpose, tables and charts must be constructed so that they are clear as well as attractive. Although clarity can be obtained by observing certain basic rules, attractiveness demands their application with imagination and originality. Thus, data presentation is at once both a science and an art.

In our discussion of statistical tables, we shall stress only basic principles sufficient to indicate proper procedures. Examples will not be given but you should look at any issue of *Statistical Abstract,* which contains all sorts of tables.

It may now be noted that *a statistical table* is a systematic arrangement of data in labeled columns and rows. Tables, classified according to function, are of two types: general-purpose tables and specific-purpose tables. The *general-purpose table,* which is also called a *primary* or *reference table,* is designed mainly for statisticians. It represents the raw data in great detail and makes no effort to draw comparisons. The general-purpose table is a repository of a large number of data, covering a variety of information on the same subject. It may, therefore, serve as the basis for a number of specific purpose tables. Because of the function of a general table, it should contain actual and absolute figures instead of rounded and percentage values. Also, it must be designed so that people can easily find the information that they are looking for.

The *specific-purpose table* is often called by other names such as *summary table, text table,* and *analytical table.* It is constructed so as to emphasize facts or relationships. In a summary table, rounded figures may be used when the values involved are large, and percentages can be employed when they facilitate comparisons or analyses. A summary table must be smaller than a general table from which it is drawn. In practice, it is much better to prepare several summary tables, each analyzing one problem, than to prepare a large summary table that analyzes several different problems.

Although practice varies, there are nevertheless generally accepted rules for the construction of statistical tables:

1. Every table must contain a unified set of relationships. In general, each table should be devoted to one topic, although data may be cross-classified in several ways. Moreover, the table should show the relationship of the parts that make up the whole. This is done by integrating the various parts of a table in an orderly and clear arrangement, as indicated by the following example.

2. When more than one table is contained in a report or book, each

TABLE Number Title

Head Note

	Master Caption		
Stub	Column Label	Column Label	} Boxhead
Row Label	Cell	Cell	
" "	"	"	
" "	"	"	} Body
" "	"	"	

Footnotes
Source note

table must have a number. The tables are conventionally numbered in sequence in a given presentation, so that they may be
consulted easily.

3. A table must have a title. This should inform the reader in a brief
   but precise manner of the answers to the questions: What is the
   nature of the data presented? What area (where) do the data
   cover? What time period (when) do the data cover? How are the
   data classified?

4. A headnote is frequently used to give additional information about
   the data that is crowded out of the title.

5. Both stub and boxhead must be clearly worded.

6. The body or field of a table contains the figures that the table is
   designed to present to the reader. The significance of each figure is
   set forth in the stub and caption entries.

7. Footnotes are used to explain anything that is not self-evident in
   the table. A numeral is generally used to key a footnote that
   explains a word in the table. A letter or some other type of
   nonnumerical symbol should be used to key a footnote that
   explains a figure. A footnote is placed immediately below the table
   and above the source.

8. The source note appears below the footnotes, if any are used, and
   below the stub and body, if no footnotes are used. The source note
   should give pertinent information about the place from which the
   data in the table were secured. When hypothetical data are
   involved, the source may say "hypothetical," or "fictitious." Very
   often in text books, when hypothetical data are used for illustration, the source note may be omitted if it is clear from the
   discussion.

9. General rulings of lines are as follows:

   a. horizontal line should be placed under the title and below the body of the table.

   b. The stub and boxhead must be separated from the figures by lines.

   c. It is useful, though not essential, that columns be separated by single lines.

   d. totals should be separated from other figures in a column by a single line.

10. Arrangement of data in the stub must follow some logical or conventional order so that reading, comparison, and analysis may be facilitated. Appropriate arrangement in a given situation depends upon the nature of the data and the purpose and emphasis of the table. Several commonly used arrangements follow:

    a. Data may be arranged alphabetically. This arrangement is most frequently used in general tables. Its chief advantage is that the reader may find the data in a lengthy table with less effort.

    b. Data may be arranged according to magnitude or size. When this arrangement is used, data may be placed in descending or ascending order. This practice facilitates comparisons between items that are relatively close to each other in value. It also has the advantage of quickly showing the reader the relative importance of each item.

    c. In presenting time series or historical data, the stub entries of a table are arranged chronologically, usually from the earlier years to the most recent years. An exception to this rule occurs when the latest figures are of primary interest, because they are published for the first time. In this instance the latest figure may be placed before others, then separated from them by an empty space or a heavy line.

    d. Data may be arranged geographically. This practice requires that the arrangement be in conformity with the customary classifications. For instance, one familiar geographical division has this sequence: New England, Middle Atlantic, East North Central, West North Central, South Atlantic, and so on.

    e. Data may be arranged according to customary classifications. For example, in the volume of the census, the word "male" is usually entered in the stub before the word "female" when distributions according to sex are being prepared. The sections of the census involving racial origin invariably list data in the stub in this order: White, Black, Spanish origin, Asian and Pacific Islands, American Indian, Eskimo, Aleutian, and Other.

    f. Tables may sometimes be prepared with stub items arranged in a manner referred to as progressive. In such an arrangement, the items under consideration usually read logically from one to the next. The conventional income statements are an illustration.

11. The totals of columns should be placed at the bottom of the columns and row totals should be placed at the extreme right of each row. This practice may be reversed if the table stresses the totals.

12. Tables should be constructed in such a way that they have a balanced appearance, that is, the table should be approximately as wide as it is long. If it is impossible to construct a balanced table, it is considered better to make the table relatively long and narrow than short and wide.

2.9 GRAPHIC PRESENTATION

In the words of that old Chinese proverb, (coined by Fred R. Barnard), "A picture is worth a thousand words." The wide use of pictures in all kinds of publications in modern times surely confirms this. The picture-language of statistics is the graph. *A graph* may be considered as a device for presenting numerical data in visual form. It can show the changes in some variable quantity, such as production, prices, sales, or employment, much more quickly and clearly than can a table of values. Although people often think that the main purpose of the graph is to present information more vividly to the reader, the graph is also capable of bringing facts to the statisticians' attention that might not have been noticed from studying a table of figures. Indeed, to present numerical results graphically is one of the first logical steps toward the analysis or interpretation of data. The investigation of numerical relationships from columns of raw figures may be difficult even for experts; the same data in graphic form may tell a simple and precise story.

Many varieties of graphs have been devised. The selection of a particular type in a given situation depends upon the characteristics of the data and the purpose the graph is to serve. Graphs are constructed by using the coordinate plane and by observing the same basic rules (except rules 9 and 11) for constructing statistical tables as given in the preceding section. In applying these same rules in constructing graphs, however, some modifications or deviations may be observed. First, although the table title must always be placed at the top, the graph title may be placed either above or below the body of the graph. Second, just as the headings for both columns and rows in a table must be clearly worded, the axes, lines, bars, and so on in a graph, must all be properly labeled. Third, if a balanced appearance is to be achieved in a graph, extreme scales should be avoided. Changes in values of the varying quantity to be emphasized should be represented by approximately a squared graph. If it is impossible to construct a balanced graph, it is considered better to draw the graph relatively short and wide than to make it long and narrow. This practice is just the opposite of table construction. Last, the principle of presenting data as attractively as possible is especially important in graph construction. As a result, adherence to the rules must be mixed with artistic considerations.

The multiplicity of graphs may be classified into the following types: (1) line or curve graphs, (2) bar charts, (3) area diagrams, (4) solid diagrams, and (5) statistical maps. In this section we shall discuss briefly the nature and use of the various types of graphs. Illustrations of the more important types of graphs will be given in the following section.

Line or Curve Graphs

As the name implies, *line* or *curve graphs* present variations in data by means of a line or curve. This type of graph is especially adaptable to the portrayal of changes in a variable over time. When charting a time series, it is customary to measure time along the horizontal axes and the related variable on the vertical axes. Points representing the varying values are shown, and, to facilitate interpretation, are connected with straight lines.

Line graphs differ from each other by differences in scale rulings. The most commonly employed are the arithmetic and semilogarithmic rulings. On an *arithmetically ruled paper,* equal distances between the coordinate lines are allocated to changes that are equal in amounts. Thus, for instance, the distance from $1 to $5 must be the same as the distance from $10 to $14. It is most important that the scale on the vertical axis of an arithmetically ruled graph begin with zero at the origin. Otherwise an erroneous impression of the extent of changes may be created. In every instance, because of the great swings of variations or the big difference between the minimum and maximum values of the variable, where the scale does not begin with zero or where the scale "jumps," as 0, 50, 100, 150, 250, 300, the fact must be clearly indicated on the graph by a scale break.

Arithmetically ruled graphs are designed to show changes in absolute amount. In interpreting this type of graph, one should bear in mind that an arithmetic progression—one whose successive values are of constant differences—will plot in a straight line. Also, equal changes are assigned equal distances.

Even when an arithmetic graph is properly constructed, it has severe limitations for many types of analysis. In the first place, it is difficult to compare relative rates of change in the series. Second, when series that differ greatly in magnitude are compared, it frequently becomes difficult to determine the extent of the fluctuations in the series with the smaller values. Third, an arithmetic graph does not help the reader to determine whether one series of data is increasing or decreasing at a more rapid rate than other series of data that are plotted in the same field. Finally, the arithmetic graph does not lend itself to comparisons between series of data that are expressed in different units.

To overcome these limitations and to enable the reader of a graph to perceive relative rates of change or to compare different series quickly and easily, economists and statisticians frequently use semilogarithmic ruling, rather than the conventional arithmetic ruling for line graphs. On the *semilogarithmic graph* changes in time along the X axis are measured as usual. On the Y scale, however, the distances between scale marks are proportional to the logarithms of the units instead of the units themselves. For example, since the logarithm of 4 is to the logarithm of 2 as the logarithm of 10 is to the logarithm of 5, the distance between 4 and 2 is the same as the distance between 10 and 5. That is, on an arithmetic scale, equal distances represent equal absolute amounts of change; equal distances in the direction of the logarithmic scale represent equal ratios of proportions or percentages of change.

One important difference between semilogarithmic ruling and arithmetic ruling is that the former can never start with zero at the origin on the axis with the logarithmic scale, even though the other axis can have the entire range of real numbers. The reason is that any change from zero to a positive value would represent an infinitely great percentage increase and, hence, cannot be shown.

The actual number employed to start a logarithmic scale depends upon the range of the variable. What should be remembered is that the number will be multiplied 10 times for a cycle of the scale, that is, the number at the top of the cycle will be 10 times the initial number. Thus, if the scale starts with 1, the numbers on the scale would follow the sequence 1, 2, 3, 4, 5, 6, 7, 8, 9, and 10. Similarly, if the scale starts with 15 it would read 15, 30, 45, 60, 75, 90, 105, 120, 135, and 150. This is due to the fact that a log scale measures relative or percentage increase, and each complete cycle represents an increase of one power of 10, as from 1 to 10, 15 to 150, or 100 to 1000.

The great advantage of the semilogarithmic graph is that one can compare relative rates of change by a glance at the slope of the curve or curves. For instance, a variable that is changing at a constant rate per unit of time will result in a straight line on such a graph. In other words, a curve of the exponential type becomes a straight line when plotted on a semilogarithmic graph. Thus, the growth curve of any sum of money at compound interest takes the form of a straight line when so plotted.

Several special types of line or curve graphs are commonly used. One of these, a *silhouette chart,* is a line graph that shows the positive and negative deviations from a zero or base line. it is constructed by plotting points that indicate the actual deviations from the base line. These points are then connected by straight lines, and the area between the curve and the base line is filled in.

The second is the *band chart*. This is a type of line graph that shows variations in the component parts as well as in the total of a series. In the construction of such a chart, the variations of the largest component part are plotted first. The next-largest component part is then added to the first component and the result is plotted. This cumulative process is continued until all the component parts are included. Each segment is then shaded or cross-hatched. The variations in the top line show the variations in the total, while variations of a particular component are represented by the width of the corresponding segment. This type of chart focuses attention on the changing relationships among the components of the total.

The third variation of the line graph is the *high–low chart,* which shows the variations over time and the changes within a period, such as a day, a week, or a month. In this type of graph, vertical bars are drawn to represent the high and the low values for each period. When a high–low graph is employed to present daily stock prices, a horizontal line is drawn on each vertical line to indicate the closing price. Illustrations of high–low graphs can be found in many daily newspapers, such as *The New York Times.*

Bar Charts

Graphs of the bar chart type are used to contrast quantities by comparing columns of varying length but of uniform width. The columns or bars may be set up either horizontally or vertically. Vertical bars are usually used when time series data are involved. Horizontal bars are frequently used to present data classified according to categories.

Bar charts can be employed effectively to compare the relative values over time, or for a stated period of several time series. They are also well adapted to the presentation of the component parts of a given aggregate: the bar chart subdivided for this purpose may be constructed by using the absolute values or made to show the percentage distribution of an aggregate.

Bar charts are sometimes constructed in pictorial form. Pictures of different heights or lengths may be used for comparative purposes.

Area Diagrams

Area diagrams attempt to compare quantities by comparing figures with varying areas. In this type of presentation, total areas of different size may be compared by varying the sizes of the figures, or a single area may be subdivided for comparison.

The most frequently used area diagram is the *pie chart,* a diagram of circular shape broken into sections. Its construction is based on the fact that each circle is divided into 360°. Let the circle equal 100%; therefore, 1% equals 3.6°. Thus, if a protractor is used to draw the chart, we must multiply the percentage value by 3.6 before plotting the sectors on the circle in degrees. The chart is usually drawn beginning at 12 o'clock with the pieces of pie going from largest to smallest in a clockwise direction. (However, this rule is often ignored by many graphers.) Since it is difficult to estimate relative values visually with any degree of accuracy, the proportionate size of the sectors of a pie chart or actual values should be indicated in the diagram. Pie charts are especially adaptable to percentage data and are particularly suited to portraying budgets. One pie may be used to show the sources of revenue and another to show expenditures.

Solid Diagrams

Solid diagrams are designed to show varying values by varying volumes. One drawback of this type of diagram is that it is extremely difficult for a reader to make accurate comparisons between the values that are represented by volumes of different sizes. Whenever other devices are available, solid diagrams should not be used for data presentation.

Statistical Maps

Statistical maps present in pictorial form, the numerical facts of geographic or spatial distributions. The proportionate quantities for different areas may be represented by different colors, by varying degrees of shading or cross-hatching, by dots of similar size with different densities of the numbers of dots, by dots of proportional sizes, and so on.

2.10 ILLUSTRATIONS OF GRAPHS

All illustrations of statistical graphs or charts in this section are reproduced, substantially unchanged, from various publications. Some of the charts are originally in multicolor and thus are much more attractive than the reproductions here. When you study these examples, you should recall the basic rules for graph construction and compare any deviations (which may be acceptable, even desirable practices from the artistic point of view), from some of the rules presented previously. It is important too for you to acquire the ability to absorb the information from these charts. You should study and interpret each graphic display by yourself, as well as you can, before reading the brief description of it in the text. A good start for this purpose is to be sure of the meaning of each variable graphed.

Chart 2.1 is an example of line graphs drawn on arithmetic scales. Both panels of the chart show vividly and artistically the runaway costs of weapons during period 1950–1982. Because of its simplicity and effectiveness no additional remarks are required to the information provided by this chart. However, the story behind the information may be of interest to students of social sciences; indeed, to the American people in general, since inflation is only a minor cause for the "less bang for the buck"!

Chart 2.2 consists of two panels again. Both are line graphs, with the upper panel drawn against the ratio, or semilog, scale. The most interesting point to be observed is that the composite-stock price index clearly seems to have a negative relationship with the earnings–price ratio on common stocks. Furthermore, this relationship would appear to be more pronounced if the composite stock price index is plotted against arithmetic scale. You should be able to explain this comment by recalling the difference between ratio and arithmetic scales.

Chart 2.3 is an illustration of a vertical bar chart. It displays the changes in manufactured exports from Central America to the U.S. from

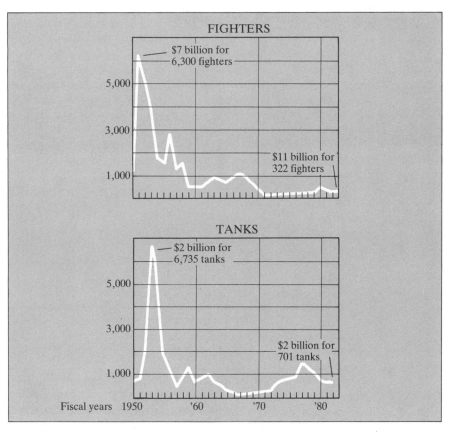

CHART 2.1 Less bang for the buck. (*Source:* Adapted from Franklin C. Spinney, "The Winds of Reform", *Time,* March 7, 1983, p. 16.)

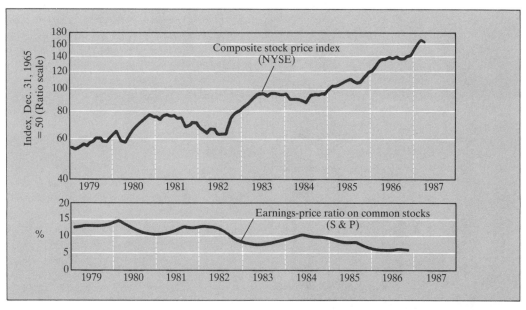

CHART 2.2 Common stock prices and yields, 1979–1987. (*Source:* Adapted from *Economic Indicators,* April 1, 1987, p. 31.)

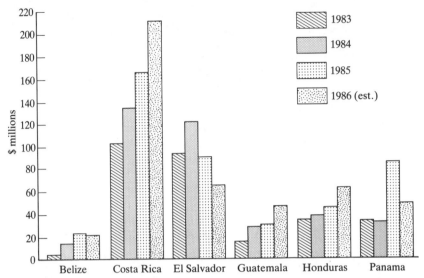

CHART 2.3 Central America: manufactured exports to the U.S., 1984–1986. (*Source:* Adapted from *Department of State Bulletin,* April, 1987, p. 67.)

1984 to 1986. Two things stand out clearly in this figure. First, Costa Rica is by far the most important exporter. Second, while Costa Rica, Guatemala and Honduras experienced continued growth of exports to the U.S., other countries' exports fluctuate from year to year with varying degrees.

The two panels in Chart 2.4 are again vertical bar charts. These charts show vividly the great discrepancy in conventional heavy

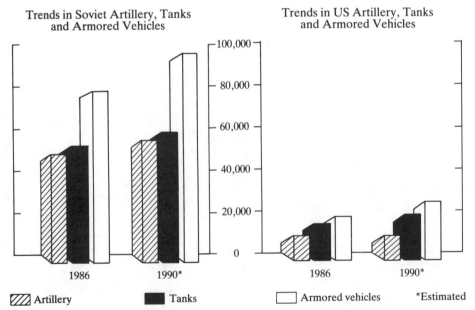

CHART 2.4 Trends of Soviet and U.S. conventional military hardwares, 1986–1990. (*Source:* Adapted from *Soviet Military Power,* U.S. Department of Defense, 1987, p. 12.)

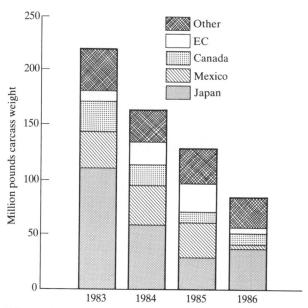

CHART 2.5 U.S. pork sales to Japan back up in '86 (*Source:* Adapted from *Agricultural Outlook,* May, 1987, p. 12.)

military weapons between the Soviet Union and the U.S., with the latter way behind either in terms 1986 existing volumes or in terms of estimated 1990 quantities.

Chart 2.5 is an illustration of component bar chart. It shows the continuous decline of U.S. pork sales to the selected countries. Overall, Japan has been the biggest importer of U.S. pork. In 1986, the extremely poor showing of U.S. pork exports was mainly because of the big drop in shipments to Mexico and EC.

The four diagrams in Chart 2.6 are all illustrations of the silhouette chart. Note that, in all of the first three (line) silhouette charts, double vertical scales are used to accommodate the differences in units for inventory and the inventory-to-sales ratio. Fluctuations in inventories from month to month and from year to year are the greatest with manufacturing, followed by retail trade, and with nondefense capital goods being the most stable. However, in terms of inventory-to-sales ratios, the reverse is true. The reasons behind these patterns of movement may be interesting to you. If so, you should read the source given to Chart 2.6. Finally, the relationship between change in inventory investment and that in GNP is not a clear one. From the fourth diagram alone one can only say that they seem to move in the same direction but with noticeable exceptions.

An example of a 100% band chart is given by Chart 2.7, which shows the changes in the composition of the total TIAA commitments from 1979 to 1985. The most striking features of these changes during the period are: (1) the decrease of long-term fixed-rate investment from nearly three-quarters to only one-third of the total commitments; (2) the increase of intermediate-term fixed-rate investment from a mere 1% to 31% of the total commitments; (3) the introduction of long-term rate-reset loans in 1980, its great increase the following year, its great

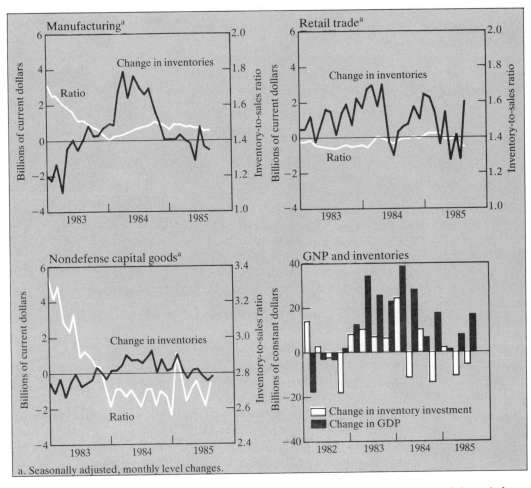

CHART 2.6 U.S. inventories and sales, 1983–1985. (*Source:* Adapted from *Economic Trends,* Federal Reserve Bank, Cleveland, December, 1985, p. 8.)

drops in 1982 and 1983, and its eventual complete disappearance since 1984. These features reflect TIAA's adoption of an investment policy to deal with uncertainties that surrounded the economy and the investment market in 1980s.

The *Economist* uses the four figures in Chart 2.8 to summarize the economic performance of President Reagan's first term in office. It was a mixed package. The greatest achievement of the Reagan administration was its ability to bring the double-digit inflation down steadily to only 2%, calculated as percentage increase from the previous month, in 1986. Unemployment rate increased from 7% to 9.5% at first and then decreased again to the original level. If the decline in unemployment, which began in 1983, can continue and unemployment can reach a level about 4.5% or so after 1986, it would be a great achievement too. On the whole, the average annual rate of increase in real GNP throughout his first term was only about 2%. This is rather disappointing relative to the previous performance of the American economy since World War II to the 1970s. The greatest failure of Reagan's first term was his trade

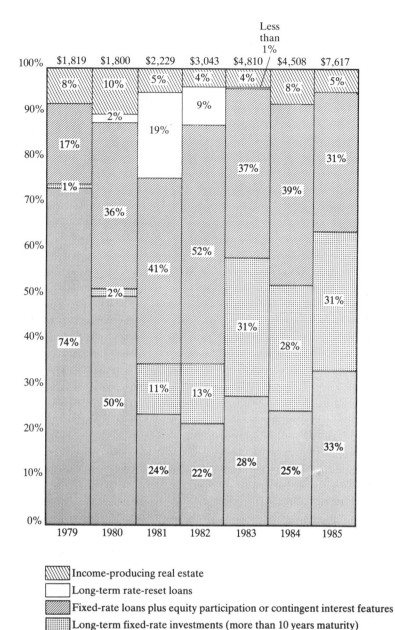

CHART 2.7 Total TIAA commitments 1979–1985 (millions). (*Source:* Adopted from *The 1985 Annual Report of TIAA and CREF,* p. 15.)

policy, which led to a continuous increase in trade deficit as well as current account balance; both reached all-time highs of about 175 and 143 billion dollars, respectively. At the time of writing of this volume (1987–1988) the trade deficit of the first half of Reagan's second term had continued its advances.

Chart 2.9 is an illustration of the band chart. This graph shows the development of federal involvement in the credit markets from 1960 to

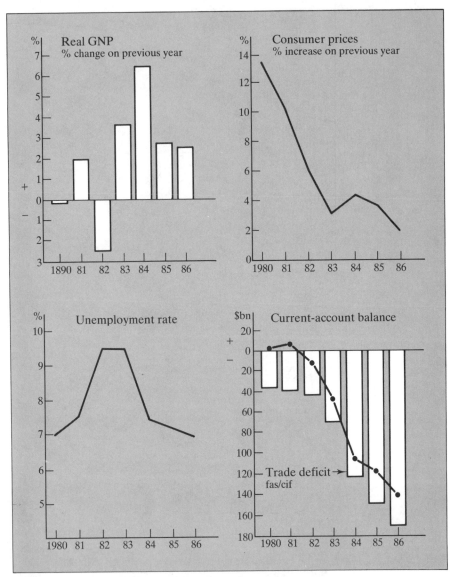

CHART 2.8 American survey. (*Source:* Adapted from *The Economist*, April, 1987, p. 21.)

1982 by type of debt outstanding, as percentage of GNP. The bottom layer of the chart represents the outstanding debt of state and local governments, which has remained stable in relation to GNP. The next layer is Federal debt outstanding less direct Federal loans (made to business and households) which has declined somewhat as a percentage of GNP since 1960. The third layer consists of debts that are loans made or guaranteed directly by government. Changes in this category seem to be quite mild relative to GNP. The fourth layer from the bottom represents deposits of commercial banks, thrift institutions, and credit unions issued by the Federal government less instruments of Federal

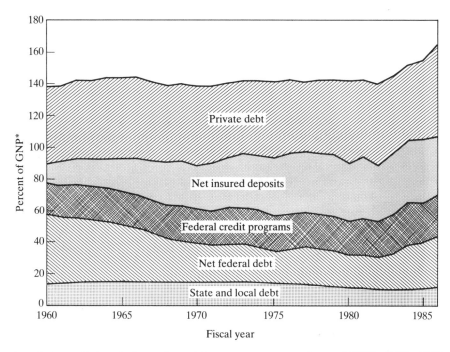

CHART 2.9 Debt of all nonfinancial sectors as percentage of GNP, 1960–1985. (*Source:* Adapted from *Economic Report of The President,* February, 1986).

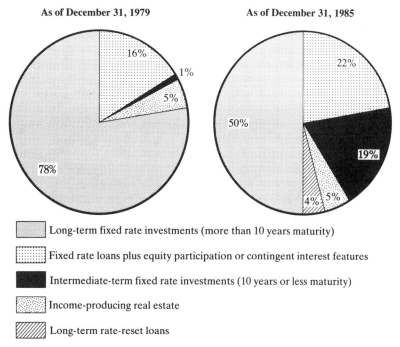

CHART 2.10 The TIAA portfolios for 1979 and 1985. (*Source:* Adapted from *The 1985 Annual Report of TIAA and CREF,* p. 14.)

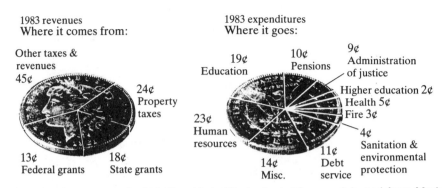

1983 revenues
Where it comes from:

Other taxes &
revenues
45¢

24¢
Property
taxes

13¢
Federal grants

18¢
State grants

1983 expenditures
Where it goes:

19¢
Education

10¢
Pensions

9¢
Administration
of justice

Higher education 2¢
Health 5¢
Fire 3¢

23¢
Human
resources

4¢
Sanitation &
environmental
protection

14¢
Misc.

11¢
Debt
service

CHART 2.11 Proposed 1983 New York City budget. (*Source:* Adapted from Mark Lieberman, "Koch Proposes $15.6b Budget," *Daily News*, N.Y., May 11, 1982, p. 2.)

debt obligations. The "net insured deposits" has increased considerably during the period 1959–1985. Completely private intermediate debt is represented by top layer. Overall, the level of government involvement as both borrower and lender has remained fairly stable between 148 and 162% of GNP throughout the whole period covered by the chart.

The two figures in Chart 2.10 are obviously examples of the pie chart. These two charts provide a comparison of TIAA's portfolios between 1979 and 1985. The most important difference between the two years' portfolios is that the composition of TIAA assets in 1985 are slightly more venturesome and much more flexible then those in 1979.

Chart 2.11 is another illustration of the pie chart with an artistic touch. The two pie charts presented the proposed 1983 budget of New

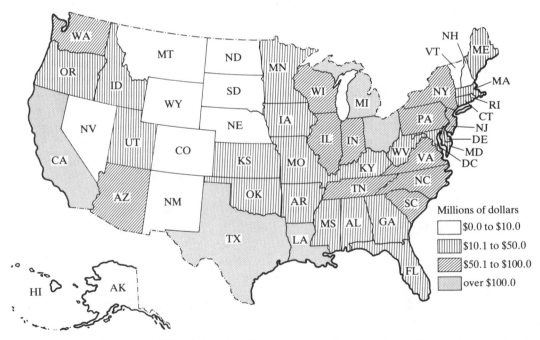

Millions of dollars

$0.0 to $10.0
$10.1 to $50.0
$50.1 to $100.0
over $100.0

CHART 2.12 Capital expenditures by manufacturers for pollution abatement, by state, 1984. (*Source:* Adapted from *Current Industrial Report, May, 1986.*)

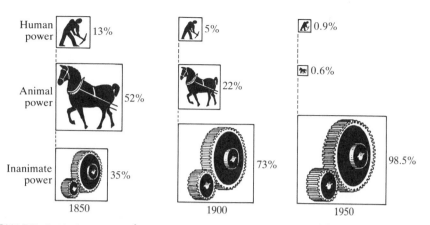

CHART 2.13 Inanimate "horsepower" has replaced muscle power. (*Source:* Adapted from T. R. Carskadon and George Soule, U.S.A. in *New Dimensions,* (New York, Macmillan, 1957), p. 6.)

York's Mayor Koch, totaling $15.6 billion. The first chart provides information on the sources of projected revenue, and the second gives information on projected expenditures. The interesting thing here is to evaluate the division of each revenue dollar. Undoubtedly, people of different persuasions would have different opinions on it. After all, this is not only economics, but also politics!

An illustration of the map graph is given by Chart 2.12. It shows clearly that, in general, the more industrialized the state, the more the state spends on capital expenditure for pollution abatement. The reason for this is of course quite obvious.

Finally, Chart 2.13 is an illustration of the pictorial area diagram. This diagram is rather out of date. It has been selected for its attractiveness and for the reason that the process illustrated by the diagram has continued since 1950s. Anyway, this chart shows the process of replacing animal and human muscle power by inanimate sources of energy from 1850 to 1950. At the beginning of this period, two-thirds of all work done in this the U.S. was done by human and animal muscle power; however, by the end of the period, 1.5% of the work was so performed. Thus, by 1950, more than 98% of the tremendously increased total volume of work energy came from inanimate sources of power that ran machines.

REVIEW QUESTIONS

2.1 What do we mean by *a priori* planning of statistical investigation? What is its importance?

2.2 Define "populations", "elementary units", and "characteristics". Provide a few examples of your own for different decision situations.

2.3 Give an example of your own to show that a population may be defined in different ways for a given decision problem.

2.4 Can the same population be used for decision making in different decision situations? If so, what is the main advantage of this possibility?

2.5 What do we mean by a "scale" or "level of measurement"? How many scales are there? Define each and point out the possible use of each "level of measurement."

2.6 Define the notion of "variable." State the different ways of classifying variables.

2.7 Is there a difference between "characteristic" and "trait"? If so, how are they differentiated? Give a few examples.

2.8 How are variables related to statistical data? States and define different types of statistical data in terms of the differences in nature of different data sets?

2.9 What are primary data? Internal data? External data of primary source? External data of secondary source? Give several examples of each type of data.

2.10 If primary data are the most reliable for an investigation, why is that the data used to solve most economic and business problems are often collected by persons or agencies other than those who employ the data for statistical studies?

2.11 Why are secondary data taken from primary sources more desirable than those taken from secondary sources?

2.12 Name the publications in which you would expect to obtain the following information. (Hint: study the Appendix to this chapter.)
   a. Annual estimate of the population of each county in United States
   b. The monthly average production of pig iron in the United States during the past forty years
   c. The number of grocery stores in each state in the United States in 1985
   d. The number of firms in New York City which employed more than 2500 workers last year
   e. United States currency in circulation
   f. Man-hours worked in textile mills in Massachusetts for the latest available date
   g. The number of unemployed for latest available four months
   h. The consumer price index for the United States for latest available month
   i. General Motors' earnings per share of common stock for the first three quarters of 1987
   j. The latest available figures for the Gross National Product and disposable income in the United States
   k. The total union membership for each year since 1930
   l. The purchasing power of the dollar as measured by consumer prices since 1945 up to the latest date available
   m. A measure of manufacturing output in the United States for the latest available month
   n. The buying power index for the county in which your home is located
   o. The number of motor vehicles produced in the United States for the latest period available
   p. The number of sedan cars exported from and imported into the United States each year during the period 1965–1988

2.13 List the advantages and disadvantages of each method of collecting data:
   a. Personal interview
   b. Telephone interview
   c. Mail questionnaire

2.14 For each of the following situations, discuss the method of data collection that would be preferable.
   a. A study by a college administration to determine the attitudes of faculty members toward a comtemplated group insurance plan
   b. A study by the Federal government to determine the attitude of physicians in the United States toward contemplated legislation for Federal medical insurance for American families
   c. A survey by a foreign-born and foreign-educated professor who wants to discover from his students whether his accent affects their understanding of his lectures
   d. A survey by a radio news commentator to determine the reactions of his listeners to his news analysis

2.16 What comments can you make on the following questions if they are directed to average citizens for information?
   a. Are you in favor of the right-to-work laws?
   b. Do you believe that George Bush would make a good president?
   c. Have you ever falsified information on your income tax returns?
   d. What is your occupation?
   e. Do you shine your shoes or do you have them shined?
   f. What is the average number of cubic feet of gas used for cooking each week during the past year at your home?

2.17 State the basic rules that should be observed in table and graph construction.

2.18 Compare the relative advantages and disadvantages of tables and graphs as a means of presenting data.

2.19 What should each of the following sets of figures look like in arithmetic-scale line graphs?
   a. 1, 2, 3, 4, 5, 6.
   b. 1, 2, 4, 8, 16, 32.
   c. 3, 9, 27, 81, 243.

2.20 Do you or do you not agree with each of the following statements?
   a. A time series that is increasing at a constant rate will plot as a straight line on an arithmetic chart
   b. On a semilog chart the same vertical distance anywhere on the scale shows the same absolute amount of change
   c. Equal rates of changes plot with equal slopes on the ratio chart
   d. Both the arithmetic chart and the semilog chart must start the vertical scale with zero
   e. Only one cycle would be required in order to plot the fluctuations of national income of the United States since 1800

2.21 In your opinion which type of graph is most appropriate to portray the following data? Why?
   a. Annual automobile production in the United States from 1971 to 1988
   b. Building permits issued in New York City compared with the total building permits issued in the United States, by month, for the latest 5 years available

c. Sales of a department store for December, 1984, subdivided into five categories
d. Revenues and expenditures in the federal budget for a given year
e. Population in the United States recorded by the 1980 census

PROBLEMS

Note: Many of the diagrams in the following problems can be drawn on your PC with the software package that comes with it. Take advantage of it.

2.1 Draw a line chart on arithmetic scale for data in Table 2.P1.

TABLE 2.P1 Annual Sales of ABC, Inc. (in Millions of Dollars)

Year	Sales	Year	Sales
1981	11.0	1986	15.8
1982	13.5	1987	20.3
1983	15.0	1988	24.6
1984	14.0	1989	23.4
1985	16.5	1990	21.5

Source: Hypothetical.

2.2 Construct a line chart on arithmetic scale for data in Table 2.P2.

TABLE 2.P2 Annual Inventory Stock (in Hundreds) of Ichibon Motor Co. just before New Models are Introduced, 1979–1990

Year	Inventory	Year	Inventory
1979	13	1985	33
1980	17	1986	38
1981	26	1987	35
1982	31	1988	34
1983	29	1989	39
1984	27	1990	41

Source: Hypothetical.

2.3 Draw a line diagram on ratio scale for data in Table 2.P3.

TABLE 2.P3 GNP (in Billions of Dollars) of the Republic of Utopia 1980–1994

Year	GNP	Year	GNP	Year	GNP
1980	150	1985	250	1990	300
1981	175	1986	235	1991	400
1982	200	1987	300	1992	375
1983	185	1988	350	1993	380
1984	230	1989	320	1994	425

Source: Hypothetical.

Study your result carefully and comment the appropriateness of using a ratio chart in this case.

2.4 Construct a vertical bar chart with data for the most recent ten years in Table 2.P3.

2.5 Draw a horizontal bar chart with information provided by the pie chart for December 31, 1985 in Chart 2.10.

2.6 Draw a silhouette chart with the data in Table 2.P4. Comment on the results.

TABLE 2.P4 Profits and Losses (in millions of dollars) of RA Inc., 1978–1983

Year	Profits	Year	Profits	Year	Profits
1978	+2.5	1983	+1.5	1989	+7.4
1979	+3.7	1984	+3.0	1990	+11.0
1980	−1.0	1985	−1.8	1991	+11.5
1981	−1.5	1986	−3.7	1992	+6.0
1982	−2.4	1987	+5.0	1993	−1.8

Source: Hypothetical.

2.7 For data in Table 2.P5 do the following.
   a. Draw a band chart showing actual amounts of data for the three categories
   b. Draw a vertical component bar chart with different shadings (Hint; one bar for each year's quantities for the three categories)
   c. Draw a 100% band chart with different shading (Hint: First convert the absolute columns of the three categories and the subtotals as percentages of the total amount, rounded to two decimal points, and then plot the resulting values)
   d. Construct a pie chart for the 1986 distribution data (Hint: The total produced of 237.5. corresponds to the total number of degrees (360) in a circular arc. Namely, 1 unit corresponds to $360°/745$. Thus, for tax liability, $(103.5)(260°/237.5) = 157°$; for dividend payment, $(89.8)(360°/237.5) = 133°$; for undistributed profits, $(46.2)(360°/237.5) = 70°$)

TABLE 2.P5 Distribution of Corporate Profits, United States 1980–1986 (billions of dollars)

Year	Tax Liability	Dividend Payment	Subtotal	Undistributed Profit	Total Profit Before Tax
1980	84.8	54.7	139.5	97.6	237.1
1981	81.1	63.6	144.7	81.8	226.5
1982	63.1	66.9	130.0	39.6	169.6
1983	77.2	71.5	148.7	58.9	207.6
1984	95.4	78.3	173.7	62.0	235.7
1985	91.8	81.6	173.4	49.8	223.2
1986	103.5	87.8	191.3	46.2	237.5

Source: Economic Indicators, April 1987, p. 8.

Appendix to Chapter Two
Sources of External Data

PUBLISHED GUIDES

In view of the huge volume of published statistical data today, it is good and effective practice to make use of published guides in locating desired information. As far as guides concerning business and economic data are concerned, the selected literature listed below is highly informative:

American Statistics Index (ASI), Washington, D.C., Congressional Information Service, Inc., updated monthly. A two-volume index of Government publications. The first volume is a standard index, and the second contains abstracts of the indexed publications. The first edition, 1973, contained all of the Federal Government statistical publications in print at that time, as well as the most significant publications since 1960.

Readers' Guide to Periodical Literature, published by the H. W. Wilson Company, New York. This publication is the major current guide to general periodicals. Its indexing service began in 1900, and is issued semimonthly from September to June and monthly in July and August, with an alphabetic annual cumulation appearing. At present, the guide indexes over 150 periodicals. Each article indexed is referred to by author and by subject.

Business Periodicals Index, published by the H. W. Wilson Company, New York. This publication is a subject index to periodicals in various fields of business. It is published monthly, except in August, and cumulated into annual volumes. It now indexes almost 200 periodicals.

Catalog of U.S. Census Publications, Washington, D.C. Covers all Bureau of the Census publications on a quarterly basis. This is an excellent guide to publications by the U.S. Bureau of the Census.

Foreign Commerce Handbook: *Basic Information and a Guide to Sources,* Washington, D.C., Chamber of Commerce of the United States, published since 1922. This volume outlines the functions of U.S. Government, intergovernmental, and private organizations, providing the foreign trade sources outlined. It also lists key addresses.

Economic Abstracts: *A Semimonthly Review of Abstracts on Economics, Finance, Trade and Industry, Management and Labour.* Published since 1953 by Martinus Nijhoff in the United States. Covers books, governmental reports, and journal articles mainly in European languages, including English. The abstracts follow in the language of the report abstracted. Subject and author indexes. Cumulated annually.

Journal of Advertising Research. Published by the Advertising Research Foundation in the United States. Includes reviews, resumes, and listing of the current literature.

Statistical Services of the U.S. Government, prepared by the U.S.

Office of Statistical Standards, Bureau of the Budget (Washington, D.C.: U.S. Government Printing Office) since 1968. Part I describes the federal statistical system; Part II gives a brief account of each of the main economic and social statistical series collected by the government; and Part III describes the principal statistical publications of federal agencies.

The guides described above are valuable even to the most experienced statistical workers. However, experience in assembling data is of more value than any published guides. researchers, therefore, must become familiar with some of the more important existing sources, which are listed and described in the following pages.

GOVERNMENT SOURCES

The federal government is by far the most important producer of secondary data in the world today. Nearly every federal agency collects statistical data: some data are collected for governmental administrative and operating purposes; others are compiled as a service for public use.

To begin with, once every ten years the Bureau of the Census published voluminous information about the American population. The original dual purpose of the periodic census was to provide a continuing basis for the apportionment among the states of membership in the House of Representatives, and for the collection of taxes, but its scope was expanded long ago to furnish data concerning various aspects of the business and economic activities of the citizens of the United States. The Census of the United States presently incorporates eight different types of census, each of which is of great interest and aid to students in business and economics. Together with other reports published by the Bureau, these censuses constitute the most fruitful single source of statistical data for a business and economic researchers. The eight types of census are: *Census of Population*; *Census of Housing*; *Census of Retail Trade, Wholesale Trade, and Selected Service Industries*; *Census of Manufacturers*; *Census of Mineral Industries*; *Census of Agriculture*; *Census of Transportation*; *and Census of Governments*.

It may be noted that the experience, resources, and authority of the Census Bureau taken together, give the census data a high reputation for validity. Also, being a complete enumeration of people and their activities census data are used by government statisticians to compare and adjust sample statistical series collected between censuses.

Two more publications by the Bureau of Census are also of great importance. The first is the *Business Condition Analysis,* a monthly publication that gives in detail many economic and business time series—such as GNP, employment and unemployment, and money and credit. It arranges statistical information in such a way as to facilitate the analysis of the course and degree of well being of the U.S. economy. The second is the *Statistical Abstract of the United States,* published annually since 1878. This volume contains more than 1000 tables that present what are considered to be the most generally useful series of data on industrial, social, political, and economic organizations and activities, collected by various governmental and nongovernmental agencies. Since the sources of these data are carefully given, the *Statistical Abstract* is also useful as a preliminary reference to locate more detailed and more recent data in a given field. A supplement to the *Statistical Abstract* called *Historical Statistics of the United States,* covers about 3000 time series extending back through to the earliest year for which data are available. This supplement was published in 1949, and in 1954 the series in the 1945 volume were brought forward seven years in the publication of *Continuation to 1952 of Historical Statistics of the United States, 1789–1945.* In addition to statistical data, *Historical Statistics* also gives a brief description of the series and information on the sources of data.

A few additional annual publications of federal agencies should also be mentioned. *Agricultural Statistics,* published by the Department of Agriculture, brings together facts on acreage, yield and production of crops, agricultural prices, imports and exports of agricultural commodities, and the like. *Minerals Yearbook,* a comprehensive record of the production and marketing of minerals in the nation is published by the Bureau of Mines. The Interstate Commerce Commission publishes *Statistics of Railways in the United States,* which contains data concerning railroad traffic, operations, equipment, finances, employment, and accidents.

Some federal agencies also issue publications that present economic and business data quarterly, monthly, or more frequently. Among these, *Survey of Current Business,* published by the Department of Commerce, is of general interest to economists and businessmen. This publication is one of the most comprehensive collections of current statistical data and contains more than 2500 series on business and economic activities in the United States. Some of the well-known and highly useful series are Gross National Product, personal and farm income, expenditures for new plant and equipment, retail and wholesale sales, manufacturers' orders and inventory, balance of international payments, production, prices, and shipments for many commodities. Each issue contains the figures for the most recent month and the twelve preceding months. A weekly supplement is issued to give certain weekly series. Moreover, a biennial supplement furnishes data for past years and assembles for all the published series, the monthly detailed information necessary for their understanding. The supplement also contains careful descriptions of the sources of the data published.

Federal Reserve Bulletin, published monthly by the Board of Governors of the Federal Reserve System, contains detailed data on money and banking, domestic and international financial transactions, and other economic data, such as production, consumer credit, and department store operations. Another monthly publication by the FRS is *Federal Reserve Charts on Bank Credit, Money Rates and Business.* It provides charts of significant indicators of financial and general business conditions. It also covers bank reserves, deposits and currency, and so on.

The Bureau of Labor Statistics publishes the *Monthly Labor Review,* which contains data on employment and payrolls in manufacturing and nonmanufacturing industries, wages and hours of labor, labor turnover, industrial disputes, consumer and wholesale prices, work stoppages, construction, and many other activities of interest to labor.

Another highly useful governmental source is *Economic Indicators,* a monthly release prepared by the Council of Economic Advisers and published by the Joint Congressional Committee on the Economic Report. It contains the most important indicators of current business activity, such as prices, employment, wages, production, purchasing power, credit, money, national output, and Federal finances. The main purpose of this publication is to keep current the statistical data contained in the *Economic Report of the President.* The companion volume, *Historical and Descriptive Supplement to Economic Indicators* is a useful aid to the use of the *Economic Indicators.* This supplement describes the procedures used in compiling the series in the Economic Indicators and explains their uses and limitations.

NONGOVERNMENTAL SOURCES

Statistical data are also collected by many private agencies and organizations. An important function of the trade associations of various industries is the compilation of statistical data concerning the particular industry and their dissemination among the members. Some of the large trade associations also make public vast quantities of data. Examples are *Automobile Facts and Figures* and *Motor Truck Facts,* published annually by the Automobile Manufacturers Association; *Life Insurance Fact Book,* put out annually by the Institute of Life Insurance; *Petroleum Facts and Figures,* issued each year by the American Petroleum Institute; and *Steel Facts,* published by the American Iron and Steel Institute; *Gas Facts,* provided by the American Gas Association; *Railroad Car Facts,* furnished by the American Railroad Institute; and *Air Transport Facts and Figures,* published by the Air Transport Association of America.

A second source is newspapers and magazines. These publications are excellent sources of current business and economic data. A few examples in this category comprise Barron's, *Business Week, The Commercial and Financial Chronicle, Dun's Review, U.S. News & World Report,* and *The Wall Street Journal.* All of these but the last-named are weeklies. The *Wall Street Journal* is published daily excepting Saturdays and Sundays.

Finally, there are agencies that furnish statistical services. Their publications are normally sold on a subscription basis and their costs to subscribers are high compared with the costs of those sources listed in the preceding paragraph. Besides supplying statistical data, these agencies also make analyses and forecasts with respect to specific business and investment problems. The well-known agencies for statistical services are Babson's Reports, Inc., Brookmire Corporation, Standard and Poor's Corporation, Moody's Investors' Service, and United Business Service.

INTERNATIONAL SOURCES

Many international agencies compile and publish statistical data of great usefulness to business management and economic analysts. The two major sources are *International Financial Statistics,* published monthly by the International Monetary Fund; and *Monthly Bulletin of Statistics,* issued by the United Nations. In the first publication, data are organized by nation; in the second, data for a large number of countries are gathered by function.

The United Nations' *Direction of World Trade* (monthly) and its *Yearbook of International Trade Statistics* are excellent sources of detailed international trade data.

Two more international sources that may be consulted are the *Annual Report* on international financial questions, put out by the Bank for International Settlement, and *International Trade,* an annual report published by the contracting parties to the General Agreement on Tariffs and Trade.

3 Arrays and Frequency Distributions

3.1 STATISTICAL RAW DATA

Statistical analysis begins when a data set is made available in accordance with the definition of a research problem. It must be realized, however, that a data set, whether it presents a population or a sample, usually contains a large number of values. Furthermore, these values, in the raw form, are almost always recorded as they are gathered. Thus, they vary from one value to another without any order or pattern. To make sense out of a raw data set, the raw data must be organized and presented in a systematic or sequential manner by way of a table or graph. When this is done, we then find that the hidden properties of data are clearly revealed and are able to determine the appropriate statistical methods that can be applied to their study.

Organization of raw data depends upon the nature of the data on hand. In this chapter, we shall concentrate on the organization and presentation of cross-sectional univariate data. Consider first a couple of examples of raw data sets. As the first example, suppose a bicycle shop has been in business for over one year and the owner is interested in learning something about the variability of its daily sales. For this problem, the manager may select a sample of days at random, say, 25 days, and then analyze sales on these days. Suppose the sales on these days selected are as recorded in Table 3.1. This set of raw data is quite simple because it contains only 25 observations and all the values are single-digit integers. Thus, if we go through the table, we immediately find that the daily sales assume six distinct values, from 0 to 5.

TABLE 3.1 Raw Data Set of Bicycle
Sales for 25 Days

1	0	1	5	2
2	1	2	0	0
0	3	2	4	3
3	2	1	4	2
2	1	4	3	2

However, the precise distribution pattern of the daily sales is still hidden and can only be revealed by some sort of proper organization.

Next, let us consider a more involved example. Suppose that we would like to study the food consumption expenditures of middle-income families in a certain geographic district in Chicago; suppose that we have selected a random sample of 80 families from this district and that from these families we have obtained their average weekly food consumption expenditures for 1986 that are recorded in Table 3.2. What information can we gather from such a set of raw data? The honest answer is: Not much! As a matter of fact, the most vivid impression we can get from the set is that the data points seem to jump up and down without any meaningful pattern at all. True, if we study the table very carefully we may discover that no family seems to spend less than $121.00 or more than $234.90 for food per week and thus it provides us with a range—the difference between highest and lowest values—of $113.90 for the average weekly food consumption expenditures of these families in 1986. But this information is certainly inadequate for us to evaluate the characteristics of the variable—the purpose for which we have supposedly collected the data. The lack of order of raw data of different magnitudes effectively conceals nearly all information underlying the data.

TABLE 3.2 Raw Data Set of Average Weekly Food Consumption Expenditures of 80 Middle Income Families in Chicago, 1986

$134.70	234.90	210.25	147.25	166.57
138.50	225.75	150.00	156.44	156.56
179.95	160.00	148.55	149.99	158.30
179.35	188.45	142.28	154.80	190.00
195.00	184.00	169.85	177.35	157.00
196.75	171.34	172.50	178.00	158.15
200.00	175.20	148.95	190.16	188.20
219.99	121.00	172.46	187.35	182.85
179.00	149.84	175.55	164.50	157.50
178.00	140.10	198.70	165.00	125.58
153.10	164.00	154.25	162.78	161.25
150.00	162.25	155.00	189.99	167.77
158.12	198.92	148.90	193.45	163.45
130.15	190.45	147.34	210.95	213.25
146.50	215.10	156.15	155.00	182.34
217.20	205.50	159.00	177.15	177.48

The sum of this set of data is $13,719.25

These two examples illustrate clearly the necessity of efficient organization of raw data before any statistical description or analysis can be made. For cross-sectional univariate data, there are two methods of organization available: arrays and frequency distributions. We now take up these methods in the order mentioned.

3.2 ARRAYS

An *array* is a quite simple method of organizing data whereby the data points are arranged according to their magnitudes. It may be either in *ascending order,* where the values are arranged consecutively from the lowest to the highest, or in *descending order,* where the values are arranged consecutively from the highest to the lowest. Arrays of ascending order are more frequently employed in practice.

Now, let us rearrange the raw data in Table 3.2 in order of magnitudes, resulting in an array of ascending order as shown in Table 3.3. Let us see what the formation of an array for our data has accomplished. It is quite simple now to see many of the characteristics of the data set under review. Just by glancing at the array we see that (1) the variable ranges in value from $121.00 to $234.90; (2) the individual values seem to follow each other without any large gaps; (3) roughly, $167.00 seems to be the value that divides all the consumption expenditures into two parts with equal numbers of items in each; (4) the greatest concentration of values is within a narrow interval, ranging approximately from $140.00 to $180.00; (5) the number of families that spend less than $150.00 is almost twice as large as those that spend more than $200.00. It can now be seen clearly that the array has a considerable advantage in terms of useful information, compared with

TABLE 3.3 Array of Average Weekly Food Consumption Expenditures of 80 Families in Chicago, 1986

$121.00	$150.00	$161.25	$177.35	$190.45
125.58	153.10	162.25	177.48	193.45
130.15	154.25	162.78	178.00	195.00
134.70	154.80	163.45	178.00	196.75
138.50	155.00	164.00	179.00	198.70
140.10	155.00	164.50	179.35	198.92
142.28	156.15	165.00	179.95	200.00
146.50	156.44	166.57	182.34	205.50
147.25	156.56	167.77	182.85	210.25
147.34	157.00	169.85	184.00	210.95
148.55	157.50	171.34	187.35	213.25
148.90	158.12	172.46	188.20	215.10
148.95	158.15	172.50	188.45	217.20
149.84	158.30	175.20	189.99	219.99
149.99	159.00	175.55	190.00	225.75
150.00	160.00	177.15	190.16	234.90
Total of this data set is				$13,719.25

Source: Table 3.2.

what is provided by the raw data set, even though the same data are used in both.

The array is often a practical and useful device in organizing data that includes only a small number of values. Thus, for example, to study the subsidies that a state grants to its cities for the operation of public transportation, the leading cities in the state may be arranged in an array according to population. It may also be informative to array the per capita income of the various states to evaluate the reasons for the differences, or to decide on Federal aid in education for the various states. The array, however, is still a very cumbersome form of data presentation, especially when a large data set is involved. Moreover, its usefulness is exhausted after a few different types of information have been obtained. Lastly, an array still has all the detail of the raw data set, which may not be required or necessary for refined analysis. In other words, we are looking at all the trees and may be missing the forest. More formally, though, we have not yet done anything to condense or summarize data into a more compact form so that unwanted detail is eliminated and more interesting properties of the data are revealed. To condense data without losing the essential detail is the purpose of a frequency distribution—a topic we now turn to for a detailed discussion.

3.3 FREQUENCY DISTRIBUTIONS

Different Types of Distribution

A *frequency distribution*, or simply a *distribution*, in general is a method of organizing and summarizing data whereby individual observations are distributed in accordance with the few distinct values the variable can take, or with a number of size-groups that are subintervals of the whole range of the values of a variable, or with a number of qualitative categories. This general definition seems a little vague, but it will become clear as we proceed.

First, from Table 3.1, we see that the daily sales assume six distinct values, from 0 to 5. If we organize this set of raw data into a distribution, it would appear as set forth in Table 3.4.

TABLE 3.4 Distribution of 25 Daily Bicycle Sales

Daily Sales	No. of Days
0	4
1	5
2	8
3	4
4	3
5	1
Total	25

Source: Table 3.1.

TABLE 3.5 Distribution of Average Weekly Food Consumption Expenditures of 80 Families in Chicago, 1986

Food Consumption Expenditures ($)	No. of Families
120.00–139.99	5
140.00–159.99	26
160.00–179.99	24
180.00–199.99	15
200.00–219.99	8
220.00–239.99	2
Total	80

Source: Table 3.2 or Table 3.3.

Next, if we wish to construct a frequency distribution for the data in Table 3.2 or in Table 3.3, we may distribute the individual consumption expenditures into a set of size-groups—subintervals. The end result would be as shown by Table 3.5.

As the last example of frequency distributions, let us consider a case in which we are interested in finding the pattern of voting registration of the undergraduates of a western state university. For this objective, suppose we have taken a sample of 100 undergraduate students of the said university and have distributed them according to party affiliations; a table like Table 3.6 would result.

Note that Tables 3.4, 3.5, and 3.6 are referred to as *frequency tables* simply because they contain frequency distributions of the variables in question. Furthermore, the first two examples are referred to as *numerical,* or *quantitative, distributions* because, in both cases, data are classified according to numerical magnitudes. Note also that Table 3.4 illustrates what is referred to as a *distribution of repetitious data,* since the individual observations of the variable take on only a few distinct values and each of these values is repeated a number of times. This type of distribution is sometimes referred to as *ungrouped distribution.* Table 3.5 is an illustration of what is called a *grouped distribution,* in the sense that the individual values are distributed in accordance with a number of size-groups or classes that are sub-intervals of the whole range of values of the variable. Table 3.6 displays

TABLE 3.6 Distribution of 100 Students' Voting Registration in a Western University

Party	No. of Students
Democratic	32
Republican	38
Liberal	10
Conservative	13
Independent	3
Other	4
Total	100

what is referred to as a *categorical,* or *qualitative, distribution*—a distribution in which the values are distributed according to several categories that differ in kind instead of in magnitude.

With just a moment's reflection, we see that the construction of a numerical distribution for repetitious data is a very simple matter and requires no more explanation, except to note that this type of distribution is only appropriate when the variable takes on only a few distinct values. The organization of a categorical distribution is also quite simple once the categories are properly designated. However, in this case, it is sometimes quite troublesome to determine the number of categories to be used. The important consideration here is that the categories must be mutually exclusive and sufficient in number to accommodate all the data. Very often it is quite easy to err by selecting overlapping categories for qualitative data. For instance, to study the various types of food sold in a supermarket, we might adopt categories that are not satisfactory, such as "meat and meat products," "vegetables," "frozen foods", and so forth. With such categories, we would have difficulty in deciding to which category an item such as "frozen meat" or "frozen vegetable" belongs.

While distributions for repetitious numerical data and qualitative data are relatively simple, there are a number of important aspects to be considered in the construction of "numerical frequency distributions of the grouped form." We now turn to a detailed discussion of this topic. To avoid constant repetition of the rather long title quoted, we simply call it a frequency distribution, or distribution, or grouped data. When distributions of repetitious data and categorical distributions are discussed, their full descriptive names will be used.

Methods of Constructing Frequency Distributions

You know by now that a frequency distribution is an arrangement of a set of raw data that shows the frequency of occurrence of values in each of several size-classes or size-groups. A tabular presentation of a summary of such data is called a *frequency table.* To distribute a set of raw data over the classes that have already been established we use either a tally sheet or the entry form. If the data are input to a computer—a widely used procedure in handling large samples—the sorting and counting can be done automatically in a single procedure. Tallying, as shown in Table 3.7 involves establishing classes and representing each item that falls in each class by one vertical or diagonal stroke; we then count the number of items in each class.

The use of the entry form is illustrated by Table 3.8. In this procedure, the classes are set up horizontally at the top in an ascending order from left to right. The actual items are entered into the appropriate classes. The items that fall into each class are then counted and recorded at the bottom of that class. The total figures in the classes constitute the class frequencies. The entry form is more laborious than tallying, but it offers certain advantages: (1) we can easily find any entries in wrong columns by scanning the columns; (2) reclassifications

TABLE 3.7 Tally Sheet of Average Weekly Food Consumption Expenditures for 80 Families in Chicago, 1986

	Tally						Frequency
$120.00–$139.99	卌						5
$140.00–$159.99	卌	卌	卌	卌	卌	1	26
$160.00–$179.99	卌	卌	卌	卌	1111		24
$180.00–$199.99	卌	卌	卌				15
$200.00–$219.99	卌	111					8
$220.00–$239.99	11						2
Total							80

Source: Table 3.6.

can often be made with little effort if the original classes are unsatisfactory; and (3) we can find out how closely the mid-value of a class agrees with the average of the values of the items in that class.

Note that both tally sheet and entry form are much easier to construct if an array of the series is available. However, the items can also be arranged, with more effort, from the raw data. In practice, an array is never constructed solely for the purpose of making a frequency distribution, since too much time and effort are required.

TABLE 3.8 Entry Form of Average Weekly Food Consumption Expenditures for 80 Families in Chicago, 1986

$120.00–139.99	$140.00–159.99	$160.00–179.99	$180.00–199.99	$200.00–219.99	$220.00–239.99
121.00	140.10	160.00	182.34	200.00	225.75
125.58	142.28	161.25	182.85	205.50	234.90
130.15	146.50	162.25	184.00	210.25	(2)
134.70	147.25	162.74	187.35	210.95	
138.50	147.34	163.45	188.20	213.25	
(5)	148.55	164.00	188.45	215.10	
	148.90	164.50	189.99	217.20	
	148.95	165.00	190.00	219.99	
	149.84	166.57	190.16	(8)	
	149.99	167.77	190.45		
	150.00	169.85	193.45		
	150.00	171.34	195.00		
	153.10	172.46	195.75		
	154.25	172.50	198.70		
	154.80	175.55	198.92		
	155.00	175.20	(15)		
	155.00	177.15			
	156.15	177.35			
	156.44	177.48			
	156.56	178.00			
	157.00	178.00			
	157.50	179.00			
	158.12	179.35			
	158.15	179.95			
	158.30	(24)			
	159.00				
	(26)				

Source: Table 3.6.

TABLE 3.9 Frequency Table for Weekly Food Consumption Expenditures for 80 Families in Chicago, 1986

Food Consumption Expenditures (class)	Midpoint, m_i	Number of Families (class frequency), f_i
120.00–139.99	130.00	5
140.00–159.99	150.00	26
160.00–179.99	170.00	24
180.00–199.99	190.00	15
200.00–219.99	210.00	8
220.00–239.99	230.00	2
Total	—	80

Source: Table 3.7 or 3.8.

The results of the tally sheet or the entry form may now be presented in a frequency table, such as Table 3.5. This is now reproduced as Table 3.9 with an additional column for the "midpoint", a concept that will be explained shortly.

The distribution achieves condensation of data by blurring the values of the data. We now know only the class frequencies for data, not the individual values. For example, in Table 3.9, the two largest observations are somewhere between $220.00 to $239.99; we no longer know that they are $225.75 and $234.90, respectively. Despite this loss, a great deal has been gained by this condensation. First, all the information revealed by the array can be obtained, approximately, with greater ease from the frequency distribution. Second, the distribution not only shows clearly the concentration of the individual values, it also brings about the pattern of the tendency for the individual values to vary above and below the concentration. Third, comparisons between two or more series can be made more readily with data formed into a frequency distribution. As will be shown later in this chapter, such comparisons are further facilitated when frequency distributions are presented in graphic form. Finally, frequency tables, as we shall see, help speed computations of many descriptive measures (parameters or statistics), assuming that the loss of detail is not serious.

3.4 PROBLEMS IN CONSTRUCTING FREQUENCY DISTRIBUTIONS

There are essentially three steps in the construction of a numerical distribution of the group form: (1) designation of the classes; (2) distribution of the observations into these classes; and (3) determination of the number of observations in each class. Since steps (2) and (3) are purely routine, here we will only consider step (1)—the designation of the classes. However, before we do this, we must first explain for future reference some of the technical terms associated with a frequency table.

The groupings 120.00–139.99, 140.00–159.99, and so on, in Table 3.9 are called *classes*. The numbers on the left of the class are called *lower class limits,* denoted as L_i, and the numbers on the right, *upper class limits,* denoted as U_i. The point halfway between the limits of each class is called the *midpoint,* or *class mark,* of that class, denoted as m_i. The number of units between the limits of a given class is called the *class interval,* denoted as c_i. When the same interval length is used for all classes, we have a distribution with *equal* or *uniform class intervals.* The number of occurrences in each class is called the *class frequency,* denoted as f_i. Obviously, the total number of frequencies in a distribution, $\sum f_i$, is equal to the sample size n or the population size N, depending upon whether the distribution is organized using sample or population data.

Now, turning our attention to the problem at hand, we note that there exist a few "rough" rules that can be used as an aid in the designation of classes. These rules are concerned with the number of classes, the size of the class intervals, and the class limits. These rules and their implications are introduced in the next few pages.

Number of Classes and Class Intervals

The number of classes used should be neither too many nor too few. A large number of classes may not condense data sufficiently to be of any practical value; a small number of classes tends to oversummarize data so that much valuable information is lost. A rule of thumb is to limit the number of classes to between 5 and 15. Obviously, the actual number of classes to be employed depends upon the number of data points and the range of their values. It also depends, less obviously, upon the use to which the data will be put. If only a broad pattern in the data is desired, a few classes may be used. If a detailed pattern is desired, more classes are needed. If great accuracy is desired in later computations from the frequency table, use of many classes becomes a necessity.

One way to determine the number of classes is to determine the size of each class interval first. When the class interval size has been determined, the number of classes can be obtained by dividing the range of the variable by the selected class interval size. Now let the number of classes be represented by k, we then have

$$k = \frac{\text{the range of the variable}}{\text{the size of class interval}} = \frac{R}{c}. \tag{3.1}$$

For instance, using our illustrated example (and from Table 3.3), $R = \$234.90 - 121.00 = \$113.90$, and for reasons to be given shortly, we have selected $\$20.00$ as the class interval. Thus, we have

$$k = \frac{113.90}{20.00} = 5.695 \doteq 6.$$

Here, the sign $\doteq$ means "approximately equal to". Indeed, 6 is the number of classes we have used for the distribution of food expenditure data. The value of k obtained by (3.1) is usually rounded up to a whole number. Because of this, it is permissible to start with a smaller value than the minimum value of the variable as the lower class limit of the first class and to end with a larger value than the maximum value of the variable as the upper class limit of the last class. This is exactly what we have done in constructing the distribution of the food expenditure data.

Finally, there are two important points to be observed in the selection of the class interval size. First, the interval should be some convenient number, such as a whole integer or multiples of 5, in order to make future computations from the distribution easier. Second, whenever possible we should use uniform class intervals, since uniformity facilitates our understanding correctly the pattern of the distribution.

Class Limits and Midpoints

After the numbers of classes and class intervals have been fixed, the remaining problem is to designate the class limits. First, and most important of all, class limits should be "mutually exclusive" and "collectively exhaustive". They should be *mutually exclusive* in order to eliminate any doubt as to the class to which a given value belongs. The class limits shown below are not mutually exclusive and should never be used:

1,000 to 1,500
1,500 to 2,000
2,000 to 2,500
etc.

With such a designation of class limits we would not know whether, say, the value of 1,500 belongs to the first or to the second class. That the classes should be *collectively exhaustive* means that there must be a class for every mathematically possible value of the variable.

The selection of proper class limits depends to a great extent whether the data are discrete or continuous and on whether the data have been rounded. It may be noted here that, irrespective of the data on hand, there are only two basic methods of designing class limits, as illustrated below.

Food Consumption Expenditures	
Non-overlapping Limits	Overlapping Limits
$120.00–$139.99	$120.00 and under $140.00
140.00– 159.99	140.00 and under 160.00
160.00– 179.99	160.00 and under 180.00
etc.	etc.

A moment's reflection will enable us to see that these basic forms of class limits are equivalent expressions. For example, a value of, say, $140.00 would be assigned to the second class using either classification.

In treating discrete data that are not rounded, such as a monetary series recorded to the nearest penny, or discrete data that can only take on integer values, the nonoverlapping form of class limits should always be used. Thus, this type of class limit is employed for the food expenditure example considered earlier. Again, suppose we were making a study of industrial accidents occurring daily in the manufacturing plants in Detroit, the following classification could be used:

No. of Industrial Accidents
0–4
5–9
10–14
etc.

When we are dealing with continuous data, the overlapping form of class limits should always be used in order to provide a continuous appearance. Furthermore, in doing so we must also simultaneously observe that the class limits are mutually exclusive. The manner in which this is achieved will be discussed shortly.

In designing the class limits, consideration must also be given to the location of *midpoints*. The midpoint of the ith class is located by using the following simple equation:

$$m_i = L_i + \frac{c_i}{2}. \tag{3.2}$$

(All symbols have been defined earlier.) For example, for the food expenditure data in Table 3.9, we have

$$m_1 = L_1 + \frac{c_1}{2} = 120.00 + \frac{20}{2} = \$130.00, \quad \text{and so on.}$$

When the class intervals are uniform, the midpoints of the successive classes will be separated from the midpoint of the first class and from each other by the width of the class interval. It is important to note that the class interval of a class is found by subtracting the lower class limit of the class from the lower class limit of the next class. It is not always possible to find the interval by subtracting the lower limit from the upper limit of a class. For example, in a classification such as 0–9, 10–19, 20–29, and so on, the class interval is 10 and not 9. The midpoints are, therefore, 5, 15, 25 and so forth, and *not* 4.5, 14.5, 24.5, etc.

Midpoints are employed to represent the individual values (which, as mentioned before, are lost in the process of constructing a distribution) for further computations. Here, we assume that all the items in a class (the class frequency) have the same value as the midpoint of that class. Clearly, this assumption almost always introduces an error. This error is called the *grouping error* and can be defined as the difference between an observed value and the midpoint of the class in which the observation is placed. A grouping error can be positive or negative. With properly selected class limits, grouping errors cancel one another, or at least partially cancel each other. In a special case, where the original data bunch at particular values, grouping errors can be minimized to a great extent if these values can be placed at or near the midpoints of the class limits used. For example, suppose we are studying the weights of adult males. An observation gathered on each male derives from his answer to the question: "How much do you weigh?" Since the answers will almost always end in 0 or 5 units of pounds in the United States, notice what heppens if we employ the following set of classes:

...; 100 but less than 105; 105 but less than 110;...

With these classes, the midpoints would be ...; 102.5; 107.5; .... Almost all the individual values are as far from these midpoints as they can be. Consequently, substantial grouping errors will be introduced when these midpoints are used for further computations. However, if we design class limits that are centred on frequently occurring observations, such as ...; 97.5–102.5; 102.5–107.5;..., we obtain midpoint values of ...; 100; 105;... as desired.

Here, in connection with the statement of class limits and the determination of midpoints, attention is called to the distinction between nominal class limits and actual or true class limits. *Nominal limits* are simply those that are stated in a frequency table. Thus, if we establish reported classes for certain observations and write 10–14, 15–19, 20–24, and so on, these same limits are then nominal. The same nominal limits are often used to accommodate data whose actual limits may be different. The *actual limits* depend upon whether and how the data are rounded. Here we consider two common cases.

First case: data are not rounded, as in the case of prices originally reported in dollars and cents. In such a case, the actual class limits are identical with the nominal class limits. The class interval is 5 and the midpoints are 12, 17, 22, and so on.

Second: data are rounded to the nearest whole unit, such as the nearest whole dollar, or the nearest whole pound. If this is the case, a reported figure of 10 actually lies between 9.5 and 10.5; a reported figure of 14 actually falls between 13.5 and 14.5; and so on. This implies that an item of 14, which would be entered into the first class of the three classes cited in the previous paragraph, may actually be as large as 14.5. Consequently, actual limits are 9.5–14.5, 14.5–19.5, 19.5–24.5, and so on, which give the same class interval and midpoints as in the first case.

It can be seen from the above discussion that the midpoints are always determined on the basis of actual limits. In order to avoid possible confusion, the student is advised to construct frequency tables with actual class limits at all times. When doing this, the problem is often with continuous data, which are usually rounded. However, the solution to this problem is quite simple, as the illustration in the second case indicates. More precisely, to determine the actual class limits for a continuous variable, all we have to do is write the class limits with one decimal point more than the originally recorded data. For example, if a data set consists of measurements of lengths rounded to one-tenth of an inch, then the nominal class limits may take the following form: ...; 11.0–11.2; 11.3–11.5; 11.6–11.8;... If we rewrite this set of classes with actual limits, using our simple rule we would have: ...; 10.95–11.25; 11.25–11.55; 11.55–11.85; .... Furthermore, these class limits have an overlapping appearance and should be interpreted as "over L_i and through U_i." With class limits so interpreted, no confusion would arise as to which class an item belongs. For example, the value of, say, 11.2, clearly belongs to the first and not the second class, since 11.2 is less than 11.25—the upper class limit of the first class and the lower class limit of the second. Thus, with this interpretation, the seemingly overlapping classes are actually mutually exclusive. In any event, it may be noted that both sets of classes have the same class intervals and midpoints. However, the second form of designation should always be used for continuous data, not only because they are real class limits, but also because it provides a continuous appearance without violating the condition that classes should be mutually exclusive.

Open-ended Classes, Varying Class Intervals, and Frequency Density

If possible, we should not employ open-ended classes and varying (or unequal) class intervals. An *open-ended* class results from the practice of writing the first class without the lower class limit or writing the last class without the upper class limit. Theoretically speaking, the interval for an open-ended class is infinity and its midpoint is either $-\infty$ or $+\infty$ (minus infinity or plus infinity). Hence, it is impossible for us to conduct further operations with open-ended classes unless a footnote is presented that gives us the total values of the frequencies therein, or a judgment is made by the investigator as to what the values for the missing class limits should reasonably be. However, the latter practice may be quite difficult at times.

Varying class intervals, that is, intervals that are of unequal sizes, should be avoided if possible, since they tend to make the interpretations of class frequencies difficult, and thus blur the true pattern of the distribution.

However, it must also be pointed out that open-ended classes and varying class intervals, despite their shortcomings, are sometimes necessary and even advantageous in situations where there are a few extremely small or a few extremely large values, or both; where data possess large gaps; where the number of observations runs into thousands or even millions. For example, Table 3.10 for the distribution of income for all the U.S. White households, which number almost 53 million, is constructed with both open-ended classes and varying class intervals.

Several things about Table 3.10 need to be explained. First of all, the class limits in column (1) are copied from the source for the table. These limits indicate that the original data are rounded to whole dollars. Hence, they are nominal limits. If we wish to convert them into actual (or true) limits they should be $2,499.5 $4,999.5, $4,999.5, $7,499.5, etc. Second, the class intervals vary in lengths from $2,500 to $15,000. These designations have produced a good deal of distortion of

TABLE 3.10 Income Distribution of 52,710 Thousands U.S. White Households in 1980

(1) Income (in current $)	(2) No. of Households (in thousands)[a]	(3) No. of Class Intervals of width $2,500	(4) Frequency Density
Under $2,500	843	1[b]	843
$2,500– $4,999	1,749	1	1,739
5,000– 7,499	2,794	1	2,794
7,500– 9,999	3,163	1	3,163
10,000– 12,499	3,742	1	3,742
12,500– 14,999	3,584	1	3,584
15,000– 19,999	7,432	2	3,716
20,000– 24,999	7,485	2	3,742
25,000– 34,999	10,964	4	2,741
35,000– 49,999	7,169	6	1,195
50,000 and over	3,795	40[c]	95
Total	52,710	—	—

[a] The original data were given in percentages for class frequencies. The class frequencies presented here are converted back to absolute numbers by multiplying 52,710 by the percentages shown.
[b] Minimum income is assumed to be $0.
[c] Maximum income is assumed to be $150,000.

Source: 1982 Statistical Abstract of the United States, Table 3, p. 13.

the true pattern of the income distribution. For example, the greatest concentration of the number of households is in the two classes before the last, ranging in income from $25,000 to $50,000 and giving the impression that many of the householders are moderately wealthy. This is indeed wonderful; but it is, unfortunately, a misleading illusion. Had we used $2,500 as the class interval all the way through, for instance, an entirely different picture would have emerged. Of course, we cannot use equal intervals of $2,500 in this case, because if we did, the number of classes would become extremely large, (and perhaps many classes would be empty). The way to correct this misleading impression, introduced by varying class intervals, is to compute what is called *frequency density*. We do this by estimating what the class frequencies would be if uniform class intervals were used. Thus, in column (3) of Table 3.10 we have the number of class intervals assuming that each is of width of $2,500. Frequency densities for the classes are then easily obtained by dividing the stated class frequencies by the number of "standardized" class intervals. The results are given in column (4). It must also be noted that in determining this set of frequency densities we have assumed that the minimum income is $0 and the maximum income is $150,000. These assumptions seem to be reasonable, since households with negative incomes and incomes over $150,000 are so very few when compared with the almost 53 million households that they can be ignored without any negative consequences as far as the true pattern of income distribution is concerned.

This rather lengthy discussion concerning the design of classes when constructing a distribution of the grouped type can be summarized in terms of the following six rules of thumb.

1. The number of classes should range from 5 to 15, unless the data content clearly requires some other number.

2. The class limits should be mutually exclusive and collectively exhaustive.

3. The size of class intervals should be some convenient number, so that the class marks could be whole integers or multiples of five.

4. Class intervals should be so designed that frequently occurring observations will fall on or near the midpoints when the data so indicates.

5. Open-ended classes should be avoided whenever possible. When they must be used, footnotes on the total values of the class frequencies should be given.

6. Uniform class intervals should be used, unless the content clearly requires unequal class intervals. When unequal class intervals are employed, frequency densities must be computed.

These rules also apply to charts and graphs as well as tables for frequency distributions. Indeed, they apply in any use of class intervals. Finally, they also serve as a checklist for spotting the trouble in distributions prepared by others.

3.5 GRAPHIC PRESENTATION OF FREQUENCY DISTRIBUTIONS

The most important function of a pictorial presentation or graph of a data set is to make it easier to understand the data than it is through numerical presentation. Even the relatively simple distribution, such as presented in Table 3.4, requires studying quite a few numbers and mentally translating them into meaningful patterns. More involved tables, such as Table 3.10, become still more difficult to interpret. Graphs do the translating for us and provide effective and simple communication of data patterns. Furthermore, unusual features that are difficult to see in columns of figures are more easily revealed by graphs. Graphs also clearly provide important statistical patterns that either call for particular analytic approaches or prohibit them. Hence, good practice often calls for graphing data before doing any important calculations.

Whether graphs are used to present final results or to commence statistical analyses, a suitable type of graph must be chosen. As far as grouped univariate data are concerned, there are three types of graphic presentations: the histogram, the polygon, and the smooth curve. We now discuss them in the order mentioned.

Histograms

A *histogram* is simply a vertical bar diagram with all the bars touching each other, without any spaces between them. Some special features used in the construction of a histogram are enumerated below.

1. The class frequencies are usually plotted against the Y axis, and the class intervals scaled on the X axis. Both X and Y axes should start at zero, with scale breaks if necessary. This recommendation is not critical for the X axis. Both axes, however, should be clearly and completely labeled.

2. A space, from half to the full size of the class interval, is left at each end of the X axis.

3. The X scale designations are usually placed at the true class limits. The bars must touch each other, without gaps, except for empty classes. Sometimes, the X scale is labeled by placing the mid-value of each class at the center of the base of the bar.

4. The X scale is equally spaced when the class intervals are uniform. In a varying class-interval distribution, the X scale should be adjusted accordingly. For instance, if two class intervals, 100 and 500, are used, then the spaces on the X axis for the classes with intervals of 500 should be five times as wide as those with intervals of 100.

5. The Y axis must be completely labeled to show whether it represents frequency or frequency density. If the class intervals are uniform, as in Table 3.9, the visual pattern in the graph will be the same whether frequencies or frequency densities are graphed. Nevertheless, it is desirable in this case to label the Y axis so that the reader knows which is being portrayed. If the class intervals are not uniform, as in Table 3.10, the visual pattern in the graph will differ, depending on whether frequencies or frequency densities are graphed; in this case it is essential to label the Y axis precisely.

6. A histogram is always regarded as composed of bars, whether they show explicitly, as in Figure 3.1, or they do not, as in Figure 3.2.

There is a difference between the interpretations of the heights as well as the areas of histogram bars, depending upon whether the vertical axes show frequency or frequency density. With the vertical axis showing frequency, the height of each bar represents frequency in that class interval. The area of each bar has no meaning, but the visual appearance of the areas of the bars causes no distortion or trouble in a histogram having equal class intervals. The reason is that when the bars are of equal width, the areas must be proportional to the heights. Namely, the areas and heights give the same visual message.

When we have unequal class intervals in any histogram using density along the vertical axis, the height of a bar represents density in that class interval. However, the area of a histogram bar now is

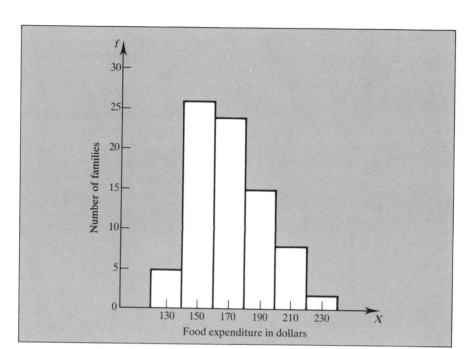

FIGURE 3.1 Histogram for average weekly food consumption expenditures of 80 Chicago families in 1986. (*Source:* Table 3.9.)

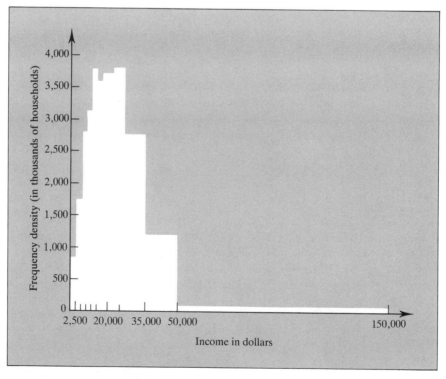

FIGURE 3.2 Histogram for income distribution of U.S. White households, 1980. (*Source:* Table 3.10.)

meaningful: it represents frequency or relative frequency. In Figure 3.2, for example, the areas correctly present the income distribution under study. The visual suggestion that most families are in the bars with the greatest areas is accurate, as is the visual impression that there are small numbers of families in the bars with small areas.

Polygons

Another way of presenting a distribution graphically is to draw a *frequency polygon*. We do this if a histogram (using frequency not frequency density) is already available, by simply placing a dot on the midpoint of the top of each bar in the histogram and then connecting these dots by straight lines (Figure 3.3(*a*)). Very often, however, a polygon is constructed without setting up the rectangles. Without the histogram, we obtain the polygon by locating the coordinates: the ordinates, which are the class frequencies, and the abscissas, which are the midpoints. These points are then joined by straight lines (Figure 3.3(*b*)).

Although the histogram is an effective and vivid graphical presentation of frequency distributions, the polygon does not represent the basic data very well. The outstanding shortcoming of the polygon is that the areas under it are usually not proportional to the frequencies. One remedy is to close the polygon at the base by extending both ends of the curve to the midpoints of two hypothetical classes at the extremes of the distribution that have zero frequencies. This practice would make the area under a polygon approximately equal to that of a histogram. Both polygons in Figure 3.3 have been drawn in this manner.

There are, nevertheless, at least two important reasons for using the frequency polygon. First, when several distributions are to be compared on the same graph, it is much clearer to superimpose frequency polygons than to superimpose histograms, especially when all the distributions have the same class limits. Second, the frequency

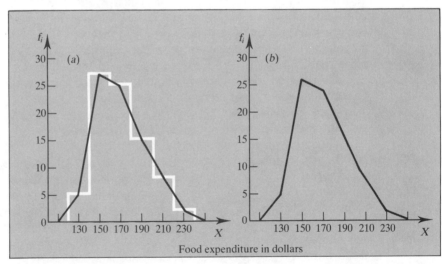

FIGURE 3.3 Frequency polygons for average weekly food consumption expenditures of 80 Chicago families in 1986. (*Source:* Table 3.9.)

polygon suggests the use of a smooth curve as an idealized representation of the population distribution. Let us now turn to see how smooth curves are drawn.

Smooth Curves

There are two basic methods of constructing smooth curves. One is to graph actual data, such as Figure 3.3(a) or 3.3(b), to which the statistical investigator may add a smooth curve drawn through the actual polygon to eliminate irregularities in the pattern of the data. This is done as if we were increasing the size of the sample continuously until all the irregularities are eliminated. This might appear to be an improper procedure, since it amounts to deliberately falsifying the actual data. Nevertheless, there are occasions when statistical problems should be answered by analyzing smoothed curves from data instead of actual data.

The second method is to fit a smooth curve to a set of actual data by a mathematical equation. it is not expected that actual data will correspond exactly to the mathematical equation, but it is a fact that many sets of actual data correspond closely to simple mathematical equations. For such sets of data, it is very helpful to analyze the mathematical equations approximating the data, because many useful but hard-to-see properties can be discovered in this way.

The smooth curves are alternatively called *population models*. They are so called because they depict the salient features of population distributions. The term "population model" also suggests generalizations of the shapes of population distributions—symmetrical, skewed, U-shaped, and so on. These generalizations are of great usefulness in statistical analysis because they provide simplified methods of describing the basic characteristics of populations. There are additional reasons for our interest in population models. One is that a population distribution is sometimes needed for decision making. Another, as will be discussed in later chapters, is that statistical inferences often require our knowledge of population models. A third reason is that a population model, being represented by a smooth curve, sometimes lends itself more readily to mathematical treatment.

As the reader can easily imagine, population models can assume an infinite variety of shapes. In the following paragraphs we shall introduce some of the population models that are more frequently encountered in business and economic statistics.

Curve (a) in Figure 3.4 is a population model of special interest and importance in statistics. Note that this curve of distribution is bell-shaped. The largest frequency densities are in the center. Smaller densities are next to the center. There are very small densities at both extremes. It is indeed strange that if a trait occurring at random is measured, the curve of the resulting distribution often resembles the one shown as curve (a). Whether we measure the tensile strength of steel bars produced by a given process, the height of men, the intelligence of students, the size of grains of rice, or errors of repeated measurements of a given characteristic, the distribution curve often

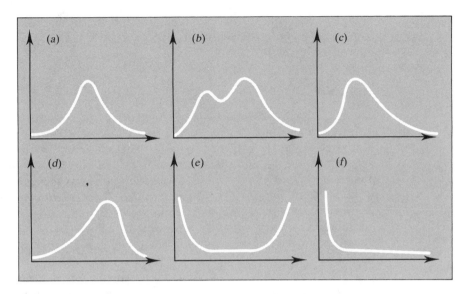

FIGURE 3.4 Principal varieties of smooth curves: (a) the normal curve; (b) the bimodal curve; (c) the positively skewed curve; (d) the negatively skewed curve; (e) the U-shaped curve; (f) the reversed J-shaped curve.

looks like a bell. The bell-shaped model is commonly called the *curve of normal distribution* or simply the *normal curve*. We shall have more to say about it in Chapter 9.

Curve (*b*) in Figure 3.4 portrays what is known as the *bimodal* distribution, meaning that it has two peaks, in contrast to a unimodal distribution, which has only one peak. This type of distribution occurs when a population contains elements that can be divided into two classes differing from each other in the characteristics being measured. We may also say that the population is not homogeneous. For instance, the distribution for all demand deposit balances in the United States would assume this model. In such a distribution we would find a prominent peak at a relatively low value for the balances held by consuming units and another distinct peak at a relatively high value for balances held by business firms and other organizations. Again if we were to study the heights of college students, a bimodal distribution would result—one concentration for men and another for women. Sometimes the reason for a bimodal distribution is unknown.

Curves (*c*) and (*d*) in Figure 3.4 are models for skewed distributions. A *skewed distribution* usually has only one peak, located at either the lower or the higher end of the curve. It is asymmetrical. When the longer tail of the curve is on the right, we say the distribution is *skewed to the right* or *positively skewed*. When the longer tail of the curve is on the left, we say the distribution is *skewed to the left* or *negatively skewed*. The positively skewed model is very common in economic and business data. For instance, the distribution of income (see Figure 3.2) is skewed to the right. Also, the distribution of the number of retail stores by amount of sales would be positively skewed, since there are many small stores and few very large ones. An example of the negatively skewed model would be the number of firms distributed according to the ratio of cost of sales to net sales in an industry. The negatively skewed model describes well a population whose variates have an upper limit. For instance, in practice the upper limit of the ratio of sales cost to net sales would be unity, or 100%. A firm seldom stays in business very long if its ratio of sales cost to net sales exceeds unity, although this can happen temporarily.

The U-*shaped curve,* as illustrated by curve (e) in Figure 3.4, describes a distribution that contains predominantly low and high values, intermediate values being relatively scarce. The U-shaped model is rather rare, but some economic series do conform to it. For instance, the distribution of the nations of the world according to their stages of economic development would reveal bunching at two extremes. Most of the countries are either highly developed or underdeveloped, with only a few at the intermediate stages. Again, the frequency distribution of the unemployed according to age groups would emerge as a U-shaped curve. This indicates that most of those who do not work are either very young or very old.

A population may also take the *reversed* J-*shaped curve,* such as curve (f) in Figure 3.4, where the frequencies of occurrence increase or decrease continuously along the horizontal scale. The reversed J-shaped curve would be a good approximation for the distribution of corporations classified according to the size of assets, or the distribution of business failures with the X axis the duration of time in operation. Can you explain why?

Thus, although the normal distribution holds a very important place in statistical analysis, there are business and economic variables that are not normally distributed. For numerous reasons we must have a knowledge of various population models. It is true that most of the time we do not know the true underlying population distributions, but we can approximate their models either by fitting a smooth curve to sample data or by pure deductive reasoning. Our ability to do so greatly facilitates our further analysis.

Graphs for Repetitious and Qualitative Distributions

Finally, the graphic representation of a distribution for repetitious data often takes the form of either a vertical line chart or a vertical bar diagram. Figures 3.5(a) and 3.5(b) are graphs for the sales data in Table 3.4. Note that in these diagrams the heights of the lines or of the bars measure the frequencies and the widths of the bars are arbitrary and have no meaning.

A categorical distribution is usually graphed as a horizontal bar chart, such as Figure 3.6, for the registration data in Table 3.6, where the vertical scale indicates the categories and the horizontal scale measures the frequencies in each category. The length of each bar is the frequency in that category. Widths of bars, as in bar charts in general, are entirely arbitrary and have no practical significance.

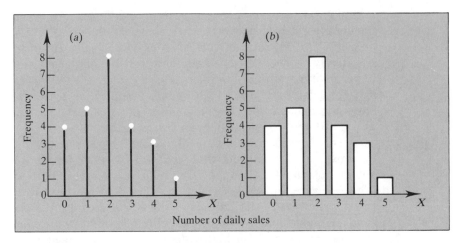

FIGURE 3.5 (a) Line and (b) bar charts for bicycle sales. (*Source:* Table 3.4.)

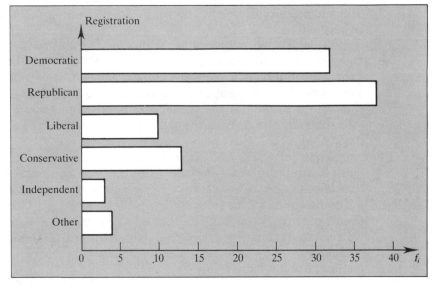

FIGURE 3.6 Horizontal bar chart for 100 college students' vote registrations. (*Source:* Table 3.6.)

3.6 RELATIVE FREQUENCY DISTRIBUTIONS

We have been concerned so far with what are called *absolute frequency distributions* since, in each case, the frequency for each repetitive value, each class, or each category, is given by an absolute number. Frequency distributions are sometimes given in a relative form, resulting in a *relative frequency distribution,* or simply a *relative distribution*. One form of such a distribution is given as proportions, which are the absolute frequencies in each and every category or class divided by the total number of observations for the distribution. In other words, relative frequencies of this form are simply f_i/n for a sample, or f_i/N for

TABLE 3.11 Relative Distributions of 80 Family Average Monthly Food Consumption Expenditures in Chicago, 1986

Food Consumption Expenditures (in dollars)	Absolute Frequency f_i	Relative Frequency in	
		Proportions, f_i/n	Percentages, $(f_i/n)100$
120.00–139.00	5	0.0625	6.25
140.00–159.99	26	0.3250	32.50
160.00–179.99	24	0.3000	30.00
180.00–199.99	15	0.1875	18.75
200.00–219.99	8	0.1000	10.00
220.00–239.99	2	0.0250	2.50
Total	80	1.0000	100.00

Source: Table 3.9.

a population. When each proportion is multiplied by 100 (i.e., to give $(f_i/n)100$ or $(f_i/N)100$) we have the other form of relative distribution, which is referred to as the *percentage distribution*. Relative distributions of both forms for the food expenditure data in Table 3.9 are shown in Table 3.11.

Several aspects of relative distributions need to be mentioned at this time. First, the sum of relative frequencies should add up to 1 or to 100%, except for rounding errors, depending upon whether they are expressed in terms of proportions or percentages. Second, the graphs for relative distributions are identical with those as for absolute distributions, except that the scale for frequencies should be labeled as proportions or percentages. Third, for grouped data with uniform class intervals, the area enclosed by the polygon or the smooth curve of a relative distribution, is 1 or 100%. Finally, when a relative distribution is constructed with varying class intervals, the relative frequencies should be converted into frequency densities in the same manner as discussed earlier and as illustrated in Table 3.12, to facilitate interpretation and avoid misleading impressions. In this connection, it must also be noted that the areas enclosed by the histogram, the polygon, or the smooth curve will for a relative distribution be less than 1 or 100%, because the relative frequency densities no longer add up to 1 or 100%.

As we move along, we shall see that relative distributions can perform many useful functions. For the time being, we may take notice of two of them. One is that a relative distribution provides the same information as an absolute distribution, but in a simpler and more precise way. For example, just by looking at Table 3.11, we can make the following precise statements.

1. Exactly 32.5% of the families spent between $140.00 and $160.00 for food per week in 1986.

2. More than two-thirds of the families spent less than $180.00 per week, while less than one-third of the families spent more than this amount for food per week.

TABLE 3.12 1980 Income Distributions of 52,710 Thousands White and 6,317 Thousands Black Households in the United States

Income (in current dollars)	Frequency Density (in thousands)		Percentage Frequency		No. of Class Intervals in $2,500	Relative Frequency Density	
	White (2)[a]	Black (3)[b]	White (4)	Black (5)	(6)	White (4)/(6)	Black (5)/(6)
Under 2,500	843	335	1.6	5.3	1	1.6	5.3
2,500– 4,999	1,739	714	3.3	11.3	1	3.3	11.3
5,000– 7,499	2,794	846	5.3	13.4	1	5.3	13.4
7,500– 9,999	3,163	657	6.0	10.4	1	6.0	10.4
10,000–12,499	3,742	575	7.1	9.1	1	7.1	9.1
12,500–14,999	3,584	486	6.8	7.7	1	6.8	7.7
15,000–19,999	3,716	404	14.1	12.8	2	7.05	6.4
20,000–24,999	3,742	322	14.2	10.2	2	7.1	5.1
25,000–34,999	2,741	186	20.8	11.8	4	5.2	2.95
35,000–49,999	1,195	66	13.6	6.3	6	2.27	1.05
50,000 and over	95	3	7.2	1.7	40	0.36	0.0025
Total	—	—	100.0	100.0	—	—	—

[a] See Table 3.10.
[b] Original data are given as in column (5) here with a total of 6,317 at the source. These densities are obtained from the converted absolute frequencies as shown in Table 3.10.

Source: Adopted from *1982 Statistical Abstract,* Table 3, p. 13.

3. While only 12.5% of the families spent more than $200.00 per week, almost 39% of the families spent less than $160.00 for food per week, and so on.

The other useful function of the polygon or the smooth curve of a relative distribution is that it lends itself more readily to the comparison of different distributions, especially when they differ greatly in the total number of observations (as illustrated by the two income distributions for White and Black households in Table 3.12). This point is clearly revealed by Figures 3.7 and 3.8. The former contains polygons of the absolute distributions in Table 3.12. It is very difficult to discover from this graph the features that are similar and different between these two distributions. More serious is the fact that incorrect impressions may be obtained from it. However, when reference is made to the polygons of the two relative distributions portrayed in Figure 3.8, several important conclusions can be drawn easily and accurately:

1. Both distributions are positively skewed, but the skewness for the Black households seems to be greater than that for the White households.

2. The income of Black households has a sharp and large concentration at the point around $7,500. In contrast, the income of White households does not concentrate as sharply and this concentration is around a range of higher incomes, which range from about $12,500 to $25,000 thus yielding a slight flat-top appearance.

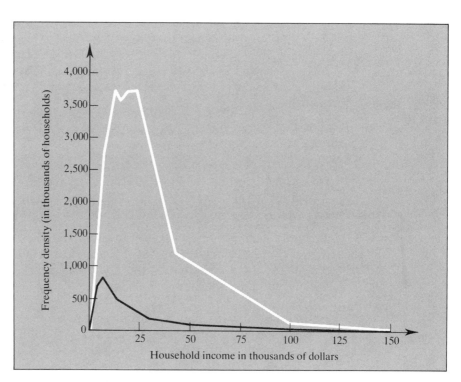

FIGURE 3.7 Absolute income distributions for White and Black households in 1980. (*Source:* Table 3.12.)

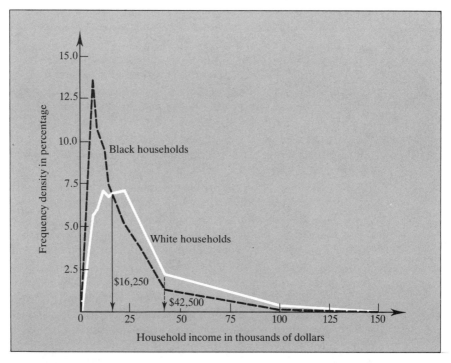

FIGURE 3.8 Relative income distributions for White and Black households in 1980. (*Source:* Table 3.12.)

3. The percentage of Black households with incomes less than about $16,250 is almost twice as large as that as for the White households. However, above this income level, the percentage of White households is greater all the way through than that of the Black households. (See the vertical line dropped from the intersection of the polygons.)

4. Above the income level of approximately $42,500, the percentage of income of White households is about twice as great as that of Black households.

5. The largest percentage of Black households have incomes between $2,500 and $12,500, while for the White households, the largest percentage is between $7,500 and $30,000.

6. The overall impression one gets from Figure 3.8 is that not only are Black households generally poorer than the White households; but also that the distribution of income for the Blacks seems to be less equitable than that for the Whites.

The comparisons of relative distributions becomes even more revealing when we deal with distributions whose minimum or maximum values, or both, differ widely from each other. You can deepen your insight into the usefulness of relative distributions by drawing different types of smooth curves and interpreting them verbally.

3.7 CUMULATIVE FREQUENCY DISTRIBUTIONS

For certain purposes it is desirable to arrange data cumulatively. Very often we may wish to answer such questions as how many people in the United States are making $20,000 or less a year? How many salesmen in the company are selling a given amount or more per week? When serial bonds secured by equipment are issued, how much of the equipment will be in use at each maturity date of the bonds? How many of the automobile tires produced by a factory can last 50,000 miles or more? How many of them can last only 35,000 miles or less? Answers to such questions can readily be found if the frequency distributions are arranged cumulatively.

Cumulative frequencies can be formed on either a "less than" or a "more than" basis, and they can be absolute or relative. Table 3.13 illustrates these two types of cumulative frequencies for the food expenditure data. In this table, F_i refers to absolute cumulative frequencies, and F_i/n stands for relative cumulative frequencies. Note, in the "less than" case, that *frequencies* are *cumulated* from smaller to greater values and therefore are referred to the upper class limits U_i. In the "more than" case, *frequencies* are *cumulated* by using the lower class limits L_i as references. Cumulative tables have many distinct advantages that lead to their wide use. Mortality tables, for example, are usually arranged in these forms.

TABLE 3.13 Cumulative Distributions of 80 Chicago Family Monthly Average Food Consumption Expenditures in 1986

| Class (in dollars) | f_i | f_i/n | Cumulative Distribution | | | |
| | | | Less than U_i | | More than L_i | |
			F_i	F_i/n	F_i	F_i/n
120.00–139.99	5	0.0625	5	0.0625	80	1.0000
140.00–159.99	26	0.3250	31	0.3875	75	0.9375
160.00–179.99	24	0.3000	55	0.6875	49	0.6125
180.00–199.99	15	0.1875	70	0.8750	24	0.3125
200.00–219.99	8	0.1000	78	0.9750	10	0.1250
220.00–239.99	2	0.0250	80	1.0000	2	0.0250
Total	80	1.000	—	—	—	—

There are also three types of graphic presentations of cumulative frequency distributions, corresponding to those for distributions in the noncumulative form. They are the step diagram, the ogive, and the smoothed cumulative curve.

The *step diagram* graphs a cumulative distribution by a series of horizontal lines drawn at levels of the cumulated frequencies in the successive classes, with the vertical and horizontal axes scaled in the same fashion as for a histogram. The endpoints of the horizontal lines may or may not be connected by vertical lines. Cumulative data of the "less than" form in Table 3.13 are so graphed in Figure 3.9.

The *ogive* is a polygon that represents a cumulative distribution in the form of a *line diagram*. Figure 3.10 is the ogive for the food

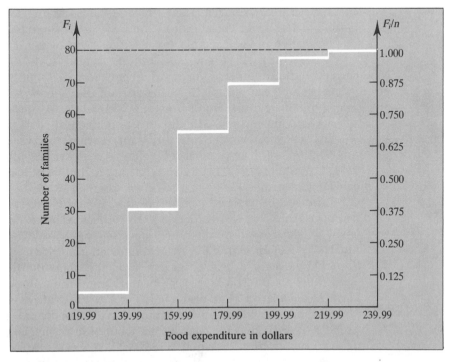

FIGURE 3.9 Step diagram for the average weekly food consumption expenditures of 88 Chicago families in 1986. (*Source:* Table 3.13.)

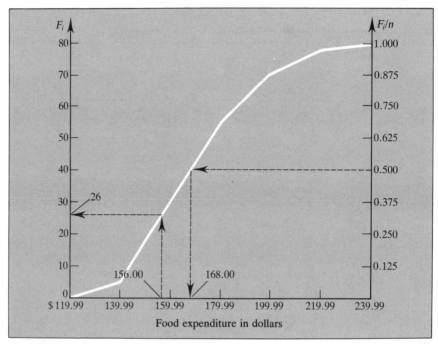

FIGURE 3.10 Ogive for the average weekly food consumption expenditures of 80 Chicago families in 1986. (*Source:* Table 3.13.)

expenditure data given in Table 3.13. Note that the cumulative frequencies of the "less than" form are plotted on the upper class limits. Clearly, cumulative frequencies of the "more than" form should be plotted at the lower class limits.

An ogive is used mainly for interpolations, which can be made in two ways. First, if a point on the horizontal scale is selected, the corresponding number, or proportion, of observations in the distribution whose values are equal to or less than the value indicated by the selected point can be found from the vertical scale. For example, if we select the point of, say, $156.00 on the horizontal scale in Figure 3.10, we then draw a vertical line up to intersect the ogive, and from this intersection we draw a horizontal line to the vertical scale on the left: we get a value of 26. This means that approximately 26 observations in the sample have values equal to or less than $156.00.

The second method of interpolation is just the reverse. This time we move from the vertical axis to the horizontal axis to find the value below which a given number, or proportion, of observations will fall. To illustrate, let us use the vertical scale on the right in Figure 3.10. Suppose we draw a horizontal line from the point 0.5 to intersect the ogive and then drop a perpendicular from the intersection to the horizontal scale: we then find a value of $168.00. This means that about 50% of the observations in the sample have values equal to or less than $168.00. This result also means that about 50% of the observations have values greater than or equal to $168.00. A value such as this, which divides the whole series into two equal parts, is called the *median*—a type of average to be discussed in the next chapter.

Just as a histogram or a polygon can be smoothed out to yield a

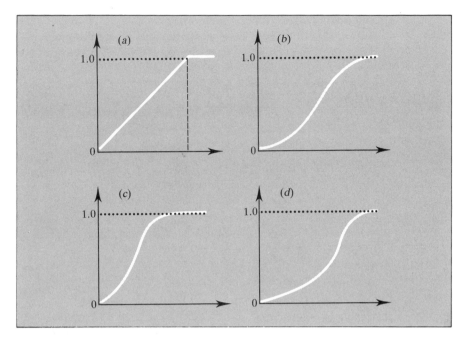

FIGURE 3.11 Smooth cumulative curves.

population model, so can a step diagram or ogive be smoothed out to represent a possible underlying population distribution function. Figure 3.11 shows four cumulative curves, or smoothed ogives, corresponding to (a) a uniform, (b) a bell-shaped, (c) a positively skewed, and (d) a negatively skewed distribution.

GLOSSARY OF FORMULAS

(3.1) $k = \dfrac{R}{c}$.

The number of classes for a distribution of the grouped form is determined by this formula. Here, k is the number of classes, R is the range of the values of the variable, and c is the size of the class interval to be employed for the distribution. In applying this equation, we should remember two things: (1) c should be some convenient number such as a whole integer or multiples of 5; and (2) k is always rounded up to a whole number.

(3.2) $m_i = L_i + \dfrac{c_i}{2}$.

The midpoint m_i of the ith class in grouped data is located by this expression, where L_i and c_i are the lower class limit and class interval for the ith class, respectively. When uniform class intervals are used, midpoints of the successive classes are separated from the midpoint of the first class and from each other by the width of the class interval. To apply this formula to a distribution of varying class intervals, the midpoint for each class must be determined independently.

REVIEW QUESTIONS

3.1 What is an array? What are the advantages and disadvantages of the array as a method of organizing a set of raw data?

3.2 Give a general definition of a frequency distribution.

3.3 What are the two forms of numerical frequency distributions?

3.4 Why is the distribution of repetitious data only appropriate when the variable can take on only a few distinct values?

3.5 How does a categorical distribution differ from a numerical distribution? What is the most important thing to consider in organizing a categorical distribution?

3.6 When is it advisable to use frequency distributions to organize data? What is the most important function of a frequency distribution?

3.7 What are the advantages of the entry form over the tally sheet form for the construction of frequency tables?

3.8 What are the reasons for the rule that the number of classes should be 5 or greater, but not greater than 15?

3.9 What objections do we have against open-ended classes and varying class intervals? Under what conditions are these practices actually desirable and necessary? What additional information should be provided when they are employed?

3.10 The class interval for a given class is always the difference between the upper and lower class limits of that class. True or false?

3.11 The nominal class limits may or may not be the same as the actual, or true class limits. Discuss this statement.

3.12 What important role do midpoints play in a distribution of the group form?

3.13 What do we mean by grouping errors? What is the important property of such errors? Does the problem of grouping errors arise in a distribution for repetitious data? Why or why not?

3.14 As an overall review of the problems involved in constructing numerical distributions of the group form, state the six rules of thumb to use, in your own words and give the reason for each.

3.15 Why are graphic presentations of numerical data important?

3.16 What is a histogram? In what sense do we say that the histogram is superior to the polygon as a graphic representation of a distribution?

3.17 What is a frequency polygon? What important functions does this type of graph serve?

3.18 Only one type of smooth curve can be fitted to a given data set. Do you agree or disagree?

3.19 Why do we sometimes call smooth curves population models?

3.20 Which smooth curve do you consider to be a good approximation of the underlying distribution of each of the following populations of variates? Give reasons.
    a. The I.Q. of students of a certain university
    b. Students' grades on difficult problems
    c. Durability of auto tires produced by a certain process
    d. Annual earnings of American lawyers
    e. Annual rates of inflation in a given year in the early 1980s of all the nations in the world
    f. The number of corporations filing corporate income tax returns classified by size of capitalization
    g. The weights of all students in a coed college
    h. The monthly rents of five-room apartments in Boston
    i. The lifespan of restaurants in any big city in the world
    j. Per capita income of all the nations in the world

3.21 What is a relative distribution? Under what circumstances are relative distributions especially effective in comparing different sets of data?

3.22 With the aid of the concept of relative frequency, can you explain why there are as many expensive cars in poor neighborhoods as in the fashionable suburbs? Also, do you think it is reasonable to expect that the weights of rats may show a greater variation in values than the weights of elephants?

3.23 For what type of problems do we need to construct cumulative distributions?

3.24 A cumulative distribution is always set up by using the upper class limits. Is this correct or incorrect?

3.25 What are the three types of graphic presentations of cumulative distributions? What is the most important function of an ogive?

3.26 Give a critical evaluation of Table 3.R1 below.

TABLE 3.R1 Distribution of Rented Two-Bedroom Apartments in Toronto, Canada, 1984

Monthly Rental	Number of Dwellings in Each Class (in thousands)
Under $100.00	327
$100.00–149.99	349
150.00–199.99	521
200.00–299.99	1,039
300.00–499.99	1,075
500.00–749.99	189
750.00–999.99	24
1,000.00 and over	9
Total	3,533

PROBLEMS

Note: Save your answers to the problems for this and the next chapters, because the same data sets and problems worked out from them may be the basis for problems in Chapters 4 and 5.

3.1 A sample of 30 MBA graduates from St. John's University in New York City had starting weekly wages in 1982 as given in Table 3.P1:

TABLE 3.P1 Raw Data Set of 30 Starting Weekly Wages in Dollars

500	400	500	450	500	450	500	650	600	550
400	550	600	500	450	450	500	550	550	500
450	500	550	600	550	450	550	550	500	600

a. Construct an array in ascending order for the data above. Analyze and comment on the information provided by the array which may not have been revealed by the raw data.

b. Construct an ungrouped (repetitious data) frequency distribution for the data (call it Table 3.S1), and comment on whether and how it is or is not superior to the array in terms of summarizing and organizing the data.

c. Would you recommend constructing a distribution of the grouped form for the set of data on hand? Why or why not?

3.2 What categories would you establish in order to construct frequency distributions for the following variables?

a. Number of policyholders of an insurance company to be classified according to the level of education of the head of the family

b. Retail stores in your home town to be classified according to types of business

c. Various foods sold in a supermarket

d. Land-use in an agricultural region

e. Number of banks distributed according to the several categories established, depending upon the specialized functions they perform

3.3 The Personnel Department of a large corporation wishes to study the pattern of absenteeism of their employees. Fifty employees' files were selected at random and the number of days of absence for each of them was counted. The following results were obtained:

TABLE 3.P2 Raw Data Set: Number of Days of Absences of 50 Employees

5–13–1–16–4–3–12–11–3–8–5–0–3–14–9–6–3–10–7–4–2–10–5–7–13
6–10–6–11–13–3–8–7–4–5–14–8–6–5–11–5–7–4–7–8–3–4–4–5–3

   a. Construct a frequency distribution for the above data by the entry form and call the frequency distribution table Table 3.S2. (*Hint:* The first class should be written as 0–2.)
   b. Are the class limits you have used nominal or actual limits, or both? Explain
   c. What is the size of the class intervals for the distribution?
   d. Locate the midpoints and record them in Table 3.S2

3.4 The following set of data in Table 3.P3 represents weights (in pounds) of 100 packages containing machine parts of a certain type. The data have already been arranged into an array in ascending order.

TABLE 3.P3 Array of Weights (in pounds) of 100 Packages of Machine Parts

92.3	98.4	100.3	101.8	104.0
93.5	98.5	100.4	101.9	104.0
94.0	98.5	100.4	101.9	104.3
94.2	98.6	100.4	102.0	104.4
94.4	98.6	100.5	102.1	104.5
94.5	98.8	100.5	102.2	104.8
95.7	98.9	100.6	102.2	104.9
95.9	99.0	100.7	102.3	105.4
96.1	99.3	100.7	102.5	105.5
96.3	99.5	100.8	102.5	105.8
96.4	99.6	101.0	102.6	105.9
96.6	99.8	101.0	102.9	106.3
97.2	100.0	101.1	103.0	106.4
97.3	100.0	101.2	103.3	106.6
97.5	100.0	101.2	103.4	107.0
97.7	100.1	101.4	103.5	107.3
97.9	100.1	101.5	103.7	107.5
98.0	100.2	101.6	103.8	107.9
98.3	100.3	101.7	103.8	108.4
98.4	100.3	101.7	103.9	109.6

Total for this sample is 10,105.2

Note: The array is arranged vertically.

   a. In constructing a frequency distribution (use a tally sheet) for data in Table 3.P3, call it Table 3.S3, it is quite reasonable to use $c = 2$ pounds. Why?
   b. There are at least three different acceptable designations of the class limits for this distribution. They are: (i) 92.0 and under 94.0, 94.0 and under 96.0, etc.; (ii) over 92 through 94, over 94 through 96, etc.; and (iii) 91.50–93.50, 93.50–95.50, etc. Do these three sets of class limits differ from each other in

terms of class intervals and/or in terms of midpoints? Which designation of class interval would you select for your distribution? Explain your choice. Call the resulting distribution Table 3.S3.

3.5 Construct a distribution by tally sheet for the following data set. Call the resulting frequency table Table 3.S4, and write the lower class limit of the first class as $280.00.

TABLE 3.P4 Array of Weekly Wage Rates of 150 Refinery Employees in New Jersey, 1982

$280.05	$280.90	$281.12	$284.49	$286.50
289.94	295.48	297.57	301.95	303.02
304.11	307.48	309.56	311.75	312.83
315.01	315.55	316.00	317.28	318.43
319.23	320.46	321.05	321.44	321.65
322.53	323.80	323.80	324.00	325.90
326.75	326.98	329.18	330.27	331.36
332.45	333.54	335.72	336.81	337.90
340.08	340.08	340.15	341.23	342.26
343.35	344.44	344.44	344.44	345.25
345.78	346.62	347.48	347.78	347.90
348.67	348.80	348.95	349.99	350.95
352.07	352.55	353.00	353.00	354.25
355.64	355.80	356.23	357.52	358.61
359.70	360.39	360.79	361.88	361.88
361.97	363.14	364.27	365.08	365.08
366.24	366.77	366.95	367.33	368.42
369.51	370.60	371.69	372.50	372.50
373.48	373.89	374.96	375.54	375.54
375.54	378.21	379.11	379.25	379.99
380.00	380.00	380.00	380.31	380.55
381.50	381.50	381.50	382.42	384.46
384.77	385.29	386.95	388.04	389.21
390.22	391.31	393.48	394.00	394.95
397.94	398.55	400.06	402.21	403.31
405.48	406.57	407.66	408.53	410.44
411.33	413.21	414.02	415.29	419.38
419.38	419.38	419.47	420.16	420.16
421.07	421.89	424.05	425.10	428.19
429.25	432.36	436.44	437.55	439.82

Total of the series is $54,332.36

Note: The array is arranged horizontally.

For the distribution you have just constructed, explain how you have determined the class interval and designed the class limits. Also give a verbal description of the pattern of the distribution.

3.6 Construct a distribution with the data in Table 3.P5 and call the table Table 3.S5. (*Hint:* use 0.10 as the first class interval and write the class limits in two decimal points, with the first lower class written as 3.60 a.u. 3.70.)

TABLE 3.P5 Array for 100 Measurements of Diameters of Steel Pipes of a Certain Make, in Inches

3.63	3.86	3.96	4.04	4.12
3.69	3.87	3.96	4.04	4.13
3.70	3.88	3.97	4.05	4.14
3.71	3.89	3.97	4.05	4.14
3.71	3.90	3.97	4.05	4.15
3.73	3.90	3.97	4.06	4.15
3.74	3.91	3.97	4.06	4.16
3.76	3.91	3.98	4.07	4.16
3.77	3.92	3.98	4.07	4.16
3.79	3.93	3.99	4.07	4.16
3.80	3.93	3.99	4.07	4.17
3.81	3.94	4.00	4.08	4.18
3.81	3.94	4.00	4.08	4.20
3.82	3.94	4.01	4.08	4.22
3.82	3.95	4.02	4.09	4.23
3.83	3.95	4.02	4.09	4.24
3.83	3.95	4.02	4.10	4.26
3.83	3.95	4.03	4.11	4.28
3.84	3.96	4.03	4.11	4.29
3.85	3.96	4.04	4.12	4.35

The total of this series is 399.17 inches

Note: the array is arranged vertically.

Verbally describe the distribution pattern of results in Table 3.S5.

3.7 Construct a vertical line chart and a vertical bar chart for the data in Table 3.S1.

3.8 Construct a histogram and a polygon for each of the distributions in Tables 3.S2 through 3.S5 inclusively.

3.9 If a smooth curve were fitted to each of the polygons you have constructed in the preceding problem, what general shape would it take: Symmetric? Positively skewed? Negatively skewed? Another pattern?

Instruction. For each of the next five problems consruct a relative frequency distribution for the data; in each case, give relative frequencies in both proportions and percentages.

3.10 Use the distribution in Table 3.S1; call it Table 3S.6.

3.11 Use the distribution in Table 3.S2; call it Table 3.S7.

3.12 Use the distribution in Table 3.S3; call it Table 3.S8.

3.13 Use the distribution in Table 3.S4; call it Table 3.S9.

3.14 Use the distribution in Table 3.S5; call it Table 3.S10.

Instructions. For the next four problems construct the "less than" and "more than" cumulative distributions for both absolute and relative frequencies for data indicated.

3.15 Use the results in Table 3.S7; call it Table 3.S11.

3.16 Use the results in Table 3.S8; call it Table 3.S12.

3.17 Use the results in Table 3.S9; call it Table 3.S13.

3.18 Use the results in Table 3.S10; call it Table 3.S14.

3.19 Draw step diagrams and ogives of the "less than" form for the cumulative distributions in Tables 3.S11 and 3.S13.

3.20 Draw step diagrams and ogives of the "more than" form for the cumulative distributions in Tables 3.S12 and 3.S14.

3.21 From the ogives you have constructed in the foregoing two problems, find the approximate value of the variable in each case that divides the values of the variable into two equal parts; that is, so that 50% of the values of the variable will be "equal to or less than" and 50% of the values of the variable will be "equal to or greater than" that value.

3.22 As has been pointed out, we seldom organize a raw data set into an array when the sample is at all large just for the purpose of obtaining more information. However, the array is an efficient and useful type of data organization when sample is small—say, 25 or less. An array is needed to determine fractile values from ungrouped data. In such a case n or N may be quite large, so a computer program is needed for the construction of such an array. Organize an array by such a program for the following set of data.

16,	12,	33,	18,	25,	37,	31,	29,	30,	42,
11,	32,	28,	26,	25,	17,	15,	22,	26,	34,
10,	41,	39,	21,	25,	34,	19,	40,	37,	36.

3.23 No computer program is available for the organization of a frequency distribution from the start. It requires one to determine the number of classes, the class limits and midpoints first. Once these quantities are given, a computer program will give us the class frequencies, absolute or relative, and cumulative frequencies, absolute or relative. Table 3.P6 contains an array (read horizontally) of 1,000 excutive business luncheon expenses of Gamma Co. for 1990—a hypothetical population cooked up for illustrative purposes. We shall use this data set a number of times in the future. For the time being, construct a frequency distribution for it with a computer program, showing absolute and relative frequencies and absolute and relative cummulative frequencies with classes written as $120 a.u. $140, 140 a.u. 180,..., and 280 a.u. 300. Call this table Table 3.S15.

3.24 *A small research project.* Write a report with at most ten typewritten pages (including tables and graphs) on the changes in the income distribution of Black households from 1960 to the most recent year. You can find such income distributions in various issues of *Statistical Abstract.*

TABLE 3.P6 Executive Business Luncheon Expenses (in dollars) of Gamma Co. for 1990

$120	$121	$121	$121	$122	$122	$122	$123	$123	$123
123	124	124	124	124	125	125	125	125	126
126	126	126	126	127	127	127	127	127	128
128	128	128	128	129	129	129	129	129	129
129	130	130	130	130	130	130	130	130	130
131	131	131	131	131	131	131	132	132	132
132	132	132	133	133	133	133	133	134	134
134	134	134	135	135	135	135	135	136	136
136	136	137	137	137	137	138	138	138	139
140	140	141	141	141	141	142	142	142	142
143	143	143	143	143	144	144	144	144	144
145	145	145	145	145	146	146	146	146	146
146	147	147	147	147	147	147	147	148	148
148	148	148	148	148	148	149	149	149	149
149	149	149	149	149	149	149	150	150	150
150	150	150	150	150	150	150	150	150	151
151	151	151	151	151	151	151	151	151	152
152	152	152	152	152	152	153	153	153	153
153	153	153	154	154	154	154	154	154	155
155	155	155	155	155	156	156	156	156	156
157	157	157	157	157	158	158	158	158	159
159	160	160	160	160	160	161	161	161	161
161	161	161	162	162	162	162	162	162	162
162	162	162	162	163	163	163	163	163	163
163	163	163	163	163	164	164	164	164	164
164	164	164	164	164	164	164	165	165	165
165	165	165	165	165	165	165	165	165	166
166	166	166	166	166	166	166	166	166	166
166	166	167	167	167	167	167	167	167	167
167	167	167	167	167	168	168	168	168	168
168	168	168	168	168	168	168	168	168	169
169	169	169	169	169	169	169	169	169	169
169	169	169	169	169	170	170	170	170	170
170	170	170	170	170	170	170	170	170	170
170	170	170	170	171	171	171	171	171	171
171	171	171	171	171	171	171	171	171	171
171	171	172	172	172	172	172	172	172	172
172	172	172	172	172	172	172	172	173	173
173	173	173	173	173	173	173	173	173	173
173	173	174	174	174	174	174	174	174	174
174	174	174	174	174	174	175	175	175	175
175	175	175	175	175	175	175	175	175	176
176	176	176	176	176	176	176	176	176	176
176	177	177	177	177	177	177	177	177	177
177	177	178	178	178	178	178	178	178	178
179	179	179	179	179	179	180	180	180	180
181	181	181	181	181	181	181	182	182	182
182	182	182	182	182	183	183	183	183	183
183	183	183	184	184	184	184	184	184	184
184	184	185	185	185	185	185	185	185	185
185	186	186	186	186	186	186	186	186	186
186	187	187	187	187	187	187	187	187	187
187	188	188	188	188	188	188	188	188	188
188	188	188	189	189	189	189	189	189	189
189	189	189	189	189	189	189	190	190	190
190	190	190	190	190	190	190	190	190	190
190	190	191	191	191	191	191	191	191	191
191	191	191	191	191	192	192	192	192	192
192	192	192	192	192	192	193	193	193	193

(continued)

TABLE 3.P6 (*continued*)

$193	$193	$193	$193	$193	$193	$194	$194	$194	$194
194	194	194	194	194	195	195	195	195	195
195	195	195	195	196	196	196	196	196	196
196	196	197	197	197	197	197	197	197	198
198	198	198	198	198	198	199	199	199	199
199	199	200	200	200	201	201	201	201	202
202	202	202	203	203	203	203	203	204	204
204	204	204	205	205	205	205	205	205	206
206	206	206	206	206	207	207	207	207	207
207	207	208	208	208	208	208	208	208	208
209	209	209	209	209	209	209	209	209	209
210	210	210	210	210	210	210	210	210	210
210	210	211	211	211	211	211	211	211	211
211	211	211	212	212	212	212	212	212	212
212	213	213	213	213	213	213	213	214	214
214	214	214	214	214	215	215	215	215	215
215	216	216	216	216	216	217	217	217	217
217	218	218	218	218	219	219	220	220	221
221	221	222	222	222	223	223	223	223	224
224	224	224	225	225	225	225	226	226	226
226	226	227	227	227	227	227	228	228	228
228	228	229	229	229	229	229	229	229	230
230	230	230	230	230	230	230	230	231	231
231	231	231	231	231	231	232	232	232	232
232	232	232	232	233	233	233	233	233	233
234	234	234	234	234	235	235	235	235	235
236	236	236	236	237	237	237	237	238	238
238	239	239	240	240	241	241	242	242	243
243	243	244	244	244	245	245	245	246	246
246	246	247	247	247	247	248	248	248	248
249	249	249	249	249	249	250	250	250	250
250	250	250	251	251	251	251	251	251	252
252	252	252	252	252	253	253	253	253	253
254	254	254	254	255	255	255	255	256	256
256	257	257	257	258	258	259	260	260	261
261	262	262	263	263	264	264	265	265	265
266	266	266	267	267	267	268	268	268	269
269	269	269	270	270	270	270	271	271	271
272	272	272	273	273	274	274	275	275	276
276	277	278	279	280	281	282	283	284	285
286	287	288	289	290	291	292	294	296	299

The total of this series is $190,640 with $N = 1,000$

Source: Hypothetical.

4 Measures of Central Tendency: Averages

4.1 PROPERTIES OF CROSS-SECTION UNIVARIATE DATA

In the preceding chapter we discussed how the data points of a data set, or the values of a variable, could be reduced to compact, comprehensible and communicable form by means of the frequency distribution. The frequency distribution is not only a method of organizing data, it is also a descriptive measure that depicts the pattern of the distribution of a variable. Indeed, it may be considered as a set of descriptive measures, since each number showing the frequency (or density) of observations in a class is a descriptive measure.

Often, however, we need descriptive measures in the form of single numbers that can focus attention more sharply on the various properties of a set of data being investigated. For example, when the family food consumption expenditures of the Soviets are compared with those of the Americans, or when the wage rates of the Japanese auto workers are compared with those of the oil refinery employees in the United States, or when deposits of commercial banks in London are contrasted with those in New York City, the use of a single number for each characteristic of each of the variables in question is clearly more advantageous in terms of simplicity, clarity, directness, and vividness than the whole of the distributions.

In general, in the context of sampling, any quantity determined from the n observations in a sample is called a statistic. Parallel functions for population data are called parameters. Corresponding

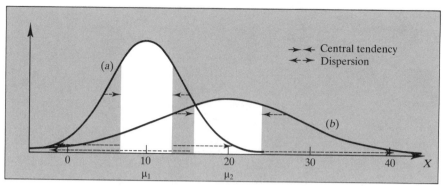

FIGURE 4.1 Graphic illustration of varying degrees of central tendency and dispersion between two distributions.

statistics and parameters are computed from sample and population data, respectively, with much the same equations, and they differ, as we shall see, only in terms of notation. Now it may be noted that although any single number derived from the n or N observations is a descriptive measure, not all possible numbers that can be applied to a set of data are of equal importance or usefulness. Some of them may even be meaningless. As far as cross-section univariate data are concerned, we are only interested, as suggested by the various patterns of smooth curves, in the four kinds of summary measured stated below:

1. *Central tendency*: This property refers to the location of the center of a distribution. It tells us where the data are or what a typical observation is.

2. *Dispersion.* This property reveals the degree of variation of individual values around the central point. It is the tendency of individual values to deviate from the measure of central tendency toward the small and large values of the variable. Both central tendency and dispersion are illustrated by Figure 4.1.

3. *Skewness.* The degree of skewness is the lack of symmetry on both sides of the peak (the point with the highest frequency density) of a distribution. (See Figure 4.2.)

4. *Kurtosis.* This characteristic refers to the degree of peakedness, or the rate at which the distribution rises and falls from left to right. (See Figure 4.3.)

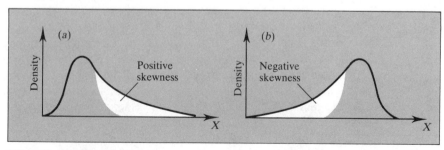

FIGURE 4.2 Graphic illustration of the degree of (a) positive skewness and (b) negative skewness.

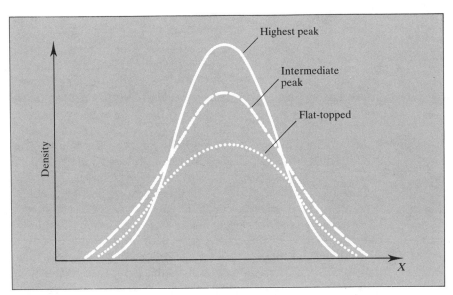

FIGURE 4.3 Graphic illustration of varying degrees of peakedness of different distributions.

These properties are especially meaningful for unimodal distributions, but they also apply to other types of distributions. To facilitate interpretation, however, we shall relate our discussion mainly to unimodal distributions. Furthermore, among these four properties, central tendency and dispersion are by far the most important from both the theoretical and practical points of view. Thus, the discussion that follows will concentrate on the measures of these two properties. Skewness and kurtosis will be introduced merely for the purpose of later cross-references. This chapter will be devoted to the measures of central tendency or averages. Dispersion, skewness and kurtosis will be topics for discussion in the next chapter.

4.2   A NOTE ON STATISTICAL NOTATION

Summary or descriptive measures of central tendency are called *averages*. An *average* can also be defined as a typical value, because it is sometimes used to represent all the values of a variable. There are many types of averages, each possessing particular properties and each being typical in some unique way. The most frequently encountered ones are given below.

1. Computed averages
   a. The arithmetic mean
   b. The geometric mean
   c. The harmonic mean
2. Position averages
   a. The median
   b. The mode

We shall later present these measures in the order mentioned. However, before doing so, we present a brief discussion on statistical notation in order to avoid possible confusion in the future.

It is rather unfortunate that statistical notation is only partially standardized. If you study the same topics in different texts or in journal articles, you can expect different authors to use somewhat different notations. This may be dismaying at the beginning, but after some experience you will finally get accustomed to notational changes. In any event, in the remainder of this section we will attempt to standardize notations that will be employed in this text.

Just as in algebra, the upper-case letter X is often used as a variable in statistics. When there are several variables involved, we may use X, Y, Z, etc., to denote each of them. The individual values that a variable can take are denoted by the corresponding lower-case letters. For example, if X is used as the heights of, say, a sample of 40 people, then x is the numerical value of one of these 40 people. Different values of a variable are identified by subscripts. Thus, the heights of the 40 people in the sample may be denoted as $x_1, x_2, \ldots, x_{40}$. In other words, a subscript refers to a particular value of a variable. In general, a *subscript* is a symbol attached to and written to the right below a main symbol. Our notation for a variable is the same for a sample or for a population. For example, x_{15} is the 15th value of X in either a sample or a population. You can tell from the context whether the data refer to a sample or to a population.

The total number of observations in a finite population is denoted as N, and in a sample is denoted as n. Thus, if X refers to a population we may express the individual values as x_i, $i = 1, 2, 3, \ldots, N$. Likewise, if X refers to a sample, then the individual values may be denoted as x_i, $i = 1, 2, \ldots, n$. The subscripts i, j, and k attached to x are the most frequently used generalized subscripts for individual values.

The distinction between descriptive measures for populations and samples is very important. We shall denote parameters by Greek letters or lower-case English letters with a tilde above each. Sample statistics will be represented by upper-case English letters, and a realized value of a sample statistic by the corresponding lower case English letter. For example, the descriptive measures to be introduced in this chapter will be denoted as follows

Name of the Measure	Parameter	Notation for Statistic	A Realized Value
Arithmetic mean	μ	$\bar{X}$	$\bar{x}$
Proportion	π	$\bar{P}$	$\bar{p}$
Geometric mean	$\tilde{g}$	G	g
Harmonic mean	$\tilde{h}$	H	h
Median	$\tilde{x}_{.5}$	$X_{.5}$	$x_{.5}$
Mode	$\tilde{x}_m$	X_m	x_m

Note that we employ upper-case letters to represent sample statistics, because they are variables. As a matter of fact they are variables of a special kind, called "random variables"—a concept to be discussed in detail in Chapter 7. For the time being, it is sufficient to point out that a statistic is a *random variable* in the sense that if many different samples of the same size are selected from the same population, the realized values of the statistic will vary from sample to sample, since different samples may include different elements of the population.

Finally, the symbol Σ (the upper case Greek letter "sigma") is often used for repetitive addition. Rather complicated additions occur quite often in statistics and the Σ sign, meaning adding up, make such additions absolutely precise. A detailed discussion on summation algebra is given in Appendix B at the end of this text. The reader is advised to study it now before proceeding to the rest of this chapter.

A word of warning is also in order here. Despite our great care in denoting various quantities, we may make exceptions at quite a few places. First, sometimes the same symbol may be used for different quantities, since we may not have enough letters, Greek or English, to go around. Second, for clarity as well as differentiation, we may sometimes use two English letters to represent a statistic, as in the next chapter. Third and lastly, some statistics are very useful for descriptive purposes, but they will not be employed for conducting inferences in this text. In such cases, the corresponding population parameters may not be explicitly given. You will be able to recognize all these exceptional cases from the context of the discussion, however, and will not be confused by them.

We move on now to introduce various summary measures, stressing sample statistics, since, as has been mentioned a number of times already, statistical investigations are usual in the context of sampling, rather than census. However, it may be pointed out that population parameters are nearly always computed with analogous formulas for samples, and that properties of sample statistics can almost always be applied to parameters. Whenever, in rare cases, there are exceptions, these exceptions will be pointed out to you.

4.3 THE UNWEIGHTED ARITHMETIC MEAN

There are two types of arithmetic means: unweighted and weighted. The unweighted arithmetic mean, because of ease of computation, long usage, and desirable mathematical properties, is the best known and most commonly used average. Sometimes it is referred to simply as "the arithmetic mean" or "the mean" or "the average," but appropriate adjectives must be used when other types of means are used.

The *mean* is defined as the sum of the observations divided by the number of observations. Thus, for a sample of n values, we have

$$\bar{X} = \frac{x_1 + x_2 + \cdots + x_n}{n} = \frac{\Sigma x}{n}. \tag{4.1}$$

For example, if we have a sample with the three values of 2 pounds, 4 pounds, and 8 pounds, then

$$\bar{x} = \frac{2 + 4 + 8}{3} \doteq 4.67 \text{ pounds.}$$

Again, for the food expenditure data in Table 3.2, we have

$$\bar{x} = \frac{\Sigma x}{n} = \frac{13,719.21}{80} = \$171.49.$$

As mentioned before, the population mean is denoted by μ (the Greek letter "mu") and obviously, $\mu = \Sigma x/N$ if the population is finite. The population mean is often the key parameter in many decision situations. Indeed, as will be seen, the chapters on inductive statistics in this book are often concerned with this parameter. It will suffice to mention here a few situations in which where the mean adequately describes the true state of the problem and thereby serves as the basis for decision. For instance, in deciding whether a shipment of cargo should be accepted, the mean may be the appropriate parameter. It may be, say, the mean durability of a shipment of automobile tires, or the mean weight of a lot of drained weight of canned meat, or the mean tensile strength of an order of steel wires. Again, in setting up the price of the products of a firm, management may use the mean of the selling prices of all the firms in the industry as the basis for decision. Finally, decisions on changes in wage rates are often made on the basis of some price index—an average of price-relatives. As a matter of fact, the wages of millions of unionized workers in this country are tied by contract to the Consumer Price Index.

The mean has a number of interesting and important mathematical properties. First, it is a typical value, in that is the center of gravity—a point of balance. It is also typical in the sense that its value can be substituted for the value of each item in the series without changing the total. Stating this symbolically, we have

$$n(\bar{X}) = \Sigma x.$$

This is obvious. After all, the mean is just the sum of the observations divided by the number of observations. When this property is used in practical applications, due allowance must be made for any rounding error.

The second mathematical property of the mean is that the algebraic sum of deviations from the mean (that is, taking into account algebraic signs) is always zero. That is,

$$\Sigma (x - \bar{X}) = 0.$$

The third mathematical property is that the sum of the squared deviations of the individual observations from the mean is less than the sum of the squared deviations from any other number. In other words,

TABLE 4.1 Numerical Demonstrations of the Mathematical Properties of the Mean

	(1) x	(2) $\bar{x}$	(3) $(x - \bar{x})$	(4) $(x - \bar{x})^2$	(5) $(x - 2)^2$	(6) $(x - 5)^2$
	1	3	−2	4	1	16
	2	3	−1	1	0	9
	6	3	+3	9	16	1
Sum	9	9	0	14	17	26

in terms of sample data,

$$\sum (x - \bar{X})^2 = \text{a minimum}$$

The basic idea of selecting a number so that the sum of squared deviations about that number is minimized has great importance in statistics. It even has a special name, the "principle of least squares." It is, for example, the rationale of the *method of least squares* used to fit the best curve through a set of scattered points, as we shall see in a later chapter. This property is also the basis of computing an important measure of dispersion presented in the next chapter.

The validity of these three properties can be easily demonstrated by a simple numerical example, as shown in Table 4.1. In this table, column (1) contains a data set whose sum is 9 and whose mean is 3. Column (2) demonstrates the first property of the mean; i.e., if each of the individual values in the data set is replaced by the mean, the sum remains at 9. Column (3) verifies the fact $\sum (x - \bar{X}) = 0$. Finally, columns (4), (5) and (6) demonstrate that $\sum (x - \bar{X})^2 = 14$, which is smaller than the sums when individual deviations are taken from the number 2 and the number 5, respectively.

4.4 THE WEIGHTED ARITHMETIC MEAN

A familiar example of the weighted mean is the averaging of a student's test scores, when the final examination counts, say, twice as much as either of the two interim tests. Suppose 60 is the minimum score for a D, 70 for a C, 80 for a B, and 90 for an A. Suppose also, that you scored 68 and 72 on the two interim tests, but that the course finally "sank in" and you scored 94 on the final. What is your average grade for the semester? The correct answer is

$$\frac{1(68) + 1(72) + 2(94)}{1 + 1 + 2} = \frac{328}{4} = 82,$$

which is a B. The numerator is calculated by multiplying each score by its weight. The denominator is the sum of the weights. You would be justifiably upset if your scores were averaged as $(68 + 72 + 94)/3 = 78$, which is a C, since this does not allow for the extra weight of the final.

The average of 82 calculated above is an example of the *weighted mean.* The average of 78 is an *unweighted mean.* The general formula for the sample weighted mean is

$$\bar{X}_w = \frac{\sum wx}{\sum w}. \tag{4.2}$$

The sum of the weights in (4.2) must not be zero, but otherwise there is no restriction on the values of the weights. Notice that w is used both as a subscript and as a main symbol in the previous equation. When w is a subscript, it means "weighted." When it is a main symbol, it means "weight."

Notice that if all the w's are set equal to 1, then (4.2) becomes the equation for the unweighted mean. It is also true that if all the w's are set equal to a constant, say c, then (4.2) again becomes the equation for the unweighted mean. So the "unweighted mean" is really a mean with equal weights.

The weights can have any interpretation appropriate to the context. In averaging test scores, the weights showed the relative importance of the tests. Consider now another situation: in a management consulting firm ten junior consultants receive $60 each per day, four seniors receive $100 each, and one "specialist" receives $200. What is the average salary? The unweighted average is (60 + 100 + 200)/3 = $120 per day. The weighted average is [10(60) + 4(100) + 1(200)]/[10 + 4 + 1] = $80 per day. If the three job titles are considered equally important, the average salary is $120. If the fifteen people are considered equally important, the average salary is $80. To get the $80 answer, the salary levels are weighted by the numbers of people receiving them. Ordinarily, of course, $80 is the correct answer and $120 is a mistake—but the reverse can be true in some situations.

As another example, suppose that the purchasing department of a supermarket chain buys paper towels from three suppliers, rotating among the suppliers. This purchasing policy is frequently used. A company likes to have several suppliers for everything it buys instead of being dependent on just one supplier, so it spreads its orders around to help every supplier stay in business. Suppose it orders 5,000 rolls of paper towels at a time from one of suppliers A or B or C, and suppose the suppliers' prices and levels of production are as shown in Table 4.2.

What is the average price? This question is rather vague, but we can make it clear by the following discussion. First, the average price

TABLE 4.2 Prices and Production for Paper Towels

Supplier	Price per Roll (x)	Supplier's Monthly Production (w)	Total Yearly Value (xw)
A	$1.25	200,000 rolls	$250,000
B	1.00	400,000 rolls	400,000
C	1.05	800,000 rolls	840,000
Totals	$3.30	1,400,000 rolls	$1,490,000

per supplier is ($3.30)/(3) = $1.10; this is the unweighted average of the three prices. Second, the average price per roll produced is ($1,490,000)/(1,400,000) ≐ $1.06; this is the weighted average of the three prices, the weights being based on monthly production levels. If your firm rotates its 5,000-roll purchases equally among the three suppliers, its average price is $1.10. If it rotates its purchases in proportion to the size of the supplier (as measured by monthly production), its average price is $1.06. If it follows some other rotation policy, its average price would be a weighted average of the three suppliers' prices, the weights being based on the quantities purchased.

When two or more averages can be calculated, as in the preceding examples, it is sometimes unclear which average is correct. The key is to determine whether the average-per-such-and-such is the one really wanted. Is it the average salary per job title? Average salary per employee? Is it the average price per supplier? Per item produced? Per item purchased? In other words, as pointed out in Chapter 1, in any statistical investigation, the first thing to do is to define the research question clearly and precisely. Sometimes several averages are interesting and relevant. If this happens, calculate and report them all.

4.5   PROPORTIONS AS MEANS

We often encounter populations whose elementary units can be classified into two categories: one as having a certain attribute; the other as not having a certain attribute. In this case we are interested in the proportion of the elements that possess that certain attribute. A proportion is thought of as a fraction or a percentage, but can be thought of as a special case of the mean. It can be computed by using the formula for the mean and the properties of the mean can be applied to it.

Suppose we are to determine the proportion (mean) of eligible voters among all of the U.S. citizens. We may first assign a value of 1 to each person qualified to vote and a value of 0 to each person not qualified. Then the sum of 1's would be $\sum x$ and the mean would be obtained by dividing the sum by the total number N of persons in the United States. Here, we are clearly talking about a finite population. In dealing with proportions, however, we usually substitute x for $\sum x$ and π (the Greek letter "pi") for μ, which stands for the population proportion. Thus, $\mu = \sum x / N$ is replaced by $\pi = x / N$. Likewise, we usually use $\bar{P}$ to represent a sample proportion, thus

$$\bar{P} = \frac{x}{n}. \qquad (4.3)$$

For instance, if a survey is to be conducted of the smoking habits of students at universities in Boston and it is found that 250 of the 800 students selected in the sample smoke cigarettes, then $x = 250$ and

$n = 800$, and

$$\bar{p} = \frac{250}{800} \doteq 0.3125, \text{ or } 31.25\%.$$

The proportion, though a very simple concept, is nevertheless, as we shall see, one of the most useful measures for many decision situations. For the time being, let us just cite a few examples in which proportions are employed in decision making. In deciding whether a lot of merchandise ordered should be accepted or rejected, the information we need is usually the proportion of defective items in the lot. In a TV network's decision on a course of action concerning a program, the relevant proportion is also the key measure to be considered. For instance, the network may decide to continue the program if 15% or more of the television viewing audience watches it, and may decide to drop the program if the rating is less than 15%. Often, a manufacturer may decide to introduce a new product if it could share a certain proportion of the total market. Again, the federal government may decide to take one type of action if the proportion of unemployment is 10% or more; to take another type of action if it is between 8 and 10%; to take still another action if it is between 5 and 8%; and to take no action at all, if it is 5% or less.

4.6* THE GEOMETRIC MEAN

The *geometric mean* of a sample is defined as the nth root of the product of the n sample values. That is,

$$G = \sqrt[n]{(x_1)(x_2)\ldots(x_n)}. \tag{4.4}$$

For example, the geometric mean of 2 pounds, 4 pounds, and 8 pounds is

$$G = \sqrt[3]{(2)(4)(8)} = \sqrt[3]{64} = 4 \text{ pounds.}$$

For the same series, $\bar{x} = 4.67$ pounds. It is always true that the arithmetic mean is greater than the geometric mean for any series of positive values, unless the items being averaged are of the same value, in which case the two averages are the same.

The computation of the geometric mean is quite easy by (4.4) on a pocket calculator. However, the interpretation of this measure and its properties are made much more obvious by reducing formula (4.4) to its logarithmic form:

$$\log G = \frac{\log x_1 + \log x_2 + \log x_3 + \cdots + \log x_n}{n}$$

$$= \frac{\sum \log x}{n}. \tag{4.5}$$

Thus, the logarithm of the geometric mean is equal to the arithmetic mean of the logarithms of the values.

It may be noted that the geometric mean is meaningful only for sets of observations that are all positive. In addition, the geometric mean possesses two mathematical properties. The first is that the product of the values of series will remain unchanged when the value of the geometric mean is substituted for each individual value. For example, the geometric mean for series 2, 4, 8, 16, and 32 is 8; therefore, we have

$$(2)(4)(8)(16)(32) = 32{,}768 = (8)(8)(8)(8)(8).$$

The other property of the geometric mean is that the sum of the deviations of the logarithms of the original observations above or below the logarithm of the geometric mean are equal; namely, $\sum (\log x - \log G) = 0$. Alternatively, we may say that the value of the geometric mean is such as to balance the ratio deviations of the observations from it. Thus, using the same numbers as before, we can see that

$$(8/2)(8/4) = 8 = (16/8)(32/8).$$

Because of this property, we may say that the geometric mean is typical in the sense that its value balances the ratio deviations from it of the items. Because of this property, the geometric mean is especially adapted to average ratios, rates of change, and logarithmically distributed series. In certain special cases of averaging ratios or percentages, such as the computation of the price index, the geometric mean can yield meaningful and logical results that the arithmetic mean cannot. For example, consider the data in Table 4.3, which shows the price changes of two commodities, A and B, from 1980 to 1985. During this period the price of A increased 100% and the price of B decreased by 50%. What was the relative average change in price?

The arithmetic mean is the wrong answer to that. As indicated by the computations in Table 4.3, the application of the mean in this case has led to a nonsensical conclusion that the prices in 1985 were, on the average, 25% higher than those in 1980, when 1980 was chosen as the base, and that the prices in 1980 were 25% higher than those in 1985 when 1985 was chosen as the base. The arithmetic mean of ratios is inconsistent.

TABLE 4.3 Prices of Commodities A and B in 1980 and 1985

| | | | Price Relatives | | | |
| | Price | | 1980 = 100 | | 1985 = 100 | |
Commodity	1980	1985	1980	1985	1980	1985
A	$50	$10	100	200	50	100
B	20	10	100	50	200	100
Arithmetic mean			100	125	125	100

However, a consistent result is reached when the geometric mean is applied:

1. If 1980 is chosen as the base, the prices of 1985 were 100% of the prices of 1980; i.e.

$$g = \sqrt{200 \times 50} = \sqrt{10,000} = 100.$$

2. If 1985 is chosen as the base, the prices of 1980, as they should be, were also 100% of the prices in 1985; i.e.,

$$g = \sqrt{50 \times 200} = 100.$$

This method reduces the large-upward-moving relative changes to ratios equal to the smaller decreasing relative changes by giving each change equal weight when the nth root of the products of the relatives is extracted.

The most useful application of the geometric mean is perhaps for averaging rates of change, since the averages of rates of change can be measured correctly only by this method. Suppose the annual sales of a manufacturing firm had increased from 10,000 to 17,280 units during the period 1985–1988 as shown in Table 4.4; what is the average rate of change per year? The average annual rate of growth can be calculated from the percentage values of the absolute sales. It is not, however, the arithmetic mean, which would be

$$\bar{x} = (60 + 96 + 300)/3 = 152,$$

implying an average rate of growth of $152 - 100$, or 52%. If sales grew at 52% per year, starting from 1985's sales of 10,000, then 1986's sales would be

$$10,000 + 0.52(10,000) = 15,200;$$

1987's sales would be

$$15,200 + 0.52(15,200) = 23,104;$$

and 1988's sales would be

$$23,104 + 0.52(23,104) = 35,118.08.$$

TABLE 4.4 Computation of the Geometric Mean of Sales Growth of a Manufacturing Firm, 1985–1988

Year	1985	1986	1987	1988
Sales	10,000	6,000	5,760	17,280
Percentage of previous year		60	96	300

Clearly, 35,118.08 is almost 200% of the actual 1988 sales of 17,280. Here, the geometric mean is required, not the arithmetic mean, and

$$g = \sqrt[3]{(60)(96)(300)} = 120,$$

implying an average annual rate of growth of $120 - 100$, or 20%. As a check, if sales grew at 20% a year, starting from 1985's sales of 10,000, then 1986's sales would be

$$10,000 + 0.20(10,000) = 12,000;$$

1987's would be

$$12,000 + 0.20(12,000) = 14,400;$$

and 1988's sales would be

$$14,400 + 0.20(14,400) = 17,280.$$

This agrees with the correct figure for 1988.

It is worth emphasizing that the 20% is a rate of compound interest, not simple interest. The percentage can be negative, indicating an average rate of decline rather than an average rate of growth. Notice, too, that each of the three percentages whose geometric mean was calculated is *percent of previous year* rather than *percent change from previous year,* or some other kind of percentage. Furthermore, interpretation of the result is made in terms of $(G - 100)$, where the 100 means 100%.

The calculation of average rate of change is based upon the assumption of a constant rate of change or that the individual values have a geometric progression. When the calculation involves a considerable number of time periods, it is usually undertaken by using a more efficient formula that is related to that for the geometric mean and is called the *average rate of growth*. This formula, as given below, also happens to be the compound interest formula:

$$R = \left(\sqrt[n]{\frac{x_t}{x_b}} \right) - 1 \qquad (4.6)$$

where

R = the average rate of growth,

n = the number of time units or time periods,

x_b = the value of the beginning period, and

x_t = the value of the end or terminal period.

Applying (4.6) to data in Table 4.4, we have the average rate of increase per decade as

$$R = \left(\sqrt[3]{\frac{17,280}{10,000}} \right) - 1$$

$$= (\sqrt[3]{1.728}) - 1 = 1.20 - 1 = 0.20, \text{ or } 20\%$$

as obtained before. Note that in both cases of the preceding two calculations $n = 3$ and not 4 since the first time period is the base for the calculations (from 1985 to 1988, there are only three year periods, not 4.) Also note that $R = G - 1$ in computing the average rate of growth.

The pattern of the distribution of a series is often an important consideration in selecting the most representative average. If the absolute values of the distribution, plotted on an arithmetic scale, are fairly symmetrical, the arithmetic mean is definitely preferable to the geometric mean. A geometric mean would appear to be more representative if a serial is logarithmically distributed. A logarithmic distribution is markedly skewed to the right, so that, if its midpoints are plotted on an arithmetic scale, a symmetrical polygon appears. A logarithmically distributed series is encountered when the series has a definite limit at one extreme and theoretical infinity at the other. A good illustration of this type of distribution is given by percentage changes in prices. In theory as well as in practice, the price of a commodity may increase infinitely from a given base, but it can never decrease more than 100%. Thus, the percentage changes, as natural numbers, would distribute themselves asymmetrically, with the range of deviations above the arithmetic mean greatly exceeding the range below. However, the logarithms of percentage changes would tend to group themselves symmetrically about the logarithm of the geometric mean. In conclusion, the geometric mean is preferred for a logarithmic distribution, because in such a distribution the deviations of ratios about central tendency tend to be symmetrical and not the absolute deviations.

4.7*   THE HARMONIC MEAN

If the reciprocal of the value of each item is taken, the arithmetic mean of the reciprocals is computed, and the reciprocal of this mean is taken, the result is known as the harmonic mean. Or, more compactly, the *harmonic mean* is the reciprocal of the arithmetic mean of the reciprocals of the observations. Symbolically, for a sample, we have

$$H = \frac{1}{\dfrac{1/x_1 + 1/x_2 + \ldots + 1/x_n}{n}} = \frac{1}{\dfrac{\sum (1/x)}{n}} = \frac{n}{\sum (1/x)}. \qquad (4.7)$$

To make computation easier, (4.6) may be rewritten as

$$1/H = \frac{1/x_1 + 1/x_2 + \ldots + 1/x_n}{n} = \frac{\sum (1/x)}{n}. \qquad (4.8)$$

The harmonic mean of the three values 2, 4, and 8 is

$$\frac{1}{h} = \frac{1/2 + 1/4 + 1/8}{3}$$

$$= 7/24;$$

$$h \doteq 3.43.$$

For the same data, the arithmetic mean is 4.67 and the geometric mean is 4. For any series of which the values are not all the same and which does not include any value of zero, the harmonic mean is always smaller than both the arithmetic mean and the geometric mean. This relationship is due to the facts that the arithmetic mean is influenced by total weights of the extreme large values; the geometric mean is influenced by the nth root of such values; and the harmonic mean is influenced merely by the reciprocals of such values.

The harmonic mean is limited to average time rates under certain conditions and certain types of prices. Nevertheless, within this limited area, the harmonic mean yields consistent results in most cases. The arithmetic mean has often been used when the harmonic mean should have been employed. For instance, during World War I, the estimate of the transport capacity of American ships was made by dividing the round-trip distance by the arithmetic mean speed of the ships to be used. The result, allowing for turn-round time, delays, and so forth, gave an estimate of shipping capacity that proved unattainable. Actually, in such a case the harmonic mean should have been used. The arithmetic average number of hours per mile could have been obtained and multiplied by the number of miles to get the mean number of hours per trip. Since the harmonic mean speed is the reciprocal of the arithmetic average number of hours per mile, such a procedure is mathematically equivalent to dividing the number of miles by the harmonic mean speed.

Because of the absolute necessity of using the harmonic mean in some cases, and the confusion between the application of the arithmetic and harmonic averages, the harmonic mean deserves more attention than it receives in most elementary textbooks. The proper use of the harmonic mean depends upon a number of considerations. First of all, we must remember that an average refers to some class of units that must be appropriate to the use that the average is to serve. As an example, suppose two workers, A and B, in a clothing factory can make two and three neckties per hour, respectively, their speeds being recorded in either one of the following two forms:

FORM 1.   Worker A: 2 neckties per hour

               Worker B: 3 neckties per hour

FORM 2.   Worker A: 30 minutes per necktie

               Worker B: 20 minutes per necktie

In the first form, time is held as a constant and production is a variable; that is, the outputs are weighted with *equal time periods*. Under this assumption, the interest is centered around the average output per hour, and it is proper to use the arithmetic mean, which in this case is 2.5 neckties per hour $(2 + 3)/(2)$. If 2.5 neckties are produced, on the average, per hour, how much time is required, on the average, to produce one necktie? The answer is 24 minutes because $(60)/(2.5) = 24$.

When the rate is expressed as in the second form, however, time is treated as the variable, and production is the constant; that is, time is weighted with *equal amounts of output*. With this change in the assumption, interest has now been shifted to the average time required to complete one unit of product: therefore, the harmonic mean should be employed. Thus,

$$\frac{1}{h} = \frac{1/30 + 1/20}{2} = \frac{5}{120};$$

$$h = 24 \text{ minutes per necktie.}$$

That is, on the average, 2.5 neckties are produced per hour: $(60)/(24) = 2.5$. It may be pointed out here, that, since workers usually work a fixed number of hours each day, the real interest in time study is the number of hours, rather than the number of outputs, which should be considered as a constant. This being the case, the ratio of form 1 (units per hour) should be stated and the arithmetic mean used. If, however, the time rates are recorded as in form 2 (length of time per unit of output), where time, the factor desired to be constant, is made variable, only the harmonic mean gives the correct answer.

The harmonic mean is especially adapted to a situation in which the observations are expressed inversely to what is required in the average. That is, for example, when average cost per unit is desired, but the data show the number of outputs per amount of cost. This point may be made clear by the following illustration.

Suppose you have spent $12.00 for 3 dozen oranges in one shop, another $12 for 4 dozen oranges and still another $12.00 for 5 dozen oranges in two other stores. What is the "average price" per dozen of oranges? You may easily make the mistake of computing the arithmetic mean for your data. Since you may reason that the average prices in the three stores are $12/3 = \$4.00$, $12/4 = \$3.00$, and $12/5 = \$2.40$, respectively, the average price per dozen oranges in the three stores must be $(4.00 + 3.00 + 2.40)/3 \doteq \$3.13$. You can see that this is incorrect for the following reason: you have spent only $36.00 for 12 dozen oranges; if the average price is $3.13, you would have spent $(3.13)(12) = \$37.56$! Or you may note that your data are expressed in the form "so many dozen oranges per dollar," but you wish to know the average of "so many dollars per dozen of oranges." These two are inverse expressions. Hence, the appropriate average can be obtained by the harmonic mean as

$$\frac{1}{h} = \frac{(1/4.00) + (1/3.00) + (1/2.40)}{3}$$

$$\doteq 0.3333;$$

$$h \doteq \$3.00.$$

Now $(3)(12) = \$36.00$—the amount of money you have spent. So, the harmonic mean is the correct average. Also, you may note that, in the present case, the weighted arithmetic mean also yields the accurate result. Here, the weights are the quantities of oranges bought.

4.8   THE MEDIAN

The *median* is, as its name indicates, the value of the middle item in a series when the items are arranged according to magnitude. For the series $2, $4, $5, $7, and $8, the median is the value of the third item, $5. If there are six items in a series, say, 3, 4, 6, 7, 8, and 10 pounds, then any value between 6 and 7 pounds would divide the series into two equal parts; therefore, any such value could become the median. In practice, for an even number of data, we usually assume the median to be halfway between the two central items. In our example, therefore, the median would be 6.5 pounds. The median may have values identical with its own on both sides of it. For instance, in the series 1, 2, 3, 4, 5, 5, 5, 6, 7, 8, 9, the median is 5.

Because of these characteristics, the *median* may now be formally defined as the value that divides a series in such a fashion that at least 50% of the items are equal to or less than it, and at least 50% of the items are equal to or greater than it. More formally, we state that

$$X_{.5} = \text{the value of } [(n + 1)/2)\text{th item.}} \tag{4.9}$$

Thus, as an example, for the food expenditure data in Table 3.3,

$$x_{.5} = [(80 + 1)/2]\text{th item} = 40.5\text{th item.}$$

That is

$$x_{.5} = (x_{40} + x_{41})/2$$

$$= (166.57 + 167.77)/2$$

$$= \$167.17.$$

Clearly, we require an ordered array to locate the value of the median from ungrouped data. Unfortunately, the construction of an array is often tedious and time-consuming.

As it is defined, the median is not influenced by values in the tails of a distribution. For example, if the sample data 1, 2, 3, 4, 5, were to change to −100, −10, 3, 15, 150, the median would remain at 3. Thus, it is a highly desirable measure of central location for skewed distributions, such as the distribution of income, provided we do not care whether the richest family, for example, earns $500,000 or $1,000,000 a year.

The median also has the interesting property that the sum of the absolute deviations of the observations from the median is less than the sum of the absolute deviations from any other point in the distribution. In symbols:

$$\Sigma \,|x - X_{.5}| = \text{a minimum}$$

and similarly for population data. The median is often selected as a measure of central tendency because of this property.

A simple application, is the decision on the optimal location of a plant. For example, suppose a restaurant chain organization has seven restaurants on a certain turnpike, as shown in Table 4.5. Each day, each restaurant must send for fresh food from a central storehouse; furthermore, suppose the servicing requires two trucks each day. Then where should the central storehouse be located to minimize the total distance from the seven restaurants?

Remembering that the sum of absolute deviations from the median is a minimum, we can easily decide that the central storehouse should be located at restaurant D or in its vicinity. The median distance of the restaurant from the turnpike's entrance is 96 miles, and from restaurant D the total amount of travel to resupply each restaurant once would be minimized at 276 miles each way. If the central storehouse is located at any other point, the sum of distances will be greater. At restaurant C, for instance, this sum is 296 miles. The student may check these computations in Table 4.5.

TABLE 4.5 Computation of Resupply Distances

Restaurant	Location in miles from turnpike entrance to restaurant	Distance From D	Distance From C
A	12	84	64
B	40	56	36
C	76	20	0
D	96	0	20
E	124	28	48
F	132	36	56
G	148	52	72
Total	—	276	296

4.9   THE MODE

The *mode* is that value in a sample or a population that appears more frequently than any other value. In simple cases, it is easy to spot the mode, provided the data are ranked. For example, if the ranked sample data are 1, 2, 3, 3, 4, 5, and 6, then the sample mode is 3. The typicalness of the mode is due to the fact that it is the value that appears the greatest number of times.

Although the mode is a simple and sometimes useful concept, its application presents many difficulties. Sometimes it is even difficult to give any definition of the mode that it is satisfactory. There may be a tie for the mode, as in 1, 2, 3, 3, 3, 4, 5, 6, 6, 6, and 7. Both 3 and 6 occur an equal number of times in this example. There may be more than one mode even though there is no tie, as in 1, 2, 2, 3, 4, 5, 5, 5, and 6. Strictly speaking, any value is a *mode* if it occurs more often than either of its neighbors. So both 2 and 5 are modes in this example. Since 5 occurs more often than 2, it is common to call 5 the *primary mode* and 2 the *secondary mode*. Sometimes there is no mode at all. For example, if we have an array of the populations of all the states in the U.S., there is no modal population for the U.S. because no population occurs more than once.

Again, very often, some observations occur more frequently than others, but there is still no mode at all. For example, if the data are 1, 2, 2, 2, 4, 4, 4, 5, 8, and 9, then no observation occurs more frequently than both of its neighbors, and so there is no mode. There are three 2s and 4s, so 2 does not occur more frequently than 4, and hence cannot be a mode, and 4 does not occur more frequently than 2 and hence cannot be a mode.

Still another troublesome situation exists when an extreme value may occur most frequently. For example, if the data are 1, 1, 1, 2, 3, 4, and 5, then 1 seems to be the mode, but it cannot be said that it occurs more frequently than both of its neighbors, the trouble being that there are no neighboring values less than 1.

Some of the difficulties can be overcome totally or in part when the data are arranged into a frequency distribution. In such a form, any tendency of the data to cluster around a certain value tends to be more clearly shown, and the problem created in the first situation may be solved. When data are grouped into classes, those items that differ in value only on the right of the decimal points may still fall in the same class irrespective of the method of rounding. Finally, a modal value may appear in grouped data even though there is no repetition of any value in the array.

In practice, disadvantages of the mode are so great and so many that it is seldom used in statistical analysis. However, it may in any case be advisable to report the mode for a set of data, because it is simple to understand and therefore helps convey some "feeling" for the data.

Even though the mode is rarely used in statistical analysis, it is rather commonly used in deciding which resulting value is correct when the same measuring or computing process is repeated several times. If, for example, seven statistics students all do the same rather complicated calculation on their pocket calculators and four of them come up with the same answer, while the fifth, sixth and the seventh each come up with different answers, it is reasonable to conclude that the frequently occurring answer is the correct answer. The same principle is sometimes used in laboratories and computer centers. Naturally, the modal answer is not necessarily correct, perhaps only the seventh student understands how to perform the calculation. Of course, it would be better to check each step of the process for validity. Sometimes, though, accepting the modal value represents a reasonable practical compromise between a very expensive checking operation on the one hand and the dangers of relying entirely on one determination on the other.

4.10   THE MEAN FOR GROUPED DATA

When samples are large, it is much more efficient to compute the descriptive measures from frequency distributions. Furthermore, as mentioned near the end of the last section, a modal value may not exist for an array, but it may emerge when data are in the grouped form. It must be pointed out at the very outset, though, that owing to grouping errors values of statistics computed from group data may differ from those computed from ungrouped data. However, if the class limits of the distributions are properly designed summary measures computed from grouped data should very closely correspond to those determined from ungrouped data, and the differences between them may be of no practical importance at all. We shall now begin with the computation of the mean from grouped data.

The mean cannot be determined exactly from a frequency distribution with class intervals, but an approximation can be obtained by using the midpoint assumption. The approximation is almost always quite satisfactory if the distribution is well constructed. Recall that the midpoint assumption refers to the practice that each of the frequencies in a given class is assumed to take on the value of the midpoint of that class. Consequently, the total value of the class frequency of the ith class is simply the product $f_i m_i$. Under this assumption, the approximate mean for a distribution of a sample with k classes becomes

$$\bar{X} \doteq \frac{f_1 m_1 + f_2 m_2 + \cdots + f_k m_k}{f_1 + f_2 + \cdots + f_k} \doteq \frac{\sum fm}{\sum f}$$

$$\doteq \frac{\sum fm}{n}. \tag{4.10}$$

This equation is applicable to distributions with equal, as well as varying class intervals. Notice that all summations in this equation are of classes, not individual observations.

TABLE 4.6 Computing the Mean for the
Food Expenditure Data

Class	f	m	fm
$120.00–$139.99	5	130.0	650.0
140.00– 159.99	26	150.0	3900.0
160.00– 179.99	24	170.0	4080.0
180.00– 199.99	15	190.0	2850.0
200.00– 219.99	8	210.0	1680.0
220.00– 239.99	2	230.0	460.0
Total	80	—	13,620.0

Source: Table 3.9.

Let us apply (4.10) to the food expenditure data in Table 3.9. We have the work sheet shown in Table 4.6.

$$\bar{x} \doteq \frac{13,620.00}{80} \doteq \$170.25.$$

This result is very close to $171.49—the mean of the ungrouped data for the food expenditures obtained earlier. The difference of $1.24 here is the net total grouping error, which is of little or no practical importance at all, since it is less than 1% of $171.49—the exact mean for our sample.

If the midpoint assumption is exactly met, then (4.10) produces exact means instead of approximate means. The sales data in Table 3.4 can be considered as an example meeting the midpoint assumption exactly. The six "class intervals" for sales in that table are just single numbers, so every observation in Table 3.4 equals the midpoint of its class interval. Equation (4.10) then produces an exact mean:

$$\bar{x} = \frac{4(0) + 5(1) + 8(2) + 4(3) + 3(4) + 1(5)}{25}$$

$$= 1.6 \text{ bicycles per day.}$$

Strictly speaking, of course, a class interval is really an interval, not just a single value. Mathematically, it is perfectly sound to let a class interval be so narrow that it contains only a single point, but this is upsetting to the common-sense meaning of the word "interval", especially if we bear in mind the distinction made at the beginning of Chapter 3, where we considered *grouped data* as the usual kind of class interval and *repetitious data* as the single-point type of class interval. Equation (4.10) produces approximate means for grouped data and exact means for repetitious data.

4.11 THE MEDIAN FOR GROUPED DATA

There are two popular ways of locating the median for grouped data; the graphic method and the algebraic interpolation method. In the *graphic method,* the median value is found by interpolation from the ogive of the distribution. We draw a horizontal line at $n/2$ from the absolute vertical scale or at the point of 0.5 from the relative scale to the ogive; then drop a perpendicular line to the horizontal scale to locate the median value. Thus, from Figure 3.10 we find the median for the food expenditures data to be $x_{.5} \doteq \$168.00$.

In the method of *algebraic interpolation,* we first find the *median class,* the class whose cumulative frequency first exceeds the value of $[(n + 1)/2]$. Then we can locate the median by use of the following formula for interpolation:

$$X_{.5} = L_{.5} + \left[\frac{(n + 1)/2 - F_p}{f_{.5}} \right] c, \qquad (4.11)$$

where

$\quad L_{.5}$ = the true lower class limit of the median class,
$\quad F_p$ = the cumulative frequency in the class immediately preceding the median class,
$\quad f_{.5}$ = the class frequency in the median class,
$\quad c$ = the true class interval of the median class.

A few comments on (4.11) are in order. First $(n + 1)/2$ indicates the position of the item in the distribution whose value is the median. Second, if $(n + 1)/2 = F_p$, then the median would fall at the lower class limit of the median class, $L_{.5}$. Third, if $[(n + 1)/2] - F_p = f_{.5}$, then the median would fall at the upper class limit of the median class, $U_{.5}$. Fourth, when the second and third conditions do not hold, then the median must fall between $L_{.5}$ and $U_{.5}$. This being the case, the ratio $[(n + 1)/2 - F_p]/f_{.5}$ would give us the position of the median in the median class. For example, if this ratio is 0.5, the median would fall on the midpoint of the median class—that is, the position of the median is 50% of the size of the median class interval above $L_{.5}$. Now, if we multiply this ratio by the size of the class interval, we obtain the value in excess of $L_{.5}$ required to obtain the value of the median. Hence, Equation (4.11) is formulated. Now, for the food expenditures data in Table 3.13, we find the median class to be the third class defined by the class limits 160.00–179.99 with $F_p = 31$, $f_{.5} = 24$, and $c = 20$. Thus,

$$x_{.5} \doteq 160.00 + \left(\frac{81/2 - 31}{24} \right) 20$$

$$\doteq \$167.92,$$

which is nearly identical with that obtained by the graphic method and slightly larger than $167.17, the median located from ungrouped data. These differences are clearly of no practical importance.

4.12   THE MODE FOR GROUPED DATA

The mode of a frequency distribution very often can be approximated by the midpoint of the *modal class*—the class with the greatest frequency

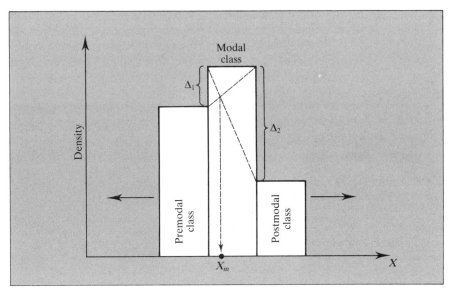

FIGURE 4.4 Geometric interpretation of the algebraic interpolation for determining the mode.

density. Thus, for the food expenditure data, $x_m = \$150$, the mid-point of the second class in Table 4.6. This method of locating the mode is quite satisfactory when frequency densities in the class immediately before the modal class (the premodal class) and immediately after the modal class (the postmodal class) are approximately equal. When this condition is not met, as suggested by Figure 4.4, more satisfactory results can be obtained by algebraic interpolation with the following equation, for a sample:

$$X_m \doteq L_m + \left(\frac{\Delta_1}{\Delta_1 + \Delta_2}\right)c, \qquad (4.12)$$

where

$\quad L_m$ = the true lower class limit of the modal class,
$\quad \Delta_1$ = the absolute value of the difference between the frequency densities in the premodal and modal classes,
$\quad \Delta_2$ = the absolute value of the difference between the frequency densities in the postmodal and modal classes,
$\quad c$ = the true class interval of the modal class.

Now, for the food expenditure data in Table 4.6, the first problem is to convert frequencies to frequency densities, since (4.12) requires densities. As it happens, this problem is very easily solved because the class intervals in Table 4.6 are uniform. Thus, absolute class frequencies are identical with frequency densities, and so we have

$$L_m = 140.00, \qquad \Delta_1 = |15 - 26| = 11,$$
$$c = 20, \qquad \Delta_2 = |24 - 26| = 2.$$

Hence,

$$x_m = 140.00 + \left(\frac{11}{11 + 2}\right)20$$

$$= \$156.92.$$

It is also interesting to note that the median and the mode, as position averages, can almost always be located from frequency distributions constructed with open-ended classes, since for these measures the individual values of each of the items in the sample are not needed. Furthermore, these measures can be obtained with equal ease for distributions with uniform or varying class intervals, since the only class interval required is that which contains the median or the mode. But it must be noted that with unequal class intervals the modal value is located with reference to frequency densities.

4.13* GEOMETRIC AND HARMONIC MEANS FOR GROUPED DATA

Geometric and harmonic means are seldom computed from group data, since, in situations where these two measures are appropriate, the samples are usually quite small. For the sake of completeness we will note that, for grouped data,

$$\log G \doteq \frac{\Sigma f(\log m)}{n}, \tag{4.13}$$

$$H \doteq \frac{\Sigma \left(\dfrac{1}{fm}\right)}{n}, \tag{4.14}$$

where, in both cases, the summations are made over all the k classes.

4.14 WHICH AVERAGE TO USE

Several types of averages have been discussed in this chapter. Except for some specific situations, different averages usually yield different values for the same set of data. Moreover, each average has a unique meaning of its own. Because of these considerations, a very important and often difficult question arises: which average should be used to describe or represent a given series? Before this question is asked, another fundamental question must be asked: should an average be used at all in a given situation?

As to whether it is appropriate to use a single number to describe a series, we must remember that an average is a measure of central tendency. Hence, unless the data show a clear, single concentration of observations, an average may not be meaningful at all. This evidently precludes the use of any average to typify a bimodal, a U-shaped, or a J-shaped distribution. With this in mind, we may then proceed to determine what average to use by first considering the following.

1. What purpose is the average designed to serve?

2. Should we permit extreme values in the series to influence the average?

3. Should the average be used for further computation?

4. What is the underlying model of the distribution? Is it symmetrical or skewed? If it is positively skewed, is it of the logarithmic type?

5. How are we to record the observations to be averaged? Natural numbers? Ratios? Rates? Averages?

6. What class of units should be used for the average? Are the observations expressed inversely to what is required in the average?

7. In what sense do we expect the average to be typical? To balance the individual values? To balance the ratios? To balance the number of items? To typify the most frequent value?

8. What weights, implicit or explicit, if any, should be used?

With answers to these questions clearly in mind we can then make a rational selection of averages with reference to the properties of the averages and the numerical relationships among them. The properties of various averages are summarized below.

The Arithmetic Mean

(a) It is affected by every observation and is influenced by the absolute magnitudes of the extreme values in the series. (b) As a computed average, it is capable of algebraic manipulation. From its basic equation $\bar{X} = \sum x/n$, when two of the magnitudes are known, the third can also be obtained. That is, $\sum x = n\bar{X}$ and $n = \sum x/\bar{X}$. (c). The sum of algebraic deviations from the mean is zero, and the sum of the squared deviations from the mean is a minimum. (d) In a sampling sense, the mean is a stable statistic. This concept will be developed in a later chapter. (e) The mean is typical in the sense that it is the center of gravity, balancing the values on either side of it.

Geometric Mean

(a) It is also affected by all items in the series, but it gives less weight to extremely high values than does the arithmetic mean. (b) It is strictly determined for positive values, but cannot be used to average negative values or values with a zero term. (c) It balances the ratio of the values to the geometric mean. (d) it is adapted to average rates of change, to ratios between measures, and to ratios of price change. (e) It is also capable of algebraic manipulation. When it is substituted for the values from which it is computed, the same product is secured.

The Harmonic Mean

(a) As a computed average, it is also affected by all observations. However, since the reciprocals are averaged, it gives more weight to the smaller values. This is just the opposite of the mean. (b) It is capable of algebraic manipulation. (c) It is adapted to average time rates and price movements. It is also useful when the observations are expressed inversely to what is required in the average.

The Median

(a) It is a position average that is affected by the number of items, not by the values of the observations. Because of this property, the median is not capable of algebraic manipulation. (b) It is thus not influenced by the magnitude of the extreme deviations from it. (c) It can be located from open-end distributions. (d) The sum of absolute deviations from the median is a minimum. (e) It is typical in the sense that it balances the number of items in the series. (f) It is meaningless for completely qualitative data, but meaningful as long as data can be ranked, such as the grades A, B, C, D, E, F. The median is the most suitable average to describe observations that are scored rather than computed or measured.

The Mode

(a) Since it is the point of greatest concentration, the mode is the most typical average for a distribution. (b) Because of this property the mode is meaningless unless the distribution includes a large number of observations and possesses a distinct central tendency. (c) Like the median, the mode is not influenced by extreme values, is not capable of algebraic manipulation, and can be located from an open-end distribution. (d) Unlike all other averages, the mode is always represented by actual items in the series. (e) The mode is the most unstable average and its exact value is often difficult to determine.

Certain numerical relationships exist among the averages.

1. For any series, except one whose observations are of identical value, the arithmetic mean is always greater than the geometric mean, which, in turn, is greater than the harmonic mean.

2. For a symmetrical and unimodal distribution, mean = median = mode.

3. For a positively skewed distribution, the mean has the largest value, the mode has the smallest value, and the median is about one-third the distance from the mean as it is toward the mode.

4. For a negatively skewed distribution, the mean is the smallest, the mode is the largest, and the median is again about one-third the distance from the mean as it is toward the mode.

The last three observations are illustrated graphically by Figure 4.5.

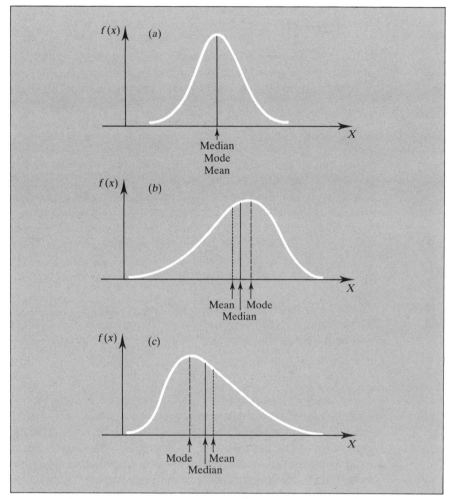

FIGURE 4.5 Illustrations of the positions of the mean, the median, and the mode for symmetric and skewed unimodal distributions.

In conclusion, it may also be pointed out that a complete description of a distribution occasionally calls for two or more of these averages. It is true that presenting two or more averages creates an added burden for the investigator as well as for the consumer of statistics. However, the extra work entailed is fully justified if it presents a more complete description of the data than is possible from a single measure.

GLOSSARY OF FORMULAS

(4.1) $\bar{X} = \dfrac{\sum x}{n}$.

The arithmetic mean of a sample is defined as the sum of the individual values of the sample, $\sum x$, divided by the size of the sample, n.

(4.2) $\bar{X}_w = \dfrac{\Sigma\, wx}{\Sigma\, w}$.

This is the equation for *the weighted arithmetic mean*. Here w is the weight assigned to each individual observation x. Note also that the weights can have any interpretation appropriate to the context.

(4.3) $\bar{P} = \dfrac{x}{n}$.

The sample proportion is defined as the number of elements that possess a certain trait or attribute, divided by the total number of observations in the sample. Note that here the sample is selected from a population whose elementary units can be classified into two mutually exclusive categories. Also observe that the population proportion π can only be determined if the population is finite.

(4.4) $G = \sqrt[n]{(x_1)(x_2)\cdots(x_n)}$.

The sample geometric mean is defined as the nth root of the product of the n sample values. This formula requires that all the individual values be positive.

(4.5) $\operatorname{Log} G = \dfrac{\Sigma \log x}{n}$.

This is a more efficient formula for the computation of the *geometric mean*. Note here that G = antilog of $\log G$. This equation says that the logarithm of the geometric mean is equal to the arithmetic mean of the logarithms of the values. The geometric mean is frequently used for averaging ratios, rates of change, and values showing a geometric progression.

(4.6) $R = \left(\sqrt[n]{\dfrac{x_t}{x_b}} \right) - 1$.

The *average rate of growth* R is defined as the nth root of the ratio of the value x_t of the end period to the value x_b of the beginning period, less 1. It is in fact the efficient formula for the geometric mean when the number of time periods is large. This formula is also called the compound interest formula. Note that n is equal to the number of observations less 1, since the initial period is the base for the computation, so that there are only $n-1$ periods involved.

(4.7) $H = \dfrac{n}{\Sigma\,(1/x)}$;

(4.8) $1/H = \dfrac{\Sigma\,(1/x)}{n}$.

The first of these two equations defines the *harmonic mean* as the reciprocal of the arithmetic mean of the reciprocals of the observations. The second equation is the *harmonic mean* expressed as a reciprocal to facilitate calculations. Clearly, $H = 1/(1/H)$. The harmonic mean is the appropriate average when ratios are being averaged and the numerators of the fractions from which the ratios were computed are the same as for all ratios. Alternatively, this measure is useful mainly in processing ratio data that have physical dimensions, such as miles per gallon, cost per mile, miles per hour, and so on.

(4.9) $X_{.5} =$ the value of the $[(n + 1)/2]$th item.

This equation indicates that, for an odd number of items, the central item is the median, and that for an even number of items, the mean of the two central items becomes the median. Of course, the data points must be in the form of an array for it to be possible to use this formula.

(4.10) $\bar{X} \doteq \dfrac{\sum fm}{n}$.

This is the definitional equation of the *mean* for grouped data derived under the midpoint assumption. It yields an approximate mean that should be very close to the exact mean if the distribution is properly constructed. For a distribution of repetitious data, this equation produces the exact mean. This equation is applicable to both equal and unequal class intervals.

(4.11) $X_{.5} = L_{.5} + \left[\dfrac{[(n + 1)/2 - F_p]}{f_{.5}}\right]c.$

This is the *algebraic interpolation formula* for computing the *median* from grouped data. The median here is interpolated as the lower class limit of the median class, $L_{.5}$, plus the proportion of distance of the class interval of the median class at which the total frequency is divided into two equal parts.

(4.12) $X_m = L_m + \left(\dfrac{\Delta_1}{\Delta_1 + \Delta_2}\right)c.$

This is the *algebraic interpolation formula* of the *mode* for grouped data. Here, Δ_1 is the absolute difference in frequency densities between the modal and premodal classes and Δ_2 is the absolute difference between the frequencies of the modal and postmodal classes. L_m is the lower class limit of the modal class.

(4.13) $\log G = \dfrac{\sum f(\log m)}{n};$

(4.14) $H = \dfrac{\sum (1/fm)}{n}.$

These two equations are for the computations of the *geometric* and *harmonic means* for grouped data. They are seldom used in practice, since, when these two measures are required, the sample is usually small.

REVIEW QUESTIONS

4.1 Compare and contrast "central tendency", "dispersion," "skewness," and "peakedness" on an abstract or general basis.

4.2 How are parameters and statistics usually differentiated in statistical notation?

4.3 If the context is that of a variable, rather than a parameter or a statistic, what is the difference between Y and y?

4.4 How is an average defined?

4.5 In what sense is each of the five averages introduced in this chapter typical?

4.6 The mean has the following mathematical properties.
   a. $n\bar{X} = \sum x$.
   b. $\sum (x - \bar{X}) = 0$.
   c. $\sum (x - \bar{X})^2 = $ a minimum.
   Give a verbal statement for each of these properties.

4.7 What are the important properties of the geometric and harmonic means respectively? Explain the fact that $\bar{X} > G > H$ all of the time for the same data set.

4.8 What are the important properties of the median?

4.9 What is a mode? A primary mode? A secondary mode?

4.10 What are the troublesome aspects of determining and using the mode?

4.11 Is the arithmetic mean always weighted? Why or why not?

4.12 Why the geometric mean cannot be used to average observations that have zero or negative values? Do you think this property to be an important disadvantage of the geometric mean? Explain.

4.13 Would it be possible for more than 50% of production workers to receive a wage lower than the mean wage of these workers in the same plant? In connection with your answer, what average would you expect to be used by the public relations man of the plant? By the business agent of the labor union?

4.14 If the average height of American soldiers were 5 feet and 8 inches, could the most typical height of American soldiers be greater or smaller than this value? Why or why not?

4.15 If a salesman says he has to call on four prospects "on the average" to make a sale, which average do you suppose he means? Explain.

4.16 Alfred Kinsey and others reported in their *Sexual Behavior of the Human Male,* that "nearly all the distribution curves on human sexual behavior are strongly skewed to the right. The means are quite regularly higher than the location of the body of the population would lead one to expect. A few high-rating individuals apparently raise the mean, this gives a distorted picture using the arithmetic mean." What average would be most appropriate under the circumstances? Why?

4.17 Gives a specific example of your own for each of the following cases.
   a. The median is preferred to the arithmetic mean.
   b. The geometric mean would be more satisfactory than the arithmetic mean.
   c. The harmonic mean must be used instead of the arithmetic mean.
   d. The mode would be preferred to the median.
   e. The median would be preferred to the mode.
   f. No average would be meaningful.

4.18 Which average—the mean, the mode, or the median—would you use in each of the following situations? Explain your choice.
   a. The average number of rooms in apartments in Queens, New York
   b. The average annual earnings of Boston lawyers
   c. The average temperature for the summer months in your native city

4.19 Indicate (but do not compute) whether you can derive the mean, the mode, or the median from the distribution tabulated below. Explain in each case.

Sales Size of Electronics Distributors in Northeastern United States

Volume Group	Number of Distributors
under $ 100,000	84
$100,000 under 250,000	144
250,000 under 500,000	98
500,000 under 1,000,000	70
over 1,000,000	54
	450

PROBLEMS

4.1 The starting annual wages, in thousands of dollars, of ten college graduates in the summer of 1983 were 15, 14, 16, 18, 16, 17, 20, 16, 19, and 22. Determine the arithmetic mean for this data set and use your result to demonstrate the three mathematical properties of the mean as stated in Review Question 4.6.

4.2 Do the same as in the preceding problem with the data set in Table 3.P1.

4.3 The prices in dollars of five different two-semester statistics text books selected at random in 1985 were $32.50, 29.95, 34.25, 35.00, and 37.75. Do the same as for the previous problem and comment on the results.

4.4 Compute the mean from
   a. Absence data in Table 3P2
   b. Weight data in Table 3.P2
   c. Wage data in Table 3.P4, and
   d. Diameter data in Table 3.P5

4.5 There are three firms in an industry producing a certain output. Their cost and production data are as given below.

Firm	Average Cost ($)	Total Production (units)
A	2.75	100,000
B	3.00	250,000
C	2.50	300,000

What is the average cost of production for the whole industry? Explain why your answer is correct.

4.6 To produce a certain make of automobile in Japan, labor of different kinds is required in quantities as follows:

skilled labor:	50 hours
semiskilled labor:	100 hours
unskilled labor:	200 hours

If hourly wage rates for these three kinds of labor are $20, $12, and $8 respectively, what is the average labor cost per hour in producing the car?

4.7 A traveling salesman made five sales trips during the months of June and July. The number of days and value of sales for each trip are tabulated below.

Trip	No. of Days	Value of Sales ($)	Sales per Day ($)
1	3	900	300
2	7	2800	400
3	10	3000	300
4	5	800	160
5	10	4000	400
Totals	35	11,500	1,560

The sales manager criticized the salesman's performance, since his mean sales per day amounted to only $312.00. The salesman, however, argued that the sales manager was wrong, since his mean sales per day were $328.57. How did each arrive at the mean sales per day? Whose average is accurate?

4.8 A manufacturing firm produces four lines of products. The net profit to sales ratios, expressed as percentages of sales, and sales volume in millions of dollars, are tabulated below.

Production Line	Ratio of Net Profit to Sales	Sales (in millions of dollars)
1	6%	1.5
2	5%	2.0
3	4%	1.2
4	7%	2.2

a. What is the total net profit for all production lines?

b. Is the overall ratio of net profit to sales for the entire firm 5.50% or 5.68%? How is each of these percentages calculated? Explain.

4.9 An economist conducted a survey on the possible differences in the rates of unemployment among Whites, Blacks, and Asians in a certain big city in the early spring of 1983. He found that 56 were unemployed among 700 Whites, 80 were unemployed among 500 Blacks, and 42 were unemployed among 300 Asians.

a. What is the rate of unemployment for each group of people?

b. What is the overall rate of unemployment if the three samples are combined? Explain how you have obtained the result. (Hint: this result can be obtained in two ways.)

4.10 A manufacturing firm produces two lines of output, A and B. It has provided the following data for its sales for 1981 and 1984.

Item	Sales	
	1981	1984
A	500,000 pounds	3,000,000 pounds
B	2,000,000 yards	400,000 yards

a. What is the percentage change from 1981 to 1984 for each output by using 1981 or 1984 as a base respectively?

b. What is the arithmetic mean for the rate of change?

c. What is the geometric mean for the rate of change?

d. Which average is the correct one in this case? Explain.

4.11 The level of employment of a rapidly growing manufacturing firm from 1981 to 1986 is given below.

	1981	1982	1983	1984	1985	1986
No. of Employees	55	60	70	75	85	100

Determine the annual average rate of growth from the above data in two different ways.

4.12 The total profit of a department store increased from $1,000,000 in 1981 to $3,500,000 in 1990. This indicates that the store's profit had been increasing by 35% per annum. Is this correct? If not, what is the correct answer?

4.13 On a certain trip, a motorist bought 10 gallons of gasoline at $1.29 per gallon, 15 gallons at $1.40 per gallon, 20 gallons at $1.45 per gallon, and 15 gallons at

$1.31 per gallon. What is the average price per gallon of gasoline paid by the motorist in terms of the harmonic mean and in terms of the weighted arithmetic mean?

4.14 Mr. X went to City B from City A by plane at 400 miles an hour and returned by train at 40 miles per hour. The distance between A and B is 1000 miles. What is his average speed? Check to see if your answer is logical.

4.15 If A can finish a certain operation in 30 minutes, B in 20 minutes, C in 25 minutes, and D in 40 minutes, what is the average time required to finish the operation?

4.16 Suppose an automobile trip to a small town starts in the heavy rush-hour traffic of a big city, then gets into the country in bad weather, and finishes in the country in good weather. Suppose the average speed for the first leg of the trip is 20 mph; for the second leg, 30 mph; and for the third leg, 55 mph.
   a. If each leg takes an hour, what is the average speed for the whole trip?
   b. If each leg is 40 miles long, what is the average speed for the whole trip?
   c. Calculate the arithmetic mean of the three speeds, and the harmonic mean of the three speeds. Which mean is correct for part (a) and which for part (b)?

4.17 Locate the median and the mode from the data set in Problem 4.1. Comment on the results.

4.18 Locate the median and the mode from the data set in Problem 4.2. Comment on the results.

4.19 Determine the median and the mode (if a mode exists) for each of the following data sets.
   a. In Table 3.S1
   b. In Table 3.P2
   c. In Table 3.P3
   d. In Table 3.P4
   e. In Table 3.P5

   Instructions. For the remainder of the problems from here on, do the following.
   1. Compute the mean.
   2. Locate the median by the graphic method and by algebraic interpolation.
   3. Locate the mode by algebraic interpolation.
   4. Comment on the results by bringing all your knowledge to these measures.

4.20 Use the wage data in Table 3.S6.

4.21 Use the absenteeism data in Table 3.S11.

4.22 Use weight data in Table 3.S12.

4.23 Use the wage data in Table 3.S13.

4.24 Use the diameter data in Table 3.S14.

4.25 *A Small Research Project.* Check the *Fortune 500 Directory* in the May 1988 issue of *Fortune* for the earnings per share of common stock and the volume of sales for the companies listed below, for the years from 1980 through 1987, and write a short essay evaluating the performances of these companies in terms of their possible future growth rates: a. IBM, b. Mobil Oil, c. General Electric, d. Greyhound, e. General Motors, and f. Kennecott Copper.

5 Measures of Dispersion, Skewness, and Kurtosis

5.1 THE INADEQUACY OF AVERAGES

The importance of averages is often exaggerated. An unqualified "average" may be virtually meaningless. One factor adding to the confusion is that with some distributions all the important averages fall closely together, while with others they fall far apart. If one says that the average height of American soldiers is five feet and eight inches, for example, we may get a very good idea of the stature of American soldiers. We do not need to ask if the average is the mean, the median, or the mode, since they would be of the same value, or nearly so. However, if we say that the average family income of a certain city is $26,000 per year, we still do not know much about the income distribution of that city unless we can find out which of the common kinds of average it is.

An average, as a single value adopted to represent the central tendency of a series, is indeed a very useful and powerful measure. However, the use of a single value to describe a distribution conceals many important facts. Decision making often demands the revelation of these concealed characteristics of the distribution. We must now, therefore, develop statistical measures to summarize those concealed characteristics.

In the first place, not all of the observations in a series are of the same value as the derived average. Almost without exception, the items included in a distribution always depart from the central value, although the degree of departure varies from one series to another.

Moreover, little can be revealed about the dispersion even when several averages are computed for the series. For instance, we cannot tell at all which distribution has a greater or smaller degree of dispersion from the information given in the table below.

	Distribution A	Distribution B
Mean	15	15
Median	15	12
Mode	15	6

Thus, a measure of the degree of dispersion or variation is needed in order to give a more complete description of the chief characteristics of a distribution or to make possible effective comparison of two or more distributions.

A second consideration is that distribution shapes differ from one data set to another. Some are symmetrical; others are not. Hence, to describe a distribution we also need a measure of the degree of symmetry or asymmetry—a description of the balance or lack of balance on both sides of the central tendency. The descriptive statistic for this characteristic is called the measure of *skewness*.

Finally, there are differences of the degree of peakedness among different distributions. This property is known as *kurtosis*. To measure kurtosis is to define the pattern of scatter of observations among the classes near the central value, as compared with the scatter of observations near both ends of the distribution.

Variation is by far the most important characteristic of a distribution: it may be either a basis for decision making or a measure for developing further statistical theory and method. Although skewness is an important characteristic for defining the precise pattern of a distribution, it is rarely calculated in business and economic series. As to kurtosis, we hardly use it at all in elementary statistics. For these reasons, we shall devote the major portion of this chapter to discussing various measures of variation, and the remaining space to skewness and kurtosis.

5.2 SIGNIFICANCE OF VARIATION

Variety is not only the spice of life, but also the essence of statistics. Quantitative data, the raw material for statistical analysis, are always characterized by differences in values among the individual observations. These quantitative differences are as important as the tendency of the items to cluster around a central value in a series. Just as we say that statistics is the science of averages, we can say that all statistical methods are techniques of studying variation. After all, different patterns of frequency distributions are caused by different degrees of variation. Furthermore, many other powerful analytical tools in statistics, such as the regression study, the testing of hypotheses, the defining of confidence limits, the analysis of fluctuations, techniques of production control, and so on, are based on the measures of variation of one kind or another.

Our immediate concern with the measures of variation is to stress their importance as a supplement to the measures of central tendency in analyzing frequency distributions. An average gives no information whatsoever for us to judge its representativeness, because it conceals the actual distribution of the items in a series. It is therefore of little use, unless the degree of variation that occurs about it is given. If it is found that the scatter about the central value is very large—that the items are widely scattered—the average is then of little use as a typical value: it does not represent most of the individual items very well. If, however, the scatter is found to be small—if the items fall very closely together and close to the center—the average then represents the series quite well: it is nearly the same size as the other items in the series. In short, the degree of variation of a series must be measured and given if we are to know how representative of the distribution the average is.

An average, though derived from the individual items of a group, often exhibits a behavior pattern different from that of the individual items. The behavior of the individual items is just as important as, if not more than, that of the average. An excellent example is the "general price level," an average of many prices, which is used by economists to reflect the value of money. When this average changes from time to time, we find that many of the individual prices often move in the opposite direction from the course taken by the average. Moreover, this average may remain stable over a period of time, while some of the individual prices may increase, others decrease, and still others remain stable. This overall stability of the average thus conceals the fact that there is a unique distribution of individual prices at each index (the general price level) and that changes are taking place continuously in the pattern of price distribution through time. Individual prices changing in different directions (even if the net change may be zero, thereby yielding a stable average) may indicate serious economic disturbances, such as alterations in the relative positions of different industries and maladjustments in output and pricing. The variation of individual prices, therefore, is also a major concern of economic theorists. Because of public policy we must pay equal attention to the general price level and to the degree of dispersion of prices over time in order to achieve economic stability without serious disturbances in the economic structure.

In production, a small amount of variation, or conversely, a high degree of uniformity of output, is often of vital importance. In mass production, the supposedly identical manufactured parts must be interchangeable. Interchangeability requires uniformity in dimensions. It can be easily imagined that the degree of variability may be as important as—perhaps more important than—the average value of manufactured items. The variability in the lifetime of light bulbs, for instance, is more crucial than the average life if the bulbs are used in inaccessible places where replacements are extremely difficult to make. The variability in the durability of motorcycle tires used by the police may be more critical than the average. Again, you may have heard the saying that even though the average strength of the links of a chain is great, the variability also significantly affects its strength.

An average, as a typical value, may be used to compare two or more series. For instance, we may compare the average annual per capita income of two nations. Such a comparison is significant in that it may reveal the relative standards of living in two countries. However, the differences in or the similarity of the material well-being of the countries cannot be told fully by such a comparison alone. The material welfare of a people depends on the size of per capita income and on the degree of variation of individual incomes. In other words, we may find that both countries may have the same annual per capita income, say, $3,500, but that in one nation the individual incomes vary from $2,000 to $20,000 whereas in the other they vary from $1,000 to over $1,000,000. It is quite likely that the majority of the people in the first nation belong to the middle class, receiving about $3,500 per person a year, whereas in the second nation there may be many very poor as well as many very rich people with a relatively small number of middle-class citizens. Thus, the wide difference in the social and economic structure—an important factor in determining welfare—between the two nations can be revealed only by the measures of variation in individual incomes together with the averages.

Perhaps the significance of variation was most vividly expressed by Darrel Huff when he wrote in his delightful little book entitled *How to Lie with Statistics*:

> There is another kind of little figure ... It is the one that tells the range of things or their deviation from the average that is given ... Place little faith in an average or a graph or a trend when those important figures are missing. Otherwise you are as blind as a man choosing a campsite from a report of mean temperature alone. You might take 61 degrees as a comfortable annual mean, giving you a choice in California between such areas as the inland desert and San Nicolas Island off the south coast. But you can freeze or roast if you ignore the range. For San Nicolas it is 47 to 87 degrees, but for the desert it is 15 to 104.

As in the case of central tendency, there are many different summary measures for dispersion. These measures are listed below in the order of our presentation.

1. Range

2. Quartile and percentile ranges

3. Average deviation

4. Variance and standard deviation

5. The coefficient of variation

5.3 RANGE

The simplest measure of dispersion is the *range,* the difference between the highest and the lowest values in the data. Common sense uses "range" as the minimum and the maximum, rather than as their difference. Statistical usage requires the difference. For a frequency distribution using class intervals, the range may be considered either as the difference between the largest and the smallest class limits or as the difference between the midpoints of the last and the first class intervals. According to our notational convention, we denote the ranges for the population, the sample, and realized value of the sample as $\tilde{r}$, R, and r respectively.

The range, though a simple concept, may be used quite fruitfully as a measure of dispersion for many purposes. It is perhaps most useful when one wants to know only the extent of the extreme dispersion under "ordinary" conditions. If either the largest or the smallest item is unusual, the range reveals nothing about the "ordinary" distribution of the items. Thus, stock market reports are frequently stated in terms of their range, by quoting high and low prices of stock over a period of time. When no exceptional movements of stock prices occur, the quoted range may measure the "ordinary" variation. When exceptional movements are present, however, the range reveals the effects of temporary disturbing conditions in the market. Consequently, a comparison of price ranges of stock through time may show the effects of exceptional factors as well as the fluctuations of stock prices caused by ordinary trading conditions.

Sometimes the range may have certain distinct advantages in measuring the dispersion of a symmetric and nearly continuous series. In such a case, the mean can be approximated by taking the average of the two extreme values, often called the *midrange.* For example, it is the practice of meteorologists to derive the daily mean temperature by averaging only the maximum and minimum temperatures instead of using, say, the 24-hourly readings of the day.

The range can also be used to advantage when the same sample size is used repeatedly, as is often true in manufacturing quality control. In this case, comparisons between ranges are not affected by differences in sample size, so it is easy to see whether dispersion is getting worse, staying about the same, or getting better.

Finally, the range is the only measure of dispersion that people without statistical training can immediately understand. For this audience, the range must be used. It should be presented in both its common-sense form (the maximum and the minimum) and its statistical form (the difference between these two). When necessary, the statistician can supplement the range by explaining a better measure of dispersion and then presenting its numerical value.

In closing our discussion on range, it must be noted that, judging from the definition of the range, we see that it is not only the simplest, but also the crudest measure of dispersion, because it is calculated from only two of the values of a variable. The range has some serious defects.

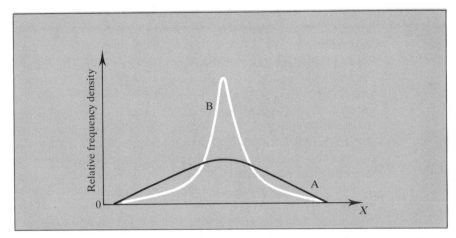

FIGURE 5.1 Illustration of two distributions with the same range but different variabilities.

It can be unduly influenced by one unusual value in a sample. Also, the range is in no way a measure of the scatter of the intervening items relative to a typical value. Figure 5.1 illustrates this. Finally, the range is highly sensitive to the size of a sample. The range tends to increase, though not proportionately, as the size of the sample increases. For this reason we cannot interpret the range properly without knowing the number of observations included in the data.

5.4 QUARTILE AND PERCENTILE RANGES

The range expresses the extreme variability of observations of a variable. It is therefore subject to the chance of erratic changes in extreme items and it fails to take into account the scatter within the range. To overcome these limitations, at least partially, the measures of interquartile and interpercentile ranges have been suggested. Both are location measures and both are related to a basic concept called "fractiles".

Fractiles, Percentiles, Deciles, and Quartiles

The notion of "fractile" is concerned with the division of the values of a variable into equal fractions and is related to the cumulative arrangement of the values of a variable. As was stated in Chapter 3, one of the most important functions of cumulative distributions is that they enable us to answer questions such as these: "What proportion of the value of the variable is less than or equal to a given value? Greater than a given value? Between any two values?" However, from a frequency distribution, such questions can only be answered with reference to the exact class limits. For example, from the relative cumulative distribution in Table 3.13, we can answer questions such as: "What proportion of the families in the sample have food expenditures of \$159.99 or less?" or the like. However, we cannot ask a question like "What is the food expenditure such that the proportion of the sample having that value or less is 0.40?" The answer to this question is not readily available from inspection of Table 3.13. It is, though, clear from the table that a proportion of 0.3875 have a value of \$159.99 or less, and a proportion of 0.6875 have values of \$179.99 or less. As a result, the food expenditure corresponding to a cumulative proportion of 0.40 must be somewhere between \$159.99 and \$179.99. It is not possible to determine the precise value from the frequency distribution, because individual values have been grouped into classes.

To determine the precise value with a cumulative proportion of 0.40, it is necessary to look at the individual values that have been organized into an array of ascending order, as shown in Table 3.3. Now, since $n = 80$, a cumulative proportion of 0.40 corresponds to a cumulative frequency of $(80)(0.40) = 32$. This means that the value having a cumulative proportion of 0.40 is the 32nd item in the array, and it is found in Table 3.3 to be \$160.00. The value that has a cumulative proportion of 0.40 is referred to as the 0.40 fractile of the distribution.

Before we formally define the term "fractile", let us illustrate further how to obtain a fractile by another example. We may do so by trying to locate the 0.08 fractile for the data in Table 3.3. Here, the cumulative proportion of 0.08 is the same as the cumulative frequency of $(80)(0.08) = 6.4$. However, it is meaningless to say that the 0.08 fractile becomes the value of the 6th item, or \$140.10. If we round 6.4 up to 7, then the 0.08 fractile would be the value of the 7th item—\$142.28. In the first case, \$140.10 has a cumulative proportion of $6/80 = 0.075$; in the second case, \$142.28 has a cumulative proportion of $7/80 = 0.0875$. Which practice should we adopt? The answer here lies with the formal definition of a fractile.

Let us denoted a cumulative proportion for a population as ϕ (the lower case Greek letter *phi*) and as F for a sample. Then *the ϕ fractile of a finite population,* or *the F fractile of a sample,* is the lowest observed value such that the cumulative proportion corresponding to that value is at least equal to ϕ for a population, or to F for a sample. So defined, we see that 0.075 is less than 0.08, while 0.0875 is "at least" equal to 0.08. The 0.08 fractile must then be the value of the 7th item—\$142.28.

In terms of some quantitative variable X, X_ϕ will denote the ϕ fractile of the distribution of a population and X_F will denote the F fractile of a sample. For the sample distribution of food expenditures in Table 3.13, just cited above, we have $x_f = x_{.08} = \$142.28$, etc. Notice that for a realized value of a fractile in a sample, the lower case English letter is used as usual. Note also that both X and F in X_F are variables.

Fractiles are often expressed in terms of percentages, rather than decimal fractions. When we do this, a fractile is called a *percentile*. Clearly, in terms of percentiles, the whole range of values of a variable is divided into 100 equal parts with 99 percentile values. Also, for example, the 0.25 fractile may be referred to as the 25th percentile. The 99 percentiles of X are denoted as $X_1, X_2, \ldots, X_{99}$. In developing equations with percentiles, we usually write them in terms of fractiles, that is, as $X_{.01}, X_{.02}, \ldots, X_{.99}$. Also, for convenience, we may denote a percentile as X_P. A realized value for it is denoted as x_p.

It is important to observe that the definition for fractile or percentile has been made with reference to discrete variables. However, in the process of using fractile or percentile to develop descriptive measures, it is often convenient and even desirable to treat the discrete variable as if it were continuous and capable of assuming any fractional values. These imaginary "fractional values" are obtained by linear interpolation. In fact, this practice was employed in locating the value of the median for a variable, in the last chapter, even though we did not explicitly point it out. Indeed, the median of a variable is actually the 0.50 fractile, or 50th percentile, of the variable.

There are two sets of fractiles (or percentiles) that are used most frequently. The first is $X_{.25}$, $X_{.50}$, and $X_{.75}$. These three fractiles divide the whole distribution into four equal parts or four quarters, thus they are often referred to as *quartiles* and are denoted, for sample data, as Q_1, Q_2, and Q_3. Here, Q_1 is the 25th percentile and is defined as that value of a variable for which 25% of the values are less than or equal to it and 75% of the values of the variable are greater than or equal to it. Q_2 and Q_3 are defined in a similar manner.

The second set of frequently used fractiles is $X_{.10}, X_{.20}, \ldots, X_{.80}, X_{.90}$. These nine fractiles divide the range of the variable into 10 equal parts. Thus, they are referred to as *deciles* and are denoted as $D_i, i = 1, 2, 3, \ldots, 9$. Clearly the first decile, D_1 is equal to $X_{.10}$ and it is that value of the variable such that 10% of the values are less than or equal to it and 90% of the values are greater than or equal to it. The other eight deciles can be defined in a similar fashion.

Note that both quartiles and deciles are points on a real line. As such, it is improper to say, for example, that a given value falls on the third quartile. It is, however, quite proper to say that such a value falls *in* the third quarter of the variable.

The Interquartile Range

To determine the *interquartile range,* we begin by locating the two quartiles $X_{.25}$ and $X_{.75}$. The process of finding quartile values parallels that of locating the median. To obtain quartiles from an array of a sample we simply first locate the rank of items by observing that

$$X_{.25} = Q_1 \text{ is the } [(n + 1)/4]\text{th item, and}$$

$$X_{.75} = Q_3 \text{ is the } [(3n + 3)/4]\text{th item.}$$

We then read off these values from the array. If fractional values occur, we make a linear interpolation between the two values corresponding to the two observations within which the fraction falls. For example, if there are 20 items in the sample, the position of q_1, or the 25th percentile of this sample is at the $(20 + 1)/4 = 5.25$th space. This indicates that the realized value of Q_1 (i.e., q_1) is that of the fifth item plus 25% of the difference between the values of the 5th and 6th items.

Thus, if these values are 10 and 12, respectively, then

$$q_1 = 10 + (12 - 10)(0.25) = 10.50.$$

Of course, if the values of the fifth and sixth items are equal, then q_1 takes the value of the fifth item and no interpolation is required.

Now, with reference to the food expenditures data in Table 3.3, we have q_1 at the $(80 + 1)/4 = 20.25$th place; hence,

$$q_1 = 154.80 + (155.00 - 154.80)(0.25) = \$154.85.$$

Similarly, q_3 is at the $[3(80) + 3]/4 = 60.75$th place; hence,

$$q_3 = 188.20 + (188.45 - 188.20)(0.75) \doteq \$188.39.$$

Finally, we note that the *interquartile range* is simply the difference between Q_3 and Q_1, and the interquartile range for a sample, denoted by QR, becomes

$$QR = Q_3 - Q_1. \tag{5.1}$$

From (5.1) we see that QR includes only the middle 50% of the distribution. That is, one-quarter of the observations at the lower end and another quarter of the observations at the upper end of the distribution are excluded. For the food expenditure data, we have

$$qr = q_3 - q_1 = 188.39 - 154.85 = \$33.54.$$

This means the middle 50% of the food consumption expenditures vary within the range of $33.54.

Obviously, a low interquartile range value indicates a small variation among the central 50% of the items: a high interquartile range value means that the variation among the central 50% of the items is large. These statements are rather vague—a difficulty we always encounter by interpreting absolute values. However, in this particular case we may get a more precise idea about the degree of dispersion in the center of the distribution by comparing the interquartile range value with that of the range for the same data set. Thus, with the food expenditure data, the range is $113.90 and the interquartile range is $33.54. These reveal that the interquartile range is only $(33.54/113.90) \doteq 0.2945$, or 29.45% of the whole range of values. Clearly the central 50% of the food expenditures vary from each other much less than those values below $x_{.25}$ and above $x_{.75}$ in this case. Algebraic interpolations for quartile values from grouped data can be made by the same principle or procedure as that for the median. This is obvious, since, as we have already mentioned, the median is identical with the second quartile. Thus,

$$Q_1 = X_{.25} = L_{.25} + \left[\frac{(n + 1)/4 - F_p}{f_{.25}} \right] c, \tag{5.2}$$

and

$$Q_3 = X_{.75} = L_{.75} + \left[\frac{(3n + 3)/4 - F_p}{f_{.75}}\right]c. \tag{5.3}$$

In these two expressions, all symbols should be clear to the reader except perhaps F_p. In (5.2) F_p refers to the cumulative frequency before the *first quartile class*; while in (5.3), it refers to the cumulative frequency before the *third quartile class*.

Applying (5.2) and (5.3) to the food expenditures data in Table 3.13, we have

$$q_1 = x_{.25} = 140.00 + \left[\frac{(80 + 1)/4 - 5}{26}\right]20 \doteq \$151.73;$$

$$q_3 = x_{.75} = 180.00 + \left[\frac{(3(80) + 3)/4 - 55}{15}\right]20 \doteq \$187.67.$$

From these results, we have

$$qr = 187.67 - 151.73 = \$35.94,$$

which, as expected, differs from the interquartile range determined from ungrouped data by \$2.40 ($= \$35.94 - 33.54$) owing to grouping errors.

Interpercentile Ranges

First, it must be observed that in locating percentile values, our focus should be on the observations whose ranks in an array are multiples of $[X_P(n) + X_P]/100$. Interpolations are again required if positions of percentiles result in fractional values. With reference to data in Table 3.3, for example, the 10th percentile or the first decile, d_1, is at the $[10(80) + 10]/100 = 8.10$th place and thus,

$$x_{.10} = d_1 = 146.50 + (147.25 - 146.50)(0.10)$$

$$\doteq \$146.58.$$

Similarly, the 90th percentile is the same as the ninth decile, d_9, and is at the $[90(80) + 90]/100 = 72.90$th place and thus,

$$x_{.90} = d_9 = 205.50 + (210.25 - 205.50)(0.90)$$

$$\doteq \$209.78.$$

With these results we can then construct what is called the *90–10 interpercentile range,* denoted as PR, or what is called *9–1 interdecile range, denoted as* DR. We shall use the second name since it is simpler in terms of notation. The equations for them are

$$PR = X_{.90} - X_{.10} \tag{5.4a}$$

$$DR = D_9 - D_1. \tag{5.4b}$$

The 9–1 interdecile range may be called simply the *interdecile range* without specifying the "9–1". However, when other decile ranges are needed, the indicated decile numbers must be specified. The same comments can be made for PR. Now, for the food expenditures data, we have

$$dr = d_9 - d_1 = 209.78 - 146.58 = \$63.20.$$

This means that the central 80% of the food consumption expenditures varies within a range of $63.20. Other interpercentile ranges can be constructed in the same manner. In particular, we note that the interquartile range is the 75–25 percentile range.

A percentile can also be located from a frequency distribution by using similar formulas as for quartiles. That is, the Pth percentile for a sample is

$$X_P = L_P + \left[\frac{(P(n) + P)/100 - F_P}{f_P} \right] c. \tag{5.5}$$

It may be instructive for the reader to try to write out what each of the symbols in this equation stands for.

Compared to the range, the interquartile and interpercentile ranges are influenced less by the extreme small or large values, because they are computed from intermediate values of a distribution. However, like the range, both the interquartile and interpercentile ranges are based on the values of only two observations without paying any attention to the other values of the variable. Thus, these measures are still quite crude in measuring dispersion by ignoring the general distribution pattern of a variable. Furthermore, since dispersion refers to the tendency of the individual values to deviate from central tendency, a good dispersion measure should somehow be related to an appropriate average. None of the measures in terms of ranges has taken this consideration into account.

We have presented a rather thorough discussion of fractiles or percentiles here, not only because they are the basis for the more adequate measures of dispersion, than the range, but also because fractiles or percentiles are often used to describe probability distributions and are frequently used in Bayesian statistics, which will be introduced in later chapters. Furthermore, percentiles can have other applications in statistical analysis. One is their use in establishing the ranking of the values of a variable, such as ranking the performances of a group of workers, or of students in a class or in a whole school. Another common application of percentiles is to use them to compare two different distributions that have different patterns of variability or that are skewed in different directions. In such cases, the first and the third quartiles or the first and the ninth deciles can describe them more accurately as well as more meaningfully than any measure of central tendency. The third application derives from the fact that quartiles and deciles, as we shall see a little later, also furnish a basis for the calculation of kurtosis.

5.5 AVERAGE DEVIATION

The search for a measure of variability that would take all observed values into account and that would characterize the dispersion of the individual values from their central tendency naturally leads us to the idea of computing a measure such as $\sum (x - \bar{X})/n$; but this measure would always equal 0 because $\sum (x - \bar{X}) = 0$. An obvious way of overcoming this difficulty is averaging the deviations but ignoring the minus signs of negative deviations. The result is the *mean absolute deviation,* or simply the *average deviation.* Using AD for the sample average deviation, we find the formulas for AD for ungrouped and grouped data, respectively, as

$$AD = \frac{\sum |x - \bar{X}|}{n}, \tag{5.6a}$$

$$AD = \frac{\sum f |m - \bar{X}|}{n}, \tag{5.6b}$$

The vertical lines in the numerators are the usual notation for absolute values.

The average deviation is easy to interpret. The more the observations differ in either direction from their own mean, the larger the average deviation. If the observations in a sample are approximately normally distributed, $\bar{X} \pm AD$ will contain about 58% of the sample's observations. Thus, when AD is small and the distribution of the observations is approximately normal, the distribution will be relatively compact, because over half of the observations will be within a small distance from the mean. Sometimes a simple variation of the average deviation is used, substituting the median for the mean. The name "average deviation" is still used despite the substitution of $\bar{X}$ by $X_{.5}$ in (5.6).

The average deviation is useful in situations where no elaborate analysis is required. We have introduced it here as the logical stepping stone to the variance, which is a superior measure of dispersion.

5.6 VARIANCE AND STANDARD DEVIATION

To overcome the difficulty that $\sum (x - \bar{X}) = 0$, we can use the squares of the deviations from the mean instead of taking their absolute values. Squared deviations not only prevent summing to zero; they are also much more adaptable to mathematical analysis than absolute values.

The *variance* is defined as the average of the squared deviations from the mean. For a sample,

$$S^2 = \frac{\sum (x - \bar{X})^2}{n - 1}. \tag{5.7a}$$

For a finite population,

$$\sigma^2 = \frac{\sum (x - \mu)^2}{N}. \tag{5.7b}$$

In Equation (5.7a), $n - 1$ is called the number of "degrees of freedom" of S^2, a concept explained in a later chapter. There is one restriction on (5.7a), namely $n > 1$. There are no restrictions on (5.7b). Note also that this is the first time we have given the equations both for the parameter and statistic explicitly, because in this case they are computed in slightly different ways.

From a practical point of view, the variance is awkward, because its unit of measurement is squared, as in square dollars or square pounds. We can eliminate this awkwardness easily by using the positive square root of the variance, which is called the *standard deviation* and is denoted by S for a sample and by σ for a population.

Equations (5.7) define S^2 and σ^2, but computations are easier if we use the following expressions:

$$S^2 = \frac{n \sum x^2 - (\sum x)^2}{n(n - 1)}; \tag{5.8a}$$

$$\sigma^2 = \frac{\sum x^2}{N} - \left(\frac{\sum x}{N}\right)^2. \tag{5.8b}$$

Now we can compute the variance merely by summing the values and summing the squares of the values; it is no longer necessary to compute the mean, then compute the deviations from the mean, and finally square those deviations.

To illustrate the process of computing the variance and standard deviation, and to suggest a use for these measures, consider the following example. Two different makes of machine, X and Y are designed to produce the same output. They cost the same. A manufacturer is trying to decide which make to buy, and has observed 10 different machines of each make in operation for 1 hour. Table 5.1 shows the hour's outputs in the first two columns. The means are $\bar{x} = 403/10 = 40.3$ units per hour and $\bar{y} = 408/10 = 40.8$ units per hour. Thus, on the basis of these data, Make Y is very slightly faster. Can anything else be determined from these data? The answer is yes, because we can measure and compare the dispersions of the hourly outputs of the two makes. Using (5.8a) for the data in Table 5.1, we find that

$$s_X^2 = \frac{10(16,405) - (403)^2}{10(10 - 1)} \doteq 18.23,$$

$$s_X \doteq \sqrt{18.23} \doteq 4.27 \text{ units per hour};$$

$$s_Y^2 = \frac{10(17,984) - (408)^2}{10(10 - 1)} \doteq 135.11,$$

$$s_Y \doteq \sqrt{135.11} \doteq 11.62 \text{ units per hour.}$$

TABLE 5.1 Work Sheet for Computations of the Mean, Variance, and Standard Deviation of Hourly Outputs of Two Makes of Machine

	x	y	x^2	y^2
	35	25	1,225	625
	36	26	1,296	676
	49	55	2,401	3,025
	44	52	1,936	2,704
	43	48	1,849	2,304
	37	24	1,369	576
	38	34	1,444	1,156
	42	47	1,764	2,209
	39	50	1,521	2,500
	40	47	1,600	2,209
Sums	403	408	16,405	17,984

Make X obviously has less dispersion than Make Y, so it appears from these data that Make X is the more dependable machine. If the manufacturer has to make a decision now, she should probably choose X because of superior dependability, despite its slightly inferior speed.

5.7 INTERPRETING AND APPLYING THE STANDARD DEVIATION

The standard deviation is the most frequently employed measure of variability in business and economics. Unfortunately, the standard deviation does not have an intuitively obvious interpretation. For example, in the new machine example in Section 5.6, $S_X \doteq 4.27$ units per hour, but it is not obvious what that says about machines of Make X. For many sets of data, there are two theorems for interpreting the standard deviation that are quite useful. They are called Chebyshev's Inequality and the Gaussian Rule which are introduced below.

THEOREM 7.1 CHEBYSHEV'S INEQUALITY. *For any data set and any constant $h > 1$, at least $1 - 1/h^2$ of the data points must lie within h standard deviations on either side of the mean.*

From this theorem, we are thus sure that at least 3/4, or 75% of the data points must lie within the interval $\bar{X} \pm 2S$; at least 8/9, or about 88.9% of the data points must be within the interval of $\bar{X} \pm 3S$; and at least 15/16, or about 94%, of the values of any variable must be included within the interval of $\bar{X} \pm 4S$. The values of 2, 3, and 4 are arbitrarily selected: Chebyshev's inequality can be applied with any number or fractions of standard deviations of a distribution, except for $h \leq 1$. This restriction is imposed because when $h = 1$, at least 0 of the observations fall within the interval from $\bar{X} - S$ to $\bar{X} + S$. This is evidently not a very useful result.

Consider the new machine example discussed earlier. We have

$\bar{X} = 40.3$ and $S_X = 4.27$. At least what percentage of outputs of the machine must be between 33.9 and 46.7 units per hour? To solve this problem we note that $hs = 46.7 - 40.3 = 40.3 - 33.9 = 6.4$ and hence $h = (6.40/4.27) \doteq 1.50$. This result means that at least $[1 - 1/(1.50)^2] \doteq 0.56$, or approximately 56%, of the machines must be producing between 33.9 and 46.7 units of output per hour. From Table 5.1, we find 9 out of the 10 values, or 9/10, are within the said range, and clearly $(9/10) > [1 - 1/(1.50)^2]$, or 56%.

The advantage of Chebyshev's Inequality is that it can be applied to variables with any distribution patterns. However, it has the drawback that it is not very precise, since the actual percentage of values falling within the range of the mean, plus and minus any number of standard deviations is nearly always much greater than the minimum given of $(1 - 1/h^2)$, especially when samples are small, such as in our current illustration.

THEOREM 7.2 GAUSSIAN RULE. *If the data are a sample and approximately normally distributed—that is, if a histogram of the data is approximately symmetric and bell-shaped—then*

1. $\bar{X} \pm 1S$ *will include approximately 68% of the data.*

2. $\bar{X} \pm 2S$ *will include approximately 95% of the data.*

3. $\bar{X} \pm 3S$ *will include approximately 100% of the data.*

We call this the *Gaussian Rule,* because it is based on the Gaussian probability distribution. The Gaussian probability distribution is the same as the normal probability distribution, and we will discuss it in detail in a later chapter.

If a population is exactly normally distributed and has a mean of μ and a standard of σ, Figure 5.2 shows what percentages of the observations in the population will fall in the intervals $\mu \pm \sigma$, $\mu \pm 2\sigma$, and $\mu \pm 3\sigma$. Some samples are almost exactly normally distributed, and the Gaussian Rule applies very nicely to them. Some samples are

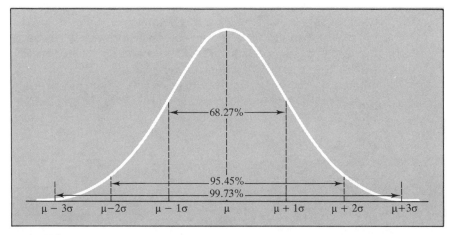

FIGURE 5.2 Percentage of items included under the normal curve for selected values of σ.

moderately close to the normal distribution, and the Gaussian Rule is only moderately accurate for such samples. Some samples are very far from the normal distribution, and the Gaussian Rule is not accurate for these samples; $\bar{X} \pm S$ might include only 60% of the observations, or as much as 80% of them, or even 100% of them. This is true, for instance, in the case of outputs produced by Machine Y in Table 5.1. The Gaussian Rule must not be applied blindly to every sample, because it applies well only to samples that are close to the normal distribution.

One application of the Gaussian Rule is for prediction based on sample data. For instance, suppose laboratory measurements show that the average burning life of a sample of 200 television picture tubes is 500 hours, that the standard deviation is 20 hours, and that the measurements are nearly normally distributed. Then, assuming that the burning lives of all television picture tubes that could be produced by the same process are normally distributed and that their mean and standard deviation are about the same as found in the sample, we can predict that practically all burning lives will be in the range of 440–560 hours, that 95% will be in the range 460–540 hours, and that 68% will be in the range 480–520 hours.

As we shall see, the standard deviation has many more applications. For the time being, we will just note that one of its functions is to serve as a standard unit of measurement when we are measuring the deviation of an observation from the mean. That is, an individual value is considered to be a particular number of standard deviations, denoted as Z, from the mean. To obtain a Z *value,* which is often called the *standardized value,* or for normally distributed data, the *standard normal deviate,* convert the difference between the individual observation and the mean into units of the standard deviation:

$$Z = \frac{X - \bar{X}}{S}.$$ (5.9)

The numerical value of Z can be positive (for an observation greater than the mean), 0 (for an observation equal to the mean), or negative (for an observation less than the mean).

The standardized value is used frequently in later chapters. Equation (5.9) can be used to compare two individual observations even when they belong to different distributions. To illustrate, suppose a student scored 94 on an intelligence test when he entered college, the mean for all entering students being 100 and the standard deviation being 15. Then

$$z = \frac{x - \bar{x}}{s} = \frac{94 - 100}{15} = -0.4.$$

The student's IQ is somewhat below average, because his score is 0.4 standard deviations below the mean. Now, suppose that by the end of his freshman year this same student achieves an average grade of 79 points, whereas the overall mean and standard deviation for the whole freshman class are 70 and 10, respectively. For his average grade,

$$z = \frac{79 - 70}{10} = +0.9.$$

His actual achievement is 0.9 standard deviations above the average for all freshmen. The student seems to be doing much better than his intelligence test indicated he would.

5.8 COEFFICIENT OF VARIATION

Often, as in the new machine example, we want to compare the variabilities in two or more sets of data. We can do this easily using variances or standard deviations when, first, the individual observations all have the same unit of measurement and, second, the means of the sets of data are all approximately equal. When either of these conditions is not met, a relative measure of dispersion should be used. One frequently used relative measure of variability is called the *coefficient of variation,* denoted by CV for a sample. This measure is the ratio of the standard deviation to the mean:

$$\text{CV} = \frac{S}{\bar{X}}. \tag{5.10}$$

Suppose a scientist in India has obtained the following data concerning the weights of elephants and rats.

Elephants	Rats
$\bar{x}_E = 24{,}000$ pounds	$\bar{x}_R = 1.05$ pounds
$s_E = 1{,}285$ pounds	$s_R = 0.16$ pounds

Clearly, just at a glance, elephant weights vary much more than do the rat weights. However, elephant weights may vary less as a percent of their mean than rat weights do. If we compute their respective coefficients of variation, we find that

$$\text{cv}(X_E) = \frac{s_E}{\bar{x}_E} = \frac{1{,}285}{24{,}000} \doteq 0.054, \quad \text{or } 5.4\%;$$

$$\text{cv}(X_R) = \frac{s_R}{\bar{x}_R} = \frac{0.16}{1.05} \doteq 0.152, \quad \text{or } 15.2\%.$$

Thus the variability of the weights of rats is almost three times greater on a relative basis than the variability of the weights of elephants. The former's standard deviation is 15.2% of its mean, whereas the latter's only 5.4% of its mean.

Again, for the machine data in Table 5.1, we have

$$\text{cv}(X) = \frac{4.27}{40.30} \doteq 0.1060, \qquad \text{or } 10.06\%;$$

$$\text{cv}(Y) = \frac{11.62}{40.80} \doteq 0.2848, \qquad \text{or } 28.48\%.$$

Thus, the dispersion of outputs produced by Machine Y are more than two and a half times as great as those produced by Machine X. Clearly, Machine X is much more dependable, because of its much greater uniformity in performance.

5.9 VARIANCE AND STANDARD DEVIATION OF GROUPED DATA

The variance and standard deviation can be computed from grouped data, that is, frequency distributions using class intervals. However, the results may be only approximately accurate. The key idea, as for the case of the mean, is the midpoint assumption: that every observation has the value of the midpoint of the class interval it occupies. Each midpoint enters the calculations as many times as there are observations in that class interval. The definitional equations for variances are as

$$S^2 \doteq \frac{\sum f(m - \bar{X})^2}{n - 1}, \qquad \text{for the sample;} \qquad (5.11a)$$

$$\sigma^2 \doteq \frac{\sum f(m - \mu)^2}{N}, \qquad \text{for the population.} \qquad (5.11b)$$

The symbols used in these equations have been defined before. When doing actual computations, we usually use the following more convenient formulas for variances:

$$S^2 = \frac{\sum fm^2 - (\sum fm)^2/n}{n - 1} \qquad (5.12a)$$

and

$$\sigma^2 = \frac{\sum fm^2 - (\sum fm)^2/N}{N} \qquad (5.12b)$$

for the sample and population, respectively. Here, as before, when descriptive measures are given for the population, we assume the population is finite. We shall, of course, make the same assumption in the future without pointing it out every time.

The summations in all these equations are over all the k classes, not over the individual observations. These equations can be applied to equal as well as unequal class intervals. However, they cannot be

TABLE 5.2 Work Sheet for Computing Sample Variance for Food Consumption Expenditures

(1) m	(2) f	(3) fm (2)(1)	(4) fm^2 (3)(1)
$130	5	650	84,500
150	26	3,900	585,000
170	24	4,080	693,600
190	15	2,850	541,500
210	8	1,680	352,800
230	2	460	105,800
Total	80	13,620	2,363,200

Source: Table 4.5.

employed when there is one or more open-ended class(es). As for ungrouped data, the positive square roots of equations (5.11) and (5.12) are the standard deviations for the sample and population, respectively.

Now, applying (5.12a) to the food consumption expenditures data in Table 4.5, we need a work sheet for the task at hand, as shown in Table 5.2.

With the sums in Table 5.2 and from (5.12a), we have

$$s^2 \doteq \frac{2,363,200 - (13,620)^2/80}{80 - 1}$$

$$= \frac{2,363,200 - 2,318,805}{79}$$

$$= \frac{4,4395}{79} \doteq 561.96.$$

From this result, we also have

$$s \doteq \sqrt{561.96} \doteq \$23.71.$$

5.10* MEASURES OF SKEWNESS

Two distributions may also differ from each other in terms of skewness, or peakedness, or both. As we shall see, measures of skewness and peakedness gain importance because theoretical considerations about statistical inference and decision making are often based on the assumption of normally distributed populations. Measures of skewness and peakedness are therefore useful to guard against mistakenly making this assumption.

Several measures of skewness are available, but we shall introduce only one, which offers simplicity in concept as well as in computation. This measure, the *Pearsonian measure of skewness,* is based on the relationships among the mean, the median, and the mode. Recall that these three measures are identical in value for a symmetric unimodal distribution, but for an asymmetric distribution the mean moves away from the mode toward the direction of the skewness with the median in-between. Consequently, the distance between the mean and the mode could be used to measure skewness. Precisely,

$$\text{skewness} = \text{mean} - \text{mode}.$$

The greater this distance, whether negative or positive, the more asymmetric is the distribution.

Such a measure, however, has two defects in application. First, because it is an absolute measure, the result is expressed in terms of the original unit of measurement of the distribution, and thus it changes when the unit of measurement changes. Second, the same absolute amount of skewness has different significance for different series with different degrees of variability. To eliminate both defects, we may introduce a relative measure of skewness. This is achieved by the *Pearsonian coefficient of skewness,* denoted SK_P; and given by

$$\text{SK}_P = \frac{\bar{X} - X_m}{S}. \tag{5.13}$$

The application of (5.13) involves another difficulty, which arises because the modal value of most distributions is only an approximation, but that the location of the median is more satisfactorily found. As we noted before, in moderately skewed distributions, the relationship

$$X_m \doteq \bar{X} - 3(\bar{X} - X_{.5})$$

holds. From this we see that

$$\bar{X} - X_m = \bar{X} - [\bar{X} - 3(\bar{X} - X_{.5})] = 3(\bar{X} - X_{.5}).$$

With this result, (5.13) can now be written as

$$\text{SK}_P = \frac{3(\bar{X} - X_{.5})}{S}. \tag{5.14}$$

This measure would be zero for a symmetric distribution, negative for a left-skewed distribution, and positive for a right-skewed distribution. More precisely, this measure varies within the limits of ±3; however, in reality, it is only rarely that the value of SK_P exceeds the limits of ±1.

Applying (5.14) to the grouped food consumption expenditures data, we have

$$\text{SK}_P = \frac{3(170.25 - 167.92)}{23.71} \doteq +0.295.$$

This result reveals that the distribution of the food consumption expenditures data is moderately positively skewed.

In conclusion, a few interesting points concerning skewness may be mentioned. The J-shaped and reverse J-shaped curves are examples of extreme left and right skewness, respectively. It is quite common to encounter positively skewed distributions in economic and business data, particularly in production and price series, which can only be as small as zero but can be infinitely large. It is believed that positive skewness is produced by multiplicative forces. For instance, income distribution is usually positively skewed, because it is affected by a large number of factors, such as education, race, sex, family background, "lucky breaks", and so on, which can be thought of as combining multiplicatively instead of additively. Negatively skewed distributions are quite rare, and it is often difficult to furnish a rational explanation for their existence.

5.11* KURTOSIS: A MEASURE OF PEAKEDNESS

In this section we present a measure of peakedness, the *coefficient of kurtosis*, denoted as K. This measure is both algebraically tractable and geometrically interpretable. It is defined as a ratio of the semi-interquartile range—that is, half of the value of the interquartile range—and the 9–1 interdecile range; namely,

$$K = \frac{\frac{1}{2}(Q_3 - Q_1)}{D_9 - D_1}. \tag{5.15}$$

By means of the coefficient of kurtosis, we classify different degrees of peakedness into the three categories of *leptokurtic, platykurtic,* and *mesokurtic* (Figure 5.3). A leptokurtic distribution (curve (a)) has most of its measurements concentrated in the center. Consequently, the difference between the two distances, $(Q_3 - Q_1)$ and $(D_9 - D_1)$ tends to be quite small. Precisely, given a specific degree of dispersion, the sharper the peak, the smaller is the difference between these two distances. Since $\frac{1}{2}(Q_3 - Q_1) < (D_9 - D_1)$ all of the time for a very peaked curve, K approaches 0.5 as the limit when $Q_3 - Q_1 \doteq D_9 - D_1$. In contrast, the more platykurtic the distribution (curve (b)), the more the 9–1 interdecile range tends to exceed the interquartile range. Thus, when the range of a variable approaches infinity and for a completely flat curve, K approaches zero. In view of these considerations, it seems reasonable to take values close to both sides of 0.25 to represent mesokurtosis (curve (c)). The choice is reinforced by the fact that for the standardized normal variable, $k = 0.2630$. (See Chapter 9 for discussion of this variable.)

With values of quartiles and deciles obtained earlier from the

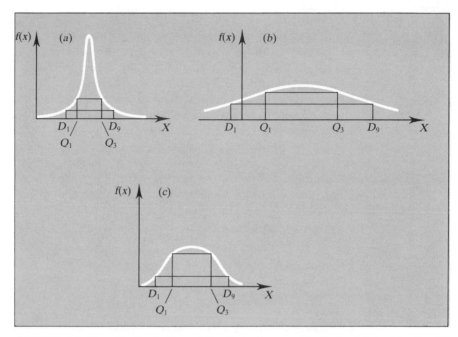

FIGURE 5.3 Graphic illustration of the three types of kurtosis: (a) leptokurtic; (b) platykurtic; (c) mesokurtic.

ungrouped data for food expenditures, we see that

$$k = \frac{(1/2)(q_3 - q_1)}{d_9 - d_1} = \frac{(1/2)(188.39 - 154.83)}{209.78 - 146.58}$$

$$\doteq 0.2655.$$

This finding indicates that the distribution of food consumption expenditures is nearly mesokurtic, because it is very close to 0.25.

5.12 WHICH MEASURES SHOULD BE USED?

With this chapter we have now finished the summary measures for cross-section univariate data. To answer the question posed here, we must first take note that this question is exclusively concerned with the measures for dispersion, since calculations of skewness and kurtosis have been introduced mainly for the purpose of further reference, and we shall have no further applications for them. Second, so far as the different measures of dispersion are concerned, several criteria can be employed for their selection in different situations.

First, if the research question asks for the value of a specific descriptive measure, that settles the issue. Some care is needed here, however, because the study may reveal that the required measure is misleading or that it does not tell the full story. If this is the case, answer more than the question requires in order to be safe and thorough.

Next, if the audience has little or no statistical training, only the range should be used without any explanation. Other measures have to be explained, at least briefly, to ensure that your audience understands them. Very often, we adopt the practice of using only the easier to understand measures in the main report, but include the more difficult ones in a technical appendix.

Third, the characteristics of each measure are often the determining factor for its adoption. Hence, it is worthwhile for us to recapitulate the characteristics of various measures of dispersion here.

The Range

(1) The range is simple to compute and easy to understand. (2) It is based on the two extreme values and is therefore a highly unstable measure. Its value may change greatly if a single observation is added to or withdrawn from its calculation. (3) This measure is the distance along the scale that includes 100% of the cases, but it gives no indication of the pattern of distribution between the two extreme values. (4) It is useful as a rough measure of the degree of variation and is a good measure for presenting variations to the general public or for use when the sample is small.

Interquartile and Interpercentile Ranges

(1) These measures are also easily calculated and readily understood. (2) QR is a distance along the scale that includes the middle 50% of the items within its range. Thus, it is not a measure of dispersion from any specific average. (3) QR is determined by the number of cases rather than by their values, and therefore is not suitable for further algebraic manipulation. (4) As a rough measure of dispersion, however, QR is superior to the range and is especially useful in the case of open-end distributions. Similar comments can be made for interpercentile ranges, or interdecile ranges.

The Average Deviation

(1) The AD is determined by the value of every item in the series. (2) It is less affected by the extreme deviations than is the variance or the standard deviation. (3) It may be computed from either the arithmetic mean or the median, though the average deviation from the latter is a minimum. (4) In a normal distribution, about 58% of the items in the series fall within the range of the mean or median ±AD. If the distribution is moderately skewed, this range will include approximately 58% of the cases. (5) Mathematically, the AD is neither as logical nor as convenient as the standard deviation. Consequently, its use is limited and it is overshadowed as a measure of variation by the superior standard deviation. Meanwhile, it should be recognized that easy computation and obvious interpretation have made the average deviation an efficient practical measure under certain circumstances.

The Variance

(1) The variance is determined by the value of every item in the series. (2) It places greater stress upon extremes than does the average

deviation, because all values are squared in computing the variance. (3) Owing to its well-defined mathematical properties, the variance is highly useful in theoretical discussions. (4) It is always computed about the mean and the sum of the squared deviations from this point is a minimum. (5) It suffers two drawbacks in practical applications. One is that it lacks an intuitive interpretation. The other is that its units of measurement are awkward, because they are squares of the original units of the data at hand.

The Standard Deviation

(1) As the positive square root of the variance, the standard deviation also possesses well-defined mathematical properties and is thus highly useful in theoretical discussions. (2) Moreover, the standard deviation does not possess the awkwardness in terms of the units of measurements that the variance does. (3) However, as for the variance, the standard deviation does not possess a clear, direct, and simple interpretation. On this point, though, the standard deviation has two advantages over the variance. First, for a learned audience, Chebyshev's Inequality and the Gaussian Rule can help. Also, for easier interpretation and comparing the dispersions of two or more variables with different means and units of measurements, the *coefficient of variation,* computed as a ratio of standard deviation to the mean, is of great value.

In closing this chapter, we note that the mean and the standard deviation are by far the two most important descriptive measures for cross-section univariate data, because of their roles in the normal distribution. This may be a mystery to you for the time being, but it will become clear to you very soon.

GLOSSARY OF FORMULAS

(5.1) $QR = Q_3 - Q_1$.

The *interquartile range,* also called *quartile deviation,* is defined as the difference between the third and the first quartiles. This measure of dispersion includes the central 50% of the values of a variable. It is not influenced by the extreme values as is the simple range, but it is still a rather crude measure, since it still ignores the values within QR and beyond it.

(5.2) $Q_1 = X_{.25} = L_{.25} + \left[\dfrac{(n+1)/4 - F_P}{f_{.25}} \right] c;$

(5.3) $Q_3 = X_{.75} = L_{.75} + \left[\dfrac{(3n+3)/4 - F_P}{f_{.75}} \right] c.$

These two equations are employed to locate the first and the third quartiles from a frequency distribution. They follow the same logic as that for the median, which in fact is Q_2 of a distribution. As with any measure determined from a grouped distribution, Q_1 and Q_3 are also subject to grouping errors.

(5.4a) $PR = X_{90} - X_{10}$.

(5.4b) $DR = D_9 - D_1$.

The 90–10 *interpercentile range,* PR, is identical with the 9–1 *interdecile range,* since, the 90th percentile is the ninth decile and the 10th percentile is the first decile. Each of these measures includes the central 80% of the values of the variable. We usually use (5.4b), because of its slightly simpler notation.

(5.5) $X_P = L_P + \left[\dfrac{(P(n) + P)/100 - F_P}{f_P} \right] c$.

We use this equation to determine the Pth percentile of a distribution, X_P. Here, L_P is the lower class limit of the class within which the Pth percentile falls; F_P is the cumulative frequency before the Pth percentile class; and f_P is the class frequency in the Pth percentile class.

(5.6a) $AD = \dfrac{\Sigma |x - \bar{X}|}{n}$.

(5.6b) $AD = \dfrac{\Sigma f |m - \bar{X}|}{n}$.

These are equations of the average deviation for ungrouped and grouped data of a sample, respectively. This measure includes approximately the central 58% of the values of a distribution if the sample is almost normally distributed. Note that the computation of AD is made with the sum of the absolute deviations (deviations with signs ignored) from the mean. Sometimes AD is calculated by replacing the mean with the median. The interpretation of AD, however, remains unchanged.

(5.7a) $S^2 = \dfrac{\Sigma (x - \bar{X})^2}{n - 1}$.

(5.7b) $\sigma^2 = \dfrac{\Sigma (x - \mu)^2}{N}$.

These are definitional equations for the *sample variance* and *population variance,* respectively. In general, the *variance* is the average of the squared individual deviations from the mean. As we shall see, the variance is a very important measure of dispersion, because of the significant role it plays in theoretical considerations. Note also that the square root of a variance is called the *standard deviation,* which is denoted by S and σ for the sample and population, respectively. Finally,

$(n - 1)$ in the denominator for S^2 is referred to as "$n - 1$ degrees of freedom,"—a concept to be explained in a later chapter.

$$(5.8a) \quad S^2 = \frac{n \sum x^2 - (\sum x)^2}{n(n - 1)}.$$

$$(5.8b) \quad \sigma^2 = \frac{\sum x^2}{N} - \left(\frac{\sum x}{N}\right)^2.$$

These are the efficient formulas for computing the variances from ungrouped data for the sample and the population respectively.

$$(5.9) \quad Z = \frac{X - \bar{X}}{S}.$$

This formula is sometimes called the *Z-transformation equation*. It transforms any variable X into a variable Z that has a zero mean and unit standard deviation. Thus, this expression converts an individual deviation of X from the mean of X into the number of standard deviations. We shall have a good deal more to say about this transformation in future chapters.

$$(5.10) \quad CV = \frac{S}{\bar{X}}.$$

The *coefficient of variation* is the ratio of the standard deviation to the mean. It can be expressed as a proportion or percentage. As a pure number, it is quite easy to interpret as well as to use it to compare the variations of two or more distributions.

$$(5.11a) \quad S^2 = \frac{\sum f(m - \bar{X})^2}{n - 1}.$$

$$(5.11b) \quad \sigma^2 = \frac{\sum f(m - \mu)^2}{N}.$$

$$(5.12a) \quad S^2 = \frac{\sum fm^2 - (\sum fm)^2/n}{n - 1}.$$

$$(5.12b) \quad \sigma^2 = \frac{\sum fm^2 - (\sum fm)^2/N}{N}.$$

The first two equations define sample variance and population variance for grouped data, respectively. The last two equations are the computational equations for the sample and population variances, respectively.

Note that, as usual, f stands for class frequencies and m, for class midpoints.

(5.13) $\text{SK}_P = \dfrac{\bar{X} - X_m}{S}$.

(5.14) $\text{SK}_P = \dfrac{3(\bar{X} - X_{.5})}{S}$.

Both formulas are the *Pearsonian coefficients of skewness*. Theoretically, both should yield the same result, because of the relationship $(\bar{X} - X_m) = 3(\bar{X} - X_{.5})$. However, owing to the unstable nature of X_m, (5.14) is preferred to (5.13) in actual application. SK_P is nearly always within the limits of ± 1, even though theoretically it could range in value from -3 to $+3$.

(5.15) $K = \dfrac{(\frac{1}{2})(Q_3 - Q_1)}{D_9 - D_1}$.

Kurtosis, the measure of peakedness, is defined here as the ratio of half of the size of the interquartile range, called the *semiquartile deviation*, to the interpercentile range. Here, K is the sample *coefficient of kurtosis*. The value of K ranges approximately from 0 to 0.5. If K is close to 0.5, the distribution is said to be leptokurtic; if K is close to 0.25 from both sides, the distribution is said to be mesokurtic; if K is close to 0, the distribution is said to be platykurtic. For the standardized normal variable, a normal variable with zero mean and unit standard deviation, $K \doteq 0.2630$.

REVIEW QUESTIONS

5.1 Why are averages often inadequate in describing many sets of data?

5.2 Can you think of some examples of your own in which, when averages are used alone in making decisions, they may lead to seriously damaging results?

5.3 Why are measures of dispersion important? Give at least two important reasons.

5.4 What is the meaning of the "range" according to common usage of the term and what according to statistical analysis?

5.5 What are the advantages and disadvantages of the range as a measure of dispersion? In view of your answer, under what circumstances should the range be used?

5.6 Define the following:
   a. Fractile or percentile
   b. $X_{.75}$, $X_{.60}$, D_4, and Q_3
   c. Interquartile range and interpercentile range

5.7 How should the interquartile and interpercentile ranges be interpreted? What are the advantages of these two measures over the range? What are the limitations that these two measures have in common with the range?

5.8 What are the two essential conditions a good measure of dispersion should possess? Does the average deviation possess these two qualities? If so, why is it seldom used for further statistical analysis?

5.9 How are the variance and standard deviation defined? What are the advantages associated with these two measures relative to the measures of variability in terms of ranges? Are these advantages also possessed by the average deviation?

5.10 As far as computational procedures are concerned, what is the difference between S^2 and σ^2?

5.11 There are definitional and computational formulas for the variance as well as for the standard deviation. Which should be used for numerical calculations? Explain. Also, what is the difference between S and σ?

5.12 What information is provided by the variance or the standard deviation? When all the observations in a data set are the same, the values of the variance and standard deviation are zero. Can you explain the reason?

5.12 What is Chebyshev's Inequality? What is it used for? Can it be applied to any set of data?

5.13 State the Gaussian Rule? What is it used for? Can it be applied to any set of data?

5.14 Can you explain why the variable Z defined as $(X - \bar{X})/S$ would always have a mean of zero and a standard deviation of 1? (Do not panic, if you cannot answer this question at this time.)

5.15 Suppose you have computed the variance or the standard deviation from repetitious data; should you expect an exact or approximate answer? Why?

5.16 What is the coefficient of variation? What are the functions it can perform?

5.17 What is the Pearsonian coefficient of skewness? What does it mean if the resulting coefficient is -1.75? -0.96? $+0.02$? $+1.0$? and $+15.9$?

5.18 How is the coefficient of kurtosis, K, defined in this text? According to this definition, what values of K would indicate that the distribution under consideration is leptokurtic, platykurtic, or mesokurtic?

PROBLEMS

Instructions: For Problems 5.1 through 5.4 inclusive, do the following and interpret the results.

   1. Determine the range.

   2. Determine the interquartile range.

   3. Determine the interpercentile range.

5.1 Use the weight data in Table 3.P3.

5.2 Use the wage data in Table 3.P4.

5.3 Use the weight data in Table 3.S3.

5.4 Use the wage data in Table 3.S4.

5.5 For the nine members of the Board of Directors of Alpha Publishing House, Inc., the years of service for each are:

$$5, 8, 10, 16, 15, 12, 14, 15, \text{ and } 18.$$

Compute σ^2 and σ for this set of data, using both definitional and computational formulas.

5.6 A sample of six salesmen of vacuum cleaners yields the following number of sales during the current week:

$$4, 3, 1, 2, 5 \text{ and } 3.$$

Compute s^2 and s for this set of data by using both definitional and computational formulas.

5.7 For the same set of data in Problem 5.5, what is the value of σ^2 (a) if each of the observations is increased by two years; (b) if each of the observations is reduced by 1.5 years?

5.8 For the same set of data in Problem 5.6, what is the value of s (a) if 2 units of sales are added to each of the observations; (b) if 1 unit of sales is deducted from each of the observations?

     The solutions you have obtained to this problem and the preceding one demonstrate a very important mathematical property of the standard deviation? What is it? Can you make a general statement of this property?

5.9 Consider the service time data in Problem 5.5 again. If each of the observations is multipled by 1.2, what is then the value of σ^2?

5.10 Consider the sales data in Problem 5.6 again. If each of the sample observations is multiplied by 2 what is then the value of s^2.

The solutions you have obtained to this problem and the preceding one demonstrate yet another interesting mathematical property of the standard deviation. What is it? Can you make a general statement of this property?

5.11 If all the 2-pound cans of dog food filled by a food processor have a mean $\mu = 32$ ounces and a standard deviation $\sigma = 0.05$ ounces, what percentage of the cans must fall within the range from 31.875 to 32.125 ounces of dog food?

5.12 A sample of customers with house charge-accounts selected from all the department stores in the United States reveals that the monthly balance in their accounts has a mean $\bar{x} = \$200.00$ and a standard deviation $s = \$50.00$. What percentage of these account balances must lie between
   a. $150.00 and $255.00?
   b. $100.00 and $300.00?
   c. $50.00 and $350.00?

5.13 If, in a very large manufacturing firm, the mean and standard deviation of the workers' monthly wages are $2,500 and $250, respectively, what percentage of the workers will receive monthly wages as follows:
   a. Beween $2,250 and $2,750?
   b. Greater than $3,000?
   c. Less than $1,750?

5.14 Compute the coefficient of variation for the sales data in Problem 5.6.

5.15 A sample of lawyers taken in Houston, Texas, reveals that their mean income in 1984 was $60,500 with a standard deviation of $5,600. A sample of lawyers drawn from Washington, D.C., shows a mean income of $85,250 with a standard deviation of $11,550 in the same year. Which sample has a greater dispersion in view of these results?

5.16 Sample data on the annual wages of professors and physicians in a certain Western state in 1987 yields the following result:

Professors	Physicians
$\bar{x}_1 = \$48,000$	$\bar{x}_2 = \$93,000$
$s_1 = \$3,100$	$s_2 = \$10,250$

Are the professors' wages more or less variable than those of the physicians?

5.17 Compute the variance and standard deviation for the weight data in Table 3.S3.

5.18 Compute the variance and standard deviation for the wage data in Table 3.S4.

5.19 Compute sk_P and k for the weight data in Table 3.S3.

5.20 Compute sk_P and k for the wage data in Table 3.S4.

Instruction: Do the rest of the problems by computer.

5.21 Determine the interquartile range, the median, and interpercentile range for data in Tables 3.P6 and 3.S15.

5.22 Compute the population mean, variance, and standard deviation for the luncheon expense data in Table 3.P6.

5.23 Compute the population mean, variance, and standard deviation for the luncheon expense data in Table 3.S15. Comment on the results obtained in this and the preceding problem.

5.24 *Two research projects.*
   a. Revise and extend the research paper you wrote about the income distribution of the Black households in Problem 3.25 with the additional knowledge you have gained from this and the preceding chapters.
   b. Do a comparative study of the income distributions of the White and Black households with data for 1970 and the most recent year. In your paper you should bring all the relevant descriptive measures into the discussion. Furthermore, you should bring in your knowledge of political, socioeconomic and legal changes during this period of time as possible explanations for the differences in changes in these two distributions. Also, you should utilize the computer to do the computations for the measures you need whenever computer programs for them are available. This may turn out to be a rather large project for this course alone. However, you may check with your professors in some economics, sociology, or political science classes you are taking now, for permission to use this report as a required term paper for one of their courses.

6 Probability Theory

6.1 INTRODUCTION

In the preceding three chapters, we have been concerned with organizing, presenting, and describing univariate sample data. Sample data are seldom studied for their own sake; instead, they are used to revise a decision maker's prior knowledge on the state of nature or to generalize about the values of population parameters that are unknown. Sample data may help us to reduce uncertainty about the state of nature, but they can scarcely eliminate uncertainty completely. Thus, a statistic can be used to estimate the true value of a parameter or to ascertain whether an assumption made about the value of a parameter is tenable. There is always some degree of uncertainty involved, since the value of a statistic almost always differs from that of the parameter and such a difference is usually unknown.

We are indeed living in a world of uncertainty. As noted by Richard Barnfield (1574–1627) in his book *The Shepherd's Content,* "Nothing more certain than incertainties; Fortune is full of fresh variety: Constant in nothing but inconstancy." Barnfield seems to imply that nothing is predictable. However, this view seems to be too pessimistic. As a matter of fact, we are not completely impotent as far as prediction is concerned. Insuring houses against fire is an example. No one can predict with any degree of accuracy which houses will burn down in a year, but the total number of houses that will be burned down can be predicted quite accurately. Hence, the chance that a house will burn down can be assessed, and this makes possible the existence of a fire insurance industry. Insurance companies can regularly pay large claims to those whose houses burn down, by collecting modest premiums from everyone whose houses are insured. This is made possible by our knowledge of "probability theory."

In reality, probability is a concept used by many people in their daily expressions and is even unconsciously used by them for many types of routine decisions. We often hear statements such as these: "The odds are 2 to 1 against my favorite football team winning the conference championship." "The chances of your candidate winning the forthcoming election look pretty good." "I am almost certain that I can pass Professor Jones' course without any trouble at all." All these are examples of expressions about some events or possibilities in terms of probability. Again, if the weatherman predicts that the chances are about 80% that it will rain today, you may "decide" to carry an umbrella with you if you go outdoors. However, if he says that the chances are only about 20% that it will rain, you may "decide" not to be bothered with the inconvenience of carrying an umbrella with you. Here, you have actually made your decision with the aid of probabilities. People talk freely about "chances" all the time, and derive some benefit from them even though they may have no definite or clear idea about the notion of probability.

From our discussion so far, you may get the impression that probability is somehow related to chance and uncertainty. This is correct, though rather vague. More formally, we say that statistics, as a method of decision making under uncertainty, is founded on probability theory, since probability is at once the language and the measure of uncertainty and risks associated with it. Thus, before learning statistical decision procedures, we must acquire an understanding of probability theory.

The study of probability theory is a very interesting but rather difficult undertaking. Mathematicians have struggled for centuries with the task of just giving a definite and clear interpretation of the word "chance" or "probability." Several rigorous theories of probability have been developed and the important ones will be discussed in this chapter.

Convenient and clear treatment of probability theory requires two types of basic knowledge: counting rules and set theory. The simple process of counting still plays an important role in all fields of scientific investigation. Sometimes, counting the number of things may become very involved and time-consuming or even impossible. This being the case, the counting process can be simplified by means of special mathematical principles that will be given in the next section. The calculation of a probability value or its interpretation can be quite confusing too at times. Difficulties with probability concepts and computations can be avoided to a great extent by proper understanding of some ideas from set theory. The notion of a set and some of the relationships among different sets have, fortunately, intuitive counterparts in everyday life and are disarmingly simple on a rigorous basis. Furthermore, the theorems we shall use concerning sets are very simple; hence, no previous study of set theory is needed for the discussion that follows.

6.2 PRINCIPLES OF COUNTING

There are two simple mathematical principles of counting large numbers of items or arrangements efficiently. They are called "permutation" and "combination", both of which, in turn, are based upon a simple concept — the principle of multiplication. Let us introduce this principle first and then the notions of permutation and combination.

Principle of Multiplication

The principle of multiplication states If an operation can be performed in n_1 ways, and then, after it is performed in any one of these ways, a second operation can be performed in n_2 ways, and after it is performed in any one of these ways, a third operation can be performed in n_3 ways, and so on for k operations, then the total number of ways, denoted as T_k for the k operations can be performed, is

$$T_k = (n_1)(n_2)(n_3) \cdots (n_{k-1})(n_k).$$ (6.1)

For example, if a department store has five entrances and six exits,

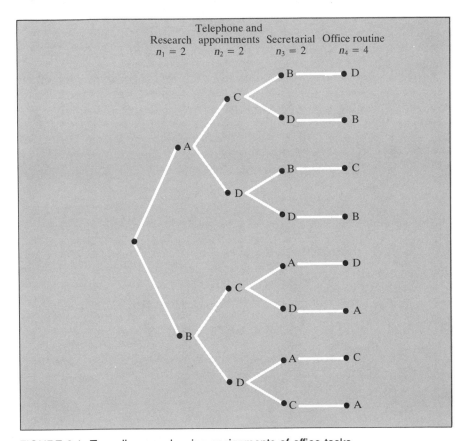

FIGURE 6.1 Tree diagram showing assignments of office tasks.

in how many different ways can one enter and leave the store? *Answer*:

$$T_k = (n_1)(n_2) = (5)(6) = 30 \text{ ways.}$$

As a second example, consider the case of Mr. Johnson who is a lawyer. Johnson has four clerks in his office—Allan, Betty, Carl, and Dora. He needs one clerk to do library research, one to operate the switchboard and make appointments, one to take dictation and do typing, and one to take care of other office routines such as filing, etc. Both Allan and Betty have some legal training and can do library research for Mr. Johnson, and only Carl and Dora can take dictation and type. All four clerks, however, can perform other routines of the office. In how many different ways can the jobs be assigned?

Clearly, there are two ways to fill the first position, (either Allan or Betty), and two ways also to fill the second position, (either Carl or Dora). After the first two positions have been filled, there are two ways to fill the secretarial position; for example, if Allan is assigned as the research person and Betty is given the telephone and appointment chores, then either Carl or Dora may take dictation and do typing. Once the first three assignments have been made, this leaves only one clerk to take care of other office routines. Hence there are $(2)(2)(2)(1) = 8$ different ways of making the job assignments in the lawyer's office. The tree diagram in Figure 6.1 portrays this conclusion.

Permutations

A *permutation* of a number of objects is the arrangement of these objects in a definite order. The *total number of permutations* of a set of N things, taken all together, is $N!$. Denoting this number by $_NP_N$, we have

$$_NP_N = N! \tag{6.2}$$

where $N!$ is read "N factorial" and is the product of all whole numbers from 1 to N; that is,

$$N! = (1)(2)(3) \cdots (N - 2)(N - 1)N. \tag{6.3}$$

In particular, we see that

$$1! = 1,$$

$$2! = (1)(2) = 2,$$

$$3! = (1)(2)(3) = 6,$$

$$4! = (1)(2)(3)(4) = 24.$$

We also note that

$$10! = 10(9!),$$

$$100! = 100(99!),$$

or, in general, if $N \geqslant n$, then

$$N! = n!(n + 1)(n + 2) \cdots (N - 1)(N). \tag{6.4}$$

For example,

$$\begin{aligned}
100! &= 99!(100) \\
&= 98!(99)(100) \\
&= 90!(91)(92) \cdots (99)(100) \\
&= 11!(12)(13) \cdots (99)(100).
\end{aligned}$$

Finally, we also define

$$0! = 1.$$

Equation (6.2) is the consequence of the direct application of the multiplicative principle. We have, in permutation, N spaces to fill. The first space can be filled with any one of the N objects, and so on in N ways. After this has been done (in any of the N ways), the second space can be filled with any of the remaining $N - 1$ objects. Likewise, the third space can be filled in $N - 2$ ways, the fourth space in $N - 3$ ways, and so forth. Therefore, by the multiplicative principle and the definition of the factorial sign, the number of ways of filling N spaces with N objects is $N!$.

In how many different ways can the ten numbers from 1 to 10 be arranged by taking all of them at one time? *Answer*:

$$_{10}P_{10} = (1)(2)(3) \cdots (9)(10) = 3{,}628{,}800.$$

The total number of arrangements of objects taken n at a time from N object, with $n \leq N$, denoted as $_NP_n$, is

$$_NP_n = \frac{N!}{(N - n)!}. \tag{6.5}$$

Assume that four signal flags are to be run up, one above the other, on a flagpole. How many different signals can be run up using six different flags four at a time? *Answer*:

$$\begin{aligned}
_6P_4 &= \frac{6!}{(6 - 4)!} = \frac{2!(3)(4)(5)(6)}{2!} \\
&= 360.
\end{aligned}$$

(Note that in a ratio of factorial signs only equal factorial signs can be canceled.)

Combinations

A *combination* is a selection of objects considered without regard to their order. The *total number of combinations* of a set of N things taken n at a time, $N \geq n$, usually denoted by $_NC_n$ or by $\binom{N}{n}$, is

$$_NC_n = \binom{N}{n} = \frac{N!}{n!(N - n)!}.$$ (6.6)

To understand (6.6), we may consider the possible selections of two letters at a time from the three letters, A, B, and C. By rearranging, we get two permutations from each of the three selections:

$$AB, \quad AC, \quad \text{and} \quad BC,$$

since each 2-subset can be arranged 2! ways. This operation yields a total of $3(2!) = 6$ permutations, as listed below.

Combinations $_3C_2$	Permutations $_3P_2$
AB	AB, BA
AC	AC, CA
BC	BC, CB

It is important to repeat that in a permutation the order counts; in a combination the order does not count. The equivalent general expression is

$$_NP_n = {}_NC_n({}_nP_n).$$ (6.7)

A traveling basketball squad has ten players. The coach must select a starting team for a forthcoming game. How many different teams of 5 players each can be designated for this purpose? Here we are not interested in the positions each of the five players on each team is to play. It is therefore a problem of combination, and

$$_{10}C_5 = \frac{10!}{5!(10 - 5)!}$$

$$= \frac{5!(6)(7)(8)(9)(10)}{5!(1)(2)(3)(4)(5)}$$

$$= 252 \text{ combinations.}$$

If, in selecting the team, the coach also has to designate positions, then the order counts and the problem is one of permutation. Hence,

$$_{10}P_5 = \frac{10!}{(10 - 5)!}$$

$$= \frac{5!}{5!}(6)(7)(8)(9)(10)$$

$$= 30,240 \text{ permutations.}$$

Note that, when a team has been selected, the number of ways the 5 players can be assigned is

$$_5P_5 = (1)(2)(3)(4)(5) = 120 \text{ ways.}$$

Thus, 30,240 assignments = (252 teams)(120 assignments per team).

Permutations for Elements That Are Alike

Our discussion on permutations so far has been confined to cases in which all the elements are different. We now consider the number of distinguishable arrangements that can be formed when some of the objects are identical.

If there are N objects, of which n_1 are alike, another n_2 are alike, another n_3 are alike, and so on, for k types of objects, then the number of permutations of N objects, taken all together, is

$$_NP_{(n_1, n_2, \ldots, n_k)} = \frac{N!}{n_1! n_2! \ldots n_k!}, \tag{6.8}$$

where $n_1 + n_2 + \ldots + n_k = N$.

For example, suppose a student is planning to display ten of his books on one shelf of his bookcase. The books are of different colors: four are red, three are blue, one is black, and two are white. How many distinct arrangements can be formed from the ten books? Here, we have

$$N = 10; \quad n_1 = 4, \quad n_2 = 3, \quad n_3 = 1, \quad \text{and } n_4 = 2.$$

Hence, by using (6.8), the answer is

$$_{10}P_{(4,3,1,2)} = \frac{10!}{4! 3! 1! 2!} = 12,600.$$

It is interesting to observe that if all of the N objects are different, then $n_1 = n_2 = \cdots = n_k = 1$ and

$$_NP_{(1,1,1,\ldots,1)} = {}_NP_N = N!.$$

Also, if there are only two types of objects, n of which are alike and

$(N - n)$ of which are alike, then we have the very special case of (6.9):

$$_{N}P_{(n, N-n)} = \frac{N!}{n!(N - n)!} = {_{N}C_{n}}.$$ (6.9)

That is, the number of different permutations that can be made of N objects, n of which are of one type and $(N - n)$ of which are of another type, is identical to the number of combinations of N objects, taken n at a time. This result also leads to the interesting concept of the *property of symmetry* in combinations:

$$\binom{N}{N - n} = \binom{N}{n}.$$

In concluding our discussion on counting procedures, it should be noted that to use the permutation and combination formulas, we must have $N \geqslant 0$, $n \geqslant 0$, $N \geqslant n$; the N objects must be distinct; and the selection must be made without replacement. *Selection* (or *sampling*) *without replacement* means that once an object has been selected from N things into a group of n objects, the same object cannot be selected again. In contrast, *selection* (or *sampling*) *with replacement* occurs in a situation where the same object can be selected into a group of n things more than once.

6.3 UNCERTAINTY, RANDOM EXPERIMENTS, SAMPLE SPACES, AND EVENTS

Basic to the discussion of probability theory are the concepts of sample space, sample points, and events, all of which are associated with the two related notions of uncertainty and random experiments.

Uncertainty and Random Experiments

Uncertainty refers to the ouctome of some process of change. If a process of change can lead to two or more possible outcomes, the outcomes are said to be *uncertain*. Furthermore, a *process of change,* or an *experiment,* is considered to be *random,* or *stochastic,* if its outcomes are uncertain. Thus, tossing a coin or a die, selecting an item from a day's production run, observing a family's weekly food expenditures, counting the number of cars that cross an intersection before an accident occurs, asking a potential voter whether or not he favors a certain candidate, and so on, are all random experiments, since in each case the process can lead to more than one possible outcome.

It is important to note that when we refer to an experiment we may have reference to a physical experiment that can actually be performed any number of times or in repetitive trials, under essentially the same conditions, or we may simply conceive a set of outcomes as a random experiment, in which case no sequence of repetitive trials is involved. For a random process, real or imaginary, all that is needed is that the outcomes be precisely defined.

Sample Spaces

A *sample space* may be considered a collection of all the possible outcomes of a random experiment. It may also be thought of as a list of the ways a data-generating process can come out. When the data-generating process is, for example, to take a random sample of size n, then the sample space contains all of the possible samples of size n. The common symbol for a sample space is S, and the outcomes (members) of S are called *sample points*. The best way to think of a *sample space* is as a set of all possible outcomes of a data-generating process. It is in this sense that a sample space is called a *universal set* sometimes. The total number of sample points in S may be denoted as $N(S)$.

There are two major reasons for working with a sample space before directly tackling a probability question. One is that, in many cases, the sample space provides a convenient device by which to calculate the answer to the probability question. The other is that, in all cases, working with the sample space provides valuable background and perspective for answering the probability question.

There are some complications concerning sample spaces. We offer the following examples as illustrations of what a sample space is and of some of the complications.

Example 1 A Coin and a Die

Toss a coin and a die once. This is the data-generating process, or the "experiment." What is the sample space for this experiment? A natural way of answering this question is deciding that the coin could come out H (for a head) or T (for a tail), and the die could come out 1, 2, 3, 4, 5, or 6. Thus, $N(S) = (2)(6) = 12$ and this sample space can be written as:

$$S = \{(H, 1), (H, 2), (H, 3), (H, 4), (H, 5), (H, 6),$$

$$(T, 1), (T, 2), (T, 3), (T, 4), (T, 5), (T, 6)\}.$$

The curly brackets indicate that S is a set. Each expression in parentheses is a possible outcome of the experiment. The order in which the points in a sample space are listed does not matter. However, it is helpful to list them in some easy-to-see order.

It is often helpful to graph a sample space. Two common methods are by the use of dots on a conventional two-dimensional graph and by a tree diagram. Figures 6.2 and 6.3 illustrate these graphical methods for the example above. Frequently, the conventional two-dimensional graph will not work. Whenever there are three or more components to the experiment, the two axes on such a graph are not sufficient. Tree diagrams will always work in principle. However, they can become extremely complex in practice.

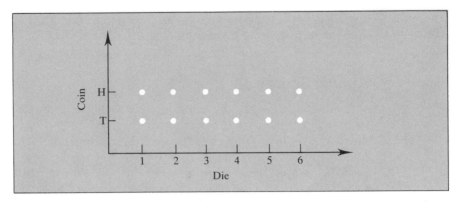

FIGURE 6.2 Representing the sample space of the coin–die example by a two-dimensional graph.

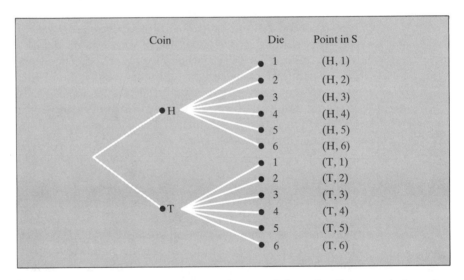

FIGURE 6.3 Representing the sample space of the coin–die example by a tree diagram.

Example 2 Secretary Pool

A certain corporation has 5 typists in the secretary pool—Alice, Betty, Carole, Dorothy, and Ellen. For convenience, we shall refer to them as A, B, C, D, and E. On a certain day, two of the secretaries are required to work overtime that night. The supervisor thinks that the fairest way to select the two typists is by a random process. What is the sample space in this case?

A natural way of answering this question is to realize that the first secretary selected could be any of 5 possibilities and the second secretary selected could be any of 4 possibilities. The first secretary selected affects which secretaries are the four available for the second selection, but there are always four of them. This leads to the following sample space, with $N(S_1) = (5)(4) = 20$; listing all the ways this selection could turn out, we have

$$S_1 = \{(A, B), (A, C), (A, D), (A, E),$$
$$(B, A), (B, C), (B, D), (B, E),$$
$$(C, A), (C, B), (C, D), (C, E),$$
$$(D, A), (D, B), (D, C), (D, E),$$
$$(E, A), (E, B), (E, C), (E, D)\}$$

Perhaps you have noticed that the above sample space distinguishes the outcomes in which the secretaries can be chosen and also the order in which they can be chosen. Does the order really matter? For example, is (A, B) really a different outcome from (B, A) since the same two secretaries are going to work overtime? No, these are not different outcomes as far as the physical realities of the experiment are concerned. We could revise the sample space by eliminating all the points that are merely rearrangements of previously listed pairs of secretaries. Calling the revised sample space S_2, it should be clear that

$$N(S_2) = {}_5C_2 = \frac{5!}{2!(5-2)!} = \frac{3!(4)(5)}{3!(1)(2)} = 10.$$

By scrapping the distinction based on order of selection, the number of points in the sample space has been cut in half. Judging from the wording of the experiment, it does not matter whether we use S_1 or S_2; both are correct sample spaces.

Example 3 Male Faculty on the Committee

The business college of a certain university has 100 instructors, 70 men and 30 women. Five instructors are to be selected to evaluate possible changes in programs which the college offers. The dean thinks a good way of selecting the committee is to draw a random sample of 5 instructors from the 100 instructors. The assistant dean, however, is worried about the possibility that random selection may produce either all men, which would upset the women, or all women, which would upset the men. If the assistant dean has a valid point, what is the sample space of selecting at random 5 faculty members?

One way of writing the sample space is by realizing the possibility that the committee will have either 0 or 1, 2, 3, 4, or 5 men. Thus, denoting the sample space as S_1, we have

$$S_1 = \{(5 \text{ men}), (4 \text{ men and 1 woman}), (3 \text{ men and 2 women}),$$
$$(3 \text{ women and 2 men}), (4 \text{ women and 1 man})(5 \text{ women})\}.$$

Here, $N(S_1) = 5$.

Another way of writing the sample space is by realizing that the first person who is randomly selected could be either a man or a woman, and the second selection could be a man or a woman, and the third selection could be a man or a woman, and so on. Then we would have $N(S_2) = 2^5 = 32$ sample points as shown below:

$$S_2 = \{(M,M,M,M,M),(M,M,M,M,W),(M,M,M,W,M),(M,M,M,W,W),$$
$$(M,M,W,M,M),(M,M,W,M,W),(M,M,W,W,M),(M,M,W,W,W),$$
$$(M,W,M,M,M),(M,W,M,M,W),(M,W,M,W,M),(M,W,M,W,W),$$
$$(M,W,W,M,M),(M,W,W,M,W),(M,W,W,W,M),(M,W,W,W,W),$$
$$(W,M,M,M,M),(W,M,M,M,W),(W,M,M,W,M),(W,M,M,W,W),$$
$$(W,M,W,M,M),(W,M,W,M,W),(W,M,M,W,M),(W,M,W,W,W),$$
$$(W,W,M,M,M),(W,W,M,W,W),(W,W,M,W,M),(W,W,M,W,W),$$
$$(W,W,W,M,M),(W,W,W,M,W),(W,W,W,W,M),(W,W,W,W,W)\}.$$

This is a correct sample space for our example. It is still quite small in the sense it has only 32 sample points. However, it is still rather laborous to write it out.

Very often, the sample space can become extremely large and, it then becomes almost impossible, or at least too time-consuming and tedious, to enumerate all the sample points. Fortunately, in most cases we only need to know the total number of points in the sample space and not what they are. Thus, for instance, with the current example, we can also construct the sample space in this case by thinking of taking a sample of $n = 5$ at random without replacement from the 100 faculty members. Now we have

$$N(S_3) = \binom{100}{5} = \frac{100!}{5!95!}$$

$$= \frac{95!(96)(97)(98)(99)(100)}{95!(1)(2)(3)(4)(5)} = 75{,}287{,}520.$$

This is indeed a very large sample space, since it contains more than 75 million points in it. However, we could have sample spaces much, much larger than this, running into billions or more sample points.

Now we can offer a more precise definition of a sample space: a *sample space* is a set containing all of the possible outcomes or sample points, of an experiment, where sample points are collectively exhaustive, and each pair of sample points is mutually exclusive. In other words, the sample space must not omit any of the possible outcomes, and must not repeat any.

Events in a Sample Space

In statistics, an *event* is defined as a subset of the sample space. An event, therefore, consists of some of the points in the sample space. Many different events can be defined in the same sample space. More precisely, if a sample space contains N sample points, then the total number of events that can be defined on it is 2^N. All the possible 2^N sets or events are the elements of what is called the *power set* of S. For example, if a coin is tossed, $S = \{H, T\}$ and the power set would contain $2^2 = 4$ "set elements", which are $\{T\}$, $\{H\}$, $\{T, H\}$ and $\emptyset$. The last element $\emptyset$ is called the *null set,* a set that contains no sample point—i.e., the empty set. Hence, we see that an event can consist of as many as all the sample points in S or as few as one or none of them. Some types of events occur over and over again in probability and statistics; we discuss these next, along with a few relationships among these events.

Simple Event

A *simple event* is a subset containing exactly one point in a sample space. It can also be called an *elementary event* or a *fundamental event.* Sometimes a *simple event* is defined as an outcome that cannot be decomposed into two or more outcomes. An example would be a "1" when tossing a die once. By contrast, "odd" can be decomposed into "1", "3", or "5", so "1" is a simple event while "odd" is not. This is a good way of defining a simple event, provided one realizes that the definition is concerned with "an outcome *considered* not to be capable of decomposition." We can, if we wish, consider the outcome of two men and three women, in the example concerning male faculty on a committee to be incapable of decomposition. This is done in S_1. Alternatively we can consider it to be capable of decomposition into (M, M, W, W, W), (M, W, M, W, W), (M, W, W, W, M), (W, M, M, W, W), (W, M, W, M, W) and (W, W, W, M, M), where the order of selection of the man for the committee is important. This is done in S_2. The amount of decomposition that is considered to be possible depends on both the experiment and the probability question. The essential consideration for our purpose is that a simple event contains exactly one point in a sample space.

Compound Event

A *compound event* is a subset containing two or more points in a sample space. A compound event is also called a *composite event.*

Impossible Event

An *impossible event* is a subset containing none of the points in a sample space. Such a subset is empty; it is called the *null set.* Conventional notation, as mentioned before, for the null set is $\emptyset$. The symbol $\emptyset$ is usually read aloud as "null set". As an example, the event of obtaining a "7" in rolling a die is the null set, because this event does not contain any sample point in this sample space; "7" is an impossible event in this sample space.

Before we proceed further, let us observe that to denote events, we use capital letters (sometimes with subscripts) as in A, B, $C, \ldots$, or $E_1, E_2, E_3, \ldots$. We use $n(\cdot)$ as the number of points in an event set, where the dot in the notation stands for the name of the event. Thus, $n(A)$ is the number of points in A; and $n(E_3)$ is the number of points in E_3, and so forth.

It may be noted that if A and B are two events defined on the same sample space S and if $n(A) = N(S)$ or $n(A) = n(B)$, then A is an *improper subset* of S or of B; if $n(A) < N(S)$ or $n(A) < n(B)$, then A is a proper subset of S or of B.

Complement of an Event

The *complement* of the event A, denoted as the event $\bar{A}$, consists of all the points in the sample space that are not in A. The symbol $\bar{A}$ is usually read aloud as "big A bar" or as "A bar".

Union of Two Events

The *union* of two events, A and B, that are defined on the same sample space is itself an event, denoted by $A \cup B$, and consists of all the points in the sample space that are in at least one of the sets A and B. That is, each point in $A \cup B$ is in A or in B or in both A and B. One way of reading $A \cup B$ is "A union B."

Intersection of Two Events

The *intersection* of two events, A and B, that are defined on the same sample space is itself an event, is denoted by $A \cap B$, and consists of all the points in the sample space that are in both A and B. One way of reading $A \cap B$ is "A intersection B."

As examples of a complement, a union, and an intersection, consider the earlier example of tossing a coin and a die once. Let the event A be "getting a head," and let the event B be "getting a 6." Then the following list shows the points in the sample space belonging to A, to B, to the complement of A, to the union of A and B, and to the intersection of A and B:

$$A = \{(H, 1), (H, 2), (H, 3), (H, 4), (H, 5), (H, 6)\};$$

$$B = \{(H, 6), (T, 6)\};$$

$$\bar{A} = \{(T, 1), (T, 2), (T, 3), (T, 4), (T, 5), (T, 6)\};$$

$$A \cup B = \{(H, 1), (H, 2), (H, 3), (H, 4), (H, 5), (H, 6), (T, 6)\};$$

$$A \cap B = \{(H, 6)\}.$$

Pictorial representations called *Venn diagrams* are often helpful as a means of illustrating relationships in set theory. In a Venn diagram, a set can have any shape. The set we are particularly interested in is a sample space, and we use a rectangle to represent a sample space. The points in the rectangle represent the sample points in the sample space. Then subsets of the sample space, such as A, or B, or $\bar{A}$, are areas within the rectangle. The three diagrams in Figure 6.4 are general visual representations of examples of the union of two events, the complement of an event and the intersection of two events.

The word "and" is often used as the meaning for " $\cap$ ", as in the event A and B. The word "or" is often used as the meaning for " $\cup$ ", as in the event A or B. When "or" refers to the union of two events, the interpretation is always "and/or," never "either/or." To illustrate this last point, "$H \cup 6$" in the preceding example is often read as "head or six" and includes all the possibilities where a head occurs, or a six

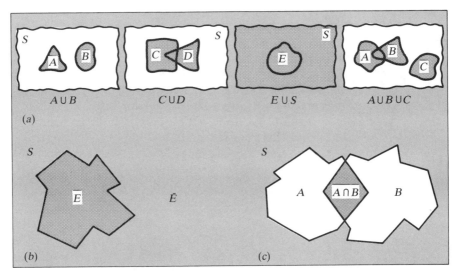

FIGURE 6.4 Venn diagrams showing (a) the union, (b) the complement, and (c) the intersection of events.

occurs, or both a head and a six occur. As another illustration, consider the earlier example of selecting two secretaries from the pool of five secretaries. The event "$A \cup B$" is often read as A or B, and includes all the possibilities where A is selected, or B is selected, or both A and B are selected.

Mutually Exclusive Events

Two events are *mutually exclusive,* or *disjoint,* if they have no points in common. Two events such as A and B are mutually exclusive if and only if $A \cap B = \emptyset$ (see Figure 6.5).

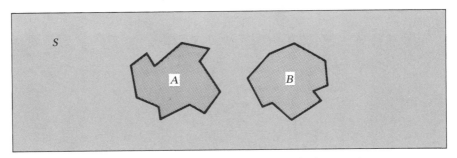

FIGURE 6.5 Venn diagram showing two mutually exclusive events.

Collectively Exhaustive Events

Two or more events are *collectively exhaustive* if their union contains every point in the sample space. The events $E_1, E_2, \ldots, E_k$, where $k \geq 2$, are collectively exhaustive if, and only if, $E_1 \cup E_2 \cup \ldots \cup E_k = S$.

Partition

Two or more events are a *partition* of a sample space if they are collectively exhaustive and every pair of events is mutually exclusive. As an illustration, consider the coin-and-die example. Let C be "getting a head on the coin and any number except 6 on the die"; let D be "getting a tail on the coin and any number except 5 or 6 on the die"; and let E be "getting a head and a 6 or getting a tail and a 6 or getting a tail and a 5." Then C, D, and E are a partition of the sample space. Figure 6.6 illustrates this general case.

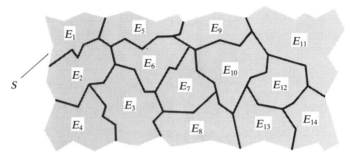

FIGURE 6.6 Venn diagram showing the partition of a sample space.

Overlapping and Joint Events

Two events are *overlapping* if they have at least one point in common. In other words, if two events are not mutually exclusive, they are

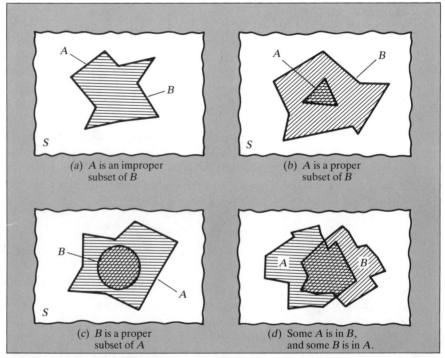

(a) A is an improper subset of B

(b) A is a proper subset of B

(c) B is a proper subset of A

(d) Some A is in B, and some B is in A.

FIGURE 6.7 Venn diagrams illustrating all the possible ways in which two events can overlap. (a) A is an improper subset of B; (b) A is a proper subset of B; (c) B is a proper subset of A; (d) some A is in B and some B is in A.

overlapping. The overlap itself is the intersection of the two events. Sometimes this intersection is called a *joint event,* which is, in a way, the opposite of a disjoint event. There are more possibilities for overlapping events than in the usual common-sense meaning of "overlapping," and Figure 6.7 illustrates these possibilities.

6.4 THE MEANING OF PROBABILITY

We mentioned earlier that mathematicians have struggled for centuries with the task of giving a precise meaning to probability. There have also been many arguments over the interpretation of the term "probability" and these arguments continue to this very day. There are, then, two points to be noted about the meaning of "probability". One is its mathematical definition; the other is its interpretation. As far as the first is concerned, there is no controversy; however, many competing views have been advanced as to the second point. We shall, in this section, provide first a discussion on mathematical probability and then introduce the three most popular schools of thought concerning the interpretation of probability.

Mathematical Probability and Probability Axioms

On a mathematical level, the notion of probability is quite straightforward. We define the *mathematical probability of an event E* as a real number, denoted as $P(E)$, which ranges in value from 0 to 1 and which measures the likelihood of the occurrence of the event E. (The notation $P(E)$ is a functional notation, not a multiplication notation, and it is read as "P of E.") In accordance with this definition, probabilities are nothing more than numbers that obey a few rules, and it does not matter what interpretation one cares to give to the numbers. These rules are quite simple with a finite sample space. Let S be such a sample space, and let A and B be any two events defined on S. Let $P(S)$, $P(A)$, and $P(B)$ be the probabilities of S, A, and B, respectively. The numerical values of $P(S)$, $P(A)$, and $P(B)$ are probabilities if and only if they satisfy the following three rules.

1. $P(A) \geq 0$, for any event A defined in S;

2. $P(S) = 1$;

3. $P(A \cup B) = P(A) + P(B)$, for any events A and B defined on S, provided A and B are disjoint.

These rules are sometimes called the *axioms of formal probability.* They offer great freedom in the ways that probability can be assigned to the points in a sample space. Each point must have a nonnegative probability, and the sum of the probabilities for all the points in the sample space must equal unity, but there is no requirement that each point's probability be "correct," "realistic," or even "reasonable". Mathematical probability then, investigates the consequences of assigning probabilities; the interest in mathematical probability is in the development of theorems giving the probabilities of more complicated events, once the probabilities of simple events have satisfied the axioms. The power of mathematical probability lies in the fact that its theorems hold for any interpretation of probability (provided that the axioms are met). A major limitation of mathematical probability is that it cannot be used, by itself, to solve any practical problems, because it provides no way of arriving at correct (or approximations of) probabilities for events in the real world. Mathematical probability, then, is strictly theoretical; something has to be added to the axioms before probability can be applied to problems in real life.

Many attempts have been made, with varying degrees of success, to provide the needed interpretation. There are three such interpretations in common use today: the classical theory, the relative-frequency theory, and the personalistic theory. Each of these three interpretations of probability is a way of adding to the axioms so that probability is made to be practical.

Classical Theory

Classical probability theory originated with the analyses of gambling games a few centuries ago. Unquestionably, it was intended to be practical, since it was developed by mathematicians to answer questions brought to them by gamblers. The crucial feature of classical probability is the assertion that all the points in a suitably constructed sample space are equally probable. By a "suitably constructed sample space" we mean one for which it is reasonable to believe that all the points are equally probable. For example, if the experiment is tossing a die, then $S = \{\text{odd}, 2, 4, 6\}$ is not suitably constructed, but $S = \{1, 2, 3, 4, 5, 6\}$ is suitably constructed. The *principle of insufficient reason* is often used in this context. This states that if we have insufficient reason to believe that one point in the sample space is more likely to occur than any other when an experiment is performed, then it is reasonable to assign equal probabilities to all points. If it is agreed that all points in a sample space are equally probable, then the following statement is true. The probability of an event is equal to the number of points in the sample space for which this event occurs, divided by the total number of points in the sample space. In symbols, let $N(S)$ be the number of points in the sample space. Then $1/N(S)$ is the probability of each point. Let E be the event whose probability is desired. Then it is possible to count the number of points in the sample space for which E occurs and let $n(E)$ be this number of points. Finally, the probability of E is

$$P(E) = n(E)\left[\frac{1}{N(S)}\right] = \frac{n(E)}{N(S)}. \qquad (6.10)$$

In other words, (6.10) states that the probability of an event is the number of ways it can occur during the running of an experiment, divided by the total number of ways the experiment can turn out.

For example, in the coin and die illustration, it should be intuitively obvious that if the coin is fair and if the die is fair, then each of the 12 points in the sample space has the same probability, namely 1/12. An argument justifying this is that a fair coin has the probability of 1/2 for H and 1/2 for T. The probability of 1/2 for H is shared equally by the six ways a fair die can come out, giving a probability of one-sixth of 1/2 for each of the points in the sample space that start with an H. Similarly, the probability of 1/2 for T is shared equally by the six ways a fair die can come out, giving a probability of one-sixth of 1/2 for each of the points in the sample space that start with a T.

If this seems to be an elaborate argument for a simple case, it is. Its importance lies in seeing how to make the argument, so that more complicated sample spaces can be examined to see whether they have equally probable points. Now, what is the probability of the event E when E is, say, getting a head and a number greater than 3? E occurs for the following points in the sample space: $(H, 4)$, $(H, 5)$, and $(H, 6)$. Therefore, $n(E) = 3$ while $N(S) = 12$, and hence

$$P(E) = \frac{3}{12} = \frac{1}{4}.$$

As a second example, consider the sample space of male faculty on the committee. What is the probability for the committee to consist of (a) 5 men? (b) 5 women? To answer this question, we use S_3, since, owing to random selection, in this sample space the sample points are equally likely. We know that $N(S_3) = \binom{100}{5}$. Now, the event "5 men" would contain $\binom{70}{5}$ points and the event "5 women" would have $\binom{30}{5}$ points. Then

(a) $$P(5 \text{ men}) = \frac{\binom{70}{5}}{\binom{100}{5}} = \frac{\frac{70!}{5!65!}}{\frac{100}{5!95!}} = \frac{12,103,014}{75,287,502} = 0.1608;$$

(b) $$P(5 \text{ women}) = \frac{\binom{30}{5}}{\binom{100}{5}} = \frac{142,506}{75,287,502} \doteq 0.0019.$$

In view of these small probabilities, the worry of the assistant dean mentioned before seems to be unfounded.

We should point out that classical theory, under the assumption of equally likely outcomes, depends upon logical reasoning. Thus, we usually meet no difficulty if we are concerned with a well-balanced coin, an unloaded die, an honest roulette wheel, or any other experiment whose outcomes are virtually equally likely to occur and can be deduced by logic. However, it is reasonable to believe that the real world has no such thing as a perfectly balanced coin, perfect die, perfectly honest roulette wheel, and so on. Therefore, the assumption of perfection will cause slightly incorrect probability assignments. What about a coin that is unbalanced, a loaded die, a crooked roulette wheel? In each of these cases, the classical approach of assigning equal probabilities would yield incorrect probability calculations.

It is also important to understand the assertions that the coin is perfect or the die is fair. These assertions may be assumptions only. This being the case, we are really dealing with mathematical probability and the results of any probability computations show only what would happen using such assumptions. Again, the assumption of fairness might be based upon repeatedly tossing the coin or rolling the die and concluding that their actual behavior is fair. Now we are really dealing with the relative-frequency theory, which we shall introduce at this point.

The Relative-frequency Theory

Relative-frequency theoreticians claim that the only valid procedure for determining event probabilities is through repetitive trials of an experiment under identical conditions. For example, when a coin is tossed, what is the probability that it will land heads up? The relative-frequency theorist would approach the problem by actually tossing the coin, say, 100 times, under the same conditions, and then calculating the proportion of times the coin fell heads. Suppose the coin fell heads 45 times out of 100; then the ratio 45/100 is used as the estimate of the probability of heads, $P(H)$, of this coin. A moment's reflection will show that even if the coin were unbiased, we might not have exactly 50 heads out of 100 tosses. In other words, we cannot expect to obtain the true probability from repeated experiments. However, if the coin were perfectly balanced, the estimate would approach the true ratio (probability) of 1/2 as the number of trials continued to increase.

This discussion leads us to the following interpretation of probability in terms of relative frequency. If an experiment is performed n times under the same conditions, and there are x outcomes, $x \leq n$, in which an event occurred, then an estimate of the probability of that event is the ratio x/n. Furthermore, the estimate of the probability of an event x/n approaches a limit, the true probability of the event, when n increases without limit; that is,

$$P(E) = \lim_{n \to \infty} \frac{x}{n},$$

where "$\lim_{n \to \infty}$" means "the limit when the number of trials increases until it approaches infinity."

Clearly, in practice we can never obtain the probability of an event as given by this limit; we can only seek a close estimate of $P(E)$ based on a large n. For convenience, we shall treat the estimate of $P(E)$ as if it were actually $P(E)$, writing the working relative-frequency definition of probability as

$$P(E) \doteq \frac{x}{n}. \tag{6.11}$$

Defining $P(E)$ as a limit as n approaches infinity does, however, emphasize that probability involves a long-run concept. This means that when we toss a balanced die six times, it is incredibly unlikely for each of the six numbers to appear once. However, if we roll the die over and over again, for a large number of times, we can expect, in the long run, or on the average, each of the six faces of the die appear about one-sixth of the time. It is exactly in this sense that we say the probability of getting any one of the numbers on a die in a random roll is 1/6. Again, if 1,000 items are selected at random from a day's production run and 75 are found to be defective, then the probability of selecting a defective item from the entire day's run is $P(D) = 75/1{,}000 = 0.075$.

Both the classical and relative-frequency theories are called *objective* definitions of probability. The classical definition is *objective* in the sense that it based on deduction from a set of assumptions. The relative-frequency definition is *objective* because the probability of an event occurring is determined by repeated empirical observations.

The Personalistic Theory

An objectivist is quite at home in talking about probability in connection with the toss of a coin or the manufacture of a mass-produced output. He can readily think of the number of automobile tires produced vis-à-vis the probability of one defective tire as the long-run ratio of the number of defective tires to the total number of tires produced. He might, however, be helpless with respect to the problem of unique events—events that occur just once or that cannot be subjected to repetitive trials of an experiment. Thus, he would not care to talk about the probability of Columbus' discovering America or of Bacon's writing the works of Shakespeare. As a result, a large class of problems is beyond the reach of the objectivist. This limitation of both the relative-frequency theory and the classical assumption of equal probabilities has prompted the birth of the personalistic view of probability.

The *personalistic,* or *subjective,* theorist regards probability as a measure of personal confidence in a particular proposition, such as a belief that Robert Kennedy probably would have become the President of the United States if he had not been assassinated in 1968. In other words, according to subjectivists, the probability of an event is whatever you think it is, using the information currently available to you. If you think a die is fair, judging from its appearance, you assign probabilities accordingly. If, after tossing it quite a few times, you think it is slightly loaded because sixes came up more often than other numbers, you assign probabilities accordingly. In general, if no trials have been run, a subjective probability can still be assigned even though it is necessarily based on personal judgment and sometimes hunches, even though other people will assign different subjective probabilities because their judgments and hunches are different. If some trials have been run, the subjective probability becomes a blend of personal judgment and hunches on the one hand, and the evidence from the trials on the other hand. If many trials have been run, the roles of judgment and hunch nearly vanish, the evidence from the trials having become so strong.

Subjectivists or Bayesians, have employed several methods to aid people in probing their judgments and hunches when assigning probabilities. Lotteries, betting odds, and reference contracts are three of these devices. At this point, we shall explain how a subjective probability can be determined by the first two methods and take up the third much later when we present Bayesian statistics.

Consider first how your subjective probability of an event can be determined in terms of lotteries. Suppose you wish to assign your own subjective probability to the event that the common stock of General Motors will at least double its price in six months by the lottery device. You should then decide which of the following hypothetical lotteries you would like to enter.

Lottery A: You win $1,000 with probability 0.5.

You win $0 with probability 0.5.

Lottery B: You win $1,000 if General Motors' stocks will at least double its price in six months.

You win $0 if General Motors' stock will not at least double its price in six months.

The prizes in the lotteries are the same, so you should prefer the lottery giving you the greater probability of winning $1,000. Now, suppose you prefer Lottery A over Lottery B; it means that you believe the probability of General Motors' stock to double its price is less than 0.5. You should then adjust the probability of winning $1,000 in lottery A downward (and, of course, also adjust the probability of winning $0 upward in Lottery A so that the sum of these two probabilities remains as 1). However, if you prefer Lottery B, it means that, in your judgment, the probability of General Motors' stock will at least double its price is greater than 0.5. You should then adjust your probability of winning $1,000 in Lottery A upward. You continue to adjust the probability of winning $1,000 in Lottery A until the two lotteries are equally attractive to you; that is, until you feel indifferent between the two lotteries. Suppose such a point is reached when you have assigned a probability of 0.10 of winning $1,000 in Lottery A, then your subjective probability for General Motors' stock will at least double its price in six months is 0.10.

To generalize the foregoing example, we offer this definition. Your *subjective probability of an event E,* denoted as $P(E)$, is the number $P(E)$ that makes you feel indifferent between the following two lotteries.

Lottery A:	You receive X with probability $P(E)$.
	You receive Y with probability $1 - P(E)$.
Lottery B:	You receive X if E occurs.
	You receive Y if E does not occur.

In these lotteries, X and Y are two prizes. The only restriction on X and Y is that they should not be equally satisfactory to you. If, in other words, you feel indifferent between the two prizes, then you would feel indifferent between the two lotteries regardless of the values selected for $P(E)$.

Personal probabilities can also be determined in terms of "odds," which are common everyday expressions of the probabilities of events occurring. Odds compare the chances in favor of an event occurring to the chances against its occurrence. When one says, for example, that the odds are 2 to 1 that A will win the next election, he means that there are two chances in three that A will win the election. To convert odds to probabilities, we note that odds of 2 to 1 can also be written as 2:1; if these odds favor the occurrence of the event then the probability of the event is $2/(2 + 1) = 2/3$.

In general, if the odds are $x : y$ in favor of an event E occurring, then $P(E) = x/(x + y)$. Furthermore, saying that the odds are $x : y$ in favor of the event's occurring is the same as saying the odds are $y : x$ against the occurrence of the event. The probability that the event will not occur is $y/(x + y)$.

Probabilities can also be converted into odds. For example, since the probability that a head will occur on a toss of a fair coin is 1/2, the odds in favor of getting a head are $1 : 1$. In general, if the probability that event E will occur is $P(E)$, then the odds in favor of the occurrence of E are $P(E) : [1 - P(E)]$ and the odds against it are $[1 - P(E)] : P(E)$.

Odds can also be viewed as the ratio of the probability $P(E)$ of the occurrence of an event to the probability $P(\bar{E})$ of its complement, as follows:

$$\text{odds in favor of } E = \frac{P(E)}{P(\bar{E})} = \frac{P(E)}{1 - P(E)}; \qquad (6.12)$$

$$\text{odds against } E = \frac{P(\bar{E})}{P(E)} = \frac{1 - P(E)}{P(E)}. \qquad (6.13)$$

Odds can be used in a decision situation to determine one's subjective probabilities for any number of events, or propositions that are mutually exclusive and completely exhaustive. For example, if your university is planning to build a new business school and there are, say, three contractors, A, B, and C, bidding for the contract. If you know something about the contractors' bidding patterns in the past, their reputations, and so on, you may wish to assess each contractor's chance of winning the contract. To do this, you may follow three simple steps.

TABLE 6.1 Determining Subjective Probabilities
in Terms of Odds

Contractor	Weight	Probability of Winning the Contract
A	5	$P(A) = 5/11$
B	4	$P(B) = 4/11$
C	2	$P(C) = 2/11$
Total	11	11/11

First, you should determine the odds according to your judgment and whatever information available for each pair of contractors. You may, for instance, reach these conclusions: so far as A and B are concerned, the odds are 5 : 4 in favor of A; so far as B and C are concerned, the odds are 2 : 1 in favor of B. Next, when these odds are determined, you should assign some numerical value as *weight* to each of the contractor's winning the contract in accordance with the odds ratios you have established. The numbers assigned are entirely arbitrary, but they must be identical to or in agreement with your odds ratios. Finally, these weights are converted into probabilities by dividing each individual weight by the total weight assigned. These steps are illustrated in Table 6.1. As an exercise, you may wish to explain why the numbers (weights) in the table are identical with your odds ratios. Also explain why, had you used another set of numbers as weights such as 10, 8, and 4, for example, you would end up with the same correct answers.

In this author's opinion, both the objective and subjective interpretations of probability have merit. The empirical approach stresses the importance of gathering evidence from trials, and it is certainly sound to urge this. There are problems, though, with this approach. It is not clear how many trials are sufficient, nor is it clear how similar the conditions must be each time a trial is run. It is impossible to assign any probability to a unique event, and virtually impossible to assign a probability to a rare event. The subjective approach insists that decisions should be guided by meager evidence if no other information is available, supplemented by the judgment of the decision maker. This is certainly sound, too; quantitative probabilistic analyses based on little or no evidence beyond personal judgment can be valuable. A major problem with the subjective approach is that a full analysis of a complicated practical problem requires distressingly large numbers of personal assessments plus distressingly complex mathematical computations. There are, as we shall see, ways of simplifying these practical problems so that analyses can be done.

The classical approach also has merit, especially when it is used to analyze a probability problem when assuming that the gambling devices are fair, or when assuming that the sampling is random, or that the sequence of good and bad parts coming off an assembly line is a random sequence. In closing, it may be observed that we view these three schools of thought as complementary to each other rather than as substitutes for each other. That is, the classical, subjective, and empirical approaches are all useful in different settings, and the interpretation of the "probability" should be whatever is appropriate to the particular circumstance.

It is also interesting to note that, even though the three schools interpret the probability of an event differently, they all define $P(E)$ as a ratio or proportion, and they all satisfy the three axioms mentioned before. Thus, once $P(E)$ is determined in any fashion, the same set of rules—probability theorems—can be applied to do the probability computations.

6.5 BASIC THEOREMS OF PROBABILITY

Aside from their purely mathematical interest, the theorems of probability are highly useful when calculating probabilities. The theorems, of course, are logical consequences of the axioms of formal probability. We present a number of the most useful elementary results. Our presentation applies fully to a "discrete sample space" but, as will be shown at the end of this chapter, requires some modification for the more complicated case of a "continuous sample space." A *discrete sample space* has a finite number of points in it, or an infinite number of points that can be put into a one-to-one correspondence with the positive integers. We do not distinguish among theorems, axioms, and definitions in the following material. Such a three-way distinction would be essential for a mathematical development of probability, but it is not vital in an introduction to applied probability.

THEOREM 6.1 *Within any sample space S, if E is an event, then*

$$0 \leqslant P(E) \leqslant 1. \tag{6.14}$$

One use of this theorem is in discovering calculating errors. If a computed probability is less than zero or greater than one, there is a mistake in the calculations.

THEOREM 6.2 *For any sample space S,*

$$P(S) = 1. \tag{6.15}$$

This means that an entire sample space is a "certainty"—it is an event that is bound to occur in one running of the experiment.

THEOREM 6.3 *Within any sample space S, if the events A and B are mutually exclusive, then the probability that A or B will occur is the sum of the probabilities of A and B. That is,*

$$P(A \cup B) = P(A) + P(B), \quad \text{for disjoint A and B.} \tag{6.16}$$

This result is sometimes called the *special additivity rule,* since it is concerned with the special case of mutually exclusive or disjoint events.

In the coin-and-die example, if A is getting a number less than 3 and B is getting a number greater than 3, then there are 4 points in the sample space possessing property A and 6 points in the sample space possessing property B, and

$$P(A \cup B) = \frac{4}{12} + \frac{6}{12} = \frac{10}{12} = \frac{5}{6}.$$

The special additivity rule can be extended to any number of events. If the events are $E_1, E_2, \ldots, E_k$, where $k \geq 3$ and all the events are within the same sample space, then

$$P(E_1 \cup E_2 \cup \ldots \cup E_k) = P(E_1) + P(E_2) + \cdots + P(E_k),$$

$$\text{for disjoint events.} \quad (6.17)$$

THEOREM 6.4 *With any sample space S, if A and B are two events, then*

$$P(A \cup B) = P(A) + P(B) - P(A \cap B). \qquad (6.18)$$

Notice that this theorem is true whether A and B are mutually exclusive or not. Because of this, it is sometimes called the *general additivity rule*. If A and B are mutually exclusive, then $P(A \cap B) = 0$, since $A \cap B$ is the null set $\emptyset$, and (6.18) becomes (6.16.) If A and B are not mutually exclusive, then $P(A) + P(B)$ gives too large an answer, because the probabilities attached to the points in the intersection of A and B are included both in $P(A)$ and in $P(B)$. The solution is to subtract out these probabilities once, and that is why " $- P(A \cap B)$" appears in (6.18). Also see Figure 6.4(*c*).

Continuing to use the coin-and-die example, suppose that A is getting a number less than or equal to 3 and B is getting a number greater than or equal to 3. Then there are 6 points in the sample space possessing property A, and there are 8 points possessing property B. There are 2 points possessing both properties, namely (H, 3) and (T, 3). Now,

$$P(A \cup B) = \frac{6}{12} + \frac{8}{12} - \frac{2}{12} = \frac{12}{12} = 1.$$

As another illustration from the coin and die example, suppose that A is getting a head and an odd number, while B is getting a head and a 1, a 2, or a 3. Then there are 3 points in the sample space possessing property A, 3 points possessing property B, and 2 points possessing both properties; namely, (H, 1) and (H, 3). Now,

$$P(A \cup B) = \frac{3}{12} + \frac{3}{12} - \frac{2}{12} = \frac{4}{12} = \frac{1}{3}.$$

Let us consider still another application of this rule. In a lot of 1,200 golf balls, 40 have imperfect covers, 32 cannot bounce, and 12 have both defects. If a ball is selected at random from the lot, what is the probability that the ball is defective?

The probability for the balls to have imperfect covers is 40/1,200, and the probability for the balls not to bounce is 32/1,200. Here we have two joint events, and a ball that has both defects is counted as a defective twice, once for its imperfect cover and once for its inability to bounce. We are told there are 12 balls that have both defects. Consequently,

$$P(\text{defective}) = P(\text{imperfect cover}) + P(\text{inability to bounce})$$
$$- P(\text{imperfect cover and inability to bounce})$$
$$= \frac{40}{1,200} + \frac{32}{1,200} - \frac{12}{1,200} = 0.05.$$

The general additivity rule can be extended to any number of events, but the extension is somewhat complicated. If, within a sample space, there are three events, A, B, and C, it can be proved that:

$$P(A \cup B \cup C) = P(A) + P(B) + P(C)$$
$$- P(A \cap B) - P(A \cap C) - P(B \cap C)$$
$$+ P(A \cap B \cap C). \tag{6.19}$$

(The reader can easily understand the logic behind this expression by studying Figure 6.8, a Venn diagram with three overlapping events.)

As an example of the application of (6.19), consider a fashionable suburb of, say, Dallas, that has 10,000 households. Among these households, many subscribe to the following three magazines: *Playboy*, M_1, *Town and Country*, M_2, and *Penthouse*, M_3. Suppose a survey has provided these data: 1,500 families subscribe to M_1, 1,450 to M_2, 1,200 to M_3, 425 to both M_1 and M_2, 510 to both M_1 and M_3, 110 to both M_2 and M_3, and 160 to all three magazines. Suppose one family is selected

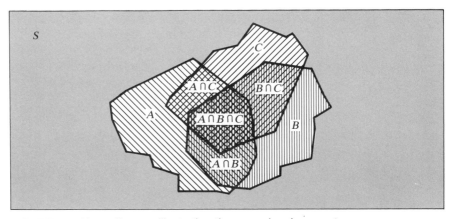

FIGURE 6.8 Venn diagram illustrating three overlapping events.

at random from this suburb, what is the probability that it subscribes to at least one of these magazines? From data provided and by (6.19), we have

$$P(M_1 \cup M_2 \cup M_3) = \frac{1,500}{10,000} + \frac{1,450}{10,000} + \frac{1,200}{10,000}$$

$$- \frac{425}{10,000} - \frac{510}{10,000} - \frac{110}{10,000} + \frac{160}{10,000}$$

$$= 0.3255.$$

THEOREM 6.5 *For any sample space S,*

$$P(\emptyset) = 0. \tag{6.20}$$

This theorem states that, if the event set is the null set, then the event is an "impossibility" for which the probability of occurrence is zero. This is quite understandable: the null set contains no sample point and, hence, no weight can be assigned to it. For example, the probability of obtaining a 7 in rolling an ordinary die is zero, since there is no such number on the die.

THEOREM 6.6 *Within any sample space S,*

$$P(A) = 1 - P(\bar{A}). \tag{6.21}$$

The probability that an event will occur, in one running of the experiment, is one minus the probability that it will not occur. This theorem is very useful. As often happens, the desired probability $P(A)$ is difficult to calculate, while $P(\bar{A})$ is simple to calculate. When this occurs, do the simple calculation and then apply (6.21).

As an example, suppose a lot of 100 bolts of woolen cloth are such that 60 bolts have no defects, 20 bolts have one defect apiece, 10 bolts have two defects apiece, 5 bolts have three defects apiece, 3 bolts have four defects apiece, and 2 bolts have five defects apiece. The probability that a randomly selected bolt will have at least one defect can be found as follows:

$$P(\text{at least one defect}) = P(1 \text{ or } 2 \text{ or } 3 \text{ or } 4 \text{ or } 5 \text{ defects})$$

$$= \frac{20}{100} + \frac{10}{100} + \frac{5}{100} + \frac{3}{100} + \frac{2}{100}$$

$$= 0.40.$$

However, it seems simpler to obtain this probability by means of the complementary event:

$$P(\text{at least one defect}) = 1 - P(\text{no defects})$$
$$= 1 - \frac{60}{100}$$
$$= 0.40.$$

We next introduce additional basic probability theorems by first introducing what is called "conditional probability."

6.6 CONDITIONAL PROBABILITY

Often, when we evaluate some event's probability, we already have some information stemming from an experiment. The availability of such information, in effect, reduces the original sample space to one of its subsets. That is, the information tells us that we are definitely in a *portion* of the sample space rather than possibly being anywhere in the sample space. Clearly, the probability of an event is different when we have some information. For example, the probability that a card drawn at random from a bridge deck will be an ace is greater if we know that the card is an honor card. The probability that a household selected at random from the whole world will have an annual income over $25,000 is different from that for a household chosen randomly from, say, the United States.

In each of the foregoing examples, attention is focused on the probability of an event in a subset, or subpopulation, of the original sample space; the probability of an event in the subset can be greater than, equal to, or less than that which is the original sample space. Each such subset is a "reduced sample space" and is specified by new conditions (information) beyond the initial conditions of the original sample space. (See Figure 6.9.) Probabilities associated with events defined on the reduced sample space are called *conditional probabilities*. We shall now present the law governing them and a few probability concepts related to them by an example.

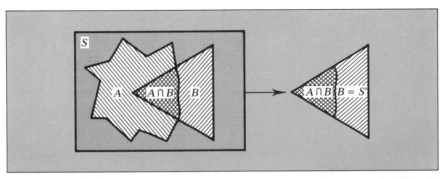

FIGURE 6.9 Venn diagram illustrating the notion of conditional probability via reduced sample space.

TABLE 6.2 Composition of a Firm's Labor Force

	College (C)	Noncollege ($\bar{C}$)	Total
Managerial (M)	50	20	70
Nonmanagerial ($\bar{M}$)	150	280	430
Total	200	300	500

The employees of a firm are cross-classified as managerial or nonmanagerial personnel, and as college graduates or not as shown in Table 6.2. This table may be considered as a sample space in which the 500 employees are the individual sample points. These sample points are equally likely to be selected if a random observation is made. Thus various types of probabilities for events defined on this sample space can be easily determined by the classical theory.

Suppose, for example, if one employee is selected at random from the sample space represented in Table 6.2, we would have

$$P(M) = \frac{n(M)}{N(S)} = \frac{70}{500} = 0.14,$$

$$P(\bar{M}) = \frac{n(\bar{M})}{N(S)} = \frac{430}{500} = 0.86,$$

$$P(C) = \frac{n(C)}{N(S)} = \frac{200}{500} = 0.40,$$

$$P(\bar{C}) = \frac{n(\bar{C})}{N(S)} = \frac{300}{500} = 0.60.$$

These probabilities are called *marginal probabilities*, since each is determined by dividing a marginal total in Table 6.2 by the grand total.

To continue this example, we can also compute

$$P(M \cap C) = \frac{n(M \cap C)}{N(S)} = \frac{50}{500} = 0.10,$$

$$P(M \cap \bar{C}) = \frac{n(M \cap \bar{C})}{N(S)} = \frac{20}{500} = 0.04,$$

$$P(\bar{M} \cap C) = \frac{n(\bar{M} \cap C)}{N(S)} = \frac{150}{500} = 0.30,$$

$$P(\bar{M} \cap \bar{C}) = \frac{n(\bar{M} \cap \bar{C})}{N(S)} = \frac{280}{500} = 0.56.$$

These probabilities are called *joint probabilities*, since each is the probability for the joint occurrence of two events. For an obvious reason, these probabilities are also called *cell probabilities*. It is interesting to note that a marginal probability is the sum of a set of joint probabilities.

For example, from previous calculations, we have

$$P(M) = P(M \cap C) + P(M \cap \bar{C})$$
$$= 0.10 + 0.04 = 0.14$$

and so on. We shall develop special theorems for joint and marginal probabilities in later sections.

Turning our attention now to our main task at hand, suppose we have learned that the selected employee is a college graduate, but still do not know whether he is managerial. Namely, we have partial information about the way the experiment turned out. Now we ask: What is the probability that the employee is managerial, in view of the fact that the employee is a college graduate?

Before we answer this question, let us note that there is a special notation for the desired probability: $P(M \mid C)$. The vertical line here does not have a standard name. Some of the ways of reading this notation are "the probability of M given C", "the conditional probability of M given C", "the probability of M given that C has occurred", and "the probability of M on the condition that C occurs".

One procedure of determining $P(M \mid C)$ is by realizing that, since we know that C has occurred, we are clearly confined to the 200 college graduates. Since the selection is random, each of these people must have an equal probability of being drawn. We also know that 50 of these 200 people are managerial. With all the information, we see that the desired probability is simply

$$P(M \mid C) = \frac{50}{200} = 0.25.$$

This result is obtained by the *method of reduced sample space*. We use the information in the condition (which is whatever comes after the little vertical line in the notation for conditional probability) to identify the portion of the sample space we know we are in—the "reduced sample space." Having identified the portion of the sample space we know we are in, we adjust the probabilities of the points in that portion so that they add up to 1. Here, we changed them from 1/500 to 1/200. In general, we multiply the original probabilities by whatever constant is needed to make the revised probabilities add up to 1. The sum of 1 is appropriate, of course, since it is *certain* that we are in that portion of the sample space, and an event that is certain has a probability of one. Finally, we get the desired probability from the reduced sample space just as we would get it from any sample space—by identifying the points possessing the desired property and adding up their probabilities, or by using theorems and equations to do the equivalent of this.

There is another method besides that of the reduced sample space. The original sample space, with the original probabilities of its points, can be used for all calculations. Sometimes, this is more convenient. The usual definition of conditional probability is in terms of the original sample space and its probabilities as shown by the following theorem.

THEOREM 6.7 *Within any sample space S, the conditional probability* *of B given that A has occurred is*

$$P(B \mid A) = \frac{(P(A \cap B)}{P(A)}, \qquad provided \; that \; P(A) > 0. \qquad (6.22)$$

If $P(A) = 0$, then $P(B \mid A)$ is not defined and has no meaning.

As an example of using (6.22), consider the probability of having selected a managerial employee given that a college graduate was selected, as in the previous example, we have

$$P(M \mid C) = \frac{P(M \cap C)}{P(C)} = \frac{50/500}{200/500} = \frac{50}{200} = 0.25.$$

This is exactly the same answer as was obtained before. It is no accident that the two methods for calculating $P(M \mid C)$ give precisely the same answer. It can be proved that the reduced-sample-space method and the method of (6.22) must result in the same answer. Of course, whichever is the easier method is the one that should be used.

6.7 JOINT PROBABILITIES AND STATISTICAL INDEPENDENCE

A *joint probability* is the probability of a joint event; that is, the probability that both A and B will occur in one running of the experiment. For example, in Table 6.2 concerning a firm's labor-force composition, what is the probability of selecting a managerial employee who is a college graduate when selection is made at random? Here, 50 points in the sample space possess the desired property (which is that of being both college graduate and managerial), and each of these points in the sample space has a probability of 1/500. The desired probability, then is $50(1/500) = 1/10$.

Next, we introduce a major distinction: independent versus dependent events. Two events are *statistically independent* if and only if their joint probability equals the product of their separate probabilities. To see whether C and M are statistically independent, we calculate $P(C)P(M) = (200/500)(70/500) = 7/125$. This result does not equal the joint probability of C and M, which is 1/10. Therefore, C and M are *statistically dependent,* not statistically independent.

As another example of computing the joint probability of two independent events, suppose a white die, W and a blue die B are tossed. What is the probability that $W \geq 5$ and $B \leq 4$? We note that the sample space consists of the 36 equally probable combinations of the white and the blue die, each die with six possible outcomes, and that the event under consideration requires that the two conditions be satisfied simultaneously. If E_1 is the event that $W \geq 5$ and E_2 the event that $B \leq 4$, then we need to know the number of sample points that both sets have in common—that is, the intersection, $E_1 \cap E_2$. In Figure 6.10,

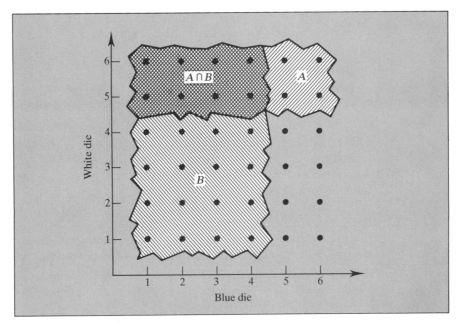

FIGURE 6.10 Graphic illustration of the intersection of two events A and B, where A is defined as W ≥ 5 and B is defined as B ≤ 4 in the sample space of tossing a White and a Blue die.

we can see that there are 8 points in the intersection set. We have then $P(E_1 \cap E_2) = 8/36$. By counting, we find that there are 12 sample points in E_1 and 24 sample points in E_2. As a result, $P(E_1) = 12/36$ and $P(E_2) = 24/36$. Thus,

$$P(E_1 \cap E_2) = \left(\frac{12}{36}\right)\left(\frac{24}{36}\right) = \frac{8}{36},$$

which illustrates that E_1 and E_2 are statistically independent.

The concepts of statistical independence and statistical dependence are very important. Usually, probability calculations for independent events are much simpler than the calculations for dependent events. Some important theorems apply only to independent events. When examining practical questions—such as whether the drug Laetrile helps to cure cancer, or whether bad housing helps to cause crime—a sample result showing statistical independence is usually interpreted as "There is no effect", while a sample result showing statistical dependence is usually interpreted as "There is an effect." We will return in later chapters to the issue of interpreting sample results.

We will now formally introduce two theorems for calculating joint probabilities. These theorems also aid us in distinguishing between statistical independence and dependence.

THEOREM 6.8 *With any sample space S, two events A and B are* statistically independent *if and only if*

$$P(A \cap B) = P(A)P(B). \tag{6.23}$$

This result is sometimes called the *special rule of multiplication*, because it can be applied only when A and B are statistically independent events.

THEOREM 6.9 *Within any sample space S,*

$$P(A \cap B) = P(A)P(B \mid A), \quad \text{provided } P(A) > 0. \quad (6.24)$$

This equation follows from multiplying each side of (6.22) by $P(A)$ and is sometimes called the *general rule of multiplication*. It is so called because the result (6.24) is true whether A and B are statistically independent or not.

Intuitively speaking, statistical independence means that the occurrence of A has no effect on the probability of B. Notice that we are talking of the *occurrence* of A and the *probability* of B. Notice, too, that we are talking about one running of the experiment, and of whether information that A has occurred in that one running of the experiment changes the probability of B, compared with no information about whether A has occurred.

For example, are the events "head" and "odd" statistically independent in the coin-and-die example? That is, does information that the die turned out to be an odd number influence the probability that the coin turned out to be a head? Of course not, and this is exactly what is meant by statistical independence. As another example, suppose two cards are selected from a deck of bridge cards simultaneously. Are the events "the first card is an ace" and "the second card is an ace" independent? The answer is clearly "No!", since the occurrence or nonoccurrence of an ace for the first card would affect the probability of the second card to be an ace differently. There is the same pattern in all of these examples: to decide whether two events are statistically independent, we compare the probability of B knowing that A has occurred with the probability of B not knowing anything about A's occurrence. In short, does information about the occurrence of A affect the probability of B? If the answer is "no," the events are statistically independent; if the answer is "yes," the events are statistically dependent.

In general, sampling *with* replacement generates independent events and sampling *without* replacement generates dependent events.

The following theorem summarizes our preceding discussion.

THEOREM 6.10 *Within any sample space S, if $P(A) > 0$, then*

1. *A and B are statistically independent if and only if*

$$P(B) = P(B \mid A), \quad and$$

2. *A and B are statistically dependent if and only if*

$$P(B) \neq P(B \mid A).$$

It is also true that, in the case when $P(A) > 0$ and $P(B) > 0$, if

$P(B) = P(B \mid A)$ then $P(A) = P(A \mid B)$, and if $P(B) \neq P(B \mid A)$ then $P(A) \neq P(A \mid B)$. We will provide some homework problems in which the readers can explore these relations for themselves.

6.8 MARGINAL PROBABILITY AND THE THEOREM OF ELIMINATION

In a cross-classification table, such as Table 6.2, as mentioned before, a joint probability refers to a cell entry while a marginal probability refers to a margin entry. Like all probabilities, marginal probabilities can be calculated by the direct method of identifying points in the sample space and then adding up their probabilities. Or, they can be calculated by adding up the proper joint probabilities. For example, in Table 6.2, the event "managerial" is subdivided into two events, "managerial and college" and "managerial and noncollege." If desired, $P(\text{managerial})$ can be calculated as $P(\text{managerial and college}) + P(\text{managerial and noncollege})$.

The method of obtaining marginal probabilities employed before is called the *theorem of elimination* or the *theorem of total probability*. It may now be formally established, with Figure 6.11 helping to reveal the underlying logic.

THEOREM 6.11 *Let H_i (for $i = 1, 2, \ldots, k$) be k mutually exclusive and collectively exhaustive nonnull events, and E be an event defined on the same sample space; given that the marginal probabilities, $P(H_i)$, and the conditional probabilities, $P(E \mid H_i)$, for all i, are known, then the marginal probability of E is defined as*

$$
\begin{aligned}
P(E) &= P(E \cap H_1) + P(E \cap H_2) + \cdots + P(E \cap H_k) \\
&= P(H_1)P(E \mid H_1) + P(H_2)P(E \mid H_2) + \cdots + P(H_k)P(E \mid H_k) \\
&= \sum P(H)P(E \mid H).
\end{aligned}
\tag{6.25}
$$

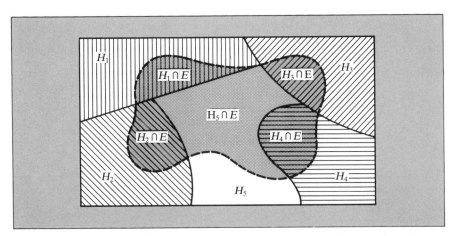

FIGURE 6.11 Venn diagram illustrating the theorem of total probability for the computation of a marginal probability $P(E)$, where the rectangle is S and the central area enclosed by the broken line is the event E.

To illustrate the application of this theorem, let us consider an example. During a local election, three candidates H_i are running for mayor of a certain city. According to one political observer, the probabilities for their victories are $P(H_1) = 0.5$, $P(H_2) = 0.3$, and $P(H_3) = 0.2$. The same observer believes that the conditional probabilities E for the current police commissioner to be reappointed, given that any one of the candidates wins are, respectively, 0.4, 0.8, and 0.5. What is the probability that E will be reappointed? By (6.25) we see that

$$P(E) = P(H_1)P(E \mid H_1) + P(H_2)P(E \mid H_2) + P(H_3)P(E \mid H_3)$$

$$= (0.5)(0.4) + (0.3)(0.8) + (0.2)(0.5)$$

$$= 0.54.$$

Thus, looking at this situation before the election, the current police commissioner has a more than even chance to be reappointed after the election.

6.9 THEOREMS GOVERNING THE INTERSECTION OF MORE THAN TWO EVENTS

Statistical Independence Generalized

Our discussion of joint probabilities and statistical independence has been limited to the intersection of two events. The discussion can now be extended to the intersection of many events. For three events, the definition of statistical independence is considerably more complicated than for two events, as is revealed by the following theorem.

THEOREM 6.12 *Within any sample space S, three events A, B, and C are* completely statistically independent *if and only if all of the following equations are true*

$$P(A \cap B) = P(A)P(B),$$

$$P(A \cap C) = P(A)P(C),$$

$$P(B \cap C) = P(B)P(C),$$
$$P(A \cap B \cap C) = P(A)P(B)P(C). \tag{6.26}$$

It can happen that the first three equations hold but that the fourth does not, and vice versa.

To calculate the joint probability of three events, the direct method can be used, or (6.26) can be used if it applies. Alternatively, the following method can be used whether the events are statistically independent or dependent.

THEOREM 6.13 *Within any sample space S,*

$$P(A \cap B \cap C) = P(A)P(B \mid A)P(C \mid A \cap B), \qquad (6.27)$$

provided $P(A) > 0$ and $P(A \cap B) > 0$.

Suppose for example, a random sample of three is drawn with replacement from a shipment of merchandise, 10 percent of which is defective; what is the probability that all three units in the sample are nondefective?

Drawing with replacement generates independent events. Hence, the probability of any item to be selected at any draw remains unchanged. Let A, B, and C, be the events of getting a nondefective unit on the first, second, and third draws, respectively. Then, using (6.26),

$$P(A) = P(B) = P(C) = 0.9,$$

$$P(A \cap B) = P(A \cap C) = P(B \cap C) = (0.9)(0.9) = 0.81,$$

$$P(A \cap B \cap C) = (0.9)(0.9)(0.9) = 0.729.$$

Now consider the repeated tossing of a fair coin. The probability of getting four heads in four tosses is $(1/2)(1/2)(1/2)(1/2) = 1/16$. If there are 100 tosses and the results are 100 heads, $P(H)$ on the 101st toss is still $1/2$ because of independence. By this time, of course, you may very well question the assumption that the coin is well balanced, since $P(100\,H) = (1/2)^{100}$, which is practically zero. Our discussion on independence here, however, does bring out the fallacy of the gambler's *maturity theory of chance,* which entertains the false idea that a long run of failures heralds a success.

Independent and Mutually Exclusive Events

It is important to clarify now the difference between mutually exclusive events and independent events. We want to know whether events are mutually exclusive when we consider the union of events or the probability that at least one of several events will occur. We are interested in independence when we consider the intersection of the events, or the probability that all of the events will occur.

Furthermore, if two events are mutually exclusive and if neither event has zero probability, then the two events must be statistically dependent. However, if two events are dependent, it does not necessarily follow that they are mutually exclusive. As a general illustration of some of these ideas, consider the two events A and B in Figure 6.12, where the 15 outcomes in S are assumed to be equally likely. Here, clearly, A and B are not mutually exclusive, since $A \cap B \neq \emptyset$. They are, however, independent, since

$$P(A) = P(A \mid B) = 5/15,$$

$$P(B) = P(B \mid A) = 6/15,$$

$$P(A \cap B) = P(A)P(B) = 2/15.$$

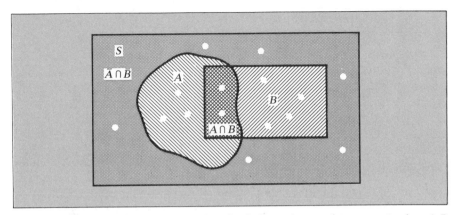

FIGURE 6.12 Venn diagram illustrating the independence of two events A and B that are overlapping.

It is interesting to note that a slight change in the definitions of A and B here, say, moving one element from $\bar{A} \cap \bar{B}$ to $A \cap \bar{B}$ would make A and B no longer independent.

Finally, if A and B are independent and if $P(A) \neq 0$ and $P(B) \neq 0$ then A and B cannot be mutually exclusive, since for two independent events, the probability that both events will occur is the product of their marginal probabilities. Given that the two marginal probabilities are both greater than zero, the product must be greater than zero. If A and B are mutually exclusive, then $A \cap B = \emptyset$, which has a zero probability. Hence, the intersection must not be the null set; that is, the events are not mutually exclusive.

To conclude our discourse on independence, let us provide the following general results (which the reader may wish to verify or explain as an exercise).

1. For any event E in S:

   a. E and the null event $\emptyset$ are independent.

   b. E and S are independent.

2. If E_1 and E_2 defined over the same sample space S are independent, then so are

   a. $\bar{E}_1$ and $\bar{E}_2$

   b. E_1 and $\bar{E}_2$

   c. $\bar{E}_1$ and E_2

6.10 ADDITIONAL EXAMPLES OF PROBABILITY PROBLEMS

The presentation of probability theory in this chapter has provided a number of powerful tools for solving probability problems. It is quite simple and straightforward to apply the basic probability theorems introduced here; but it is often not as simple to identify which rule should be applied for any given problem. One way to overcome this difficulty is to first identify the proper sample space in which the event or events in the problem are defined. We shall provide a few more examples here to enable you to have a deeper understanding of these rules.

Example 4 Male Faculty on the Committee

With reference to this example, we have solved the problem of determining the probability of selecting 5 men on the committee, which is 0.1608, by using S_3, where all the sample points are equally likely to occur, because the selection is made at random. Now, suppose we wish to solve the problem via S_1, where the 32 sample points are not equally likely. This amounts to determining the probability of the first sample point listed in S_2, (M, M, M, M, M), which in turn means the selection of 5 men from the 100 instructors. Recall there are 70 men among the 100 instructors and by the general multiplicative rule, (for dependent events), we have

$$P(5 \text{ men}) = P(M_1 \cap M_2 \cap M_3 \cap M_4 \cap M_5)$$
$$= P(M_1)P(M_2 \mid M_1)P(M_3 \mid M_1 \cap M_2)P(M_4 \mid M_1 \cap M_2 \cap M_3)$$
$$P(M_5 \mid M_1 \cap M_2 \cap M_3 \cap M_4)$$
$$= \left(\frac{70}{100}\right)\left(\frac{69}{99}\right)\left(\frac{68}{98}\right)\left(\frac{67}{97}\right)\left(\frac{66}{96}\right)$$
$$= 0.1608,$$

as before. As a matter of fact, this example illustrates the determination of probabilities of sample points in any discrete sample space where the sample points are not equally likely.

Example 5 Match Box

There are four matches in a box. Two are red and two are black. If two matches are selected at random without replacement, what is the probability that the sample selected consists of one red and one black match?

To solve this problem, we first note that the sample space in this case is

$$S = \{(R_1, R_2), (R_1, B_2), (B_1, R_2), (B_1, B_2)\}.$$

Next, we note that the event in question contains the two sample points (R_1, B_2) and (B_1, R_2), which are mutually exclusive. Thus, the solution becomes

$$P(1R \text{ and } 1B) = P(R_1 \cap B_2) + P(B_1 \cap R_2)$$
$$= P(R_1)P(B_2 \mid R_1) + P(B_1)P(R_2 \mid B_1)$$
$$= \left(\frac{2}{4}\right)\left(\frac{2}{3}\right) + \left(\frac{2}{4}\right)\left(\frac{2}{3}\right)$$
$$= \frac{2}{3}.$$

This problem can also be solved as follows

$$P(1R \cap 1B) = \frac{\binom{2}{1}\binom{2}{1}}{\binom{4}{2}} = \frac{2}{3}.$$

The point here is this: Does the solution of 2/3 here seem to be contradictory to your common sense or your understanding of the problem? If so, you should try to fully understand the solution obtained in both ways, before moving on to the next example.

Example 6 Royal Flush in Spades

During the "roaring twenties," a big gambler was reported to have said that he would die a very happy man if he could get a royal flush in spades in a poker game just once in his whole life. He said this, evidently, because the odds against getting such a poker hand are overwhelming. Let us see exactly what the probability of obtaining a royal flush in spades is.

Here, the event is the single example point of A, K, Q, J, 10, all spades in any order, in a sample space where $N(S) = {}_{52}C_5$. Thus,

$$P(A, K, Q, J, 10 \text{ in spades}) = \frac{\binom{5}{5}}{\binom{52}{5}} = \frac{1}{2,598,960}.$$

This probability is practically 0. Alternatively, we see that the odds in favor of such a hand are as small as $1 : 2,598,959$. This is even smaller than $1 : 1,919,190$: the odds in favor of winning the first prize of $1,000,000 or more for a $1 bet in the original New York State Lottery when winning the first prize required picking the six correct numbers from a total of 44 numbers.

Example 7 Five Coins

Suppose five coins are tossed; what is the probability of obtaining exactly two heads and three tails? In this case, we have 2^5 different ways in which the five coins can fall. The number of cases of two heads and three tails, by the general expression for permutations, is ${}_5P_{(2,3)}$. Therefore,

$$P(2H \cap 3T) = \frac{{}_5P_{(2,3)}}{2^5} = \frac{5!/(2!3!)}{32}$$

$$= \frac{\dfrac{3!(4)(5)}{3!(1)(2)}}{32} = \frac{10}{32} = 0.3125.$$

Example 8 Repair Team

Mr. A is one of a team of ten service men. For a certain job, three service men are required. If the three are to be selected at random, what is the probability that Mr. A will be included? This probability can be obtained by the multiplicative rule for probabilities by finding the complement of the probability that A would remain unselected after three draws:

$$P(\text{A included}) = 1 - P(\text{A not included})$$
$$= 1 - (9/10)(8/9)(7/8) = 3/10.$$

This probability can also be found by determining the total number of trios that could be formed from among the ten service men and then determining the number of these that would include A. Both are problems of combinations, since order is of no significance. The total number of groups that can be formed from ten by taking three at a time is

$$\binom{10}{3} = \frac{10!}{3!(10-3)!} = \frac{7!(8)(9)(10)}{7!(1)(2)(3)} = 120.$$

There are 120 groups of three that could be selected. to find out how many of these would include A, find how many pairs may join A to form a group of three. Such pairs must be selected from among the nine other service men, so we need the number of combinations of nine things taken 2 at a time.

$$\binom{9}{2} = \frac{9!}{2!7!} = 36.$$

The probability that A will be a member of the trio selected then becomes 36/120 or 3/10 as before.

Example 9 Window Display

A store manager is arranging ten different pieces of merchandise in the three sections of a show window. If he puts the ten items into the three sections at random, what is the probability that he puts three items in one section, five in another section, and two in yet another section?

To construct a sample space for this experiment, let us label the three sections in the show window as a, b, and c so that we can tell them apart. Now, the sample space would consist of sample points which are all possible sequences of ten letters, where each letter in the sequence may be a, b, or c. By the multiplicative principle, the total number of sample points in S is

$$3^{10} = 59,049.$$

We assign a probability of 1/59,049 to each sample point, since the manager is to put the items into the three sections at random.

Next, we consider the event E^* as putting three items in one section, five in another, and two in yet another. This event can be split into six mutually exclusive and exhaustive subsets as below:

A is the event "3 in a, 5 in b, and 2 in c";

B is the event "5 in a, 2 in b, and 3 in c";

C is the event "2 in a, 3 in b, and 5 in c";

D is the event "3 in a, 2 in b, and 5 in c";

E is the event "5 in a, 3 in b, and 2 in c";

F is the event "2 in a, 5 in b, and 3 in c."

Since these events are disjoint, we have

$$P(E^*) = P(A) + P(B) + P(C) + P(D) + P(E) + P(F).$$

Let us now concentrate on one of these subsets, say A. The sample points of S that are in A have 3 a's, 5 b's, and 2 c's arranged in any order. By (6.8), the total number of possible different arrangements of 3 a's, 5 b's, and 3 c's is

$$_{10}P_{(3,5,2)} = \frac{10!}{3!5!2} = 2520.$$

Hence,

$$P(A) = \frac{_{10}P_{(3,5,2)}}{3^{10}} = \frac{2520}{59,049}.$$

Finally, the number of sample points in the remaining events is clearly the same as that in A. Thus, the six events A, B, C, D, E, and F have equal probabilities, and

$$P(E^*) = P(A) + P(B) + P(C) + P(D) + P(E) + P(F)$$
$$= 6\left(\frac{2520}{59,049}\right) \doteq 0.256.$$

A Card Game

Cards are dealt face-up from well-shuffled bridge deck, one at a time, until the first king appears. What is the probability that the first king appears (a) at the third card? (b) At the rth card? (c) at the rth card or sooner?

There may be a number of ways to construct the sample space for this experiment. One way that is convenient for our present discussion is as follows. There are 4 kings K, and 48 nonkings $\bar{K}$, in the deck. The sample space then may be thought to consist of all the possible arrangements of 4 Ks and 48 $\bar{K}$s in 52 numbered positions. The total number of arrangements is then $_{52}P_{(4,48)} = (52!/(4!48))$, which is equal to $_{52}C_4$.

Now, the event that the first king appears at the third card is the case (in the sample space) in which the first three symbols of each of its elements must be $\bar{K} - \bar{K} - K$, since the first king is at the third place. The number of sample points in this event set is therefore all possible arrangements that can be made with the remaining 3 Ks and 46 $\bar{K}$s; that is, $(49!)/(3!46!)$. Therefore, we have,

(a) $$P(\text{1st king at the 3d card}) = \frac{\dbinom{49}{3}}{\dbinom{52}{4}} = 0.0681.$$

Next, if the first king appears at the rth card, then the remaining 3 Ks and $[48 - (r - 1)]$ $\bar{K}$s can form $\dbinom{52 - r}{3}$ arrangements. Hence,

(b) $$P(\text{1st king at the } r\text{th card}) = \frac{\dbinom{52 - r}{3}}{\dbinom{52}{4}}, \quad r = 1, 2, 3, \ldots, 49.$$

Finally, if we let E be the event "first king at the rth card or earlier," then $\bar{E}$ is the event "4 kings after the rth card." The number of sample points belonging to $\bar{E}$ is the number of arrangements that can be made in the remaining $(52 - r)$ cards taken 4 Ks and $(48 - r)\bar{K}$s, since the first r symbols of every member in this event are all nonkings. This number is $(52 - r)!/4!(48 - r)!$. Thus,

(c) $$P(E) = 1 - P(\bar{E}) = 1 - \frac{\dbinom{52 - r}{4}}{\dbinom{52}{4}}.$$

If $r = 10$, for example,

$$P(E) = 1 - \frac{\dbinom{52 - 10}{4}}{\dbinom{52}{4}} = 1 - \frac{111{,}930}{270{,}725} = 0.41345,$$

which reveals that there is almost 59% of a chance that a king will appear at the 10th card or sooner.

6.11 INFINITE SAMPLE SPACES

Throughout this chapter we have been assuming that a random experiment can have only a finite number of outcomes. On occasion the random phenomenon of interest may generate a sample space that is infinite. Infinity, furthermore, may be countably infinite or uncountably infinite.

Countably Infinite Sample Spaces

A sample space is *countably infinite* if it can be put into a one-to-one correspondence with the set of positive integers so that it can be enumerated as 1, 2, 3, ... That is, when the sample space is countable, we can denote it as $S = \{e_1, e_2, e_3, \ldots\}$. Then we need to assign a number of $P(e_i)$ to each outcome e_i such that

$$0 \leqslant P(e_i) \leqslant 1, \quad \sum_{i=1}^{\infty} P(e_i) = 1.$$

Furthermore, if $E = \{e_i : i \in I_E\}$, where I_E stands for a subset of positive integers, and the symbol $\in$ means "a member of", it will be assigned a probability

$$P(E) = \sum_{i \in I_E} P(e_i).$$

Here I_E may be infinite, since S is infinite, but the sum in $P(E)$ is finite, since $\sum P(e_i)$ is at most 1.

As an example, let us consider the experiment in which a well-balanced coin is tossed indefinitely and a tally is kept of the number of trials until the first head occurs. The sample space clearly consists of integers 0, 1, 2, ... We get the outcome i if the sequence

$$\underbrace{TTT \ldots TH}_{i}$$

emerges. It is easy to see that the probability of such a sequence is $(1/2)^{i+1}$. That is,

S	0	1	2	3	...
Probability	1/2	$(1/2)^2$	$(1/2)^3$	$(1/2)^4$	...

It can also be verified that

$$\frac{1}{2} + \frac{1}{2^2} + \frac{1}{2^3} + \ldots = 1.$$

We see that the countably infinite case is exactly the same as the finite case. As a result, all the definitions and consequences obtained before the finite case can be carried over to the countably infinite case. For this reason we sometimes lump the finite and countable cases together under the name *discrete sample spaces*.

Uncountably Infinite Sample Spaces

A sample space is *uncountably infinite,* or *continuous,* if it is not countable. Assigning probabilities to individual elementary outcomes, as in the discrete cases, does not work in the case of continuous sample space. In most uncountably infinite cases the probability of each individual outcome must be zero. The way out of this difficulty is to assign probabilities to composite events rather than to individual outcomes.

When continuous, the sample space may be a set of ordinary real numbers, such as the interval $(0, 1)$ or the whole real line $(-\infty, \infty)$, or it may be a set of four points in a plane. In the former case, events may be defined in terms of intervals; in the latter, in terms of areas. Once events can be clearly defined in either case, event probabilities can be assigned, and the rules for discrete cases can then be applied.

Let us restrict our attention to the case of assigning probabilities to events that are intervals. Let the sample space be the set of real numbers on the interval from 0 to 1. It seems appropriate to say that $P(S) = 1$ here as for any other type of sample space. Intuitively, it also seems reasonable to say that a random selection from this sample space will produce a number less than 0.5 with a probability of 0.5. Similarily, the probability that the number selected at random will fall between 0.75 and 0.85 is 0.10.

Now let us define three interval events on this sample space as follows:

$$A = \{x : 0.6 < x < 0.9\},$$

$$B = \{x : x > 0.7\},$$

$$C = \{x : x < 0.5\}.$$

If we assign to each event a probability that is the proportion of its length to the total length of the sample space, we have

$$P(A) = 0.3, \quad P(B) = 0.3, \quad \text{and} \quad P(C) = 0.5.$$

From the definitions of these events, we may derive other events on the same sample space via set operations. Thus, for example,

$$A \cup B = \{x : 0.6 < x < 1.0\},$$

for which

$$P(A \cup B) = 0.4.$$

Alternatively, we note that

$$A \cap B = \{x : 0.7 < x < 0.9\}$$

and

$$P(A \cap B) = 0.2;$$

hence

$$P(A \cup B) = P(A) + P(B) - P(A \cap B)$$
$$= 0.3 + 0.3 - 0.2$$
$$= 0.4.$$

Intuitively, we also see that the following results hold:

$$\bar{C} = \{x : x \geq 0.5\},$$

$$P(\bar{C}) = 0.5$$
$$= 1 - P(C)$$
$$= 1 - 0.5;$$

$$B \cup C = \{x : x < 0.5 \text{ or } x > 0.7\},$$
$$P(B \cup C) = P(B) + P(C)$$
$$= 0.5 + 0.3$$
$$= 0.8;$$

$$B \cap C = \emptyset,$$
$$P(B \cap C) = 0 \neq P(B)P(C).$$

The last two results indicate that B and C are mutually exclusive but are not independent.

From our example of "selecting a number of random" we may take notice of two important properties. First, a set whose probability is computable as an interval. Given two interval events, A and B, we see that $\bar{A}$, $\bar{B}$, $A \cup B$, and $A \cap B$ are again intervals. Second, the assignment of probability is additive. That is, if A and B are any two sets consisting of intervals and if they are disjoint, then the sum of the lengths of the intervals in $A \cup B$ is just the length of A plus the length of B. These are clearly consistent with the axioms given earlier for the finite sample space.

Turning our attention to another example of interval events and their probabilities on an uncountably infinite sample space, let us consider a stopwatch with a minute hand and with numerals on the circumference from 0 to 10, indicating minutes. If the watch is started and then stopped at your command while you are blindfolded, what is the chance that the minute hand will stop exactly at the numeral 4? By exactly, we mean 4.000... minutes with zeros carried on forever. Clearly, there is no chance at all. Yet the watch must stop somewhere, and the probability that it stops is 1. Or we may ask: "If the watch stops at a random time, what is the probability that the minute hand stops between the numbers 2 and 4?" Many people would say the probability is 0.2, since the space between the numerals 2 and 4 is 2/10 of the circumference.

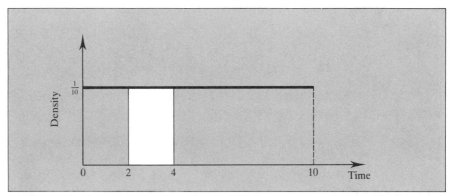

FIGURE 6.13 Graphic illustration of probability as an area under the density curve of a continuous random variable via the stopwatch example.

To express the foregoing probability as an area, we may construct what is called an area probability graph. The total area under the graph is the total probability of the continuous sample space and must equal 1. For our example, the base should extend from 0 to 10 along the time axis T. (Note that on the circumference of the watch, 0 and 10 coincide.) Since the watch can stop at random at any point between 0 and 10, we may assign equal probabilities to two time intervals with equal widths. If their probabilities are to be measured by areas, the altitudes of the corresponding rectangles should have equal heights. Hence, because the total area under it must equal 1, the area graph is bounded above by a straight line parallel to the T axis at a distance 1/10 above the axis. Figure 6.13 gives us this area graph. The black area in this figure represents the probability that the watch stops between 2 and 4. The area of the rectangle is $(4 - 2)(1/10) = 0.2$, the same as the probability obtained intuitively.

GLOSSARY OF FORMULAS

(6.1) $T_k = (n_1)(n_2)(n_3) \cdots (n_{k-1})(n_k)$.

This is the *principle of multiplication,* which gives the total number of ways that k operations, each with n_i, $i = 1, 2, \ldots, k$, ways to arrange the objects, can be performed.

(6.2) $_N P_N = N!$

(6.3) $N! = (1)(2)(3) \cdots (N - 1)(N - 2)N$.

The first equation gives the total number of permutations, arrangements of objects in which order is important, of a set of N things, taken all together. The second equation defines $N!$ ("N factorial") as the product of whole numbers from 1 to N.

(6.4) $N! = n!(n + 1)(n + 2) \cdots (N - 1)(N)$.

This expression is derived from (6.3) and is used to manipulate equations expressed in terms of factorial signs. Note that here, $n \leq N$, and that in a ratio of factorial signs only equal factorials can be canceled.

(6.5) $_NP_n = \dfrac{N!}{(N - n)!}$.

This equation defines the total number of permutations of N objects taken n at a time with $n \leq N$. With permutations, order is of significance.

(6.6) $_NC_n = \dbinom{N}{n} = \dfrac{N!}{n!(N - n)!}$.

The total number of combinations of N things taken n at a time with $n \leq N$ is defined by this equation. For a combination, order is of no significance. Furthermore, $_NC_n$ combinations are equally likely.

(6.7) $_NP_n = {}_NC_n({}_nP_n)$.

This equation says that the total number of permutations is equal to the total number of combinations multiplied by the total number of permutations as specified, provided $N < n$. For example: $_{10}P_4 = {}_{10}C_4({}_4p_4)$.

(6.8) $_NP_{(n_1, n_2, \ldots, n_k)} = \dfrac{N!}{n_1!n_2! \ldots n_k!}$.

If there are N objects, of which n_1 are alike, n_2 are alike, etc., for k types of objects, with $\sum n_i = N$, $i = 1, 2, 3, \ldots, k$, then the total number of permutations of N objects, taken all at a time, is defined by this formula. Sometimes, this quantity is also denoted as $\left(\begin{smallmatrix} N \\ n_1, n_2, \ldots, n_k \end{smallmatrix} \right)$.

(6.9) $_NP_{(n, N-n)} = \dfrac{N!}{N!(N - n)!} = {}_NC_n$.

This is the special case of (6.8). Here, all the N objects are divided into two mutually exclusive categories; that is, n are alike and $(N - n)$ are alike. This relationship between permutation and combination also demonstrates the symmetric property of combinations: $_NC_{(N-n)} = {}_NC_n$. It is interesting to note that $_NC_N = {}_NC_0 = 1$ just as $0! = 1$ by definition.

(6.10) $P(E) = \dfrac{n(E)}{N(S)}$.

Under the assumptions of mutually exclusive and equally likely outcomes in the sample space, the *classical interpretation* views the probability of an event as a ratio of the points in that event set to the total number of points in the sample space.

(6.11) $P(E) = \dfrac{x}{n}$,

The *relative-frequency theory* insists that event-probabilities can be established only by repeated trials of an experiment. According to this school of thought, the probability of an event is the ratio of the number of favorable outcomes for the event, x, to the total number of trials, n. $P(E)$ here is only an estimate of the true probability of E.

(6.12) Odds in favor of $E = \dfrac{P(E)}{P(\bar{E})} = \dfrac{P(E)}{1 - P(E)}$;

(6.13) Odds against $E = \dfrac{P(\bar{E})}{P(E)} = \dfrac{1 - P(E)}{P(E)}$.

These two equations view odds as the ratio of probabilities of E to the probability of its complement $\bar{E}$. Odds are one of the procedures to determine subjective event-probabilities.

(6.14) $0 \leqslant P(E) \leqslant 1$.

This expression states the fact that the probabiiity of any event E ranges from 0, if E is the null set or an impossible event, to 1, if E is equal to S, the sample space, which represents a certainty.

(6.15) $P(S) = 1$.

This means the probability of a sample space is 1, since S is a certainty—an event that is bound to occur.

(6.16) $P(A \cup B) = P(A) + P(B)$.

This is the *special additive rule* for mutually exclusive events. This rule states that if A and B are mutually exclusive, then the probability that either A or B will occur is the sum of their separate probabilities.

(6.17) $P(E_1 \cup E_2 \cup \ldots \cup E_k) = P(E_1) + P(E_2) + \cdots + P(E_k)$.

This is the extension of the additive rule to k disjoint events. From this extension, we see that $P(E_1 \cup E_2 \cup \cdots \cup E_k) = P(S) = 1$. This states that if the k events are mutually exclusive and exhaustive, then the k events are said to form a partition of the sample space S.

(6.18) $P(A \cup B) = P(A) + P(B) - P(A \cap B)$.

The *general additive rule* for two overlapping, or joint, events states that if A and B are not mutually exclusive, then the probability that either A or B will occur is the sum of their separate probabilities less the probability that both A and B will occur. If $P(A \cap B)$ is not deducted from $P(A) + P(B)$, then we would have counted the intersection AB twice.

(6.19) $P(A \cup B \cup C) = P(A) + P(B) + P(C) - P(A \cap B) - P(A \cap C)$
$$- P(B \cap C) + P(A \cap B \cap C).$$

This is the additive rule for three joint events. It is interesting to note the necessity of the last term in this formula.

(6.20) $P(\emptyset) = 0.$

Since the null set is empty, it represents an impossible event. Its probability of occurrence is 0.

(6.21) $P(A) = 1 - P(\bar{A}).$

A and $\bar{A}$ are complementary events and their union is the sample space. Thus, $P(A) = P(S) - P(\bar{A}) = 1 - P(\bar{A}).$

(6.22) $P(B \mid A) = \dfrac{P(A \cap B)}{P(A)}.$

The *conditional probability of B given A* is the joint probability of A and B divided by the marginal probability of A. This formula requires that $P(A) \neq 0$. Note that the denominator of a conditional probability is always the probability of the "conditional event." For example, $P(A \mid B) = P(B \cap A)/P(B)$. Also note that while $P(A \cap B) = P(B \cap A)$; $P(A \mid B)$ and $P(B \mid A)$ may not be equal, since $P(A)$ and $P(B)$ may be different.

(6.23) $P(A \cap B) = P(A)P(B).$

This is the *special rule of multiplication*. It says that if A and B are independent events, then the probability of their joint occurrence is the product of their marginal probabilities. Note that A and B are independent if and only if (6.23) holds. The application of this rule also requires that $A \neq \emptyset$.

(6.24) $P(A \cap B) = P(A)P(B \mid A).$

This is called the *general rule of multiplication,* which is applicable for dependent as well as independent events, since for independent events, $P(B \mid A) = P(B)$ and $P(A \mid B) = P(A)$. For (6.24) to hold, $P(A) > 0$. Furthermore, if $P(A) = P(A \mid B)$ and $P(B) = P(B \mid A)$, then (2.24) reduces to (6.23).

(6.25) $P(E) = \sum P(H)P(E \mid H).$

The marginal probability of E, by the theorem of elimination, is defined as the sum of a set of joint probabilities. Here, the summation is over all the k mutually exclusive and collectively exhaustive events H_i—events that form a partition of S.

(6.26) $P(A \cap B \cap C) = P(A)P(B)P(C).$

This is an extension of (6.23) for three independent events. For this formula to hold, *A, B,* and *C* must also be pairwise-independent. As a matter of fact, (6.23) can be extended to any number of independent events with similar restrictions (requirements) as for three events.

(6.27) $P(A \cap B \cap C) = P(A)P(B \mid A)P(C \mid A \cap B)$.

This is an extension of (6.24) for three dependent events. This rule can be extended to any number of events similar to this case without any restrictions.

REVIEW QUESTIONS

6.1 What is the meaning of uncertainty?

6.2 How is a random experiment defined?

6.3 In what sense do we say that probability is the foundation of modern statistics?

6.4 What is a factorial, such as 15!?

6.5 What is the difference between a permutation and a combination? What are the restrictions on the use of the formulas?

6.6 How are $_NC_n$ and $_NP_{(n,N-n)}$ related? Use a numerical example of your own to verify this relationship.

6.7 What is the symmetric property of combinations? Explain and demonstrate the validity of this property by a numerical example.

6.8 What is the difference between selecting (sampling) with replacement and selecting (sampling) without replacement?

6.9 On a particular Sunday evening, the weatherman of a national T.V. station included the following in his forecast for New York City. "The probability of precipitation is 25% for Monday." According to objective probability, can you argue that the quotation is nonsense because the event of precipitation on the Monday is unique and therefore, cannot have a probability calculated for it? Try to find a way of making sense out of the quotation—and of justifying the numerical choice of 25%—using objective probability.

6.10 How is a sample space defined? Why should we work with a sample space before directly tackling a probability question?

6.11 Can there be two or more sample spaces for an experiment, all of which are correct? Give an example of your own.

6.12 How is an event defined? What do we mean by (1) a simple event, (2) a compound event, (3) the complement of an event, (4) the union of two events, and (5) the intersection of two events?

6.13 How do we differentiate mutually exclusive events from overlapping events? Use Venn diagrams to illustrate the difference.

6.14 What is a partition of a sample space?

6.15 Are joint and overlapping events the same? Why or why not?

6.16 Two dice are rolled. What is the sample space of the sum of the two dice? Draw a two-dimensional diagram to represent this sample space; then define three events A, B, and C, such that
   a. A and B are complementary events.
   b. A and C are mutually exclusive events.
   c. B and C are overlapping events.

6.17 How is the mathematical probability of an event E defined? What are the three rules that must be satisfied if $P(E)$ is to be a probability?

6.18 How is the probability of an event defined by the classicists, relative-frequency theoreticians and subjectivists, respectively? In what sense may we consider these three schools of thought as complementary to each other, rather than as substitutes for each other?

6.19 Cite examples of your own to illustrate how an event probability is assigned by the classical, relative-frequency and subjective theories, respectively.

6.20 How are odds converted to probabilities? For example, if you say the odds are 5 to 1 in favor of your football team's winning a conference championship, what is the probability that it will lose the championship?

6.21 How are probabilities converted to odds? For example, if a financial writer says he believes the probability is 0.80 that a particular corporation will overcome its current difficulties and return to profitability without going bankrupt, what is he saying the odds are in favor of the corporation in overcoming its difficulties?

6.22 The expression $P(A \cup B) = P(A) + P(B)$ always holds irrespective of what kind of event A and B are. Is this true? Explain your answer.

6.23 Let E and $\bar{E}$ be complementary events, then it would always be true that $P(E) = 1 - P(\bar{E})$. Is this correct? Why or why not?

6.24 Is it always true that $P(E) = n(E)/N(S)$ If not, when is it true and when is it not true?

6.25 How does a reduced sample space arise? How do we use it to calculate a conditional probability.

6.26 How are marginal and joint probabilities defined? What is the relationship between them?

6.27 Differentiate and illustrate the dependence and independence of two events. How are dependent and independent events generated, respectively?

6.28 Some economists believe that high wages cause inflation (the so-called cost-push theory) and some economists believe just the opposite: that inflation causes high wages (the so-called demand-pull theory). In any event, in your judgement, are high wages and inflation dependent or independent events? Or, neither? Justify your answer.

6.29 Some economists believe that high defense spending creates high federal deficit that, in turn, creates inflation. If these economists are right, are the three events statistically dependent? Could you provide a possible explanation for their conclusions?

6.30 Does the law $P(A \cap B) = P(A)P(B)$ hold all the time? If not, when does it and when does it not hold?

6.31 Under what conditions can we conclude that the four events $A, B, C,$ and D are statistically independent?

6.32 If A and B are mutually exclusive, are they also statistically independent? Explain.

6.33 If A and B are statistically independent, are they also mutually exclusive? Explain.

6.34 Why can we treat discrete infinite sample space the same way as a discrete finite sample space? Explain.

6.35 When we say $P(E) = 0$ with reference to a discrete sample space, we mean $E = \emptyset$. What does $P(E) = 0$ mean with reference to a continuous sample space? Also, how are events defined if the sample space is continuous? Give examples.

PROBLEMS

6.1 At a given hour, there are 5 drivers and 4 taxis in the garage of a taxi company. In how many different ways can one driver and one taxi be assigned to a job? Use a tree diagram to demonstrate the result.

6.2 A travel agency offers trips to 10 summer resorts either by air, by rail, or by bus. In how many different ways can such a trip be arranged?

6.3 How many automobile license plates can be made by using two letters followed by a four-digit number?

6.4 Find the number of license plates for the previous problem if repetition of a letter is not allowed.

6.5 How many different deals are there in a bridge game?

6.6 The director of the audit division of the Federal Internal Revenue Service has been given a list of 120,000 tax returns for examination. Because of staff shortage, only half of these returns can be reviewed during the next two months, a quarter of the returns can be referred to further study, and the rest must be filed for future action. In how many different ways can these 120,000 tax returns be arranged?

6.7 If S is a set such that $N(S) = h$, what is the number of ordered subsets of elements of S each containing k elements?

6.8 A consulting firm sends out teams of 3 men on certain types of jobs. It has a total force of 10 consultants. The first man selected is the leader of the team and the second man assigned is the assistant leader of the team. How many different teams can be formed?

6.9 A survey of economists is conducted to determine the appropriate policies for fighting inflation and unemployment in 1982. Each economist is asked to rank 5 policies from a list of 10 policies suggested by the investigator. How many differently ranked policies are possible from each economist?

6.10 A manufacturer receives a lot of 1000 metal parts, 100 of which are defective. The following acceptance decision rule is established: (1) a random sample of 30 parts is to be selected; (2) if more than 3 parts in the sample are defective, the entire lot is rejected; (3) otherwise, the lot is accepted.
a. How many different samples of 30 are possible under this decision rule?
b. How many of the possible samples will lead to the rejection of the lot?

6.11 Three items are drawn with replacement from a lot of merchandise. Each item is to be identified as defective or nondefective. List all the sample points for this experiment by means of a tree diagram.

6.12 A factory employs 60 female and 40 male workers. In order to discuss working conditions with the workers, the management would like to select 3 workers at random as representatives. How many sample points would (1) S_1 contain if the selection is made with replacement? (2) S_2 if the selection is made without replacement? Are the sample points in S_1 and S_2 equally likely? Explain your answer.

6.13 Continue with the preceding problem: If the sample points are given in terms of the number of male representatives and in terms of simple events, would you expect $N(S_1)$ to be different from $N(S_2)$? Why or why not? (Hint: In order not to miss any sample point, the best way to obtain the sample points is by way of a tree diagram.)

6.14 Many newspapers publish betting odds on future sporting events. The following example is for a horse race (the 8th race at Aqueduct on December 26, 1982):

Code	Horse	Odds	Code	Horse	Odds
A1	Hour of love	20–1	F6	Hitting Irish	12–1
B2	Tina Tin Too	5–1	G7	Posed	12–1
C3	French Flick	10–1	H8	Suspicious	20–1
D4	Cheap Seats	4–1	I9	Lady Dean	3–1
E5	Patella	8–1	J10	Fancy Noskra	5–1

Convert each of these 10 given odds to the probability of winning the race. (Note: Your probabilities should add to more than 1.00, to allow for betting taxes and the racetrack's operating expenses.)

6.15 Convert each of the following probabilities that an event will occur into odds: 0.10, 0.20, 0.30, 0.40, 0.50, 0.60, 0.70, 0.80, and 0.90. (Note: probabilities under 0.50 are usually converted to odds against, while probabilities over 0.50 are usually converted to odds in favor.)

6.16 A card is drawn from a well-shuffled bridge deck. What is the probability that it is an ace? A king of diamonds? A black card?

6.17 In a lot of 100 manufactured items, 7 are defective. An item is drawn at random from the lot; what is the probability that it is defective?

6.18 What is the probability that a sum of 7 or 11 will occur if a pair of fair dice are tossed?

6.19 Four MBA graduates, call them A, B, C and D, from your school are all applying for the same position at a financial firm. According to your judgment, A and B have even odds to be hired, the odds are 3 : 2 in favor of B comparing B to C, and the odds are 2 : 1 in favor of C compared to D. What are your subjective probabilities for each to get the job if your judgment is correct?

6.20 A marketing research firm is interested in the buying habits of families in Atlanta. The Anderson family is among those the firm is studying. The firm is interested in the Anderson's purchases of liquid detergents and scouring powders during the next three months. If it is found that the Andersons may buy up to four containers of liquid detergent and up to three cans of scouring powder during the said period of time, what is the sample space showing the amount of each product to be purchased. Present this sample space by a two-dimensional diagram. For simplicity, let us assume the sample points in S are equally likely. What is the probability that the Anderson family will purchase:
a. Four containers of liquid detergent and three cans of scouring powder?
b. Two containers of liquid detergent and two cans of scouring powder?
c. Three containers of liquid detergent or two cans of scouring powder?

6.21 Mr. Sanders holds a ticket in a lottery, sponsored by a church, that sells 10,000 tickets and that offers one first prize, two second prizes, and three third prizes. What is the probability that he will win the first prize? The second prize? The third prize? Any prize?

6.22 If a die is rolled, what is the probability that either an even number or a number divisible by 3 will occur?

6.23 Steel pipes produced by a certain process are considered to be acceptable if the diameters of the pipes are between 2.55 and 2.58 inches; otherwise they are considered defective units. One day's production has provided the following data:

Length of diameter	No. of steel pipes
Shorter than 2.55	26
Between 2.55 and 2.58	950
Longer than 2.58	24
Total	1,000

If one pipe is selected at random for observation, what is probability that it is an acceptable unit? An unacceptable unit?

6.24 A certain output is known to be subject to three types of defects, A, B, and C. Among 100 units produced one day, the inspector on the assembly line reported the following results.

Defect	No. of Pieces
A	30
B	35
C	20
A ∩ B	5
A ∩ C	5
B ∩ C	4
A ∩ B ∩ C	2

If an item is selected at random from the day's production, what is the probability that it is defective?

6.25 What is wrong with each of the following statements?
   a. The probability for John to pass this course is less than zero.
   b. The probability that a new restaurant will be profitable is 0.35, but it is three times as likely that it will suffer a loss.
   c. The probabilities for the three candidates for Governor of a given state to be victorious are 0.4, 0.5, and 0.3, respectively.

6.26 A movie producer feels that the odds are 8 to 1 his new movie will be rated R, 4 to 1 it will be rated as X, and 16 to 7 that it will receive neither of these two ratings. Are these odds consistent? Explain your answers.

6.27 There are three radar systems installed along the coast of Maine to detect incoming alien objects either from the air or from the sea. These systems function independently and each has a probability of 0.05 of failure. What is the probability that an incoming object is not detected by any of the three systems?

6.28 In accordance with the decision rule stated in Problem 6.10, what are the probabilities that the lot (a) will be accepted? (b) will not be accepted?

6.29 Determine the probabilities for the sample points in the sample spaces, S_1 and S_2, as stated in Problem 6.12.

6.30 Recall that three events, A, B, and C, are said to be completely independent if and only if the following two conditions are satisfied: (1) $P(A \cap B \cap C) = P(A)P(B)P(C)$; (2) all events are statistically independent in pairs.

    a. Let a fair die be rolled and, in this sample space, let A be an even number, B a number equal to or greater than 3, and C a number divisible by either 3 or 5 without remainder. Show that in this case, while $P(A \cap B \cap C) = P(A)P(B)P(C)$; A, B, and C are not completely independent.

    b. Two fair coins are tossed. If A is the event "head on the first coin," B is the event "head on the second coin," and C is the event "the coins match," show that A, B, and C are pairwise independent events, but they are not completely independent.

6.31 In a lot of 20 TV picture tubes, 5 are known to be defective. A random sample of 3 is selected without replacement. What is the probability of no defectives in the sample? Exactly one defective? Exactly two defectives? Three defectives?

6.32 Among 1000 students of a certain college, 100 are known to be registered as Republicans. If five students are selected at random with replacement, what is the probability of observing more than one registered Republican in the sample?

6.33 For the preceding problem, what is the desired probability if sampling is made without replacement? Can you explain the nearly identical results for these two problems?

6.34 A major American Oil Company, under the contract with the government of ROC is drilling test wells off the coast of Kowshung as well as off the coast of Keelung. It feels that the probability of oil at the first site is 0.55 and that at the second site is 0.85. Assuming statistical independence, calculate:

    a. P (both sites produce oil).

    b. P (exactly one site produces oil).

    c. P (neither site produces oil).

6.35 Of 800 radios shipped by truck, 100 had superficial damage only, 10 had major damage only, 20 had both types of damage, and the rest had no damage at all. If one radio is observed at random, what is the probability that

    a. it is in perfect condition?

    b. it had major damage?

    c. it has major or superficial damage?

6.36 A political scientist estimates the probability for President Reagan's re-election in 1984 to be 0.95 and the probability of a sizeable increase in defense expenditure during Reagan's second term to be 1.00. What would be the scientist's probability estimate that both events will occur?

6.37 One out of five potential customers entering a certain department store buys something there. Assuming statistical independence, what is the probability that none of the next five people entering the store will purchase nothing?

6.38 During a depressed year, the 1000 manufacturing workers in a certain town have been cross-classified as follows:

		Employed: E	Unemployed: U	Total
White:	W	500	150	650
Black:	B	250	100	350
Total		750	250	1000

If one worker is selected at random, find:
a. $P(E)$;
b. $P(U)$;
c. $P(W)$;
d. $P(B)$;
e. $P(E \mid W)$;
f. $P(U \mid W)$;
g. $P(E \mid B)$;
h. $P(U \mid B)$.

6.39 All things being equal, an individual's income increases with his age. If the probability that an individual is over 45 years and earns more than $35,000 a year is 0.15, and if the probability that an individual makes more than this figure is 0.25, what is the probability that an individual is over 45 years if his income exceeds $35,000?

6.40 A company is considering a site for a new plant. The probability that the site is satisfactory for raw material supply and finished product consideration is 0.70. Given the probability that the site is acceptable from the product-market aspect is 0.90, what is the probability that the site is acceptable from the materials supply point of view?

6.41 Two slates of candidates for the board of directors, A and B, are competing for control of a corporation. The probabilities that these two slates will win are 0.7 and 0.3, respectively. If A wins, the probability of introducing a new product is 0.8; and if B wins, the corresponding probability is 0.6. What is the probability that the new product will eventually be introduced?

6.42 A, B and C are bidding on a contract for the construction of a bridge in Boston. The probabilities that A, B and C will get the contract are 0.5, 0.3, and 0.2 respectively. If A gets it, he will select E as the subcontractor with probability 0.7. If B or C gets it, E will be chosen with probabilities of 0.6 and 0.4, respectively. Before the (main) contract is awarded, what is the probability that E will eventually get the subcontract?

6.43 Eight executives of a firm drive their cars to their office each day and park at one of three parking lots. If the lots are selected at random, what is the probability of having 5 of the 8 cars in one parking lot, 2 in another, and 1 yet in another on a given day?

6.44 Let the sample space be $S = \{X : 0 < x < 12\}$, where x is a real number and is selected at random. Given the following events:

$$A = \{x : x < 8\},$$
$$B = \{x : 6 < x < 9\},$$
$$C = \{x : x < 7\}.$$

Determine $P(A)$, $P(B)$, $P(C)$, $P(A \cup B)$, $P(B \cup C)$, $P(A \cup C)$, $P(A \cap B)$, $P(B \cap C)$, and $P(A \cap C)$.

6.45 Consider the stopwatch example in the text. What are the following probabilities?
   a. $P(5 < T < 10)$.
   b. $P[(0 \leq T \leq 2) \text{ or } (7 \leq T \leq 9)]$.
   c. $P(T \leq 8)$.
   d. $P[(0 < T < 4) \text{ and } (2 < T < 5)]$.

7 Random Variables and Probability Distributions

This chapter is a continuation of the study of probability theory. Probability theory encompasses much more than just calculating probabilities of various isolated events by the basic theorems introduced in the previous chapter. Indeed, the application of probability theory and statistics to decision making springs from the need for procedures that will enable decision makers to analyze complex relationships among events in a precise and orderly way. Logical treatment of such relationships, as in pure mathematics, is accomplished by means of the notion of "functions". In fact, in any scientific study, the concept of function is so important that, without it, little progress can be made in the use of mathematics for real-world problems.

Throughout this text, we shall introduce many types of mathematical functions related to probability and statistics. In this chapter, we provide a general presentation of two basic statistical functions: random variables and probability distributions. Then, in the next two chapters, we take up some special random variables and their distributions that are encountered frequently in real-world situations.

7.1 RANDOM VARIABLES

There are at least two popular ways to define random variables. The first is related to the classical and relative-frequency interpretations of probability. As such, it is only natural that a random variable was originally formulated in terms of a clearly delineated sample space or in terms of a well-defined random process. In the previous chapter, we saw how events can be defined on a sample space. Some events are numerical and others are qualitative. In analyzing such events, it is generally preferable that they be numerical in nature, since this facilitates mathematical manipulations. To achieve this, we may assign a number to each sample point on the sample space. The rule we use in assigning a specific value to each and every sample point in a sample space is a *random variable*. Alternatively, we say that a *random variable* is a real-valued function defined on a sample space. To say the same thing in a more intuitive manner, a *random variable* is simply a quantity that has a set of values that are derived from a sample space. Consider now some examples in accordance with this definition.

Example 1 The Number of Heads

Suppose two coins are tossed, we would have the following sample space:

$$S\{(H, H), (H, T), (T, H), (T, T)\}.$$

The sample points in this S are qualitatively described. Let us now define on this S a random variable called, say, the number of heads in tossing two coins and denote it by X. To define X here is to convert the qualitative sample points into numerical values by counting the number of heads in S. Such a *count* is a random variable, since it assigns a numerical value to each of the sample points in S. We can express this functional relationship between the count and S in the following way:

$$X = \begin{cases} 0 & (T, H), \\ 1 & \text{for} \quad (T, H) \quad \text{or} \quad (H, T), \\ 2 & (H, H). \end{cases}$$

This functional relationship is illustrated graphically by Figure 7.1, which shows the mapping of a sample space into the range of a

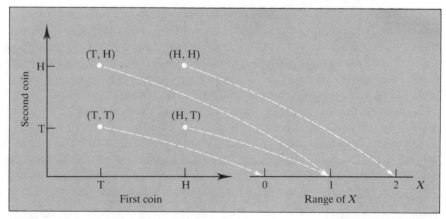

FIGURE 7.1 Mapping the sample points in a sample space into the range of a random variable.

random variable. In general, the set of all possible values that a random variable can assume is called the *range*. For our current example, the range for X is $\{0, 1, 2\}$.

Example 2 The Sum of Rolling Two Dice

If a crap shooter's point is 5, then his only interest in the next roll of the two dice would be that the sum of the two dice be equal to 5, irrespective of how each of the dice turns up. Thus, we would adopt the rule of describing the outcome of a roll by adding the number of spots appearing on the upper faces of the two dice. Let Y be the quantity (sum) defined by this *rule*; Y is then a random variable. The S on which Y is defined, the range of Y, and the number of sample points corresponding to each possible value of Y are as shown in Table 7.1. After brief inspection of Table 7.1, the following observations, which are true in all cases about the relationship between random variables and sample spaces, can be made.

1. Each sample point is assigned a specific possible value of the random variable, though the same specific value can be assigned to two or more sample points.

2. Each possible value of a random variable is an event, since it is a subset defined on a sample space.

3. All the values of a random variable constitute a set of events that are mutually exclusive and completely exhaustive; that is, they form a partition of S.

The second way of defining a random variable is influenced by the subjective interpretation of probability. Now a *random variable* is simply considered as an uncertain quantity—a quantity whose value is not known with certainty. Reflecting on this definition for a moment, you will conclude that it is quite consistent with the previous one. For example, suppose our crap shooter mentioned before is about to roll the

TABLE 7.1 Defining Y: The Sum of Rolling Two Dice

Range of Y: Sum of Spots	Number of Sample Points	Corresponding Sample Points in S
2	1	$(1, 1)$
3	2	$(1, 2), (2, 1)$
4	3	$(1, 3), (2, 2), (3, 1)$
5	4	$(1, 4), (2, 3), (3, 2), (4, 1)$
6	5	$(1, 5), (2, 4), (3, 3), (4, 2), (5, 1)$
7	6	$(1, 6), (2, 5), (3, 4), (4, 3), (5, 2), (6, 1)$
8	5	$(2, 6), (3, 5), (4, 4), (5, 3), (6, 2)$
9	4	$(3, 6), (4, 5), (5, 4), (6, 3)$
10	3	$(4, 6), (5, 5), (6, 4)$
11	2	$(5, 6), (6, 5)$
12	1	$(6, 6)$
Total	36	—

dice. He is not sure at all which sum is actually going to occur. Clearly, the sum is a random variable that satisfies the first as well as the current definition. However, many students find it easier to think of random variables as uncertain quantities produced by chance or randomness. For instance, intuitively, you should not have any difficulty in identifying the number of customers arriving at a teller's window in a bank during lunch hour each day, the sales of cars of a car dealer each week, the number of people visiting the Museum of Natural History in New York City each weekend, the number of defective items in each day's production run of a certain output, and so on, as random variables, without the sample space in each case being explicitly and formally specified. This is just fine. You must now be advised, however, that whichever definition you use, you should always keep in mind that for each random variable there is always an underlying appropriate sample space.

Let us try to bring out some additional implications of random variables by considering in detail a more realistic and slightly more complex example.

Example 3 Daily Sales of TV Sets

Suppose a television shop has been open for the last 300 business days. Let the experiment be that of randomly choosing one day's sales tickets. (In practice, the experiment would be that of choosing a few day's sales tickets at random and then analyzing what had been drawn into such a sample of days. The motive might be auditing the accounting system to see how accurately it records sales activity, or a special study of sales that goes into more detail than is provided by the shop's regular financial reports). In the simple case of choosing one day's sales tickets, the sample space would have 300 points in it, each point consisting of a day's sales tickets.

Many different random variables can be defined over this sample space. One possible random variable is the number of sales tickets, another is total revenue, another is the number of TV sets sold, and so on. We can define our random variable so that it is relevant to whatever problem we are trying to solve, and we can define several random variables over the same sample space if we need to. Suppose the objective here is to predict future demand for TV sets by analyzing daily sales from the past. Suppose the random variable Q is defined as one day's sales of TV sets; then Q will have some range. Suppose also that the daily sales are 0, 1, 2, 3, 4, 5, or 6 TV sets: the range of Q is $\{0, 1, 2, 3, 4, 5, 6\}$.

Observe the contrast between 300 piles of daily slips and the random variable Q, which varies in value between 0 and 6. Obviously, it is much more convenient and easier to analyze Q than the points in S. This is a major reason for defining random variables and then working with them instead of working merely with the points in S. Of course, a random variable describes only some particular feature of the sample points in S, so we must choose the random variable or random variables with great care to assure that relevant features of a sample space are properly considered.

A comment on notation is appropriate here. As usual, we use capital letters for random variables and lower-case letters for values of random variables. In this connection, we may often say that the random variable equals some numerical value such as, say, in $Q = 4$ for the television shop example. Or, we may often state something such as $Q = q$, where Q stands for the random variable and q stands for a particular, but unspecified, value that Q can take. It is important to note that statements such $Q = 4$ and $Q = q$ should not be taken literally, because each is a shorthand way of stating something more complicated; namely applying the rule Q to a point in S, resulting in the number 4 or in the unspecified, but possible, value of q.

Finally, we may point out that a random variable may be discrete or continuous. A *discrete random variable* is one that takes on only a finite, or a countably infinite, number of values. We have so far been concerned only with discrete random variables. A *continuous random variable* is one that can take on any real value within a specified range. An example of a continuous random variable is the time taken for one telephone conversation chosen at random from a day's telephone calls, provided that time is regarded as measurable to any degree of accuracy. In the sections that follow, we explore some useful properties of discrete random variables, one at a time first; then we discuss the various aspects of two or more associated discrete random variables; and then in Chapter 9, we provide a brief treatment of continuous random variables, in connection with our presentation of special continuous probability models.

7.2 PROBABILITY DISTRIBUTIONS FOR RANDOM VARIABLES

As has been pointed out, all the possible values a random variable can assume are events defined over a sample space. As events, they must have probabilities. Thus if X is a random variable that can assume K possible values, then corresponding to each of the K values there is a probability associated with it. Let x_i and p_i represent the possible values of X and their associated probabilities respectively. The set of ordered pairs (x_i, p_i), $i = 1, 2, \ldots$, is called the *probability distribution* of the random variable X. When X is discrete, its probability distribution is often called a *probability mass function*, which abbreviates to PMF. In order to determine more readily the probabilities associated with the values of a random variable, we can express the PMF of a random variable in a more obvious and practical manner. If we denote by $f(x)$ the probability that the random variable will assume the value x; then the PMF of X can be written as

$$f(x) = P(X = x). \tag{7.1}$$

TABLE 7.2 PMF of X; The Number of Heads in Tossing Two Coins

x:	0	1	2	Total
$f(x)$:	1/4	2/4	1/4	4/4

To be qualified as a PMF, (7.1) must satisfy

(1)
$$f(x) \geq 0,$$

(2)
$$\sum f(x) = 1.$$

Here, the summation is over all the K probability values of X.

Probability mass functions are often presented as tables. Using the random variables introduced in the previous section as examples, we see that if the coins are fair, then Table 7.2 presents the PMF of X—the number of heads in tossing two coins. Similarly, if the dice are perfect, then Table 7.3 presents the PMF of Y—the sum of rolling two dice. Finally, consider the random variable Q—the daily sales of TV sets. Suppose every day's pile of sales tickets were examined and we found that 30 days had no sales, 60 days had 1 sale each, 90 days had 2 sales each, 60 days had 3 sales each, 36 days had 4 sales each, 18 days had 5 sales each, and 6 days had 6 sales each. Then, when we select one day's sales tickets at random, the probability of getting a day with no sales is $P(Q = 0) = 30/300 = 0.10$; the probability of getting a day with 1 sale is $P(Q = 1) = 60/300 = 0.20$; and so on. Table 7.4 presents the complete probability distribution of Q.

Note that the probabilities in Tables 7.2, 7.3 and 7.4 are objective probabilities. Furthermore, those for X and Y are classical probabilities and those for Q are relative frequencies. Probabilities assigned to the values of a random variable can also be subjective, as the following example shows.

TABLE 7.3 PMF of Y: The Sum of Rolling Two Dice

y:	2	3	4	5	6	7	8	9	10	11	12	Total
$f(y)$:	1/36	2/36	3/36	4/36	5/36	6/36	5/36	4/36	3/36	2/36	1/36	36/36

TABLE 7.4 PMF of Q: Daily Sales of TV Sets When One Day is Observed at Random

q:	0	1	2	3	4	5	6	Total
$f(q)$:	0.10	0.20	0.30	0.20	0.12	0.06	0.02	1.00

Example 4 Inflation Rate in the 1980s

Suppose that, in the spring of 1981, a Wall Street economist is trying to predict the average rate of inflation during the 1980s. Of course, the sample space has many many points on it because there are so many possibilities for the state of the U.S. economy in the 1980s. The Wall Street economist is concentrating on just one of the many random variables that could be defined over this sample space, namely the average rate of inflation from the price level of 1980 to the price level of 1990. Let I be this random variable. Instead of working with the sample space to get the probability distribution of I, the economist finds it convenient to work directly with the probabilities of the various values of I. He believes that under one of President Reagan's economic plans, of fighting inflation with tight money policy and deep cuts into many types of expenditure for social services, the double-digit inflation rate in the 1970s will most probably not continue during the 1980s. He decides to concentrate on 4 values of I (3%, 5%, 7% and 9%) as possible values of the average annual rate of inflation. Let the probabilities of each of these inflation rates be p_1, p_2, p_3, and p_4, respectively. The economist believes that the rates of 3% and 9% are equally likely—in other words, that $p_4 = p_1$. He also believes that the 5% rate is three times as likely as the 3% rate (that is, $p_2 = 3p_1$), and that the 7% rate is twice as likely as the 3% rate (that is, $p_3 = 2p_1$). Of course, the four probabilities must add to 1, so

$$p_1 + p_2 + p_3 + p_4 = 1.$$

Substituting for p_2, p_3 and p_4, we obtain

$$p_1 + 3p_1 + 2p_1 + p_1 = 1,$$

from which it follows that $7p_1 = 1$ and therefore $p_1 = 1/7$. Then

$$p_2 = 3p_1 = \frac{3}{7}; \quad p_3 = 2p_1 = \frac{2}{7}; \quad \text{and} \quad p_4 = p_1 = \frac{1}{7}.$$

The probability distribution of I is shown in Table 7.5.

The probabilities in Table 7.5, being subjective in nature, express the economist's degrees of belief in the various possible rates of inflation. Different economists, faced with the same amount and type of information, may assign entirely different probabilities from those shown in Table 7.5. Nevertheless, different decision makers of the subjective school of thought must observe the following two conventions in assigning probabilities to the values of a random variable: (1) none of

TABLE 7.5 PMF of I: Inflation Rate in the 1980s

i:	3%	5%	7%	9%	Total
$f(i)$:	1/7	3/7	2/7	1/7	7/7

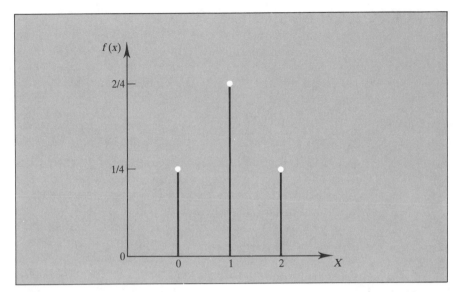

FIGURE 7.2 Graph of the PMF for number of heads in tossing two coins. (*Source:* Table 7.2.)

the values should have a probability of 0 or 1 and; (2) the sum of the probabilities assigned to all the values must equal 1. Much more can be said about the subject of determining the numerical values of subjective probabilities, but we will delay our discussion of this topic until we take up Bayesian statistics much later.

The probability distribution of a random variable can also be presented graphically. For discrete random variables, the graphs are usually in the form of vertical line or bar charts, with probabilities, $f(x)$ or $P(X = x)$, plotted on the vertical scale and the values of the random variable on the horizontal scale. Figures 7.2, 7.3 and 7.4 are vertical line

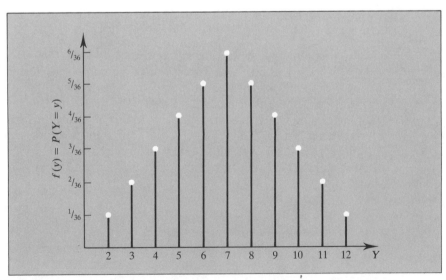

FIGURE 7.3 The PMF for the sum of rolling two dice. (*Source:* Table 7.3.)

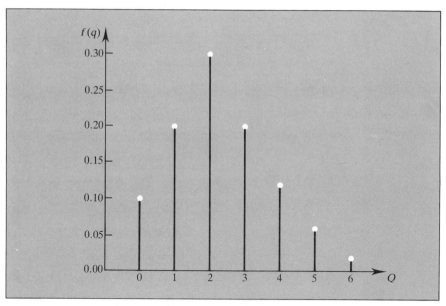

FIGURE 7.4 The PMF for daily sales of TV sets. (*Source:* Table 7.4.)

charts for our illustrative examples of random variables X, Y and Q. There are other correct ways of graphing PMFs. Chapter 2, on graphs, applies to graphs of probability distributions just as it does to any other graph.

The PMF of a random variable can be presented algebraically as well as tabularly or graphically. An algebraic presentation gives a function that shows, for each value in the range of the random variable, what the probability is for that value. For example, consider the random variable Y in Table 7.3. We see that for each value of Y in the first row there is an associated probability shown in the second row. Thus, the second row can be considered as a function of the first row. This functional relationship can be expressed algebraically as

$$f(y) = \begin{cases} (y-1)/36, & \text{if } y = 2, 3, 4, 5, 6; \\ (13-y)/36, & \text{if } y = 7, 8, 9, 10, 11, 12; \\ 0, & \text{elsewhere.} \end{cases}$$

7.3 THE CUMULATIVE MASS FUNCTION

In connection with random variables, we often need to ask questions such as "What is the probability that a random variable will assume a value equal to or less than a particular prescribed number of interest?" The answer to such a question, similar to the case of empirical distributions, is given by the *cumulative distribution function,* which, for a discrete case, is also called the *cumulative mass function* and is abbreviated to CMF. Formally, the CMF of a discrete random variable is defined as follows. If X is a discrete random variable and x is any real

TABLE 7.6 PMF and CMF for Q

q	$f(q)$	$F(q)$
0	0.10	0.10
1	0.20	0.30
2	0.30	0.60
3	0.20	0.80
4	0.12	0.92
5	0.06	0.98
6	0.02	1.00
Total	1.00	—

Source: Table 7.4.

number, then the CMF of X, denoted as $F(x)$, showing the probability that X takes on a value equal to or less than x, is

$$F(x) = P(X \le x) = \sum_{x_i \le x} f(x). \tag{7.2}$$

Here, $x_i \le x$ attached to the summation sign says that the value of $F(x)$ corresponding to x is just the sum of the probabilities of the possible values of X that lie below and at the value x. Thus, a CMF is immediately defined from the corresponding PMF of a random variable. Table 7.6, for instance, shows the CMF for Q—the daily sales of TV sets, obtained by applying (7.2).

In a sense, Table 7.6 is incomplete, because a CMF has nonzero values for additional values of Q beside those presented in the table. For example, we should have $P(Q \le 1/2) = 0.10$, $P(Q \le 95/100) = 0.10$, $P(Q \le 2) = 0.30$, and so on. However, it is assumed from the context that these statements are true, and many others like them, so no additional entries are needed in Table 7.6. If you still have doubt on this point, consider $P(Q \le \sqrt{2})$. We obtain this cumulative probability by adding the probabilities for all values of the random variable that possess the specified property. Here, this specified property is $Q \le \sqrt{2}$. Since $\sqrt{2} \doteq 1.414$, there are two values of Q—0 and 1—having this property. From Table 7.6, we see that $P(Q \le 1) = 0.30$; hence, $P(Q \le \sqrt{2})$ is also 0.30.

Graphs of CMFs often have vertical jumps in them, producing a staircase appearance. In fact, a function of this type is often referred to as a *step function*, because such a graph looks like a set of steps. Figure 7.5 illustrates this graphical pattern for the CMF of Q in Table 7.6. This graph shows that the CMF starts at $-\infty$ on the horizontal axis, although its vertical height is always between 0 and 1 inclusive. Every CMF ranges from $-\infty$ to $+\infty$, with its height between 0 and 1.

Cumulative mass functions can be presented algebraically, too. There is no convenient algebraic expression of the CMF for the TV sales example, but there is for the simple random variable D when a fair die is rolled. In this case, each of the six possible values of D has a

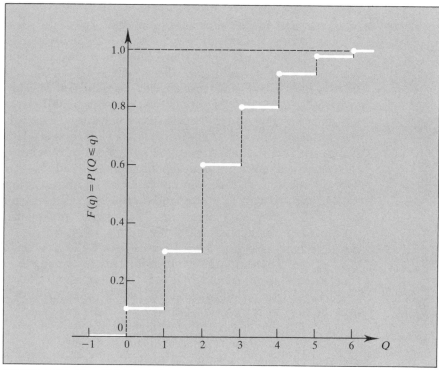

FIGURE 7.5 The CMF for daily sales of TV sets. (*Source:* Table 7.6.)

probability of 1/6. To state the CMF for D algebraically, we have

$$F(d) = P(D \leq d) = \frac{d}{6}, \quad \text{for } d = 1, 2, 3, 4, 5, 6.$$

To summarize, we may observe that a CMF must possess the following properties.

1. $0 \leq F(x) \leq 1$.

2. $F(a) \leq F(b)$, if $a < b$.

3. $F(\infty) = P(X \leq \infty) = 1$ and $F(-\infty) = P(X \leq -\infty) = 0$.

Please note that property (2) implies that a CMF is a nondecreasing function and that, if $a \leq b$, $P(a \leq X \leq b) = F(b) - F(a)$. This last result, as we shall see, enables us to obtain the probabilities of the individual terms (values) of random variables from probability tables that are cumulatively arranged.

7.4 EXPECTED VALUES OF RANDOM VARIABLES

We discussed in Chapters 4 and 5 how a sample or a population can be characterized by various descriptive measures applied to its distribution. The descriptive measures were specified in terms of central tendency, dispersion, skewness, and peakedness. In a similar manner, the properties of a random variable can be described in terms of its probability distribution. Furthermore, this is done by applying the same measures, such as the mean, the variance, the standard deviation, the fractile, and so on, to a probability distribution. In our discussion of descriptive measures for random variables, we shall stress the mean as a measure of central tendency and the variance (or its related measure, the standard deviation) as a measure of dispersion. This emphasis is due to the fact that the mean and variance of a random variable are of the greatest importance in decision making procedures. The mean is the subject matter of this section; variance is that of the next. Other measures of central tendency and dispersion will be taken up briefly in Section 7.7. Summary measures of skewness and peakedness will be presented in connection with the notion of "moments" of probability distributions in Section 7.8.

Before we begin the immediate task at hand, let us make two observations that are relevant to the discussion that follows. First, frequency distributions presented in Chapter 3 are called *empirical distributions* in the sense that they are distributions of the observed or realized values of variables. Probability distributions, however, are referred to as *theoretical distributions* in the sense that they are deduced by logical reasoning. Alternatively, a probability distribution is theoretical, because it shows how the total probability of 1 is distributed among all the possible values of a random variable, and these values are what we may expect to occur when an experiment is performed. Thus, a probability distribution is predictive in nature and this is the reason why it can aid us in making decisions under conditions of uncertainty.

Second, an empirical distribution may be constructed from a set of sample data or that of population data; but a theoretical distribution is always a population distribution, because a random variable is considered as a population. A random variable is a population in that it takes on all the possible outcomes of a random process as its values. Another way of saying the same thing is that the possible values of a random variable exhaust all the sample points in a sample space that is a universal set. Thus, descriptive measures for random variables are called, by statistical convention, parameters.

The Meaning of Expected Value

The mean of a random variable is called by many names, such as the *expected value,* the *mathematical expectation,* or the *expectation.* The expected value is the most frquently employed term. The *expected value* of a random variable X is a weighted average of the values that X can assume with probabilities for the values of X as weights. Thus, let X be a random variable with PMF $f(x)$; the expected value of X, denoted as $E(X)$ or μ_X, is then by definition

$$E(X) = \mu_X = x_1 f(x_1) + x_2 f(x_2) + \cdots + x_K f(x_K)$$

$$= \sum x f(x).$$

(7.3)

Applying (7.3) to the random variables presented in Tables 7.2, 7.3, 7.4 and 7.5, we have the following.

1. For the number of heads in tossing two coins

$$E(X) = \mu_X = \sum xf(x)$$

$$= 0(1/4) + 1(2/4) + 2(1/4) = 1 \text{ head.}$$

2. For the sum of rolling two dice

$$E(Y) = \mu_Y = \sum yf(y)$$

$$= 2(1/36) + 3(2/36) + \cdots + 12(1/36) = 7 \text{ points.}$$

3. For the daily sales of TV sets

$$E(Q) = \mu_Q = \sum qf(q)$$

$$= 0(0.10) + 1(0.20) + \cdots + 6(0.02) = 2.3 \text{ sets.}$$

4. For the inflation rate in the 1980s

$$E(I) = \mu_I = \sum if(i)$$

$$= 3(1/7) + 5(3/7) + 7(2/7) + 9(1/7) = 5.86\%.$$

The expected value, as a measure of central tendency, tells us where the center of the mass of the probability distribution of a random variable is located. It is also the average value of a random variable if the same random experiment is repeated over and over again. As such the expected value need not be a possible value of the random variable, as $E(Q)$ or $E(I)$ above illustrates.

The expected value is a very basic concept and is employed in decision theory, management science, systems analysis, game theories, and many other fields of intellectual endeavor. Some of these applications will be discussed in future chapters in this text. Meanwhile, in order to enable you to have a better understanding and deeper appreciation of this measure, let us consider one more realistic example. Suppose the probability that a house of a certain type will burn down in any 12-month period is 0.004. An insurance company offers to sell the owner of such a house a $120,000 one-year-term fire-insurance policy for a premium of $690. What is the company's expected gain from such a contract?

The "gain" G here is a random variable with possible values of $690 if the house does not have a fire accident, and $-$119,310$ if the house burns down during the year covered by the policy, with probabilities of 0.996 and 0.004, respectively. With the statement of the problem, we see that, from the point of view for the company, we have

$$E(G) = (690)(0.996) + (-119,310)(0.004) = \$210.00.$$

The expected gain for an insurance policy of any kind must be positive for the insurance company in order to enable the company to pay for administrative and selling costs, and to build up reserves for paying its beneficiaries and policy holders. From the buyer's viewpoint, however, insurance, like any game of chance that is run for profit, has a negative expected value. Thus, it can be anticipated that, from the gamblers' viewpoints, the expected value for any game in a casino or lottery drawing is negative—no one can win from the gambling house or lottery issuing agent in the long run. Let us demonstrate this by taking the following example of lottery drawing in New York State.

The New York Lotto guarantees to award a minimum of $3,000,000 to the winner of the first prize. To win it, one must have all six winning numbers in the betting slip. These six numbers are selected at random without replacement from a total of 54 numbers. Thus, there are $_{54}C_6 = 25,827,166$ possible ways to select six numbers. Also, it is required to play at least two games for one dollar; that is, one has two chances out of 25,827,166 to win the first prize. Suppose you are one of those minimum players, how much do you expect to win per drawing?

Let the amount of winning per drawing be random variable W, which clearly has the two possible values of $-\$1$ (if you do not win) and $2,999,999 (if you do win). From the previous explanation of the lottery, the respective probabilities for these two values are 0.999999923 and $2(0.000000077) = 0.000000154$. Thus,

$$E(W) = (-1)(0.999999923) + (2,999,999)(0.000000154)$$

$$= -\$0.50.$$

This amount, a *minus* 50 cents, is the money you expect to win per drawing if you play the minimum number of two games (i.e., a dollar) each drawing over and over again. In other words, you are expected to lose 50 cents on the average per drawing if you continue to bet $1 in every drawing.

Our analysis of the New York Lottery is a simplified version of the game, since we left out a number of factors about the game in the study. First of all, the Lottery also offers 2nd, 3rd and 4th prizes with varying amounts of payoff. Secondly, $3,000,000 is often the minimum payoff for the first prize. It is often more than this because if there were no first prize winners in the previous drawings the prize money is rolled over to next drawings. For instance, one week in mid-summer of 1988, the award for the first prize was over $21,000,000! Finally, there may be more than one winner for each of the prizes. If this is the case, then each of the prizes is shared equally by the winners of that prize. In any event, even when all these and other minor factors have been included in our evaluation, the expected winning of this game is still negative.

Indeed, a lottery is a sure and easy way to raise money. No wonder many states in the Union are running the game today.

The Expected Value of a Function of a Random Variable

We have stated that the expected value is a very important decision parameter in a variety of situations, and we have seen that the expected value of a random variable is easily determined once its PMF is specified. In the process of making decisions, however, we may encounter a random variable, say, Y, whose PMF is not readily available. When this happens, we may find, though, that Y is functionally related to another variable, say, X, whose PMF is known. In such a case, the expected value of Y can be computed in terms of $f(x)$. Precisely, if $Y = g(X)$ and if $f(x)$ is known, then we have

$$E[g(X)] = \sum g(x)f(x). \tag{7.4}$$

It is important to note that $g(x)$ in (7.4) is not a PMF. It represents, instead, the values of Y in terms of X as specified by $Y = g(X)$, as the following example illustrates.

Dr. Santina Puzo is a psychiatrist. She practices at Sutton Place in New York City. The number of patients she sees each day is a random variable X that ranges in value from 5 to 10. Furthermore, past experience indicates that the PMF of X is as follows:

$$f(x) = \begin{cases} x/36, & \text{if } x = 5, 6, 7; \\ (15 - x)/36, & \text{if } x = 8, 9, 10; \\ 0, & \text{otherwise.} \end{cases}$$

Dr. Puzo's net income per day, Y, is also a random variable and it is related to X by the following functions:

$$Y = g(X) = \$10(X^2 - 2X + 5).$$

We wish to determine the expected net income per day for Dr. Puzo. First, from the two functions given above, we can determine $q(x)$ and $f(x)$ as shown below:

x:	5	6	7	8	9	10
$f(x)$:	5/36	6/36	7/36	7/36	6/36	5/36
$g(x)$:	$200	$290	$400	$530	$680	$850

Next, by (7.4), we see Dr. Puzo's daily expected net income is

$$E(Y) = E[g(X)] = \sum g(x)f(x)$$

$$= 200(5/36) + 290(6/36) + 400(7/36) + 530(7/36)$$

$$+ 680(6/36) + 850(5/36)$$

$$= \$488.33.$$

Properties of Expectations

There are a number of mathematical properties of expectations that can aid us to compute expected values with greater ease. We shall introduce these properties now via a simple random variable X with the following PMF:

x:	−1	0	2
$f(x)$:	0.3	0.1	0.6

For X, we have

$$E(X) = (-1)(0.3) + (0)(0.1) + (2)(0.6) = 0.9.$$

If we add a constant b to a random variable X, then the expectation of the new random variable $(X + b)$ has the same expectations as X, plus the constant. That is, $E(X + b) = E(X) + b$. For instance, if we add 3 to our illustrative random variable X, we have

$$E(X + 3) = (-1 + 3)(0.3) + (0 + 3)(0.1) + (2 + 3)(0.6) = 3.9$$

$$= E(X) + 3.$$

This relationship is just what we would expect, since if X is increased by b for all its values, it will be increased by b on the average.

Next, multiplication by a constant gives $E(aX) = aE(X)$. That is, if we multiply each value of X by a constant a, its average value will be multiplied a times. Consider, for instance, the expectation of the variable $3X$ for our illustrative problem. Clearly,

$$E(3X) = (-3)(0.3) + (0)(0.1) + (6)(0.6) = 2.7$$

$$= 3E(X).$$

Finally, the first two properties indicate that in multiplying X by a constant a and adding a constant b to the results, we multiply the mean of X by a and add b to the result. For example,

$$E(3X + 4) = (-3 + 4)(0.3) + (0 + 4)(0.1) + (6 + 4)(0.6) = 6.7$$

$$= 3E(X) + 4.$$

To formalize the foregoing discussion, we introduce an intuitively obvious theorem below.

THEOREM 7.1 MATHEMATICAL PROPERTIES OF EXPEC-TATION. *If X is a random variable with $E(X)$ and if a and b are any numerical constants, then the random variable $Y = aX + b$ would have its expectation defined as*

$$E(Y) = E(aX + b) = aE(X) + b. \tag{7.5}$$

From the above theorem, we can also understand that if X is a random variable with $E(X) = \mu_X$, then $E(X - \mu_X) = 0$. It is also clear that if X is a random variable and it can take on only a single value—a constant, say, c—then $E(X) = c$. You can easily verify these two conclusions in examples of your own.

7.5 VARIANCES AND STANDARD DEVIATIONS OF RANDOM VARIABLES

The expected value is useful in providing us with a picture of the long-run average result we expect when a random experiment is performed over and over again. However, it tells us nothing about how outcomes may disperse from one trial of the experiment to another. For this, we need measures of variability. We shall, in this section, introduce the two most important measures of dispersion for random variables: the variance and the standard deviation.

The Meaning of Variance

Let X be a random variable with mean $E(X) = \mu_X$; *the variance of X,* denoted as $V(X)$ or σ_X^2, is the mean of the squared deviations of X from its expectation. Symbolically,

$$V(X) = \sigma_X^2 = E(X - \mu_X)^2$$

$$= \sum (x - \mu_X)^2 f(x), \tag{7.6a}$$

where the summation is over all the K values of X. For actual computations, it is much more convenient to use the equivalent of (7.6a) expressed as

$$V(X) = E(X^2) - \mu_X^2. \tag{7.6b}$$

As illustrations of applying (7.6b), let us use information provided in Tables 7.2 through 7.5, inclusive, again.

1. For the number of heads in tossing two coins

$$V(X) = E(X^2) - \mu_X^2$$
$$= [0^2(1/4) + 1^2(2/4) + 2^2(1/4)] - 1^2 = 0.5.$$

2. For the sum of rolling two dice

$$V(Y) = E(Y^2) - \mu_Y^2$$
$$= [2^2(1/36) + 3^2(2/36) + \cdots + 11^2(2/36) + 12^2(1/36)]$$
$$- 7^2 \doteq 5.83.$$

3. For the daily sales of TV sets

$$V(Q) = E(Q^2) - \mu_Q^2$$
$$= [0^2(0.10) + 1^2(0.20) + \cdots + 6^2(0.02)] - (2.3)^2 = 2.05.$$

4. For the inflation rate in the 1980s

$$V(I) = E(I^2) - \mu_I^2$$
$$= [3^2(1/7) + 5^2(3/7) + 7^2(2/7) + 9^2(1/7)] - (5.86)^2 \doteq 3.23.$$

Properties of Variance

Unless we use a computer, the calculation of variances, even by (7.6b), is quite time-consuming if the values of the random variables are either very large or very small. To save time and effort, we rely upon a procedure that involves shifting the origin of the values of a variable and changing the unit of measurement—changing the scale.

We note, first, that if a random variable is always equal to a constant c, then its expectation will be c. Furthermore, such a variable will never differ from its expectation, and so the variation about this expectation will be zero, giving a variance of zero. Second, if we add a constant to a random variable X, then $E(X)$ will be increased by the same constant. However, the difference $[X - E(X)]$ remains unchanged and, therefore, $V(X)$ is unaffected by addition of the constant to X. Third, if we multiply each value of a random variable by a number, say, a, then we also multiply its expectation by a, so that the quantity $[X - E(X)]$ will be a times as large as before. The square $[X - E(X)]^2$ will evidently be a^2 times as large as before; that is, if $Y = aX$, then

$$[Y - E(Y)]^2 = [aX - aE(X)]^2$$
$$= [a(X - E(X))]^2$$
$$= a^2[X - E(X)]^2.$$

Consequently, if a random variable is multiplied by a constant a, the variance of the variable is multiplied by a^2. In particular, if a random variable is multiplied by $a = -1$, we have $V(-X) = V(X)$.

These observations are formalized by the theorem below.

THEOREM 7.2 MATHEMATICAL PROPERTIES OF THE VARIANCE. *If X is a random variable with $V(X) = \sigma_X^2$, and if a and b are any two numerical constants, then the variable $Y = aX + b$ would* *have as its variance*

$$V(Y) = V(aX + b) = \sigma_{aX+b}^2 = a^2 \sigma_X^2. \qquad (7.7)$$

As an example of applying (7.7) consider a random variable X with the following PMF:

x:	5050	5100	5150
$F(x)$:	0.1	0.4	0.5

To simplify the determination of $V(X)$, we first define a new random variable Y

$$Y = \frac{X - 5100}{50}$$

whose PMF is clearly given by

y:	-1	0	1
$f(y)$:	0.1	0.4	0.5

For Y, we have

$$E(Y) = (-1)(0.1) + (0)(0.4) + (1)(0.5) = 0.4,$$

$$E(Y^2) = (-1)^2(0.1) + (0)^2(0.4) + (1)^2(0.5) = 0.6,$$

and therefore the variance of Y is

$$\sigma_Y^2 = E(Y^2) - \mu_Y^2 = 0.6 - (0.4)^2 = 0.44.$$

Now, we may find σ_X^2 on the basis of σ_Y^2 by recalling that, from the definition of Y, we must have

$$X = 50Y + 5100.$$

Therefore, by (7.7),

$$\sigma_X^2 = \sigma_{50Y+5100}^2 = \sigma_{50Y}^2$$
$$= (50)^2 \sigma_Y^2 = 2500 \sigma_Y^2$$
$$= 2500(0.44) = 1100.$$

The reader should go through the example above, recalling various properties of variance at every step.

The Standard Deviation

For applications, it is more convenient to have a measure of variability in the original units instead of their square. This leads to the introduction of the standard deviation, which is simply the (positive) square root of the variance. If X is a random variable with $V(X) = \sigma_X^2$, then the standard deviation of X, denoted by σ_X, is

$$\sigma_X = \sqrt{V(X)}. \tag{7.8}$$

Corresponding to the properties of variance, we see that the following relations hold true for standard deviation:

$$\sigma_{cX} = |c|\, \sigma_X \tag{7.9}$$

and

$$\sigma_{X+c} = \sigma_X. \tag{7.10}$$

Can you give a verbal interpretation of each of these two expressions?

7.6 CHEBYSHEV'S INEQUALITY

To describe a probability distribution completely, we need to know the PMF of the random variable. Useful information about a PMF is provided if the expectation and standard deviation of the random variable are known. Difficulty arises when we attempt to interpret the value of the standard deviation. Intuitively, we see that a standard deviation measures the spread of a probability distribution. Thus, when σ is small, the probability is high that we will get a value close to the expectation; and when σ is large, we are more likely to get a value far away from the expectation. However, if we wish to be more specific than these rather vague statements, we must again rely upon Chebyshev's Inequality, which was introduced in Chapter 5 in connection with our attempt to interpret standard deviations for empirical distributions. For a probability distribution, this inequality can be stated in the following theorem.

THEOREM 7.3 CHEBSHEV'S INEQUALITY FOR PROBABILITY DISTRIBUTION. *If X is a random variable with finite expectation μ and finite standard deviation σ, then for any $h > 1$,*

$$P(|X - \mu| < h\sigma) \geq 1 - 1/h^2, \text{ or} \tag{7.11a}$$

$$P(|X - \mu| \geq h\sigma) \leq 1/h^2. \tag{7.11b}$$

There are several observations about (7.11) that can be made. First, (7.11a) says that the probability for X to take on a value x that is within $h\sigma$ of its expectation is at least $1 - (1/h^2)$, no matter what value h happens to have. While (7.11b) states that the probability that X assumes a value x outside the closed interval from $\mu - h\sigma$ to $\mu + h\sigma$ is never greater than $1/h^2$. These interpretations of Chebyshev's inequality reveal that the two forms of (7.11a) and (7.11b) are clearly consistent, since $(|x - \mu| < h\sigma)$ and $(|x - \mu| \geq h\sigma)$ are complementary events.

Second, if h is less than 1, then $1 - (1/h^2)$ is less than zero or $1/h^2$ is greater than 1, but we know that the probability of any event ranges from 0 to 1. In other words, Chebyshev's inequality is trivial for values of h less than 1. Thus, we use this inequality only when h is greater than 1.

Third, in the statement of Chebyshev's theorem it is required that both μ and σ be finite. This will always be the case when th number of values for X is finite.

Finally, the significance of Chebyshev's Inequality lies in its complete universality; it can be applied to any random variable. In the process of achieving such a general result, however, this inequality is not particularly tight in terms of the bound achieved on particular distributions. Thus, it does not provide a practical method of estimating probabilities, since the right-hand side of (7.11b) for example, is usually larger than the left-hand side. In this connection, it may be noted that this inequality does provide us with a convenient interpretation of the concept of variance (or standard deviation) and that it can be used to provide a simple proof for the law of large numbers in a later chapter.

Let us illustrate the application of Chebyshev's Inequality by way of an example. Consider a random variable X with the following probability distribution:

x:	1	2	3	4	5
$f(x)$:	0.1	0.1	0.2	0.3	0.3

What is the probability that is associated with values of X up to 2σ and 3σ, respectively, from its expectation? For X here, we have

$$\mu = 3.6 \quad \text{and} \quad \sigma = \sqrt{1.64} \doteq 1.28062.$$

For these values, we find that

(a)
$$P(|X - \mu| < 2\sigma) = P[(\mu - 2\sigma) < X < (\mu + 2\sigma)]$$
$$\doteq P(1.03876 < X < 6.16124)$$
$$= P(2) + P(3) + P(4) + P(5)$$
$$= 0.9,$$

which is much greater than $1 - 1/4 = 3/4$.

(b)
$$P(|X - \mu| < 3\sigma) \doteq P(-0.24186 < X < 7.44186)$$
$$= P(1) + P(2) + P(3) + P(4) + P(5)$$
$$= 1,$$

which is also greater than 8/9 as the Chebyshev Inequality dictates.

Consider another example. Suppose a report made by a city agency in New York states that there were more than 2000 restaurants in New York City that lost money in the year of 1984, and that the mean loss was $25,000, with a standard deviation of $3,000. The report, however, did not reveal how these losses were distributed. Now, if one of these restaurants is selected at random, what is the minimum probability that its loss was between $19,000 and $31,000? What is the maximum probability that its loss was either less than $17,500 or more than $32,500?

Here we have the random variable L whose expectation is $25,000 and standard deviation is $3,000. Clearly, $19,000 is $2\sigma_L$ below $E(L)$ and $31,000 is $2\sigma_L$ above $E(L)$. From (7.11a), we know that the probability that the loss of a randomly selected restaurant will fall within this range is at least $(1 - (1/2)^2) = 0.75$. Likewise, $17,500 and $32,500 are $2.5\sigma_L$ below and above $E(L)$, respectively. Hence, by (7.11b), we see that the probability that the loss of a randomly selected restaurant will fall outside this range is at most $1/(2.5)^2 = 0.16$.

7.7 ADDITIONAL MEASURES OF CENTRAL TENDENCY AND DISPERSION FOR RANDOM VARIABLES

Expectation, variance, and standard deviation, as you may recall from our discussion of descriptive measures for empirical distributions, are not the exclusive summary values of central tendency and dispersion. Two other common measures of central tendency are the median and the mode. Then there are measures of dispersion based on fractiles. There is also the average deivation for measuring variability.

The *median* of a random variable, $\tilde{x}_{.5}$, is a number such that $P(X \leqslant \tilde{x}_{.5}) \geqslant 0.5$ and $P(X \geqslant \tilde{x}_{.5}) \geqslant 0.5$. This definition implies that for a discrete random variable, there may or may not exist a unique value as *the* median. For example, in the case of tossing two coins, the median for the number of heads is 1, since

$$P(X \leqslant 1) = 3/4 \geqslant 0.5; \qquad P(X \geqslant 1) = 3/4 \geqslant 0.5.$$

However, in the case of rolling one die, we note that

$$P(D \leqslant 3) = 3/6 = 0.5, \qquad P(D \geqslant 3) = 4/6 > 0.5;$$
$$P(D \leqslant 4) = 4/6 > 0.5, \qquad P(D \geqslant 4) = 3/6 = 0.5.$$

Hence, either 3 or 4 may be considered as a median. In fact, for this case, any number in the closed interval between 3 and 4, inclusive, satisfies the definition of the median and, therefore, a median value for D.

The *mode* of a discrete random variable, $\tilde{x}_m$, if it exists, may be defined as the value of the random variable that has the highest probability of occurrence. Thus, for the number of heads in tossing two coins, $\tilde{x}_m = 1$ with the highest probability of 2/4 and, for the sum of rolling two dice, $\tilde{y}_m = 7$, with the highest probability of 6/36. However, the number of spots showing in rolling one die has no mode because all the six possible values of D have equal probabilities of 1/6 each.

Recall also that the median is but one of a family of descriptive measures based on the notion of fractiles. In Chapter 5, the fractile of a variable was defined as the lowest observed value such that the cumulative relative frequency for that value is at least equal to ϕ. Corresponding to this, for a probability distribution, the ϕ *fractile* can be defined as the smallest value of the random variable such that the cumulative probability for that value is at least ϕ. Namely, for a random variable X, the ϕ *fractile* is the smallest value of X that will satisfy $P(X \leq x) \geq \phi$. Now, since $P(X \leq x) = F(x)$, the ϕ *fractile* can also be defined as the smallest value of X for which $F(x) = \phi$. This leads to the conclusion that if we denote the ϕ fractile of the PMF of X by $\tilde{x}_\phi$, we have $F(\tilde{x}_\phi) \geq \phi$.

To illustrate how the ϕ fractile is determined for a discrete random variable, let us use the random variable Q in Table 7.6, where $F(q)$ is already given in the third column of the table. Suppose we wish to determine the 0.80 fractile for Q, we find in the $F(q)$ column $F(3) = 0.80$, hence the 0.80 fractile for Q is 3.

It is important to note that for discrete random variables, the cumulative probability of the ϕ fractile is usually not equal to ϕ exactly. For example, if we wish to obtain the 0.55 fractile for Q, we cannot find a cumulative probability for Q equal to 0.55 precisely in the $F(q)$ column of Table 7.6. However, we find that $F(1) = 0.30$ and $F(2) = 0.60$. From these observations, we see that 2 is the smallest q-value for which the cumulative probability is at least 0.55 and, by definition, 2 is the 0.55 fractile even though $F(2) = 0.60$. More often than not, in a discrete case, the actual cumulative probability of the ϕ fractile turns out to be greater than ϕ because probabilities for the values of a discrete random variable "jump" from one value to the next.

Consider those values of a random variable X that have probabilities greater than 0; then the range of X is simply the difference between the largest and smallest of these values. Again, when 0.25 and 0.75 fractiles are determined, we can compute the *interquartile range* of X as $\tilde{x}_{.75} - \tilde{x}_{.25}$. Similarly, with 0.10 and 0.90 fractiles available, we would have the *interpercentile* or *interdecile range* as $\tilde{x}_{.90} - \tilde{x}_{.10}$ or as $\tilde{d}_9 - \tilde{d}_1$. Obviously, all these measures correspond to those for empirical distributions.

Finally, the *average deviation* of a discrete random variable with mean μ is defined as the mean of the absolute deviations of X about μ. That is to say that here the average deviation is also an expected value and it may expressed algebraically as $E(|X - \mu|) = \sum (|x - \mu|)f(x)$. The summation here is over all the K possible values of X.

7.8 MOMENTS OF PROBABILITY DISTRIBUTIONS

Besides central tendency and variability, a PMF may be characterized by the degree of skewness and by the degree of peakedness, or kurtosis. Descriptive measures for these properties can be defined in terms of "moments" of a probability distribution. *Moments* are simply the expectation of different powers of the random variable. Thus, the kth moment of a discrete random variable X about the origin is defined as

$$E(X^k) = \sum x^k f(x).$$

The summation here is over all K values of X. We note that the first moment about the origin is the expected value of a random variable.

Moments can also be defined about any other fixed point. In particular, moments about the expectation are of special interest. For instance, the second moment about the mean,

$$\mu_2 = E[(X - \mu)^2],$$

is the variance of X. Just as the mean and the variance measure the location and dispersion of a distribution, respectively, so do higher moments measure other properties of a distribution. Thus,

$$\mu_3 = E[(X - \mu)^3],$$

the third moment about the mean, can be used to determine whether a distribution is symmetric or skewed. Since all deviations in μ_3 are cubed, negative and positive deviations will tend to cancel each other out, giving $\mu_3 = 0$, if the distribution is symmetric about μ. If the distribution is skewed to the right, then $\mu_3 > 0$. On the other hand, given a left (negatively) skewed distribution, we would have $\mu_3 < 0$. Note that μ_3 alone is a rather poor measure of skewness, since the size of μ_3 is influenced by the units used to measure the values of X. To eliminate the dimensionality of X, we may form a relative measure defined as (μ_3/σ^3).

1. When $\mu_3/\sigma^3 = \pm 1$, the distribution is highly skewed.

2. When $0.5 < |\mu_3/\sigma^3| < 1$, the distribution is moderately skewed.

3. When $0 < |\mu_3/\sigma^3| < 0.5$, the distribution is nearly symmentric.

The fourth moment about the expectation,

$$\mu_4 = E[(X - \mu)^4],$$

is always positive and it can be used to reflect the degree of peakedness. Again, we may introduce a relative measure such as (μ_4/σ^4) in order to eliminate the dimensionality. Here, (μ_4/σ^4) measures the degree of kurtosis. When this ratio is equal to 3, the distribution is said to be *mesokurtic* with reference to a "normal distribution" as discussed in Chapter 5. When it is less than 3, the distribution is said to be *platykurtic*, and when it is greater than 3, the distribution is said to be *leptokurtic*.

Moments higher than μ_4 are only of theoretical interest and are usually difficult to interpret. In practice, while expectation and variance usually do not describe a probability distribution completely, they are adequate for many purposes, as we shall see in our discussion of statistical inferences in later chapters. The third and fourth moments about the mean, as we have just mentioned, are sometimes useful. From our point of view, these last measures have been introduced mainly for reference purposes; we shall under no circumstances be called upon to compute them.

7.9 STANDARDIZED RANDOM VARIABLES

As we shall see, it is always much more convenient to evaluate a random variable that is standardized than one that is not. A *standardized random variable* is one with zero expectation and unit variance. Any random variable can be standardized by subtracting its expectation from it and dividing the result by its standard deviation. That is, if we let X be a random variable with mean μ_X and standard deviation σ_X, the corresponding standardized random variable, denoted as Z, is

$$Z = \frac{X - \mu_X}{\sigma_X}.$$

The expectation of a standardized variable is always 0, since

$$E(Z) = E\left(\frac{X - \mu_X}{\sigma_X}\right) = \frac{E(X) - E(X)}{\sigma_X} = 0,$$

where $E(X)$ and σ_X are constants over all the possible values that X can assume.

The variance of a standardized variable is always unity, since

$$V(Z) = E(Z^2) - [E(Z)]^2 = E\left[\frac{X - E(X)}{\sigma_X}\right]^2 - 0^2$$

$$= \frac{E[(X - \mu_X)^2]}{\sigma_X^2} = \frac{\sigma_X^2}{\sigma_X^2} = 1,$$

which indicates, of course, that σ_Z is also unity.

Clearly, from our previous discussions on functions of random variables, the Z transformation does not in any way change the pattern of the original probability function. The probability of any Z value is simply the probability of the corresponding value of the original random variable. We also note that each X value corresponds to one, and only one, Z value. The transformation of X into Z has the effect of changing the scale of the original variable by converting the individual deviation of the original variable from the original units of measurement to standardized units, that is, to units of σ_X.

7.10 JOINT PROBABILITY DISTRIBUTIONS

Our discussion on probability distributions up to now has been exclusively concerned with distributions of single random variables. As such, they are often referred to as *univariate probability distributions*. In many realistic decision situations, more than one random variable may be generated in the same experiment. For instance, if we wish to study the relationship between the diameter and tensile strength of steel wires, we may consider the measurements of diameter and tensile strength as two random variables, whose values are determined by outcomes of the experiment of measuring of steel wire selected at random from the population of a day's production run. Equally, family income, liquid assets, and consumption expenditures can be considered as three random variables whose values are the results of observations made of a family chosen at random from the households of a certain state. Needless to say, even more random variables may be associated with the outcomes of an experiment in some situations.

Our interest in two or more random variables simultaneously is to discover the possible joint effects between or among them, since some or all of them may be interdependent. Thus, they must be analyzed in terms of their possible impact on some objective the decision maker wishes to achieve.

When we are concerned with two random variables, the corresponding probability distribution is called the *bivariate probability distribution*. The probability functions for three or more random variables are referred to as *multivariate probability distributions*. In the discussion that follows, we shall mainly be concerned with bivariate probability distributions. Also, since in this section we are dealing exclusively with discrete random variables, the bivariate and multivariate probability distributions can also properly be called *joint probability mass functions*.

Joint Probability Distribution of Two Random Variables

To study the relationship between two variables, we are naturally interested in knowing the probability that each takes on a particular value—namely, the joint probability distribution of the two variables under consideration. As an illustration, consider the tossing of four coins. If we let X be the number of heads and Y be the number of "runs," then the sample space of this experiment is as given in Table 7.7.

Note that the notion of a *run* refers to a succession of individual letters, numbers, or symbols uninterrupted by a different letter, number, or symbol. Thus, for example, the sequence of numbers 1134445 has four runs. In Table 7.7, the sample outcome HHHH has one run, the sample outcome HTTH has three runs, and so on.

To find the joint probability distribution of X and Y defined above, we may ask: What is the probability that X and Y jointly take on the values, say, (0, 1)? Similar questions can be raised for all other possible

TABLE 7.7 Sample Points, Number of Heads, and Number of Runs in Tossing Four Coins

Sample Point	Number of Heads, X	Number of Runs, Y
HHHH	4	1
HHHT	3	2
HHTH	3	3
HTHH	3	3
THHH	3	2
HHTT	2	2
HTHT	2	4
HTTH	2	3
THTH	2	4
TTHH	2	2
THHT	2	3
HTTT	1	2
THTT	1	3
TTHT	1	3
TTTH	1	2
TTTT	0	1

ordered pairs of values of (x_i, y_j). When we have the entire sample space available, answers to such questions can be deduced from the listings of the sample points corresponding to the joint values of X and Y. For instance, from Table 7.7, we see that when $X = 0$, Y always equals 1, and there is only one such pair of values among the total of 16 pairs. Since these 16 pairs of values are equally likely, we conclude that $P(X = 0 \text{ and } Y = 1) = 1/16$. The probability when $X = 0$ and $Y = $ any value other than 1 is zero. Likewise, for $X = 1$, $Y = 2$ twice and $Y = 3$ twice. Hence, $P(X = 1 \text{ and } Y = 2) = 2/16$ and $P(X = 1 \text{ and } Y = 3) = 2/16$. Also, when $X = 1$ and $Y = $ any value other than 2 or 3, the probability is zero. When probabilities of all possible joint events, $P(X = x_i \cap Y = y_j)$, have been determined in this fashion, then we have a joint probability distribution of X and Y, and these results may be presented in a two-way table as in Table 7.8. The graph of a joint probability distribution of two variables is constructed in a three-dimensional space. Data in Table 7.8 are shown by Figure 7.6.

TABLE 7.8 Joint Probability Distribution of Number of Heads and Number of Runs for Four Coins

		X: Number of heads					Row Total
		0	1	2	3	4	
	1	$\frac{1}{16}$	0	0	0	$\frac{1}{16}$	$\frac{2}{16}$
Y: Number	2	0	$\frac{2}{16}$	$\frac{2}{16}$	$\frac{2}{16}$	0	$\frac{6}{16}$
of Runs	3	0	$\frac{2}{16}$	$\frac{2}{16}$	$\frac{2}{16}$	0	$\frac{6}{16}$
	4	0	0	$\frac{2}{16}$	0	0	$\frac{2}{16}$
Column Total		$\frac{1}{16}$	$\frac{4}{16}$	$\frac{6}{16}$	$\frac{4}{16}$	$\frac{1}{16}$	$\frac{16}{16}$

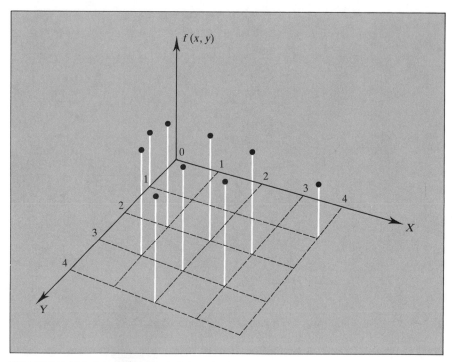

FIGURE 7.6 Joint distribution of the number of heads and the number of runs for the experiment of tossing four coins. (*Source:* Table 7.8.)

To generalize: Let X be a random variable with possible value x_i, $i = 1, 2, \ldots, I$ and Y be a random variable with possible values $y_j, j = 1, \ldots, J$; then the joint probability function of X and Y gives the probability that X takes on the value x_i and Y takes on the value of y_j for each ordered pair (x_i, y_j), or

$$f(x_i, y_j) = P(X = x_i \cap Y = y_j), \qquad \text{for all } (x_i, y_j). \qquad (7.12)$$

To be a probability distribution, (7.12) must satisfy

$$f(x_i, y_j) \geq 0, \qquad \text{and} \qquad \sum_{i=1}^{I} \sum_{j=1}^{J} f(x_i, y_j) = 1.$$

From the definition of the joint probability distribution (7.12) above, we can also deduce that the corresponding joint cumulative mass function of X and Y must be

$$F(x, y) = P(X \leq x \cap Y \leq y)$$

$$= \sum_{x_i \leq x} \sum_{y_j \leq y} f(x, y), \qquad \text{for any } x \text{ and } y. \qquad (7.13)$$

Marginal and Conditional Distributions

Our discussion of joint probabilities in the preceding chapter led us to consider marginal and conditional probabilities. Now, the consideration

TABLE 7.9 Marginal Distributions of X and Y

x_i	$f(x_i) = P(X = x_i)$	y_j	$g(y_j) = P(Y = y_j)$
0	1/16	1	2/16
1	4/16	2	6/16
2	6/16	3	6/16
3	4/16	4	2/16
4	1/16	—	—
Total	16/16	—	16/16

of joint probability distributions directs us to introduce marginal and conditional probability distributions. The headings across the top of Table 7.8, together with the column totals at the bottom, provide us with the PMF for X by itself. Similarly, the PMF for Y by itself can be found in the first and the last columns of the table. These are called *marginal distributions* because they are found at the margins of the table. For our illustrative example, the marginal distributions for X and Y are as shown in Table 7.9.

The general expressions for marginal distributions of X and Y may be written, respectively,

$$f(x_i) = \sum_{j=1}^{J} f(x_i, y_j) \tag{7.14a}$$

and

$$g(y_j) = \sum_{i=1}^{I} f(x_i, y_j). \tag{7.14b}$$

For example, with the data in Table 7.8, we have

$$P(X = 1) = f(1) = \sum_{j=1}^{4} f(1, y_j)$$

$$= f(1, 1) + f(1, 2) + f(1, 3) + f(1, 4)$$

$$= 4/16;$$

$$P(Y = 2) = g(2) = \sum_{i=1}^{5} f(x_i, 2)$$

$$= f(0, 2) + f(1, 2) + f(2, 2) + f(3, 2) + f(4, 2)$$

$$= 6/16;$$

and so on. (See Table 7.9.)

Another type of distribution that can be derived from a joint distribution is the *conditional probability distribution*. This notion is analogous to the concept of conditional probability. Thus, from the equation for two (possibly dependent) events, A and B,

$$P(A \cap B) = P(A)P(B \mid A) = P(B)P(A \mid B),$$

we can, in terms of probability distribution notation, write

$$f(x_i, y_j) = f(x_i)g(y_j \mid x_i) = g(y_j)f(x_i \mid y_j).$$

From this result, the conditional probability distributions for X and Y, respectively, can be expressed as follows:

$$f(x_i \mid y_j) = \frac{f(x_i, y_j)}{g(y_j)}, \qquad g(y_j) > 0; \tag{7.15a}$$

and

$$g(y_j \mid x_i) = \frac{f(x_i, y_j)}{f(x_i)}, \qquad f(x_i) > 0. \tag{7.15b}$$

Using our current example, we see that the probability of, say, observing two runs, given that the number of heads is 1, is

$$P(Y = 2 \mid X = 1) = \frac{2/16}{4/16} = \frac{1}{2}.$$

Likewise, the probability of the occurrence of one head, given that the number of runs is one, is

$$P(X = 1 \mid Y = 1) = \frac{0}{2/16} = 0.$$

Independence of X and Y

In evaluating joint distributions, the question of dependence and independence between the variables becomes relevant for determining how well the value of one variable can be predicted on the basis of the value of another. Recall that, in terms of event probabilities, independence is present if and only if the conditional probability of an event is equal to its marginal probability. This condition can be carried over to joint probability distributions. Hence, if X and Y are independent variables, we must have

$$f(x_i \mid y_j) = f(x_i) \qquad \text{for all } i \text{ and } j \text{ for which } g(y_j) \neq 0;$$
$$g(y_j \mid x_i) = g(y_j) \qquad \text{for all } i \text{ and } j \text{ for which } f(x_i) \neq 0.$$

Alternatively, we may say that X and Y are independent if and only if

$$f(x_i, y_j) = f(x_i)g(y_j) \qquad (7.16)$$

for all values of X and Y.

In our illustrative example, X and Y are dependent, not independent. Consider, for example, the ordered pair $(0, 1)$. For this point we find from Table 7.8

$$P(X = 0 \cap Y = 1) = 1/16;$$

but from the marginal distributions in Table 7.9, we have

$$P(X = 0) = 1/16 \quad \text{and} \quad P(Y = 1) = 2/16.$$

Hence,

$$P(X = 0)P(Y = 1) = (1/16)(2/16) = 1/128,$$

which does not equal $1/16$.

It is interesting to note that if two random variables are dependent, their joint distribution can be derived only when there is sufficient information about the sample space so that joint probabilities can be determined directly, or by analytical deduction. Without such information, we must rely on empirical estimates based on relative frequencies of joint events. Of course, if two random variables are independent, their joint distribution can be easily synthesized from their respective marginal distributions.

Our discussion of the bivariate case can readily be extended to multivariate distributions. Aside from added computational labor, joint distributions of three or more variables do not pose new analytical problems. Thus, we simply state here that the joint probability mass function of k random variables $f(x_1, x_2, \ldots, x_k)$ is specified to be nonnegative and its sum over the k-dimensional space is unity.

7.11 EXPECTED VALUE AND VARIANCE OF A FUNCTION OF TWO VARIABLES

The notion of expected value can be extended to functions of two or more random variables. Given two random variables X and Y, we are particularly interested in the following three types of functions:

$$h(X, Y) = X + Y,$$
$$h(X, Y) = X - Y,$$
$$h(X, Y) = (X)(Y).$$

Expectation of a Function of Two Random Variables

The expectations of $h(X, Y) = X + Y$ and $h(X, Y) = X - Y$ are governed by the following theorem.

THEOREM 7.4 THE ADDITIVE (DIFFERENCE) LAW OF EXPECTATION. *If X and Y are any two random variables with $E(X)$ and $E(Y)$, respectively, then the expectation of their sum or of their difference is the sum or difference of their separate expectations. Thus,*

$$E(X + Y) = E(X) + E(Y) \qquad (7.17a)$$

$$E(X - Y) = E(X) - E(Y). \qquad (7.17b)$$

These results follow directly from the definition of expectation, and thus

$$E(X \pm Y) = \sum_i \sum_j (x_i \pm y_j) f(x_i, y_j)$$

$$= \sum_i x_i f(x_i) \pm \sum_j y_j f(y_j). \qquad (7.18)$$

These results can easily be demonstrated.

Consider our current example, as it can be verified easily; the expected number of heads is $E(X) = 2$, and the expectation of the number of runs is $E(Y) = 2.5$. Now, from Table 7.8 and by (7.18), we see that

$$E(X + Y) = (0 + 1)(1/16) + (1 + 2)(2/16) + (1 + 3)(2/16)$$

$$+ (2 + 2)(2/16) + (2 + 3)(2/16) + (3 + 2)(2/16)$$

$$+ (3 + 3)(2/16) + (4 + 1)(1/16) + (2 + 4)(2/16)$$

$$= 72/16 = 4.5,$$

which is equal to $E(X) + E(Y)$, as the addition law of expectation dictates. The reader may verify that $E(X - Y) = 2 - 2.5 = -0.5$ for the same example.

Theorem 7.5 below governs the expectation of the function $h(X, Y) = (X)(Y)$.

THEOREM 7.5 THE PRODUCT LAW OF EXPECTATION. *If X and Y are two random variables with $E(X)$ and $E(Y)$, respectively, and if X and Y are statistically independent, then the expectation of their product is equal to the product of their separate expectation. Thus,*

$$E(XY) = E(X)E(Y). \qquad (7.19)$$

Recalling the condition for independence of X and Y as specified by (7.16), and by the definition of expectation, we see that

$$E(XY) = \sum_i \sum_j x_i y_j f(x_i) g(y_j). \qquad (7.20)$$

TABLE 7.10 The Joint PMF of Two Independent Variables

		Values of X			
		1	2	3	Row Total
Values	0	0.04	0.20	0.16	0.40
of Y	1	0.06	0.30	0.24	0.60
Column Total		0.10	0.50	0.40	1.00

Source: Hypothetical.

It is important to observe that if X and Y are independent, then they must satisfy (7.19). However, dependence does not preclude equality between $E(XY)$ and $E(X)E(Y)$; in some special situations, we find that (7.19) holds even though X and Y are dependent random variables.

You can verify on your own, for the four-coin experiment, that $E(XY) \neq E(X)E(Y)$, since the number of heads and the number of runs are not independent random variables. Consider now, however, the joint probability distribution in Table 7.10, where X and Y are statistically independent, since each cell in the table contains a joint probability that is the product of the corresponding row and column totals. Being independent variables, as calculations below indicate, X and Y in Table 7.10, clearly satisfy (7.19):

$$E(X) = (1)(0.10) + (2)(0.5) + (3)(0.4) = 2.3,$$

$$E(Y) = (0)(0.4) + (1)(0.6) = 0.6,$$

$$E(XY) = [(1)(0)](0.04) + [(1)(1)](0.06) + [(2)(0)](0.20) + [(2)(1)](0.30)$$
$$+ [(3)(0)](0.16) + [(3)(1)](0.24) = 1.38$$

$$E(XY) = 1.38 = E(X)E(Y) = (2.3)(0.6).$$

The Variance of a Function of Two Random Variables

The additive property of expectations also holds for variances, provided the random variables are independent. Hence, we have the following theorem.

THEOREM 7.6 THE ADDITIVE (DIFFERENCE) LAW OF VARIANCES. *If X and Y are independent random variables and if their variances are $V(X)$ and $V(Y)$, respectively, then the variance of their sum or of their difference is the sum of their separate variances. That is,*

$$V(X + Y) = V(X) + V(Y) \tag{7.21}$$

and

$$V(X - Y) = V(X) + V(Y). \tag{7.22}$$

Intuitively, (7.21) seems quite simple and direct, but (7.22) is clearly against our common sense. We therefore provide an example to demonstrate the validity of (7.22). Using information in Table 7.10 again, we have

$$V(X) = [1^2(0.10) + 2^2(0.50) + 3^2(0.40)] - (2.30)^2 = 0.41;$$

$$V(Y) = [0^2(0.40) + 1^2(0.60)] - (0.60)^2 = 0.24;$$

$$\begin{aligned} V(X - Y) &= [(1 - 0)^2(0.04) + (1 - 1)^2(0.06) + (2 - 0)^2(0.20) \\ &\quad + (2 - 1)^2(0.30) + (3 - 0)^2(0.16) + (3 - 1)^2(0.24)] \\ &\quad - [(1 - 0)(0.04) + (1 - 1)(0.06) + (2 - 0)(0.02) \\ &\quad + (2 - 1)(0.30) + (3 - 0)(0.16) + (3 - 1)(0.24)]^2 \\ &= 3.54 - 2.65 = 0.65, \end{aligned}$$

which, as expected, is identical with

$$V(X) + V(Y) = 0.41 + 0.24 = 0.65$$

owing to fact that X and Y are independent in this case.

Dependence of *X* and *Y*: Covariance

The notion of statistical dependence between two random variables has so far been brought up only indirectly via our discussion of statistical independence. In this subsection, we shall present a general theorem for the variances of a sum that enables us to differentiate independent random variables from those that are dependent. This law is based on a measure called covariance.

First, by definition, the *covariance* of two random variables X and Y is the expectation of the product of their paired deviations from their separate expectations. In symbols,

$$\text{Cov}(X, Y) = E[(X - \mu_X)(Y - \mu_Y)]. \tag{7.23}$$

From this definition, we see that the commutative law holds for covariance;

$$\text{Cov}(X, Y) = \text{Cov}(Y, X).$$

Second, it can verified that (7.23) can be converted into the following convenient form for computation:

$$\text{Cov}(X, Y) = E(XY) - E(X)E(Y). \tag{7.24}$$

Third, as the name implies, covariance measures the covaribility, or association of the values, between X and Y. As it shall be seen in a later chapter, this quantity furnishes a basis for us to measure the degree or strength of association between two or more variables. Our immediate concern with $\text{Cov}(X, Y)$, is to present the following theorem.

THEOREM 7.7 THE GENERAL LAW OF THE VARIANCE OF A SUM *Let X and Y be two random variables, dependent or independent, with finite variances, V(X) and V(Y), respectively. Let covariance be as defined by (7.23). Then the variance of the sum of X and Y is given by*

$$V(X + Y) = V(X) + V(Y) + 2\,\text{Cov}(X, Y). \qquad (7.25)$$

This theorem implies that if X and Y are independent, then $\text{Cov}(X, Y) = 0$; otherwise, X and Y are dependent. Thus, Theorem 7.6 is actually a special case of Theorem 7.7.

Let us now consider a numerical example for the determination of dependence between two random variables via Theorem 7.7. Suppose the marketing research team of a manufacturing firm has established from past data a joint probability mass function between sales X of a certain commodity and levels of advertising expenditures Y for the commodity, as shown by Table 7.11.

In Table 7.11, we have

$X = 0$ if sales are less than 50,000 units per quarter,

$\quad = 1$ if sales are between 50,000 and 100,000 units per quarter,

$\quad = 2$ if sales are more than 100,000 units per quarter;

$Y = 0$ if advertising expenditures are less than \$50,000 per quarter,

$\quad = 1$ if advertising expenditures are between \$50,000 and \$100,000 per quarter;

$\quad = 2$ if advertising expenditures are over \$100,000 per quarter.

With data in Table 7.11, we first have

$$E(X) = 1.20, \quad E(Y) = 1.24, \quad V(X) = 0.56 \quad \text{and} \quad V(Y) = 0.5824.$$

Next, by (7.24), we obtain

$$\begin{aligned}
\text{Cov}(X, Y) &= E(XY) - E(X)E(Y) \\
&= [(0)(0)(0.10) + (0)(1)(0.06) + (0)(2)(0.04) \\
&\quad + (1)(0)(0.08) + (1)(1)(0.22) + (1)(2)(0.10) \\
&\quad + (2)(0)(0.02) + (2)(1)(0.08) + (2)(2)(0.30)] - [(1.20)(1.24)] \\
&= 1.78 - 1.488 = 0.292.
\end{aligned}$$

TABLE 7.11 The Joint PMF of Sales X and Advertising Expenditures Y

		\multicolumn{3}{c}{X}		
		0	1	2	Row Totals
	0	0.10	0.08	0.02	0.20
Y	1	0.06	0.22	0.08	0.36
	2	0.04	0.10	0.30	0.44
Column Totals		0.20	0.40	0.40	1.00

Source: Hypothetical.

Finally, by (7.25), we get

$$V(X + Y) = V(X) + V(Y) + 2\,\mathrm{Cov}(X, Y)$$

$$= 0.56 + 0.5824 + 2(0.292) = 1.7264.$$

From the preceding results we see that the covariance term has increased the sum of the variances of X and Y, $(0.56 + 0.5824 = 1.1424)$ by more than 51% to give the variance of $(X + Y)$. In general, when the values of one variable are positively associated with those of another, $\mathrm{Cov}(X, Y) > 0$ and thus, as in our current example, the $V(X + Y)$ would be increased from $V(X) + V(Y)$ by the amount of covariance. Clearly, if the values of one variable are negatively associated with those of another, $\mathrm{Cov}(X, Y) < 0$, the $V(X + Y)$ would then be decreased from $V(X) + V(Y)$ by the amount of covariance. For our current example, X and Y are dependent variables because $V(X + Y) \neq V(X) + V(Y)$, or because $\mathrm{Cov}(X, Y) \neq 0$.

In closing our discussion in this section on the expectation and variance of the bivariate case, let us point out that the laws governing the expectations of the sum and the difference of two random variables are universal, in the sense that they can be applied whether the random variables are independent or not. However, the laws governing the expectation of the product and the variances of the sum or the difference require that the random variables must be independent. A general law for the variance of the sum of two random variables is provided, though, by Theorem 7.7. Furthermore, all the theorems introduced in this section can be extended to cover any number of random variables without any modifications, except that statistical independence must be observed, as in the bivariate case just mentioned.

GLOSSARY OF FORMULAS

(7.1) $f(x) = P(X = x)$.

The values of a random variable X together with their probabilities comprise the *probability distribution* of X. If X is discrete, its probability distribution is also called a *probability mass function*, PMF. A PMF gives the probability that X assumes a particular value x. This equation is subject to the restrictions that $f(x) \geq 0$ and $\sum f(x) = 1$.

(7.2) $F(x) = P(X \leq x) = \sum_{x_i \leq x} f(x)$.

This equation defines the *cumulative mass function*, CMF, of a discrete random variable X. It says that the probability of X to take on a value less than or equal to x is the sum of the probabilities of those values of X that are equal to or less than x. Thus, $F(x)$ is obtained by adding up the probabilities of the possible values of X that lie below and at the value of x. Since the total probability of a distribution is 1, we can say that $P(X > x) = 1 - P(X \leq x)$.

(7.3) $E(X) = \mu_X = \sum xf(x)$.

The *expected value* of a discrete random variable X is defined here as the weighted average of the values that X can take with probabilities for these values as weights. The expected value tells us where the center of the mass of the probability distribution is located. It is also the average value of X we expect to have in the long run when the same random experiment is repeated over and over again.

(7.4) $E[g(X)] = \sum g(x)f(x)$.

If Y is a function of X, then the expected value Y can be determined by this formula. Here, $g(x)$ are values of Y in terms of X as specified by $y = g(x)$ and $f(x)$ is the PMF of X.

(7.5) $E(Y) = E(aX + b) = aE(X) + b$.

This equation states the mathematical properties of expectation. Precisely, it says that (1) if a constant b is added to a random variable X, then the new random variable $Y = (X + b)$ has the same expectation of X plus the constant b; (2) if X is multiplied by a constant a, then the new random variable (aX) has as its expectation, the expectation of X times a.

(7.6a) $V(X) = \sigma^2 = \sum (x - \mu_X)^2 f(x)$;

(7.6b) $V(X) = E(X^2) - \mu_X^2$.

The first of this pair of formulas, defines the *variance of a random variable* X as the mean of the squared deviations of X from its expectation. It is the sum of squared deviations weighted by the probabilities of the values that X can assume. The second expression is an equivalent of the first and is a more convenient formula for computing $V(X)$.

(7.7) $V(aX + b) = \sigma_{aX+b}^2 = a^2 \sigma_X^2$.

This equation states the important mathematical properties of a variance. (1) When a constant, say, b, is added to X, the new random variable $(X + b)$ will have the variance of X. (2) When X is multiplied by a constant, say, a, the new random variable (aX) will have a variance that is equal to $V(X)$ times a^2. These properties enable us to compute $V(X)$ with much less effort when X can take on very large or very small values.

(7.8) $\sigma_X = \sqrt{V(X)}$;

(7.9) $\sigma_{cX} = |c|\,\sigma_X$;

(7.10) $\sigma_{X+c} = \sigma_X$.

Equation (7.8) defines the standard deviation of a random variable as the (positive) square root of the variance of that variable. Equations (7.9) and (7.10) express the mathematical properties of standard deviations, which correspond to those of the variance. Specifically, (7.9) says that if X is multiplied by a constant c, then cX has a standard deviation equal to the standard deviation of X multiplied by the absolute value of c; (7.10) says, that if a constant c is added to X, then $(X + c)$ will have the standard deviation of X. This also means that shifting the origin will not change the standard deviation.

(7.11a) $P(|X - \mu| < h\sigma) \geq 1 - 1/h^2$;

(7.11b) $P(|X - \mu| \geq h\sigma) \leq 1/h^2$.

These are the alternative forms of Chebyshev's Inequality for probability distributions. The first says that the minimum probability that the value of a random observation of X will lie within the range $\mu \pm h\sigma$ is $1 - 1/h^2$. The second says the maximum probability that the value of a random observation of X will lie outside the range $\mu \pm h\sigma$ is $1/h^2$. The most important property of this theorem is that it can be used irrespective of the distribution pattern of the random variable.

(7.12) $f(x_i, x_j) = P(X = x_1 \cap Y = y_j)$, for all (x_i, y_j).

This equation defines the *bivariate joint probability mass function* of two random variables X and Y. It is a function that gives the joint probability of X that takes on the value of x_i, and Y that takes on the value of y_j, for all possible ordered pairs of values (x_i, y_j).

(7.13) $F(x, y) = P(X \leq x \cap Y \leq y) = \sum_{x_i \leq x} \sum_{y_j \leq y} f(x_i, y_j)$.

This equation defines the *bivariate cumulative mass function*. It indicates, similar to the univariate case, that the cumulative probabilities of X and Y are obtained simply by adding (cumulating) the joint probabilities of (x_i, y_j), for any x and y.

(7.14a) $f(x_i) = \sum_{j=1}^{J} f(x_i, y_j)$; $g(y_j) = \sum_{i=1}^{I} f(x_i, y_j)$.

These are the general expressions of the marginal distributions for X and Y respectively, derived from the joint distribution of X and Y. Each marginal probability here is simply the sum of a column total or of a row total found in a joint probability table.

(7.15a) $f(x_i \mid y_j) = \dfrac{f(x_i, y_j)}{g(y_j)}$, $g(y_j) > 0$;

(7.15b) $g(y_j \mid x_i) = \dfrac{f(x_i, y_j)}{f(x_i)}$, $f(x_i) > 0$.

From a joint PMF, we can also derive the conditional distributions for X and Y respectively. The conditional distribution of X, given Y, is the joint probability function divided by the marginal distribution of Y as shown by (7.15a). Similarly, the conditional distribution of Y, given X, is the ratio of the bivariate PMF to the marginal PMF of X, as in (7.15b).

(7.16) $f(x_i, y_j) = f(x_i)g(y_j)$.

This expression states the fact that if X and Y are independent variables, then the probability for all pairs of values of X and Y is equal to the product of their marginal probabilities.

(7.17a) $E(X + Y) = E(X) + E(Y)$;

(7.17b) $E(X - Y) = E(X) - E(Y)$;

(7.18) $E(X \pm Y) = \sum_i \sum_j (x_i \pm y_j)f(x_i, y_j)$.

Equations (7.17a) and (7.17b) state that the expectation of $(X + Y)$ and that of $(X - Y)$, is the sum of, or the difference between, the expectations of X and Y. This property holds whether X and Y are independent or dependent random variables. Equation (7.18) is the computational formula for (7.17a) and (7.17b).

(7.19) $E(XY) = E(X)E(Y)$;

(7.20) $E(XY) = \sum_i \sum_j x_i y_j f(x_i)g(y_j)$.

Equation (7.19) says that if X and Y are independent random variables, then the expectation of the product of X and Y is equal to the product of their separate expectations. Equation (7.20) is the computational formula for the expected value of the product of X and Y.

(7.21) $V(X - Y) = V(X) + V(Y)$;

(7.22) $V(X + Y) = V(X) + V(Y)$.

These equations provide the additive/difference laws of variance. If X and Y are independent, then the variance of their *sum* or *difference* is the *sum* of their separate variances.

(7.23) $\text{Cov}(X, Y) = E[(X - \mu_X)(Y - \mu_Y)]$.

The covariance of two random variables X and Y is defined as the expectation of the product of their paired deviations from their separate expectations. Note that $\text{Cov}(X, Y) = \text{Cov}(Y, X)$.

(7.24) $\text{Cov}(X, Y) = E(XY) - E(X)E(Y)$.

When neither of the two random variables X and Y has a zero mean, then their covariance can be defined by this expression. This may also be considered as the efficient formula for computing Cov(X, Y) in this special case.

(7.25) $V(X + Y) = V(X) + V(Y) + 2\,\text{Cov}(X, Y)$.

This expression gives us the general law of the variance of a sum. When X and Y are independent, then Cov(X, Y) = 0. Otherwise, X and Y are dependent.

REVIEW QUESTIONS

7.1 What are the two ways to define a random variable? What is the range of a random variable?

7.2 A random variable must assume numerical values. Is this correct? Explain.

7.3 What is the relationship between a random variable and a sample space?

7.4 Can more than one random variable be defined on the same sample space? If not, why not? If the answer is yes, provide an example of your own.

7.5 In general, how is probability distribution defined for discrete random variables? What is a PMF?

7.6 What are the restrictions on a PMF?

7.7 What is a cumulative mass function for a random variable? What function does a CMF perform? Are there any restrictions on a CMF? If so, what are they?

7.8 What is the expected value of a random variable? What does it measure? How should it be interpreted?

7.9 What do we mean when we say that the random variable Y is a function of the random variable X? What is the use of such a function?

7.10 Give a verbal interpretation to the relationship between $E(aX + b)$ and $E(X)$. What use can we have for this relationship?

7.11 How are the median, the mode, and the fractile of a discrete random variable defined?

7.12 What is the variance of a random variable? What does it measure? Why is it an awkward measure in practice?

7.13 Give a verbal interpretation to the expression $V(aX + b) = \sigma^2_{aX+b} = a^2\sigma^2_X$. What is the use for this mathematical expression?

7.14 What is the standard deviation of a random variable? What are the important mathematical properties of this measure?

7.15 Can the expected value of a random variable be negative? The variance? The standard deviation? Explain in each case.

7.16 What is the function of Chebyshev's Inequality? How should it be interpreted as expressed by (7.11a)? By (7.11b)?

7.17 What do we mean by the "moments" of a probability distribution? What use can we have for the notion of "moments"?

7.18 What is a joint probability distribution in general? What is the difference between a bivariate PMF and a multivariate PMF?

7.19 What are the two conditions for a joint probability distribution of two random variables?

7.20 Given a joint probability distribution between two random variables, say X and Y:
a. How are marginal distributions of X and Y defined?
b. How are conditional distributions for X and Y defined?

7.21 The expression $E(X \pm Y) = E(X) \pm E(Y)$ holds, if and only if X and Y are independent. Is this correct?

7.22 The expression $E(XY) = E(X)E(Y)$ holds if and only if X and Y are dependent. Is this correct?.

7.23 What is the relationship between the variance of the sum of random variables and the sum of the variances of the random variables? Does it matter whether the random variables are pairwise independent or not?

7.24 Is it always true for any two random variables X and Y, that $V(X \pm Y) = V(X) + V(Y)$ and $V(XY) = V(X)V(Y)$? Explain.

7.25 How is covariance defined? In what sense can we use this measure to determine whether X and Y are independent?

PROBLEMS

7.1 The following array shows the number of boxcars that are unloaded each day, X by a warehouse crew during the past 200 working days. Determine the probability distribution of X.

x:	5	6	7	8	9	10
Number of days:	25	60	46	34	20	15

7.2 The warehouse section of a department store receives various types of goods from its suppliers. Historical records show that, during the past 55 working days, the warehouse manager recorded 6 trucks arriving on each of 10 of those days, 7 trucks arriving on each of 25 of those days, 8 trucks arriving on each of

15 of those days, and 9 trucks arriving on each of 5 of those days. Determine the probability distribution of the random variable "number of truck arrivals during one day."

7.3 A manufacturing company has just developed a new product. The company is starting to decide whether it should make and sell the new product. Management estimates that, if the new product captured 20% of the market, it would be nicely profitable; capturing 15% of the market would result in breaking even; and 10% of the market would result in a substantial loss. Management seems to be quite optimistic about the new product. It currently believes that the odds are about 5 to 4 in favor of a 20% market share, 3 to 6 in favor of a 15% market share, and 1 to 8 in favor of a 10% market share. What is the subjective probabiliity distribution of the share of the market for the new product, according to management's current judgment?

7.4 A construction company is planning to put up a commercial building on land acquired a few years ago. Of crucial importance is the mortgage interest rate during the next two or three years. Suppose you are the financial adviser to the company, and suppose you think the rate the construction company will have to pay will be one of the following: 12%, 14%, 16%, 18%, or 20%. Establish a probability distribution for the random variable "mortgage interest rate" for the next few years, according to your judgment.

7.5 Determine the CMF for each of the random variables in Problems 7.1 and 7.2.

7.6 The number of machine breakdowns in a large manufacturing firm during one week has the following summarized probability distribution:

b:	5	10	15	20	25
$P(B = b)$:	0.25	0.30	0.25	0.15	0.05

Using this distribution, compute $E(B)$, $V(B)$, σ_B, and $P(B \leq 18)$.

7.7 The numbers of industrial accidents that occur in a day in the chemical plants in a certain area are given, approximately, by the following distribution:

a:	0	1	2	3	4	5
$P(A = a)$:	0.1	0.2	0.2	0.3	0.1	0.1

Using this distribution, compute $E(A)$, $V(A)$, σ_A, $P(A \leq 3)$, $P(A \geq 4)$, and $P(A > 4)$.

7.8 Suppose the mortality table used by American life insurance companies shows that there are 12 deaths per 1000 persons for 30-year-old males. Mr. Kosco is 30 years old and buys $10,000 of one-year term life insurance for a premium of $180. Let the random varible X be the financial result for the insurance company from Mr. Kosco's policy. What is the range of X? Determine the probability distribution of X and compute $E(X)$.

7.9 A car dealer offers every potential customer a trial run of 30 miles in the type of car the customer is interested in buying, plus a free lunch or dinner for the customer. All of this costs about $50. If the customer does not buy a car, the dealer loses $50, but if the customer does buy a car, the dealer's average profit is about $500 (from which the trial run and the free meal must be deducted). In the past, 20% of the customers bought cars after the trial runs and free meals. What is the expected profit for the dealer in this situation?

7.10 The Beta Company has purchased 80 electronic components from a supplier who claims that only 2% of the components it sells are defective and that the defective components are mixed at random with the good components. Each defective component in Beta's purchase will cost Beta $250 in repair costs. If the supplier is right, what is the expected number of defective components? What is the expected repair cost?

7.11 A gambler who has $700 plays a single-die game with the following system: At the first toss of the die, he bets $100 on even numbers and quits if he wins. If he loses, he bets $200 on even numbers at the second toss and quits if he wins. If he loses again, he bets his final $400 on even numbers at the third toss. The single-die game returns the bet plus an equal amount for a win on even numbers. Show that this game is *fair* because, for this game, $E(G) = 0$.

7.12 A salesman regularly schedules five calls a day. He is certain of making at least one sale out of the five calls, and may make as many as five sales if he is in his best form and extremely lucky. The probabilities of his making various numbers of sales in a day are specified by the PMF below:

$$f(x) = \begin{cases} \dfrac{6 - x}{15}, & \text{if } x = 1, 2, 3, 4, 5; \\ 0, & \text{otherwise.} \end{cases}$$

a. Prepare a probability table for this PMF.
b. Determine the CMF for X.
c. Compute $E(X)$, $V(X)$, and σ_X.
d. How should the result of $E(X)$ in (c) be interpreted?

7.13 A manufacturing company specializes in producing an expensive piece of hand-made furniture. The monthly demand for its product is a random variable X that, according to past records, approximately obeys the PMF:

$$f(x) = \begin{cases} \dfrac{x - 3}{14}, & \text{if } x = 5, 6, 7, 8; \\ 0, & \text{otherwise.} \end{cases}$$

The profit function per month, as a function of demand, is known to be

$$Y = g(y) = \$1{,}200(X^2 - X + 10)$$

a. Prepare a table showing $f(x)$ and $g(y)$.
b. Determine the expected profit per month.

7.14 A retailer on Fifth Avenue in New York City sells a low-volume, but extremely high-quality article. Experience indicates that sales of this article per month is a random variable V that obeys the PMF:

$$f(v) = \begin{cases} 0.05(33 - v), & \text{if } V = 27, 28, 29, 30, 31; \\ 0, & \text{otherwise.} \end{cases}$$

The retailer's monthly profit from this article, as a function of V, is defined by

$$R = g(r) = \$250(V^2 - V).$$

a. What is the probability that the monthly demand is at most 29? At least 28?
b. What is the expected monthly demand?
c. What is the expected monthly profit?

7.15 A census of the full professors in American state universities revealed that their annual mean income was $43,500 with a standard deviation of $2,100 in 1988.
 a. What is the maximum probability that the annual income of a randomly selected professor would be either less than $40,000 or more than $47,000?
 b. What is the minimum probability that the annual income of a randomly selected professor will fall within a range from $38,000 to $49,000?
 c. Determine a range of the professors' annual incomes, with μ at the center of the range, that will guarantee that at least 80% of the professors will have annual income within that range.
 (Hint: Since the exact probability distribution here is unspecified, the answers to the questions can be obtained by applying Chebyshev's inequality.)

7.16 The daily number of customers served by a large branch of Citibank on any working day is a random variable with $E(C) = 500$ and $\sigma_C = 34$. However, the exact distribution of C is unknown. With what probability can we assert that between 449 and 551 customers will be served on any working day? With what probability can we assert that the number of customers that will be served is either less than 415 or more than 585 on any working day?

7.17 A random variable X has the following PMF:

x:	-1	0	1
$f(x)$:	$\frac{1}{5}$	$\frac{3}{10}$	$\frac{1}{2}$

Find the PMF for $2X$, $X + 1$, X^2, and $(X - 0.3)^2$. Verify also that $E(2X) = 0.6$, $E(X + 1) = 1.3$, $E(X^2) = 0.7$, and $E[(X - 0.3)^2] = 0.610$.

7.18 Let X be a random variable with the following PMF:

x:	10,025	10,050	10,075
$f(x)$:	0.2	0.3	0.5

Show that $V(X) = 381.25$.

7.19 If the variance of random variable X is 0.8, what is the variance of the random variable $5X$? $2X$? $X/2$?

7.20 A random variable X takes on the value 1 with probability π and the value 0 with probability $(1 - \pi)$. Show that $E(X) = \pi$ and $V(X) = \pi(1 - \pi)$.

7.21 Show that if X is a random variable that can take on values $1, 2, 3, \ldots, n$ with $1/n$ as the proabability of each value, then

$$E(X) = \frac{n + 1}{2} \quad \text{and} \quad V(X) = \frac{n^2 - 1}{12}.$$

Hint: $\qquad 1 + 2 + \cdots + (n - 1) + n = [n(n + 1)]/2$

and

$$1^2 + 2^2 + \cdots + (n - 1)^2 + n^2 = [n[n + 1)(2n + 1)]/6.$$

7.22 A competitive game of skill is played by teams of two players, each of whom can score 0, 1, 2, or 3 points. The score of the team is the sum of the points gained by the two players. For each such team, the PMFs of the two players, respectively, are as follows:

PMF of Player X

x:	0	1	2	3
$f(x)$:	0.1	0.3	0.4	0.2

PMF of Player Y

y:	0	1	2	3
$g(y)$:	0.3	0.1	0.4	0.2

Assuming independence of X and Y, derive
a. the joint probability distribution of X and Y;
b. the probability distribution of the total score T of the two players.

7.23 For the preceding problem, compute $E(X)$, $E(Y)$, $E(T)$, and check that $E(T) = E(X) + E(Y)$ and that $E(XY) = E(X)E(Y)$.

7.24 In an oligarchic industry the two leading firms, A and B, control 50 and 30% of the market, respectively. If a random sample of two buyers is selected at random for observation, what is the joint probability distribution of the number of buyers patronizing each firm in the sample?
Hint: Let X and Y be the numbers of customers for A and B, respectively; then the sample space can be constructed as follows:

Sample Point	Joint Event $= (x, y)$	Probability
AA	(2,0)	(0.5)(0.5) = 0.25
AB	(1,1)	(0.5)(0.3) = 0.15
BA	(1,1)	(0.3)(0.5) = 0.15
AC	(1,0)	(0.5)(0.2) = 0.10
CA	(1,0)	(0.2)(0.5) = 0.10
BB	(0,2)	(0.3)(0.3) = 0.09
BC	(0,1)	(0.3)(0.2) = 0.06
CB	(0,1)	(0.2)(0.3) = 0.06
CC	(0,0)	(0.2)(0.2) = 0.04

where $P(A) = 0.5$, $P(B) = 0.3$, and $P(C) = P(\overline{A \cup B}) = 0.2$.

7.25 For the preceding problem show that $E(X) = 1, E(Y) = 0.6, E(X + Y) = 1.6$, and $E(XY) = 0.3$.

7.26 Compute $E(X)$, $E(Y)$, and $E(XY)$ for the joint distribution below. Show that $E(XY) = E(X)E(Y)$ for this distribution. Does your result indicate that X and Y are independent? Explain your answer.

		\multicolumn{4}{c}{Values of X}	
		0	1	2	3	$g(y_i)$
Values of Y	1	$\frac{1}{8}$	0	0	$\frac{1}{8}$	$\frac{2}{8}$
	2	0	$\frac{2}{8}$	$\frac{2}{8}$	0	$\frac{4}{8}$
	3	0	$\frac{1}{8}$	$\frac{1}{8}$	0	$\frac{2}{8}$
$f(x_i)$		$\frac{1}{8}$	$\frac{3}{8}$	$\frac{3}{8}$	$\frac{1}{8}$	$\frac{8}{8}$

7.27 Let the joint probability distribution of X and Y be defined as

$$f(x_i, y_j) = \left(\frac{1}{54}\right)(3x_i + 2y_j - 4), \qquad x_i, y_j = 1, 2, 3.$$

a. Construct a joint probability table.
b. Give the marginal probability distributions for X and Y, respectively.
c. Give the conditional distributions of X and Y, respectively.
d. Verify that X and Y are independent.

7.28 Do the same as for the preceding problem, given that

$$f(x, y) = (1/33)(x + y + 2),$$

$$x = 1, 2, \qquad \text{and} \qquad y = 1, 2, 3.$$

7.29 Use Theorem 7.7 to verify that in the four coins example, the number of heads X and the number of runs Y are dependent variables.

7.30 The joint distribution below indicates that X and Y are statistically independent. Is this correct? Explain or demonstrate.

Joint distribution of Employment Status Y and Age Group (in years) X

		\multicolumn{3}{c}{X}	
		Under 20	20 to 40	Over 40	
Y		0	1	2	Total
Unemployed	0	0.020	0.020	0.015	0.055
Employed	1	0.180	0.480	0.285	0.945
Total		0.200	0.500	0.300	1.000

8 Special Discrete Probability Models

8.1 INTRODUCTION

The main purpose of any science is to discover the relationship between two or more variables so that a model, a principle, a theory, or a law can be established. A *model,* is a simplified picture of reality that tells us how one variable is influenced by or related to another variable or other variables. It is important to note that a model is designed merely to capture the necessary essential features of reality; it is not constructed to be an exact replica of reality. This is done by leaving out all irrelevant variables in a real-world situation so that we can observe clearly what we intend to observe. All scientists follow this practice. Thus, the physicists construct their law of gravity in a "vacuum", the economists formulate their theory of demand by keeping in their minds the restriction "other things being equal", and so forth.

In general, a model consists of two parts: (1) a set of assumptions or initial conditions, and (2) a conclusion derived by logic from the initial conditions. We see that a model is derived by logical reasoning rather than by actual physical experiments even though physical experiments are often designed to verify the validity of models after the models have been constructed. Models can be classified into two kinds: deterministic and probabilistic. A *deterministic model* is one that enables us to say that given certain initial conditions, certain states or outcomes are definitely to follow. In other words, a deterministic model provides us a clear-cut cause-and-effect explanation—certain specific conditions cause the subsequent unique state. All models in pure mathematics and many models in natural sciences are deterministic in nature.

In many situations a clear-cut relationship can never be established, because of uncertainty; here we can have only probabilistic models. A *probabilistic model* enables us to say only that, given certain initial conditions, certain states will occur with such-and-such probabilities. That is, given the initial conditions, a probabilistic model enables us to deduce a probability distribution for possible subsequent states, which are values of a random variable.

In this chapter, we present some *special discrete probability models,* and in the next we present some *special continuous probability models*—probability distributions for random variables that are appropriate mathematical models for real-world situations under sets of specific conditions. Such models are important to the extent that they can help us predict the behavior of future repetitions of an experiment. They are also of practical interest, since, if we have precise mathematical formulations for various situations frequently encountered in statistical analysis, computations of probabilities involved can be reduced to routine operations. Moreover, mathematical analysis of the probability model can help us see relationships we might not even think of looking for otherwise.

In the discussion that follows, whenever the required mathematical reasoning is not beyond the reader's reach we shall actually derive the mathematical expression for each special model from a set of assumptions. We shall also rely extensively on prepared tables, so that computational labor can be minimized. You should take notice at this stage, however, that it is more important for you to match a problem with the correct model than to memorize the model's detailed mathematical development.

8.2 THE DISCRETE UNIFORM PROBABILITY MODEL

We begin our study of special probability models with a very simple, but important, one called the *discrete uniform model*. The importance of this model rests with the fact that it furnishes the theoretical foundation as well as the practical means of selecting a simple random sample. From the very first chapter of this text we have mentioned the simple random sample a number of times, but we have up to now neither given it a precise definition nor presented a method for its selection. It is both convenient and necessary to do so now for two reasons. First, as we shall see immediately, all the special discrete probability models introduced in this chapter are actually generated by the process of random sampling. Second, when we commence the discussion of statistical inferences from Chapter 10 on, we shall be exclusively concerned with simple random samples.

Probability Mass and Cumulative Mass Functions of a Discrete Uniform Variable

A *discrete uniform random variable* results from the performance of a random experiment that can terminate in N mutually exclusive and equally likely ways. Consider, for example, N numbers; one on each of the N identical chips are placed in a box and mixed thoroughly, and then one chip is drawn from the box. The random variable so generated will clearly have as its *probability mass function,* PMF, as given by

$$f_u(x \mid N) = \frac{1}{N}, \qquad x = 1, 2, \ldots, N. \tag{8.1}$$

Here, the subscript u attached to f indicates that f_u stands for the functional notation for a uniform random variable. We shall use similar notations for other special probability models for quick and precise identifications. Now, (8.1), as a PMF, gives the probability that X can assume any specific value x as $1/N$; it is therefore called the *discrete uniform* or *rectangular probability model.* Note also that this model has N as its single parameter.

The *cumulative mass function* of a *discrete uniform random variable,* CMF, can be expressed by the following simple equation:

$$F_u(x) = P(X \leq x) = \frac{x}{N}, \qquad x = 1, 2, \ldots, N. \tag{8.2}$$

We have encountered the discrete uniform probability model before, though it was not given such a name. For instance, the probability distribution of the number of spots on a perfect die generated by tossing the die once is uniform because the probability associated with each and every one of the six possible outcomes of this experiment is a constant 1/6. The PMF and CMF of this random variable are simply

$$f_u(x \mid 6) = \frac{1}{6}, \qquad x = 1, 2, \ldots, 6$$

and

$$F_u(x) = \frac{x}{6}, \qquad x = 1, 2, \ldots, 6.$$

Simple Random Sampling and Simple Random Samples: An Application of the Discrete Uniform Probability Model

In this subsection we accomplish three things: (1) we define simple random sampling and simple random samples; (2) we bring out the relationship between the discrete uniform probability model and simple random sampling; (3) we explain the rationale that shows that the discrete uniform probability model furnishes a practical means of selecting simple random samples.

Simple random sampling, as the name implies, is a sampling procedure that generates simple random samples. A simple random sample, abbreviated to SRS, may be defined in three different but equivalent ways. When a sample of size n is drawn from a population with N elements, the sample is a *simple random sample* if any of the following is true. Also, if any one of the following is true, so are the other two.

1. All n items of the sample are selected independently of one another and all N items in the population have the same chance of being included in the sample. The "independence" of the selections is interpreted in the usual way for sampling with replacement. That is, the selection of a particular item in one draw has no influence on the probabilities of selection in any other draw. When sampling without replacement, an allowance must be made for the impossibility of selecting the same item a second time. Here, "independent" selection means that the selection of a particular item in one draw has no influence on the probabilities of selection in any other draw, except that the same item cannot be drawn twice.

2. At each selection, all remaining items in the population have the same chance of being drawn. If sampling is made with replacement, each item has a probability of $1/N$ of being drawn at each selection. If sampling is made without replacement, the probability of selection of each item remaining in the population at the first draw is $1/N$, at the second draw is $1/(N - 1)$, at the third draw is $1/(N - 2)$, and so on.

3. All the possible samples of a given size n are equally likely to be selected. Thus, if sampling is made with replacement, each possible sample has a probability of $1/N^n$ of occurring; if sampling is made without replacement, each possible sample has a probability of $1/{}_N P_n$ of occurring. The probabilities $1/{}_N P_n$, assume that the various possible samples respect the order of selection, so that reordering the distinct terms in a possible sample makes it a different possible sample. If order is ignored, each possible sample has probability of $1/{}_N C_n$ of occurring.

At this point, two observations may be made. First, the distinction between an SRS selected with replacement and one selected without replacement only exists when sampling is made from a finite population. Furthermore, we often call an SRS selected with replacement an *unconditional* SRS, and one selected without replacement as a *conditional* SRS. Second, when sampling is made from an infinite population, drawing with or without replacement would produce SRSs with identical properties, provided that all observations drawn into the sample are made from the same population and that these observations are made independently. Also, when an SRS is selected from a very large population, or when the size of the sample is less than or equal to 5% of the population size, the population can in effect be treated as if it were infinite, since then the changes in probability from one selection to another are negligible.

Let us now move on to explain the relationship between the selection of an SRS and the discrete uniform probability model. Consider first the case of simple random sampling without replacement. Suppose we have a population of ten elements with values ranging consecutively from 1 to 10. We wish to draw from it a conditional simple random sample of size $n = 3$. To do this, we may first write each one of the ten numbers on ten physically identical chips and put them in a jar. Next, we select one chip randomly at a time wtihout replacement until three chips have been selected. By this procedure, the probabilities associated with all selections are uniform. For the first choice, we have $f_u(x \mid 10) = 1/10$. For the second choice, we have $f_u(x \mid 9) = 1/9$. For the third choice, we have $f_u(x \mid 8) = 1/8$. Finally, let us evaluate the probability of drawing a sample that contains any three items, say 1, 3, and 7. Such a sample can be obtained by drawing, first, any one of the three numbers, with a probability of 3/10; by drawing second, either of the two remaining numbers, with a probability of 2/9; and by drawing third, the remaining number, with probability of 1/8. By the product rule for dependent events, we have the probability of getting this sample as follows:

$$(3/10)(2/9)(1/8) = \frac{3!7!}{10!} = \frac{1}{\dfrac{10!}{3!7!}} = \frac{1}{\dbinom{10}{3}},$$

here, $_{10}C_3$ is the total number of samples of size three from a population with ten items. From similar reasoning, each and every one of the possible samples has the same probability of $1/(_{10}C_3)$ of being selected. As a result, the procedure has yielded an SRS.

The preceding arguments constitute a verification of the statement that all combinations are equally likely. We may now generalize that if a sample of size n is to be drawn without replacement from a population with N items, then there are $_NC_n$ possible samples, each of which has a probability of $1/(_NC_n)$ of occurring. This means that the distribution of all the possible samples, itself is uniform with a PMF of

$$f_u(x \mid r) = \frac{1}{\dbinom{N}{n}},$$

where $r = {_NC_n}$, the number of possible samples of size n, and x stands for one of the r possible samples.

Next, let us consider the case of drawing an unconditional SRS of size n from a population of size N. Owing to sampling with replacement, we see that there would be a constant probability of $1/N$ to draw each and every one of the n items from the population. Furthermore, there would be N^n possible samples with equal probability of occurring. For example, let the population be one with only three items whose values are 1, 2, and 3. If an unconditional SRS of $n = 2$ is to be drawn from the said population, we would then have a sample space whose sample points are the possible samples of size 2 as given below:

$$S = \{(1, 1), (1, 2), (1, 3), (2, 1), (2, 2), (2, 3), (3, 1), (3, 2), (3, 3)\}.$$

where $N(S) = 9 =$ all the possible samples $= 3^2 = N^n$. Each of these possible samples clearly would have a probability of 1/9 to be drawn. Again, the possible samples in S would have a uniform distribution with the PMF

$$f_u(x \mid r) = \frac{1}{N(S)}$$

where $r = N(S)$, the total number of sample points in S and, as before, x stands for one of the r possible samples.

It seems that what we need is an "N-sided" die to generate a uniform population of N items. However, such a die is clearly impractical to construct. It might seem reasonable to place, say, N identical chips or balls into a large drum, rotated until the chips or balls are thoroughly mixed, and then select n items from the drum. In practice, though, one cannot expect to achieve a truly uniform distribution by such mixing or by similar experiments. The mixing is just not thorough enough to insure true randomness. For example, statisticians discovered substantial departures from the uniform distribution when balls were placed in a large container to select draftees for the U.S. Army in 1940 and again, three decades later, when the U.S. "draft lottery" first started. Thus, such physical experiments are very poor methods of selecting random samples. The only way, in practice, to draw a random sample is to use a table of random digits, where the table has been thoroughly tested to insure that its digits or numbers are random.

Most tables of random numbers are constructed to approximate very closely the situation in which the digits represent the outcomes of a series of random selections from a population whose values are 0, 1, 2, 3, 4, 5, 6, 7, 8, 9, and uniformly distributed as:

$$f_u(x \mid 10) = \frac{1}{10}, \qquad x = 0, 1, 2, \ldots, 9.$$

To obtain such a series, some physical process is devised to give good positive evidence that each of the ten digits has indeed a probability of 1/10 of occurring on each trial and that the separate trials are independent. Then the process is set in motion; thousands of digits or more are generated and written down in the order in which they occur. These digits are then tested for randomness. Table I in Appendix C is a short table of random digits generated by the use of a "pseudorandom-number generator" on a computer. The most extensive and best known table of random digits is Rand Corporation's *A Million Random Digits,* generated by an electronic roulette wheel.

Finally, to illustrate the use of a table of random digits for drawing a simple random sample of 500 items from a population of 8,900 items. We would begin by acquiring or preparing a list of the individual items in the population, such as names of employees, retail prices, households, or the like. Such a list is the frame or the sampled population as defined in Chapter 1. Next, we assign each item in the frame a serial number from 0001 to 8900. then we obtain our sample in the following fashion.

1. Enter the table in a haphazard manner by blindly pointing a finger to it. In a table with two or more pages, blindly pick a page and then blindly pick a spot on the selected page. "Blindly" is meant literally—close your eyes. The number under the finger becomes the starting point. Then the table may be read vertically, horizontally, or diagonally, provided it has been tested in all these directions. If in doubt, read it horizontally just as you would ordinarily read a printed page. The table can be used in any systematic way once the haphazard start is made.

2. Read all the four-digit numbers in the table without skipping any. Since our serial numbers have four digits, our random number needs four digits. If the number is 8900 or smaller, record it. If the number if greater than 8900, do not record it. (If the sample is to be drawn without replacement, do not record a number when it appears a second time). If 0000 is read, we regard it as the serial number just before 0001 or just after 9999, but we make our choice of meaning before using the table. Here it does not matter, since neither meaning would be recorded. Proceed in this way until we obtain five hundred numbers. (This procedure is quite general. If N is between 101 and 1,000, use three-digit random numbers; if N is between 10,001 and 100,000, use five-digit random numbers; and so on.)

3. Take from the list those five hundred items that have the corresponding recorded numbers, for these are the members of the desired simple random sample.

Simple random sampling is certainly a practical procedure if the population is not large and if it is relatively easy and inexpensive to find the sampling units, or to prepare the frame. It could also be a practical procedure for large populations whose elements are concentrated within a small area. For instance, the study of all expense vouchers of a large corporation, the investigation of the attitudes of all the employees toward a pension plan in a big company, the survey of student's study habits at a given university, and so on, can easily be made by a simple random sample.

One drawback of applying simple random sampling to large populations is that the population must be numbered. Note that it is not necessary literally to number every item in the population, but it has to be done at least conceptually. "Conceptually" here means that once a selecting serial number has been read from a table of random digits, there is absolutely no doubt which item in the population has been selected. Theoretically, we could obtain simple random samples by numbering all the eligible voters, all the households in America, all automobile owners, all retail stores, or all refugees from other countries, and so forth. Such a procedure, however, would be extremely costly and might even be physically impossible. As a matter of fact, many economic and business data cannot be effectively gathered by simple random sampling. Consequently, instead of using simple random sampling, we often employ other kinds of random sample designs, as presented in the Appendix to Chapter 10.

Despite the practical difficulty of drawing an SRS, we will consider only this type of sampling in our later work on statistical inferences. There are two reasons for this practice. On the one hand, an SRS possesses many desirable properties that provide great convenience in developing theorems in sampling; on the other hand, any other probability sampling plans involve simple random sampling at some stage.

Even though our main concern is with an SRS, other types of sampling plans will also be introduced in the Appendix to Chapter 10. To avoid boring repetition, when we mention a "sample" without any adjective before it, we shall always mean the simple random sample. The abbreviation SRS will also be frequently employed in our future presentations.

8.3 THE BERNOULLI PROBABILITY MODEL

We shall now consider another simple probability model called the Bernoulli model. Our interest in this model is mainly for the purpose of furnishing a basis for the binomial probability model, which is appropriate for a vast number of real-world situations. The Bernoulli model (named in honor of Jacques Bernoulli, who lived during the latter half of the seventeenth century) applies to a random variable that can only assume two values. For simplicity, let the two values be 0 and 1, with π' and π as their respective probabilities, where $\pi' = 1 - \pi$; then the *probability mass function*, PMF, of a *Bernoulli variable* is simply

x	$f(x)$
0	π'
1	π
Sum	1

For the PMF above, we note that

$$\sum xf(x) = \pi \quad \text{and} \quad \sum x^2 f(x) = \pi.$$

Consequently, we have for the Bernoulli variable

$$E(X) = \mu_X = \pi \tag{8.3}$$

and

$$V(X) = \sigma_X^2 = E(X^2) - \mu_X^2 = \pi - \pi^2 = \pi(1 - \pi) = \pi\pi'. \tag{8.4}$$

The Bernoulli model has a single parameter π (the probability of success); it is appropriate whenever one is interested in an experiment that would result in an event E or its opposite $\bar{E}$, such as success or failure, hit or miss, yes or no, pass or fail, in favor of or against, defective or nondefective, and so on. Also note that, in statistical terminology, "favorable" or "successful" outcome does not necessarily imply outcomes that are "desirable" in practice.

In general, a Bernoulli variable may be considered as a single random observation from a population, infinite or finite, whose elementary units may be classified into two mutually exclusive categories. Many decision problems are concerned with populations of this kind and they are often called *dichotomous populations*. Some examples of such populations are as follows.

1. A coed college with 10,000 students, of which 5,500 are males and 4,500 are females.

2. A shipment of 1,000 transistors, of which 150 are defectives and 850 are nondefectives.

3. The tossing of a coin continuously and indefinitely, where the results are half heads and half tails.

4. The set of positive integers, where half are even numbers and the other half are odd numbers.

In dealing with the above and similar populations, we may know whether a process is Bernoulli or not all the time, but we may not know the value of the parameter π. With a fair die, for instance, we may know the process is Bernoulli with probability of 1/6 as a success (for say, one) and the probability of 5/6 of a failure (other numbers). However, if we are given a die and told it is not fair, the process of rolling the die may still be Bernoulli, but the value of the parameter π is now unknown to us. Thus, we may have a Bernoulli process with a known or an unknown parameter. Many business processes can be characterized for analytical purposes, as Bernoulli, even though they are not truly Bernoulli in every respect. If the "fit" is close enough, we may assume the Bernoulli model is a reasonable characterization.

Suppose a production process is employed to produce a certain output, 10% of which is defective and 90% good; then the process is Bernoulli with $\pi = 0.10$ and $\pi' = 0.90$, provided π remains stable at 0.10 for each unit of output and defective and good outputs are mixed in a random order. For this process, we have $E(X) = 0.10$ and $V(X) = 0.10(0.90) = 0.09$.

We have assumed that the production process is set for a long run of output and the probability of defective output is sufficiently stable. If, however, the process is subject to fast wear, then more defective units will be produced as the end of the run approaches, and π is not stable. In many production processes, the occurrence of defective and non-defective output is sufficiently randomized to be considered as Bernoulli. In other cases, the probability of success may remain stable through a production run, but it may change from one run to another owing to, for example, machine settings. In such a case the process could still be considered as Bernoulli, but consideration must be given to the change in the probability of success from run to run.

8.4 THE BINOMIAL PROBABILITY MODEL

Binomial Variables

A *binomial random variable* may be considered as the sum of n independent Bernoulli variables. More precisely, a variable is *binomial* if it is generated under the following three postulates.

1. There must be a fixed number n of repeated trials that are statistically independent.

2. Each trial must be a Bernoulli process—that is, each trial must result in either a "success" or a "failure".

3. All trials must have identical probabilities of success, π, so that the probability of a failure also remains at a constant value of π' that is equal to $(1 - \pi)$.

These conditions are satisfied if sampling is made from an infinite dichotomous population or if sampling is made with replacement from a finite dichotomous population. These conditions are also approximately satisfied if a relatively small sample is selected without replacement from a very large dichotomous population, since the population can be considered effectively as infinite, as explained before.

A random variable that counts the number of successes under the foregoing conditions is called a *binomial variable*; it is discrete and has $n + 1$ possible values. For example, the number of heads in tossing three coins is a binomial variable and it has the four possible values of 0, 1, 2, and 3; there are $3 + 1$ values.

The Binomial Probability Mass Function

The probability mass function of a binomial variable attempts to answer this question: If we conduct an experiment under the stated conditions n times, (i.e., if an SRS of size n is selected with replacement from a dichotomous population), what is the probability of obtaining exactly x

successes? To be more precise, and for the purpose of deriving a general mathematical expression for the binomial PMF by way of answering a question such as this, let us consider a concrete example. Suppose in a lot of television transistors, 10% is known to be defective and suppose an SRS of $n = 5$ is drawn with replacement from the lot; we would have the number of defectives in the sample as a binomial variable with the values of 0, 1, 2, 3, 4, and 5. Let X stand for this variable, we now may ask: What is the probability for X to take on each of these values?

To answer the question posed above, we note that, because of statistical independence, the probability of selecting a defective item d at any draw in the sequence of five selection is $\pi = 0.10$ and that of selecting a good item g in the sequence is $\pi' = 0.90$. Now, consider $P(X = 0)$. For $X = 0$, all the items in the sample of five must be good—the sequence must be $ggggg$. The probability for this sequence, by the rule of multiplication for independent events, is $(0.90)(0.90)(0.90)(0.90)(0.90) = (0.90)^5 = 0.59049$. Thus, $P(X = 0) = 0.59049$. Next, consider $P(X = 1)$. For $X = 1$, we would have the following five sequences: $ggggd, gggdg, ggdgg, gdggg, dgggg$. For any of these sequences, say, the first, the probability is $(0.90)(0.90)(0.90)0.90)(0.10) = (0.10)(0.90)^4 = 0.06561$. Since we have here five sequences that are mutually exclusive and each with a probability of 0.06561 to occur, we have, by the special rule of addition, $P(X = 1) = 5(0.06561) = 0.32805$. Probabilities for other values of X can be obtained in a similar manner. By generalizing the procedure employed here, we can then derive the mathematical expression of the *probability mass function for a binomial random variable* as

$$f_b(x \mid n, \pi) = \binom{n}{x} (\pi)^x (\pi')^{n-x}, \qquad x = 0, 1, 2, \ldots, n. \qquad (8.5)$$

Thus, a binomial PMF has the two parameters n and π with $n = 1, 2, 3, \ldots$ and $0 < \pi < 1$.

The logic for (8.5) must be fully understood. First of all, this equation gives us the probability of obtaining x successes and $(n - x)$ failures in n trials of the Bernoulli process. Next, the term $(\pi)^x (\pi')^{n-x}$ is the probability of any sequence of x successes and $(n - x)$ failures. The total probability of x successes and $(n - x)$ failures is obtained by multiplying the probability of a single sequence by the total number of sequences that are mutually exclusive and equally likely. The total number of equiprobable sequences, as you may recall, is equal to the number of distinct permutations of two kinds of objects, such as here, when x are alike and $(n - x)$ are alike. You may also recall that, in this special case, the number of permutations is identical with the number of combinations. Because of this identity, and because of notational convenience, statisticians always use the term $_nC_x$ to specify the operation $n!/x!(n - x)!$ in (8.5). Finally, the term $_nC_x$ is often called the *binomial coefficient,* and the binomial model derives its name from the fact (8.5) is the general term of the "binomial expansion" of $(\pi' + \pi)^n = 1^n = 1$.

Returning to our previous example, we see that the number of defectives in the sample of five has the following specific binomial PMF:

$$f_b(x \mid 5, 0.10) = \binom{5}{x}(0.10)^x(0.90)^{5-x}, \qquad x = 0, 1, 2, 3, 4, 5.$$

From this function, we have then

$$f_b(0 \mid 5, 0.10) = \binom{5}{0}(0.10)^0(0.90)^5 = \frac{5!}{0!5!}(0.10)^0(0.90)^5$$
$$= (1)(1)(0.59049)$$
$$= 0.59049;$$

$$f_b(1 \mid 5, 0.10) = \binom{5}{1}(0.10)(0.90)^4 = \frac{5!}{1!4!}(0.10)(0.90)^4$$
$$= 5(0.10)(0.65610)$$
$$= 0.32805;$$

$$f_b(2 \mid 5, 0.10) = \binom{5}{2}(0.10)^2(0.90)^3 = \frac{5!}{2!3!}(0.10)^2(0.90)^3$$
$$= (10)(0.01)(0.7290)$$
$$= 0.07290;$$

$$f_b(3 \mid 5, 0.10) = \binom{5}{3}(0.10)^3(0.90)^2 = \frac{5!}{3!2!}(0.10)^3(0.90)^2$$
$$= (10)(0.001)(0.8100)$$
$$= 0.00810;$$

$$f_b(4 \mid 5, 0.10) = \binom{5}{4}(0.10)^4(0.90) = \frac{5!}{4!1!}(0.10)^4(0.90)$$
$$= 5(0.0001)(0.90)$$
$$= 0.00045;$$

$$f_b(5 \mid 5, 0.10) = \binom{5}{5}(0.10)^5(0.90)^0 = \frac{5!}{5!0!}(0.10)^5(0.90)^0$$
$$= (1)(0.00001)(1)$$
$$= 0.00001.$$

These results add up to 1, as they should.

The Binomial Cumulative Mass Function

The *cumulative mass function* CMF *of a binomial variable,* like that of any discrete random variable, gives the probability of obtaining r successes or less, in n trials, with $r \leq n$, and is obtained by adding the probabilities of the individual terms of the binomial variable equal to or

TABLE 8.1 The PMF and CMF of a
Binomial Variable with $\pi = 0.1$ and
$n = 5$

x	$f_b(x)$	$F_b(x)$
0	0.59049	0.59049
1	0.32805	0.91854
2	0.07290	0.99144
3	0.00810	0.99954
4	0.00045	0.99999
5	0.00001	1.00000
Sum	1.00000	—

less than r. In symbols, we have

$$F_b(r \mid n, \pi) = f_b(0 \mid n, \pi) + f_b(1 \mid n, \pi) + \cdots + f_b(r \mid n, \pi)$$

$$= \sum_{x=0}^{r} f_b(x \mid n, \pi). \tag{8.6}$$

Equation (8.6) simply specifies the summation of the binomial probabilities of the individual terms with r as the upper limit of the summation. Applying this formula to our current example of the number of defective transistors in a sample of five, for instance, we have

$$F_b(0) = \sum_{x=0}^{0} f_b(x \mid 5, 0.10) = \sum_{x=0}^{0} \binom{5}{0}(0.10)^0(0.90)^5 = 0.59049;$$

$$F_b(1) = \sum_{x=0}^{1} f_b(x \mid 5, 0.10) = f_b(0) + f_b(1)$$

$$= \binom{5}{0}(0.10)^0(0.90)^5 + \binom{5}{1}(0.10)(0.90)^5$$

$$= 0.59049 + 0.32805 = 0.91854;$$

and so on. The complete CMF for this example is presented, together with the PMF, in Table 8.1.

The Use of Binomial Cumulative Probability Table

Equations (8.5) and (8.6) are definitional equations and their applications seem quite straightforward from the simple example we have employed. However, as you can easily imagine, when n is large, computations with these equations become very time-consuming and laborious. Fortunately, they are seldom required for computational purposes, since extensive binomial probability tables are available. Table II in Appendix C contains cumulative binomial probabilities for selected values of n and π. This table can also be used to obtain the individual terms of binomial probabilities as the following examples will demonstrate. Tables such as this often have large gaps in the values of

π as well as of n. When we cannot use the table, we can compute the binomial probabilities by computer.

Example 1 Interviewing the Labor Force of a Manufacturing Town

Eighty percent of the workers in a certain manufacturing town are known to be union members. In a survey of the town's labor situations, an economist has selected an SRS with $n = 20$ for interview. For this experiment, let us try to answer the following questions.

1. What is the probability that the sample will contain 15 union members or less?

2. What is the probability that the sample will contain at least 15 union members?

3. What is the probability that the sample will contain exactly 15 union members?

Before answering these questions, it may be observed that it has not been specified in the foregoing presentation whether sampling is made with or without replacement. In this experiment, however, the sample is evidently very small relative to the whole labor force in the town—i.e. the population. As a result, the probability of drawing a union member, even without replacement, at any selection would remain approximately at $\pi = 0.80$; in other words, the population here can effectively be treated as if it were infinite and, thus, the binomial model can be employed as a very close approximation. Now, with the aid of Table II, the foregoing questions can be answered quite easily as indicated below.

1. $P(X \leq 15) = F_b(15 \mid 20, 0.80) = 0.3704$;

2. $P(X \geq 15) = 1 - P(X \leq 14) = 1 - F_b(14 \mid 20, 0.80)$
   $= 1 - 0.1958 = 0.8042$;

3. $P(X = 15) = f_b(15 \mid 20, 0.80)$
   $= F_b(15) - F_b(14)$
   $= 0.3704 - 0.1958 = 0.1746.$

These probabilities are of course read directly from Table II. However, you should try to understand the calculations for the last two probabilities by recalling what you have learned from the last chapter. It would also be quite instructive to try to give verbal explanations of the manipulations in (2) and (3).

Example 2 An Acceptance Decision Rule

The purchasing agent of the U.S. Navy has to decide whether to accept or reject a shipment of 100,000 rain coats. The shipment has 10% defective units. Suppose he adopts a decision rule such as this: (a) take an SRS with $n = 15$, accept the shipment if the sample contains 1 defective unit or less; (b) reject the shipment if there are more than 2 defectives in the sample; (c) if the sample contains exactly 2 defectives, then take another sample of 35 and if the number of defectives in the combined sample is 3 or less, accept the shipment. According to this decision rule, what is the probability that

1. the shipment will be accepted with the first sample?

2. a second sample will be taken?

3. the shipment will be accepted with the combined sample?

According to this decision rule, the shipment will be accepted if the sample of $n = 15$ contains 1 or less units of defectives, and the probability for this to occur is

$$P(X \leqslant 1) = F_b(1 \mid 15, 0.10) = 0.54904.$$

Next, a second sample will be taken only when the first sample contains exactly 2 defective units, and

$$P(X = 2) = F_b(2) - F_b(1) = 0.81594 - 0.54904 = 0.26690.$$

Finally, the shipment will be accepted with the combined sample, with $n = 15 + 35 = 50$ if it contains 3 or less defectives, and

$$P(X \leqslant 3) = F_b(3 \mid 50, 0.10) = 0.2569.$$

These results indicate that if the fraction defective in the shipment is indeed 0.10, then it is very unlikely that it will be accepted under this rule. If the Navy can tolerate 10% or less defectives, the purchasing agent's decision rule seems to be too conservative or too cautious.

The Expectation and Variance of a Binomial Variable

A binomial variable X, the number of successes in n independent trials, may be considered as a sum

$$X = X_1 + X_2 + \cdots + X_n,$$

where each X_i is a Bernoulli variable with expectation π. Thus, the expectation of the binomial variable may be thought of as the sum of expectations of the n Bernoulli variables. That is,

$$E(X) = E(X_1) + E(X_2) + \cdots + E(X_n)$$
$$= \underbrace{\pi + \pi + \cdots + \pi}_{(n \text{ times})} = n\pi$$

That is, for a binomial variable

$$E(X) = n\pi. \tag{8.7}$$

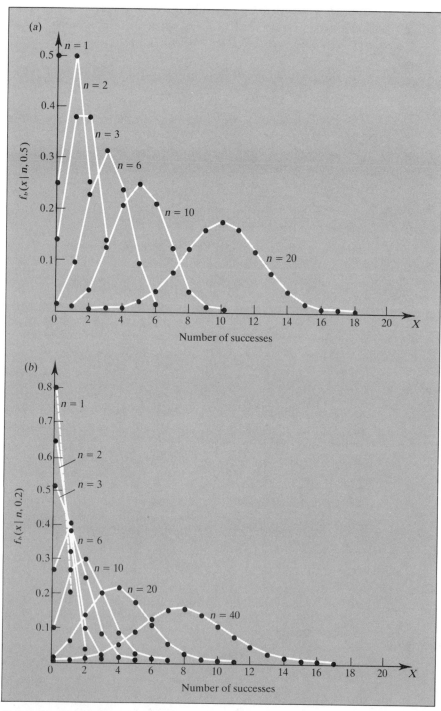

FIGURE 8.1 Binomial distributions with (a) $\pi = 0.5$ and (b) $\pi = 0.2$ for a few selected values of n.

Furthermore, the Bernoulli variables are identical and independent. As such, their variances are also additive. That is, the binomial variable, as the sum of n Bernoulli variables, must have as its variance the sum of the variances of n Bernoulli variables:

$$V(X) = V(X_1) + V(X_2) + \cdots + V(X_n)$$
$$= \underbrace{\pi\pi' + \pi\pi' + \cdots + \pi\pi'}_{\text{(the sum of } n \text{ products)}} = n\pi\pi'$$

That is,

$$V(X) = n\pi\pi' \qquad (8.8)$$

Thus, for the example of union members, we have

$$E(X) = n\pi = 20(0.9) = 18 \text{ union members,}$$

and

$$V(X) = n\pi\pi' = 20(0.9)(0.1) = 1.8.$$

As usual, the square root of this variance is the standard deviation. For our current example, we have

$$\sigma_X = \sqrt{n\pi\pi'} = \sqrt{1.8} \doteq 1.34 \text{ union members.}$$

Before concluding our discussion of the binomial probability model, we should note that the binomial distribution is symmetric when $\pi = 0.5$, and skewed when $\pi \neq 0.5$. When $\pi < 0.5$, it is skewed to the right; when $\pi > 0.5$, it is skewed to the left. The interchange of π and π' in any binomial distribution would yield its mirror image. The skewness of a binomial distribution, regardless of the size of π, becomes less and less pronounced as n continues to increase. Some of these properties are revealed by Figure 8.1.

8.5 THE MULTINOMIAL PROBABILITY MODEL

The binomial model, which deals with independent trials with two outcomes each, is but a special case of the *multinomial probability law*, which is concerned with sampling from a population whose elements can be classified into three or more mutually exclusive categories. The extension from a binomial model to a multinomial model is in principle a rather simple one, whereby we merely replace the binomial coefficient with the multinomial coefficient in the data generating process.

When we sample from a population that consists of k, $k > 2$, mutually exclusive types of elements, then each trial is capable of yielding k possible outcomes, E_i, $i = 1, 2, \ldots, k$, with respective probabilities of occurrence $\pi_1, \pi_2, \ldots, \pi_k$. The sum of these probabilities is obviously unity. If a simple random sample of size n is selected, the n selections are independent, and the π's remain constant from one trial to another. Under these circumstances, we may wish to answer the question: What is the probability of obtaining exactly x_1 occurrences of E_1, x_2 occurrences of $E_2, \ldots$, and x_k occurrences of E_k, given that $x_1 + x_2 + \cdots + x_k = n$?

To answer this question, we note that the n trials are independent and, thus, the probability of any stated sequence of outcomes is equal to the product of their separate probabilities; that is, $(\pi_1)^{x_1}(\pi_2)^{x_2} \cdots (\pi_k)^{x_k}$. Furthermore, the number of distinct sequences yielding the stated number of results of each kind is equal to the number of ways to permute n things taken all together at one time when x_1 are alike, x_2 are alike, $\ldots$, and x_k are alike. Since all these sequences are mutually exclusive and have equal probabilities of occurrence, the total probability of $(x_1, x_2, \ldots, x_k \mid \pi_1, \pi_2, \ldots, \pi_k)$ is then the sum of all the sequence probabilities. This total has

$$_nP_{(x_1, x_2, \ldots, x_k)} = \frac{n!}{x_1! x_2! \cdots x_k!}$$

terms, and this notation is called the *multinomial coefficient*. Thus, similar to the binomial case, the *probability mass function of a multinomial variable* is

$$f_m(x_1, x_2, \ldots, x_k \mid \pi_1, \pi_2, \ldots, \pi_k) = \frac{n!}{x_1! x_2! \cdots x_k!} (\pi_1)^{x_1}(\pi_2)^{x_2} \cdots (\pi_k)^{x_k}, \quad (8.9)$$

where

$$\pi_1 + \pi_2 + \cdots + \pi_k = 1; \quad x_1 + x_2 + \cdots + x_k = n,$$

$$x_i = 0, 1, 2, \ldots, k.$$

It is interesting to note that since x's have a fixed total—any one of them can be eliminated and replaced by the expression of n minus the sum of the others; and that any one of the π's can be expressed as 1 minus the sum of the others. Owing to these two properties, we may consider the multinomial probability model as a joint distribution of $k - 1$ discrete variables, and as possessing k independent parameters. However, (8.9) gives us the symmetric form of this model and it is the simplest mathematical statement.

Finally, we note that the sum of the PMF of the multinomial variable, taken over all possible values of the x's, as 1 can be seen from the fact that $f_m(x_1, x_2, \ldots, x_k)$ is the general term of the multinomial expansion of $(\pi_1 + \pi_2 + \cdots + \pi_k)^n = 1^n = 1$.

Consider first a simple example of the application of (8.9). Fifteen dice are tossed together; what is the probability that each of the odd numbers will appear exactly twice and that each of the even numbers will appear exactly three times? There are six outcomes in a single trial, each with a probability of 1/6. Now, if we denote x_1 as the number of times that a 1 appears, x_2 as the number of times that a 2 appears, and so on, then we have the desired probability as

$$f_m(2, 3, 2, 3, 2, 3 \mid 1/6, 1/6, 1/6, 1/6, 1/6, 1/6)$$

which is equal to

$$\frac{15!}{2!3!2!3!2!3!} (1/6)^2 (1/6)^3 (1/6)^2 (1/6)^3 (1/6)^2 (1/6)^3 \doteq 0.0016.$$

Now, let us provide a more thorough example. Suppose that a certain commodity is controlled by three stores, E_1, E_2, and E_3, in a certain town. Their respective shares of the market are known to be 0.40, 0.35 and 0.25. If an SRS of 4 is selected from the customers of this commodity, what is the distribution of the trade division among the three stores?

Clearly, the experiment above qualifies as a multinomial process with $n = 4$, $\pi_1 = 0.40$, $\pi_2 = 0.35$ and $\pi_3 = 0.25$. Now, let x_1, x_2 and x_3 denote the respective number of customers of E_1, E_2 and E_3; we have the following multinomial PMF:

$$f_m(x_1, x_2, x_3) = \frac{4!}{x_1! x_2! x_3!} (0.40)^{x_1} (0.35)^{x_2} (0.25)^{x_3};$$

$$(x_1 + x_2 + x_3) = 4, \qquad x_i = 0, 1, 2, 3, 4.$$

Thus,

$$f_m(4, 0, 0) = \frac{4!}{4!0!0!} (0.40)^4 (0.35)^0 (0.25)^0 = 0.0256,$$

$$f_m(3, 1, 0) = \frac{4!}{3!1!0!} (0.40)^3 (0.35)(0.25)^0 = 0.0896,$$

and so on. The whole distribution is presented in Table 8.2.

Sometimes, in the repeated trials of a multinomial process, we may be interested in the probability of the exact number of occurrences for

TABLE 8.2 Multinomial PMF with $n = 4$, $\pi_1 = 0.40$, $\pi_2 = 0.35$ and $\pi_3 = 0.25$; PMF of the Trade Share Example

(x_1, x_2, x_3)	$f_m(x_i)^*$	(x_1, x_2, x_3)	$f_m(x_i)^*$	(x_1, x_2, x_3)	$f_m(x_i)^*$
4, 0, 0	0.0256	2, 0, 2	0.0600	0, 4, 0	0.0150
3, 1, 0	0.0890	1, 3, 0	0.0686	0, 3, 1	0.0429
3, 0, 1	0.0640	1, 2, 1	0.1470	0, 2, 2	0.0459
2, 2, 0	0.1176	1, 1, 2	0.1050	0, 1, 3	0.0219
2, 1, 1	0.1680	1, 0, 3	0.0250	0, 0, 4	0.0039

* The overall sum of $f_m(x_i)$ is 1.0000.

only a few, instead of all of the k possible outcomes. For example, suppose that failures of a certain electronic mechanism may be due to six different causes, $E_1, \ldots, E_6$ with respective probabilities 0.40, 0.30, 0.10, 0.10, 0.05 and 0.05 of occurring. These causes are known to be independent and simultaneous defects are only a very remote possibility. If failures are observed at random, say, six times, what is the probability that the failures contain two instances of E_1 and E_2 each?

To solve this problem, we first note that, among the six possible outcomes, we are only interested in the probability of x_1 occurrences of E_1 and x_2 occurrences of E_2. The occurrences of each of the four other outcomes are not required. As such, we actually have a new experiment that can be thought of as having only three outcomes, E_1, E_2 and E_p, with the last representing the occurrence of any of the other four outcomes in the original experiment, where the subscript p stands for "pooled". The corresponding probabilities now can be restated as π_1, π_2, and π_p, with $\pi_p = \pi_3 + \pi_4 + \pi_5 + \pi_6$. With these designations, we see that $x_p = n - (x_1 + x_2)$. Similarly to (8.9), we then have

$$f_m(x_1, x_2, x_p \mid \pi_1, \pi_2, \pi_p) = \frac{n!}{x_1!\, x_2!\, x_p!} (\pi_1)^{x_1}(\pi_2)^{x_2}(\pi_p)^{x_p}$$

for our present problem, which can be generalized for k outcomes with any number of a given type of particular outcomes specified. Turning to the numerical calculations for our current example, we have $\pi_p = 0.10 + 0.10 + 0.05 + 0.05 = 0.30$ and $x_p = 6 - 4 = 2$. Hence,

$$f_m(2, 2, 2 \mid 0.4, 0.3, 0.3) = \frac{6!}{2!2!2!} (0.4)^2(0.3)^2(0.3)^2$$

$$= 0.11664.$$

Since it can be shown that in the multinomial model the number of occurrences of each possible type of outcome in n independent trials can be considered as a binomial variable, thus expectation and variance of each can be given as

$$E(X_i) = n\pi_i, \qquad\qquad i = 1, 2, \ldots, k; \qquad\qquad (8.10)$$
$$V(X_i) = n\pi_i(1 - \pi_i)$$
$$= n\pi_i\pi_i', \qquad\qquad i = 1, 2, \ldots, k. \qquad\qquad (8.11)$$

In concluding this section, we may observe that computation of multinomial probabilities can become time-consuming and tedious when n is at all large. Tabulations of these probabilities are cumbersome and impractical, because of the vast variety of choices of π_i, x_i and n. When inferential situations arise in which the multinomial probability model is required, we often resort to its approximation by other probability models, such as the chi-square test on frequencies which will be introduced in Chapter 26. We have presented a brief discussion of the multinomial model here because it is at once very interesting and not conceptually difficult. Furthermore, it is quite easy to apply when n is small and this occurs not too infrequently in actual situations.

8.6 THE HYPERGEOMETRIC PROBABILITY MODEL

The derivations of the binomial and multinomial probability distributions require statistical independence among the successive trials. This is realizable when we are dealing with infinite populations or when we conduct random sampling with replacement from finite populations. The *hypergeometric probability model* that we now present applies to sampling from finite populations without replacement.

The Hypergeometric Mass Function

A *hypergeometric variable,* as in the case of the binomial model, is called the number of successes and is generated from the following set of conditions.

1. Sampling is made without replacement from a dichotomous population of size N.

2. The result of each draw can be classified into two mutually exclusive categories, such as success and failure.

3. Successive selections are statistically dependent.

4. The drawing is repeated a fixed number of times n.

Under those conditions, as in the binomial case, we again may wish to answer the question: What is the probability of obtaining exactly x successes in n trials? As usual, this question is answered by the probability mass function of the random variable under consideration.

To derive the PMF under the foregoing conditions, consider a population of N items, k of which possess a certain characteristic and $(N - k)$ of which do not possess such a characteristic. Obviously, if a random selection of an item is made from such a population, the result must be either one of the k's (successes) or one of the $(N - k)$'s (failures). It is also clear that, since the n random selections are made without replacement from the population, all the n outcomes are dependent, and the probability of success changes from one draw to the other. It is under these conditions that we wish to determine the probability of obtaining exactly x items that are of type $k,$ or of obtaining successes, in a random sample of size n.

With the stated conditions, we now proceed to formally establish the PMF of a hypergeometric variable. To do this, let us first observe that the total number of ways to draw n items from N things is $(_NC_n)$. Next, note that to draw exactly x items of a certain characteristic is the same as to draw $(n - x)$ items that do not possess the characteristic from a total of $(N - k)$ items available. Thus, the total number of ways to draw x k's and $(n - x)$ non-k's is $(_kC_x)_{N-k}C_{n-x}$. Finally, because of random sampling, all items that are still available after any number of selections has been made, are equally likely to be chosen. As a result, we can assign equal probabilities to each of the $_NC_n$ points in the sample space. These arguments lead us to conclude that the *probability mass function of a hypergeometric variable, X,* which answers the question of obtaining exactly x successes in n trials, is

$$f_h(x \mid N, n, k) = \frac{\binom{k}{x}\binom{N - k}{n - x}}{\binom{N}{n}}. \tag{8.12}$$

Equation (8.12) is defined in terms of the three fixed numbers, N, n and k, which are the parameters of the hypergeometric probability mass function. It is important to take notice now of two important facts about probability models and the parent populations from which the former are generated. First, when a probability model is generated by the random sampling process, the model is a mathematical function of the parent population. The parameters of the model are often different from those of the original population. For example, in our current discussion, the parameters of the hypergeometric model are N, n and k, but only N and k are the parameters of the dichotomous population in question, while n is not. Again, in the binomial case, the parameter of the population is π, but the binomial model has π and n as its parameters. Second, each special probability model is a family of distributions; that is, each PMF defines not one, but many probability distributions. Each of these distributions follows the same mathematical rule for assigning probabilities to the possible values of the random variable, but the particular probabilities assigned are dependent upon the values of the parameters of the mathematical function, and each of these parameters, in general, could assume a vast number of values. For example, given the population parameter π, we would have a different binomial distribution for each possible value of n. Again, for the same n, a different binomial distribution results if the population parameter π changes. Similar comments can be made for the hypergeometric probability model. In this connection, however, it must also be noted that in the case of the discrete uniform model, the population and the function share the same parameter N. Also, in the case of the Bernoulli model, both the population and the function share the same parameter π. This happens because in each of the two cases we are concerned with a single random observation from the population, and as a consequence, the random variable so generated would have the same distribution as the parent population. (These observations, as we shall see in the following chapter, also apply to continuous probability models.)

Returning to our present presentation, let us cite an example of the application of (8.12). A television repairman has 5 picture tubes for a certain make of television in his stock. Without his knowing, 2 of the tubes are defective. In answering the calls for repair one day, he needs two picture tubes of this kind and he selects 2 out of the 5 tubes at random on his way out to work. What is the probability that his sample contains no defective tubes; one defective tube; two defective tubes?

A moment's reflection will indicate to you that the number of defective items in the repairman's sample is a hypergeometric variable with $N = 5$, $n = 2$ and $k = 2$. Therefore,

$$P(X = 0) = f_h(0 \mid 5, 2, 2) = \frac{\binom{2}{0}\binom{5-2}{2-0}}{\binom{5}{2}}$$

$$= \frac{\binom{2}{0}\binom{3}{2}}{\binom{5}{2}} = \frac{(1)(3)}{10} = \frac{3}{10},$$

$$P(X = 1) = f_h(1 \mid 5, 2, 2) = \frac{\binom{2}{1}\binom{3}{1}}{\binom{5}{2}} = \frac{6}{10},$$

$$F(X = 2) = f_h(2 \mid 5, 2, 2) = \frac{\binom{2}{2}\binom{3}{0}}{\binom{5}{2}} = \frac{1}{10}.$$

These results indicate that the repairman has 3 chances in 10 of completing both jobs, 6 chances in 10 of completing only one of the two jobs, and 1 chance in 10 of completing neither of the two jobs.

The Hypergeometric Cumulative Mass Function

The *cumulative mass function of a hypergeometric variable* X gives the probability of X to take on a value of r or less, $r \leq n$. It thus simply specifies the summation of the hypergeometric probabilities as defined by (8.12) from $x = 0$ to $x = r$, as in any discrete case. Symbolically,

$$F_h(r \mid N, n, k) = \sum_{x=0}^{r} f_h(x \mid N, n, k). \tag{8.13}$$

Applying (8.13) to our previous example, we have

$$F_h(0) = \sum_{x=0}^{0} f_h(x \mid 5, 2, 2) = f_h(0) = \frac{3}{10};$$

$$F_h(1) = \sum_{x=0}^{1} f_h(x \mid 5, 2, 2) = f_h(0) + f_h(1) = \frac{3}{10} + \frac{6}{10} = \frac{9}{10};$$

$$F_h(2) = \sum_{x=0}^{2} f_h(x \mid 5, 2, 2) = f_h(0) + f_h(1) + f_h(2)$$

$$= \frac{3}{10} + \frac{6}{10} + \frac{1}{10} = \frac{10}{10}.$$

The Hypergeometric Probability Table

Table III in Appendix C gives values for both $f_h(x)$ and $F_h(x)$ for $N = 10$. This table is a small part of the *Tables of the Hypergeometric Probability Distribution,* tabulated by G. J. Lieherman and D. B. Owen and published by the Stanford University Press in 1961. These tables provide individual and cumulative hypergeometric probabilities for $N = 2, 3, 4, \ldots, 50, 60, 70, 80, 90, 100$, as well as for selected values of N between 100 and 1,000. There is also an appendix with these tables that provides 15-place logarithms for $1!, 2!, \ldots, 2{,}000!$.

In using tables for hypergeometric distributions, one should observe a very interesting property: when k and n are interchanged, there will be no effect on the hypergeometric probabilities. That is,

$$f_h(x \mid N, n, k) = f_h(x \mid N, k, n) \qquad (8.14a)$$

and

$$F_h(r \mid N, n, k) = F_h(r \mid N, k, n). \qquad (8.14b)$$

To illustrate the use of Table III, let us consider this example. Professor Vanessa Smith is an easy grader. She gives her students only As and Bs. In one of her classes with ten students, she has given 6 As and 4 Bs in the final examination. If four examination papers are selected at random without replacement, what is the probability for us to find that (1) all 4 are As; (2) 3 or less are As; (3) 2 or more are As?

To solve this problem, we see that the number of As in the sample is a hypergeometric variable with $N = 10$, $n = 4$ and $k = 6$. Hence

1. $P(X = 4) = f_h(4 \mid 10, 4, 6) = f_h(4 \mid 10, 6, 4) = 0.071429;$
2. $P(X \leq 3) = F_h(3 \mid 10, 4, 6) = F_h(3 \mid 10, 6, 4) = 0.0928571;$
3. $P(X \geq 2) = 1 - P(X \leq 1) = 1 - F_h(1 \mid 10, 4, 6)$
   $\qquad = 1 - F_h(1 \mid 10, 6, 4) = 1 - 0.119048 = 0.880952.$

Before we proceed further, you must understand the procedure of obtaining these results and check Table III to make certain that these results are accurate.

The Expectation and Variance of the Hypergeometric Variable

To derive the expectation of a hypergeometric variable, note that this variable X may also be considered as a sum, just as in the binomial case, of n variables X_i, except that in the hypergeometric model $X_1, \ldots, X_n$ are dependent. But, because the additive property of expectation does not require the independence of X_i, it is still true that $E(X) = E(X_1) + \cdots + E(X_n)$, where each $E(X_i)$ is the probability (k/N) of success at the ith trial if it is not known what has happened at the preceding, or what will happen at subsequent, trials. Thus, the expectation of the hypergeometric variable X becomes

$$E(X) = n\left(\frac{k}{N}\right). \tag{8.15}$$

The variance is not additive for dependent variables. It can be shown, however, that in the hypergeometric case the variance is given by

$$V(X) = n\left(\frac{k}{N}\right)\left(\frac{N-k}{N}\right)\left(\frac{N-n}{N-1}\right). \tag{8.16}$$

We note that if sampling is made with replacement, then the binomial model is appropriate and $V(X) = n\pi\pi' = n(k/N)[(N-k)/N]$. When sampling without replacement is assumed for the hypergeometric model, a *finite population correction factor* $[(N-n)/(N-1)]$ is introduced. This correction factor approaches 1 when n is very small relative to N. This is the reason why we can still use the binomial model, as mentioned before, in such a situation.

Returning to the example of Professor Smith's grades, we have

$$E(X) = 4\left(\frac{6}{10}\right) = 2.4 \text{ As}$$

and

$$V(X) = 4\left(\frac{6}{10}\right)\left(\frac{4}{10}\right)\left(\frac{10-4}{10-1}\right) = 0.64.$$

Also, from the value of $V(X)$, we see that

$$\sigma_X = \sqrt{V(X)} = \sqrt{0.64} = 0.80 \text{ As}.$$

8.7 THE POISSON PROBABILITY MODEL

Many events occur not as the definite number of outcomes of an experiment, as in the binomial or hypergeometric cases, but rather at random points of time, space, or volume. The number of automobile accidents on a certain highway per week, the number of errors on each page of typewritten material, the number of bacteria in a given cubic inch of water, the number of atoms disintegrating per second in radioactive material, the number of meteorites located on one square foot of desert land, the number of deaths occurring in 100,000 air passenger-miles, the number of hydrogen atoms in a cubic light-year of intergalactic space, the demand for service per hour on a cashier or a saleswomen of a department store, on a clerk at a factory, on a tollbooth of a bridge or tunnel, on a cargo-handling facility of a port, on the trunk lines of a telephone exchange, or on a maintenance man at a machine shop, the number of defects on the surface of a table, on an item of glassware, or on a piece of fabric, the number of bomb hits per square mile in Vietnam in 1972, and so on, are all examples of random variables generated by what is called the Poisson process, attributed to the French mathematician S. D. Poisson (1781–1840).

Each of the above-mentioned random variables seems to be characterized by the following assumptions.

1. The number of occurrences of the event in any specified unit (of time, space or volume) is independent of the number of occurrences in any other specified unit.

2. The mean number of occurrences of the event is proportional to the size of the specified unit.

3. The probability of two or more occurrences of the event in a very small specified unit is negligible.

4. The probability of a single occurrence of the event in a very small specified unit remains constant from one such unit to another.

Let us use an example to make the foregoing four assumptions absolutely clear. Suppose the demand per hour for trunk lines of a telephone exchange follows a Poisson process, then we would have the following four characteristics. First, the number of trunk lines demanded in any hour would not be affected by the number of trunk lines demanded in any other hour. Second, if the number of trunk lines demanded is, say, at an average rate of 10 per hour, then there would be a mean rate of 5 per half an hour, 2.5 per quarter of an hour, etc. Third, given a mean demand for trunk lines of 10 per hour, the demand for any trunk line during the course of, say, a second, would practically have a probability of zero and it can therefore be neglected. Fourth, if there is say, a, 0.0005 probability for the demand of a single trunk line during any second, that probability remains constant for every second.

The Poisson Probability Mass Function

It is not as easy as it is with binomial and hypergeometric models to convince ourselves that the assumptions of the Poisson case are reasonable. A further complication is the fact that the occurrences of an event in a specified unit (of time, space, and volume) need not necessarily behave as a Poisson process. Again, in some situations when the Poisson model seems appropriate, the independence condition may not be satisfied. However, it is time to face the reality that models sometimes do not always give us completely accurate probabilities, since some assumptions are not satisfied at all times. However, they still provide us with fairly accurate probabilities, provided the violations of some of the assumptions are not crucial. In any event, if the assumptions in the previous subsection are satisfied, then the Poisson variable would have the following PMF, which gives us the probability of obtaining exactly x occurrences (successes) of a phenomenon in a specified unit of time, space, or volume:

$$f_p(x \mid \lambda) = \frac{e^{-\lambda}\lambda^x}{x!}, \qquad x = 0, 1, 2, \ldots. \qquad (8.17)$$

Here, e is a constant and is approximately equal to 2.71828 and λ is the mean number of successes per specified unit and is the single parameter of a Poisson probability distribution. To compute Poisson probabilities directly from (8.17), we compute $f_p(x)$ for $x = 0$, $x = 1$, and so on, until we reach a value of X for which $f_p(x)$ is so small that it is practically zero.

To illustrate the application of (8.17), all we need is a statistical calculator with an exponential key. Now, as an example, consider this case. Jeanne Sato claims that she averages 0.5 errors per page in typing. Suppose a sample page is selected at random from all her typed material for a certain day for observation. What is the probability that there will be no errors, one error, two errors, and so forth, on the page?

It may be noted that the errors in this case may not be independent of one another. For example, if she were tired or upset about something that day, she would make more errors on that day's typing. Or, if she had, by chance, made more errors on a page than usual, she might have become upset, and more errors might have been made much sooner. In any event, assuming the Poisson process is appropriate, what is the probability that there will be no errors, one error, two errors, and so on? The desired probabilities are calculated

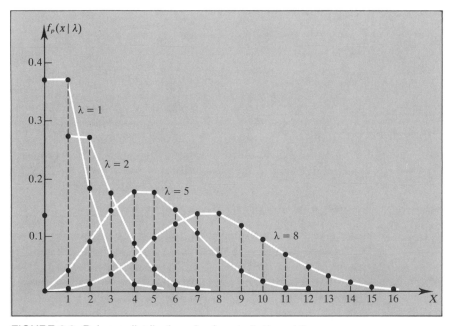

FIGURE 8.2 Poisson distributions for $\lambda = 1$, 2, 5, and 8.

below:

$$f_p(0) = (e^{-0.5})(0.5)^0/0! = (0.60653)(0.5)^0/1 \doteq 0.6065,$$

$$f_p(1) = (e^{-0.5})(0.5)^1/1! = (0.60653)(0.5)^1/1 \doteq 0.3033,$$

$$f_p(2) = (e^{-0.5})(0.5)^2/2! = (0.60653)(0.5)^2/2 \doteq 0.0758,$$

$$f_p(3) = (e^{-0.5})(0.5)^3/3! = (0.60653)(0.5)^3/6 \doteq 0.0126,$$

$$f_p(4) = (e^{-0.5})(0.5)^4/4! = (0.60653)(0.5)^4/24 \doteq 0.0016,$$

$$f_p(5) = (e^{-0.5})(0.5)^5/5! = (0.60653)(0.5)^5/120 \doteq 0.0001,$$

$$f_p(6) = (e^{-0.5})(0.5)^6/6! = (0.60653)(0.5)^6/720 \doteq 0.0000.$$

The Poisson distribution, as revealed by these results is positively skewed. However, as Figure 8.2 shows, the skewness decreases continuously as the value of λ increases. From this example we also detect the fact that $f_p(x)$ is nonincreasing in X when the value of X is large. This observation justifies our practice as stated in the last sentence in the previous paragraph.

The Poisson Cumulative Mass Function

The *cumulative mass function* of a Poisson variable is given, as usual for discrete cases, as a summation of the individual terms of the Poisson probability mass function. Symbolically,

$$F_P(r \mid \lambda) = \sum_{x=0}^{r} f_p(x \mid \lambda). \tag{8.18}$$

For the typist example just considered, we have, for instance

$$F_P(1) = \sum_{x=0}^{1} f_P(x \mid 0.5)$$

$$= f_P(0) + f_P(1)$$

$$\doteq 0.6065 + 0.3033 = 0.9098.$$

This finding indicates that if the typist's claim is true, it is very unlikely for us to find 2 or more errors on the page of her typing that we have selected at random for observation.

The Use of Poisson Probability Tables

Extensive Poisson probability tables for the individual terms, as well as cumulative terms, are available. For example, *Poisson's Exponential Binomial Limit* by E. C. Molina, published by D. Van Nostrand, 1949, gives both individual and cumulative terms to at least six decimal places for

$$\lambda = 0.001(0.001)0.010(0.01)0.30(0.10)0.150(1)100.$$

Table VI in Appendix C contains cumulative sums for some values of λ. The following examples illustrate the use of this table.

A lawyer's office receives an average of four telephone calls per hour. What is the probability that the office will receive (1) fewer than three calls during the next hour? (2) exactly four calls during the next hour? (3) three or more calls during the next hour? (4) more than 6 calls during the next two hours? (5) between 5 and 9 calls during the next two-and-a-half hours?

To obtain the desired probabilities, we note that the number of calls received by the lawyer's office qualifies as a Poisson variable with $\lambda = 4$ per hour. Thus

1. $P(X < 3) = P(X \leqslant 2) = F_P(2 \mid 4) = 0.23810;$

2. $P(X = 4) = F_P(4 \mid 4) - F_P(3 \mid 4)$
$$= 0.62884 - 0.43347 = 0.19537;$$

3. $P(X \geqslant 3) = 1 - P(X \leqslant 2) = 1 - F_P(2 \mid 4)$
$$= 1 - 0.23810 = 0.7619.$$

To answer the fourth question, we see that the specified unit has changed from 1 hour to two hours and, hence, $\lambda = 2(4) = 8$. So,

4. $P(X > 6) = 1 - P(X \leqslant 6) = 1 - F_P(6 \mid 8)$
$$= 1 - 0.31337 = 0.68663.$$

Finally, for the fifth question, the time unit now becomes 2.5 hours, thus $\lambda = 2.5(4) = 10$ and

5. $P(5 \leqslant X \leqslant 9) = F_P(9 \mid 10) - F_P(4 \mid 10)$
$$= 0.45793 - 0.02925 = 0.42868.$$

A manufacturer of woolen piece goods claims that the average number of flaws in his products is one per two square yards. A sample square yard of his product, selected at random, shows three flaws. What is the probability of obtaining three or more flaws in any one square yard if the manufacturer's claim is valid?

Here, we have a Poisson variable with $\lambda = 0.5$ per square yard, and the desired probability is

$$\sum_{x=3}^{\infty} f_P(x \mid 0.5) = 1 - \sum_{x=0}^{2} f_P(x \mid 0.5) = 1 - F_P(2 \mid 0.5)$$

$$\doteq 1 - 0.98561 = 0.01439.$$

In view of this result, what can we conclude about the manufacturer's claim? It is unlikely that the claim is true, owing to the very small probability.

A certain city in the United States has, on the average, twelve traffic deaths every three months. What is the probability that in any one month, there are (1) more than four traffic deaths and (2) exactly four traffic deaths? Since $\lambda = 4$ per month,

1. $P(X > 4) = \sum\limits_{x=5}^{\infty} f_P(x \mid 4) = 1 - F_P(4 \mid 4)$
$\doteq 1 - 0.62884 = 0.37116;$

2. $P(X = 4) = F_p(4 \mid 4) - F_P(3 \mid 4)$
$\doteq 0.62884 - 0.43347 = 0.19537.$

Expectation and Variance of the Poisson Variable

It can be shown the Poisson variable has the unique property that its expected value is identical with its variance. Namely,

$$E(X) = \lambda \qquad (8.19)$$

and

$$V(X) = \lambda \qquad (8.20)$$

8.8 RELATIONSHIPS AMONG THE DISCRETE PROBABILITY MODELS

Before closing our discussion, let us point out that all the discrete random variables that we have covered in this chapter are closely related. First of all, if you think back to what you have learned about these models, you will come to the conclusion that all models are generated from the process of simple random sampling. As such, these random variables may be viewed as sample statistics, and their PMFs may be considered as "sampling distributions"—a notion we shall elaborate on in detail in Chapter 10.

Next, it has been stated that the binomial variable is but the sum of n independent and identical Bernoulli variables, and that the binomial model is merely a special case of the multinomial model. As a matter of fact, it can be verified that the respective probabilities of the possible values of one of the x's in the multinomial PMF follow the binomial probability law. Recall, also, that both the binomial and hypergeometric variables are generated by sampling from dichotomous populations, with two differences: (1) The binomial variable can be generated from infinite, as well as finite populations; while the hypergeometric variable is always generated from finite populations. (2) When sampling from finite populations, binomial variables result if sampling is made with replacement; hypergeometric variables emerge if sampling is made without replacement. Both differences become negligible, however, when sampling is conducted under the condition that the sample size is very small relative to the population. Finally, the PMF for the Poisson variable was originally formulated by Poisson as a limited form of the binomial PMF as n approaches infinity and π approaches zero. As such, the Poisson distribution may be viewed as that for the rare events originally governed by the binomial probability law: That is, the Poisson distribution is the limit of the binomial distribution.

We have made the remarks immediately above in order to lead us to the more important task on hand: the approximations of probabilities of one model by the probability law of another. First, let us consider the possibility of approximating the hypergeometric probabilities by use of the binomial probability model. Suppose that 30,000 of the 100,000 members of a labor union are in favor of a strike over some seemingly unresolvable issues in a labor negotiation. If 10 union members are selected at random without replacement, then the probability that exactly x members in the sample are in favor of a strike is given by the hypergeometric law as

$$f_h(x \mid 100{,}000, 10, 30{,}000) = \frac{\binom{30{,}000}{x}\binom{100{,}000 - 30{,}000}{10 - x}}{\binom{100{,}000}{10}}.$$

(Note that $f_h(0 \mid 100{,}000, 10, 30{,}000) = 0.0282418$ calculated by computer.) If, however, the sample of 10 is drawn at random with replacement, then the probability of each independent trial remains constant at 30,000/100,000, or 0.3, and the binomial model is appropriate for the number of members in favor of a strike in the sample, and the probability function becomes

$$F_b(x \mid 10, 0.3) = \binom{10}{x}(0.3)^x(0.7)^{10-x}$$

(Again note that $f_b(0 \mid 10, 0.3) = 0.0282475$. This agrees with the corresponding hypergeometric probability to five decimal places.)

Now, the ratio of those in favor of a strike to the total number of union members will change only very slightly when a sample as small as 10 is drawn without replacement from a population as large as 100,000. In other words, when n is very small and N is very large, the probability of success will not change significantly from one draw to another, and successive draws can in effect be considered as independent. Thus, we would expect the binomial probability to approximate very closely the hypergeometric probability. In our numerical example, as shown by setting $x = 0$ before, we would expect $f_b(x \mid 10, 0.3)$ to yield very close approximations to $f_h(x \mid 100{,}000, 10, 30{,}000)$. In general, it can be shown that if n, and therefore x, is very small compared to both k and $N - k$, then

$$\frac{\binom{k}{x}\binom{N-k}{n-x}}{\binom{N}{n}} \doteq \binom{n}{x}\left(\frac{k}{N}\right)^x\left(\frac{N-k}{N}\right)^{n-x} \qquad (8.21)$$

This says that if a small sample is taken from a large population, then nonreplacement (the hypergeometric model) and replacement (the binomial model) give approximately identical results. A rule of thumb is that $n \leq 0.05N$. This rule is called the 5% rule and will be discussed in detail in Chapter 10.

The practical importance of (8.21) is that, when conditions for its validity are met, we can obtain a close approximation of a hypergeometric probability by the more easily computed binomial probability. This approximation improves, given n, as N increases. That is, the binomial model is the limit of the hypergeometric model as N approaches infinity.

While the binomial model can be used to approximate the hypergeometric probabilities, the binomial model, in turn, can be approximated by the Poisson distribution. It can be shown that if n is large and π is small, then the binomial and Poisson models are related by the following equation:

$$\binom{n}{x}(\pi)^x(\pi')^{n-\pi} \doteq e^{-n\pi}\left[\frac{(n\pi)^x}{x!}\right], \qquad (8.22)$$

where an individual binomial term can be replaced by a corresponding Poisson term with $\lambda = n\pi$.

When we find it convenient to approximate the binomial model by the Poisson model, we must be sure to know what is meant by large n and small π. As a rule of thumb, if $n > 100$ and $\pi < 0.01$, the binomial and Poisson probabilities agree approximately (to three decimal places) for every value of the random variable. Furthermore, for those x values for which $[(x - n\pi)^2/n] < 0.01$, the two models agree to within 1%. Finally, if π is sufficiently small, satisfactory approximations of the binomial model by the Poisson model can be made even when n is as small as 10. Given a small π, then the larger the n the better the results. Given n, then the smaller π is the more satisfactory are the approximations.

Table 8.3 gives the binomial probabilities for $x = 0, 1, 2, 3, 4$, and 5 with $n = 10$ and $\pi = 0.1$, and with $n = 20$ and $\pi = 0.05$, respectively.

TABLE 8.3 Binomial Distributions and Their Poisson Approximations

x	0	1	2	3	4	5
$f_b(x \mid 10, 0.10)$	0.349	0.387	0.194	0.057	0.011	0.0015
$f_b(x \mid 20, 0.05)$	0.358	0.377	0.189	0.060	0.013	0.0022
$f_P(x \mid 1)$:	0.368	0.368	0.184	0.061	0.015	0.0031

In each case the Poisson approximations are the same, since $\lambda = 10(0.1) = 20(0.05) = 1$.

The numerical illustrations reveal that Poisson approximations of the binomial probabilities are quite good even when n is as small as 10 or 20, and that for $n = 20$ the approximations are better than for $n = 10$. However, in practice, it would make no sense to approximate binomial probabilities by the Poisson values, when the former can be read directly from tables. Speed is gained without sacrificing accuracy only when n is large and π is sufficiently small, and when the binomial probabilities cannot be obtained from published tables.

Suppose that the probability that a newborn baby will die of a certain disease is 0.00002; what is the probability that out of 100,000 newborn babies (1) four or more, (2) exactly four will die of this disease? The probabilities required are clearly binomial.

1. The probability that four or more will die of this disease is

$$
\sum_{x=4}^{100,000} \binom{100,000}{x}(0.00002)^x(0.99998)^{100,000-x}.
$$

Rather than trying to evaluate this seemingly formidable expression, we would be well advised to approximate it by the Poisson law, with

$$
\lambda = n\pi = 100,000(0.00002) = 2.
$$

So,

$$
\sum_{x=4}^{100,000} f_P(x \mid 2) = 1 - \sum_{x=0}^{3} f_P(x \mid 2) = 1 - F_P(3 \mid 2)
$$

$$
= 1 - 0.85712 = 0.14288.
$$

2. The probability of exactly four deaths is

$$
F_P(4 \mid 2) - F_P(3 \mid 2) = 0.94735 - 0.85712
$$

$$
= 0.09023.
$$

In concluding, let us observe that just as the hypergeometric model takes the binomial model as its limit, so the binomial model takes the Poisson model as its limit. Thus the Poisson can also be employed to approximate the hypergeometric probability via the binomial distribution, under appropriate conditions. We shall see in the next chapter, moreover, that all of these probabilities can be approximated by a single continuous probability model—the normal probability law—under appropriate conditions.

GLOSSARY OF FORMULAS

(8.1) $f_u(x \mid N) = 1/N, \quad x = 1, 2, \ldots, N;$

(8.2) $F_u(x) = P(X \leq x) = x/N, \quad \text{for } x = 1, 2, \ldots, N.$

These two equations are the *probability mass function*, PMF, and *cumulative mass function*, CMF, of *a discrete uniform random variable*, respectively. The discrete probability model has the single parameter N and is appropriate when a random observation made from a population with N items yields N mutually exclusive and equally likely outcomes. This model is the basis of generating random digits as well as the rationale for the selection of simple random samples.

(8.3) $E(X) = \pi;$

(8.4) $V(X) = \pi\pi'.$

The expectation and variance of a Bernoulli variable are defined by these two equations. A *Bernoulli variable* is generated by a random observation made from a dichotomous population. As such, it can take on two possible values, 0 and 1. Here, "1" represents a successful outcome arbitrarily with a probability of π to occur; "0" arbitrarily represents a failure with a probability π' to occur, where $\pi' = 1 - \pi$. Also, π of a Bernoulli variable is the single parameter. The Bernoulli process is the basis of the binomial probability model.

(8.5) $f_b(x \mid n, \pi) = \binom{n}{x}(\pi)^x(\pi')^{n-x}; \quad x = 1, 2, \ldots, n;$

(8.6) $F_b(r \mid n, \pi) = \sum_{x=0}^{r} f_b(x \mid n, \pi);$

(8.7) $E(X) = \mu_X = n\pi;$

(8.8) $V(X) = \sigma_x^2 = n\pi\pi'.$

This group of equations is concerned with the binomial probability model. A *binomial variable* is the number of successes with $n + 1$ values and is generated by sampling from infinite dichotomous populations or sampling with replacement from finite dichotomous populations. Thus, the n trials are independent and the probability π of success remains constant for all trials. Equation (8.5) is the binomial PMF, which gives the probability of obtaining exactly x successes in n trials. Equation (8.6) is the binomial CMF, which gives the binomial probability of obtaining r or fewer successes. Note that a binomial variable has as its parameters n and π, both of which are fixed. Since a binomial variable can be considered as the sum of n independent and identically distributed Bernoulli variables, the additive property holds for both its expectation and variance, as indicated by the last two equations, (8.7) and (8.8), in this group.

(8.9) $f_m(x_1, x_2, \ldots, x_k \mid \pi_1, \pi_2, \ldots, \pi_k)$

$$= \frac{n!}{x_1!, x_2!, \ldots, x_k!} (\pi_1)^{x_1}(\pi_2)^{x_2}, \ldots, (\pi_k)^{x_k},$$

where $\sum \pi_i = 1$, $\sum x_i = n$, and $x_i = 0, 1, 2, \ldots k$;

(8.10) $E(X_i) = n\pi_i$;

(8.11) $V(X) = n\pi_i(1 - \pi_i) = n\pi_i\pi_i'$.

This group of equations is concerned with the *multinomial probability model,* which is generated by sampling from populations whose elements can be classified into three or more mutually exclusive categories. The populations may be finite or infinite, but statistical independence, as in the binomial case, must be insured. Equation (8.9) is the multinomial PMF, which gives the probability of obtaining exactly x_k successes of the kth kind of outcome when n independent trials are made. Note that π_i refers to the probability of success of the ith outcome in each trial. It is possible to modify (8.9) to cover a situation in which we are only interested in the probability of the exact number of occurrences of a few outcomes, instead of the occurrences of all the exact numbers of all possible outcomes. Finally, Equations (8.10) and (8.11) reflect the fact that in the multinomial case, the number of occurrences of each type of outcome for n independent trials may be treated as an individual binomial variable whose expectation and variance, therefore, are identical to those of a binomial case.

(8.12) $f_h(x \mid N, n, k) = \dfrac{\dbinom{k}{x}\dbinom{N-k}{n-x}}{\dbinom{N}{n}}$;

(8.13) $F_h(r \mid N, n, k) = \displaystyle\sum_{x=0}^{r} f_h(x \mid N, n, k)$;

(8.14a) $f_h(x \mid N, n, k) = f_h(x \mid N, k, n)$;

(8.14b) $F_h(r \mid N, n, k) = F_h(x \mid N, k, n)$;

(8.15) $E(X) = n\left(\dfrac{k}{N}\right)$;

(8.16) $V(X) = n\left(\dfrac{k}{N}\right)\left(\dfrac{N-k}{K}\right)\left(\dfrac{N-n}{N-1}\right)$.

This group of equations is associated with the *hypogeometric probability model,* in which a *hypergeometric random variable* is generated by sampling without replacement from finite dichotomous populations. It is the number of successes in n dependent trials and it possesses three parameters, N, n, and k by which its PMF (8.12) and CMF (8.13) are defined. Equations (8.14a) and (8.14b) express the interesting property of hypergeometric distributions, in which n and k can be interchanged without changing the hypergeometric probabilities. Since the additive property for expectation holds for independent, as well as dependent variables, the expected value of a hypergeometric variable, being a sum, is simply the sum of the separate expectations of X_i as shown by (8.15). However, owing to statistical dependence, the variance of a hypergeometric variable must be modified by a *finite population correction factor* $[(N - n)/(N - 1)]$—the last term on the right-hand side of (8.16). If $n \leqslant 0.05N$, then this factor can be eliminated from (8.16) to compute $V(X)$ without significant difference in results.

$$(8.17) \quad f_P(x \mid \lambda) = \frac{e^{-\lambda}\lambda^x}{x!},$$

$$(8.18) \quad F_P(r \mid \lambda) = \sum_{x=0}^{r} f_P(x \mid \lambda);$$

$$(8.19) \quad E(X) = \lambda;$$

$$(8.20) \quad V(X) = \lambda.$$

The *Poisson probability model* is governed by these four equations. The *Poisson variable* is the number of occurrences of a given phenomenon or event per specified unit of time, space, or volume and it can take on the integer values $0, 1, 2, \ldots$. The PMF, (8.17), of a Poisson variable gives the probability of obtaining exactly x successes in a specified unit. Its CMF, (8.18), as usual for discrete cases, is simply the summation of the individual terms of Poisson probabilities as given by (8.17). The Poisson variable is completely defined by a single parameter λ, which is the mean number of occurrences per specified unit. The Poisson probability model has two interesting and unique properties: (1) the value of λ is proportional to the specified unit and (2) its expectation and variance are identical; i.e., $E(X) = V(X) = \lambda$. The second property is revealed by equations (8.19) and (8.20).

$$(8.21) \quad \frac{\binom{k}{x}\binom{N-k}{n-x}}{\binom{N}{n}} \doteq \binom{n}{x}\left(\frac{k}{N}\right)^x\left(\frac{N-k}{N}\right)^{n-x}.$$

This equation states the fact that when a small sample is taken from a large population, say, $n \leqslant 0.05N$, the hypergeometric probability is approximately equal to the binomial probability. Thus, under such a condition, a hypergeometric probability can be satisfactorily approximated by the binomial probability with $(k/N) \doteq \pi$ and $(N - k)/N \doteq \pi'$.

$$(8.22) \quad \binom{n}{x}(\pi)^x(\pi')^{n-x} \doteq e^{-n\pi}\left[\frac{(n\pi)^x}{x!}\right].$$

This formula says that the binomial PMF is approximately equal to the Poisson PMF under the condition that n is large and π is small. To approximate a binomial probability by the Poisson law, we simply set $\lambda = n\pi$.

REVIEW QUESTIONS

8.1 What is a model?

8.2 What is the difference between deterministic and probabilistic models?

8.3 What is the importance of a model or a theory?

8.4 How is the uniform discrete probability model generated? What is its parameter?

8.5 What do we mean by a simple random sample?

8.6 Use an example of your own to demonstrate that:
   a. Each random observation from a population in an SRS is uniformly distributed.
   b. If all the possible samples of the same size are selected at random with or without replacement, the distribution of the possible samples can be characterized by a discrete uniform probability distribution.

8.7 A table of random digits can be considered as an SRS selected from a population with the ten integers from 0 consecutively to 9. How can this be so, in view of the fact that a table of random digits can run into the thousands, hundreds of thousand or even a million or more digits, while the parent population has only 10 digits?

8.8 Suppose you are to select a simple random sample of size 20 from a population of 500 by using Table I in Appendix C. How would you go about it if:
   a. The sample is to be selected with replacement?
   b. The sample is to be selected without replacement? (Write down the random digits you have selected for the two types of samples.)

8.9 What is a dichotomous population? Cite a few examples of your own for such a population.

8.10 What is a Bernoulli variable? How is it generated? What is its parameter? What is the most important function of the Bernoulli probability model?

8.11 What is a binomial variable? Under what conditions is it generated? What are its parameters in terms of which the binomial PMF and CMF are defined? What are the important properties of a binomial PMF?

8.12 In what sense do we say that the binomial probability model is but a special case of the multinomial probability model? Can you think of some situations where the multinomial model is appropriate?

8.13 What is a hypergeometric variable? How is it generated? How does it differ from a binomial variable? What are its parameters?

8.14 It has been pointed out that the PMF of a binomial variable is positively skewed if π is less than 0.5 and negatively skewed if $\pi > 0.5$, and that the skewness decreases continuously with the increase in the size of n. Can the same statements be applied to the PMF of a hypergeometric variable? Why or why not?

8.15 There is a very interesting property of the distribution of hypergeometric variables. What is it? What is its practical importance?

8.16 Does a special probability model always have the same parameter(s) as the population from which the former is derived? Give examples to support your answer.

8.17 In the previous chapter we said that a random variable is identical with a population. In this chapter we said that each of the special random variables is in effect a sample statistic. Are these two statements contradictory to each other? Why or why not?

8.18 What is a Poisson variable? Under what conditions is it derived? How does it differ from the binomial and hypergeometric variables? What is the unique property of the expectation and variance of a Poisson variable?

8.19 In what sense do we say that the PMF of each special random variable actually defines a family of probability distributions?

8.20 How is the hypergeometric model related to the binomial model? Under what conditions can we approximate hypergeometric probabilities by the binomial probability law?

8.21 How is the binomial model related to the Poisson model? Under what conditions can we approximate the binomial probabilities by the Poisson probability law?

8.22 In view of your answers to the preceding two questions, do you think that the hypergeometric probabilities can also be approximated by the Poisson probability law? If so, how would you go about it?

PROBLEMS

8.1 The American version of a roulette wheel is constructed by dividing the circumference into 38 arcs of equal lengths, numbered from 00, 0, 1 and consecutively to 36. A ball is placed in the wheel and the wheel is spun. After the wheel comes to rest, the position of the ball is observed. What probability model is appropriate for this experiment? Give general expressions for its PMF and CMF.

8.2 For the preceding experiment, what is the probability that the ball will be in the arc with the number 00? From 10 to 20 exclusive? That it is even? That it is greater than 30?

8.3 The traffic light at a certain intersection is green for 35 seconds, yellow for 5 seconds, and red for 10 seconds. Assuming a rectangular distribution, what is the probability that a motorist, arriving at the intersection at random time, will go through without stopping? will have to wait? [*Note:* Solve only the obvious, simple version of this problem.]

8.4 If 100 perfect coins are tossed:
  a. What is the probability that exactly 50 heads turn up?
  b. What is the probability that the number of heads will not deviate from 50 by more than 10?

8.5 It was estimated that 40% of George Wallace's supporters were inclined to vote for Richard Nixon in the 1972 Presidential election. In a random sample of two selected from among Wallace's supporters, what are the probabilities that 0, 1 or 2 were inclined to vote for Nixon?

8.6 Five fair ordinary dice are tossed. Would you agree that the probability of obtaining no ace is the same as that of obtaining five aces? If not, what are the exact respective probabilities?

8.7 The probability that A will make a profit on any business deal is 0.7. What is the probability that he will make a profit exactly seven times in ten successive statistically independent deals?

8.8 A certain make of computer has a probability of 0.05 of giving wrong results owing to electrical or mechanical failure. To improve the accuracy of calculations, the operator feeds the same data into five such statistically independent computers and accepts as accurate, the answer that the majority of the computers give. For one calculation, what is the probability that a majority of the computers are operating properly? Discuss whether this is the same as the probability that the same answer by a majority of the computers is a correct answer.

8.9 Write down the expression without evaluation of this statement: The probability of obtaining exactly 51,000 heads in 100,000 tosses of a perfect coin.

8.10 Mr. Smith has purchased five electronic tubes produced by a certain manufacturer. This product is known to be defective 2% of the time.
  a. What is the probability that all the five tubes purchased are perfect?
  b. Upon making the purchase, Mr. Smith adopted the following decision rule: If more than one tube in the purchase is defective, the tubes will be returned and the order canceled. If there is exactly one defective tube, the defective will be returned for replacement. If the replacement is also defective, the order will be canceled. Assuming the replacement sent to Mr. Smith is a random selection, determine the probability of canceling the order.

8.11 A production process is shut down for adjustment whenever a random sample of five items, selected with replacement, yields two or more defectives. Find the probability that the process will be shut down after an inspection if it is producing:
  a. 20% defectives
  b. 10% defectives
  c. 5% defectives

8.12 A production process is considered to be in statistical control if the fraction defective of output produced is less than or equal to 0.10. To determine whether the process is out of control, two plans have been suggested.

    I. The process is judged out of control if five or more defectives are found in a sample of 25.

    II. The process is judged out of control if two or more defectives are found in a sample of 10.

Evaluate the efficiency of these two plans with respect to:
a. Concluding falsely that a good process is out of control.
b. Detecting a process that is producing 20 percent defectives.

8.13 According to a political scientist, the voting population of a certain city in New York State consists of 46% Democrats, 40% Republicans, 11% Conservatives, and 3% Liberals. In a random sample of five, what is the probability for the sample to contain:
a. two Democrats and one each of the other categories?
b. three Democrats and two Republicans?
c. no Liberals?

8.14 A single missile of a certain variety has a probability of 1/4 of shooting down a jet bomber, a probability of 1/4 of damaging it, and a probability of 1/2 of missing it. Also, two damaging shots will down the plane. If four such missiles are fired, what is the probability of shooting down a jet bomber?

8.15 In a lot of ten manufactured parts, two are known to be defective. If a random sample of two parts is drawn without replacement, show that the probabilities that there will be 0, 1, or 2 defectives are 0.62, 0.36, and 0.02, respectively.

8.16 Defective guidance mechanisms have been mistakenly mounted on 3 of a group of 9 missiles. It is not known which missiles have the defective mechanisms. If a random sample of 3 is taken without replacement, what is the probability that the sample will contain no defective missile? One defective missile? More than one defective missile?

8.17 A certain make of automobile tire has a flat, owing to external causes, on the average of once in every 2,500 miles. Assuming that occurrences follow the Poisson law, what is the probability that
a. more than one flat will occur in a 500-mile run?
b. no flat will occur in a trip of 5000 miles?

8.18 If a Poisson variable has a variance of 2.5, what is its probability mass function?

8.19 Flaws in a certain kind of woolen piece goods occur at random with a mean number of one flaw per 100 square feet. What is the probability that a roll measuring 50 by 10 feet will have no flaws? (*Hint:* $\lambda = 50(10)/100 = 5$.)

8.20 A book contains 150 misprints distributed randomly throughout its 600 pages. Assuming a Poisson distribution, determine
a. its mean per page.
b. the probability that a page observed at random contains at least two misprints.

8.21 Automobiles arrive at a tollbooth at random at the rate of 300 cars per hour. what is the probability that
   a. one car arrives during a given 1-minute period?
   b. at least two cars arrive during a given 1-minute period?
   c. no cars arrive during a period of T minutes?

8.22 A taxi company has, on the average, 8 flat tires per week. During the past week, 16 flat tires occurred. If the Poisson model is appropriate here, what is the probability of having 16 or more flat tires per week? What conclusion can you draw from this result?

8.23 Accidents on a certain highway occur at random at a rate of 20 per month. What is the probability that at least 1 accident occurs in a given half-month interval?

8.24 It is known that the mean number of defects per sheet of carpet of a certain make is 2. What is the probability that any sheet of carpet will contain more than 2 defects?

8.25 Suppose that cars pass a certain traffic intersection at a rate of 30 cars per hour.
   a. What is the probability that during a 2-minute interval no car will pass the intersection, or at least 2 cars will pass it?
   b. If you observed the number of cars passing the intersection during each of thirty 2-minute intervals, would you be surprised if you found twenty or more of these intervals had the property that either none or at least 2 cars had passed the intersection during that time?

8.26 A sample of 100 is taken without replacement from an incoming shipment of 10,000 light bulbs. Three defective bulbs are found in the sample. What is the approximate probability for this sample result, if it is known that there are 500 defective bulbs in the shipment? (*Hint:* Use the Poisson approximation.)

8.27 The probability that a person in the 50–60 age group will die from a certain rare disease during a period of one year has been estimated to be 0.00001. If a life insurance company has 100,000 policyholders in this age group: What is the approximate probability that the company must pay off more than four claims in one year, because of death from this disease?

8.28 An intercontinental ballistic missile has 10,000 parts. The probability that each part will succeed is 0.99998, and all parts work independently. The failure of any part can make the flight a failure. What is the probability of a successful flight? (*Hint:* $\mu = np = 0.2$.)

8.29 A company will accept a shipment of 1,000 articles if, in a conditional random sample of 50, there is at most 1 defective item. If the shipment is 10% defective, what is the approximate probability that the shipment will be accepted?

8.30 What is the Poisson approximation of the preceding probability? Do you think the Poisson is better than the binomial approximation in this case? Explain.

Note: All the problems for this chapter so far can be solved with the aid of published probability tables or by approximating one kind of probability by another. Two things must be noticed now. One is that published probability tables always have gaps between the parameter values. The other is that very often conditions required to approximate one probability by another may not be ideal. In both cases, it may become very laborious and time-consuming to evaluate the exact probabilities in many situations without the use of computers. All the rest of the problems for this chapter are to be solved by computer.

8.31 It is known that 50 among the 400 assembly line workers in a certain factory did not graduate from high schools. If an unconditional SRS with $n = 10$ is selected from these workers, what are the probabilities of $0, 1, 2, \ldots$, and 10 workers in the sample who are not high-school graduates?

8.32 In the preceding problem if a conditional SRS is selected, what are the probabilities of $0, 1, \ldots$, and 10 workers in the sample who are not high-school graduates?

8.33 In a small rural community with 150 families, only 114 families have TV sets. Let the number of successes be the number of families that do not have TV sets in a sample of $n = 12$; establish the probability mass function and cumulative mass function for the random variable, assuming
a. an unconditional SRS;
b. a conditional SRS.

8.34 A factory produces 100 units of a certain output each day with 8% defectives. If an unconditional SRS with $n = 10$ is selected for inspection, what is the probability that the sample contains exactly 1 defective unit? If 20 units are selected at random from one day's total output for shipment, what is the probability that the shipment contains exactly 2 defective units? What is the probability it contains 2 defective units or less?

9 Special Continuous Probability Models

9.1 GENERAL COMMENTS ON CONTINUOUS RANDOM VARIABLES

It is often convenient and sometimes necessary to consider experiments in which some random phenomenon is observed and measured and in which the measurement yields a continuous random variable. From a practical point of view, the notion of a continuous random variable is somewhat unrealistic, since all empirical data are discontinuous owing to limitations in the accuracy of measuring instruments. Nevertheless, we can think of and use a mathematical model in which the data are continuous and measured with complete accuracy, to approximate the real-world situations. As long as the mathematical model captures the essential features of the real-world situation, then analyses based on the model will provide reasonably accurate predictions of what will happen in the real world. Thus, mathematical models for continuous random variables are highly useful, although they are not completely realistic.

As promised, we shall in this chapter present a few special continuous probability models that are frequently encountered and extremely useful in applied situations. Before we do so, however, we shall bring out some of the basic and important ideas about continuous random variables in general in order to facilitate our discussions of the special continuous probability models to be introduced.

When a random variable X is defined on a continuous sample space, such as time, length, or weight, then X is a *continuous random variable.* If X is continuous, it has uncountably many possible values. Continuity, therefore, leads us to two important departures from our discussion on discrete random variables. First, the probability mass function PMF, denoted as $f(x)$, in the discrete case specifies probabilities for specific values of X. However, for a continuous random variable, the corresponding function $f(x)$ is called a *probability density function,* abbreviated as PDF. Unlike a PMF, a PDF does not specify probabilities for specific individual values of the random variable. This is because, with uncountable possible values that X can take, $f(x) = P(X = x) = 0$ for each and every x. Thus, for a continuous random variable, an event must be defined in terms of an interval of values, such as $(a \leqslant X \leqslant b)$ for $a < b$.

Graphically, a PDF can be viewed as a mathematical function that describes the curve, called the *density curve* of $f(x)$. So viewed, for any value of $X, f(x)$ is simply the ordinate (height) of the curve erected at x. The probability of an event, such as $P(a \leqslant X \leqslant b)$, is then represented by the area under the density curve enclosed by the two ordinates erected at the two points a and b. This is shown by Figure 9.1.

As a probability density function, $f(x)$ must satisfy the following two conditions.

1. $f(x) \geqslant 0$. That is, $f(x)$ cannot be negative for any values of X beween $-\infty$ and ∞.

2. The area under the density curve described by $f(x)$ must be equal to 1, which is the total probability of X.

The distribution function of a continuous random variable is called the *cumulative density function,* or CDF. As in the discrete case, the CDF of a continuous random variable specifies the probability that an observed value of X is equal to or less than a given value x. However, the graph of cumulative density function is smooth; that is, there are no jumps in probability for X to assume any one of its possible values as in the discrete case. In general, if $f(x)$ is a PDF of X, then the correspond-

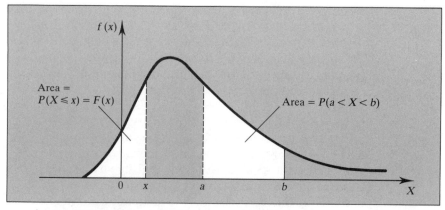

FIGURE 9.1 Graphic illustrations of (*a*) an event probability as the area and (*b*) the CDF as an area under the density curve of a continuous X below x.

ing CDF of X is given as

$$F(x) = P(X \leqslant x) = \int_{-\infty}^{x} f(u)\,du.$$

The expression on the right-hand side of this equation is called a "definite integral." The integral sign $\int$ used in the continuous case is the counterpart of the summation sign $\sum$ employed in the discrete case. In words, a CDF says that for a continuous random variable, $P(X \leqslant x)$ is given by the definite integral of its density function evaluated between $-\infty$ and x. Alternatively, it simply states the fact that the probability for X to be equal to or less than x is the area under the density curve for X from $-\infty$ to x as illustrated, again, by Figure 9.1. Observe that since x is the upper limit of the integration in the above expression, $f(u)\,du$ is a "dummy" expression used in place of $f(x)\,dx$ in the integrand. In this practice, u is used as a "dummy variable" and any letter other than x can be used as a "dummy" for x. It should be stressed that a dummy variable is simply a substitution required for mathematical propriety and it does not denote a different variable.

It may be mentioned here that cumulative mass and cumulative density functions are often collectively referred to as *cumulative distribution functions* and both are abbreviated to CDF. In actuality, both are "distribution functions." As such, the word "cumulative" is redundant in this context, since a distribution function is cumulative by definition. In any event, in this text we shall always call the distribution function of a discrete random variable as the cumultive mass function, CMF, and reserve the notation CDF to mean the cumulative density function for a continuous random variable.

A PDF is often called a *distribution density*. This new name is based on the fact that we think of a density function as the rate at which probability would accumulate if we were to sweep from the left to the right on the axis of the values of the continuous random variable. Over the intervals of the axis where probability is uniformly distributed, for example, the rate (density) would be constant. Hence, $f(x)$ can be viewed as a measure of the concentration of probability within an interval. To say the same thing in a different way, $f(x)$ can be interpreted as the rate of change of $F(x)$ in the continuous case.

In general, if the probability density function PDF is at a constant height over an interval, the probability that the random variable will take on a value within that interval is simply the height of the PDF times the width of the interval. So stated, we see that this is a height times a width, which is an area on the graph; hence an area under the density curve represents a probability. When the PDF is not at a constant height over the interval whose probability is desired—when the PDF is moving upward or downward with changing rates of accumulation from left to right—then life gets difficult from a mathematical viewpoint. Integral calculus is required to evaluate the areas under the density curve, and sometimes even calculus does not work very well and complicated numerical approximations have to be employed. However, you should not worry about such complexities;

since, on those occasions when we have to work with that kind of PDF, we provide numerical tables in which the desired probabilities can be easily found. The computations of the descriptive measures from continuous random variables with any kind of PDF also need calculus. We shall provide the formulas for such measures that are the results of calculus computations. So our discussion on continuous probability models will by no means be more difficult than that on discrete probability models in the previous chapter.

Now, since $F(x)$ is nondecreasing, it follows that $f(x) \geq 0$. Furthermore, if $a < b$, we must have

$$P(a \leq X \leq b) = P(X \leq b) - P(X \leq a) = F(b) - F(a).$$

From our discussions of $f(x)$ and $F(x)$ so far, we see that $F(-\infty) = 0$, $F(\infty) = 1$. $F(\infty) = 1$ follows logically from the fact that the total area under the curve described by $f(x)$ is equal to 1.

In the evaluation of continuous probabilities, let us take note of a peculiarity that refers to the fact that for a continuous random variable the probability of any specific value is zero, and thus the probability that the random variable is in some interval is precisely the same, whether endpoints are included or excluded. For example, if $a < b$, then $P(a \leq X \leq b) = P(a < X < b) = P(a < X \leq b) = P(a \leq X < b)$. This is so because the area under the PDF for the interval consisting of a single number, say, a, is graphically speaking, the area in a line; but a line has zero width and hence zero area.

Continuous probabilities are usually evaluated from the CDF of the random variable in question by recalling the fact that $P(a < X < b) = F(b) - F(a)$. Consider a simple example. If a random variable X has density given by Figure 9.2, it would have the following CDF:

$$F(x) = \begin{cases} 0, & x < 0, \\ x^2 & 0 \leq x \leq 1, \\ 1, & x > 1. \end{cases}$$

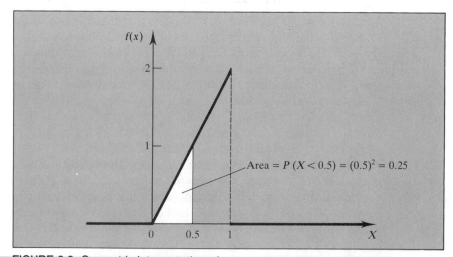

FIGURE 9.2 Geometric interpretation of an area probability under a PDF.

From this CDF, we see that

$$P(X \leqslant 0.5) = F(0.5) = 0.5^2 = 0.25;$$

$$P(0.5 < X < 0.8 = F(0.8) - F(0.5)$$

$$= 0.8^2 - 0.5^2 = 0.39;$$

$$P(0.5 \leqslant X \leqslant 1.38) = F(1.38) - F(0.5)$$

$$= 1 - 0.25 = 0.75;$$

$$P(X > 0.9) = 1 - P(X \leqslant 0.9) = 0.19;$$

etc.

It has already been pointed out that precise definitions of descriptive measures for continuous random variables require a knowledge of calculus, which is not assumed for the reader of this text. For the sake of completeness, however, we shall roughly evaluate these concepts by arguing in terms of discrete approximations.

To introduce the notions of expectation and variance for a continuous random variable, we shall, for convenience, assume that we have a variable X whose value ranges from $X = a$ to $X = b$. Let this interval be subdivided into n equal parts, each of which has length of $\Delta x = (b - a)/n$. Denote the left endpoint of the ith subinterval as x_i (for $i = 1, 2, \ldots, n$). Round down all values in the ith subinterval to x_i. The rounded values of X may be considered as a new random variable X', which is discrete, since it can only assume the endpoint values, $x_1, x_2, \ldots, x_n$. Now, the probability that X' can take on any one of these possible values, say, x_5, is the probability that the original variable X takes on a value that would be rounded down to x_5. This occurs if X takes on a value in the fifth subinterval; namely,

$$P(X' = x_5) = P(x_5 \leqslant X < x_5 + \Delta x) \doteq f(x_5)\, \Delta x.$$

Here, $f(x_5)$ is not the probability that X' equals x_5; rather, $f(x_5)$ is the probability density for $X = x_5$. This approximation becomes more and more exact as n, the number of subintervals, increases.

Now, by the formula for the expectation of a discrete random variable, we have

$$E(X') = \sum_{i=1}^{n} x_i P(X' = x_i)$$

$$\doteq \sum_{i=1}^{n} x_i f(x_i)\, \Delta x.$$

Here, as just above, $f(x_i)$ is the probability density for $X = x_i$. In this expression, as n approaches infinity, Δx approaches zero. Hence, we expect the discrete variable X' to approach the continuous variable X. That is, the "limit" of the foregoing expression for $E(X')$ should be taken as the expectation, $E(X)$, of X.

By the same line of reasoning,

$$V(X') = E[(X' - E(X'))^2]$$

$$= \sum_{i=1}^{n} (x_i - \mu')^2 P(X' = x_i)$$

$$\doteq \sum_{i=1}^{n} (x_i - \mu)^2 f(x_i)\, \Delta x.$$

Once more, $f(x_i)$ is the probability density for $X = x_i$. Thus, $V(X')$ should be considered as $V(X)$ as $n \to \infty$ and $\Delta x \to 0$.

It may also be noted that if X is continuous, then the median of X must satisfy

$$P(X \leq \tilde{x}_{.5}) = P(X \geq \tilde{x}_{.5}) = 0.50.$$

The mode of X is the value $\tilde{x}_m$ that corresponds to the maximum ordinate of the density curve if the density curve is unimodal. Finally, we may also point out that, owing to the fact that a cumulative density function CDF increases continuously, it is almost always possible to determine a unique value for any fractile for which the cumulative probability will be exactly equal to ϕ. Furthermore, since fractiles are defined in terms of the CDF of a random variable, they can be conveniently obtained from the graph of a CDF. This is done simply by

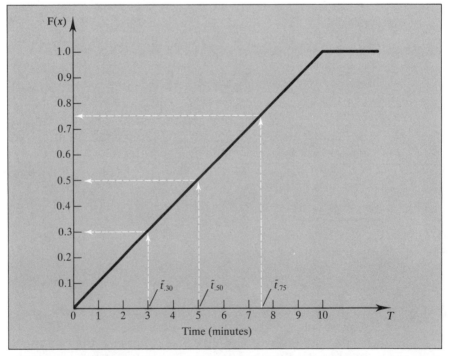

FIGURE 9.3 Illustration of locating fractiles of a continuous random variable from its CDF. (*Source:* The stopwatch example in Chapter 6.)

giving values of the horizontally plotted variable corresponding to the vertical axis for $F(x)$. The ordinate of this graph increases continuously from 0 to 1. If we divided this range into 100 equal parts, the corresponding values on the horizontal scale would be the fractiles or percentiles. For example, consider Figure 9.3, which is the graph of the CDF of the stopwatch example in the last section of Chapter 6. From this graph, and by interpolation, we find that $F(3)$, $F(5)$, and $F(7.5)$, for instance, are $\tilde{t}_{.30}$, $\tilde{t}_{.50}$, and $\tilde{t}_{.75}$, respectively.

With this much background of the various basic aspects of continuous random variables, we are now ready to take up our main task at hand: the presentation of special continuous probability models. If you have already gained a good idea about what has been said so far, you should find discussions in the remaining part of this chapter relatively easy.

9.2 THE CONTINUOUS UNIFORM PROBABILITY MODEL

The simplest continuous probability model is perhaps the one called the *continuous uniform, or rectangular, model*. This model arises when a continuous random variable can only assume values in a certain finite interval for finite numbers a and b, and when its density is constant over the whole interval from a to b. Thus, for a continuous rectangular model, the probability for any event that is a subinterval of the length (a, b) is just the ratio of the length of that interval to the length of (a, b); but the probability of any event that has no points in common with (a, b) is zero. Thus, if X is a continuous uniform, or rectangular, variable, then its PDF is simply

$$f_r(x) = \begin{cases} \dfrac{1}{b - a}, & \text{if } a \leq x \leq b, \\ 0, & \text{otherwise.} \end{cases} \tag{9.1}$$

It can be shown that from (9.1) we can obtain the CDF of a continuous uniform random variable as

$$F_r(x) = \begin{cases} 0, & \text{if } x \leq a, \\ \dfrac{x - a}{b - a}, & \text{if } a \leq x \leq b, \\ 1, & \text{if } x \geq b. \end{cases} \tag{9.2}$$

The PDF and CDF of a continuous uniform random variable are portrayed by Figures 9.4(a) and 9.4(b), respectively. A continuous rectangular probability model is quite analogous to a uniform distribution of mass along a line, such as a uniform rope or a steel wire. There are many random phenomena for which it seems plausible to expect a

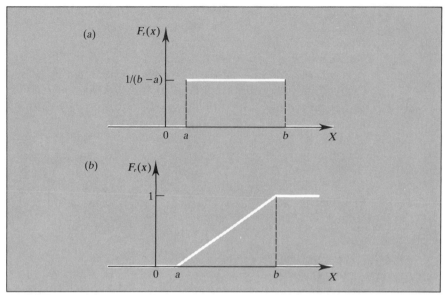

FIGURE 9.4 Graphs of (a) the PDF and (b) the CDF of a continuous uniform random variable.

uniform probability law. For example, suppose you are shooting with a machine gun at a line marked from 0 to 1. If you are always sure to hit the line and if you feel that any two subintervals of equal length on the line having equal chance of being hit, then you are led to conclude that the point at which the bullet hits the line has a probability density function as specified by (9.1). Another interesting example of this model is in the evaluation of rounding errors when measurements are recorded to a specific degree of accuracy. Here, for example, if the ages of students at a university are recorded to the nearest day, it would be assumed that the difference in days between the true age and the recorded age is some number between -0.5 and 0.5 and the error is uniformly distributed throughout this interval.

Clearly, from (9.1) and (9.2), we see that the rectangular model has a and b as its parameters. Its expectation and variance are, respectively,

$$E(X) = \frac{(a + b)}{2} \tag{9.3}$$

and

$$V(X) = \frac{(b - a)^2}{12}. \tag{9.4}$$

Note that when a random variable is uniformly distributed over the interval (a, b), its density is symmetrical about the center of the interval—$(a + b)/2$—and thus this value is both the mean and median of the variable. Obviously, a uniform random variable possesses no mode.

As an application of (9.2), consider this example. Subway trains on a certain line in New York City run every half-hour between midnight and six o'clock in the morning. What is the probability that a man entering the station at a random time during this period will have to wait at least 20 minutes to get on a train? Here, the random variable, T = time to the next train, under the assumption of random time of the man's arrival, is uniformly distributed on $0 < t < 30$. Thus, the probability that he has to wait at least 20 minutes to board the train is

$$P(T > 20) = 1 - F_r(t) = 1 - F_r(20)$$

$$= 1 - \frac{20 - 0}{30 - 0} = 1/3.$$

Also, for this example,

$$E(T) = \frac{(0 + 30)}{2} = 15 \text{ minutes}$$

and

$$V(T) = \frac{(30 - 0)^2}{12} = 75.$$

From the value of $V(T)$, we also have

$$\sigma_T = \sqrt{75} \doteq 8.66 \text{ minutes.}$$

9.3 THE EXPONENTIAL MODEL

The exponential probability model has as its origin the Poisson process. Recall that a Poisson probability is related to the likelihood of occurrence of a specific number of successes in a finite specified unit, where the number of successes is the random variable. Now, if we reverse the roles of a Poisson variable and its finite specified unit, we have what is called an exponential variable. Precisely, an *exponential variable X* is the interval of time, or space, required to get any two consecutive specific successes. For example, if the arrivals of automobiles at a tollbooth follow the Poisson law, then the length of time between successive arrivals of automobiles is an exponential variable.

The exponential model is of great importance in applied probability theory, because it can be used to describe a great variety of random situations. In management science one often encounters such operational problems as determining the number of tollgates required at highway entrances or exits, the number of telephone lines in a given area, the number of helpers at a cafeteria, and so forth. Each of these situations has a common feature—the existence of a variable demand over time for service that can be satisfied by a specific number of servers. This variable demand over time is found to obey the exponential law. Recent studies reveal that the exponential model also characterizes well such phenomena as the life of an electronic tape and the time intervals between breakdowns of electrical mechanisms, or between accidents, and so on.

From the examples above, we see that the exponential probability model arises in response to the question: If a sequence of events occurs in time according to the Poisson law at a rate of λ events per unit of time, how long do we have to wait in order to observe the first occurrence of the event? The answer to this question suggests a method of constructing the exponential probability model from a Poisson process. Let us denote by X the variable time between events and proceed to determine the cumulative density function of X by evaluating the event $X > x$ for any specific time. The event $X > x$ has not yet occurred in the time interval $(0, x)$. By the Poisson law, its probability is

$$P(X > x) = P[\text{no occurrence in } (0, x)]$$

$$= e^{-\lambda x} \frac{(\lambda x)^0}{0!}$$

$$= e^{-\lambda x}.$$

This expression gives the upper-tail probability of an exponential variable. From this result too it can be shown that the PDF and CDF, respectively, of an exponential variable are given as follows:

$$f_e(x) = \lambda e^{-\lambda x}$$

$$= \frac{1}{\beta} e^{-x/\beta}, \qquad \text{for } x \geq 0; \tag{9.5}$$

$$F_e(x) = P(X \leq x) = 1 - e^{-\lambda x}$$

$$= 1 - e^{-x/\beta}, \qquad \text{for } x \geq 0. \tag{9.6}$$

From the previous two expressions, we see that an exponential distribution is completely defined by a single parameter β—the mean of an exponential variable. Also, for an exponential varible, we have

$$E(X) = \beta = \frac{1}{\lambda} \tag{9.7}$$

and

$$V(X) = \beta^2 = \frac{1}{\lambda^2}. \tag{9.8}$$

It may be noted that in (9.5) and (9.6) we have used the letter e with two different meanings. When it is used as subscript in the functional notation, e stands for "exponential," and when it is employed on the right-hand sides of the equations it stands for the base of the natural logarithms (as employed for the Poisson model in the last chapter). Furthermore, in the previous expressions, x is the time interval between occurrences of the Poisson variable, and λ is the mean number of occurrences per time unit of the Poisson variable. The fact that

$\beta = 1/\lambda$ is a natural result, since the exponential variable is the time between successive Poisson occurrences. In this connection, we see that β can be interpreted as the average time interval between Poisson occurrences, or the expected time until the first occurrence of a Poisson event. Also note that, in the Poisson case, the expectation and variance are equal; in the exponential case, the expectation and standard deviation are equal. Finally, the exponential distribution is sometimes called the *negative exponential model*, because the slope of its density curve is negative everywhere. The decreasing density function of an exponential variable reveals that the probability of long time intervals between occurrences should be less than the probability of shorter time intervals. This, together with the fact that an exponential distribution is completely defined by β, is illustrated by Figure 9.5.

Exponential probabilities can be obtained by evaluating (9.6) with the aid of a statistical calculator.

Consider this example. The distribution of length of life during which a certain make of computer operates effectively—that is, hours of effective operation before the first breakdown—is exponential with $\beta = 360$ hours. What is the probability that the computer will operate effectively for less than 180 hours, or more than 720 hours? If three such computers are selected at random for life testing, what is the probability that one will last 180 hours or less, another will last between 180 and 720 hours, and another more than 720 hours?

For this problem, the PDF for X is clearly

$$f_e(x) = \frac{1}{360} e^{-x/360}, \qquad 0 \leqslant x \leqslant \infty,$$

whose graph is shown by Figure 9.6. The corresponding CDF can be given as

$$F_e(x) = 1 - e^{-x/360}.$$

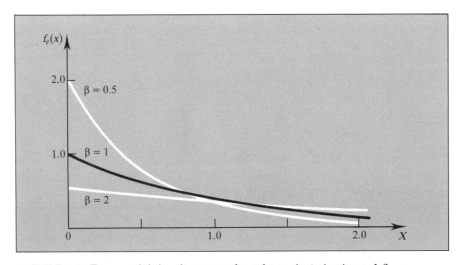

FIGURE 9.5 Exponential density curves for a few selected values of β.

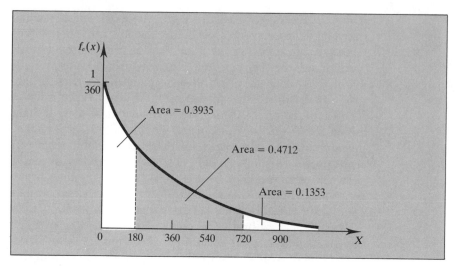

FIGURE 9.6 The density curve of an exponential random variable with $\beta = 360$.

From this CDF, we have

$$P(X \leq 180) = F_e(180) = 1 - e^{-180/360} = 1 - e^{-0.5}$$

$$\doteq 1 - 0.6065 \doteq 0.3935,$$

$$P(X > 720) = e^{-720/360} = e^{-2}$$

$$\doteq 0.1353,$$

and

$$P(180 \leq X \leq 720) = F_e(720) - F_e(180)$$

$$\doteq (1.0000 - 0.1353) - 0.3935$$

$$\doteq 0.4712.$$

Finally, the probability that a random sample of three will contain one computer in each of these three ranges is given by the multinomial law, and

$$P[(X \leq 180) \cap (180 < X < 720) \cap (X > 720)]$$

$$\doteq \frac{3!}{1! \, 1! \, 1!} (0.3935)(0.4712)(0.1353)$$

$$\doteq 0.1505.$$

9.4 THE BETA PROBABILITY MODEL

In its standard form, the beta probability model refers to a continuous random variable the admissible values of which lie between 0 and 1. As such, this model is suitable for describing the random behavior of percentages or proportions and it can be developed in many ways. However, for our later applications of this model in the study of Bayesian statistics, it is most convenient and useful to develop it from its relationship with the binomial probability model.

Recall that the binomial variable is the number of successes, X, in n independent Bernoulli trials with a constant probability π of success for each of the n trials. Here, π, being a population parameter, according to the classical interpretation, is a constant whether it is known or not. Occasions may arise when the probability of success in the Bernoulli process is unknown and we wish to estimate its value. Now, according to the Bayesian approach, or the subjective interpretation of probability (for reasons to be stated in a later chapter), π is considered as a random variable, and being a probability, it is capable of assuming any one of the uncountable real values between 0 and 1. It can be shown that, so interpreted, the random behavior of this continuous variable π is characterized by the *beta probability model* and its density function is defined in terms of two parameters, x, the number of successes, and n, the number of independent trials, with $n > x > 0$, as follows:

$$f_\beta(\pi \mid x, n) = \left[\frac{(n - 1)!}{(x - 1)! \, (n - x - 1)!} \right] \pi^{x-1}(1 - \pi)^{n-x-1}, \qquad 0 \leqslant \pi \leqslant 1.$$

$$(9.9)$$

As you may have noticed, the above density function corresponds to the binomial mass function if we simply substitute $(n - 1)$ by n, $(x - 1)$ by x, and $(n - x - 1)$ by $(n - x)$. However, you must keep in mind that the binomial distribution is discrete, whereas the beta distribution is continuous. Also, you should observe that in the binomial model X is the random variable and n and π are the parameters, but in the beta model π is the random variable and x and n are the parameters.

It is important to note that for (9.9) it is necessary that $n > x > 0$, but n and x need not be integers. Also, when n and x are not integers, the factorial terms in (9.9) must be replaced by mathematical functions known as *gamma functions*, denoted as $\Gamma(n)$, $\Gamma(x)$, and $\Gamma(n - x)$. It can be shown, in general, that

$$\Gamma(n) = \int_0^\infty x^{n-1}e^{-x} \, dx = (n - 1)\Gamma(n - 1).$$

Also, by definition,

$$\Gamma(1) = 1,$$
$$\Gamma(2) = (1)\Gamma(1) = 1,$$
$$\Gamma(3) = (2)\Gamma(2) = (2)(1),$$
$$\Gamma(4) = (3)\Gamma(3) = (3)(2)(1), \text{ etc.,}$$

and thus

$$\Gamma(n) = (n - 1)\Gamma(n - 1) = (n - 1)(n - 2) \cdots (3)(2)(1) = (n - 1)!.$$

This result indicates that if x and n are integers, the gamma functions are equal to the corresponding factorial terms in (9.9). So, for our purpose of applying (9.9), we need not be overly concerned with the mathematical concepts of gamma functions. We have mentioned them here merely for the purpose of future reference.

Given the two parameters x and n of the beta model, it can be shown that the expectation and variance of π becomes respectively,

$$E(\pi) = \frac{x}{n} \tag{9.10}$$

and

$$V(\pi) = \frac{x(n - x)}{n^2(n + 1)}. \tag{9.11}$$

To evaluate beta probabilities, we may take notice of the close relationship between the binomial and beta distributions. If x and n are integers, then the CDF of a beta variable is related to the CMF of a binomial variable as follows:

$$P_\beta(\pi \le \pi_0 \,|\, x_0, n) = P_B[X \ge x_0 \,|\, (n - 1), \pi_0],$$

$$\text{if } \pi_0 \le 1/2; \tag{9.12a}$$

$$P_\beta(\pi \le \pi_0 \,|\, x_0, n) = P_B[X < (n - x_0) \,|\, (n - 1), (1 - \pi_0)],$$

$$\text{if } \pi_0 \ge 1/2. \tag{9.12b}$$

In these expressions, P_β and P_B represent the cumulative probabilities for beta and binomial variables, respectively. Note the P_B must be manipulated into the usual form before entering the cumulative binomial table. Also, π_0 and x_0 stand for the particular specified values of π and x, respectively. Furthermore, these relationships clearly imply that for $\pi_0 \le 0.5$ the lower tail of the beta distribution corresponds to the upper tail of the binomial distribution. Finally, to obtain beta probabilities via the binomial model, requires that both n and x be integers, since the binomial variable can only assume integer values. However, beta distributions are continuous and n and x may be nonintegers. To evaluate beta probabilities with noninteger values of n and x, more detailed tables are needed, such as K. Pearson's *Tables of the Incomplete Beta-Function*, or tables of fractiles such as tables for "Beta Cumulative Functions", which appear in *Analysis of Business Decisions Under Uncertainty* by Robert Schlaifer, published by McGraw-Hill Company, Inc. in 1969.

For example, suppose that a beta distribution is defined by $n = 11$ and $x_0 = 5$; what is the probability that π is less than or equal to $\pi_0 = 0.30$? By (9.12a), we have

$$P_\beta(\pi \le 0.3 \,|\, 5, 11) = P_B[X \ge 5 \,|\, (11 - 1), 0.3]$$

$$= 1 - F_B(4 \,|\, 10, 0.3)$$

$$\doteq 1 - 0.84973$$

$$\doteq 0.15027.$$

Again, for the same beta distribution above, what is the probability that π is less than or equal to $\pi_0 = 0.7$? By (9.12b) we see that

$$P_\beta(\pi \leqslant 0.7 \mid 5, 11) = P_B[X < (11 - 5) \mid (11 - 1), (1 - 0.7)]$$
$$= P_B(X < 6 \mid 10, 0.3)$$
$$= F_b(5 \mid 10, 0.3)$$
$$\doteq 0.95265.$$

In concluding this section, it may be pointed out that beta distributions are capable of assuming various shapes with different values of n and x. In particular, let us observe the following.

1. If $x = 1$ and $n = 2$, the beta distribution is a rectangular distribution; if $x \leqslant 1$ or $(n - x) \leqslant 1$, the distribution is either unimodal or U-shaped.

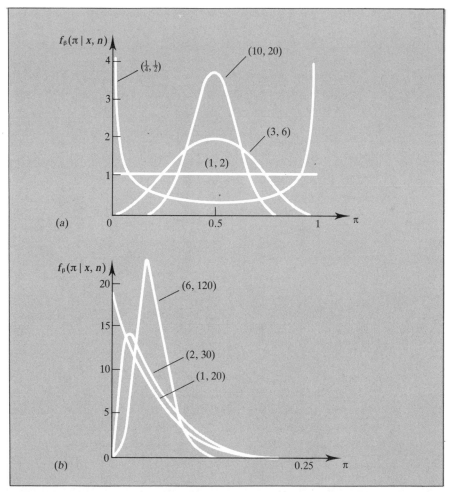

FIGURE 9.7 Illustration of β density curves for various selected pairs of parameters (x, n).
Note: If the values of x and n are interchanged, the β density curves would be the mirror images of those in (b).

2. If $x = 0.5n$ or if $E(\pi) = 0.5$, the beta distribution is symmetric about 0.5.

3. If $x < 0.5n$, the beta distribution is positively skewed; if $x > 0.5n$, it is negatively skewed.

4. If $x > 1$ and if $n > 2$, the beta distribution is unimodal, with the mode defined as

$$\tilde{x}_m = \frac{x - 1}{n - 2}. \tag{9.13}$$

These properties are portrayed by Figure 9.7.

9.5 THE GENERAL NORMAL PROBABILITY MODEL

There are many special probability distributions, but surely the most important one is the *normal probability model,* which is also called the *Gaussian probability model.* If a random variable X is continuous, if it is capable of assuming any real number from $-\infty$ to $+\infty$, and if its PDF is given by

$$f_n(x \mid \mu, \sigma) = \frac{1}{\sigma\sqrt{2\pi}}\, e^{-(1/2)[(x - \mu)/\sigma]^2}, \qquad -\infty < x < \infty, \tag{9.14}$$

then X is said to be a normal variable. In this expression, μ and σ are real numbers with $-\infty < \mu < +\infty$ and $\sigma > 0$, e, and π are constants with $e \doteq 2.7183$ and $\pi \doteq 3.1416$. The CDF of a normal variable is generally given as

$$F_n(x \mid \mu, \sigma) = \int_{-\infty}^{x} \frac{1}{\sigma\sqrt{2\pi}} e^{-(1/2)[(t - \mu)/\sigma]^2}\, dt. \tag{9.15}$$

From these two expressions, we see that a normal probability model is completely defined by the two parameters, μ and σ. Furthermore, it can be shown that, for a normal variable X, $E(X) = \mu$, and $V(X) = \sigma^2$. Of course, when the variance is σ^2, the standard deviation is σ. You should not worry about your inability to comprehend these two seemingly formidable equations at this time, since, as you will see very shortly, normal densities can easily be evaluated by (9.14), and normal probabilities can readily be obtained from published tables. You are, however, advised to learn about the mathematical properties of the normal probability density and cumulative density function by referring to Figure 9.8 constantly. Furthermore, since we shall refer to the PDF and CDF of a normal variable so frequently in the future, we introduce at this point some special notations for them by using $n(x \mid \mu, \sigma)$, or simply $n(\mu, \sigma)$, as the normal density function and by using $N(x \mid \mu, \sigma)$, or simply $N(\mu, \sigma)$, as the normal cumulative density function.

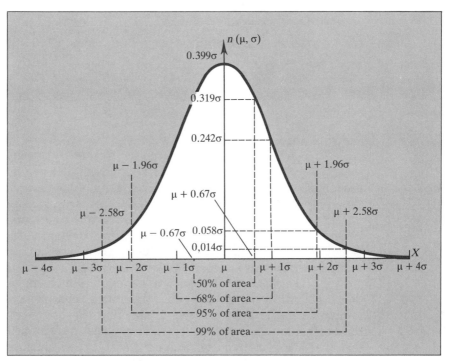

FIGURE 9.8 Graph of the general normal density function showing the areas (probabilities) a few standard deviations below and above the mean. (*Source:* Table VI of Appendix C.)

Mathematical Properties of Normal Distributions

(1) A normal distribution has μ and σ as its parameters in the sense that the area under its density curve (normal probability) is completely defined by the values of μ and σ. (See Figure 9.8). As such, the working part of the normal density is the exponent $-(x - \mu)^2/2\sigma^2$, since it contains a particular value of the normal variable X and the parameters μ and σ of the distribution. The greater the deviation of a particular value of X from μ, the smaller (i.e. the more negative) is the numerator of this exponent. The deviation is squared; hence, two different values of X showing the same absolute deviation from μ have the same probability density. This reflects the fact that a normal distribution is symmetric about μ: namely, $n(\mu - x \mid \mu, \sigma) = n(\mu + x \mid \mu, \sigma)$. For example, as the reader will learn immediately,

$$P(\mu - 0.67\sigma < X < \mu) = P(\mu < X < \mu + 0.67\sigma)$$

$$\doteq 0.25;$$

$$P(\mu - 0.67\sigma < X < \mu + 0.67\sigma) \doteq 0.50;$$

$$P(\mu - \sigma < X < \mu) = P(\mu < X < \mu + \sigma)$$

$$\doteq 0.34;$$

$$P(\mu - \sigma < X < \mu + \sigma) \doteq 0.68;$$

$$P(\mu - 1.96\sigma < X < \mu) = P(\mu < X < \mu + 1.96\sigma)$$

$$\doteq 0.475;$$

$$P(\mu - 1.96\sigma < X < \mu + 1.96\sigma) \doteq 0.95;$$

and so forth.

(2) The fact that the exponent $-(x - \mu)^2/2\sigma^2$ is negative indicates that the greater the deviation of X from μ, the smaller will be the probability density of X. That is, both tails of the normal distribution experience decreasing density, since the further X is from μ, the lower the height of the density curve becomes. In this connection we see that, when the value of X is identical with μ, the exponent is zero, and so the density is $1/\sigma\sqrt{2\pi}$, the largest value of the normal density. Thus, the normal distribution is unimodal, with the modal value at $X = \mu$.

(3) The normal distribution has an infinite range, so that its density curve never touches the X axis. As a consequence, any interval of numbers will have a positive probability. However, the probability of an interval far away from μ is negligibly small, as can be seen from the fact that the density curve falls off quickly, more than 99% of its area being enclosed by $\mu \pm 3\sigma$. This property enables us to use the normal distribution to approximate other distributions for which the true range is finite.

(4) A change in the value of μ displaces the whole normal distribution to the right or left, while a change in the value of σ alters its shape without moving it to the right or left. These facts indicate that the normal distribution is really a family of distributions (see Figure 9.9). This is true, of course, for all special probability distributions. It has been mentioned here because the student often thinks of *a* normal distribution as *the* normal distribution.

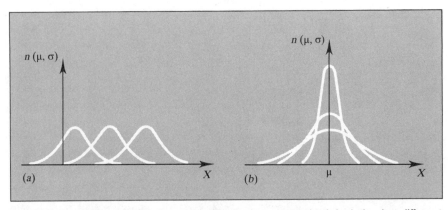

FIGURE 9.9 Normal distributions: (*a*) with the same standard deviation but different means; (*b*) with the same mean but different standard deviations.

(5) A linear transformation of a normal variable results in a new normal variable. That is, if X is a normal variable, then $Y = a + bX$ is also a normal variable.

(6) If $X_1, X_2, \ldots, X_n$ are independent normal variables, then their sum S is also a normal variable. Furthermore, because of independence, the additivity property holds for both the expectation and the variance. That is, the expectation of S is the sum of the expectations of the n normal variables, and the variance of S is the sum of the variances of the n normal variables.

The Importance of Normal Distributions

The normal distribution was first discovered by De Moivre as the limiting form of the binomial model in 1733. It was also known to Laplace no later than 1774, but through a historical error it has been credited to Gauss, who first made reference to it in 1809. Throughout the eighteenth and nineteenth centuries various efforts were made to establish the normal model as the underlying law ruling all continuous random variables: thus the name "normal". These efforts failed. The normal model has, nevertheless, become the most important probability model in statistical analysis, for a number of reasons.

First, many continuous random variables, such as heights of adult males, diameters of auto tires of a certain make, tensile strengths of steel wires produced by a certain process, and the like, are normally distributed or approximately normally distributed because of what is known, or presumed to be true, of the measurements themselves. In this connection, it is particularly interesting to note that "errors" of repeated measurements of a given dimension are hypothesized to follow the normal probability law. Any measurement of observation is assumed to represent a true magnitude plus an error. Each error has a magnitude itself, resulting from a vast collection of factors operative at the moment of measurement. Each factor has but a tiny effect on the size and direction of the error; furthermore, errors of measurement work independently with equal force to push the observed measurement up or down, and therefore cancel out in the long run. Thus we think of errors of measurements as reflections of chance variations that are normally distributed with zero expectation. These are often called "random errors" in laboratories, as distinguished from "systematic errors", which are quite different.

Second, as we shall see, the normal distribution serves as a good approximation for many discrete distributions, such as the binomial or the Poisson model.

Third, in theoretical statistics, many problems can be solved easily under the assumption of a normal population. In applied work we often find that methods developed under the normal probability law yield satisfactory results, even when the assumption of a normal population is not fully met.

Finally, and most important of all, as we shall find in the following chapter, distributions of many sample statistics computed from large samples approach the normal distribution as a limit. As a result, our work on statistical inference is made easier.

Let us now turn to study the standardized normal distribution, which enables us to compute probabilities for any general normal distribution simply by looking at published normal probability tables.

9.6 THE STANDARD NORMAL PROBABILITY MODEL

The PDF and CDF of the Standard Normal Variable

As pointed out in Chapter 7, it is often much easier to work with a random variable that is standardized than with the original random variable. Recall that if X is a random variable with mean μ and standard deviation σ, then $Z = (X - \mu)/\sigma$ is a standard random variable with mean 0 and standard deviation 1.

The Z transformation is especially useful, and even indispensable, when we are concerned with continuous random variables for which the cumulative density functions involve integrals that cannot be reduced to elementary functions. This is certainly true with normal variables. Now, if X is a normal variable with $E(X) = \mu$ and $V(X) = \sigma^2$, then the Z transformation yields a normal variable with $\mu = 0$ and $\sigma^2 = \sigma = 1$. Here, Z is called *the standard*, or *standardized, normal variable*. It is also often called *the standard normal deviate*. Corresponding to $n(\mu, \sigma)$ and $N(\mu, \sigma)$, the PDF and CDF respectively of Z are expressed as follows:

$$f_n(z \mid 0, 1) = \frac{1}{\sqrt{2\pi}} e^{-(1/2)z^2} \tag{9.16}$$

and

$$F_n(z \mid 0, 1) = \int_{-\infty}^{z} \frac{1}{\sqrt{2\pi}} e^{-(1/2)t^2} \, dt. \tag{9.17}$$

The PDF and CDF of Z are shown in Figure 9.10.

For convenience, as for the general normal probability model, we shall denote the PDF of Z as $n(z \mid 0, 1)$ or simply as $n(0, 1)$, and the CDF

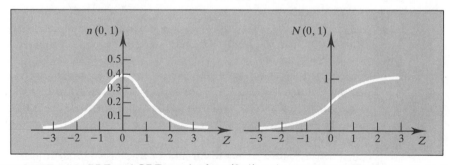

FIGURE 9.10 PDF and CDF graphs for $n(0, 1)$.

of Z as $N(z \mid 0, 1)$ or simply as $N(0, 1)$. Furthermore, we shall also use the notation $n(\mu, \sigma)$ to represent a normal variable with mean μ and standard deviation σ, and use $n(0, 1)$ to represent the standard normal variable from time to time. Employing the same notation, say, $n(\mu, \sigma)$ as the PDF of a normal variable as well as the normal variable itself should create no confusion, since we would know what it stands for in each case from the context of discussion.

To repeat: if X is $n(\mu, \sigma)$, then $Z = (X - \mu)/\sigma$ is $n(0, 1)$. This transformation from X to Z has the effect of reducing X to units of standard deviations away from the mean. In other words, given a value of X, the corresponding value of Z tells us how far away and in what direction X is from its mean μ, in terms of its standard deviation σ. For example, $Z = 1.5$ means that the particular value of X is 1.5σ above (to the right of) μ. Similarly, $Z = -2$ means that the particular value of X is 2σ below (to the left of) μ. This property of the standard normal variable enables us to evaluate normal probabilities for any $n(\mu, \sigma)$ from a single probability table for $N(0, 1)$. Precisely, any general normal CDF can be converted into a standard normal CDF by the Z transformation as follows:

$$N(x \mid \mu, \sigma) = P(X \leqslant x)$$

$$= P[(\mu + \sigma Z) \leqslant x]$$

$$= P\left(Z \leqslant \frac{x - \mu}{\sigma}\right)$$

$$= N\left(\frac{x - \mu}{\sigma} \,\middle|\, 0, 1\right)$$

$$= N\left(\frac{x - \mu}{\sigma}\right). \tag{9.18}$$

As we see immediately, with a table for the cumulative density function of the standard normal variable, such as Table VI in Appendix C, (9.18) is all we need to evaluate the probabilities of any normal variable. Also, if we wish to sketch the density curve of any $n(\mu, \sigma)$, Equation (9.14) can easily be applied via (9.18) with the aid of a statistical calculator, or use of Table V.

Example 1 Soybean Yields

An agricultural experimental station wishes to find out the effects of applying a new chemical fertilizer for the cultivation of soybeans. It divides its 1,000 acres of land into 2,000 equal plots for the experiment. By the end of the season, it is found that the yield of soybeans, measured in pounds, of the 2,000 plots is normally distributed with $\mu = 2,425$ and $\sigma = 115$. That is, the population of weights in question is $n(2,425, 115)$. Now, if we wish to sketch the density curve for this normal population, we may apply (9.16) and (9.18) to compute the densities in the following manner.

If $X = \mu = 2{,}425$, we have

$$n(2{,}425 \mid 2{,}425,\ 115) = n\left(\frac{2{,}425 - 2{,}425}{115}\ \middle|\ 0,\ 1\right)$$

$$= n(0 \mid 0,\ 1) = \frac{1}{\sqrt{2\pi}}\,e^{-(1/2)0^2}$$

$$\doteq \frac{1}{\sqrt{(2)(3.1416)}}\,e^0$$

$$\doteq \frac{1}{2.50663}\,(1) \doteq 0.3994,$$

which is the maximum ordinate (density) at $E(X) = 2{,}425$ or at $E(Z) = 0$.

If $X = \mu + 0.5\sigma = 2{,}482.5$, we have

$$n(2{,}482.5 \mid 2{,}425,\ 115) = n\left(\frac{2{,}482.5 - 2{,}425}{115}\ \middle|\ 0,\ 1\right)$$

$$= n(0.5 \mid 0,\ 1) = \frac{1}{\sqrt{2\pi}}\,e^{-(1/2)0.5^2}$$

$$= \frac{1}{\sqrt{2\pi}}\,e^{-0.125}$$

$$\doteq (0.39894)(0.88253) \doteq 0.35207.$$

If $X = \mu - 0.5\sigma = 2{,}367.5$, we have owing to the symmetry property of the normal curve,

$$n(2{,}367.5 \mid 2{,}425,\ 115) = n(-0.5 \mid 0,\ 1)$$

$$\doteq 0.35207.$$

If $X = \mu \pm 1\sigma = 2{,}540,\ 2{,}310$, then

$$n(2{,}540 \mid 2{,}425,\ 115) = n\left(\frac{2{,}540 - 2{,}425}{115}\ \middle|\ 0,\ 1\right)$$

$$= n(+1 \mid 0,\ 1) = \frac{1}{\sqrt{2\pi}}\,e^{-(1/2)1^2}$$

$$= \frac{1}{\sqrt{2\pi}}\,e^{-0.5}$$

$$\doteq (0.39894)(0.60653) \doteq 0.24197.$$

Similarly,

$$n(2{,}310 \mid 2{,}425,\ 115) = n(-1 \mid 0,\ 1)$$

$$\doteq 0.24197.$$

The last two results are clearly densities that are 1σ above and 1σ below the mean, respectively. If densities for a few more selected values of X are determined in the same way and the top points of these ordinates are connected with a smooth curve, then the density curve for the normal variable in question would look like Figure 9.11(a). In practice, we do not even have to do these computations when normal

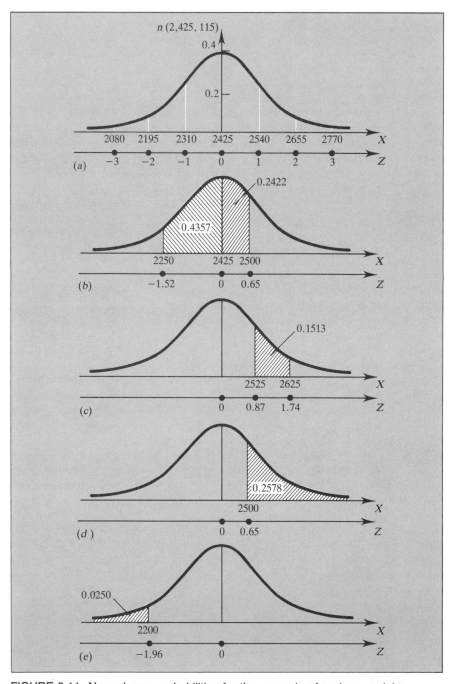

FIGURE 9.11 Normal area probabilities for the example of soybean weights.

densities are required, since they can be found directly from Table V in Appendix C.

Now, suppose the yield of soybeans of a single lot is selected at random for observation, what is the probability that it will have a weight

1. between 2,250 and 2,425 pounds?

2. between 2,250 and 2,500 pounds?

3. between 2,525 and 2,625 pounds?

4. greater than 2,500 pounds?

5. less than 2,200 pounds?

By employing (9.18), we get the following answers.

(1) $P(2,250 \leq X \leq 2,425) = P(X \leq 2,425) - P(X \leq 2,250)$

$$= N\left(\frac{2,425 - 2,425}{115}\right) - N\left(\frac{2,250 - 2,425}{115}\right)$$

$$\doteq N(0) - N(-1.52)$$

$$\doteq 0.5000 - 0.0643 \quad \text{[from Table VI]}$$

$$= 0.4357.$$

(See Figure 9.11(b).)

(2) $P(2,250 \leq X \leq 2,500) = N\left(\frac{2,500 - 2,425}{115}\right) - N\left(\frac{2,250 - 2,425}{115}\right)$

$$\doteq N(0.65) - N(-1.52)$$

$$\doteq 0.7422 - 0.0643 \quad \text{[from Table VI]}$$

$$= 0.6779.$$

(See Figure 9.11(b), where $0.4357 + 0.2422 = 0.6779$.)

(3) $P(2,525 \leq X \leq 2,625) = N\left(\frac{2,625 - 2,425}{115}\right) - N\left(\frac{2,525 - 2,425}{115}\right)$

$$\doteq N(1.74) - N(0.87)$$

$$\doteq 0.9591 - 0.8078 \quad \text{[from Table VI]}$$

$$= 0.1513.$$

(See Figure 9.11(c).)

(4) $P(X > 2,500 = 1 - P(X \leq 2,500)$

$$\doteq 1 - N(0.65)$$

$$\doteq 1 - 0.7422 \quad \text{[from Table VI]}$$

$$= 0.2578.$$

(See Figure 9.11(d).)

(5)
$$P(X < 2{,}200) = N\left(\frac{2{,}200 - 2{,}425}{115}\right),$$

$$\doteq N(-1.96)$$

$$= 0.0250 \quad \text{[from Table VI]}.$$

(See Figure 9.11(e).)

Before you move on to the next example, be sure that you understand the application of (9.18) in these calculations and check from Table VI whether the probability values are correct.

Example 2 Method to Be Used

There are two methods of setting up a machine process. The time required to complete the operation of each method is known to be normally distributed. The first method is characterized by a normal distribution with a mean time of 53 minutes and a standard deviation of 5 minutes. The second method has a mean of 55 minutes and standard deviation of 3 minutes. If there are only 60 minutes available to set up the machine one day, which method should be employed?

One way to solve this problem is to select the method that has a greater probability of setting up the machine in less than or equal to 60 minutes. Thus, by the first method, we have

$$P(X \leqslant 60) = N(60 \mid 53, 5) = N\left(\frac{60 - 53}{5}\right)$$

$$= N(+1.40) = 0.9192.$$

By the second method, we have

$$P(X \leqslant 60) = N(60 \mid 55, 3) = N\left(\frac{60 - 55}{3}\right)$$

$$= N(+1.67) = 0.9525.$$

So the second method should be used if there are only 60 minutes available. Note that this problem can also be solved by selecting the method that has a smaller probability of requiring more than 60 minutes for the completion of the task. Of course, the final answer is the same.

Example 3 Decision on the Length of a Product

A product consists of four components that are produced independently. The overall length of this product is the sum S of the lengths of the four components X_1, X_2, X_3, and X_4, all normal random variables with means and variances as follows:

$$\mu_1 = 2 \text{ inches}, \qquad \sigma_1^2 = 0.010;$$

$$\mu_2 = 1 \text{ inch}, \qquad \sigma_2^2 = 0.006;$$

$$\mu_3 = 0.5 \text{ inches}, \qquad \sigma_3^2 = 0.004;$$

$$\mu_4 = 1.5 \text{ inches}, \qquad \sigma_4^2 = 0.011.$$

What is the probability that the overall length for S will meet the specification of 5 ± 0.10 inches?

Here, the desired probability is $P(4.9 < S < 5.1)$. Since lengths of the four components are independent and normally distributed, S must be also normally distributed and we must have

$$\mu_s = \mu_1 + \mu_2 + \mu_3 + \mu_4 = 5 \text{ inches}$$

and

$$\sigma_s = \sqrt{\sigma_1^2 + \sigma_2^2 + \sigma_3^2 + \sigma_4^2} = \sqrt{0.031} \doteq 0.176 \text{ inches}.$$

Consequently,

$$P(4.9 < S < 5.1) \doteq N(0.57) - N(-0.57)$$

$$= 0.4314.$$

This result indicates that, on the average, only 43% of the items produced can be expected to meet the predesignated specifications. This is a very low percentage for problems of this kind; management should either increase the precision of producing the components (reducing variability in production) or relax the standards if relaxation does not impair the product's usefulness.

Example 4 Labor-Saving Machine

It is estimated that a certain machine, on the average, can replace 10,000 man-hours, with a probability of 0.25 that the saving in terms of mean time would be more than 10,500 hours and a probability of 0.25 that the saving would be less than 9,500 hours per week. Now, assuming that a specific normal distribution will fit these estimates, what is the probability that the machine will actually replace less than 9,000 man-hours per week?

To solve this problem, we must first find the value of the standard deviation for this distribution. To do so, we note that the central 50% of the area of a normal distribution is enclosed by $\mu \pm 0.67\sigma$. For the problem, we have

$$\frac{10,500 - 9,500}{2} \doteq 0.67\sigma.$$

That is, if we shift in either the positive or negative direction by 500 hours from the mean, we shift 0.67σ away from the mean. So

$$500 \doteq 0.67\sigma$$

and

$$\sigma \doteq \frac{500}{0.67} \doteq 746 \text{ hours.}$$

With this, the desired probability is seen to be

$$P(X \leq 9,000) \doteq N\left(\frac{9,000 - 10,000}{746}\right)$$

$$\doteq N(-1.34)$$

$$\doteq 0.0901.$$

Obviously, the probability that the machine will replace more than 9,000 man-hours per week is greater than 0.90.

Example 5 **Interpercentile Range for Soybean Yields**

Suppose we wish to compute an interpercentile range for the yields of soybeans considered in Example 1. To do this, we need the 0.10 and 0.90 fractiles of the variable X which is weights of soybean yields. Recall that the variable considered is $n(2,425, 115)$. Fractile values of any normal variable can be obtained with the aid of the table for $N(0, 1)$ (Table VI, Appendix C).

Let us consider the determination of $\tilde{x}_{10}$ first via Table VI. This is done by first scanning the table for the cumulative probability of 0.10. Unfortunately, this exact cumulative probability cannot be found in the table. However, the table does provide us with the information that $N(-1.20) = 0.1151$ and $N(-1.30) = 0.0968$. With these two values, we can find the approximate z-value by linear interpolation, which would correspond to 0.1000 as below:

$$\frac{\tilde{z}_{10} - (-1.20)}{(-1.30) - (-1.20)} = \frac{0.1000 - 0.1151}{0.0968 - 0.1151}.$$

Solving for $\tilde{z}_{10}$, we have

$$\tilde{z}_{10} = -1.2825.$$

This means that $N(-1.2825) = 0.10$. Next, applying the Z transformation formula, we may write

$$\tilde{z}_{10} = \frac{\tilde{x}_{10} - \mu}{\sigma}.$$

From this, we obtain

$$\tilde{x}_{10} = \mu + \tilde{z}_{10}\sigma.$$

Finally, by substitution,

$$\tilde{x}_{.10} = 2{,}425 + (-1.2825)(115) \doteq 2{,}277.51 \text{ pounds.}$$

To determine the 0.90 fractile, we note that the exact cumulative probability of 0.90 also does not appear in Table VI. However, we do find $N(+1.28) = 0.8997$ and $N(+1.29) = 0.9015$. Again, by linear interpolation, we obtain $N(+1.2825) \doteq 0.90$. Namely, $\tilde{z}_{.90} = +1.2825$. With this result, we have

$$\tilde{x}_{.90} = \mu + \tilde{z}_{.90}\sigma$$
$$= 2{,}425 + (1.2825)(115)$$
$$\doteq 2{,}572.49.$$

The desired interpercentile, or interdecile, range for our example can now be determined. This is,

$$\widetilde{dr} = \tilde{x}_{.90} - \tilde{x}_{.10}$$
$$= 2{,}572.49 - 2{,}277.51$$
$$\doteq 295 \text{ pounds.}$$

Thus, the central 80% of the yields of soybeans vary within the range of 295 pounds.

9.7 NORMAL APPROXIMATIONS TO DISCRETE PROBABILITIES

At the end of Chapter 8, we showed how the hypergeometric probabilities could be approximated by the binomial probabilities, which, in turn, could be approximated by the Poisson probabilities, under certain conditions in each case. We also pointed out then that all these discrete probability distributions could be approximated by a single probability law—the standard normal probability model. The subject matter of this section is how the normal probability law can be employed to approximate such discrete probabilities.

Normal Approximation to the Binomial and Hypergeometric Probabilities

The binomial distribution becomes smoother and more symmetric as n increases. In fact, a binomial distribution approaches the normal distribution as a limit (as n approaches infinity) with $\mu = n\pi$ and $\sigma = \sqrt{n\pi\pi'}$. This suggests that the binomially distributed number of successes can be approximated by a normally distributed variable. As a rule of thumb, the normal approximation to the binomial distribution is satisfactory, provided that both the conditions $n\pi \geq 5$ and $n\pi' \geq 5$ are

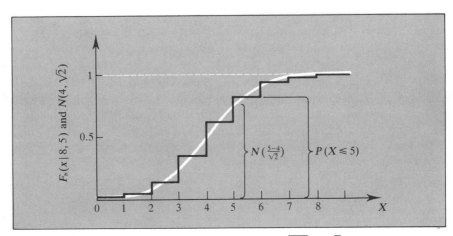

FIGURE 9.12 Graph showing the fit of $N(np = 4, \sqrt{npq} = \sqrt{2})$ to a binomial CMF with $n = 8$ and $\pi = 0.5$.

met. When these conditions are met, the CMF of the binomial variable X can be approximated by the CDF of Z as follows:

$$P(X \leqslant x) \doteq N\left(\frac{x - n\pi}{\sqrt{n\pi\pi'}}\right). \tag{9.19}$$

Figure 9.12 graphs an example of the CMF for the binomial distribution with $n = 8$ and $\pi = 0.5$. It consists of a series of steps with the cumulative normal distribution $N(\mu = 4$ and $\sigma = \sqrt{2})$, drawn through them. Even though the smooth curve is slightly above 0 for all values of X between $-\infty$ and 0, and is slightly below 1 for all values of X between 8 and $+\infty$, the curve goes through about the middle of each of the horizontal segments. As an example of applying (9.19), suppose we want $P(X \leqslant 5)$ for the binomial variable in question. From (9.19) we get

$$P(X \leqslant 5) \doteq N\left(\frac{x - n\pi}{\sqrt{n\pi\pi'}}\right)$$

$$\doteq N\left(\frac{5 - (8)(0.5)}{\sqrt{8(0.5)(0.5)}}\right) = N\left(\frac{5 - 4}{\sqrt{2}}\right)$$

$$\doteq N(+0.71) \doteq 0.7611,$$

which is not a very good approximation of the exact binomial probability of $P(X \leqslant 5) = 0.8555$.

The preceding conclusion leads us to the observation that in applying normal approximation, a compensation should be made for the fact that the binomial variable is discrete and n is finite. The conventional correction consists of changing the deviation from μ by half unit on the grounds that the discrete value, say, $X = a$ should correspond on a continuous scale to the interval $(a - \frac{1}{2}) \leqslant X \leqslant (a + \frac{1}{2})$. Thus, to estimate $P(X \leqslant a)$ for which $a \leqslant (\mu - \frac{1}{2})$, we should set $a \leqslant (\mu - \frac{1}{2})$ up as $[(a + \frac{1}{2}) - \mu]/\sigma = [(a + \frac{1}{2}) - n\pi]/\sqrt{n\pi\pi'}$ on the right-hand side of (9.19). Graphically speaking, to approximate, say, $P(X \leq 5)$, for example, we really want the height of the horizontal line segment over the X-axis between 5 and 6. It is obvious from Figure 9.12 that the height of the normal CDF above $X = 5$ is not as close an approximation as we can get. The height of the normal CDF above $X = 5\frac{1}{2}$ is a better approximation. In general, if we add $\frac{1}{2}$ to the numerator of the right-hand side of (9.19), we will improve the approximation. The quantity $\frac{1}{2}$, is called the *continuity correction factor*, or CCF. When we modify (9.19) by introducing the CCF, we get

$$P(X \leq x) \doteq N\left(\frac{x + \frac{1}{2} - n\pi}{\sqrt{n\pi\pi'}}\right). \tag{9.20}$$

Now, with (9.20), we have

$$P(X \leq 5) \doteq N\left(\frac{5 + \frac{1}{2} - 8(0.5)}{\sqrt{8(0.5)(0.5)}}\right)$$

$$\doteq N(+1.06) \doteq 0.8554.$$

The exact binomial probability (to four decimal places) is 0.8555. Thus, (9.20) produces a very close approximation in this example.

As another example based on the current case,

$$P(X = 4) = P(X \leq 4) - P(X \leq 3)$$

$$\doteq N\left(\frac{4 + \frac{1}{2} - 4}{1.41421}\right) - N\left(\frac{3 + \frac{1}{2} - 4}{1.41421}\right)$$

$$\doteq N(+0.35) - N(-0.35)$$

$$\doteq 0.6368 - 0.3632$$

$$\doteq 0.2736,$$

which approximates the exact binomial probability of 0.2734. Again, this approximation is almost identical with the exact answer. In addition, we see that

$$P(X \geq 5) = 1 - P(X \leq 4) \doteq 1 - N(0.35) \doteq 0.3632,$$

which approximates the exact binomial probability of 0.3633.

Finally, again with the same example, we find that

$$P(X \leq 1) \doteq N\left(\frac{1 + \frac{1}{2} - 4}{\sqrt{2}}\right)$$

$$\doteq N(-1.77) \doteq 0.0384,$$

with approximate binomial probability of 0.0352. This time the error of approximation is bigger than the previous results, but still quite good.

With the use of the CCF, the normal approximations are very close to the binomial probabilities, even though $n = 8$ is a small value of n. These close approximations were obtained partly because $\pi = 0.5$. In general, given n, the closer π is to 0.5, the closer the approximation is. Also, given π, the larger n is, the closer the approximation is. Furthermore, given n and π, approximations of X values close to $E(X)$ are better than those of X values close to 0 or to n.

It may be noted here also that precise mathematical evaluations of the error in normal approximation are extremely difficult and their results are difficult to report. However, extensive empirical investigation suggests that when $n\pi \, (= \mu_X)$ is "far" from 0 and n—the extreme values of X, the approximation is quite good. If $n\pi$ is at least $3\sqrt{n\pi\pi'} = 3\sigma$ from either 0 or n, then it seems that the maximum error in evaluating a single term is at most 0.011, and in a cumulative term at most 0.025.

As can be verified, for $n = 8$ and $\pi = 0.5$, the maximum errors, in individual as well as cumulative terms are both 0.004. Yet $n = 8$ does not quite put $n\pi$ a distance 3σ from extreme values of X. For $n = 40$, $\pi = 0.2$, $n\pi$ is more than 3σ from both extremes, and the maximum errors are 0.010 and 0.015 for individual terms and for cumulative terms, respectively.

The normal distribution can be used to approximate hypergeometric probabilities. if the condition as stated in the previous chapter for the binomial approximation to the hypergeometric model, (i.e., if $n \leqslant 0.05N$) is met, and if the conditions on (9.19) for the normal approximation to the binomial model, (i.e., $n\pi \geqslant 5$ and $n\pi' \geqslant 5$), are met, then the normal approximation to the hypergeometric is obtained by using (9.19) or (9.20), recognizing that $\pi = k/N$ and that $\pi' = (N - k)/N$. For the same reason given before, (9.20) would always give closer approximations than (9.19). Furthermore, comments made for the accuracy in approximation for the binomial also hold here.

Normal Approximation to the Poisson Probabilities

Recall that the PMF of a Poisson variable is positively skewed; however, the skewness decreases and the Poisson distribution becomes more symmetric as λ increases. As a matter of fact, as it can be shown that a Poisson variable approaches normality as λ becomes sufficiently large. For most practical purposes the normal approximation of the Poisson probability is adequate for $\lambda > 10$. Again, as in any discrete case, the approximation is closer if the continuity correction factor CCF is employed in the process. Thus, given $\lambda > 10$, the CMF of a Poisson variable can be given in terms of the standard normal CDF as follows:

$$F_P(x \mid \lambda) \doteq N(x \mid \lambda, \sqrt{\lambda}) \doteq N\left(\frac{x + \frac{1}{2} - \lambda}{\sqrt{\lambda}}\right). \tag{9.21}$$

For the application of (9.21), consider the following example. During peak hours, customers arrive at a bank according to the Poisson process with an average of $\lambda = 1$ per minute.

(1) During a given 12-minute period during the peak hours, what is the probability that 9 or fewer customers will arrive at the bank?

Clearly, for a 12-minute period, $\lambda = 12$ and by (9.21), we have

$$F_P(9 \mid 12) \doteq N\left(\frac{9 + \frac{1}{2} - 12}{\sqrt{12}}\right)$$

$$\doteq N\left(\frac{9.5 - 12}{3.4641}\right)$$

$$\doteq N(-0.72) \doteq 0.2358,$$

which approximates the exact Poisson probability of 0.2424 taken from Molina's tables.

(2) During a 20-minute period during the peak hours, what is the probability that (a) 15 or fewer customers will arrive at the bank, (b) exactly 25 customers will arrive at the bank?

Now, $\lambda = 20$ and

(a)
$$F_P(15 \mid 20) \doteq N\left(\frac{15 + \frac{1}{2} - 20}{\sqrt{20}}\right)$$

$$\doteq N(-1.01) = 0.1562,$$

which approximates the exact Poisson probability of 0.1565.

(b)
$$f_p(25 \mid 20) = F_P(25 \mid 20) - F_P(24 \mid 20)$$

$$\doteq N\left(\frac{25 + \frac{1}{2} - 20}{\sqrt{20}}\right) - N\left(\frac{24 + \frac{1}{2} - 20}{\sqrt{20}}\right)$$

$$\doteq N(+1.23) - N(+1.01)$$

$$= 0.8917 - 0.8438 = 0.0469,$$

which approximates the exact Poisson probability of 0.0446. Thus, we see, as expected, that the approximation becomes better as λ becomes larger.

As a second example, suppose a department store manager discovers that the number of units of a certain kind of merchandise demanded by customers in a given period of time obeys the Poisson law with $\lambda = 121$. What stock x of this merchandise should the store have on hand at the beginning of the time period in order to have a probability of 0.95 that the store will be able to supply immediately all customers who wish to buy it during the time period under consideration?

The problem here is to find the number x such that the probability is 0.95 that there will be x or fewer occurrences of this event which obeys a Poisson process with $\lambda = 121$. Hence, we seek the integer x such that

$$\sum_{x=0}^{x} e^{-\lambda}\frac{\lambda^x}{x!} = \left[\sum_{x=0}^{x} e^{-121}\left(\frac{121^x}{x!}\right)\right] \geq 0.95.$$

Note that λ is so large here that the normal approximation to the Poisson would be quite satisfactory. Now we note that the previous sum is approximately equal to

$$N\left(\frac{x + \frac{1}{2} - 121}{\sqrt{121}}\right),$$

where x should be selected so that $(x + \frac{1}{2} - 121)/\sqrt{121} \doteq 1.64$, since 95% of the area under the density curve of $n(0, 1)$, as can be found from Table VI, lies below $N(+1.64)$. Solving for x from this expression, we have

$$x \doteq 1.64\sqrt{121} + 121 - \tfrac{1}{2}$$

$$\doteq 139 \text{ units.}$$

This result says that if the manager stocks 139 units of the merchandise at the beginning of the period in question, the store will be able with a probability of 0.95 to supply immediately the customers who demand the item.

In closing, it may be observed that the normal approximation of discrete probabilities is based on one form of a quite general set of "central limit theorems" (discussed in the next chapter) that evaluate the limiting distributions of sums of random variables. These limiting distributions are usually normal. The significance of these theorems is that they enable us to obtain approximate probabilities for sums using the standard normal distribution without ever knowing the exact distribution of the sum. Exact distributions are often hard to get, so we are grateful and delighted for such approximations.

GLOSSARY OF FORMULAS

(9.1) $f_r(x) = \begin{cases} \dfrac{1}{b - a}, & \text{if } a < x < b, \\ 0, & \text{otherwise;} \end{cases}$

(9.2) $F_r(x) = \begin{cases} 0, & \text{if } x \leq a, \\ \dfrac{x - a}{b - a}, & \text{if } a \leq x \leq b, \\ 1, & \text{if } x \geq b; \end{cases}$

(9.3) $E(X) = (a + b)/2;$

(9.4) $V(X) = (b - a)^2/12.$

This group of formulas defines the continuous uniform or rectangular probability model. A random variable X = (real number x: $a < x < b$) is said to have a uniform distribution if its probability density function is constant over the interval (a, b), as indicated by (9.1). The last three equations give, respectively, the CDF, the expectation, and the variance of a continuous uniform variable.

(9.5) $f_e(x) = (1/\beta)e^{-x/\beta}$;

(9.6) $F_e(x) = 1 - e^{-x/\beta}$;

(9.7) $E(X) = \beta = 1/\lambda$;

(9.8) $V(X) = \beta^2 = 1/\lambda^2$.

Equations (9.5) and (9.6) in this group are the PDF and CDF of an exponential variable derived from a Poisson process. The exponential variable is then considered as the time interval between Poisson occurrences. Note that here λ is the Poisson average number of occurrences per unit of time or space. Note also that the expectation of the exponential distribution is the reciprocal of the mean of the Poisson model and, as such, it should be interpreted as the expected time until the first occurrence of a Poisson event. Finally, the expectation and the standard deviation of the exponential model are identical, as shown by Equations (9.7) and (9.8).

(9.9) $f_\beta(\pi \mid x, n) = \left(\dfrac{(n - 1)!}{(x - 1)! \, (n - x - 1)!} \right) \pi^{x-1}(1 - \pi)^{n-x-1}, \qquad 0 \leq \pi \leq 1$;

(9.10) $E(\pi) = \dfrac{x}{n}$;

(9.11) $V(\pi) = \dfrac{x(n - x)}{n^2(n + 1)}$;

(9.12a) $P_\beta(\pi \leq \pi_0 \mid x_0, n) = P_B[X \geq x_0 \mid (n - 1), \pi_0]$, if $\pi_0 \leq 1/2$;

(9.12b) $P_\beta(\pi \leq \pi_0 \mid x_0, n) = P_B[X < (n - x_0) \mid (n - 1), (1 - \pi_0)]$, if $\pi_0 \geq 1/2$;

(9.13) $\tilde{x}_m = \dfrac{x - 1}{n - 2}$.

This group of equations governs the beta probability model. This model is concerned with a continuous random variable π whose admissible values range from 0 to 1. The main function of this model is for the estimation of the unknown probability of success in the Bernoulli process. As shown by its density function, a beta model is completely defined by the two parameters x and n, with $n > x > 0$. See (9.9). The expectation and variance of a beta variable are as defined by (9.10) and (9.11), respectively. The beta model is capable of assuming a great variety of distribution patterns with different pairs of values for x and n. When it is unimodal, its mode is defined by (9.13). When x and n are integers, the cumulative probabilities of a beta variable can be obtained via the CMF of a corresponding binomial variable, as indicated by equations (9.12a) and (9.12b).

$$(9.14) \quad f_n(x \mid \mu, \sigma) = \frac{1}{\sigma\sqrt{2\pi}} e^{-(1/2)[(x-\mu)/\sigma]^2}, \qquad -\infty < x < \infty;$$

$$(9.15) \quad F_n(x \mid \mu, \sigma) = \int_{-\infty}^{x} \frac{1}{\sigma\sqrt{2\pi}} e^{-(1/2)[(t-\mu)/\sigma]^2} \, dt.$$

These are the PDF and CDF of a normal variable, respectively. A normal variable is continuous and it ranges in value from $-\infty$ to ∞. It is defined by two parameters: μ, with $-\infty < \mu < \infty$, which is the mean of a normal variable; and σ, with $\sigma > 0$, which is the standard deviation of a normal variable. Also, in these formulas, $e \doteq 2.7183$ and $\pi \doteq 3.1416$.

$$(9.16) \quad f_n(z \mid 0, 1) = \frac{1}{\sqrt{2\pi}} e^{-(1/2)z^2};$$

$$(9.17) \quad F_n(z \mid 0, 1) = \int_{-\infty}^{z} \frac{1}{\sqrt{2\pi}} e^{-(1/2)t^2} \, dt.$$

The PDF and CDF of a standardized normal variable are defined by these two equations. A standardized normal variable is one with mean 0 and standard deviation 1. Any normal variable X with mean μ and standard deviation σ can be converted into a standard normal variable by the transformation $Z = (X - \mu)/\sigma$. The standardized normal probability model is of great importance since probabilities of any normal variable can be evaluated by this simple Z transformation and the table for $N(0, 1)$.

$$(9.18) \quad N(x \mid \mu, \sigma) = P(X \leq x) \doteq N\left(\frac{x - \mu}{\sigma}\right).$$

The cumulative probability of any normal variable can be evaluated by this simple equation. Here, $(x - \mu)/\sigma$ is the value z of Z which corresponds to the value x of X. When a value of Z is so determined, the probability that $X < x$ for the normal variable in question can be found from the table for $N(0, 1)$.

$$(9.19) \quad P(X \leq x) \doteq N\left(\frac{x - n\pi}{\sqrt{n\pi\pi'}}\right);$$

$$(9.20) \quad P(X \leq x) \doteq N\left(\frac{x + 1/2 - n\pi}{\sqrt{n\pi\pi'}}\right).$$

When $n\pi > 5$ and $n\pi' > 5$, binomial probabilities can be satisfactorily approximated by the normal probabilities. However, since we are approximating discrete binomial probabilities here by the continuous normal probabilities, approximations will improve if a continuity correction factor of 1/2 is employed as in (9.20). These two equations can also be used to approximate hypergeometric probabilities provided the conditions for binomial approximations of the hypergeometric probabilities are satisfied and the conditions of the normal approximations for binomial probabilities are satisfied. Now, of course, we have $\pi \doteq k/N$ and $\pi' = 1 - k/N = (N - K)/N$.

$$(9.21) \quad F_P(x \mid \lambda) \doteq N(x \mid \lambda, \sqrt{\lambda}) \doteq N\left(\frac{x + 1/2 - \lambda}{\sqrt{\lambda}}\right).$$

This equation is employed to approximate Poisson probabilities by the normal probabilities. As a rule of thumb, approximations may be satisfactory when $\lambda > 10$. Of course, normal approximations improve when λ becomes larger. Also, note that in this expression the CCF of 1/2 is employed to improve the approximations.

REVIEW QUESTIONS

9.1 If X is a continuous random variable, what is $f(x)$? What are the restrictions that $f(x)$ must have?

9.2 What is the meaning of a distribution density?

9.3 How is the probability of a continuous random variable measured?

9.4 What does $F(x)$ stand for if X is a continuous random variable? What is the relationship between $f(x)$ and $F(x)$ in such a case?

9.5 What is the difference between a CMF and a CDF? Explain this difference verbally and graphically.

9.6 How should the statement that $P(X = 115) = 0$ be interpreted if X is a discrete random variable? If X is a continuous variable?

9.7 If X is a continuous random variable and if $a < b$ in the range of X, is it true that

$$P(a \leqslant X \leqslant b) = P(a \leqslant X < b) = P(a < X \leqslant b) = P(a < X < b)?$$

Would your answer be the same if X were a discrete random variable? Justify your answers.

9.8 What is the difference between the definition of a fractile for discrete and continuous distributions? What is the reason for this difference?

9.9 Why are continuous probability models unrealistic from a practical point of view? If this is the case, why should we study them?

9.10 How is the continuous uniform probability model defined? Do you think it might have practical uses in describing business and economic data? If so, give some examples.

9.11 How is the exponential probability model related to the Poisson probability model? What is the general shape of an exponential density curve? What influence does such a distribution pattern have on the probabilities of an exponential model?

9.12 Explain why the expectation of an exponential variable is the reciprocal of that of a Poisson variable.

9.13 How is a beta variable defined? How is it related to the binomial variable?

9.14 What are the parameters of a beta probability model? What pairs of values of these parameters would produce beta density curves that are
a. positively skewed?
b. negatively skewed?
c. uniform?
d. U-shaped?
e. unimodal?

9.15 How is a normal variable defined? What are its parameters?

9.16 Can you explain the reason or reasons for the particular shape of a normal distribution?

9.17 Why does the normal distribution hold the most honorable position in probability theory?

9.18 Under what conditions would the binomial, the hypergeometric, and the Poisson distributions, respectively, approach the normal distribution?

9.19 In normal approximations of binomial, hypergeometric and Poisson probabilities, a continuity correction factor CCF should be used. What is its value and why should it be used?

PROBLEMS

9.1 Let the sample space be $S = \{x: 0 < x < 12\}$, where x is a real number and is selected at random. Given the following events:

$$A = \{x: x \leq 8\},$$

$$B = \{x: 6 < x < 9\},$$

$$C = \{x: x > 7\}.$$

Determine $P(A)$, $P(B)$, $P(C)$, $P(A \cup B)$, $P(B \cup C)$, $P(A \cup C)$, $P(A \cap B)$, $P(B \cap C)$, and $P(A \cap C)$.

9.2 Consider the stopwatch example in the text. What are the following probabilities?
a. $P(5 < T < 10)$.
b. $P(0 < T < 2$ or $7 < T < 9)$.
c. $P(T > 8)$.
d. $P(0 < T < 4$ and $2 < T < 5)$.

9.3 Suppose the continuous random variable B has the following PDF:

$$f(b) = \begin{cases} 0 & \text{for } b < 0, \\ 0.02b & \text{for } 0 \leqslant b \leqslant 10, \\ 0 & \text{for } b > 10. \end{cases}$$

a. Graph this PDF.
b. What is $P(-2 \leqslant B \leqslant 0)$?
c. What is $P(0 \leqslant B \leqslant 2)$?
d. What is $P(B = 2)$?
e. What is $P(2 \leqslant B \leqslant 10)$?

f. What is $P(B = 10)$?
g. What is $P(2 < B \leqslant 10)$?
h. What is $P(2 \leqslant B < 10)$?
i. What is $P(2 < B < 10)$?
j. What is $P(2 \leqslant B \leqslant 8)$?

(*Hint:* The area of any triangle is one-half the base times the height.)

9.4 Suppose the continuous random variable C has the following PDF:

$$f(c) = \begin{cases} 0 & \text{for } c < 4, \\ 3/2 - (9/8)(c - 4) & \text{for } 4 \leqslant c \leqslant 5\frac{1}{3}, \\ 0 & \text{for } c > 5\frac{1}{3}. \end{cases}$$

a. Graph this PDF.
b. What is $f(4)$?
c. What is $P(C = 4)$?
d. What is $P(5 \leqslant C \leqslant 5\frac{1}{3})$?
e. What is $P(4 \leqslant C \leqslant 4\frac{1}{3})$?

f. What is $P(4 < C \leqslant 4\frac{1}{3})$?
g. What is $P(4 \leqslant C < 4\frac{1}{3})$?
h. What is $P(4 < C < 4\frac{1}{3})$?
i. What is $P(6 < C < 7)$?
j. What is $P(4\frac{1}{3} < C < 5\frac{1}{3})$?

9.5 The life of a certain make of radio tube is exponentially distributed with $\beta = 1,000$ hours. What is the probability that a tube will last
a. less than 1,000 hours?
b. more than 1,200 hours?

9.6 A certain digital computer, which operates 24 hours a day, suffers breakdowns at a rate of 0.1 per hour. Suppose the computer has operated satisfactorily for 10 hours; what is the probability that it will continue to operate satisfactorily during the next 10 hours? (*Hint:* An interesting property of the exponential probability model is that the distribution of future life remains the same as the initial distribution. For such computers, an old one is just as good as a new one.)

9.7 Ships arrive at a certain port according to the Poisson probability law with a mean time of 2 hours between any two consecutive arrivals. What is the probability distribution of the time intervals between ship arrivals in this case? Sketch a density curve for this distribution.

9.8 Consider the preceding problem again, what is the probability that
a. five hours will elapse with no ships arriving?
b. at most three ships will arrive during a five-hour interval?

9.9 The distribution of the life, in months, of a certain business enterprise is exponential with $1/\lambda = 70$. What is the probability that a new firm of this type of business will fail within
   a. 10 months after its birth?
   b. 20 months after its birth?

9.10 Given a beta distribution with $n = 16$ and $x = 5$, what is $P_\beta(\pi \leq 0.30)$?

9.11 Given the same beta distribution as in the preceding problem, what is $P_\beta(\pi \geq 0.70)$?

9.12 Suppose you would like to estimate the potential market share of a new product which your firm has already decided to commercialize. Suppose in a simple random sample with $n = 51$ selected from a very large population of potential customers, you find that 16 of these customers indicate that they like the product. Assuming independence, what is $P_\beta(\pi \leq 0.30)$? Now suppose that it has been estimated that the new product will be profitable if and only if the market share for it is greater than 0.30. What is the probability for it to be profitable?

9.13 Students' I.Q.'s are known to be normally distributed with $\mu = 100$ and $\sigma = 15$. Sketch the density curve. If a student is observed at random, determine:
   a. $P(X \leq 95)$;
   b. $P(X \leq 118)$;
   c. $P(90 \leq X \leq 110)$;
   d. $P(100 \leq X \leq 125)$;
   e. $P(X \leq 35)$;
   f. $P(X > 160)$.

   (*Note:* In evaluating normal probabilities we shall adopt the convention that $N(z) \leq N(-4.00) = 0$ and that $N(z) \geq N(+4.00) = 1$.)

9.14 Let X be $n(\mu, \sigma) = n(100, 7)$. Determine:
   a. $P(X = 80)$;
   b. $P(X > 100)$;
   c. $P(|X - 95| > 5)$;
   d. $P(|X - 100| < 10)$.

9.15 If Y is $n(65, 6)$, what are
   a. $P(Y = 36)$?
   b. $P(Y > 60)$?
   c. $P(Y < 55)$?
   d. $P(|Y - 65| < 9)$?

9.16 Given that X is a normal variable with $\mu = 10$ and $P(X > 12) = 0.1587$, what is the probability that X will be included in the interval $(9, 11)$?

9.17 Inside diameters of steel pipes produced by a certain firm are $n(10, 0.1)$ measured in inches. Pipes with diameters beyond the range 10.25 ± 0.12 inches are considered as defectives.
   a. What is the probability of a defective item?
   b. If the process is adjusted so that the inside diameters will be distributed as $n(10.10, 0.10)$, will the probability of a defective item be the same as before?

c. If the process is adjusted so that the inside diameters will be distributed as $n(10.05, 0.06)$, what is the probability that 95.44% of the pipes produced will meet the specifications?

9.18 The weights of a certain product in pounds are known to be normally distributed with $\mu = 180$ and $\sigma^2 = 4$. If one unit of this produce is observed at random, what is the weight of this unit if the probability of its occurrence is
a. greater than 0.10?
b. less than 0.05?

9.19 Suppose an automatic machine is set to fill tomatoes into cans with a mean weight of 12 ounces and a standard deviation of 0.04 ounces. Assuming the weights are normally distributed, what is the probability that a single can will contain
a. less than 11.90 ounces?
b. more than 12.08 ounces?
c. between 11.88 and 12.16 ounces?

9.20 Suppose that in the previous problem, we know that 10,500 cans are filled per week. How many of the cans will contain weights
a. more than 12 ounces?
b. less than 11.08 ounces?
c. between 11.92 and 12.08 ounces?

9.21 If W is a normal variable and if $P(W < 10) = 0.8413$ and $P(W < -10) = 0.0668$, what would be $E(W)$ and $V(W)$, respectively?

9.22 There are two procedures for getting fighter planes ready to take off. Procedure A requires a mean time of 27 minutes with a standard deviation of 5 minutes. For procedure B, $\mu = 30$ and $\sigma = 2$ minutes, respectively. Which procedure should be used if the available time is 30 minutes? 34 minutes?

9.23 Assume that $Y = [(X_1 + X_2)/2] - X_3$, where X_i are independent normal variables with $\mu_1 = 20$, $\mu_2 = 16$, $\mu_3 = 25$, $\sigma_1^2 = 5$, $\sigma_2^2 = 9$, and $\sigma_3^2 = 7$.
a. How is Y distributed?
b. What are $E(Y)$ and $V(Y)$?

9.24 If $Y = X_1 - X_2$, where X_1 is $n(27, 3)$ and X_2 is $n(25, 4)$, and X_1 and X_2 are independent, what is $(P(Y > 5)$?

9.25 A large flashlight is powered by five batteries. Suppose the life of a battery is normally distributed with $\mu = 120$ hours and $\sigma = 10$ hours. The flashlight will cease functioning if one or more of its batteries go dead. Assuming the lives of the batteries are independent, what is the probability that the flashlight will operate for more than 100 hours?

9.26 Suppose that 20% of the population of a large city actually watch a particular television program and that a random sample of 64 city residents will be selected. Let the random variable X be the number of residents in the sample who watch the program.
a. Calculate μ_X.
b. Calculate σ_X.

    c. What is $P(X \leqslant 19)$ without the CCF (continuity correction factor)? With the CCF?

    d. What is $P(X \leqslant 6)$ without the CCF? With the CCF?

    e. What is $P(7 \leqslant X \leqslant 19)$ without the CCF? With the CCF? (*Hint:* for each part of this question, calculate $P(X \leqslant 19)$ and $P(X \leqslant 6)$ and then subtract.)

    f. How important is the effect of the CCF in parts (c), (d), and (e)?

9.27 Suppose that 20% of the population of a large city actually watch a particular television program and that a random sample of 1,600 city residents will be selected. Let the random variable Y be the number of residents in the sample who watch the program.

    a. Calculate μ_Y.

    b. Calculate σ_Y.

    c. What is $P(Y \leqslant 352)$ without the CCF? With the CCF?

    d. What is $P(Y \leqslant 287)$ without the CCF? With the CCF?

    e. What is $P(288 \leqslant Y \leqslant 352)$ without the CCF? With the CCF? (*Hint:* for each part of this question calculate $P(Y \leqslant 352)$ and $P(Y \leqslant 287)$ and then subtract.)

    f. How important is the effect of the CCF in parts (c), (d), and (e)?

9.28 In many clerical operations, an error rate of 5% is acceptable, but anything above that is not. Random samples of 1,000 clerical items will be drawn from time to time to see whether the error rate is acceptable. Let the random variable X be the number of defective items in a sample of 1,000 items.

    a. Graph the PDF of X, assuming that the error rate is at the maximum that is acceptable, 5%. It is enough to calculate the height of the PDF for $x = \mu_X$, $x = \mu_X \pm \sigma_X$, and $x = \mu_X \pm 2\sigma_X$ and then to draw the rest of the PDF freehand. The result will be a sketch graph rather than a careful graph, but that is adequate for this problem.

    b. A decision rule of the following kind is desired: The clerical process is considered to be in control unless the number of defectives in the sample exceeds x_c, where x_c is the "critical value of x" and is such that $P(X > x_c \mid n = 1,000, \pi = 0.05) = 0.05$. Using your graph from part (a), calculate the numerical value of x_c.

9.29 Repeat Problem 9.28 for a different clerical operation for which the maximum acceptable error rate is 3%, not 5%. In part (a), draw the PDF assuming that the error rate is 3%. In part (b), the key equation is $P(X > x_c \mid n = 1,000, \pi = 0.03) = 0.05$.

9.30 The number of defects of a certain make of 9 by 12 feet carpet obeys the Poisson law with 2 defects per carpet. Suppose 25 such carpets are selected at random for inspection; what is the approximate probability that the sample will contain

    a. 32 defects or fewer?

    b. 52 defects or more?

    c. between 40 and 60 defects?

9.31 Continue with the previous problem. Suppose a retailer has ordered 100 such carpets of the type in the previous problem, and would only accept the order if there are less than 10 defects in a random sample of 15 selected from the shipment. What is the approximate probability that the shipment will be rejected?

9.32 The daily demand for Racing Forms sold at a candy store follows the Poisson process with a mean number of 49 papers per day. How many units should the store order each day so that it can satisfy its customers 99% of the time?

10 Sampling Distributions

10.1 INTRODUCTION

Having learned the various basic aspects of probability theory, we are ready to venture into analytical statistics, which is concerned with inferential and decision procedures. It has been pointed out that sample statistics are rarely obtained for their own sake; instead, they serve mainly as a basis either for generalizing about unknown population parameters in making inferences, or for revising one's prior degrees of belief about the uncertain states of nature in making decisions.

Statistical inference involves methods that enable us to infer from limited data (samples) to what is true of larger sets of data (populations). Statistical decision theory involves procedures that enable us to select the "best" of available acts in a given situation. In both cases "errors" are unavoidable. Inductive conclusions may be erroneous owing to chance variability in random sampling; hence a sample statistic is usually expected to be different from its corresponding parameter, which is an unknown but constant value. Decision may be erroneous because sample information cannot completely eliminate uncertainty attached to the states of nature. In order to have a measure of confidence in our inductive conclusions or final decisions, we must devise methods of appraising such errors.

Statistical errors originate in chance variations of the values of a statistic computed from random samples. Recall that a statistic was said to be a random variable. Now we are able to explain why. A sample statistic computed from a simple random sample is a *random variable* in the sense that it is an uncertain quantity—the value of a sample statistic, owing to chance variations in random sampling, will vary from one sample to another for samples of the same size selected from the same population. Of course, when one sample has been selected and a statistic has been computed, the statistic is then a constant—a realized value of the sample statistic—and it is no longer a random variable. In general, when we think of a statistic we have in mind all the possible values of the statistic that we expect to occur—not what we have already obtained. Indeed, statistical errors are often called sampling errors. Let $\hat{\theta}$ be any statistic and θ be the corresponding parameter, then *sampling error* can be defined as the absolute difference, denoted as ε, between them. In mathematical terms, we have

$$\varepsilon = |\hat{\theta} - \theta| . \tag{10.1}$$

Sampling errors, being chance events resulting from the data-generating process of random sampling, can be evaluated only in terms of the probability functions of sample statistics. The probability function of a sample statistic is called the *sampling distribution* of that statistic. Just as probability theory is the foundation of modern statistics because it is at once the language and measure of uncertainty, sampling distributions are the theoretical justifications of statistical inferences because they have well-defined properties that are precisely related to the properties of the corresponding parent populations. Thus, from the properties of sampling distributions, we can develop methods of assessing probabilities of erroneous inferences or decisions and gain in the process a calculated degree of confidence in inductive conclusions.

The purpose of this chapter is to introduce procedures for gathering evidence and to translate data into probabilistic terms amenable to inference about the true state of nature. We shall be concerned with the construction of sampling distributions and the evaluation of their properties. To this end, our discussion begins with a review of a very fundamental concept called the sum of random variables, which is needed for the presentation of the Law of Large Numbers and the Central Limit Theorem, which, in turn, are indispensable for many arguments and conclusions concerning the properties of sampling distributions.

10.2 SUMS OF RANDOM VARIABLES

In the discussion that follows we will be only interested in what are called independent and identical random variables. One way to generate such variables is via simple random sampling with replacement. First of all, we know that any random observation from a population will generate a random variable that has a distribution identical to that of the parent population. Next, if we select an unconditional simple random sample of size n, then we would have a set of random variables X_i, $i = 1, 2, \ldots, n$, that are independent and identical. Being identical variables, each X_i would have the population mean μ as its expectation and the population variance σ^2 as its variance.

Now, if X_i are independent and identical random variables, then the additive property would hold for both the expectation and variance of their sum S. That is, let

$$S = X_1 + X_2 + \cdots + X_n, \tag{10.2}$$

then

$$
\begin{aligned}
E(S) &= E(X_1 + X_2 + \cdots + X_n) \\
&= E(X_1) + E(X_2) + \cdots + E(X_n) \\
&= \mu n
\end{aligned}
\tag{10.3}
$$

and

$$
\begin{aligned}
V(S) &= V(X_1 + X_2 + \cdots + X_n) \\
&= V(X_1) + V(X_2) + \cdots + V(X_n) \\
&= \sigma^2 n.
\end{aligned}
\tag{10.4}
$$

We are interested in the sum of random variables for a number of reasons. First, a random variable under study may be inherently an additive combination of ingredients. For example, the binomial variable with parameters n and π is merely the sum of n independent and identical Bernoulli variables with a common parameter π. Second, the property of additivity holds for many special and important random variables. For instance, the sum of two or more binomial variables is again a binomial variable; the sum of n Poisson variables, or exponential variables, or normal variables, is again a Poisson, or exponential, or normal variable. Finally, many sample statistics are computed from sums of independent and identical random variables. For instance, the sample mean is the sum of n sample values multiplied by a constant $1/n$; the sample variance is computed with the sum of n squared deviations from the sample mean divided by $(n - 1)$; and so forth.

Theoretically speaking, computation of probabilities involving a sum of n variables can be made directly from an n-fold integral or an n-fold sum. However, such computations are usually extremely difficult, if not impossible, and the resulting distributions are very complicated, except for a few exceptional cases such as the binomial, Poisson, exponential, and normal probability models. Fortunately, thanks to two important theorems, the evaluation of variables that are sums becomes a relatively simple matter. These two theorems are the Law of Large Numbers and the Central Limit Theorem which we shall now introduce in the order mentioned.

10.3 THE LAW OF LARGE NUMBERS

A French mathematician, Poisson, published in 1837 the first general formulation of a scientific law that is called the *Empirical Law of Large*

Numbers because it applies to a large number of trials of an experiment. Since then this law has been further developed and expressed in a number of ways. One of its modern and useful versions is connected with independent and identical random variables. Given n such random variables, we can introduce new random variables such as S defined by (10.2) and $\bar{X}$ defined as

$$\bar{X} = \frac{1}{n}(X_1 + X_2 + \cdots + X_n) = \frac{1}{n}(S).$$

Clearly, this new random variable is the arithmetic average of X_i, or the sample mean that we have studied in detail before. It is easy to see that this new random variable would have $E(\bar{X}) = E(S)/n = \mu n/n = \mu$ and $V(\bar{X}) = E[(S)(1/n)] = (\sigma^2 n)(1/n)^2 = \sigma^2/n$. The latter result, as you may recall, is due to the property that when a random variable is multiplied by a constant, say $1/n$, its variance increases $(1/n)^2$ times.

From the last quantity, $V(\bar{X}) = \sigma^2/n$, we deduce the important fact that the variance of the sample mean approaches zero as n approaches infinity. By Chebyshev's Inequality, we know that if a random variable has a small variance then the probability will be close to 1 that the value of an observation from the random variable will be approximately equal to the mean of the random variable. Now, since the sample mean itself is a random variable, by taking a large enough sample we can make the probability of the sample mean as close to the population mean as we wish—that is, close to 1. In other words, if the sample size is large enough, then the probability that the sample mean will differ from the population mean by more than an arbitrarily prescribed positive difference is close to zero. These statements are alternative ways of expressing what is called the *Law of Large Numbers*. The generality that $\bar{X}$ approaches μ in probability is called *Khintchine's Theorem*, which was published in 1929. Let us now state this mathematically as in Theorem 10.1.

THEOREM 10.1 KHINTCHINE'S THEOREM OF THE LAW OF LARGE NUMBERS

If X_i, $i = 1, 2, \ldots, n$, are independent and identically distributed random variables, and if $\mu = E(X_i)$ exists, then for any arbitrarily prescribed difference $\varepsilon > 0$,

$$P(|\bar{X} - \mu| < \varepsilon) \to 1, \qquad \text{as } n \to \infty; \qquad (10.5a)$$

$$P(|\bar{X} - \mu| \geq \varepsilon) \to 0, \qquad \text{as } n \to \infty. \qquad (10.5b)$$

To observe the validity of the above statements, let us replace X by $\bar{X}$, σ^2 by $V(\bar{X}) = \sigma^2/n$, and μ by $\mu = E(\bar{X})$ in Chebyshev's Inequality, to find

$$P(|\bar{X} - \mu| \leq \varepsilon) \geq 1 - \frac{\sigma^2}{n\varepsilon^2};$$

$$P(|\bar{X} - \mu| \geq \varepsilon) \leq \frac{\sigma^2}{n\varepsilon^2}.$$

Since σ and ε are positive quantities, the ratio $\sigma^2/n\varepsilon^2$ in the preceding inequalities approaches zero as n approaches infinity. This proves that the results in Equations (10.5) are valid.

Now, we may note that $\bar{X} = S/n = \bar{P}$, ($X_i = 0$ or 1, $i = 1$, $2, \ldots, n$), where $\bar{P}$ is the relative frequency or the sample proportion. From this observation, we can deduce that the Law of Large Numbers can also be stated in terms of $\bar{P}$ and its corresponding parameter, π. In fact, the first general formulation of the Law of Large Numbers, known as *Bernoulli's Theorem*, was made by Jacob Bernoulli and published posthumously as early as in 1713. The mathematical expression of this theorem is as follows.

THEOREM 10.2 BERNOULLI'S THEOREM OF THE LAW OF LARGE NUMBERS *If S represents the number of successes in n independent and identical Bernoulli trials, with probability π of success in each trial, if $\bar{P} = S/n$, and if $\varepsilon > 0$, then*

$$P(|\bar{P} - \pi| < \varepsilon) \to 1, \quad as\ n \to \infty; \quad (10.6a)$$

$$P(|\bar{P} - \pi| \geq \varepsilon) \to 0, \quad as\ n \to \infty. \quad (10.6b)$$

Intuitively, the Bernoulli law states that if n is sufficiently large and a fixed integer, then the sample proportion would have a high probability of being close to π.

In closing this section, we may point out that the Law of Large Numbers is the philosophical justification for all attempts to estimate probability empirically. It justifies, for instance, the relative-frequency theory of probability. Furthermore, it assures a high level of probability that a sample average is close to the unknown but constant population mean if n is large. This clearly implies that the accuracy of estimates will always increase with increases in the sample size. Obviously, much of analytical statistics could not exist without a theorem of this kind.

10.4 THE CENTRAL LIMIT THEOREM

We have just shown the validity of the Law of Large Numbers by mathematical expression of the following fact: that by averaging an increasingly large number of observations of the value of a quantity we can obtain increasingly more accurate measurements of the expectation of that quantity. It must be noted now, however, that the center of the distribution of a sum S moves off to infinity, and the variance of a sum becomes larger and larger as n increases—since, as we know, $E(S) = \mu n$ and $V(S) = \sigma^2 n$. It becomes useful for us to learn more about the distribution of a sum.

Under certain mild restrictions, the distribution of the sum of a large number of identically distributed independent random variables, whatever distributions the summands possess, has approximately a normal distribution. This is the essence of what is called the *Central Limit Theorem*, CLT, a name given it by G. Polya in 1920. The value of this theorem is that it requires virtually no conditions on the distribution patterns of the individual random variables being summed. As a result, it furnishes a practical method of computing approximate probability values associated with sums of arbitrarily but independent and identical random variables. No wonder that among all probability laws this theorem is considered the most remarkable theoretical formulation from both practical and theoretical viewpoints.

The Central Limit Theorem, first introduced by De Moivre early in the eighteenth century, has been expressed in many forms. One important and basic version is stated in Theorem 10.3 below.

THEOREM 10.3 THE CENTRAL LIMIT THEOREM *If X_i, $i = 1, 2, \ldots, n$, are n independent and identical random variables, if $\mu = E(X_i)$ and $\sigma^2 = V(X_i)$ exist, and if S is the sum of X_i, with $E(S) = \mu n$ and $V(S) = \sigma^2 n$, then the quantity $(s - \mu n)/\sigma\sqrt{n}$ approaches $n(0, 1)$ as n approaches ∞. Thus, when n is sufficiently large, the approximate CDF of S can be stated as*

$$P(S \leq s) \doteq N\left(\frac{s - \mu n}{\sigma\sqrt{n}}\right). \tag{10.7}$$

Too bad that no one has ever been able to give an intuitive explanation why this wonderful and amazing theorem is true, but its validity has been demonstrated over and over again by empirical evidence. Furthermore, its computational significance is quite clear. Without a theorem such as the CLT, most of us would be helpless in dealing with the evaluation of probabilities involving sums of random variables.

As to how large n should be for (10.7) to hold, there is no standard answer. This depends upon the closeness of approximation required and the actual distribution forms of X_i. If the summands are normally distributed, then (10.7) provides exact probabilities no matter how small n is. If nothing is known about the distribution patterns of X_i, the rule of thumb is that n must be 25 or greater for satisfactory approximations. Of course, approximations improve when n becomes larger. The tendency of a sum toward normality is illustrated by Figure 10.1, in which distributions of the sums of points on tossing 1, 2, 3 and 4 fair dice are drawn. This figure shows, besides the evident tendency toward normality as n increases, that both the mean and the variance of the sum of identically distributed random variables increase with the increase in n.

Let us apply the CLT to an example. A food-processing factory produces canned ground beef with a mean of 5 ounces and a variance of 0.3 ounces^2 per can. Assume that the can weights are statistically independent. A box of 60 cans has a mean weight of $(60)(5) = 300$ ounces and a variance of $(60)(0.3) = 18$ ounces^2. By the CLT the weight of a box, denoted by W, would be approximately normally distributed. This information would allow us to determine by employing (10.7)

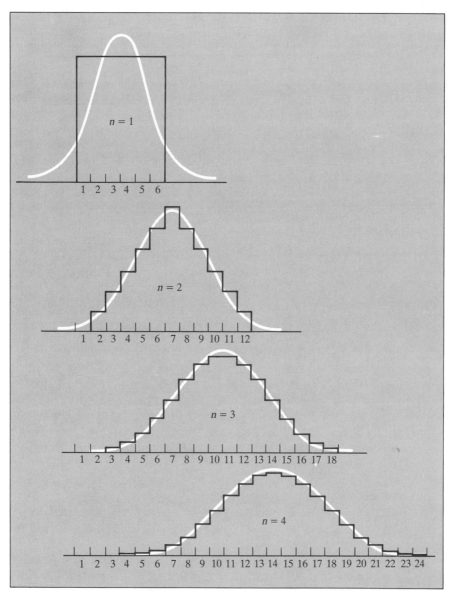

FIGURE 10.1 Graphic illustration of the central limit theorem with distributions of the sums of points on tossing 1, 2, 3, and 4 perfect dice.

probabilities for various events concerning W such as

$$P(W \leq 290 \text{ ounces}) = N\left(\frac{290 - 300}{\sqrt{18}}\right) = N(-2.36) = 0.0091,$$

$$P(W > 310 \text{ ounces}) = 1 - N\left(\frac{310 - 300}{\sqrt{18}}\right) = 1 - 0.9909 = 0.0091,$$

$$P(290 \leq W \leq 310) = N\left(\frac{300 - 300}{\sqrt{18}}\right) - N\left(\frac{290 - 300}{\sqrt{18}}\right) = 0.9818,$$

and so forth.

10.5 METHODS OF CONSTRUCTING SAMPLING DISTRIBUTIONS

It may be noted at the very beginning that sampling distributions can only be constructed for random, or probability samples. However, as will be seen in the Appendix to this chapter, there are many kinds of probability samples, and sampling distributions constructed for different kinds of probability samples are different in some respects. Also, as has been mentioned a number of times before, we are only interested in the most basic and important types of probability samples—the simple random sample, SRS, in this text. Thus, our discussion of the construction of sampling distributions will be based on SRSs only.

Simple random sampling using the method of serial number and selection by random digits as presented in Chapter 8, has three very valuable features. First, it permits use of all the theorems of probability to analyze sample results, because the probability of selecting each of the possible samples in the sample space can be calculated. As a matter of fact, for any particular sample size n, simple random sampling (with or without replacement), produces a sample space with equally probable points. This feature has very useful consequences, which we describe later. Second, this kind of sampling completely eliminates any possibility of selection bias. The investigator cannot distort the sample by selecting certain kinds of items against other kinds of items. The table of random digits does all the selecting in an unbiased manner. Third, anyone familiar with the proper techniques for drawing a simple random sample can review the procedure used to draw a sample to see whether correct methods were followed. This is important because the notion of "random sample" has been abused outside the academic world, and many samples alleged to be random are not random samples at all. On review, they often turn out to be samples with serious sources of selection bias due to the role of the investigator's judgment played in the selection.

There are two main methods of constructing sampling distributions. First, there is the method of *replicated sampling*. By this procedure, many simple random samples, say, 10,000, of the same size, say, 50, are selected from the same population. Then the sample statistic in question is computed from each sample. Finally, the resulting values of the sample statistic are organized into a relative frequency distribution that becomes an approximation of the exact sampling distribution of the sample statistic in question. Obviously, we would never employ such a method by hand calculations. Instead, we use computers. The computer selects the samples, computes the sample statistic, keeps track of how many times each of the possible values of the statistic actually result from the 10,000 samples. The end product is a frequency distribution that is an approximation of the exact sampling distribution of the statistic. (See Problem 10.39 for example.)

The second method is the *method of deduction*. By this method a sampling distribution of any statistic is deduced under a set of assumptions:

1. We assume that the population to be sampled is completely known; that is, we assume that we know how the population is distributed and the values of its parameters.

2. We assume the sample statistic to be evaluated.

3. We assume a specific size n of the sample.

4. We assume simple random sampling.

Under these assumptions, together with our knowledge of probability theory, we then deduce the sampling distribution of a statistic drawn from the assumed population.

The method of deduction is the one we shall use in our subsequent discussion of sampling distributions, because of its simplicity and efficiency. Let us, therefore, comment in a more detailed fashion on the assumptions listed above. We assume the population is known in order to see what would happen when sampling was conducted if this were the true population. If we fix in mind the known population all the time, the deductive results can then be compared with empirical results of the sample statistic later, thereby furnishing the foundation for our inferential conclusions about the actual population. This assumption also carries with it the obvious implication that when different specifications are made about the population, then different sampling distributions of the same statistic would be deduced.

The assumption of specifying the sample statistic in a given situation is an obvious one, since different sample statistics can be calculated from the same sample drawn from the same population. Hence, there would be a class of deduced sampling distributions for each statistic specified.

Given a known population, and a statistic of interest, we must specify the sample size, since samples of different sizes drawn from the same population would generate different sampling distributions for the same sample statistic. So, when we talk about a sampling distribution, we always have a fixed value n in mind.

The assumption of simple random sampling is made merely for the sake of theoretical simplicity. Other kinds of random sampling plans, such as those discussed in the Appendix to this chapter can also generate sampling distributions, but the procedures required to do so are much more involved. Recall that simple random sampling is of two types: with or without replacement. These two procedures yield identical results when sampling is made from infinite populations. When populations are finite, sampling with replacement produces observations that are independent; sampling without replacement yields observations that are statistically dependent. Therefore, in principle, the probabilities of selecting each and every of the n items from the population remain constant by the first method; such probabilities change from one draw to another by the second method. However, as shall be shown, the differences in probabilities for selection between the two methods are negligible when the sample size is relatively small compared to the size of the population. Furthermore, when it is necessary to take into account such differences, the deduced conclusions from sampling with replacement can be easily modified to coincide with those obtained if sampling without replacement is employed. Thus, in the presentation that follows we assume simple random sampling with replacement first and then make the necessary modifications for the properties of sampling distributions deduced under the assumption of sampling without replacement.

Theoretically speaking, deduced sampling distributions are exact sampling distributions. However, our special interest in this chapter is to consider sampling distributions that would approach the normal probability model under different conditions owing to the influence of the CLT. Hence, the final sampling distributions may turn out to be approximations of the deduced results, only depending upon the conditions specified.

In the remainder of this chapter we introduce sampling distributions of a few frequently encountered statistics that are used for inferences so far as cross-section univariate data are concerned.

10.6 SAMPLING DISTRIBUTIONS OF $\bar{X}$

Deduced Sampling Distribution of $\bar{X}$ for Different Sample Sizes

For illustration, let us make the following assumptions.

1. The population consists of the ten integers from 0 consecutively to 9. For this population, the distribution is uniform, with $\mu = 4.5$ and $\sigma^2 = 8.25$.

2. The statistic is the sample mean $\bar{X}$.

3. Let $n = 1, 2,$ or 4.

4. Simple random sampling with replacement is used.

For the case of $n = 1$, the sampling distribution of $\bar{X}$ can be deduced very easily. There are 10 ways the sample could come out: 0, 1, 2, ..., and 9. Each of these samples has a probability of 0.1 to be drawn. Clearly, $\bar{X}$ has ten possible values 0, 1, 2, ..., and 9. Finally, each of these values clearly has a probability of 0.1 of occurrence also. The first two columns of Table 10.1 give the *sampling distribution of $\bar{X}$ with n = 1 selected with replacement from a population of ten digits ranges from 0 consecutively to 9*. This is the full name of the sampling distribution just deduced. Very often, however, we simply call it the *sampling distribution of $\bar{X}$*, or *distribution of $\bar{X}$*, and just keep other specifications in mind.

With $n = 2$, there are $10^2 = 100$ possible samples. Furthermore, a moment's reflection will enable you to see that the possible values of $\bar{X}$

TABLE 10.1 Sampling Distributions of $\bar{X}$ for $n = 1, 2,$ and 4

$n = 1$		$n = 2$		$n = 4$			
$\bar{x}$	$f(\bar{x})$	$\bar{x}$	$f(\bar{x})$	$\bar{x}$	$f(\bar{x})$	$\bar{x}$	$f(\bar{x})$
0	0.1	0.0	0.01	0.00	0.0001	4.75	0.0660
1	0.1	0.5	0.02	0.25	0.0004	5.00	0.0633
2	0.1	1.0	0.03	0.50	0.0010	5.25	0.0592
3	0.1	1.5	0.04	0.75	0.0020	5.50	0.0540
4	0.1	2.0	0.05	1.00	0.0035	5.75	0.0480
5	0.1	2.5	0.06	1.25	0.0056	6.00	0.0415
6	0.1	3.0	0.07	1.50	0.0084	6.25	0.0348
7	0.1	3.5	0.08	1.75	0.0120	6.50	0.0282
8	0.1	4.0	0.09	2.00	0.0165	6.75	0.0220
9	0.1	4.5	0.10	2.25	0.0220	7.00	0.0165
		5.0	0.09	2.50	0.0282	7.25	0.0120
		5.5	0.08	2.75	0.0348	7.50	0.0084
		6.0	0.07	3.00	0.0415	7.75	0.0056
		6.5	0.06	3.25	0.0480	8.00	0.0035
		7.0	0.05	3.50	0.0540	8.25	0.0020
		7.5	0.04	3.75	0.0592	8.50	0.0010
		8.0	0.03	4.00	0.0633	8.75	0.0004
		8.5	0.02	4.25	0.0660	9.00	0.0001
		9.0	0.01	4.50	0.0670		

would range from 0 to 9 in multiples of 0.5, as shown in the third column of Table 10.1. Next, since all 100 samples are equally probable, we have, for example,

$$P(\bar{X} = 0) = P[\text{drawing the sample } (0, 0)]$$
$$= 1/100 = 0.01;$$

$$P(\bar{X} = 0.5) = P[\text{drawing the sample } (0, 1) \text{ or } (1, 0)]$$
$$= 0.01 + 0.01 = 0.02;$$

$$P(\bar{X} = 1.0) = P[\text{drawing the sample, } (0, 2) \text{ or } (1, 1) \text{ or } (2, 0)]$$
$$= 0.01 + 0.01 + 0.01 = 0.03; \text{ etc.}$$

The complete distribution of $\bar{X}$ for $n = 2$ is given in the third and fourth columns in Table 10.1.

Finally, with $n = 4$, we would have a total of $10^4 = 10,000$ possible samples; each has a probability of 0.0001 of occurrence. The possible values of $\bar{X}$ again range from 0 to 9 but in multiples of 0.25 in this case. The probability of each of these possible values can be computed as before by keeping in mind the 10,000-sample sample space. For example,

$$P(\bar{X} = 0) = P[\text{drawing the sample } (0, 0, 0, 0)] = 0.0001;$$

$$P(\bar{X} = 0.25) = P[\text{drawing the sample } (0, 0, 0, 1) \text{ or } (0, 0, 1, 0)$$
$$\text{or } (0, 1, 0, 0) \text{ or } (1, 0, 0, 0)]$$
$$= 0.0001 + 0.0001 + 0.0001 + 0.0001$$
$$= 0.0004; \text{ etc.}$$

The last four columns of Table 10.1 present the complete distribution of $\bar{X}$ for $n = 4$.

Properties of Sampling Distributions of $\bar{X}$

As for any random variable, the two most important properties of any statistic are its central tendency and dispersion. As usual, the central tendency of a random variable is measured by its expected value, and by its dispersion, which is measured by its variance or standard deviation.

The Expectation of $\bar{X}$

The expected value of $\bar{X}$ is denoted as $E(\bar{X})$ or $\mu_{\bar{x}}$, and can be computed in the usual way as for any random variable. You can easily verify from information provided in Table 10.1 that, for each sample size,

$$E(\bar{X}) = \sum \bar{x}f(\bar{x}) = 4.5$$

which is identical with the population mean μ. This is a general property of the sample mean. It can be proven that, for an SRS, drawn with or without replacement, the following relationship always holds:

$$E(\bar{X}) = \mu_{\bar{x}} = \mu. \tag{10.8}$$

The Variance and Standard Error of $\bar{X}$

The variation of sample means in a sampling distribution is measured by the variance of $\bar{X}$, $V(\bar{X}) = \sigma_{\bar{X}}^2$, or by the standard deviation of $\bar{X}$, $\sigma_{\bar{X}}$. The standard deviation of a statistic is generally called the *standard error* of that statistic, since it measures the dispersions of the various values of the statistic from its expectation. Such dispersions are in effect sampling errors. For our example, as the reader can easily verify again with information provided by Table 10.1, we have

$$\text{for } n = 1: \quad V(\bar{X}) = \sum \bar{x}^2 f(\bar{x}) - [E(\bar{X})]^2$$

$$= 28.50 - (4.5)^2 = 8.25;$$

$$\text{for } n = 2: \quad V(\bar{X}) = 24.375 - (4.5)^2 = 4.125;$$

$$\text{for } n = 4: \quad V(\bar{X}) = 22.3125 - (4.5)^2 = 2.0625.$$

Recall that, for the parent population in our example, $\sigma^2 = 8.25$. Thus, the above results reveal that for $n = 1$, $V(\bar{X}) = \sigma^2/1$, for $n = 2$, $V(\bar{X}) = \sigma^2/2$, and for $n = 4$, $V(\bar{X}) = \sigma^2/4$. This clearly suggests that $V(\bar{X}) = \sigma^2/n$. This result is again universal. Indeed, as can be proved, for an unconditional SRS, we would always have

$$V(\bar{X}) = \sigma_{\bar{X}}^2 = \frac{\sigma^2}{n}. \tag{10.9}$$

To determine the standard error of $\bar{X}$, we simply take the square root of its variance. Thus, from (10.9), we have, for an unconditional SRS,

$$\sigma_{\bar{X}} = \frac{\sigma}{\sqrt{n}}. \tag{10.10}$$

From (10.9) and (10.10), we can see that if we wish to reduce the variations in the values of sample means in the sampling distributions of $\bar{X}$, all we have to do is to increase the sample size. This is obvious since in (10.9) we are dividing a constant σ^2 by n: the variance of the mean is inversely proportional to n. In (10.10), we are dividing a constant σ by $\sqrt{n}$: the standard error of the mean is inversely proportional to $\sqrt{n}$. This "bunching effect" is also visually obvious from Figure 10.2. This process continues when the sample size continues to

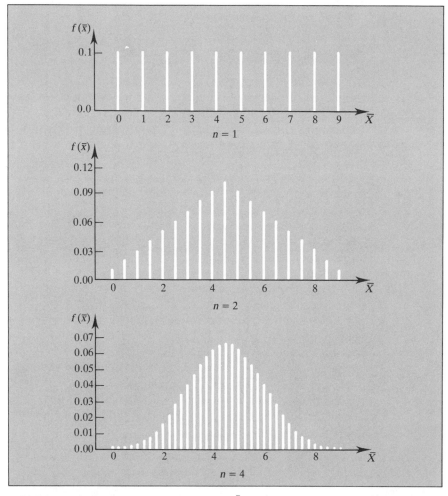

FIGURE 10.2 Sampling distributions of $\bar{X}$ with $n = 1$, 2, and 4, respectively, selected at random from a population of ten digits ranging from 0 consecutively to 9. *Note:* The population distribution is identical with $n = 1$.

increase, making a stronger and stronger "bunching effect". You should not be surprised by this result, since it is clearly implied by our discussion of the Law of Large Numbers.

There is another interesting and very important property of the sampling distribution of $\bar{X}$, again provided by the visual impression of Figure 10.2. That is, when n increases, the distribution of $\bar{X}$ seems to become closer to a normal distribution. We see, in Figure 10.2, that when $n = 4$, the graph of the PMF of $\bar{X}$ already resembles the density curve of a normal variable. It is easy to imagine that when n becomes even larger, the distribution of $\bar{X}$ would become even closer to a normal distribution. As a matter of fact, the Central Limit Theorem is often stated in terms of the sample mean. This should be a natural consequence, since the sample mean is merely a linear combination of the sum of n independent and identical random variables. But how large should n be before we can use normal approximation for the distribution of $\bar{X}$? There is no standard answer to this question; it depends upon different conditions that prevail. We will return to a full discussion of this point very shortly.

The Conditional SRS and the FPCF

We now pose this question: How are sampling distributions of the sample mean deduced under the same assumptions as before except that the method of simple random sampling without replacement is employed? The answer is that there is no difference at all in the procedure of deduction except that the effects of sampling without replacement must be taken into account. This new assumption would produce a few minor modifications and one major modification on the properties of sampling distributions of the mean. All these modifications, furthermore, are only required if we are sampling from finite populations. Even when we are sampling from finite populations, as we shall see, these modifications can be ignored without any harm in a situation where the sample size is 5% or less of the size of the population.

In general, if a sample of size n is selected without replacement from a population of size N, then there would be $_NC_n$ equiprobable possible samples. There are two consequences here with the condition of nonreplacement in sampling. One is that the n observations in each possible sample are statistically dependent. The other is that the range of the possible values of the sample mean may be different for a fixed n from that when sampling with replacement is used. This second point is always true when all the items in the population have different values.

Next, we recall the fact that the additive property of expectations holds for both independent and dependent random variables. Thus, we would have $E(\bar{X}) = \mu$ whether sampling is made with or without replacement.

Third, for an unconditional SRS, we have demonstrated that $\sigma_{\bar{X}}^2 = \sigma^2/n$. This implies that the variance of $\bar{X}$ depends only upon the dispersion of the population and the sample size; it has nothing to do with the size of the population. In other words, we assumed that population size has no effect at all on the variance and standard error of the $\bar{X}$. One basic theoretical justification of this is that sampling with replacement in effect treats a finite population as if it were infinite. However, when the population is finite, the population size N does have some effect upon the variance and standard error of $\bar{X}$ under the condition of nonreplacement. We take care of this effect by defining $\sigma_{\bar{X}}^2$ and $\sigma_{\bar{X}}$ respectively for a conditional SRS as follows:

$$\sigma_{\bar{X}}^2 = \left(\frac{\sigma^2}{n}\right)\left(\frac{N-n}{N-1}\right) \tag{10.11}$$

and

$$\sigma_{\bar{X}} = \left(\frac{\sigma}{\sqrt{n}}\right)\sqrt{\frac{N-n}{N-1}}. \tag{10.12}$$

Here, $\sqrt{(N-n)/(N-1)}$ is called the *finite population correction factor*, FPCF. We shall comment on this quantity in detail later. For the time being, let us provide an example to demonstrate the validity of Equations (10.11) and (10.12).

Suppose an SRS of $n = 2$ is drawn without replacement from the population of 10 digits considered before, we would then have $_{10}C_2 = 45$ possible samples as listed in the following sample space.

$$\begin{aligned} S = \{&(0, 1), (0, 2), (0, 3), (0, 4), (0, 5), (0, 6), (0, 7), (0, 8), (0, 9), \\ &(1, 2), (1, 3), (1, 4), (1, 5), (1, 6), (1, 7), (1, 8), (1, 9), (2, 3), \\ &(2, 4), (2, 5), (2, 6), (2, 7), (2, 8), (2, 9), (3, 4), (3, 5), (3, 6), \\ &(3, 7), (3, 8), (3, 9), (4, 5), (4, 6), (4, 7), (4, 8), (4, 9), (5, 6), \\ &(5, 7), (5, 8), (5, 9), (6, 7), (6, 8), (6, 9), (7, 8), (7, 9), (8, 9)\} \end{aligned}$$

From a glance at this sample space, we can see that the sample means range in value from 0.5 to 8.5 in multiples of 0.5. Bearing in mind that all the 45 possible samples are equally likely, probabilities for various possible values of the sample mean can be easily determined as shown in Table 10.2. From the deduced sampling distribution of $\bar{X}$ in Table 10.2, you can easily verify that

$$E(\bar{X}) = \sum \bar{x}f(\bar{x}) = 4.5,$$

and that

$$\begin{aligned} V(\bar{X}) &= \sum \bar{x}^2 f(\bar{x}) - [E(\bar{X})]^2 \\ &\doteq 23.9167 - (4.5)^2 \\ &\doteq 3.67 \end{aligned}$$

Now, let us see if the latter result agrees with the theoretical formula for $V(\bar{X})$. If it does, the theoretical formula for $\sigma_{\bar{X}}$ must hold too.

TABLE 10.2 Sampling Distribution of $\bar{X}$ for a Conditional SRS with $n = 2$ Drawn from a Population of Ten Digits

$\bar{x}$	Number of Samples	$f(\bar{x}) = P(\bar{X} = \bar{x})$
0.5	1	$1(1/45) = 1/45$
1.0	1	$1(1/45) = 1/45$
1.5	2	$2(1/45) = 2/45$
2.0	2	$2(1/45) = 2/45$
2.5	3	$3(1/45) = 3/45$
3.0	3	$3(1/45) = 3/45$
3.5	4	$4(1/45) = 4/45$
4.0	4	$4(1/45) = 4/45$
4.5	5	$5(1/45) = 5/45$
5.0	4	$4(1/45) = 4/45$
5.5	4	$4(1/45) = 4/45$
6.0	3	$3(1/45) = 3/45$
6.5	3	$3(1/45) = 3/45$
7.0	2	$2(1/45) = 2/45$
7.5	2	$2(1/45) = 2/45$
8.0	1	$1(1/45) = 1/45$
8.5	1	$1(1/45) = 1/45$
Total	45	$45/45$

By (10.12) and with information provided previously, we have

$$V(\bar{X}) = \left(\frac{8.25}{2}\right)\left(\frac{10 - 2}{10 - 1}\right) \doteq 3.67,$$

which is identical with that obtained by the definitional equation for variance of random variables.

Next, it may be noted that the only difference between equations (10.10) and (10.12) is that the latter includes the additional factor $\sqrt{(N - n)/(N - 1)}$, the FPCF. The FPCF does seem to have considerable effect in reducing $\sigma/\sqrt{n}$ in our example. This is due to the fact that the sample size used is as large as 20% of the population size. The FPCF is always less than 1 unless $N = \infty$ or $n = 1$. However, we would expect this effect to decrease continuously as n becomes a smaller and smaller proportion of a finite N. To elaborate on this point, we first note that

$$\text{FPCF} = \sqrt{\frac{N - n}{N - 1}} \doteq \sqrt{1 - \frac{n}{N}}. \tag{10.13}$$

In this expression, n/N is the proportion of the sample size to the population size. Now, if $n = 0.20N$ as in our example, we have

$$\text{FPCF} = \sqrt{1 - 0.2} \doteq 0.8944272.$$

Next, if $n = 0.10N$ and $0.05N$, respectively, then

$$\text{FPCF} = \sqrt{1 - 0.1} \doteq 0.9486333;$$
$$\text{FPCF} = \sqrt{1 - 0.05} \doteq 0.9746794.$$

The last result is practically equal to 1 and the FPCF would have very little effect on $\sigma/\sqrt{n}$. Because of this we always ignore the FPCF in the computation of the standard error when $n \leq 0.05N$. This practice is often called the 5% *rule*. We shall use this rule all the time in our future work. Our discussion on FPCF also reveals the fallacy of the common sense notion that sample size must be at least 10% or even 20% of the population in order for the sample to be reliable. The truth of the matter is that, given σ, the sample size alone determines the reliability of the sample result.

Finally, it may be noted that both the Law of Large Numbers and the CLT hold for conditional SRSs. If anything, the bunching effects and tendency toward normality operate more strongly because of the effect of FPCF on the standard error. Of course, we should always use (10.12) for the standard error when the Central Limit Theorem is applied if $n > 0.05N$.

Generalization and Examples

Let us generalize the findings and conclusions reached on sampling distributions of $\bar{X}$ by the following theorem and then provide some examples for its application.

THEOREM 10.4 SAMPLING DISTRIBUTION OF $\bar{X}$ *If an SRS of size n is drawn from a population of size N with mean μ and standard deviation σ, then the sampling distribution of $\bar{X}$ would have its expectation identical to μ and its standard error as defined by (10.10) for an unconditional SRS and as defined by (10.12) for a conditional SRS. Furthermore, the quantity $(\bar{X} - \mu)/\sigma_{\bar{X}}$ approaches $n(0, 1)$ if n approaches ∞. Thus, for a sufficiently large n, the CDF of $\bar{X}$ can be expressed as*

$$P(\bar{X} \leq \bar{x}) \doteq N\left(\frac{\bar{x} - \mu}{\sigma_{\bar{X}}}\right) \tag{10.14}$$

The last two sentences that lead to (10.14) in Theorem 10.4 can in effect be considered as the CLT stated in terms of sample mean. However, it does not say precisely how large is "sufficiently large" for n before we can apply (10.14). This vagueness is due to the fact that the quantity $(\bar{x} - \mu)/\sigma_{\bar{X}}$ approaches $n(0, 1)$ with varying speeds under different sets of conditions. These conditions involve the distribution patterns of the parent populations and whether their standard deviation are known. We shall summarize these conditions according to various empirical research results in the following way.

I. WITH σ KNOWN

1. If the population is exactly normal, then the quantity $(\bar{X} - \mu)/\sigma_{\bar{X}}$ is exactly $n(0, 1)$ for $n \geq 1$. (See Figure 10.3a).

2. If the population is symmetric with respect to its mean or is moderately skewed, then the quantity $(\bar{X} - \mu)/\sigma_{\bar{X}}$ is approximately $n(0, 1)$ for $n \geq 20$. (See Figure 10.3b.)

3. If the population is extremely skewed, such as a reversed J-shaped

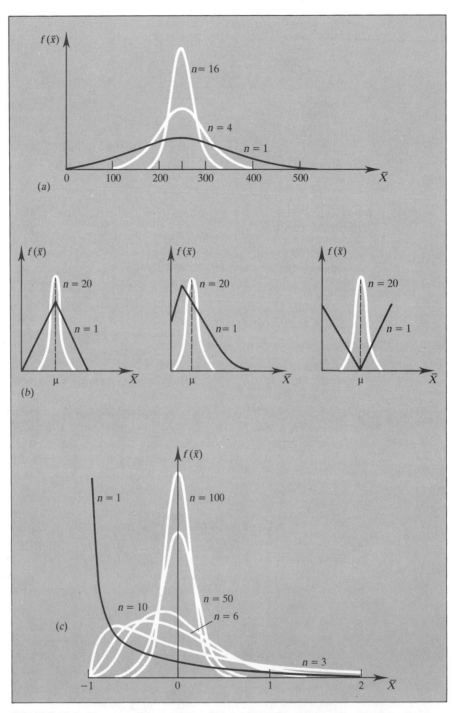

FIGURE 10.3 Demonstrations of the Central Limit Theorem with sampling distributions of $\bar{X}$, generated from different population distributions. (a) Distribution of $\bar{X}$ drawn from a normal population with $\mu = 150$ and $\sigma = 100$. (b) Distributions of $\bar{X}$ drawn from symmetric and moderately skewed population distributions. (c) Distributions of $\bar{X}$ drawn from extremely skewed distributions, with $\mu = 0$ and $\sigma = 1$.

distribution, the quantity $(\bar{x} - \mu)/\sigma_{\bar{x}}$ is approximately $n(0, 1)$ for $n \geq 50$. (See Figure 10.3c.)

II. WITH σ UNKNOWN

1. If the population is exactly normal, the quantity $(\bar{x} - \mu)/S_{\bar{x}}$ is approximately $n(0, 1)$ for $n \geq 30$.

2. If the population is symmetric with respect to its mean or moderately skewed, then the quantity $(\bar{x} - \mu)/S_{\bar{x}}$ is approximately $n(0, 1)$ for $n \geq 50$.

3. If the population is extremely skewed, such as a reversed J-shaped distribution, then the quantity $(\bar{x} - \mu)S_{\bar{x}}$ is approximately $n(0, 1)$ for $N \geq 150$.

The requirements listed above are rules of thumb, but they are quite satisfactory in ordinary situations as specified. If anything, these rules may appear to many statisticians as conservative or too cautious. Even with these rather conservative rules, rare occasions can arise in which the population departs radically from normality or in which the population may contain a few "outliers". Much greater sample sizes are then required in order to have close normal approximations. An *outlier* refers to a datum that is any extremely small or extremely large value and lies many standard deviations away from the mean. An example would be personal incomes in Texas, where a few oil magnates earn incomes in the hundreds of millions of dollars or more per annum. These values are way above the mean personal incomes in the state. In such a case, even when $N \geq 500$, we may still not obtain satisfactory normal approximations. Frequently, an outlier may turn out to be an invalid datum and it would be eliminated once errors had been detected. So all is well! However, when an outlier is a valid datum, it becomes quite troublesome in statistical analysis. Fortunately, the rare populations are very rare indeed and so our rules of thumb apply to many populations. Finally, as you have already noted, when σ is unknown, we denote the standard error as $S_{\bar{x}}$, which is a statistic and is computed by replacing σ by the sample standard deviation S in Equation (10.10) or (10.12). As a statistic, $S_{\bar{x}}$ is also subjected to random variations and this is the reason why n must be much greater under the same conditions in order to obtain satisfactory normal approximations, as implied by the preceding rules.

Let us now consider some numerical examples for the application of (10.14). In doing this we shall use conditional random samples here as well as in future examples in this chapter because, in practice, we usually employ simple random sampling without replacement. The reason is that a conditional SRS may often yield more information than an unconditional SRS because the same item of the population cannot enter the same sample more than once. You should, however, keep in mind why the FPCF is or is not used in each case.

Example 1 Distribution of Mean Weight

As the first example, let us use again the case of the weights of soybeans of the agricultural experimental station that was used in the last chapter. Recall that the population of weights considered was $n(2,425,115)$ with $N = 2,000$. Now, if a sample with $n = 25$ is drawn from the population, what is the probability that the sample mean would (1) fall between 2,360 and 2,490? (2) be less than 2,325 pounds? (3) be greater than 2,495 pounds?

To obtain the desired probabilities, we first note that the distribution of the mean in this case is exactly normal, with

$$E(\bar{X}) = \mu = 2,425 \text{ pounds}$$

and

$$\sigma_{\bar{X}} = \frac{\sigma}{\sqrt{n}} = \frac{115}{\sqrt{25}} = 23 \text{ pounds.}$$

With these preliminary calculations and by (10.14) that we see that

$$(1) \quad P(2,360 \leqslant \bar{X} \leqslant 2,490) = N\left(\frac{2,490 - 2,425}{23}\right) - N\left(\frac{2,360 - 2,425}{23}\right)$$

$$\doteq N(+2.83) - N(-2.83)$$

$$\doteq 0.9977 - 0.0023$$

$$\doteq 0.9954.$$

This result indicates that nearly all the sample means would fall within the interval specified.

$$(2) \qquad P(\bar{X} \leqslant 2,325) \doteq N\left(\frac{2,325 - 2,425}{23}\right)$$

$$\doteq N(-4.35) \doteq 0,$$

which reveals that it is virtually impossible for the sample mean to be 2,325 pounds or less if $\mu = 2,425$ and $n = 25$.

$$(3) \qquad P(\bar{X} > 2,495) = 1 - P(\bar{X} \leqslant 2,495)$$

$$= 1 - N\left(\frac{2,495 - 2,425}{23}\right)$$

$$\doteq 1 - N(+3.04)$$

$$\doteq 1 - 0.9997$$

$$\doteq 0.0003.$$

Thus, it is almost impossible to obtain a sample mean greater than 2,495, which is greater than the population mean by only 70 pounds.

Example 2 Distribution of Mean Wage

Suppose there are 500 workers in a small manufacturing town. Their annual wages are known to have a mean of $25,000 and a standard deviation of $1,400. If a sample of $n = 64$ is drawn from this population,

1. is it reasonable to speculate that all the sample means will fall within the range from $24,345 to $25,655?

2. is it possible for the sample mean to be less than $24,000 or greater than $26,000?

To answer the questions posed, we observe first that the population may be moderately skewed to the right. However, $n = 64$ is large enough for the distribution of the mean to be approximately normal, and thus, for this distribution, we have

$$E(\bar{X}) = \mu = \$25,000,$$

and

$$\sigma_{\bar{X}} = \left(\frac{\sigma}{\sqrt{n}}\right)\sqrt{\frac{N - n}{N - 1}}$$

$$= \left(\frac{1400}{\sqrt{64}}\right)\sqrt{\frac{500 - 64}{500 - 1}}$$

$$\doteq \$163.58.$$

With these results, our answer to the first question is "yes", since

$$P(24,345 < \bar{X} < 25,655) \doteq N\left(\frac{25,655 - 25,000}{163.58}\right) - N\left(\frac{24,345 - 25,000}{163.58}\right)$$

$$\doteq N(+4.00) - N(-4.00)$$

$$\doteq 1 - 0 \doteq 1.$$

The answer to the second question is "no", since

$$P[(\bar{X} \leq 24,000) \cup (\bar{X} \geq 26,000)] \doteq N(-6.11) + [1 - N(+6.11)]$$

$$\doteq 0 + 0 = 0.$$

Suppose for the current example the population mean is actually unknown and is merely assumed to be $25,000, then the answer to the first question would indicate that we are virtually certain that if we were to use the sample mean to estimate the population mean (with $\sigma = \$1,400$ and $n = 64$) the error in this case must be less than $655. This error is only 2.5% of the assumed population mean of $25,000.

Example 3 Distribution of Mean Sales

A new wholesale merchandising outlet has made over 10,000 sales since it has been in business. It is known that the mean amount per sale is $4,500 but the standard deviation is yet unknown. If a sample of 100 invoices is selected from all the invoices, what would be the probability that the sample mean will be

1. over \$4,650?

2. between \$4,300 and \$4,700?

3. different from the population mean by \$150?

For this problem the population distribution is not specified and σ is unknown. However, we suspect that the sales amount of a business of this kind may be moderately skewed to the right and we can use the sample standard deviation S to compute the standard error, since $n = 100$ is sufficiently large in this case. Now, suppose from the sample, we have $s = \$1,050$, then the sampling distribution of the mean would be approximately normal with

$$E(\bar{X}) = \mu = \$4,500$$

and

$$s_{\bar{X}} = \frac{s}{\sqrt{n}} = \frac{1,050}{\sqrt{100}} = \$105.$$

With these findings, the desired probabilities are:

(1)
$$P(\bar{X} > 4,650) \doteq 1 - N\left(\frac{4,650 - 4,500}{105}\right)$$

$$\doteq 1 - N(+1.43) \doteq 1 - 0.9236 \doteq 0.0764;$$

(2) $$P(4,300 \leqslant \bar{X} \leqslant 4,700) \doteq N\left(\frac{4,700 - 4,500}{105}\right) - N\left(\frac{4,300 - 4,500}{105}\right)$$

$$\doteq N(+1.90) - N(-1.90) \doteq 0.9713 - 0.0287 \doteq 0.9426;$$

(3) $$P((\bar{X} \leqslant 4,350) \cup (\bar{X} \geqslant 4,650)) \doteq P(|\bar{X} - 4,500| \geqslant 150)$$

$$\doteq 2N\left(\frac{-150}{105}\right) \doteq 2N(-1.43)$$

$$\doteq 2(0.0764) \doteq 0.1528.$$

The last result can be interpreted in the following way. If 10,000 samples of $n = 100$ are drawn, then 1,528 of the 10,000 sample means would differ from the population mean by \$150 or more.

Example 4 Distribution of Mean Life

The manufacturer of a certain make of transistors claims that the lives of the transistors are distributed exponentially with $\beta = 500$ hours. If a sample of size 120 is drawn from such a population and yields a sample mean of 400 hours, what conclusion can we reach?

If the lives of the transistors are exponentially distributed with $E(\bar{X}) = \mu = \beta = 500$, it would also have a standard deviation $\sigma = \beta = 500$. Now, with $n = 120$, we would expect the distribution of $\bar{X}$ to be approximately normal with

$$E(\bar{X}) = \mu = \beta = 500$$

and

$$\sigma_{\bar{x}} = \frac{\sigma}{\sqrt{n}} = \frac{500}{\sqrt{120}} \doteq 45.64.$$

Hence,

$$P(\bar{X} \leqslant 400) \doteq N\left(\frac{400 - 500}{45.64}\right) \doteq N(-2.19) \doteq 0.0143.$$

If the manufacturer's claim is true, then the sample result obtained is a very rare event indeed.

In closing our illustrations of the applications of (10.14), it is interesting to note that the CLT applies to discrete as well as continuous sampling distributions. More explicitly, we assert that when the distribution of sample mean is discrete, the application of (10.14) can still give satisfactory normal approximations if a continuity correction factor CCF is incorporated into (10.14). In the case of $\bar{X}$, CCF = $1/(2n)$ instead of $1/2$ is used for normal approximations to the binomial or Poisson probabilities, because when the possible values of the observations are integers, the possible values of the mean are spaced every $1/n$.

For example, in Table 10.1, with $n = 4$, we have $P(\bar{X} \leqslant 1.75) = 0.0330$ and $P(\bar{X} = 5.25) = 0.0592$. The normal approximations to these exact probabilities are, respectively:

$$P(\bar{X} \leqslant 1.75) \doteq N\left(\frac{\bar{x} + (1/2n) - \mu}{\sigma_{\bar{x}}}\right)$$

$$\doteq N\left(\frac{1.75 + 1/(2 \times 4) - 4.5}{\sqrt{2.0625}}\right)$$

$$\doteq N\left(\frac{1.875 - 4.5}{1.43614}\right)$$

$$\doteq N(-1.83) \doteq 0.0336$$

and

$$P(\bar{X} = 5.25) = P(\bar{X} \leqslant 5.25) - P(\bar{X} \leqslant 5.00)$$

$$\doteq N\left(\frac{5.25 + 1/(2 \times 4) - 4.5}{1.43164}\right) - N\left(\frac{5.00 + 1/(2 \times 4) - 4.5}{1.43164}\right)$$

$$\doteq N(+0.61) - N(0.44)$$

$$\doteq 0.7291 - 0.6700 = 0.0591.$$

These are indeed very satisfactory approximations of the exact probabilities given in Table 10.1, since they agree to three decimal places.
However, you are reminded that these excellent results are obtained
because the population is symmetric. If populations are skewed, a much
larger n is required to obtain close approximations.

10.7 SAMPLING DISTRIBUTIONS OF $\bar{P}$

We have pointed out before that a sample proportion is a special case of
a sample mean, in which the values are all 0s or 1s. As such, results
about sampling distributions of means apply to proportions too. Alternatively, a sample proportion can also be considered as a binomial or
hypergeometric variable—the number of successes, divided by the
sample size n. This version views $\bar{P}$ as the *proportion of success* and it is
actually more conveinent to use in discussions of the distributions of $\bar{P}$
since the properties of $\bar{P}$ can be easily derived from those of binomial
and hypergeometric probability distributions. Let us begin with a
simple illustration for the derivation of a sampling distribution of $\bar{P}$ and
see how the binomial and hypergeometric probability models can help in
the process of deduction.

Deducing the Distributions of $\bar{P}$

For this purpose, we make the following assumptions.

1. *Population*: 1000 TV picture tubes of a certain make of which 200
   are known to be defective. The proportion of defectives in this
   population is $\pi = 0.20$.

2. *Statistic*: sample proportion of defectives, $\bar{P}$.

3. *Sample size*: $n = 5$.

4. *Method of sampling*: simple random sampling.

If an SRS of five items were drawn from this dichotomous
population, we would have a binomial or hypergeometric variable,
(depending on whether sampling made with or without replacement),
with initial values of 0, 1, 2, 3, 4, and 5. the only values $\bar{P}$ can take on
then are 0.0, 0.2, 0.4, 0.6, 0.8, and 1.0. Next, since n is only $(0.005)N$
here, the probabilities for each possible sample proportion will be
virtually identical whether the sample observations are independent or
dependent. We will assume statistical independence in computing the
respective probabilities for its slight edge in simplicity.

For $\bar{P} = 0.0$, the sample must contain 5 failures (good tubes) and
there is only one such possible sample: $(0, 0, 0, 0, 0)$. Hence,

$$P(\bar{P} = 0.0) = (1 - \pi)^5 = \pi'^5 = (0.8)^5 = 0.32768.$$

For $\bar{P} = 0.2$, a sample must contain 1 success (defective tube) and

4 failures. There are $_5C_1 = 5$ mutually exclusive possible samples with these results, such as $(1, 0, 0, 0, 0)$, $(0, 1, 0, 0, 0)$, and so on. Hence,

$$P(\bar{P} = 0.2) = 5(\pi)(\pi')^4 = 5(0.2)(0.8)^4 = 0.40960.$$

For $\bar{P} = 0.4$, a sample must contain 2 successes and 3 failures and there are $_5C_2 = 10$ possible samples with these results such as $(1, 1, 0, 0, 0)$ or $(1, 0, 1, 0, 0)$ and so on. Hence,

$$P(\bar{P} = 0.4) = 10(0.2)^2(0.8)^3 = 0.20480.$$

For $\bar{P} = 0.6$, a sample must contain 3 successes and 2 failures.

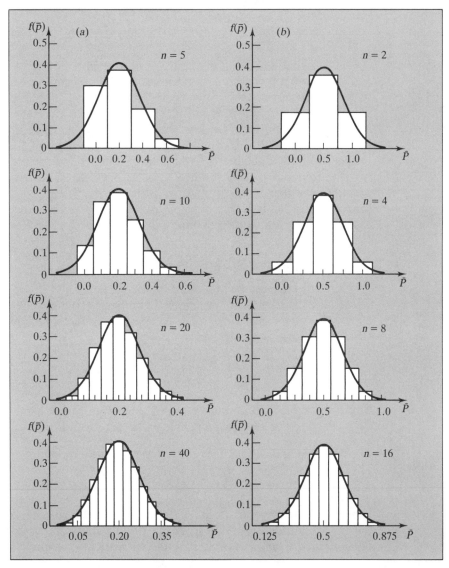

FIGURE 10.4 Demonstrations of the CLT with sampling distributions of $\bar{P}$ generated from binomial populations with (a) $\pi = 0.2$ and (b) $\pi = 0.5$.

Again, there are $_5C_3 = 10$ possible samples with these results such as $(0, 0, 1, 1, 1)$, $(0, 1, 0, 1, 1)$ and so on. Hence,

$$P(\bar{P} = 0.6) = 10(0.2)^3(0.8)^2 = 0.05120.$$

For $\bar{P} = 0.8$, a sample must contain 4 successes and 1 failure, and there are $_5C_4 = $ samples with these results, such as $(0, 1, 1, 1, 1)$, $(1, 0, 1, 1, 1)$, and so on. Hence,

$$P(\bar{P} = 0.8) = 5(0.2)^4(0.8) = 0.00640.$$

For $\bar{P} = 1.0$, a sample must contain all successes and there is only one such sample: $(1, 1, 1, 1, 1)$. Hence,

$$P(\bar{P} = 1.0) = (0.2)^5 = 0.00032.$$

The exact sampling distribution of $\bar{P}$ with $n = 5$, $\pi = 0.2$ deduced above is shown by the top diagram on the left column of Figure 10.4.

As you may have already recognized, the probabilities for the values of $\bar{P}$ in our example are binomial probabilities. Hence, to find the sampling distribution of $\bar{P}$ like the one we have just deduced, it is not necessary to make the calculations that we have given for illustrative purposes. Instead, Table II in Appendix C can be used. Indeed, the few distributions of $\bar{P}$ presented in Figure 10.4 are all drawn with binomial probabilities looked up from that table. Furthermore, as we shall see shortly, even Table II can be replaced by Table V for $N(0, 1)$ for greater ease owing to simple approximations.

Properties of Distributions of $\bar{P}$

As usual, we are most interested in the properties of distributions of $\bar{P}$. Recall that either a binomial or hypergeometric variable has as its expectation $\mu_X = n\pi$. Now, since $\bar{P}$ is such a random variable divided by the sample size, we would have

$$E(\bar{P}) = \frac{n\pi}{n} = \pi. \tag{10.15}$$

Next, since for a binomial variable the standard error is defined as $\sigma_X = \sqrt{n\pi\pi'}$, the standard error of $\bar{P}$ for an unconditional SRS, denoted as $\sigma_{\bar{P}}$, must be

$$\sigma_{\bar{P}} = \sqrt{\frac{n\pi\pi'}{n^2}} = \sqrt{\frac{\pi\pi'}{n}}. \tag{10.16}$$

The standard error of $\bar{P}$ for a conditional SRS can be derived from (10.16) by simply adjusting it with a finite population correction factor, FPCF. Thus, when sampling is made without replacement, we have

$$\sigma_{\bar{P}} = \sqrt{\frac{\pi\pi'}{n}} \sqrt{\frac{N-n}{N-1}}. \tag{10.17}$$

Again, the FPCF can be ignored when $n \leq 0.05N$, and (10.17) becomes (10.16).

Finally, as demonstrated by Figure 10.4, both the bunching effect due to the Law of Large Numbers and the tendency toward normality due to the CLT operate on the distributions of $\bar{P}$. Note also that the speed with which distributions of $\bar{P}$ tend toward normality depends on the values of π, as shown vividly by Figure 10.4.

Generalization and Examples

To summarize the finding of sampling distributions of $\bar{P}$, we provide the following theorem.

THEOREM 10.5 SAMPLING DISTRIBUTIONS OF $\bar{P}$ *If an SRS of size n is selected from a dichotomous population with parameter π, then the sampling distribution of $\bar{P}$ would have $E(\bar{P}) = \pi$, and a standard error as defined by (10.16) for an unconditional SRS and as defined by (10.17) for a conditional SRS. Furthermore, the quantity $(\bar{p} - \pi)/\sigma_{\bar{P}}$ approaches $n(0, 1)$ as n approaches ∞. Thus, for sufficiently large n, the CDF of $\bar{P}$ can be written as*

$$P(\bar{P} \leq \bar{p}) \doteq N\left(\frac{\bar{p} - \pi}{\sigma_{\bar{P}}}\right). \tag{10.18}$$

We are confronted with the same question again as for the case of the sample mean: What size of n is sufficiently large for us to obtain satisfactory normal approximations by employing (10.18)? The answer, just as in the binomial case, is that satisfactory approximations can be obtained here provided that $n\pi \geq 5$ and $n\pi' \geq 5$. These are again rules of thumb. As you can see from Figure 10.4, when $n\pi = 8(0.5) = 4$ or when $n\pi = 20(0.20) = 4$, the normal approximations already appear to be quite satisfactory even when the stated conditions are not met. However, when π is close to 0 or 1, these conditions may not be sufficient. For example, if $\pi = 0.01$ or 0.001, even with $n = 500$ or 2,000, the normal approximations may still be unsatisfactory. Fortunately, populations with $\pi \leq 0.01$ and with $\pi \geq 0.99$ are very rare in real situations. So the rules $n\pi \geq 5$ and $n\pi' \geq 5$ will be satisfactory for most practical purposes.

It may also be noted that when samples are rather small, say, 200 or less, even when the rules of thumb are met a CCF of $1/2n$ should be employed in the application of (10.18) in order to obtain more accurate normal approximations. Here, again the number 200 is arbitrarily selected. You are reminded once more that all the numerical examples below are given under the assumption of conditional SRSs. So you must take notice why the FPCF is or is not used in each case for the computation of $\sigma_{\bar{p}}$.

Example 1 Distribution of Voting Proportion

There are four candidates competing for their party's nomination in the primary for the governorship of a certain state. A knowledgable political scientist believes that the front runner, Mr. Jones, will receive 30% of the votes. Assuming the scientist's assessment is correct and a sample of $n = 500$ has been taken, what is the sampling distribution $\bar{P}$ in this case?

Given the population with $\pi = 0.30$ and a sample of $n = 500$, the distribution of $\bar{P}$ would be approximately normal with

$$E(\bar{P}) = \pi = 0.30,$$

$$\sigma_{\bar{P}} = \sqrt{\frac{\pi\pi'}{n}} = \sqrt{\frac{0.30(0.70)}{500}}$$

$$\doteq 0.0205.$$

For this distribution: (1) What is the probability that the sample proportion will be less than or equal to 0.25? between 0.28 and 0.32? (2) If the said state has the rule that there is to be a run-off election of the first two winners unless the first winner receives at least 33% of the votes, what is the probability that Mr. Jones will be a clear winner?

The desired probabilities for the first question are

$$P(\bar{P} \leq 0.25) \doteq N\left(\frac{0.25 - 0.30}{0.0205}\right) \doteq N(-2.44) \doteq 0.0073;$$

$$P(0.28 \leq \bar{P} \leq 0.32) \doteq N\left(\frac{0.32 - 0.30}{0.0205}\right) - N\left(\frac{0.28 - 0.30}{0.0205}\right)$$

$$\doteq N(+0.98) - N(-0.98)$$

$$\doteq 0.8365 - 0.1635 \doteq 0.6730.$$

The first result indicates that it is almost impossible for Mr. Jones to receive less than 25% of the votes if $\pi = 0.30$ and $n = 500$. The second result means that the odds are about $2:1$ in favor of Mr. Jones' obtaining a vote ranging from 28 to 32%.

To answer the second question, we note that Mr. Jones can receive a clear victory if and only if he can get 33% or more of the votes:

$$P(\bar{P} \geq 0.33) \doteq 1 - N\left(\frac{0.33 - 0.30}{0.0205}\right)$$

$$\doteq 1 - N(+1.46)$$

$$\doteq 1 - 0.9278 \doteq 0.0722.$$

In view of this rather small probability, a run-off election will most likely be held.

Example 2 Distribution of Proportion Defectives

A sample of $n = 50$ is drawn from a population of 200 transistors, 160 of which are known to be nondefectives. What is the probability that the sample will contain (1) less than 70% nondefective items, (2) more than 75% of nondefective items?

For this problem, we have

$$E(\bar{P}) = 160/200 = 0.80; \quad CCF = 1/2(50) = 0.01;$$

$$\sigma_{\bar{P}} = \sqrt{\frac{0.8(0.2)}{50}} \sqrt{\frac{200 - 50}{200 - 1}} \doteq 0.0491.$$

From these preliminary calculations, we have

(1) $$P(\bar{P} \leqslant 0.70) \doteq N\left(\frac{0.70 + 0.01 - 0.80}{0.0491}\right)$$

$$\doteq N(-1.83) \doteq 0.0336.$$

This is a very unlikely result if π is indeed 0.80.

(2) $$P(\bar{P} \geqslant 0.75) \doteq 1 - N\left(\frac{0.75 + 0.01 - 0.80}{0.0491}\right)$$

$$\doteq 1 - N(-0.81)$$

$$\doteq 1 - 0.2090 = 0.7190.$$

Thus, if $\pi = 0.80$ and $n = 50$, almost 72% of the sample proportions will have values greater than 0.75—a quite likely result.

10.8 SAMPLING DISTRIBUTIONS OF $\Delta\bar{X}$

Many decision situations are concerned with the evaluation of a possible difference between two population means μ_1 and μ_2. Are the annual mean incomes of lawyers in England and U.S.A. the same? Is the mean time required to complete a certain task by one procedure different from that by another procedure? Are the mean durabilities of two different makes of auto tires different? Is the mean number of defective units of a certain output produced by one manufacturing process really greater than that produced by another process? These questions, like many others of a similar nature, are examples in which we need to pass judgment on the possible difference between μ_1 and μ_2. We shall denote this difference by $\Delta\mu(=\mu_1 - \mu_2)$.

An obvious way of evaluating $\Delta\mu$ is to compare two sample means $\bar{X}_1$ and $\bar{X}_2$, obtained from an SRS with n_1 drawn from one population and from an SRS with n_2 drawn from the other population. Precisely, we wish to throw some light on $\Delta\mu$ by using the difference between the two sample means, denoted as $\Delta\bar{X}(=\bar{X}_1 - \bar{X}_2)$. The method that is used for this purpose depends upon whether the two samples are independent or dependent. The procedure we develop now applies to independent samples only. The case of dependent samples will be taken up in a later chapter. Two *samples* are said to be *independent* if the probabilities of observations drawn into one sample are the same irrespective of the observations selected into the other sample. The condition of independence here is statistical independence: the probability of any particular value in one sample is not affected by any value selected into the other sample.

To gain some insight about $\Delta\mu$ on the basis of $\Delta\bar{X}$, we, as before, need to know the properties of the sampling distribution of the difference between two sample means. It turns out, as you can easily imagine, that the properties of the distribution of $\Delta\bar{X}$ can be deduced from those of $\bar{X}_1$ and $\bar{X}_2$. This is done by the following theorem.

THEOREM 10.6 SAMPLING DISTRIBUTIONS OF $\Delta\bar{X}$ *If an SRS with n_1 is drawn from one population with μ_1 and σ_1^2 and an SRS is drawn from another population with μ_2 and σ_2^2, and if the two samples are independent, the distribution of $\Delta\bar{X}$ would have*

$$E(\Delta\bar{X}) = \mu_{\Delta\bar{x}} = \Delta\mu \qquad (10.19)$$

and

$$\sigma_{\Delta\bar{x}} = \sqrt{V(\bar{X}_1) + V(\bar{X}_2)}. \qquad (10.20)$$

Furthermore, if both $\bar{X}_1$ and $\bar{X}_2$ are normally or approximately normally distributed, then $\Delta\bar{X}$ will also be normally or approximately normally distributed. Whence, the CDF of $\Delta\bar{X}$ can be written as

$$P(\Delta\bar{X} \leq \Delta\bar{x}) \doteq N\left(\frac{\Delta\bar{x} - \Delta\mu}{\sigma_{\Delta\bar{x}}}\right). \qquad (10.21)$$

Note that in (10.20), $V(\bar{X}_1) = \sigma_1^2/n_1$ and $V(\bar{X}_2) = \sigma_2^2/n_2$ as defined by equations (10.9) and (10.11), respectively.

To illustrate the application of (10.21), consider the following example. There are two lots of aluminum-alloy channels from two different sources. The first lot contains 1,000 channels whose mean stiffness in pounds per square inch (psi) is known to be 5,000 psi with a variance of 10,000 psi². The second lot contains 200 channels with a mean and variance of 4,900 psi and 9,800 psi², respectively. Suppose a sample of size 40 is drawn from the first lot and a sample of size 35 is drawn from the second lot, what is the distribution of $\Delta\bar{X}$?

The statement of the problem provides the following data:

Population I	Population II
$N_1 = 1,000$	$N_2 = 200$
$\mu_1 = 5,000\text{ psi}$	$\mu_2 = 4,900\text{ psi}$
$\sigma_1^2 = 10,000\text{ psi}^2$	$\sigma_2^2 = 9,800\text{ psi}^2$
$n_1 = 40$	$n_2 = 35$

The characteristic of stiffness, like many other manufacturing dimensions, may be normally or approximately normally distributed. In any event, with $n_1 = 40$ and $n_2 = 35$, the distributions of $\bar{X}_1$ and $\bar{X}_2$ would be approximately normal even if the corresponding parent populations were moderately skewed. Hence, the distribution of $\Delta \bar{X}$ in this case would be approximately normal with

$$\mu_{\Delta \bar{x}} = 5000 - 4900 = 100 \, \text{psi}$$

and

$$\sigma_{\Delta X} \doteq \sqrt{\frac{\sigma_1^2}{n_1} + \left(\frac{\sigma_2^2}{n_2}\right)\left(\frac{N_2 - n_2}{N_2 - 1}\right)}$$

$$\doteq \sqrt{\frac{10,000}{40} + \left(\frac{9800}{35}\right)\left(\frac{200 - 35}{200 - 1}\right)}$$

$$\doteq 21.98 \, \text{psi}.$$

Note that the standard error here is computed without FPCF for $V(\bar{X}_1)$ since $n_1 = 0.04N_1 < 0.05N_1$, and the FPCF is used to compute $V(\bar{X}_2)$ since $n_2 = 0.175N_2 > 0.05N_2$. This distribution of $\Delta \bar{X}$ is portrayed in Figure 10.5. We see that the whole distribution lies above zero. This is a desirable result since $\Delta \mu$ is positive in this case.

If we desire, probabilities for various sample results can now be computed by employing (10.21). For example,

$$P(50 < \Delta \bar{X} < 150) \doteq N\left(\frac{150 - 100}{21.98}\right) - N\left(\frac{50 - 100}{21.98}\right)$$

$$\doteq N(+2.27) - N(-2.27)$$

$$\doteq 0.9884 - 0.0116$$

$$\doteq 0.9768,$$

which reveals that nearly 98% of the values of $\Delta \bar{X}$ would fall within the range specified. Again,

$$P(\Delta \bar{X} > 170) \doteq 1 - N\left(\frac{170 - 100}{21.98}\right)$$

$$\doteq 1 - N(+3.18)$$

$$\doteq 1 - 0.9993 \doteq 0.0007.$$

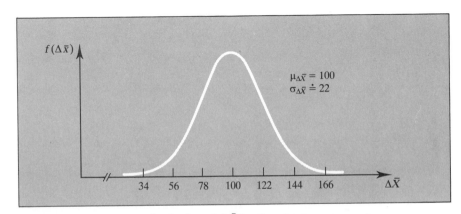

FIGURE 10.5 Sampling distribution of $\Delta \bar{X}$ for the aluminum example.

Thus, it is virtually impossible to have a value of $\Delta \bar{X}$ greater than 170 psi if $\Delta \mu = 100$ psi.

10.9 SAMPLING DISTRIBUTIONS OF $\Delta \bar{P}$

It has been pointed out before that it is often more convenient to work with proportions of successes than with numbers of successes. We consider problems in which proportions are definitely necessary. These situations involve comparing sample results obtained from two independent samples selected from two different dichotomous populations. In such cases, we must work with proportions of successes, not with numbers of successes, unless both samples are of the same size. For example, if 122 units of a certain type of electronic mechanism of Make I are found to be defective in a sample of 1,100 and if 155 units of the same type of product of Make II are found to be defective in a sample of 1,450, what conclusions can we reach regarding the possible differences of quality between the two makes of product? Clearly, these two sets of figures cannot be compared in any meaningful way unless they are first converted into proportions. Precisely, what we need here is a probability model for the difference between two proportions. In so far as the two sample proportions can be interpreted as sample means, the method of the previous section can be employed.

Let the possible difference between the parameter values of the two dichotomous populations be $\Delta \pi (= \pi_1 - \pi_2)$, and let the possible difference between two sample proportions, calculated from two independent samples, be $\Delta \bar{P} (= \bar{P}_1 - \bar{P}_2)$, we can then learn something about $\Delta \bar{P}$, given $\Delta \pi$, on the basis of the distribution of $\Delta \bar{P}$. Such a distribution can be presented as the following theorem, corresponding to Theorem 10.6.

THEOREM 10.7 SAMPLING DISTRIBUTIONS OF $\Delta \bar{P}$ *If an SRS with n_1 is drawn from a dichotomous population with π_1 and an SRS with n_2 is drawn from another dichotomous population with π_2, and if the two samples are independent, then the distribution of $\Delta \bar{P}$ has*

$$E(\Delta \bar{P}) = \mu_{\Delta \bar{P}} = \Delta \pi \qquad (10.22)$$

and

$$\sigma_{\Delta \bar{P}} = \sqrt{V(\bar{P}_1) + V(\bar{P}_2)}. \qquad (10.23)$$

Furthermore, if both $\bar{P}_1$ and $\bar{P}_2$ are approximately normally distributed, then $\Delta \bar{P}$ will also be approximately normally distributed. The CDF of $\Delta \bar{P}$, therefore, can be given as

$$P(\Delta \bar{P} \leq \Delta \bar{p}) \doteq N\left(\frac{\Delta \bar{p} - \Delta \pi}{\sigma_{\Delta \bar{P}}}\right). \qquad (10.24)$$

Let us now consider a numerical example. Suppose in a certain college town, there were respectively 21,000 male and 22,500 female registered voters in 1984. Suppose also that just before the presidential election in that year a census was taken and found that 55% of the male voters and 60% of the female voters were in favor of President Reagan's reelection. Now, suppose a sample of 1,600 had been taken from the male voters and another sample of 1,600 had been taken from the female voters, what would be the distribution of $\Delta \bar{P}$ in this case?

From the statement of the problem, we have the following information:

Male voters	Female voters
$N_1 = 21,000$	$N_2 = 22,500$
$\pi_1 = 0.55$	$\pi_2 = 0.60$
$n_1 = 1,600$	$n_2 = 1,600$

Since $n_1 = n_2 = 1,600$, the distribution of $\Delta \bar{P}$ would be approximately normally distributed with

$$E(\Delta \bar{P}) = \Delta \pi = 0.55 - 0.60 = -0.05.$$

The standard error of $\Delta \bar{P}$ in this case can be computed as follows:

$$\sigma_{\bar{P}_1} = \sqrt{\frac{\pi_1 \pi_1'}{n_1}} \sqrt{\frac{N_1 - n_1}{N_1 - 1}}$$

$$= \sqrt{\frac{0.55(0.45)}{1600}} \sqrt{\frac{21,000 - 1600}{21,000 - 1}} \doteq 0.0120;$$

$$\sigma_{\bar{P}_2} = \sqrt{\frac{\pi_2 \pi_2'}{n_2}} \sqrt{\frac{N_2 - n_2}{N_2 - 1}}$$

$$= \sqrt{\frac{0.60(0.40)}{1,600}} \sqrt{\frac{22,500 - 1660}{22,500 - 1}} \doteq 0.0118;$$

$$\sigma_{\Delta \bar{P}} = \sqrt{V(\bar{P}_1) + V(\bar{P}_2)}$$

$$\doteq \sqrt{(0.0120)^2 + (0.0118)^2} \doteq 0.0168.$$

This distribution of $\Delta \bar{P}$ is shown graphically by Figure 10.6. Various

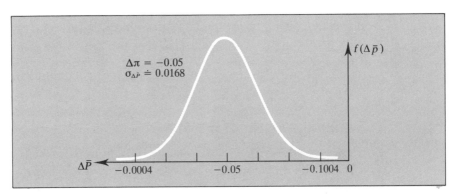

FIGURE 10.6 Sampling distribution of $\Delta \bar{P}$ for the voting example.

probabilities of sample results that are of interest can be computed by (10.24). For instance,

$$P(\Delta\bar{P} \leq 0) \doteq N\left[\frac{0 - (-0.05)}{0.0168}\right]$$

$$\doteq N(+2.98) = 0.9986.$$

With this very high probability, we can assert that it is virtually a certainty that the sample results will indicate $\Delta\bar{P}$ to be negative; that is, proportionally less male voters than female voters were in favor of Reagan's reelection in 1984 in that town. We could, if we wish, also determine the probability that the value of $\Delta\bar{P}$ will differ from $\Delta\pi$ by at most, say, 3 percentage points, as follows:

$$P(|\Delta\bar{P} - \Delta\pi| \geq 0.03) \doteq 2N\left(\frac{-0.03}{0.0168}\right)$$

$$\doteq 2N(-1.79) \doteq 2(0.0369)$$

$$\doteq 0.0734.$$

Thus, 7.34% of the sample results will fall outside the range from -0.08 to -0.02: a rather rare event.

10.10* SAMPLING DISTRIBUTIONS OF OTHER STATISTICS

We have so far presented sampling distributions for four statistics: $\bar{X}$, $\bar{P}$, $\Delta\bar{X}$ and $\Delta\bar{P}$. These are also the distributions we shall be concerned with in our introduction to statistical inferences in the next three chapters. There are, of course, other important statistics for cross-section univariate data, such as variance, standard deviation, median, and other position measures related to median to be considered. However, inferences about population variance and standard deviation are usually conducted with what are called "chi-square" distributions, and those about median and other position measures are often done with what are called "nonparametric methods", introduced in later chapters. We can, if we wish, employ the standard normal distribution for these tasks, too, even though we rarely do. For sake of completeness and future references, we provide a brief discussion of the sampling distributions of these statistics.

Sampling Distributions of S^2

If an unconditional SRS with size n is selected from a population with σ^2, then the distribution of sample variance would have

$$E(S^2) = \sigma^2. \tag{10.25}$$

Furthermore, if the parent population is normal and if it possess the fourth moment, $\mu_4 = E(X - \mu)^4$, then the standard error of S^2 is defined as

$$\sigma_{S^2} = \sigma^2 \sqrt{\frac{2}{n-1}}. \tag{10.26}$$

Finally, if the parent population is normally distributed and if $n \geqslant 100$, then the distribution of S^2 would be approximately normally distributed.

Sampling Distribution of S

If an unconditional SRS of $n \geqslant 100$ is drawn from a normal population with σ, the distribution of S will be approximately normal with

$$E(S) \doteq \sigma \tag{10.27}$$

and

$$\sigma_S = \frac{\sigma}{\sqrt{2(n-1)}}. \tag{10.28}$$

Note that, as we shall explain in detail in the next chapter, when the expected value of a statistic is equal to the value of the corresponding parameter, the statistic is said to be an "unbiased estimator" of the corresponding parameter. When this condition is not precisely met as in the case of S, for which $E(S)$ is only approximately equal to σ, the statistic is said to be a "biased estimator". It is also interesting to observe that S^2 for an unconditional SRS is an unbiased estimator for σ^2, but S is a biased estimator for σ. In this case we say that taking the square root introduces bias.

Sampling Distributions of Median and Related Measures

If the parent population is normal and if $n \geqslant 30$, the distribution of the median, $X_{.5}$, is approximately normal with

$$E(X_{.5}) = \mu \tag{10.29}$$

and

$$\sigma_{X_{.5}} = \frac{1.2533\sigma}{\sqrt{n}}. \tag{10.30}$$

It may be observed that when we are sampling from a normal population $E(X_{.5}) = E(\bar{X}) = \mu$ but $\sigma_{X_{.5}}$ is greater than $\sigma_{\bar{x}}$ by a factor of 1.2533.

Recall that X_5 is a position measure that divides a variable into two equal parts. Recall also that a variable may be divided into four equal parts by the three quartile measures, Q_1, Q_2 and Q_3. For an SRS, distributions of Q_1 and Q_3 have the same standard error, defined as

$$\sigma_{Q_1} = \sigma_{Q_3} = \frac{1.3626\sigma}{\sqrt{n}}. \qquad (10.31)$$

Furthermore, if the parent is normal and if $n \geqslant 30$, distributions of Q_1 and Q_3 will be approximately normal with expectations very nearly equal to the first and third quartiles of the population, respectively.

Recall that measures that divide a set of data into ten equal parts are called deciles: D_i, $i = 1, 2, \ldots, 9$. If the parent population is normal and if $n \geqslant 30$, distributions of D_i would be approximately normal with expectations nearly equal to the corresponding population deciles. Standard errors of D_i are defined as follows:

$$\sigma_{D_1} = \sigma_{D_9} = \frac{1.7094\sigma}{\sqrt{n}}, \qquad (10.32)$$

$$\sigma_{D_2} = \sigma_{D_8} = \frac{1.4288\sigma}{\sqrt{n}}, \qquad (10.33)$$

$$\sigma_{D_3} = \sigma_{D_7} = \frac{1.3180\sigma}{\sqrt{n}}, \qquad (10.34)$$

$$\sigma_{D_4} = \sigma_{D_6} = \frac{1.2680\sigma}{\sqrt{n}}. \qquad (10.35)$$

Note that the standard error of D_5 is obviously that of X_5. Note also how the multiplier factor decreases as the decile value comes closer to the median.

All sampling distributions introduced in this section have been deduced under the assumption that the parent populations are normal. In addition, these distributions are approximately normal if the sample sizes are as large as specified. As such, probabilities of sample results for these statistics can also be evaluated by the standard normal probability law. We can make the following generalization: If the distribution of a statistic $\hat{\theta}$ is approximately normal, then the ratio $(\hat{\theta} - \theta)/\sigma_{\hat{\theta}}$ is approximately $n(0, 1)$. Here, $\hat{\theta}$ stands for any statistic; θ is the parameter corresponding to $\hat{\theta}$, and $\sigma_{\hat{\theta}}$ is the standard error of the statistic in question and let $\hat{\theta}_0$ be a specified value of the statistic. We can then express a generalized approximate CDF for $\hat{\theta}$ as follows:

$$P(\hat{\theta} \leq \hat{\theta}_0) \doteq N\left(\frac{\hat{\theta}_0 - \theta}{\sigma_{\hat{\theta}}}\right). \qquad (10.36)$$

10.11 SIGNIFICANCE OF SAMPLING DISTRIBUTIONS

From our discussions in this chapter, we can actually view a sampling distribution as mainly a description of a population derived from a parent population. The parent population is the universal set that contains all the elementary units with known characteristics. The elements of the derived population, the sampling distribution, are groups of the elementary units of the parent population, each with size n. So stated, we can easily understand why the properties of a sampling distribution are related to those of the parent population in some fixed ways.

In reality, we usually do not know the true value of a parameter, we just assume it to be such and such a value. Then we behave as if our assumption were true. Under this assumption, given the statistic and sample size, we would have a unique sampling distribution of that statistic. While all the values of a sampling distribution are possible, some of them are highly improbable. If one of the highly improbable values does occur, then we would have doubt about the validity of our assumption and say that the assumption is inconsistent with the sample result—i.e. with empirical fact. We so conclude not with certainty, as with pure mathematical deterministic models, but with a degree of confidence that is stronger the smaller is the probability of the occurrence of the observed sample result. This method of rejecting the validity of our assumption is based upon a principle that might be called the *principle of reduction to improbability*.

With the properties of sampling distributions, we can not only pass judgment on whether some specific assumption about a population parameter is valid, we can also determine a range, as many of our examples in this chapter have implied, within which the unknown population parameter might be expected to fall with a high probability in view of the facts observed in the sample. In addition, if in a situation where we wish a sampling error to be some small specific positive number, such as 0.10, 0.01, or even 0.001, we can always find a standard error small enough to satisfy the specification by finding the appropriate sample size. In short, without the notion of sampling distributions, we can never conduct statistical inferences. This is why we stated at the very beginning of this chapter that sampling distributions are the theoretical justification of inductive statistics.

In closing, it should be said that many of the most common inferential problems can be handled by a single probability distribution—the standard normal probability model—with reasonable accuracy. Thus, for the dual objective of explaining the principles of inductive reasoning and revealing how to treat many important inferential problems, the standard normal model suffices. In other words, you are equipped now with the fundamental knowledge and skill to handle many problems of inductive statistics. We turn to these tasks in the next three chapters. Inferential problems requiring other probability models will be taken up subsequently.

GLOSSARY OF FORMULAS

(10.1) $\varepsilon = |\hat{\theta} - \theta|$.

Sampling error is defined as the absolute difference between the value of a statistic $\hat{\theta}$ and the corresponding value of a parameter θ. It is produced by chance fluctuations in random sampling.

(10.2) $S = X_1 + X_2 + \cdots + X_n$;

(10.3) $E(S) = \mu n$;

(10.4) $V(S) = \sigma^2 n$.

Here, S is defined as the sum of n independent and identical random variables. As such, the expected value of S is the sum of the means of X_i and the variance of S is the sum of the variances of X_i.

(10.5a) $P(|\bar{X} - \mu| < \varepsilon) \to 1$, as $n \to \infty$;

(10.5b) $P(|\bar{X} - \mu| \geq \varepsilon) \to 0$, as $n \to \infty$.

(10.6a) $P(|\bar{P} - \pi| < \varepsilon) \to 1$, as $n \to \infty$;

(10.6b) $P(|\bar{P} - \pi| \geq \varepsilon) \to 0$, as $n \to \infty$.

Equations (10.5) are the mathematical expression of *Khintchine's Theorem of the Law of Large Numbers,* Equations (10.6) are the statement of *Bernoulli's Theorem of the Law of Large Numbers*. In general, this law states that in averaging an increasingly large number of observations of a quantity, there is a high probability for the sample average to become closer to the unknown, but constant, population parameter.

(10.7) $P(S \leq s) \doteq N\left(\dfrac{s - \mu n}{\sigma\sqrt{n}}\right)$.

This is the equation that expresses the remarkable Central Limit Theorem, CLT. The CLT is stated here in terms of the sum of independent and identical random variables as defined by (10.2). As a rule of thumb, the application of (10.7) requires that $n \geq 25$ when distribution patterns of X_i are unknown. The CLT is operative for a number of sampling distributions, such as for the sample mean, the sample proportion, the difference between two sample means and the difference between two sample proportions.

(10.8) $E(\bar{X}) = \mu$;

(10.9) $V(\bar{X}) = \sigma^2/n$;

(10.10) $\sigma_{\bar{X}} = \sigma/\sqrt{n}$;

(10.11) $\sigma_{\bar{X}}^2 = \left(\dfrac{\sigma^2}{n}\right)\left(\dfrac{N-n}{N-1}\right)$;

(10.12) $\sigma_{\bar{X}} = \left(\dfrac{\sigma}{\sqrt{n}}\right)\sqrt{\dfrac{N-n}{N-1}}$.

This group of equations governs the sampling distributions of the mean. The expectation of the sample mean is equal to the mean of the parent population for both unconditional and conditional SRSs. The variance and standard error for an unconditional SRS are given by (10.9) and (10.10), respectively. The corresponding measures for a conditional SRS are given by (10.11) and (10.12), respectively. Note that the only difference between these two sets of equations is that, for the second, a finite population correction factor, FPCF = $\sqrt{(N-n)/(N-1)}$, is employed. The FPCF is used to take care of the possible effects of population size N on the standard error. However, such effects are practically negligible when n is small relative to N. Thus, in general, given σ, the reliability of a sample result is exclusively related to the size of the sample and has little, if anything, to do with the size of the population.

(10.13) $\text{FPCF} = \sqrt{\dfrac{N-n}{N-1}} \doteq \sqrt{1 - \dfrac{n}{N}}$.

This is the modified version of the FPCF, where n/N is the ratio of sample size to the population size. This new version of FPCF is instructive in revealing the fact that when $n \leqslant 0.05N$, FPCF practically equals 1 and it can then be dropped when we compute the standard error of the means by (10.12). This practice is often called the 5% rule.

(10.14) $P(\bar{X} \geqslant \bar{x}) \doteq N\left(\dfrac{\bar{x} - \mu}{\sigma_{\bar{X}}}\right)$.

When n is sufficiently large under a variety of conditions, the sampling distribution of the mean is normal or approximately so owing to the CLT. Thus the CDF of $\bar{X}$ can be stated as Equation (10.14). This equation can also be applied to an exact discrete sampling distribution of the mean with the incorporation of a continuity correction factor of $1/2n$ in the usual fashion.

(10.15) $E(\bar{P}) = \pi$;

(10.16) $\sigma_{\bar{P}} = \sqrt{\dfrac{\pi\pi'}{n}}$;

(10.17) $\sigma_{\bar{P}} = \sqrt{\dfrac{\pi\pi'}{n}} \sqrt{\dfrac{N-n}{N-1}}$;

(10.18) $P(\bar{P} \leqslant \bar{p}) \doteq N\!\left(\dfrac{\bar{p} - \pi}{\sigma_{\bar{P}}}\right)$.

This set of equations describes the sampling distributions of sample proportions. $\bar{P}$ being a special case of $\bar{X}$, the distribution of $\bar{P}$ has the same properties as that of $\bar{X}$. Equations (10.16) and (10.17) are the standard error formulas for unconditional and conditional SRSs, respectively. Again, when $n \leqslant 0.05N$, the FPCF can be dropped from (10.17) for computational purposes. For sufficiently large n, distributions of $\bar{P}$ are approximately normal and therefore their probabilities can be evaluated by Equation (10.18). Again, (10.18) can be used to approximate the probabilities of an exact but discrete distribution of $\bar{P}$, but a CCF of $1/2n$ must be incorporated into this equation for better approximations when $n \leqslant 200$.

(10.19) $E(\Delta\bar{X}) = \Delta\mu$;

(10.20) $\sigma_{\Delta\bar{X}} = \sqrt{V(\bar{X}_1) + V(\bar{X}_2)}$;

(10.21) $P(\Delta\bar{X} \leqslant \Delta\bar{x}) \doteq N\!\left(\dfrac{\Delta\bar{x} - \Delta\mu}{\sigma_{\bar{X}}}\right)$.

To throw light on the possible difference between two population means, $\Delta\mu = \mu_1 - \mu_2$, we use the properties of the distribution between two sample means, $\Delta\bar{X} = \bar{X}_1 - \bar{X}_2$, computed from two independent samples. Equation (10.20) is established from the well-known property of variance that the variance of the difference between two independent random variables is the sum of their separate variances. When both $\bar{X}_1$ and $\bar{X}_2$ are normally or approximately normally distributed, $\Delta\bar{X}$ is also normally or approximately normally distributed and, as a consequence, (10.21) can be applied to evaluate the distributions of $\Delta\bar{X}$. In computing $\sigma_{\Delta\bar{X}}$, you must pay attention to whether the sample is conditional or unconditional and whether $n_1 \leqslant 0.05N_1$ and $n_2 \leqslant 0.05N_2$.

(10.22) $E(\Delta\bar{P}) = \Delta\pi$;

(10.23) $\sigma_{\Delta\bar{P}} = \sqrt{V(\bar{P}_1) + V(\bar{P}_2)}$;

(10.24) $P(\Delta\bar{P} \leqslant \Delta\bar{p}) \doteq N\!\left(\dfrac{\Delta\bar{p} - \Delta\pi}{\sigma_{\Delta\bar{P}}}\right)$.

This group of equations governs the distribution of $\Delta\bar{P}$ under the assumption of two independent samples. For the application of (10.23), you must determine whether the FPCF should be used in computing $V(\bar{P}_1)$ and $V(\bar{P}_2)$. Distributions of $\Delta\bar{P}$ obey the CLT too. Thus, for sufficiently large n_1 and n_2, the CDF of $\Delta\bar{P}$ can be given as the CDF of

$n(0, 1)$ as shown by (10.24). To apply (10.24) when $n_1 \leqslant 200$ or $n_2 \leqslant 200$, a CCF of $1/2n_1$ or $1/2n_2$ should be used.

(10.25) $E(S^2) = \sigma^2$;

(10.26) $\sigma_{S^2} = \sigma^2 \sqrt{\dfrac{2}{n-1}}.$

If an unconditional SRS with $n \geqslant 100$ is drawn from a normal population with σ^2, then the distribution of S^2 will be approximately normal with expectation and standard error as defined by these two equations, respectively. Equation (10.26) can only be derived if the population possesses the fourth moment.

(10.27) $E(S) \doteq \sigma$;

(10.28) $\sigma_S = \dfrac{\sigma}{\sqrt{2(n-1)}}.$

If an SRS with $n \geqslant 100$ is drawn from a normal population with σ, then the sampling distribution of S is approximately normal with an expectation that is nearly equal to the population parameter σ and a standard error as defined by (10.28).

(10.29) $E(X_{.5}) = \mu$;

(10.30) $\sigma_{X_{.5}} = \dfrac{1.2533\sigma}{\sqrt{n}}.$

When an SRS is selected from a normal population, the distribution of the median, $X_{.5}$, would have the population mean μ as its expectation. The standard error of $X_{.5}$ is that of the mean multiplied by 1.2533. Furthermore, when $n \geqslant 30$, the distribution of $X_{.5}$ is approximately normal.

(10.31) $\sigma_{Q_1} = \sigma_{Q_2} = \dfrac{1.3626\sigma}{\sqrt{n}}.$

When an SRS is drawn from a normal population and when $n \geqslant 30$, the distributions of quartiles, Q_i, $i = 1, 2, 3$, is approximately normally distributed with $E(Q_i) \doteq \tilde{q}_i$. The standard error for Q_2 is identical with that of the median. The standard errors of Q_1 and Q_2 are equal and are defined by (10.31).

(10.32) $\sigma_{D_1} = \sigma_{D_9} = \dfrac{1.7094\sigma}{\sqrt{n}}$;

(10.33) $\sigma_{D_2} = \sigma_{D_8} = \dfrac{1.4288\sigma}{\sqrt{n}}$;

(10.34) $\sigma_{D_3} = \sigma_{D_7} = \dfrac{1.3180\sigma}{\sqrt{n}};$

(10.35) $\sigma_{D_4} = \sigma_{D_6} = \dfrac{1.2680\sigma}{\sqrt{n}}.$

If an SRS with $n \geqslant 30$ is selected from a normal population, then the sampling distributions of the nine deciles would be all approximately normal with $E(D_i) \doteq \tilde{d}_i$, $i = 1, 2, 3, \ldots, 9$. The standard errors of D_i are as defined by this group of equations. Note that the standard error of D_5 is identical with that of $X_{.5}$.

(10.36) $P(\hat{\theta} \leqslant \hat{\theta}_0) \doteq N\left(\dfrac{\hat{\theta}_0 - \theta}{\sigma_{\hat{\theta}}}\right).$

The right-hand side of this formula is a generalized CDF for $n(0, 1)$ and it is defined as the ratio of the difference between a specified sample value and the true value of the corresponding parameter, and the standard error of the statistic. Whenever a sampling distribution of a statistic is normally or approximately normally distributed under a variety of conditions, this formula can be applied simply by replacing these general notations with the specific ones for the statistic in question.

REVIEW QUESTIONS

10.1 What do we mean by identical and independent random variables? How can they be generated?

10.2 Why is the notion of the "sum of identical and independent random variables" important in the discussion of sampling distributions?

10.3 What are the important properties of the distribution of the sum of a set of independent and identical random variables?

10.4 What do we mean by sampling errors? How do they arise?

10.5 What is a sampling distribution? Why are sampling distributions important in the study of inductive statistics?

10.6 Give a verbal and intuitive statement of the Law of Large Numbers.

10.7 The Law of Large numbers has been stated in terms of two theorems: what are the similarities between them?

10.8 What role does Chebyshev's inequality play in the discussion of the Law of Large Numbers?

10.9 What use or uses do we have with the Law of Large Numbers in the discussion of sampling distributions?

10.10 We have stated the Law of Large Numbers in terms of the mean and the proportion; do you think that this law can also be stated in terms of other statistics, such as S^2, $X_{.5}$, and so on? Why or why not?

10.11 State the Central Limit Theorem in your own words. Why is this theorem considered as the most amazing theorem in probability theory?

10.12 State the CLT in terms of the sample mean and the sample proportion, respectively.

10.13 We know that the CLT can be applied to $\bar{X}$, $\bar{P}$, $\Delta\bar{X}$, and $\Delta\bar{P}$. Can it also be applied to S^2, S, $X_{.5}$, and other position measures taken up in this chapter? Why or why not?

10.14 State the two different methods of constructing sampling distributions.

10.15 What are the assumptions we must make in deducing a sampling distribution? What are the implications of each of these assumptions?

10.16 Explain as fully as you can the statement: "The properties of sampling distributions are closely related to the properties of the parent populations."

10.17 Why do we call the standard deviation of a sampling distribution the standard error?

10.18 What is the FPCF? What is it used for? Under what condition can it be ignored in computations?

10.19 The greater the ratio n/N is, the more reliable is the sample result. Is this a true statement? Explain your answer fully.

10.20 It is nearly always true that the size of the population has no effect on the reliability of sample results at all. Do you agree? If you do, what then is responsible for the reliability of sample results? Defend your answer.

PROBLEMS

10.1 A delivery truck is loaded with three different kinds of cartons containing food products. The weight of each kind of carton is a random variable. There are 10 cartons of one kind, 40 cartons of another kind, and 80 cartons of a third kind. Mean weights and standard deviations for these cartons are, respectively 100, 10, 50; and 5, 25, and $\sqrt{20}$—all in pounds. What is the probability that the load on the truck is more than 5,100 pounds?

10.2 An ordinary die is tossed 60 times.
   a. What is the mean of the sum of the points?

b. What is the variance of the sum of the points?
c. What is the probability that the total number of points is less than 200? Between 150 and 250 points?

10.3 Deduce the sampling distribution of $\bar{X}$ under the following assumptions:
1. *Population*: Annual dividends on one share of each of the four common stocks owned by an investor—$2.00, $4.00, $6.00, $8.00.
2. *Sample statistic*: $\bar{X}$.
3. *Sampling size*: $n = 2$.
4. *Sampling method*: Simple random sampling with replacement. For the deduced sampling distribution of $\bar{X}$, verify by demonstration that
a. $E(\bar{X}) = \mu$.
b. $V(\bar{X}) = \sigma^2/n$.
c. $\sigma_{\bar{x}} = \sigma/\sqrt{n}$.

10.4 Deduce the sampling distributions of $\bar{X}$ under the same conditions as in Problem 10.3, except that sampling without replacement is now employed. Then verify by demonstration that $E(\bar{X}) = \mu$ and $\sigma_{\bar{x}} = (\sigma/\sqrt{n})[\sqrt{(N-n)/(N-1)}]$.

10.5 Consider the "Defective Woolen Mill," which produced 6 rolls of woolen piece goods during a particular time period, and where roll A had 3 defects, roll B had 4 defects, roll C had 4 defects, roll D has 5 defects, roll E had 6 defects, and roll F had 8 defects.
a. Let the random variable X be the number of defects in 1 roll. For the population of 6 rolls, calculate μ_X, σ_X^2, and σ_X.
b. Using SRS without replacement and $n = 3$, list every sample in the sample space, and calculate $\bar{x}$ for each sample.
c. Using your answer to part (b) calculate the sampling distribution of $\bar{X}$.
d. Using your answer to part (c), calculate $\mu_{\bar{x}}$, $\sigma_{\bar{x}}^2$, and $\sigma_{\bar{x}}$.

10.6. Suppose that a lot of 1,000 fried chicken dinners has a mean weight of 12 ounces and a standard deviation of 0.6 ounce and that the distribution of weights departs somewhat from the normal distribution. What is the probability that, in a random sample of 100 without replacement from this population, the total weight will be
a. less than 1,190 ounces?
b. more than 1,195 ounces?
c. between 1,190 and 1,195 ounces?
(*Hint*: That the combined weight will be between 1,190 and 1,195 ounces is the same as that the sample mean will be between 11.90 and 11.95 ounces.

10.7 Packages to be delivered by a factory have a mean weight of 300 pounds and a standard deviation of 50 pounds, and the weights are almost exactly normally distributed. What is the probability that 25 packages taken at random from 16,000 packages and loaded on a truck will exceed the capacity of the truck, which is 8,200 pounds?

10.8. The Chamber of Commerce of a city with a population over 400,000 claims the annual incomes of families in that city have a mean of $28,000 and a standard deviation of $1,200. Suppose a simple random sample of $n = 100$ families is selected from the city and the sample mean is $25,000. In view of this evidence, what conclusion can be reached about the claim? (*Hint*: How probable is it that such a sample would have a mean that differs from $28,000 by $3,000 or more, either above or below?)

10.9 The breaking strengths of 1,000 ropes are close to normally distributed with $\mu = 500$ pounds and $\sigma = 25$ pounds. If a simple random sample of 81 ropes is drawn without replacement, what is the probability that the sample mean will be less than 495 pounds? greater than 505 pounds? between 490 and 510 pounds?

10.10 The annual net incomes of a national chain of 250 drug drotes are almost exactly normally distributed with $\mu = \$100,000$ and $\sigma = \$21,000$.
   a. If 9 of these stores are selected at random without replacement, what is the probability that the sample mean will fall within $10,000 of the population mean?
   b. Answer part (a), assuming that $n = 100$ and the selections are made with replacement.
   c. Answer part (a), assuming that $n = 100$ and the selections are made without replacement.

10.11 A cat food cannery claims that its major product—canned tuna fish—has a mean net weight of 8 ounces with a standard deviation of 0.32 ounce.
   a. If the company's claim is correct, what fraction of the individual cans will contain less than 7.50 ounces? More than 8.35 ounces?
   b. A government inspector randomly selects 64 cans of the product and finds the mean weight to be 7.45 ounces. If the company's claim is correct, what is the probability of this sample mean or any smaller sample mean? In view of this probability, what can be said about the company's claim?

10.12 The reliability of a rocket is the probability π that an attempted launching will be successful. It has been established that the reliability of a certain type of rocket is 0.9. A modification of this rocket is made and is being evaluated. Which of the following sets of evidence throws more doubt on the hypothesis that the modified design is exactly 90% reliable?
   a. Of 120 modified rockets tested, 95.00% performed successfully.
   b. Of 80 modified rockets tested, 96.25% performed successfully.
   (*Hint*: In each case, calculate the probability of getting the actual value of $\bar{P}$ or any higher result, assuming that π is 0.9.)

10.13 Which of the following sets of evidence throws more doubt on the hypothesis that exactly 50% of the voters favor candidate A over candidate B in a presidential election?
   a. Of 10,000 voters sampled, 51% are in favor of A.
   b. Of 1,000 voters sampled, 51% are in favor of A.
   (*Hint*: In each case, calculate the probability of getting the actual value of $\bar{P}$ or any higher result, assuming that π is 0.5.)

10.14 In a large union, 46% of the members are against the current union leadership. What is the probability that a poll would show a majority against the leadership if the poll consisted of
   a. 100 union members?
   b. 1,000 union members?

10.15 It is known that 5% of the radio transistors produced by a certain manufacturer are defective. If the manufacturer sends out 1,000 lots, each containing 100 transistors, in how many of these lots can we expect to have
   a. fewer than 90 good resistors?
   b. at least 98 good transistors?

10.16 There are 10 employees in a department of a financial firm, 4 of whom are females. The employees wish to select a committee of 3 to represent them in discussions of working conditions with the supervisor of the department. Suppose a simple random sample of 3 will be selected from the 10 employees, without replacement, and suppose we are interested in the sampling distribution of the proportion of female employees in the sample.
   a. How many possible samples are there, disregarding the order of selection into a sample?
   b. What are the possible values of the sample proportion?
   c. What is the probability of each of the values of the sample proportion?
   d. What is the probability that the sample will contain 2 or fewer females?

10.17 In the summer of 1987, it is known that 65% of American voters are in favor of President Reagan's defense policy. Suppose 500 voters are randomly selected. Compute:
   a. $P(\bar{P} \leqslant 0.63)$.
   b. $P(\bar{P} \geqslant 0.685)$.
   c. $P(0.60 \leqslant \bar{P} \leqslant 0.70)$.

10.18. A simple random sample of $n = 20$ tubes is selected with replacement from a lot of 100 television picture tubes, 80 of which are known to be nondefective. What is the probability that the sample proportion of nondefective tubes will be less than 0.70? greater than 0.85?

10.19 A certain make of ball bearing has a mean weight of 0.5 ounce and a standard deviation of 0.02 ounce. Two random samples are taken independently without replacement from a certain day's production of 145,000 ball bearings, with $n_1 = 500$ and $n_2 = 800$.
   a. What is the probability that the two sample means will differ by more than 0.002 ounce?
   b. What is the probability that the two sample means will differ by less than 0.001 ounce?
   c. Nothing was said about whether the population of 145,000 weights has a normal distribution. Does it matter? Why?

10.20 Two different makes of TV picture tubes, A and B, possess the following parameters: $\mu_A = 1,400$ hours, $\sigma_A = 200$ hours, $\mu_B = 1,200$ hours, and $\sigma_B = 100$ hours. Tube lives for both makes are almost exactly normally distributed. A random sample of 125 tubes is drawn independently from a large population of each make.
   a. What is $P(\Delta X \geqslant 160$ hours)?
   b. What is $P(\Delta x \geqslant 250$ hours)?

10.21 Repeat Problem 10.20 for the following sample sizes:
   a. $n_A = 25$ and $n_B = 225$.
   b. $n_A = 50$ and $n_B = 200$.
   c. $n_A = 167$ and $n_B = 83$.
   d. $n_A = 225$ and $n_B = 25$.

e. If the sampling budget allows a total of 250 observations, discuss briefly why the two sample sizes should be proportional to the population standard deviations—that is, why n_A and n_B should satisfy the equation $n_A/n_B = \sigma_A/\sigma_B$. Use your answers from the last problem.

f. Both populations were specified to be almost exactly normal. Does this matter? Why?

10.22 Annual mean incomes and their standard deviations for physicians and lawyers in a large Western city are known to be as follows:

Physicians	Lawyers
μ_P = $75,000	μ_L = $62,000
σ_P = $11,500	σ_L = $13,000

Now, suppose 100 physicians and 120 lawyers are selected at random for observation. For $\Delta\bar{x} = \bar{x}_p - \bar{x}_L$, calculate:

a. $P(\Delta\bar{X} \leq \$16,000)$
b. $P(\Delta\bar{X} \geq \$14,000)$
c. $P(\$14,000 \leq \Delta\bar{X} \leq \$16,000)$

10.23 Alpha and Beta Motor Companies have introduced a new model each. A sample of 9 cars made by Alpha and 12 cars made by Beta yields the following miles-per-gallon performance:

Alpha	Beta
$\bar{x}_\alpha$ = 40 m.p.g.	$\bar{x}_B$ = 35 m.p.g.
s_α = 5 m.p.g.	s_β = 4 m.p.g.

Assuming that miles-per-gallon performance is normally distributed for each new model, do you think there is a difference between μ_α and μ_β? Explain. (*Hint*: Assume $\Delta\mu = 0$ and calculate $P(|\Delta\bar{X}| \geq 5)$.)

10.24 A liberal arts college has 100 faculty members, 60 of whom have doctoral degrees. Two samples, with $n_1 = n_2 = 30$, are drawn from this 100-member faculty, independently, with replacement. Let $\Delta\bar{P} = \bar{P}_2 - \bar{P}_1$.

a. What are the numerical values of π_1, π_2, $\Delta\pi$, σ_{p_1}, and σ_{p_2}?
b. What is $P(|\Delta P| \geq 0.2)$?

10.25 Repeat Problem 10.24, except that now the sampling is without replacement.

10.26 Two different TV rating services, C and D, both take a simple random sample of the 71,000,000 American households having TV. Service C observes 1,200 families. Service D observes 1,600 families. Sampling without replacement is used. Suppose the population proportion watching a particular program is 0.16.

a. What is the probability that the two services will agree except for one-tenth of a percentage point—that is, what is $P(|\Delta\bar{P}| \leq 0.001)$?
b. What is the probability that the two services will agree except for a whole percentage point—that is, what is $P(|\Delta P| \leq 0.01)$?

10.27 Repeat Problem 10.26, except that now the population proportion watching a particular program is only 0.04.

10.28 Two different department stores in a given city, A and B, are believed to have the same proportions of customers who charge their purchases, and these proportions are $\pi_A = \pi_B = 0.35$. In doing an audit, company A's accountant selects a random sample of 150 sales slips and finds 60 charge customers, whereas company B's accountant draws a random sample of 200 sales slips and finds 65 charge customers. Thus $\Delta \bar{p} = \bar{p}_A - \bar{p}_B = 0.400 - 0.325 = 0.075$. Assume that π_A and π_B really are both 0.35.
   a. Calculate $P(|\Delta \bar{P}| \geqslant 0.075)$.
   b. Decide whether or not the accountants found an unusually large difference between $\bar{p}_A$ and $\bar{p}_B$.
   c. Explain your answer to part (b).

10.29 A factory orders a certain kind of mechanical part in bulk from each of two suppliers. The assembly line draws 200 of supplier I's parts daily and 400 of supplier II's parts daily. Machines automatically discard unusable parts, and past records show that 10% of supplier I's parts and 7% of supplier II's parts have been discarded. Assuming that unusable parts are mixed at random with good parts, determine on what proportion of the days the difference between the two discard rates will be less than $1\frac{1}{2}$ percentage points. That is, what is $P(|\Delta \bar{P}| < 0.015)$?

10.30 A real estate speculator is contemplating two investment plans, one in California and the other in Florida. In his judgment, both plans have four-year means of 200% return on investment; that is, $\mu_1 = \mu_2 = 2.00$. They also have the same variances of returns on investment in individual lots of land, and $\sigma_1^2 = \sigma_2^2 = 0.35$. If he invests in $n_1 = 60$ lots of land in California and $n_2 = 70$ lots of land in Florida, what is the probability that the mean yields of the two investments will differ by less than 3.5%?. That is, find $P(|\Delta \bar{X}| \leqslant 0.035)$.

10.31 Two different salesmen have had the same success rate when calling on customers in the past, $\pi_1 = \pi_2 = 0.25$, and this rate is expected to continue in the future. During the next two months, each salesman will call on the same number of customers: $n_1 = n_2 = 450$. For each salesman, the successes occur at random among his calls on customers. For the next two months, calculate:
   a. $E(\Delta \bar{P})$
   b. $\sigma_{\Delta \bar{p}}$
   c. $P(|\Delta \bar{P}| > 0.015)$

10.32 Weights of American soldiers are normally distributed, with a variance of 100 pounds². If a random sample of 200 is drawn from this population, what are the expectation and standard error of the sampling distribution of S^2?

10.33 For the preceding problem, what is the probability that S^2 will be greater than 101? Less than σ^2? Different from σ^2 by 1.5?

10.34 Tensile strengths of steel wires are normally distributed with a standard deviation of five pounds. Many samples of 100 each are drawn at random, and standard deviations are computed for these samples. Find the expected value and the standard error of the distribution of S.

10.35 For the last problem, what percentage of samples would have standard deviations greater than 5.71 pounds? Less than 4.148 pounds?

10.36 A normal population has $\mu = 100$ and $\sigma = 5$. If a random sample of 250 is drawn from this population, is it likely for this sample to have a median of 91 or less?

10.37 If the first quartile of a population with $\sigma = 10$ is 11, what is the probability for Q_1 with $n = 100$ to be less than 10?

10.38 If the third quartile of random variable, with $\sigma^2 = 81$, is 75, what is the probability for Q_2 with $n = 81$ to be greater than 77?

10.39 Construct a sampling distribution of the sample mean by the replicated method on the computer by following the instructions below:
   a. Use the population given by the data set in Table 3.P6.
   b. Select 500 samples with $n = 25$ each. Sampling is to be made without replacement.
   c. Compute the sample means for the samples selected.
   d. Organize the computed sample means into a relative frequency distribution. The result is a computer-simulated sampling distribution of the sample mean.

   (*Note*: Because the computer is instructed to take the sample at random, each student may come out with a slightly different sampling distribution. However, the following points must be true if you have executed the canned computer program properly. (1) The distribution must resemble a normal distribution. (2) The mean of the sample means must be very close to the population mean. (3) The standard deviation, or the standard error, computed by the definitional equation for frequency distribution must be very close to that computed from $\sigma/\sqrt{n}$).

Appendix to Chapter 10
Alternate Sampling Designs

So far we have only been concerned with simple random sampling, because, as stated on numerous occasions, this volume (as any other basic statistics text) is exclusively concerned with this kind of sampling. However, there are many kinds of samples other than SRSs that can be obtained by other kinds of sampling methods. The purpose of this appendix is to make you aware of such methods and their possible uses. Our discussion here is confined to the general nature of these alternate sampling designs without getting into their technical aspects. Before this main task, we shall answer two important questions that have been mentioned or hinted at but have not been given formally:

1. What are the reasons for sampling?

2. What is the theoretical basis of sampling?

10A-1 REASONS FOR SAMPLING

With the great strides made in the theory of sampling during the past few decades, it is now possible to measure the properties of massive amounts of data with calculated accuracy on the basis of samples. Consequently, nearly all statistical surveys today, whether they are for decision making in business, for policy formulation in government, or for the development of social and economic theories, are in the form of sampling.

Apart from the fact that reliable results can be obtained from sound sampling procedures, there are other important reasons for their wide adoption. In the first place, populations under investigation may be infinite, and in such cases sampling is the only possible procedure. Even in the case of finite populations, sampling is very often the only practical procedure, because a finite population may consist of tens of thousands, millions, or even tens of millions of elements and its complete enumeration is practically impossible. Consider the case of consumers' preferences for the styling of automobiles or the case of the outcome of a presidential election. The population for the first includes millions of automobile buyers and that of the second contains tens of millions of eligible voters. If a census were to be taken of either population, the costs of locating, visiting, and interviewing would be prohibitive.

In other cases the measurement of a population often requires the destruction of the elements in it. For example, if the producer wants to find out whether the tensile strength of a lot of steel wires meets the specified standard, pressure is put on the steel wire until it breaks. A census then would mean complete destruction of all the steel wires, and there would be no product left after the completion of examination.

What should not be forgotten, either, is that for many types of data the population is not accessible. In practice, we have to deal with whatever part of the data is available. In time series analysis, for instance, studies are inevitably made of samples because only since the recent past reliable data have been made available. It may be possible to extend the record to earlier days but this can be done only by introducing serious errors due to the unreliability of the data and without much reduction in sampling error. Obviously, we can extend the record into the future only by waiting patiently and watchfully.

Finally, even when it is financially, practically, and physically possible to observe the entire population, sampling may still be the most efficient procedure. Results obtained by the study of a sample may be just as accurate as or even more accurate than the findings from a complete count of the universe. As has been explained before, any statistical survey—by sampling or census—always contains some error. Statistical errors are of two kinds: nonsampling and sampling. Non-sampling error is usually large for a census but it can be reduced greatly or completely with well-conducted sampling. Moreover, nonsam-pling error often cannot be estimated objectively, whereas this is usually possible for sampling error. For these reasons, not only may the total error be expected to be smaller in a sampling survey but sample results can also be used with a greater degree of confidence because of our knowledge of the probable size of the error. This point is vividly illustrated by the effective use of samples by the Bureau of the Census to check the accuracy of the census.

In concluding these remarks and our previous discussion on sampling distributions, we may point out that all the reasons for sampling may be summarized by a general principle: In dealing with numerical data there always comes a point beyond which the increase in information from additional observations is not worth the increase in costs.

10A-2 THEORETICAL BASS OF SAMPLING

In sampling we find a powerful instrument with which to predict the behavior of mass phenomena. It is indeed a great scientific achievement "toward an intellectual mastery of the world around us," commented Roy Jastram in his *Elements of Statistical Inference*, "to generalize logically and precisely about thousands of values which we have not seen, simply upon the evidence afforded by, say, fifty or a hundred of those values." The theory of sampling that makes possible this kind of inference has as its foundation the permanent characteristics of mass data, which can be summarized simply and precisely by the phrase "unity in diversity."

On the one hand, the elementary units of any population are affected by a multiplicity of forces. This vast complex of forces, moreover, though related, acts upon the individual elements with a considerable degree of independence. These causes explain variations from unit to unit in the population. We thus find that brothers, although similar in most respects, may differ from each other, with varying degrees, in personality, temperament, habits, intelligence, physical features, and so forth. Oranges from the same tree may differ in size, in color, in weight, and in sweetness. Differences in diameters, in weight, in tensile strength, and in length always exist among steel bars coming off the same production process. No golf player has ever driven a ball exactly the same distance twice. In the stock market, on any day, one finds that some stock prices increase, others decrease, and still others remain relatively unchanged. And so on—the list can be extended indefinitely.

Although diversity is a universal quality of data, there is virtually no actual statistical population whose elements would vary from each other without limit. Thus, rice varies, to a limited extent, in length, weight, color, protein content, and so forth, but it can always be identified as rice. Adolescents in a human population may differ from each other in height, but no ordinary individual is as short as, say, three feet or as tall as, say, eight feet. Economic goods can never have prices as low as zero and, practically, they can never have prices that are beyond the reach of even millionaires.

The facts that any population has characteristic properties and that variations in its elements are definitely limited make it possible for us to select a relatively small random sample that can portray fairly well the traits of the population.

Another interesting and important property of data is regularity or uniformity. The related but independent forces that produce variability in a population are often so balanced and concentrated that they tend to generate equal values above and below some central value around which most of the values tend to cluster. In any school, both "A" and "F" students are in the minority, but most are "C" students. The balances of savings accounts in any bank may vary from a few dollars to over ten thousand. However, only a small number of the balances would be less than $100 or more than $10,000, and the majority would cluster within a small range somewhere between these two values. Most business firms carrying the same line of merchandise usually stock their inventories at some intermediate level; few would adopt a high or low inventory policy. The concentration of inventory size at some intermediate level is the result of trial and error. These who keep inventories too low would often be out of stock and those keeping inventories too high would lose interest on tied-up capital or suffer physical depreciation and obsolescence of merchandise. Thus, paradoxically, the individual items in a population tend to vary from each other and at the same time conform to some standards. We have therefore both diversity and uniformity in data.

Because of statistical uniformity, if a large random sample is selected, characteristics of this sample will differ very little from those in the population. Because of diversity, if a number of random samples are taken, although quite similar in many respects (because of uniformity), the samples will never agree completely with one another (because of diversity).

Uniformity or regularity refers to the tendency of the measurable characteristics to cluster around some "center of gravity." The measure for such a central tendency, as you may recall, is an average from which individual observations diverge in some definite pattern.

Averages are more stable than individual values. Moreover, averages become more stable when more observations are included in the sample. Thus if a fair coin is tossed a few times, it may easily come up all heads or no heads at all. If a coin is tossed twenty or thirty times, however, such extreme occurrences are much less likely. When the number of trials is increased indefinitely, we would eventually approach the completely stable limit of half heads and half tails. Again, the number of traffic accidents per month may fluctuate wildly, from month to month, in the City of Rosebud, in Texas. Its 1980 population was about 2,000. There may be months with no accidents at all and other months with two accidents. The percentage increases from zero to two is infinity. If the annual average is one accident per month, the variation of a particular month from the annual average can easily be −100% or +100%. If we deal with larger amounts of data, say the whole state of Texas, the fluctuations in percentage terms are much less, either on a month-to-month basis or on a deviation-from-the-annual-average basis.

The basic reason the larger amounts of data tend to exhibit less fluctuations is a tendency of the small units of data to "cancel each other out." For example, if Rosebud has a bad month with two accidents, some other small city is likely to have a good month with no accidents, so that the total number of accidents for the month is about the same for the whole state even though individual cities are experiencing large amounts of month-to-month variation. The same "cancellation" effect can be expected as a sample size increases. If a small sample has one large observation in it, that will force the sample mean up. But in a large sample such a large observation is likely to be "balanced" by a small observation, so that the sample mean is not much affected by either extreme observation. However, this explanation is dangerously near the fallacious "doctrine of the maturity of chance," which states that, as a run of bad luck continues, the probability of luck on the next trial increases. This simply does not happen in random sampling.

Notice that the statement about the "cancellation effect" said nothing about when in the sampling process the small observation was likely to occur. It merely said it was likely somewhere in the sample. A much better way of looking at the reason for the stability of averages is the "swamping" effect in large samples, rather than any "compensating" or "cancellation" effect. That is, in a large sample, a few unusual observations scarcely affect the mean because there are so many other and more typical observations. The outlying observations are swamped by the typical observations. In a small sample, there is just not the opportunity to have a great many typical observations swamp an outlying observation, so averages based on small samples exhibit more variability than averages based on large samples.

The increase in the stability of an average as sample size increases makes it possible to calculate how large a sample should be in order that its average possess a desired amount of stability (a low enough standard error). An important fact in this connection is that statistical theory does not say anything about how large the sample needs to be in order that the sampling distribution of the sample mean be approximately normal, so that it easy to interpret the meaning of the standard error of the mean. After all, if the sampling distribution of the mean were sharply nonnormal, even for large samples (say 10,000 observations), the central limit theorem would lose any practical usefulness, and the standard error of the mean would become a more-or-less uninterpretable descriptive measure of variation in the sample mean. It just happens that, in a very wide assortment of cases, small samples are large enough for approximate normality in the sampling distribution of the mean.

In practice, in making inferences we usually take only one sample. Whether the sample is large or small, we are almost certain that its characteristics are not exactly those of the population. How can we be sure, then, about the degree of dependability of our conclusions? The answer to such a question is "randomness." Objective measurement of sampling errors requires that the sample be random. This is so because this knowledge can be obtained by applying the mathematical laws of probability, which, in turn, can be applied only to random samples.

10A-3 ALTERNATE SAMPLING DESIGNS

Sampling designs can be conveniently grouped as random sampling and nonrandom sampling. Random sampling is also referred to as *probability sampling,* since if the sampling process is random, the laws of probability can be applied; thus the pattern of sampling distribution needed to interpret and evaluate a sample is provided. The term *random sample* is not used to describe the data in the sample but the process employed to select the sample. Thus, randomness is a property of the sampling procedure rather than of an individual sample. As will be shown, randomness can enter a process of sampling in a number of ways and therefore random samples may be of many kinds.

Nonrandom sampling is a process of sampling selection without the use of randomization. A nonrandom sample, in other words, is selected on a basis other than probability considerations, such as expert judgment, convenience, or other criteria. The most important aspect of nonrandom sampling to remember is that it is subject to sampling variability, but there is no way of knowing the pattern of variability in the process.

We shall now describe various sampling procedures according to following this outline.

 I. Random sampling
  1. Unrestricted or simple random sampling
  2. Restricted random sampling
   a. Stratified random sampling
   b. Cluster sampling
   c. Systematic sampling
  3. Double, multiple, and sequential sampling

II. Nonrandom sampling
   1. Judgment sampling
   2. Quote sampling
   3. Convenience sampling

10A-4 UNRESTRICTED RANDOM SAMPLING

We discussed unrestricted random sampling, or simple random sampling, in great detail in Chapter 8. It suffices to remind you that the one drawback of applying this procedure to large populations is that the population must be numbered. Note that it is not necessary literally to number every item in the population, but it has to be done at least conceptually. "Conceptually" here means that once a selecting serial number has been read from a table of random digits, there is absolutely no doubt which item in the population has been selected. Theoretically we could obtain simple random samples by numbering all the eligible voters, all the households in America, all automobile owners, all retail stores, or all refugees from other countries, and so forth. Such a procedure, however, would be extremely costly and might even be physically impossible. As a matter of fact, many economic and business data cannot be effectively gathered by simple random sampling. Consequently, instead of using simple random sampling, we often employ other kinds of random sampling designs.

Greater efficiency and the desire to have a probability sample when it is impractical to use simple random selection are the basic reasons for using other kinds of random sampling. However, every kind of random sampling uses simple random sampling in some fashion. That is, more complicated random sampling embeds simple random sampling someplace in a more elaborate sampling design.

10A-5 STRATIFIED SAMPLING

Stratified random sampling is one of the random methods that, by using available information concerning the population, attempts to design a more efficient sample than that obtained by the simple random procedure. The process of stratification requires that the population be divided into groups or classes called *strata*. Then a sample is taken from each stratum by simple random methods, and the resulting sample is called a *stratified sample*.

A stratified sample may be either *proportional* or *disproportionate*. In a proportional stratified sampling plan, the number of items drawn from each stratum is proportional to the size of the stratum. For instance, if the population is divided into four strata, their respective sizes being 10, 20, 30, and 40% of the population, and a sample of 500 is to be drawn, the desired proportional sample may be obtained in the following manner:

From stratum one	$500(0.10) = 50$ items
From stratum two	$500(0.20) = 100$ items
From stratum three	$500(0.30) = 150$ items
From stratum four	$500(0.40) = \underline{200 \text{ items}}$
Size of the entire sample	$= \overline{500 \text{ items}}$

It is evident from the above example that proportional stratification yields samples that represent the universe with respect to the proportion in each stratum in the population. This procedure is satisfactory if there is no great difference in dispersion from stratum to stratum. But it is certainly not the most efficient procedure when standard deviations differ substantially in the various strata, for, as has been repeatedly pointed out, the most important consideration for sample size is not the size but the variation of the population. This indicates that in order to obtain maximum efficiency in stratification, we should assign greater representation to a stratum with large dispersion and smaller representation to one with small variation.

For instance, suppose we want to measure how much people spend on recreation in Cleveland, Ohio. Much information is readily available from the U.S. Bureau of the Census on rents by city neighborhood. We can use this information to stratify Cleveland to our advantage. We know that in low-rent neighborhoods people do not have much money available for recreation, so the standard deviation of recreational expenditures will be small. In high-rent neighborhoods, people earn much more and therefore have many more choices on how to spend their money. Some spend a great deal on recreation, others a moderate amount, others very little. So in high-rent neighborhoods the standard deviation of recreational expenditures will be large. Medium-rent neighborhoods will be in between. Our real goal is a low overall standard error of mean recreation expenditures per family in the entire sample. We can best achieve this goal by deliberately underrepresenting the low-rent neighborhoods in our sample, since only a few observations there will be enough to give precise information on their recreational expenditures. We would deliberately overrepresent the high-rent neighborhoods in our sample, because many observations will be needed to get precise information on their recreational expenditures in view of the great variability of the data here. Medium-rent neighborhoods would be in between and could come out being neither underrepresented nor overrepresented.

A sample thus obtained is a *disproportionate stratified sample*. Disproportionate stratified sampling also includes the procedures of taking an equal number of items from each stratum irrespective of its size, or of giving only a small representation to one or more strata whose members are too expensive to investigate although some representation of them is nevertheless valuable. The term *optimum allocation* is suggested for stratified methods that take both variation and size of each stratum into consideration in determining its representation in the sample. Sometimes optimum allocation also makes allowances for differing costs of investigation from stratum to stratum.

Efficiency in stratification can be further increased when the nature of the data permits, by classifying the strata into substrata, which in turn may be subdivided into smaller groups. For instance, knowing that voting preferences are often influenced by differences in sex, religion, race, educational standards, and economic status, in conducting a presidential election poll we may subdivide the population according to these aspects. If we have two levels for sex, three for religion, three for race, three for education, and four for economic status, there are $(2)(3)(3)(3)(4) = 216$ cross-classifications in the population. Each of these is a substratum. This refinement in stratification of grouping the population with respect to several relevant characteristics simultaneously is referred to as cross-stratification.

Previous discussions may have indicated that stratification is most effective in dealing with heterogeneous or highly skewed populations, such as income data or detail sales. In such situations we can stratify the population in such a manner that (1) within each stratum there is as much uniformity as possible, and (2) among various strata differences are as great as possible. Consequently, we are able to obtain a sample with a smaller sampling error (or a smaller sample with the same precision) as compared with simple random sampling.

Thus, before deciding on stratification, we must have some knowledge of the traits of the population. Such knowledge may be based upon past data, preliminary observation from pilot studies, expert judgment, or simply intuition or good guesses. If we actually have great variation within each stratum, despite our attempt to form nearly uniform strata, we will still have a stratified random sample. No definitions or absolute requirements will have been violated. Our overall standard error requirements will have been violated. Our overall standard error will be high, so our sample results may be poor or useless—but that is another matter.

Subjective judgment used in dividing the universe into strata does not mean that stratified samples are not probability samples. By employing simple random selection from each stratum, some probability of each item's being drawn is ensured and this probability is known, even though in disproportionate sampling the probabilities that individual items will be selected are not equal.

As a probability sample, the weighted arithmetic average of the stratum sample means is an unbiased estimate of the universe mean. In the case of proportional sampling, where each item has an equal probability of being chosen, the estimate of the universe mean is merely the arithmetic average of the entire sample because it is weighted in just these proportions. However, the mean of the disproportionate sample must be derived with proper weights or serious biases may result. The proper weights are the relative proportions of the population in the various strata.

Finally, the precision of estimates in stratified sampling can be measured provided the sample is sufficiently large. As an absolute minimum, two observations must be selected from each stratum. Appropriate formulas for evaluating sampling errors in stratification can be found in more advanced books on sampling.

10A-6 CLUSTER SAMPLING

Cluster sampling refers to the procedure of dividing the population into groups called clusters and drawing a sample or cluster to represent the population. When the clusters, which are primary units, are drawn, we can either include in the sample all the elementary units in the selected clusters or take a sample of smaller primary units or elementary units from the selected clusters. When all the elementary units in the cluster are observed, we have what is known as *single-stage sampling*. When a sample of elementary units is drawn from the selected clusters, we have a type of design called *two-stage sampling* or *subsampling*. At both stages a simple random sample is selected. When cluster sampling involves more than two stages in selecting the final sample, it is called *multistage sampling*. For instance, we may take colleges—primary units—as the first stage, then draw departments as the second stage, and choose students—the elementary units—as the third and last stage. When the clusters—the primary units—are geographical areas, cluster sampling becomes the widely used *area sampling*. In any case, our objective is to study the elementary units even though initially primary units are taken.

Principles that dictate maximum efficiency in cluster sampling are the opposite of those used in stratification. In cluster sampling, it is efficient to have (1) differences among the elementary units in the same cluster as large as possible and (2) differences among the clusters as small as possible. Evidently these requirements are very difficult to meet, for in most populations similar elementary units tend to cluster together. For instance, rich people tend to live in the same neighborhood in a city, while the poor families are concentrated in another area. Again, better students tend to be in the departments of natural sciences, whereas less able students usually take liberal arts and social sciences. (This last illustration is a sad but nevertheless a true situation in many countries.)

This difficulty causes cluster sampling to have a greater standard error in practical work than stratified sampling has, for the same number of elementary units in the sample, even though the former also yields unbiased estimates. The fact that cluster sampling provides less precision for a sample of equal size does not mean that it cannot be more efficient than other random designs. If the cost per elementary unit is much lower in cluster sampling, many more elementary units can be included in the sample. (And it is usually the case that the cost per interview in cluster sampling is lower than for other types of random designs. Lower cost is most evident in area sampling, when interviewers' time and traveling costs are cut down.) Consequently, it is possible to have a larger cluster sample that can yield the same precision with lower cost than a simple or stratified random sample. Alternatively, it is possible with the same cost, to have a cluster sample large enough to have greater reliability than either simple or stratified sampling. In other words, despite the drawbacks in difficulty of achieving heterogeneity within each cluster and uniformity among different clusters, cluster sampling can still be a more efficient design.

10A-7 SYSTEMATIC SAMPLING

Another frequently used random design is the *systematic sampling plan,* which generates what are called *systematic random samples.* To obtain a systematic random sample we may again number the sampling units in the population serially from 1 to N and determine first what is called the *sampling interval, $k = N/n$.* Next, a number is selected at random from the first sampling interval. If this number is say, a, with $a \leq k$, then the sample with size n would have as its members the sampling units whose serial numbers correspond to $a, a + k, a + 2k, a + 3k, \ldots$.

For instance, suppose we wish to take a systematic sample of, say, 200 from a population of 10,000 union members. We first determine the sampling interval, which is $k = 10,000/200 = 50$. Next, we select a random number from 01 to 50. suppose this number turns out to be 12; then we would start with the 12th union member in the serial-numbered population and select every 50th one thereafter—the 62nd, 112th, 162nd, and so forth, for our sample.

Note that a systematic sample is not a simple random sample, since the sampling units selected are not independent. Also, with systematic sampling, only k samples of size n can possibly be selected: each of the remaining $_NC_n - k$ samples has a zero probability of being drawn.

Systematic sampling is really single-stage cluster sampling, where only one cluster is drawn into the sample. To see this, consider again the union membership sample just discussed. The possible samples are: cluster 1, which has members number 1, 51, 101, 151, ...; cluster 2, which has members number 2, 52, 102, 152, ... ; cluster 3, which has members number 3, 53, 103, 153, ...; and so on through cluster 50, which has members number 50, 100, 150, 200, ... Every union member belongs to one and only one cluster, and there is no overlapping among the clusters. The random start, which selects the first union member to be drawn into the sample, actually selects the whole cluster to be drawn into the sample, and no other union members enter the sample. Thus one cluster is selected at random. This leads to a theoretically disastrous result for systematic sampling. Since only one item (that is, one cluster) was selected at random, no standard errors of any kind can be computed. To compute a standard error, one has to have at least two random selections.

In practice, systematic samples are often treated as if they were simple random samples. In the union example, the 200 union members in the sample would be treated as 200 observations in a simple random sample. This appears to permit standard error computation. This procedure, of course, is completely unjustified. The statistical analysis of sample results must be appropriate to the sampling design actually used. Sometimes attempts are made to analyze the systematic sample actually obtained to show that its observations are about what one would expect in simple random sampling, so that treating them as a simple random sample is justified. However, there is no way that such justifications can really be convincing. The unobserved cluster can be anything, and there is no way of knowing for sure whether the observed cluster is so special that it seriously misrepresents the population.

Two solutions are immediately at hand to solve the problem of validly computing standard errors from systematic samples. One is to use simple random sampling instead of systematic sampling. Then the assertion that the data can be treated as a simple random sample is, of course, entirely true. Once people realize how easy it is, in many cases of great practical importance, to take simple random samples instead of systematic samples, this solution becomes very practical indeed. There remain cases, though, in which simple random sampling is hard to achieve while systematic sampling is easy to achieve. Here, the strongly recommended solution is *replicated systematic sampling*. Since one has to have at least two clusters selected at random to permit valid computations of standard errors, go ahead and take two clusters into the sample. The total number of elementary units in the sample need not increase; merely redefine the clusters so that each is half as large as before, and then draw two clusters. In the union-membership example, make the sampling interval 100 instead of 50. Then there will be 100 clusters of 100 members each, instead of 50 clusters of 200 members each. The 100 clusters would be the following: cluster 1 with members number 1, 101, 201, . . . ; cluster 2 with members number 2, 102, 202, . . .; and so forth through cluster 100 with members number 100, 200, 300, ... Next, select two random starting points, without replacement, thus guaranteeing that exactly two clusters will be selected at random into the sample. While the techniques for computing standard errors from cluster samples are not present in this book, they are described in great detail in many books on survey sampling. Suffice it to say that standard errors can validly be computed when two clusters have been randomly drawn into a sample.

There are other possible solutions besides simple random sampling and replicated systematic sampling. Ordinarily a sampling expert is needed to make the best choice from among all the possibilities available. In a large, expensive, important survey, a sampling expert will be on the survey staff. For a small, cheap, relatively unimportant survey, either of the solutions recommended here will be adequate and much superior to ordinary systematic sampling.

Systematic sampling has the great advantage of simplicity in design. It is easy to select every kth item from a list or file. However, slightly more difficult selection procedures have the great advantage of permitting valid measurements of sampling error.

Systematic sampling becomes a less representative design than simple random sampling if we are dealing with populations having hidden *periodicities*. For example, if the sales of every seventh day of the calandar year are included, the sample will contain, say, all Mondays or all Fridays. If there is a definite repetitive weekly pattern in sales (which is usually the case), our sample is not representative at all of sales for the whole year; consequently the sample results will be seriously in error. Similarly, serious errors will result if we are to test the quality of a product coming off an assembly line by taking every fiftieth item for observation when the machinery happens to have a defect that produces imperfections in every fiftieth piece. These errors will not be biases, since the random start ensures that the expected value of the estimator will equal the parameter (after any adjustments for mathematical bias). The errors will be sampling errors, since chance alone determines which series of data wind up in the sample. The sampling errors are serious, though, because they will be large when periodicities are involved and because in systematic sampling it is impossible to measure the sampling errors.

Up to now we have discussed various random procedures as independent designs. In practice, we often combine two or more of these methods into a single design. For instance, in sampling for an estimate of the labor force, the Bureau of Census uses a plan that includes many types of random sampling. In this survey approximately 2000 primary units—clusters that are whole counties or contiguous counties—were set up and then grouped into 55 strata. After that, random selections were made from the strata. Next, these selected primary units were divided into segments to determine the elementary units (households) to be included in the final sample. At each stage, probability methods were used for selection so that proper formulas could be applied to measure the reliability of the sample results.

10A-8 DOUBLE, MULTIPLE, AND SEQUENTIAL SAMPLING

All the sampling designs presented previously may be referred to as *single sampling,* since each design is used to obtain a single sample from which an estimate is made or a hypothesis is tested. The application of sampling for testing the quality of incoming material from a vendor or of a particular lot of products coming off a manufacturing process or of clerical work has led during the past few decades to popular use of double, multiple, and sequential sampling designs. These sampling plans will be discussed in detail in Chapter 14 on statistical quality control.

10A-9 JUDGMENT SAMPLING

Judgment sampling, is also called *purpose sampling.* It is the method of selecting the items into a sample on the basis of "judgment" of the sampler, who thinks that the result will be representative. In other words, the items in the population that are thought to be typical or representative, according to the knowledge of the investigator, are drawn into a judgment sample. In judgment sampling, then, the probability that an individual item will be chosen is unknown. Consequently, statistical inference cannot be conducted and judgment sampling leads to point estimates only. Furthermore, only the expert sampler can interpret the precision of results obtained from this plan; these results cannot be objectively evaluated.

Even though the principles of sampling theory are not applicable to judgment sampling, it is often used in solving many types of economic and business problems. The use of judgment sampling is justified under a variety of circumstances. When only a small number of sampling units is in the universe, simple random selection may miss the more important elements, whereas judgment selection would certainly include them in the sample. A study of the steel industry would be questionable if the United States Steel Corporation were not included in the sample. Similarly, without General Motors in the sample, a survey of the automobile industry would be equally unsatisfactory.

Judgment sampling is sometimes used because we must keep the size of the sample small: it may be difficult to locate some of the sampling units or necessary to keep sampling costs down. In such situations, probability sampling becomes impractical because wide confidence intervals are attached to small random samples. Thus the sample estimates, though unbiased and measurable, are of little value in decision making.

Again, in solving everyday business problems and making public policy decisions, executives and public officials are often pressed for time and cannot wait for probability sampling designs. Judgment sampling is then the only practical method, since estimates can be made available quickly that will enable businessmen and governmental officials to arrive at solutions to their urgent problems that are better than decisions made without any statistical data. And again, when we want to study some unknown traits of a population, some of whose characteristics are known, we may then stratify the population according to these known properties and select sampling units from each stratum on the basis of judgment. This method is used to obtain a more representative sample. Its justification lies in the assumption that such a sample is more representative with respect to the unknown characteristics of that population.

Finally, judgment sampling may be used to conduct pilot studies. It has been mentioned that, in order to have effective stratification, knowledge of the population traits is essential. Pilot studies are one way of getting this desired information. Judgment samples, like pilot studies, are then merely exploratory surveys made before other sampling designs, such as stratified sampling, are adopted.

In any case, the reliability of sample results in judgment sampling depends on the quality of the sampler's expert knowledge or judgment. If it is good and is carefully and skillfully applied, judgment samples may be expected to be representative and to yield valuable results. On the other hand, when a sample is obtained with poor judgment, serious biases will be present.

10A-10 QUOTA SAMPLING

Under the procedure known as *quota sampling* each interviewer is given a quota—a certain number of persons—to be interviewed. The interviewers are often instructed to distribute their interviews among the individuals within their quotas in accordance with some specified characteristics, such as so many in each of several income groups, so many in each race, so many with certain political or religious affiliations, and so on. One important reason for employing quota smpling is to obtain some of the merits of stratification at lower costs. More often than not, however, in the selection of sampling units an interviewer's judgment becomes the overriding factor. Interviewers often tend to interview better-educated or neatly dressed persons, or to question anyone who happens to be at home, or to ignore those sampling units who are not readily accessible. As a consequence, a quota sample actually depends on the interviewer's judgment and convenience. Because results always contain unknown biases, the sample cannot be treated as a random variable.

Quota sampling is widely used in public opinion studies. It occasionally produces satisfactory results if the interviewers are carefully trained and if they follow their instructions closely. More often, however, the satisfactory results obtained by quota sampling are due to the "success by gratuity of the universe," which means a lack of correlation between the selection of elements and the characteristics under study. In other words, quota sampling is sometimes successful because of the chance circumstance that certain traits of individuals that induce interviewers to include those individuals in the sample have no relationship whatsoever to the traits being investigated.

10A-11 CONVENIENCE SAMPLING

The method of *convenience sampling* is also called the *chunk*. A chunk is a fraction of the population taken for investigation because of its convenient availability. Thus, a chunk is selected neither by probability nor by judgment but by convenience. A sample obtained from readily available lists, such as telephone directories or automobile registrations, is a convenience sample and not a random sample, even if the sample is drawn at random from the lists. Failure to recognize this difference often leads samplers astray.

A chunk—which is merely a convenient slice of the universe—can hardly be representative of the population. Its results are usually greatly biased and unsatisfactory. Formerly, the chunk was frequently used in public opinion survey when interviewers stopped near the railroad station or the bus depot or in front of office buildings to interview people. Today, accountants still use convenience sampling to analyze or audit accounts. Their practice is to take for analysis a small slice of, say accounts payable, in some convenient manner, such as all accounts under the letter "L," to verify the total population, say, of all accounts payable of the firm.

Finally, it may be mentioned that convenience sampling is useful in making pilot studies. Questions may be tested and preliminary information may be obtained by the chunk before the final sampling design is decided upon.

11 Classical Theory of Estimation

11.1 INTRODUCTION

We have learned that sampling distributions can aid us to make probabilistic statements about unknown sample results from our knowledge of known populations. Such a process illustrates the method of deduction—the logical procedure of reasoning from the universal to the particular. In the application of sampling distributions, however, we do just the reverse. Namely, the purpose of sampling is to use the known sample results to draw conclusions about populations that are unknown. Now, the process illustrates the method of induction—the logical procedure of reasoning from the particular to the universal. Generalizations about unknown population properties on the basis of sample information made available, as we have stated many times before, are called statistical inference or inductive statistics.

Classical inferential procedures embrace two theories. One is called *estimation,* whereby we use a realized value of a sample statistic to guess about the unknown value of the corresponding parameter; the other, *hypothesis testing,* whereby we use sample result to assess whether an assumed value of a parameter (a hypothesis) is tenable or otherwise. It may be stressed at the very outset that both theories are decision oriented. As we shall see that estimation does not end with an estimate of parameter value and that testing does not end with a conclusion of rejecting or not rejecting a hypothesis. Instead, the ultimate objective of both methods is to make a decision with the result or conclusion in estimation or testing. The classical theory of estimation is the subject matter of this chapter and that of testing will be taken up in the next two chapters.

An obvious but important fact about estimation is that we may be wrong no matter how we go about it. Owing to random variations in sampling, we could never expect a sample result to be the same as the corresponding parameter and a sample result will occasionally misrepresent the parameter by a serious amount. Hence, the best we can hope for is an uncertain conclusion about the unknown but constant parameter.

The uncertainties and inaccuracies inherent in estimation can be held to low levels, however, which makes estimation an invaluable tool in scientific investigation, public policy formulations, and business decision making. Medical scientists and health authorities may wish to estimate the effectiveness of a new drug, the number of people having a certain kind of illness, the need for more physicians in different geographical regions, and so on. Estimates of the effects of closing income-tax loopholes on investment, of average and marginal propensities to consume, of population growth, of productivity changes, of the amount of inflation, and of the elasticity of demand for various commodities are needed by economists for theoretical studies or policy recommendations.

From time to time the federal government requires estimates about the level of unemployment, the number of poor families, crop yields, levels of imports and exports, and so on, in order to make economic policy. When considering new legislation, legislators may call for estimates of waste in defense programs, of housing shortages, of proportions of state or city revenues devoted to welfare, of numbers of immigrants from different countries, of voters' preferences on various issues, and the like.

Business and manufacturing executives constantly call for estimates of one kind or another, whether for day-to-day operations or long-range planning. A sales manager may wish to estimate weekly demands for products in order to establish inventory policies. A marketing expert may wish to estimate the difference in sales increases resulting from two different advertising programs. A production manager may need frequent estimates of the fraction defective in the output of a factory. Financial estimates, such as future sales, revenues, costs, or returns on possible investments, are required by management for a variety of reasons.

When an estimate is required for whatever reason, there are available two kinds of estimation: point estimation and interval estimation. A consumer survey, for example, may show that 25% of those in the sample indicate preference for a certain new product. We can then use this observed value of $\bar{p} = 0.25$ as a *point estimate* for π. We may, if we wish, also construct an interval with the Gaussian rule and the point estimate to produce an *interval estimate* such that "π is between 0.22 and 0.28 with a "confidence" of, say, 0.99." The specific values such as 0.25 and from 0.22 to 0.28 are called *estimates*. The formula employed to compute an estimate is called an *estimator,* which is identical with a statistic. The whole process of using an estimator to calculate an estimate from a sample is called *estimation*.

11.2   POINT ESTIMATION

The Nature of Point Estimation

As we have just seen, a *point estimate* is simply a realized value of a sample statistic, or of an estimator. From this point on, we shall use $\hat{\theta}$ as a general notation for an estimator and θ as that of a population parameter. It may seem obvious that we should use the sample mean to estimate the population mean or the sample proportion to estimate the population proportion. That is, we often estimate a parameter by using the obviously analogous statistic. But exceptions may arise too. For instance, we usually use S^2 to estimate σ^2, but the denominator of S^2 is $(n - 1)$. The obvious analogous statistic would have n in the denominator and, hence, our formula for S^2 departs slightly from the obvious analogous statistic.

Both estimation and testing are considered classical decision procedures. To illustrate how a point estimate can aid us to make decisions, let us consider an example. Hashemoto, Inc., is a firm manufacturing parts of TV sets. The company has been asked by a TV set producer to submit a bid for 25,000 units of a new design of color picture tubes with detailed specifications. To decide on the amount of the bid, the company's cost analyst and chief engineer have arrived at the following conclusions after careful study. First, undertaking the project requires a fixed set-up cost of $12,000. Second, there will be a variable cost of $30 for materials per unit plus $5 per hour of production time. Third, the production time is a random variable whose mean μ is unknown since the design of the picture tube is completely new. In any event, using μ as the true average time per unit of production, the total cost function can be expressed as follows:

$$TC = \$12{,}000 + 25{,}000(\$30 + \$5\mu).$$

The cost analyst and chief engineer consider that 15% of the total production cost would be a reasonable figure to cover profits and other possible contingencies. Therefore, Hashemoto, Inc. should submit its bid with the following amount:

$$\text{Amount of bid} = 1.15[(\$12{,}000 + 25{,}000(\$30 + \$5\mu)].$$

Thus, if the company knows μ, then the decision on the amount to bid can readily be made. However, μ is unknown, and the best that can be done is to have an estimate for it. As we shall see immediately, a good estimator for μ is $\bar{X}$. Now, suppose Hashemoto, Inc. has actually made a trial run and found the mean time required to produce a single unit of the picture tubes to be eight hours. That is, $\bar{x} = 8$. Using 8 as an estimate for μ, we have

$$\text{Amount of bid} = 1.15[\$12{,}000 + 25{,}000(\$30 + (\$5)(8)]$$

$$= \$2{,}026{,}300.$$

According to the decision function then, Hashemoto, Inc. should submit its bid in the amount just obtained.

In any event, point estimation is a very useful procedure in decision making, and the formulas for point estimation (the estimators) are usually quite simple. There are, nevertheless, three important questions to be considered about estimators. First, what is a good estimator? Second, how can good estimators be found? Third, what is the rationale behind point estimation?

To the first question, the answer is that a good estimator should possess all, or nearly all, of the following desirable characteristics: unbiasedness, consistency, efficiency, and sufficiency. These four characteristics are not listed in order of importance; no one of them is always more important than the other three. We try to get all four characteristics, but we often have to settle for compromises wherein the estimators do not fully possess all four characteristics. These compromises mean that there are many situations wherein the choice of an estimator is somewhat judgmental, not being entirely dictated by crisp and precise mathematical theorems. We hope that this situation is surprising to you. In the middle of a rather long book about a mathematical subject, we have to admit that statistical formulas are not always strictly determined by mathematics. There is some room for personal preferences! We next explain what the four desirable characteristics are.

Desirable Properties of point Estimators

Unbiasedness

An estimator, being a random variable, is capable of assuming many possible values, while a parameter is an unknown but is constant. Obviously, any estimate will vary randomly from the value of a parameter. It is, however, reasonable to ask whether the average of all possible values of an estimator is equal to the value of a parameter in the long run. This leads us to the definition of unbiasedness: An *estimator* $\hat{\theta}$ is said to be an *unbiased estimator* for θ if the expected value of $\hat{\theta}$ is equal to θ. That is, if $\hat{\theta}$ is unbiased, then

$$E(\hat{\theta}) = \theta.$$

From this definition, we see that if an estimator is biased, then the bias must be the quantity

$$|E(\hat{\theta}) - \theta|.$$

Recall from our discussions in the previous chapter that $E(\bar{X}) = \mu$, $E(\bar{P}) = \pi$, $E(\Delta\bar{X}) = \Delta\mu$, and $E(\Delta\bar{P}) = \Delta\pi$. Thus, $\bar{X}$, $\bar{P}$, $\Delta\bar{X}$, and $\Delta\bar{P}$ are unbiased estimators for μ, π, $\Delta\mu$, and $\Delta\pi$, respectively. Also, for an unconditional SRS, $E(S^2) = \sigma^2$. However, it can be shown that if sampling is made without replacement, then

$$E(S^2) = \left(\frac{N}{N-1}\right)\sigma^2 \neq \sigma^2.$$

except for $N = \infty$. Thus S^2 is a biased estimator for σ^2 with conditional SRSs. It can be proved too that $E(S) \neq \sigma$ for both kinds of SRS, so S is ordinarily a biased estimator for σ. It is interesting to observe that for an unconditional SRS, $E(S^2) = \sigma^2$ whereas $E(S) \neq \sigma$. This discovery clearly violates common sense. Taking the square root introduces bias. The moral here is that expectations are tricky and often do not behave in accordance with our intuitions.

It is best for an estimator to be unbiased. However, small amounts of bias are acceptable if the estimator has other desirable properties. The only unacceptable situation is a large amount of bias. A detailed examination of the amounts of bias in the estimators just mentioned is beyond the scope of this book, but such examinations can be made. They show that, for most practical situations, the amounts of bias are small enough to be unimportant. One cannot count on this for every estimator of every possible parameter; estimators must be examined for bias and shown to have little or no bias before they are acceptable.

In general, there are three kinds of bias. First, there is *selection bias*, which arises from the injection of personal judgment into the drawing of the sample. Bias of this kind evidently does not exist with simple random sampling. The second kind of bias is called *frame bias* and is produced by the difference that exists between the frame and the population. This type of bias can be eliminated or reduced to a great extent by preparing the frame with extreme care or by thorough examination to establish that a ready-made frame really is a good representation of the corresponding population. Finally, we have what is called *mathematical bias,* which is due solely to the mathematical characteristics of the formula used to estimate the parameter. This kind of bias is our major focus, because many estimators are mathematically biased. Fortunately, mathematical bias is usually quite small. Furthermore, mathematical bias can often be eliminated by minor adjustment, such as by computing S^2 with $(n - 1)$ as the denominator instead of n; or it may become negligibly small as n increases. For example, had we computed the variance with n as the denominator and denote it as $\hat{S}^2$, we would have

$$E(\hat{S}^2) = E\left[\frac{1}{n} \sum (x - \bar{X})^2\right] = E\left(\frac{n-1}{n} S^2\right) = \left(\frac{n-1}{n}\right)\sigma^2 = \sigma^2 - \frac{\sigma^2}{n}.$$

The bias here is the quantity $(-\sigma^2/n)$. This negative bias, however, will vanish as n approaches infinity. Owing to this property, $\hat{S}^2$ is said to be an asymptotically unbiased estimator for σ^2. In general, $\hat{\theta}$ is said to be an *asymptotically unbiased estimator* for θ if

$$\lim_{n \to \infty} E(\hat{\theta}) = \theta.$$

Thus, mathematical bias is not particularly damaging by itself especially if it is small and if the mathematically biased estimator possesses other desirable properties.

Consistency

Even though an estimate is usually not identical with the parameter being estimated because of sampling error, which is the difference $|\hat{\theta} - \theta|$, we do expect a good estimator to produce estimates that are close to the parameter or at least have a high probability of being close. In other words, a good estimator should possess the property of *consistency*, which means that we can make the probability that an estimator differs from the actual value of a parameter by more than any specific quantity as small as we wish by increasing the sample size sufficiently. Thus, given some arbitrarily selected constant $\varepsilon > 0$, to be consistent the estimator $\hat{\theta}$ must satisfy

$$P(|\hat{\theta} - \theta| > \varepsilon) \to 0 \qquad \text{as } n \to \infty.$$

Clearly, by this criterion we see that all statistics brought up in the last chapter are consistent estimators.

At this point, it is interesting to pose this question: Is the sample median just as good as the sample mean as an estimator of μ as far as unbiasedness and consistency are concerned? The answer is yes if the population is symmetric, since then $\tilde{x}_{.5} = \mu$. The answer is no if the population is skewed, since then $\tilde{x}_{.5} \neq \mu$. For a skewed population, and when the sample size increases without limit, the sample mean will approach μ in value and the sample median will approach $\tilde{x}_{.5}$ in value, but $\tilde{x}_{.5} \neq \mu$. Hence, the sample mean is a consistent estimator of μ, but the sample median sometimes is not. In this connection we say that the sample mean is a better estimator of μ than the sample median in terms of both unbiasedness and consistency.

Efficiency

An estimator $\hat{\theta}_1$ is said to be *more efficient* than another estimator $\hat{\theta}_2$ for θ if the former has a smaller variance than the latter. This property seems to be an intuitively clear concept. Obviously, the smaller the variance of an estimator, the more concentrated is the distribution of the estimator around its own mean, and, therefore, the better is the estimator provided that its mean equals the parameter.

A good illustration of relative efficiency in estimators is the estimation of μ by the sample mean and the sample median. If the population is normally distributed, then both $\bar{X}$ and $X_{.5}$ are unbiased and consistent estimators of μ. Yet we claim that the sample mean is better than the sample median as an estimator of μ. This claim is made on grounds of efficiency. We know that $V(\bar{X}) = \sigma^2/n$ and that $V(X_{.5}) \doteq 1.57080\sigma^2/n$. These indicate that $V(\bar{X}) \doteq 0.64V(X_{.5})$ and that the sample mean is more efficient than the sample median as an estimator of μ.

If one estimator can be more efficient than another, it seems reasonable to think of an estimator that is *most efficient* for the parameter being estimated. The most efficient estimator, in terms of our understanding of relative efficiency, must possess variance as small as possible. That is, we think of the most efficient estimator $\hat{\theta}$ as a *minimum-covariance estimator* such that

$$E\{[\hat{\theta} - E(\hat{\theta})]^2\} < E\{[\hat{\theta}^* - E(\hat{\theta}^*)]^2\},$$

where $\hat{\theta}^*$ is any other estimator of θ.

The lower bound of the variance of an estimator can be found by what is called the Cramer–Rao inequality. It states that, for example, under suitable but reasonable conditions, if $\hat{\theta}$ is an estimator of μ, then the variance of $\hat{\theta}$ cannot be less than σ^2/n—that is, $V(\hat{\theta}) \geq \sigma^2/n$. Here, $\hat{\theta}$ could be the sample mean, the sample median, or some other sample statistic. Whatever it is, its variance has a lower bound of σ^2/n. We know that $V(\bar{X}) = \sigma^2/n$. Thus, besides being unbiased and consistent, the sample mean is a minimum-variance estimator of μ.

Sufficiency

Sufficiency is a rather difficult concept. Intuitively, we say that an estimator is a *sufficient estimator,* or a *sufficient statistic,* if it conveys as much sample information as possible about the parameter that no additional information will be supplied by any other estimator calculated from the same sample, and, if the value of a sufficient statistic is obtained, the sample values themselves do not provide further information about the parameter.

For example, we usually consider the sample mean as an excellent choice for estimating μ. However, the sample mean is but one of the many reasonable statistics that might be employed to estimate μ. To mention just three, the sample median, the average of the maximum and minimum values in the sample, and the average of the first and third quartiles of the sample could be used. It can be shown that each of these three statistics might be better than the sample mean to estimate μ in special cases. Yet, we insist that $\bar{X}$ is generally better than any one of the three statistics just mentioned, since none of them has used all the information in the sample and, therefore, none is a sufficient statistic for μ.

Alternatively, we note that the computation of a sample statistic is essentially a process of reducing the sample data. As such it is desirable to reduce sample data as far as possible without losing any pertinent information. It can be proved that no pertinent information is lost when reducing sample data to $\bar{X}$ or $\bar{P}$, so $\bar{X} = \hat{\mu}$ and $\bar{P} = \hat{\pi}$ are sufficient statistics. It may be mentioned in passing that there are many problems in estimation for which sufficient statistics do not exist.

Having established the desirable properties of a good estimator, we next look for methods that might generate good estimators. We must note at this time no known method of estimation can produce estimators with all of the desirable properties all of the time. We shall be concerned with only the two most frequently used methods: the method of maximum likelihood and the method of least squares. The first will be introduced in the following section and the second in a later chapter. Sometimes the two methods produce exactly the same estimators; sometimes they do not.

11.3 THE METHOD OF MAXIMUM LIKELIHOOD

This method of estimation is based on the notion that different values of a parameter in a population tend to generate different samples. Hence any sample may be more likely to have been drawn from some parameter values than from others. It seems reasonable, then, to select that value from among all the possible values of a parameter that makes the probability of obtaining the particular value of the empirical evidence that has been observed as large as possible. Let us bring out the underlying logic of the method of maximum likelihood more vividly via an example.

After taking a sample of ten professors with replacement at a certain college, we find three to be in favor of organizing a faculty union. Given this sample result, we would like to know: Should we believe that the population proportion is 0.0, 0.1, 0.2, ..., 0.9, or 1.0? (There are other possible values of π, but these suffice to introduce the example.)

To answer this question, we note that the sample proportion in this case is a binomial variable. If the true proportion π is, say, 0.1, then we would have

$$P(\bar{P} = 0.3 \mid \pi = 0.1) = \binom{10}{3}(0.1)^3(0.9)^7$$

$$\doteq 0.0574.$$

If the true proportion is, say, 0.2, then we have

$$P(\bar{P} = 0.3 \mid \pi = 0.2) = \binom{10}{3}(0.2)^3(0.8)^7$$

$$\doteq 0.2013.$$

Similarly, we can compute the probability that the sample proportion is 0.3 given any other possible value of π specified in the query. These probabilities are as tabulated below.

Value of π	$P(\bar{P} = 0.3)$	Value of π	$P(\bar{P} = 0.3)$
0.0	0.0000	0.6	0.0425
0.1	0.0574	0.7	0.0090
0.2	0.2013	0.9	0.0008
0.3	0.2668	0.9	0.0000
0.4	0.2150	1.0	0.0000
0.5	0.1172		

Note that $\pi = 0$ and $\pi = 1$ are both impossible, since the sample has some professors favoring the union (ruling out $\pi = 0$) and some not favoring the union (ruling out $\pi = 1$).

Now, if we think that the true proportion can assume any value between 0 and 1 instead of just those given above, we are thinking of

the function

$$L(x) = P(\bar{P} = 0.3 \mid \pi = x),$$

that is defined for all x's satisfying the inequality $0 \leqslant x \leqslant 1$ as the *likelihood function* for π and the observed sample result $\bar{p} = 0.3$ with $n = 10$. Here, x is a population proportion, not a sample number of successes. This function, a conditional one, gives the probability of a particular sample result given each and every one of the possible values of the parameter. We may graph this function by plotting the values shown above and connecting them by a smooth curve. In doing so we obtain what is called the *likelihood curve* for π with $\bar{p} = 0.3$ and $n = 10$, as portrayed by Figure 11.1.

With results as above, the question is which value of π makes the observed sample outcome most likely. We would choose the value which makes the probability $P(\bar{p} = 0.3)$ as high as possible. This value, according to our previous calculations, is $\pi = 0.3$. We are led to the following conclusion: In our sample of ten we found that three were in favor of the organization of a faculty union; among all possible values of π, the value $\pi = 0.3$ makes this empirical evidence most likely; we therefore estimate π to be 0.3. Having done this, we have found a *maximum likelihood estimate* of π. Note that the *maximum likelihood estimator* of π is simply the sample proportion $\bar{P}$.

Thus, the *maximum likelihood estimator*, MLE, of a parameter for a given sample is the value of the parameter that maximizes the probability (or probability density) of the sample. If the sample is a simple random sample, taken from a population $f(x; \theta)$, the probability of the sample is given by the likelihood function:

$$L(\theta) = f(x_1 \mid \theta)f(x_2 \mid \theta)\ldots f(x_n \mid \theta).$$

Thus, the maximum likelihood estimate is found to be the value of θ that maximizes $L(\theta)$.

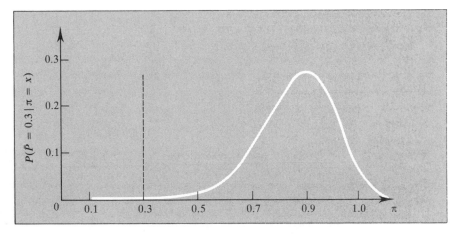

FIGURE 11.1 The likelihood curve for π with $\bar{p} = 0.30$.

It may be noted that $\bar{X}$, $\bar{P}$, and $\hat{S}^2$—are maximum likelihood estimators. This method may not always generate unbiased estimators, but they are usually consistent, efficient, and sufficient. This method is important not only because it provides an easy way of generating estimators with many desirable properties, but also because it furnishes a general framework for inferences. A theoretical proposition, or an assumption about a state of nature, is plausible to the extent that it accords well with empirical evidence—that is, it assigns high probabilities to those sample results that actually occur. Many inferential procedures, as we shall see, are directly or indirectly involved with the principle of maximum likelihood.

It is interesting to note that the principle of maximum likelihood also provides a rational for point estimation. By using a maximum likelihood estimator, MLE, to calculate an estimate for a parameter, we have in effect maximized the probability of correctly estimating the value of the parameter.

11.4 INTERVAL ESTIMATION

Given a point estimator and the method of generating it, we may know whether the estimator possess some or all of the desirable properties. This knowledge, however, is not complete for the purpose of using $\hat{\theta}$ to replace θ, since there is always an error in estimation owing to random fluctuations in the estimates. It is desirable to have a measure of "precision"—the size of the sampling error—attached to the estimator.

The basic characteristics of the distribution of $\hat{\theta}$ are its expectation and variance, defined in the usual fashion. The (positive) square root of $V(\hat{\theta})$ is the standard error of $\hat{\theta}$, denoted as $\sigma_{\hat{\theta}}$, and it measures the dispersion of $\hat{\theta}$. When $\sigma_{\hat{\theta}}$ is small and $\hat{\theta}$ is unbiased, a large proportion of estimates will lie within a small range from the true value of the parameter; when $\sigma_{\hat{\theta}}$ is large and $\hat{\theta}$ is unbiased, a small proportion of estimates will lie within a small range from the true value of the parameter. Consequently, the *precision* of an unbiased estimator is measured by the standard error of the estimator; that is, the smaller $\sigma_{\hat{\theta}}$ is, the more precise is the estimator, or the smaller is the smpling error in replacing θ by $\hat{\theta}$. If $\hat{\theta}$ is biased, its precision is measured by $E[(\hat{\theta} - \theta)^2]$ instead of $E\{[\hat{\theta} - E(\hat{\theta})]^2\}$. It is then good practice whenever an estimate is reported, to give the standard error of the estimate also. If, for some reason, a more formal statement on the estimate and its precision is required, we may construct what is called an "interval estimate".

In this section, we provide a general statement of interval estimation and restrict ourselves to cases where the sampling distributions of the statistics are normal. (Other cases will be covered in more advanced material in later chapters.) The general description of a *confidence interval,* as given in Theorem 11.1, will then be applied to a few specific situations.

THEOREM 11.1 CONFIDENCE LIMITS *In a sample space with sample sample-points, if the statistic $\hat{\theta}$ is normally distributed with* $E(\hat{\theta}) = \theta$ *and standard error* $\sigma_{\hat{\theta}}$, *if* z_c *and* $1 - \alpha$ *are such that* $P(|\hat{\theta} - \theta| < z_c\sigma_{\hat{\theta}}) = 1 - \alpha$, *and if L and U are the* lower *and* upper confidence limits, *respectively, defined as*

$$L, U = \hat{\theta} \mp z_c\sigma_{\hat{\theta}}, \tag{11.1}$$

then for any sample result, the symmetric $1 - \alpha$ *confidence interval is* (L, U) *such that* $P(L < \theta < U) = 1 - \alpha$ *in the sample space.*

Let us first take note of the fact that a confidence interval for a parameter is constructed with the following four quantities:

$\hat{\theta}$ The sample statistic or the point estimator,

$\sigma_{\hat{\theta}}$ The standard error of the estimator,

z_c A *confidence coefficient,* or a *critical value,* or a *confidence multiplier* that is a specific value of Z, *and*

$1 - \alpha$ A *confidence probability,* which is called the *degree of confidence* or the *level of confidence.*

The theorem implies that *interval estimation* refers to the estimation of a parameter by a *random interval* whose endpoints L and U are functions of observed random variables such that the probability that the inequality $L < \theta < U$ is satisfied and which is expressed in terms of a predetermined number $1 - \alpha$. Alternatively, we say that L and U are *random endpoints* since their values depend upon that of $\hat{\theta}$, which is a random variable.

Very often, the level of confidence is set at 0.95 or 0.99. When $1 - \alpha = 0.95$, the corresponding value of $z_c = 1.96$, and the result of applying (11.1) produces a 95% confidence interval. When $1 - \alpha = 0.99$, we have $z_c = 2.58$, and the application of (11.1) yields a 99% confidence interval. Of course, if it is desired, confidence intervals with other degrees of confidence, such as 0.90, 0.98, etc., can also be calculated. In such cases, the appropriate z_c values can be found from the table for $N(0, 1)$.

Finally, the minus-plus sign ($\mp$) in (11.1) means that, when we compute L the minus sign is used, and that when we compute U the plus sign is used. More explicitly, we have

$$L = \hat{\theta} - z_c\sigma_{\hat{\theta}}, \quad \text{the lower confidence limit;}$$

$$U = \hat{\theta} + z_c\sigma_{\hat{\theta}}, \quad \text{the upper confidence limit.}$$

To illustrate the application of (11.1), let us use the case portrayed by Figure 11.2. This figure shows that the distribution of the estimator $\hat{\theta}$ is normal with $E(\hat{\theta}) = \theta$. Each dot under the density curve for $\hat{\theta}$ is thought of as a possible value of the estimator, or a group of estimates of equal values. The horizontal scale measures the value of $\hat{\theta}$, and the

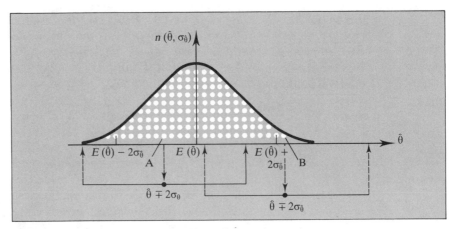

FIGURE 11.2 Illustration of 95.45% confidence intervals.

vertical scale measures the probability densities associated with these values. Now, if we wish to construct, say, a 95.45% interval estimate for θ, then $z_c = 2$. Clearly, if $\hat{\theta}$ assumes a value represented by any dot within the limits of $E(\hat{\theta}) \mp 2\sigma_{\hat{\theta}}$, then the interval will cover θ, which is identical with $E(\hat{\theta})$. See, for example, the interval constructed with the dot identified as A. Since $E(\hat{\theta}) \mp 2\sigma_{\hat{\theta}}$ includes 95.45% of the values of $\hat{\theta}$, we know that on the average, or in the long run, 95.45% of the time intervals of the size $\hat{\theta} \mp 2\sigma_{\hat{\theta}}$ will include θ, the parameter being estimated. If $\hat{\theta}$ happens to be one of the extreme values that are outside of the interval of two standard errors from the expectation, then the interval $\hat{\theta} \mp 2\sigma_{\hat{\theta}}$ will not include θ. See, for example, the confidence interval constructed from the dot identified as B. However, $\hat{\theta}$ deviates from its expectation by two standard errors or more at most 4.55% of the time. This means that if we set $1 - \alpha = 0.9545$ in estimating θ we would have a 95.45% confidence interval. We can easily make similar demonstrations and statements for confidence intervals by using Figure 11.2 in the same fashion.

Let us now make more explicit interpretations of interval estimation. The classical statisticians interpret a confidence interval in this way. If samples of the same size were repeatedly drawn from the same population, and if a confidence interval were computed with the same level of confidence for each sample, then in the long run the relative frequency of those intervals that included the parameter would approach $1 - \alpha$ as a limit. However, this classical probability concept for the interpretation of confidence intervals has been attacked by many Bayesians as the most disputed technical concept of modern statistics. This criticism perhaps rests on the fact that, in reality, we only construct a single confidence interval for estimation. When the interval is constructed, all the values for computing L and U become constants and the interval is no longer a random variable. No probability (except 0 or 1) can be attached to a realized interval for the inclusion of the parameter. It either does or it does not. And we do not know which, since the parameter is unknown.

Because of this criticism, an outstanding statistician, Nerzey

Neyman, introduced in 1937 the notion of *confidence* as an alternative to the concept of probability so far as interval estimation is concerned. With this alternate concept, we call an interval estimation a *confidence interval* instead of a *probability interval*. Thus, even though a single interval is constructed with $1 - \alpha$, we may not know whether or not it covers the parameter being estimated; we have, nevertheless, a level of confidence of $1 - \alpha$ that it will. Furthermore, if the level of confidence is 0.95, we do know that if the same estimation function is employed for various samples of the same size, 95% of the intervals will cover the parameter and 5% of them will not. If we can be correct 95% or 99% of the time, we can ordinarily behave as if each of our intervals covered the parameter. This may be properly called *inductive behavior*.

In concluding this section, let us point out an obvious fact. We generally prefer a shorter than a wider confidence interval, since the shorter the interval the more precise is our estimate. However, when n is fixed, the level of confidence and the degree of precision vary inversely. If we insist upon a given width of the interval and a given level of confidence, the size of the sample must be allowed to vary. As will be shown in the last section of this chapter, methods are available to determine the proper sample size that satisfies simultaneously any specified degree of precision and level of confidence.

11.5 CONFIDENCE INTERVALS FOR μ

When we need to compute an interval estimate for an unknown but constant population mean under the condition that the population standard deviation is known and that the distribution of $\bar{X}$ is normal or approximately so, we can use (11.1) to determine the confidence limits in the following way:

$$L, U = \bar{X} \mp z_c \sigma_{\bar{X}}. \tag{11.2}$$

If the population standard deviation is unknown, we can replace $\sigma_{\bar{X}}$ by $S_{\bar{X}}$ in (11.2) and obtain

$$L, U = \bar{X} \mp z_c S_{\bar{X}}. \tag{11.3}$$

The application of both (11.2) and (11.3) requires that the sizes of the sample must satisfy the rules of thumb stated in the previous chapter in connection with our discussion on the distributions of $\bar{X}$.

As an example of interval estimation for μ, let us consider this problem. A new machine process has been adjusted to fill cooked pork beans into cans. More than 100,000 cans are filled during the first day. A sample of $n = 100$ drawn from these filled cans yields the following data: $\bar{x} = 1.98$ pounds and $s = 0.32$ pound. In view of these sample results, what are the 95% and 99% confidence limits for μ?

Even though σ is unknown here, n is large enough for the distribution of means to be approximately normal. Thus, by (11.3), we have the 95% confidence interval for μ as

$$1.98 \mp 1.96\left(\frac{0.32}{\sqrt{100}}\right) \doteq 1.917 \text{ to } 2.043,$$

or

$$1.917 < \mu < 2.043.$$

The 99% confidence interval for μ, by (11.3) again, is

$$1.98 \mp 2.58\left(\frac{0.32}{\sqrt{100}}\right) \doteq 1.897, \text{ to } 2.063,$$

or

$$1.897 < \mu < 2.063.$$

It is important to take note of the fact once more that, given the same sample information, the 95% interval estimate is shorter, or more precise, than the 99% interval estimate. Thus, when n is fixed, in the process of gaining greater assurance (higher level of confidence), we have to sacrifice some precision in estimation.

Now, as an example of using interval estimation as a decision procedure, let us consider our current illustration again. Suppose the factory wants to fill the cans with a mean $\mu = 2$ pounds with a minimum mean weight in the cans of 1.95 pounds, so that the customers will get full value, and with a maximum mean weight in the cans of 2.05 pounds, so that calculated profits will not be reduced. What decisions should the factory make so far as the filling process is concerned in view of the previous estimating results?

To answer the question posed, we first note that both intervals contain the specified value of μ. Next, we find that the lower confidence limits in both intervals are less than 1.95 pounds. Finally, even though the upper confidence limit of the 99% confidence interval is slightly greater than the maximum weight specified, that of the 95% confidence interval is slightly less than the specified maximum mean weight. When the factory considers all the information provided, it might reach the conclusion that the machine process is not properly set and it might decide to reset the machine upward slightly or to reduce the variations from can to can somewhat in order meet all its specifications. Of course, another alternative is to take still a larger sample for observation before a final decision is made whether the machine process should be left alone or be reset.

11.6 CONFIDENCE INTERVALS FOR π

We know that distributions of $\bar{P}$ are asymptotically normal with $E(\bar{P}) = \pi$ and $\sigma_{\bar{P}} = \sqrt{\pi\pi'/n}$. If we know the value of π of the dichotomous population, we can construct an interval estimate for π, as suggested by (11.1), as follows:

$$L,U = \bar{P} \mp z_c \sigma_{\bar{P}}. \qquad (11.4)$$

With a moment's reflection you should realize that (11.4) cannot be used to construct a confidence interval for π in practice, since π is unknown, which amounts to the fact that the standard error of $\bar{P}$ is unknown. If π were known, of course, we would not need to estimate it. However, (11.4) does serve an important purpose, which will be taken up later, for the determination of the required sample size in estimating π.

Since we do not know the value of π, which amounts to not knowing $\sigma_{\bar{P}}$, we use an estimate of π to compute the standard error of π. Then the confidence limits for π are given by the formula

$$L,U = \bar{P} \mp z_c S_{\bar{P}} \qquad (11.5)$$

where $S_{\bar{P}}$ is a slightly biased estimator for $\sigma_{\bar{P}}$ and is defined as

$$S_{\bar{P}} = \sqrt{\frac{\bar{P}(\bar{P}')}{n}} \qquad \text{for an unconditional SRS;}$$

and as

$$S_{\bar{P}} = \sqrt{\frac{\bar{P}(\bar{P}')}{n}} \sqrt{\frac{N-n}{N-1}}, \qquad \text{for a conditional SRS.}$$

Confidence limits defined by (11.5) require a large sample size. Intuitively, we can see that the more the sample proportion deviates from 0.5, the larger n should be. W. G. Cochran has given us working rules on this point as presented in Table 11.1. According to this table, for example, if $\bar{P} = 0.1$, the sample size should be at least 600 for use of the normal approximation to construct a 95% confidence interval. If a degree of confidence higher than 95% is desired, n must be increased by about 10% over the values shown in Table 11.1.

TABLE 11.1 Guide to Using the Normal Approximation for Confidence Limits for π

If $\bar{p}$ Equals or is Close to	Use Normal Approximation When Constructing a 95% Confidence Interval Only if n is at Least Equal to
0.5	30
0.4 or 0.6	50
0.3 or 0.7	80
0.2 or 0.8	200
0.1 or 0.9	600
0.05 or 0.95	1400

Source: Reprinted, with some modifications, from W. G. Cochran, *Sampling Techniques* (New York: John Wiley & Sons, Inc., 1953), p. 41.

An example is in order. A sample of $n = 500$ has been selected from all the manufacturing firms throughout the United States: 80 of the firms in the sample report that they are planning to increase their investment expenditures during the next two years. What is the 99% confidence interval for π—the proportion of all manufacturing firms in the United States that will increase their investment expenditures? We have, for this problem,

$$\bar{p} = \frac{80}{500} = 0.16$$

and

$$s_{\bar{p}} = \sqrt{\frac{\bar{p}(\bar{p}')}{n}} = \sqrt{\frac{0.16(0.84)}{500}} \doteq 0.0164.$$

With these preliminary calculations, the desired 99% confidence limits become

$$L,U = \bar{p} \mp z_c s_{\bar{p}} = 0.16 \mp 2.58(0.0164) = 0.118 \text{ to } 0.202.$$

Thus, we are 99% confident that the true proportion of American manufacturing firms that will expand their investment expenditures during the next two years would range from 11.8% to 20.2%.

Interval estimation for π can be improved, especially when n is rather small by introducing the CCF of $1/(2n)$ in the determination of the confidence limits. In doing so, we have

$$L = \left(\bar{P} - \frac{1}{2n}\right) - z_c S_{\bar{P}}, \tag{11.6}$$

$$U = \left(\bar{P} + \frac{1}{2n}\right) + z_c S_{\bar{P}}. \tag{11.7}$$

These expressions reduce to (11.5) if n is large. Furthermore, these equations are still approximations, since the relationship between z_c and $1 - \alpha$ is determined under the assumption that $\bar{P}$ is normally distributed, whereas it is actually only approximately normal. However, when $n \leq 200$, equations (11.6) and (11.7) do produce more satisfactory confidence limits for π. As an exercise, you might work out our previous example, using these formulas; you will see that they will yield practically the same results as obtained before by using (11.5).

11.7 CONFIDENCE INTERVALS FOR $\Delta\mu$

When two independent samples have been selected from two different populations, we may, from the realized difference between the two sample means, make some conclusions about the true difference between the two population means by the method of interval estimation. If the standard deviations of both populations are known, the confidence limits for $\Delta\mu$ can be given as

$$L,U = \Delta\bar{X} \mp z_c\sigma_{\Delta\bar{X}}. \qquad (11.8)$$

When the population standard deviations are unknown, we have

$$L,U = \Delta\bar{X} \mp z_c S_{\Delta\bar{X}}, \qquad (11.9)$$

where $S_{\bar{X}}$ is defined as

$$S_{\Delta\bar{X}} = \sqrt{\frac{S_1^2}{n_1} + \frac{S_2^2}{n_2}}.$$

An automobile manufacturing company has recorded observations of two different makes of batteries used in its cars. Forty observations of make A showed a mean life of 32 months. Forty-five observations of make B showed a mean life of 30 months. Past experience indicates that the standard deviations for both makes of batteries are the same—4 months. What are the confidence limits for the true difference in mean life between the two types of batteries with $1 - \alpha = 0.95$?

For this problem, we have $\Delta\bar{x} = \bar{x}_1 - \bar{x}_2 = 32 - 30 = 2$ and

$$\sigma_{\Delta\bar{x}} = \sqrt{\frac{4^2}{40} + \frac{4^2}{45}} \doteq 0.87.$$

From these data, we have

$$L,U \doteq 2 \mp 1.96(0.87) \doteq 0.2948 \text{ to } 3.7052,$$

or

$$0.2948 < \Delta\mu < 3.7052.$$

Suppose we wish to have a greater assurance that the confidence interval we compute actually includes $\Delta\mu$. We may proceed to compute a 99% confidence interval with the same sample data:

$$L,U \doteq 2 \mp 2.58(0.87) \doteq -0.2446 \text{ to } 4.2446,$$

or

$$-0.2446 < \Delta\mu < +4.2446.$$

It is interesting to note that with a level of confidence of 0.95, both the confidence limits are positive, indicating that there is a positive difference between the two population means at that degree of confidence. However, with $1 - \alpha = 0.99$, the lower confidence limit is negative, implying that the interval contains zero as well as some negative and positive values. In other words, we can no longer conclude that $\Delta\mu$ is positive: it could possibly be zero or even negative. A close look at the 99% confidence interval reveals that L is very close to 0 and U is way above zero. These observations lead us to the speculation that there may indeed be a positive difference between the two population means even with $1 - \alpha = 0.99$. If this were the case, larger samples would reveal such a difference more clearly and decisively.

11.8 CONFIDENCE INTERVALS FOR $\Delta\pi$

In this case, if we know the values of π_1 and π_2 of the two dichotomous populations under consideration, then given two independent samples the confidence limits for $\Delta\pi$ can be simply determined by employing (11.1) again in the following manner:

$$L,U = \Delta\bar{P} \mp z_c \sigma_{\Delta\bar{P}}. \tag{11.10}$$

The trouble, as in the case of estimating π, is that to apply (11.10) we must know the values of π_1 and π_2—but if we do know these two values, we do not need to estimate $\Delta\pi$. Again, however, (11.10), just as (11.4), does serve an important function that enables us to determine the appropriate sample size as discussed in the next section. For the time being, we just take note of the fact that confidence limits for $\Delta\pi$ are always computed with estimated standard errors of $\Delta\bar{P}$ as

$$L,U = \Delta\bar{P} \mp z_c S_{\Delta\bar{P}}, \tag{11.11}$$

where

$$S_{\Delta\bar{p}} = \sqrt{\frac{\bar{P}_1(\bar{P}_1')}{n_1} + \frac{\bar{P}_2(\bar{P}_2')}{n_2}}.$$

An economist would like to estimate the true difference between the proportion of Republicans who are in favor of abolishing the corporate profit tax (because it amounts to double taxation) and the proportion of Democrats favoring the same measure. He takes a sample of 500 from each population and finds that 90% of Republicans and 55% of Democrats are in favor of the measure. What is the 99% confidence interval estimate for $\Delta\pi$?

From the statement of the problem, we have

$$\bar{p}_1 = 0.90, \qquad \bar{p}_2 = 0.55, \qquad \Delta\bar{p} = 0.35,$$

and

$$s_{\Delta\bar{P}} = \sqrt{\frac{\bar{p}_1(\bar{p}_1')}{n_1} + \frac{\bar{p}_2(\bar{p}_2')}{n_2}}$$

$$= \sqrt{\frac{0.90(0.10)}{500} + \frac{(0.55)(0.45)}{500}}$$

$$\doteq 0.026.$$

Hence,

$$L, U = 0.35 \mp 2.58(0.026) \doteq 0.283 \text{ to } 0.417.$$

The economist should be 99% confident that the difference between the two population proportions would fall in the interval

$$0.283 < \Delta\pi < 0.417.$$

This result also implies that it is almost a certainty that, proportionally, more Republicans than Democrats are in favor of the abolition of corporate profit tax.

11.9 DETERMINATION OF SAMPLE SIZE

Confidence Interval, Precision, and Sample Size

We have seen that the application of interval estimation is quite simple and straightforward. There is, nevertheless, a fine point that needs further exploration. That is, when the sample size is fixed, the degree of precision varies inversely with the level of confidence. In many decision situations, however, we may find that levels of both precision and confidence are predetermined and required to be satisfied simultaneously. This leads to the consideration of appropriate sample sizes that can meet both objectives. The determination of the sample size is a very important and basic aspect of any sampling plan. After all, if the sample drawn is unnecessarily large, it might turn out to be extremely expensive and wasteful. If the sample selected is too small, the sample result may not be reliable enough for the decision at hand.

The classical solution to this problem is to find the sample size that can satisfy the specified level of confidence and the maximum error in estimation. This is done by specifying the maximum probability that the estimate will be in error more than a given amount. Precisely, in an interval estimate for θ by $\hat{\theta}$, the error in estimation is $\varepsilon = |\hat{\theta} - \theta|$. If $\hat{\theta}$ differs from θ by a maximum amount permitted by the confidence interval, the maximum error must be half of the width of that interval and it must be less than the quantity $z_c \sigma_{\hat{\theta}}$. That is, if we construct, say, a 95% confidence interval for θ, we are 95% certain that $1.96\sigma_{\hat{\theta}} < \varepsilon$. This is the same as saying that

$$P(1.96\sigma_{\hat{\theta}} < \varepsilon) = 0.95.$$

This last interpretation leads us to consider what is called the risk of an interval estimate. Such a *risk* is defined as the probability that the error in estimation will be equal to or greater than $z_c \sigma_{\hat{\theta}}$; that is, risk = $P(\varepsilon \geq z_c \sigma_{\hat{\theta}})$. For example, if $1 - \alpha = 0.95$, then the risk is

$1 - 0.95 = 0.05$, or, in general, the value of α. Here, α is the probability that the estimated parameter will not fall inside of the confidence interval with $1 - \alpha$.

An interesting consequence of the relationship between the error of estimation and the risk in estimation is that it gives us a clue to the determination of the minimum desired sample size that can satisfy simultaneously specified levels of confidence and precision. Also, for the sake of simplicity, we shall ignore the possible effects of the FPCF on the sample size, because such effects are usually so minute as to be of no important consequence.

Determining *n* When Estimating μ

In an interval estimation for μ, the maximum error is

$$\varepsilon = z_c\left(\frac{\sigma}{\sqrt{n}}\right).$$

Solving this for n, we obtain

$$n = \frac{z_c^2\sigma^2}{\varepsilon^2}. \tag{11.12}$$

It may be observed that a difficulty usually arises in the application of (11.12). This springs from the fact that the use of (11.12) requires that the population standard deviation σ be known. However, more often than not, when μ is unknown, σ is also unknown. Three methods have been suggested by various statisticians to overcome this difficulty.

First, if, from our previous experience, the value of σ for a similar population is known, we may use it as the approximate value of σ required for the problem in hand. This is justified because we often find that similar populations may differ to a great extent from each other in terms of means but they may differ only slightly from each other in terms of dispersion. For example, if a new production process has been designed mainly to increase the mean speed, its variability may remain about the same as that of the old process. This being the case, the value of σ for the old process may be used quite satisfactorily as an approximation for that of the new process. Again, income distribution in England may differ by a considerable amount from that of, say, Sweden in terms of their means, but there may be only a small degree of difference in terms of dispersion. If we happen to know the σ of one, it can then be used as that of the other. In this connection, if previous sample surveys have been made with similar populations, the findings of such studies can be used to arrive at an approximation of the σ we need.

Second, if we encounter an entirely new situation, and if data on similar populations, whether parameters or statistics, are not available, we may conduct a small "pilot" study about the population under investigation. The standard deviation of this pilot sample may be used as an approximation for σ.

In the absence of previous data and a feasible pilot study, we may obtain an approximation of the value of σ by employing the Gaussian rule, by which we know that if the population is normally distributed, then $\mu \mp 3\sigma$ will include nearly 100% of the values of the population. This rule should hold approximately if the population has a clear central tendency; that is, if it is reasonably mound-shaped and not extremely skewed. In other words, for such a population, the standard deviation should be approximately 1/6 of its range. Thus, we may use one-sixth of the range of the population values as an educated guess for the value of σ.

As an illustration of the application of (11.12), let us return to the example in Section 11.5 in which a new machine process was adjusted to fill cooked pork beans into cans. For this example, the standard deviation σ is unknown but the sample standard deviation computed from a sample with $n = 100$ is found to be 0.32. Here, n is quite large and the value of s should be a good estimate for σ. Recall also, from the 99% confidence interval constructed before, that the maximum error in estimation is

$$2.58(0.032) = 0.08256.$$

Now, suppose the factory would like to have an interval estimate of the mean weight with $1 - \alpha = 0.99$ and $\varepsilon = 0.05$, what should be the minimum sample size?

By (11.12), using s for σ, we have

$$n = \frac{2.58^2(0.32)^2}{(0.05)^2} \doteq 273.$$

This result means if a sample of $n = 273$ is drawn, the probability is no greater than 0.01 that the error of estimation will be greater than 0.05 pound.

Determining n When Estimating π

From (11.4), we see that the maximum error of estimating π is

$$\varepsilon = z_c \sqrt{\frac{\pi\pi'}{n}}.$$

Solving for n from this expression, we obtain

$$n = \pi\pi'\left(\frac{z_c}{\varepsilon}\right)^2. \tag{11.13}$$

An unfortunate aspect of this result is that we need the value of π, which is unknown, in fact it is what we wish to estimate, in order to determine n. This is actually a more severe difficulty than that of estimating μ when σ is unknown. However, there do exist two

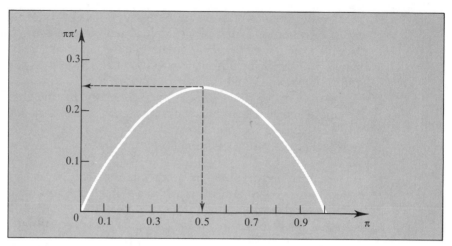

FIGURE 11.3 Illustrating that the maximum value of $\pi\pi'$ is at $\pi = \pi' = 0.5$.

procedures for us to overcome this difficulty. First, if we are completely ignorant of the possible value of π, we may assume $\pi = 0.5$. The logic of this practice, is that the maximum value of $\pi\pi'$ is 0.25 when $\pi = 0.5$. This is portrayed in Figure 11.3. In any event, the use of 0.5 as the value of π assures that the resulting value of n will be large enough to provide the desired precision and degree of confidence. Second, if we know, from whatever information available, that the value of π could possibly fall within some range, then we use the endpoint that is closer to 0.5 to represent π in applying (11.13). For example, if we judge that the value of π may range from, say, 0.20 to 0.30, we use 0.30 as π. Similarly, if we have reason to believe that the value of π cannot be smaller than 0.75 or greater than 0.85, then we use 0.75 to represent π in applying (11.13).

Suppose the producer of a new TV program wishes to ascertain the proportion of all viewers watching TV who are tuned in to his show. He is willing to assume an error of 3 percentage points at a level of confidence of 0.99. How large a sample should be taken?

First, assume $\pi = 0.50$, then by (11.13), we see that

$$n = (0.50)(0.50)\left(\frac{2.58}{0.03}\right)^2 = 1{,}849.$$

This result indicates that if we take a sample of 1,849, the probability is at least 0.99 that the sample proportion will differ from the true value of π by at most 3 percentage points.

Next, suppose the producer knows that, in the past, programs similar to his new show shared approximately 20 to 25% of the TV audience: he may then use 0.25 as the value of π, and the sample size required becomes

$$n = (0.25)(0.75)\left(\frac{2.58}{0.03}\right)^2 \doteq 1{,}387.$$

From the two results just obtained, the common practice of sample surveys of this kind of setting $n = 1{,}600$ seems to be quite appropriate.

Determining n When Estimating $\Delta\mu$

When $\Delta\mu$ is estimated with two sample means computed from two independent samples with n_1 and n_2, respectively, we know from (11.8)

$$\varepsilon = z_c \sqrt{\frac{\sigma_1^2}{n_1} + \frac{\sigma_2^2}{n_2}}.$$

Now, let $n_1 + n_2 = n$, the combined sample size. We may solve the previous expression for n and obtain

$$n(= n_1 + n_2) = z_c^2 \left(\frac{\sigma_1 + \sigma_2}{\varepsilon}\right)^2. \tag{11.14a}$$

Next, to determine n_1 and n_2, we distribute n in the following way:

$$n_1 = \frac{n\sigma_1}{\sigma_1 + \sigma_2} \tag{11.14b}$$

and

$$n_2 = \frac{n\sigma_2}{\sigma_1 + \sigma_2}. \tag{11.14c}$$

When σ_1 and σ_2 are unknown, each of the three procedures established for the case of estimating μ can be employed to guess about the values of σ_1 and σ_2 in the application of these expressions.

For illustration let us return to the example for estimating the possible difference between the mean lives of two different kinds of batteries. In that example, $\sigma_1 = \sigma_2 = 4$ months. With $n_1 = 40$ and $n_2 = 45$, we had the rather inconclusive results that the 95% confidence interval did indicate that $\Delta\mu > 0$, but that the 99% confidence interval did reveal that $\Delta\mu$ might be zero or even negative. We suggested, though, that there might indeed be a positive difference between the mean lives and that this difference might be brought out with larger samples.

Now, suppose the auto company wishes to have a 99% confidence interval estimate for $\Delta\mu$ with a maximum error of 0.8 months. How large should be n, n_1, and n_2? By (11.14), we have

$$n = 2.58^2 \left(\frac{4 + 4}{0.8}\right)^2 = 666;$$

$$n_1 = \frac{666(4)}{4 + 4} = 333;$$

$$n_2 = \frac{666(4)}{4 + 4} = 333.$$

In this case, that $n_1 = n_2$ is clearly due to the fact that $\sigma_1 = \sigma_2$.

Let us change this example slightly. Suppose both makes of batteries are new brands and that the auto company knows neither the means nor the standard deviations of their lifetimes. How should the company go about determining the appropriate sample sizes for the same level of significance and maximum error specified before?

To answer this question, let us consider the samples taken before as pilot studies and suppose that from them we have obtained $s_1 = 4.4$ and $s_2 = 3.8$. Then using these two values for σ_1 and σ_2, respectively, we get

$$n = 2.58^2\left(\frac{4.4 + 3.8}{0.8}\right)^2$$

$$= 699.33803 \doteq 700;$$

$$n_1 = \frac{700(4.4)}{4.4 + 3.8} = 375.60975 \doteq 376;$$

$$n_2 = \frac{700(3.8)}{4.4 + 3.8} = 324.39024 \doteq 324.$$

A couple of comments are in order regarding these results. First, as has been mentioned before, all sample sizes determined by our formulas are minimum values required, so in general we always round the final results upward into whole integers. This has been the practice in our previous examples. This is also what we have done for the total sample size n in our current example. However, you may have noticed that we did not do so for n_2. We did what we did in order to force $n_1 + n_2 = n$. Second, the values of n_1 and n_2 are related to σ_1 and σ_2 by the condition that $(n_1/n_2) = (\sigma_1/\sigma_2)$. This requirement seems plausible. If one population has greater dispersion than the other, the size of the sample drawn from the former should be proportionally greater than that selected from the latter, so that both samples may have the same degree of reliability.

Determining n When Estimating $\Delta\pi$

The case of estimating $\Delta\pi$ is similar to that of estimating $\Delta\mu$. Given n_1 and n_2 as the sizes of two independent samples with $n = n_1 + n_2$ and given the maximum error as

$$\varepsilon = z_c\sqrt{\frac{\pi_1\pi_1'}{n_1} + \frac{\pi_2\pi_2'}{n_2}},$$

we then have

$$n(= n_1 + n_2) = z_c^2\left(\frac{\sqrt{\pi_1\pi_1'} + \sqrt{\pi_2\pi_2'}}{\varepsilon}\right)^2; \qquad (11.15a)$$

$$n_1 = \frac{n\sqrt{\pi_1\pi_1'}}{\sqrt{\pi_1\pi_1'} + \sqrt{\pi_2\pi_2'}}; \qquad (11.15b)$$

$$n_2 = \frac{n\sqrt{\pi_2\pi_2'}}{\sqrt{\pi_1\pi_1'} + \sqrt{\pi_2\pi_2'}}. \qquad (11.15c)$$

Of course, neither π_1 nor π_2 is known in the estimation of $\Delta\pi$. Solutions to the problem of applying (11.15) are similar to those we have presented before in connection with estimating π. That is, when we have no information whatsoever available, we set $\pi_1 = \pi_2 = 0.5$. When it is possible, we may use "guesstimates" (guessed estimates arrived at with whatever relevant information is in our command) of the values of π_1 and π_1 in the same manner as suggested previously.

Now, suppose an automobile manufacturing company has constructed a mock model for a new sports car with special appeal to the youth market. The company suspects that the proportion of males who like the designed style may be different from that of females. To find out the potential difference, $\Delta\pi$, at a level of confidence of 0.95 with a maximum error of 4 percentage points, how large should the company take n_1, the sample size for the males, and n_2, the sample size for the females?

To solve this problem under the assumption that the manufacturer has no idea of the respective proportions, π_1 and π_2 can be both set to equal 0.5. Then, by (11.15a),

$$n = 1.96^2 \left(\frac{\sqrt{0.5(0.5)} + \sqrt{(0.5)(0.5)}}{0.04} \right)^2$$

$$\doteq 2{,}401.$$

Clearly, since $\pi_1 = \pi_2$ in this case, we would have

$$n_1 = n_2 = (1/2)n \doteq 1{,}201.$$

Here, if we wish to force $n_1 + n_2 = n$, we may set either n_1 or n_2 as 1,200 and the other as 1,201. This slight variation would produce hardly any significant difference in results!

A few words of caution are in order before closing our discussion on the determination of sample sizes. First of all, in the cases of estimating μ and $\Delta\mu$, exact determination of sample sizes is only possible if the population standard deviation(s) is(are) known. Insofar as the value(s) of $\sigma(s)$ is(are) "guesstimate(s)," the resulting sample size(s) can only be considered as approximations. In the cases of estimating π and $\Delta\pi$, sample sizes can never be exactly determined because the value(s) of $\pi(s)$ is(are) always unknown. You may consider that these revelations are rather disappointing after you have worked so hard in learning these methods. Such feelings are inappropriate, since the approximate sample sizes determined by the methods you have learned are sufficient for most decision situations in which estimation is required.

GLOSSARY OF FORMULAS

(11.1) $L,U = \hat{\theta} \mp z_c \sigma_{\hat{\theta}}$.

This is the generalized expression of confidence limits for a symmetric interval estimate of a parameter under the assumption that the estimator $\hat{\theta}$ is normally or approximately normally distributed. Here, z_c is a critical value of $n(0, 1)$ whose exact value depends upon the level of confidence, $1 - \alpha$. If $1 - \alpha = 0.95$, then $z_c = 1.96$, and if $1 - \alpha = 0.99$, then $z_c = 2.58$. The quantity $z_c \sigma_{\hat{\theta}}$ is half the size of an interval estimate and it measures the maximum error in estimating θ. The sign $\mp$ means that when we compute L, "minus" is used and when we compute U, "plus" is used. Finally, the length of a confidence interval may be thought as the precision of estimation and it varies inversely with the level of confidence.

(11.2) $L,U = \bar{X} \mp z_c \sigma_{\bar{X}};$

(11.3) $L,U = \bar{X} \mp z_c S_{\bar{X}}.$

These two equations are the application of (11.1) for the specific case of constructing interval estimates for μ. When σ is unknown, (11.3) is used, where $S_{\bar{X}}$ is an estimator for $\sigma_{\bar{X}}$.

(11.4) $L,U = \bar{P} \mp z_c \sigma_{\bar{P}};$

(11.5) $L,U = \bar{P} \mp z_c S_{\bar{P}}.$

The first equation here follows directly from (11.1) for the specific case of constructing confidence intervals for π. However, π is unknown and is to be estimated, so in practice we can only use (11.5) to obtain the confidence limits for π. We always compute $S_{\bar{P}}$ as $\sqrt{(\bar{P}(\bar{P}'))/n}$, which is very slightly mathematically biased.

(11.6) $L = \left(\bar{P} - \dfrac{1}{2n}\right) - z_c S_{\bar{P}};$

(11.7) $U = \left(\bar{P} + \dfrac{1}{2n}\right) + z_c S_{\bar{P}}.$

Interval estimation for π can be improved somewhat when n is rather small, say, $n \leq 100$, by incorporating the CCF in constructing L and U as shown by equations (11.6) and (11.7). However, both (11.6) and (11.7) will yield practically identical results to those of (11.5) if n is at all large.

(11.8) $L,U = \Delta \bar{X} \mp z_c \sigma_{\Delta \bar{X}};$

(11.9) $L,U = \Delta \bar{X} \mp z_c S_{\Delta \bar{X}};$

Equation (11.1) is now converted into these two formulas for the specific case of computing confidence limits for $\Delta \mu$. When σ_1 and σ_2 are unknown, we use (11.9) in practice. In either case $\Delta \bar{X}$ must be computed from two independent samples.

(11.10) $L,U = \Delta \bar{P} \mp z_c \sigma_{\Delta \bar{P}};$

(11.11) $L,U = \Delta \bar{P} \mp z_c S_{\Delta \bar{P}}.$

These two equations follow directly again from (11.1) for the specific case of estimating $\Delta \pi$. In practice, neither π_1 nor π_2 is known, so we employ (11.11) to compute the confidence limits for $\Delta \pi$. To use (11.11), it is required that the two samples must be independent.

(11.12) $n = \dfrac{z_c^2 \sigma^2}{\varepsilon^2}.$

This equation determines the minimum sample size that can satisfy predetermined levels of both confidence and precision (maximum error) for the case of estimating μ. When σ is unknown, it is replaced by a "guesstimate" arrived at one of the three methods presented in the text.

(11.13) $n = \pi \pi' \left(\dfrac{z_c}{\varepsilon} \right)^2.$

This equation is employed for the determination of the minimum sample size required so that the specified levels of confidence and estimation precision can be simultaneously satisfied. In using this equation, the unknown π may be set at 0.5 when no knowledge of any kind is available regarding the value of π. It may also be set at any approximate value according one's judgment with whatever information available.

(11.14a) $n = z_c^2 \left(\dfrac{\sigma_1 + \sigma_2}{\varepsilon} \right)^2;$

(11.14b) $n_1 = \dfrac{n \sigma_1}{\sigma_1 + \sigma_2};$

(11.14c) $n_2 = \dfrac{n \sigma_2}{\sigma_1 + \sigma_2}.$

The first of this group of equations determines the total sample size n required when estimating $\Delta \mu$ so that the predetermined confidence level and degree of precision can be satisfied. Then n is distributed between the two independent samples to obtain n_1 and n_2, as indicated by (11.14b) and (11.14c). The logic of these two equations is dictated by the condition that $n_1/n_2 = \sigma_1/\sigma_2$. When σ_1 and σ_2 are unknown, "guesstimates" are employed as discussed for estimating μ.

(11.15a) $n = z_c^2 \left(\dfrac{\sqrt{\pi_1 \pi_1'} + \sqrt{\pi_2 \pi_2'}}{\varepsilon} \right)^2;$

(11.15b) $n_1 = \dfrac{n\sqrt{\pi_1\pi_1'}}{\sqrt{\pi_1\pi_1'} + \sqrt{\pi_2\pi_2'}}$;

(11.15c) $n_2 = \dfrac{n\sqrt{\pi_2\pi_2'}}{\sqrt{\pi_1\pi_1'} + \sqrt{\pi_2\pi_2'}}$.

The formulas in this group are similar to those in the previous set. They are formulated to determine the total sample size n, and the sizes n_1 and n_2 of the two independent samples given $1 - \alpha$ and $z_c\sigma_{\Delta\bar{p}}$ in estimating $\Delta\pi$. In the application of these expressions, π_1 and π_2 are both set to equal 0.5 or any other approximate values, or "guesstimates", according to our knowledge.

REVIEW QUESTIONS

11.1 What is the difference in reasoning between the derivation and application of sampling distributions?

11.2 Differentiate the three terms estimator, estimate, and estimation.

11.3 Name the desirable properties of point estimators and define each precisely.

11.4 What are the sources of bias? Which source is our main focus? Why?

11.5 Given an intuitive explanation for the principle of maximum likelihood, explain why this principle also provides a rationale for point estimation.

11.6 How is an interval estimate defined? What is the motivation for its use?

11.7 How are confidence limits constructed? Confidence limits constructed for different parameters are not only different in form but also different in principles. Is this true? Explain.

11.8 How should an interval estimate be interpreted? Be specific.

11.9 It can be said that both the maximum error of an estimation and the estimation precision are measured by the same quantity $z_c\sigma_{\hat{\theta}}$. Why?

11.10 Given the size of sample, how do the levels of confidence and precision vary together? Why?

11.11 What is the purpose of determining the sample size when we construct confidence intervals?

11.12 How do we go about producing a guesstimate for an unknown σ in the application of (11.12)?

11.13 How do we go about producing a guesstimate for π in the application of (11.13)?

11.14 In the determination of n, n_1 and n_2 for the estimation of $\Delta\mu$, n should be distributed between n_1 and n_2 in such a way that the condition $n_1/n_2 = \sigma_1/\sigma_2$ is satisfied. Why?

11.15 In the case of estimating $\Delta\pi$, explain how the total sample size should be distributed between n_1 and n_2 along the lines of your answer for the previous question.

11.16 In general, a narrow interval estimate is preferred over a wide one. One way to obtain a narrow confidence interval is to set z_c close to 0. If we set $z_c = 0$, what would then happen to length of the interval estimate and to the level of confidence?

11.17 Other things being equal, a high level of confidence is more desirable than a low level of confidence. One way to obtain a high degree of confidence is to set the confidence level very close to 1. If we set $1 - \alpha = 1$, we would have a 100% interval estimate; but what would happen to the width of the confidence interval then?

11.18 Suppose an SRS is selected from all the eligible voters two months before a national election and another SRS is selected from the same population just one week before the election. In both samples the same questions are asked and we are interested in finding out whether there has been a change in the proportion of the voters favoring a certain candidate. Can (11.11) be used for evaluation in this case? Why or why not?

PROBLEMS

11.1 One estimator is said to be more efficient than another if the former has a smaller standard error than the latter. *Efficiencies* of estimators are simply the ratio of sample sizes which will make the two different estimates with approximately the same precision. An efficiency of, say, 0.70, for instance, indicates that the value of an estimator obtained from a sample with $n = 70$ will have the same accuracy as the alternative estimate produced by a sample of $n = 100$. We know that $V(\bar{X}) = \sigma^2/n$ and $V(X_5) \doteq 1.56\sigma^2/n$, so the efficiency of X_5 as an estimator for μ is only 0.64 of that of $\bar{X}$. Can you explain why? Now, suppose we attempt to estimate μ by X_5 with $n = 1000$; how large should n be if we attempt, as we should, to estimate μ by $\bar{X}$ in order to have the same degree of precision in estimation?

11.2 It has been pointed out that S is a biased estimator for σ even though $E(S^2) = \sigma^2$ for unconditional SRSs. However, the bias of S can be corrected by a correction factor C, which is always greater than 1. C approaches 1 when n approaches infinity. A technical explanation of this factor has been given by A. Hald in his *Statistical Theory With Applications*, (New York, John Wiley and Sons, 1952) on pp. 299–300. According to this note, $C = 1.253$ with $n = 2$ and it decreases continuously with larger n. When $n = 10$, $C = 1.028$. For $n > 10$, the values of C can be determined by the formula:

$$C \doteq 1 + \frac{1}{4(n-1)}.$$

C values determined by this expression are accurate to three decimal places. With C, we have $E(CS) = \sigma$. In any event, we see that S is as an asymptotically unbiased estimator for σ. Demonstrate this fact by computing C with $n = 20$, 50, and 100. Use the results obtained to explain why the bias of S is not serious at all in practice and why the correction factor can be ignored when $n \geqslant 50$.

11.3 An odd professor of economics I know dislikes odd numbers. So every time he has to estimate μ of some population, he takes an SRS and uses only the even numbers in the sample to compute the sample mean. Namely, he simply discards readings of odd numbers. By his practice, can we say that his estimator is
a. Unbiased?
b. Consistent?
c. Efficient?
e. Sufficient?
Explain for each of your answers.

11.4 A company is considering submitting a bid to produce 20,000 units of a certain electronic component. Its engineering department, after analyzing the specifications of component, has reached the following preliminary conclusions.
a. A fixed cost of $5,000 is required to undertake the project.
b. The variable costs would be $10 per unit for raw materials, plus $8 per hour of production time.
If the firm uses μ to represent the mean of the variable time, what is the total cost function for the 20,000 units? The firm considers that 20% of total cost of production would cover a reasonable level of profits and other possible contingencies, how should the amount of his bid be expressed? Finally, the firm makes a trial run of 16 components and finds the mean time required to produce an item is 0.4 hours; that is $\bar{x} = 0.4$. Using this value as a point estimate for μ, what is the amount the company should submit in its bid? If the variable production time is known to be normally distributed with $\sigma = 0.05$ hours, what is the 95% confidence interval for μ?

11.5 The lives of light bulbs produced by a certain factory are known to be normally distributed with $\sigma = 12$ hours. A sample of 36 light bulbs are drawn and found to have a mean life of 160 hours. Construct a 95% confidence interval for μ and interpret the result. In this problem the size of the population is not specified. Is this omission crucial here?

11.6 A sample of $n = 164$ home owners who purchased new homes in 1985 in Queens, New York, showed a mean annual property tax payment of $3,200 and a standard deviation of $150. Construct 95% and 99% confidence intervals for the mean annual property tax payment of all the people who purchased new homes in Queens in 1985. In this problem, neither the population size nor the population distribution is specified. Furthermore, the population standard deviation is unknown. Under these conditions, do you think the confidence intervals you have just constructed are justified? Explain.

11.7 The mean weight of trucks traveling on a new section of a highway in a certain state is unknown. A state highway department inspector was interested in finding out what this mean is. He selected a sample of 64 trucks passing through the new section of the highway at the weighting station and found that $\bar{x} = 16.2$ tons and $s = 4.5$ tons. Calculate a 95% interval estimate for μ. In this problem, what would be the distribution pattern of all the trucks' weights according to your judgment? If this pattern is far from normal, what happens to your interval estimate of μ?

11.8 The research department of Gamma, Inc., a manufacturing company that produces a single and rather involved machine, consisting many components, has designed a new method for assembling the machine. The management would like to undertake a sample study to estimate μ—the mean time in minutes required to assemble a machine by the new method. This sample survey will consist of assembling 36 machines. The sample mean time will be used as a point estimator for μ. From this estimate of μ, the cost of assembling an order of 2,000 machines will be estimated. From past experience, it seems reasonable to assume that the assembling time is normally distributed with $\sigma = 4$ minutes. Suppose, the firm's total cost function is given as

$$C = \$25,000 + 2,000(\$500 + \$2.50\mu),$$

and suppose the assembling of the 36 machines yields $\bar{x} = 30$ minutes.
a. What is the estimate of the total cost of the order?
b. What is the 98% confidence interval for the mean time of the new method?

11.9 Sun Rise Oil, Inc., has 400 gas stations throughout the southeastern states. A sample of 81 stations reveals that the mean price of premium no-lead gasoline sold per gallon in these stations to be $1.40 with a standard deviation of $0.045. Assuming the population of prices per gallon is approximately normal, determine the 98% confidence interval for the mean price of all the 400 stations.

11.10 A computerized accounting system handled 150,000 transactions last month. A manual follow-up was made to determine whether the computerized system is operating satisfactorily. A sample of 1,500 transactions were selected and showed that 45 of these transactions had errors.
a. What is the unbiased estimator for π?
b. Calculate the 95% and 99% confidence intervals for π.
c. The company feels that the errors are under control if $\pi \leqslant 0.015$. In view of your answers to (b), are the errors in control? Explain briefly.
d. Do you think that the sample size is large enough in this case? If not, does it affect your answers to (c)? Why or why not?

11.11 Of the 284 people voting in a straw poll in a large city for the Democratic or Republican candidates for mayor, the Democrat received 152 votes. Therefore, in the sample, $\bar{p} = 152/284 \doteq 0.5352$.
a. Calculate the 95% confidence interval for π.
b. Calculate the 99% confidence interval for π.
c. In view of your answers to part (a) and (b), how secure is the Democrat's lead over the Republican?
d. Does it matter that, here, nothing is said about the randomness of the sample? If the sample were not random, what effect would there be on the interpretation of your answers to parts (a) and (b)?

11.12 This is the same as Problem 11.11 except that 2,556 people in the straw poll voted for the Democratic or Republican candidate and 1,368 people voted for the Democrat. In this sample, then $\bar{p} = 1,368/2,556 \doteq 0.5352$.
a. Calculate the 95% confidence interval for π.

b. Calculate the 99% confidence interval for π.

c. In view of your answers to parts (a) and (b), how secure is the Democrat's lead over the Republican?

d. Compare your answers to Problems 11.11(c) and 11.12(c). Discuss briefly what happened when the sample size increased from 284 to 2,556 even though $\bar{p}$ remained the same in both samples.

e. Does it matter that, in Problem 11.11, nothing is said about the randomness of the sample? If the sample were not random, what effect would there be on the interpretation of your answers to parts (a) and (b).

11.13 The advertising director of Beta Co. is considering the possibility of purchasing a one-minute weekly "spot" commercial for his company's new product on a national popular television program that is presented every Friday night. During discussion with the manager in charge of ad sales of the TV station, the director learned that the price for a one minute of spot time is determined by the function

$$\text{price} = \$6,500 + \$350,000(\bar{P}).$$

where $\bar{P}$ is the estimator of the proportion of households that watch the program across the nation. Furthermore, the TV station always uses the ratings of TV programs obtained by Alpha National TV Survey, Inc. Alpha has installed automatic devices on the televisions of 1500 homes selected at random throughout the nation. According to its records, 360 families were registered to have watched the program in question the previous Friday.

a. What is the price of a one-minute spot commercial time on this program?

b. If the ad director would only be willing to purchase the commercial time for that price provided that he could be 98% confident that the value of π is at least 0.2, what would his decision be in view of the Alpha data?

11.14 Two cities are separated by a river. The Chamber of Commerce in city A claims that the mean family income of that city is $500 more than that of city B. The Chamber of Commerce in city B disputes this, and a statistician is hired to settle the argument. She attacks this problem by estimating the true difference between the family income in averages in the two cities. A sample is drawn from each city, and the following results are obtained.

Sample from A	Sample from B
$n_1 = 514$	$n_2 = 627$
$\bar{x}_1 = \$23,468$	$\bar{x}_2 = 22,919$
$s_1^2 = 29,043,221$	$s_2^2 = 41,948,337$

If the statistician constructs a 99% confidence interval with these data, what will she get? In view of this finding, what conclusion can be reached in the quarrel between the cities? In this problem, neither the population distributions nor their standard deviations are known. Would these considerations affect in any way the conclusion reached?

11.15 It is known that the durabilities of two different makes of automobile tires are normally distributed and have identical standard deviations, $\sigma_1 = \sigma_2 = 1,500$ miles, but it is unknown whether their mean durabilities are the same. To find out the possible value of $\Delta\mu$, 16 of each make of tires have been tested, and it has been found that $\bar{x}_1 = 45,000$ miles and $\bar{x}_2 = 45,500$ miles. If you construct a 95% confidence interval for $\Delta\mu$, what conclusion can you reach? Could you reach the same conclusion with a 99% confidence interval for $\Delta\mu$ in this case? Explain the similarities and differences in your conclusions.

11.16 The mean and the standard deviation of the maximum load supported by 100 cables produced by Alpha Company are found to be 20 tons and 1.1 tons, respectively. The mean and standard deviation of 100 cables produced by Beta Company are found to be 16 tons and 0.8 tons, respectively. Assuming both populations are normally distributed, give the 95% and 99% confidence intervals for the true difference in mean maximum loads.

11.17 A large foreign bank in New York City is considering building a branch in an affluent suburb of that city. There are two sites in the trade area A and B, available that are about 20 blocks apart. The price of site A is almost 50% higher than that of site B. However, the management feels site A would still be preferable if the family mean income of the households around site A were substantially higher than that of those households around site B. To finalize the decision, a sample survey is conducted with the following result.

Sample from Area A	Sample from Area B
$n_1 = 210$	$n_2 = 180$
$\bar{x}_1 = \$46,500$	$\bar{x}_2 = \$42,450$
$s_1^2 = 4,410,000$	$s_2^2 = 3,802,500$

a. What is the 98% confidence interval for $\Delta\mu$?
b. Suppose the bank would decide to select A if and only if $\Delta\mu$ is at least as large as $3500, with a confidence probability of 0.98. What would be the bank's decision in view of the result in (a)? Explain.

11.18 In a random sample of 700 women, 315 favor federal aid to private schools. In a random sample of 450 men, 108 favor federal aid to private schools. Determine the 95% and 99% confidence intervals for the difference in the proportions of all women and all men who favor such aid.

11.19 It has been found that 30 out of 300 TV picture tubes produced by process I are defective and that 18 out of 225 tubes produced by process II are defective. Assuming random sampling, find the 99% confidence interval for the true difference in the defective proportions.

11.20 A new remedy for chronic headaches is being tested, and 19 of 160 patients receiving the new pill find immediate relief, whereas 19 of 260 patients receiving a conventional pill find immediate relief. In view of these results, can we reasonably conclude that there may be no real difference in the proportions of patients who find immediate relief from the two kinds of pills? Why or why not?

11.21 Let the data of Problem 11.10 be sample 1. The next month, an independent simple random sample of 1,800 transactions, was selected from 157,220 transactions. Of these, 36 transactions had errors; the error rate in sample 2 was $36/1,800 = 0.02$. Comparing the two samples, we find that $\Delta\bar{p} = \bar{p}_2 - \bar{p}_1 = -0.01$; the sample error rate declined by 1 percentage point from 3% to 2%. We

are interested in whether we can conclude that the population error rate declined.
a. Calculate the 95% confidence interval for $\Delta\pi$.
b. Calculate the 99% confidence interval for $\Delta\pi$.
c. Can we conclude that the population error rate declined? Discuss briefly.
d. Do the values of n_1, $\bar{P}_1$, n_2, and $\bar{P}_2$ meet the requirements of the rule of thumb that justifies using Equation (11.11)? Discuss briefly.

11.22 When railroads merge, the new and larger company can often attract additional traffic from competing railroads. Naturally, the competing railroads do not like this prospect, and they often object to the proposed merger in proceedings before the U.S. Interstate Commerce Commission. The commission can, if it wants to, approve the merger subject to such terms and conditions as it finds to be just and reasonable. (Sections 11343–11345 of the Interstate Commerce Act, covering railroad mergers, grant this power to the commission.) So one of the strategies of the competing railroads is to ask for some terms and conditions that will offset the traffic they expect to lose. One of the issues is how much traffic will be lost to the new company, and one of the problems is whether the judgments of the new company about future diverted traffic are about the same as the judgments of the competing railroads. To cast some light on whether diversion judgments are the same, a study of the same traffic population can be run, wherein the proposed new company draws a sample and judges how much of the sample traffic will be diverted to it, and a competitor draws its own sample from the same population and judges how much of its sample traffic will be diverted to the new company. The samples are drawn from the same population, so the results can differ only because the judgments differ or because of sampling error. Suppose the traffic population consists of records of actual railroad freight car movements, and suppose the data are as follows:

SAMPLE 1:
FROM PROPOSED NEW COMPANY
Method: SRS without replacement.

$N_1 = 16,425$
$n_1 = 2,403$
$\bar{p}_1 = 115/2,403 \doteq 0.0479$, or 4.79%

SAMPLE 2:
FROM COMPETING RAILROAD
Method: SRS without replacement, and samples 1 and 2 are independent.

$N_2 = 16,425$
$n_2 = 2,733$
$\bar{p}_2 = 157/2,733 \doteq 0.0574$, or 5.74%

The sample proportions of diverted traffic differ by $\Delta p = \bar{p}_2 - \bar{p}_1 \doteq 0.0095$, or 0.95%, nearly a whole percentage point. It appears that either the new company is underestimating the diverted traffic or the competing railroad is overestimating the diverted traffic. We are interested in whether this conclusion from $\Delta\bar{p}$ is justified concerning the whole traffic population; we want to know what $\Delta\pi$ could reasonably be in view of this sample evidence. That is, could sampling error alone account for the difference between $\bar{p}_1$ and $\bar{p}_2$, with both railroads judging the diverted traffic in the same way?
a. Calculate the 95% confidence interval for $\Delta\pi$.
b. Calculate the 99% confidence interval for $\Delta\pi$.
c. In view of your answers to parts (a) and (b), could the diversions be judged the same way in both samples, with sampling error alone accounting for the difference in the sample results? Discuss briefly.
d. Do the values of n_1, $\bar{p}_1$, n_2, and $\bar{p}_2$ meet the specifications for the rule of thumb that justifies using equations (11.11)? Discuss briefly.

11.23 Suppose sample 1 is a political poll taken two months before the election, using SRS. Suppose sample 2 consists of asking the same people the same questions one month before the election. We are interested in whether the population percentage favoring the candidate has increased, judging from these sample results. Can equations (11.11) be used? Why or why not?

11.24 Suppose that, in Problem 11.22, SRS without replacement was used to select one sample of railroad traffic, which was then submitted to both railroads to determine whether they judged the traffic diversions in the same way. Can equations (11.11) be used? Why or why not?

11.25 Suppose we know that the standard deviation of a day's output from a production line is $\sigma = 100$ units. We wish to estimate the daily mean output, μ, within 50 units with 95% confidence. What sample size is required; that is, how many days should be randomly chosen for observation?

11.26 A certain bank wishes to estimate the mean balance owed by the thousands of customers holding MasterCards. If a 98% confidence interval with a total width of $100 is desired, how many cardholders should be sampled? Assume that the standard deviation of the balances is $\sigma = \$325$.

11.27 The auditor of a large bank wishes to estimate the proportion of monthly checking-account statements that have mistakes, and he specifies a confidence level of 0.99 for getting a sample proportion within 0.2 percentage point (or 0.002) of the true proportion.
a. If there is no information at all on what the true proportion might be, what sample size is needed?
b. If, for the kind of mistake the auditor is particularly interested in finding, past experience suggests a true proportion of 0.01, what sample size is needed?

11.28 *Playboy* magazine claims to have over 2,500,000 subscribers. The senior vice-president of the magazine, wishes to estimate the proportion of subscribers who have incomes of $30,000 or more a year. If a 95% confidence interval with a total width of 0.10 is desired, determine how many subscribers must be sampled (a) given that the vice-president has no idea at all what the proportion is and (b) given that the vice-president knows the proportion is about 0.30. What function or functions do you think such information can perform?

11.29 The credit manager of a casino in Atlantic City would like to know what proportion of the casino's customers with approved credit take advantage of the casino's "installment payment plan" for paying their losses. He would like to estimate the proportion within 5 percentage points at 95% level of confidence, but he has no idea at this moment how large the proportion might be. How large a sample must he select?

11.30 Returning to Problem 11.15, suppose we wish to construct a 99% confidence interval for $\Delta\mu$ with a total width of 400 miles. How large should be n, n_1 and n_2 be?

11.31 Consider Problem 11.16 again. Suppose in the process of estimating $\Delta\mu$, we specify $1 - \alpha = 0.95$ and the maximum error to be 0.25 tons. How large should n, n_1 and n_2 be?

11.32 Consider Problem 11.18 again. Suppose we want to have 95% confidence interval for $\Delta\pi$ with a total width of 1.5 percentage points; i.e. 0.015. What must the sizes of n, n_1, and n_2 be?

11.33 Do the following on a computer.
a. Select 100 SRSs with $n = 25$ each from the population data in Table 3.P6.
b. Determine the sample means.
c. Construct 95% confidence intervals for μ with results obtained in (b).
d. Comment on your results in (c) in view of what you have learned about interval estimation.

12 Classical Theory of Testing. I: The Fixed Sample-Size Case

12.1 A FIRST LOOK AT TESTING

We often hear that facts speak for themselves. However, this statement is seldom true. Facts can become meaningful only when they are combined with ideas. In statistics, facts are numerical individual observations or descriptive measures derived from them. These facts, standing alone, are of little use to us unless we have some ideas about how to interpret them in order to make them into powerful tools. Suppose, for example you are determined to find out whether a particular coin is fair, you may toss it 10,000 times and get 5,070 heads and 4,930 tails. What do these numerical facts imply about the fairness of the coin? We cannot answer such a question until we have some idea of what we mean by a fair coin and of how empirical evidence is related to conclusions reached about a population. From a statistical point of view, we can easily specify that a "fair" coin as one for which $P(\text{H}) = 0.5$ on each toss of the coin and for which the outcomes of all tosses of the coin are statistically independent. It is more difficult to specify how sample result should bear on conclusions about a population. One approach we have already learned is the idea of interval estimation. Here, we may construct, say, a 99% confidence interval for π. Assuming an unconditional SRS, such an interval becomes

$$\bar{p} \mp z_c s_{\bar{p}} = 0.507 \mp 2.58 \sqrt{\frac{0.507(1 - 0.507)}{10,000}}$$

$$\doteq 0.494 \text{ to } 0.520.$$

455

Since $\pi = 0.5$ falls within this confidence interval, we conclude that, as far as the proportion of heads is concerned, the coin is fair, or at least the coin is reasonably fair.

There is another concept for dealing with problems such as our current example. It is the second branch of statistical inference, called the *classical theory of testing*. This theory, in common practice, means that one states two different "hypotheses" that embody one's ideas about what facts might be in the population and then employs sample evidence to decide which hypothesis is more reasonable. These hypotheses are conventionally called the *null hypothesis*, denoted as H_0, and the *alternative hypothesis*, denoted as H_1. For our current example, H_0 may be stated as "The coin is fair" and H_1 as "The coin is not fair." In symbols, and with reference to the proportion of heads, these hypotheses may be stated as

$$H_0: \pi = 0.5 \quad \text{and} \quad H_1: \pi \neq 0.5.$$

With the procedure of testing, the core is whether, after we have tentatively assumed that H_0 is true, analysis shows a "probabilistic inconsistency" between sample evidence and the specified value of a parameter in H_0. If it does not, we do not reject H_0. If it does, we then reject H_0 in favor of H_1.

The notion of a "probabilistic inconsistency" used above is not a standard or conventional phrase, but merely this author's choice of ordinary English words for the concept at the heart of statistical testing. This phrase means that in order to reject the null hypothesis we do not insist that the sample evidence be impossible if the hypothesis is true. Instead, it is only required that the sample evidence be improbable to the specified degree if H_0 is true. Furthermore, we say that a probabilistic inconsistency exists when the sample result is one of the extreme, or highly improbable, values if H_0 is true. All the extreme values of the statistic that are inconsistent with H_0 form what is called the *region of rejection*, which comprises the tail-end(s) of the sampling distribution of the statistic. All the less extreme, or more probable, values of the statistic are considered to be consistent with H_0 and are said to form the *region of nonrejection* in a sampling distribution. The dividing line(s) between these two regions, as will be explained in detail later, depends upon the form of the alternative hypothesis and the "level of significance" that we choose to assign in a given test. The *level of significance*, denoted as α, is the probability of rejecting a true H_0.

The foregoing concepts are best explained by the graphic illustration of the sampling distribution of $\bar{P}$ with $\pi = 0.5$, as in Figure 12.1. This figure is a normal curve, since for $n = 10,000$ and $\pi = 0.5$, the normal approximation of the binomial distribution is excellent. Now, let us see how this figure can be applied to the coin-tossing example for the purpose of determining the regions of rejection and of nonrejection by setting $\alpha = 0.01$. Fundamentally, the region of rejection consists of the values of the statistic that are so extreme, if H_0 is true, that actually observing any of these values would constitute a probablistic inconsistency, so that H_0 would be rejected. "Extreme" is a vague word, and

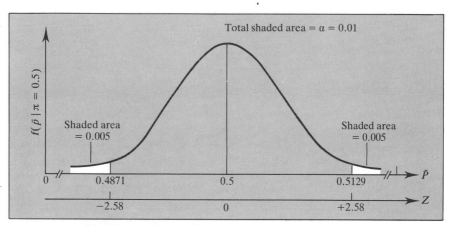

FIGURE 12.1 Graphic illustration of locating the region of rejection in testing for the coin-tossing example.

the major function of α is to make precise what is meant by "extreme" in our context.

In our current example, H_1 is stated as $\pi \neq 0.5$, thus either an extremely small or an extremely large value of $\bar{P}$ would lead us to reject H_0. The region of rejection in effect consists of two subregions, one in each tail-end as shown in Figure 12.1. In this case, where the region of rejection is two-tailed, the conventional practice is to divide α in half, using $\alpha/2$ in each tail. For the portion in the lower tail, we start with $\bar{P} = 0$—the most extreme small value of $\bar{P}$. Then we consider the less and less extreme small values of $\bar{P}$ by moving rightwards along the horizontal axis until we have accumulated a probability of 0.005 in the lower tail. While we do not know yet what value of $\bar{P}$ has such a cumulative probability in the lower tail, we do know that $N(-2.58) = 0.005$. Thus, we write $z = -2.58$ on the graph. We treat the portion in the upper tail in exactly the same way. Starting with $\bar{P} = 1.0$—the most extreme large value of $\bar{P}$, we move leftwards along the horizontal scale; we stop when we have accumulated a probability of 0.005 in the upper tail. Again, we do not yet know the value of $\bar{P}$ for the terminal point but, again, we do know that $1 - N(+2.58) = 0.005$ and so we write $z = +2.58$ on the graph. Having determined the stopping points for both tails in terms of Z-values, it becomes a simple matter to solve for the unknown values of $\bar{P}$ by normal approximations of the binomial probabilities as follows:

$$z = \frac{\bar{p} - \pi_0}{\sigma_{\bar{P}}} = \frac{\bar{p} - \pi_0}{\sqrt{\dfrac{\pi_0(1 - \pi_0)}{n}}}$$

$$= \frac{\bar{p} - 0.5}{\sqrt{\dfrac{0.5(1 - 0.5)}{10,000}}} = \frac{\bar{p} - 0.5}{0.005},$$

where π_0 denotes the null hypothetical parameter value that is assumed to be true. From this formulation we see that $\bar{p} = 0.005z + 0.5$. Hence, for $z = -2.58$, we have

$$\bar{p} = 0.005(-2.58) + 0.5 = 0.4871,$$

and for $z = +2.58$, we have

$$\bar{p} = 0.005(+2.58) + 0.5 = 0.5129.$$

These results are entered on Figure 12.1 on the horizontal scale for $\bar{P}$, and now we see that the region of rejection is

$$0 \leqslant \bar{P} < 0.4871 \cup 0.5129 < \bar{P} \leqslant 1.$$

The observed value of $\bar{p} = 0.507$ is in the region of nonrejection, so H_0 is not rejected. There is no probabilistic inconsistency between sample evidence and the hypothesis that $\pi = 0.5$. As for the conclusion reached before in terms of the confidence interval, we are again at least reasonably sure that the coin is fair.

It must be pointed out now, however, that the nonrejection of H_0 does not mean that we have proved that H_0 is true. This is the reason we have deliberately stated our conclusion in a weaker manner: "We do not reject the null hypothesis." Indeed, it is impossible to prove, except for a few rare cases, that the null hypothesis is true when sample evidence is used. We can only prove that the null hypothesis is true or that it is false with a census, or complete enumeration, of the population. Once sample evidence leads us to reject H_0, we adopt the appropriate belief and behave as if we have proved one of the hypotheses true and the other false, even though we must always bear in mind that there is the chance, however slight, the sample evidence may have misled us.

The chance of being misled by the sample evidence can be controlled in hypothesis testing. In the coin example, we arrange matters to that, if H_0 is true, there is a probability of 0.99 of getting a sample result for which we do not reject H_0 and a probability of only 0.01 of obtaining a sample result that would mislead us. This is the essence of how errors can be controlled by keeping their occurrences to low probabilities when sample evidence is used to determine whether H_0 or H_1 is the more reasonable. We return shortly to a more thorough explanation of this.

12.2 HYPOTHESES, ERRORS, AND RISKS IN STATISTICAL TESTING

Testing as a Decision Procedure

Statistical hypothesis testing is called by many other names, such as *tests of hypotheses, tests of significance, decision procedures,* or simply *testing.* As a decision procedure, the classical theory of testing is concerned with the special case wherein the decision maker is confronted with having to select one of two courses of action, say a_1 and a_2, that are contradictory in nature. Examples include buying or not buying a new machine, accepting or rejecting a given shipment of output, and introducing or not introducing a new product.

It is assumed that it would be clear whether a_1 or a_2 were the better act if we knew the value of a particular parameter of the population in question. Such knowledge is usually unattainable; we are forced to make an assumption about the numerical value of the parameter and then settle for such knowledge as can be obtained from a random sample. If the sample data do not constitute a probabilistic inconsistency with our assumption, we decide that a_1 is the better act. If the sample data do constitute a probabilistic contradiction of our assumption, we decide that a_2 is the better act. Hence, the ultimate purpose of testing is not just to decide whether H_0 should be rejected in favor of H_1. Instead, the rejection or nonrejection of H_0 leads to the selection of a more rational or better act in a given decision situation.

The coin-tossing example of the previous section is an informal and brief introduction to the classical theory of hypothesis testing. We move now to present a more formal discussion of the various aspects of the subject.

Formulation of Hypotheses

Obviously, statistical testing begins with the formulation of hypotheses. A *statistical hypothesis,* in formal terms, is an assumption about the distribution of a random variable. We may specify a hypothesis by giving the type of distribution and the value(s) of the parameter(s) that define it. Examples of this type of hypothesis would be:

1. X is normally distributed with $\mu = 100$ and $\sigma = 10$.

2. Y is a binomial variable with $\pi = 0.25$.

In practice, however, the population distribution is often implicitly assumed, and a hypothesis is specified with assumed value(s) of the parameter(s). Examples of this type of hypothesis are:

3. The mean wage rate of auto workers is \$450 per week; that is, $\mu = \$450$ per week.

4. The defective fraction of output produced by a certain process is equal to or less than 5%; that is, $\pi \leq 0.05$.

A statistical hypothesis may be thought of as a set of "elementary" hypotheses. In this connection, a statistical hypothesis may be simple or composite. A *simple hypothesis* is a complete specification of a probability distribution. Hypothesis (1) above is such a hypothesis, since with the information in it we can write down the specific density function of X. A *composite hypothesis* is any statistical hypothesis that is not a simple hypothesis. Hypothesis (2) above is an illustration of this, since the distribution of Y is not completely defined without the specification of n.

A *simple hypothesis* may be also defined as one that contains only a single state, or element, of the parameter set. In contrast, a *composite hypothesis* is one that contains two or more states, or elements, of the parameter set. Thus, hypothesis (3) is simple, while hypothesis (4) is composite.

In general, we think of a composite hypothesis as being made up of the set of all simple hypotheses consistent with it. Hence, for example, the hypothesis $\pi \leq 0.05$ is to be interpreted as being "composed" of all simple hypotheses of the form $\pi = \pi_0$, where π_0 is any single number in the range from 0 to 0.05. When we say that a composite hypothesis is true we mean that some one of the simple hypotheses that make it up is true.

As stated before, a convenient way of specifying what is required of a testing procedure is to focus attention on two possible sets of values of the parameter, or two statistical hypotheses: H_0, the *null hypothesis* and H_1, the *alternative hypothesis*. Here, H_0 is the set of simple hypotheses which, if any of them is true, would make a_1 (accepting H_0 and acting accordingly) a better act; H_1 is the set of simple hypotheses which, if any of them is true, would make a_2 (rejecting H_0 or accepting H_1 and acting accordingly) a better act. Thus, the choice between a_1 and a_2 is associated with the nonrejection or rejection of H_0.

The designation between the null and alternative hypotheses is arbitrary. Typically, however, the null hypothesis is specified in an exact manner, such as "There is no difference in mean income between physicians and professors," "The production process is in control," or "There has been no increase in real per capita income in India since it became independent." A null hypothesis, in other words, "nullifies" the effect of a "treatment" and it corresponds to the absence of effects of the variable being investigated. The alternative hypothesis is usually less sharply formulated: It is often stated as a range of values that would prevail if the variable being studied did have some effect. Thus, the null hypothesis is often specified in a way that is opposite to what one believes to be true, and the alternative is stated as the opposite of the null hypothesis.

In testing terminology we speak of testing a null hypothesis against an alternative hypothesis under the tentative assumption that the null hypothesis is true. However, we must realize that we are really making a decision between two actions, or between H_0 and H_1. There are three main types of tests, each of which is identified by the way H_0 and H_1 are formulated. First, there is the *double-tail test,* or *two-side test,* for which the hypotheses are of the following general form:

$$H_0: \theta = \theta_0; \qquad H_1: \theta \neq \theta_0.$$

This type of test is appropriate if we are concerned that the value of a parameter may be either too small or too large for some specific purpose. Suppose, for example, a machine part is produced and that it is to be fitted with other parts in order to assemble a complete machine. One of the critical dimensions, say, the length, of this machine part is specified to have a mean of 2.5 inches. If the part is either too short or too long (in accordance with specified tolerance limits), it will not fit and will be useless. Thus, the producer should test the following pair of hypotheses from time to time with sample data to see whether or not the manufacturing process is in control:

H_0: $\mu = 2.5$, a_1: the process is in control, leave it alone;

H_1: $\mu \neq 2.5$, a_2: the process is out of control, take corrective action.

Second, there is the *lower-tail test,* or *left-tail test,* for which the hypotheses may be formulated as

$$H_0: \theta \geq \theta_0; \qquad H_1: \theta < \theta_0.$$

This type of test is employed when we are concerned that the value of a parameter is not small enough for some specific objective. Suppose, for example, that it has been well established by medical scientists that if the average nicotine content of cigarettes is 25 milligrams or more, lung cancer is likely to develop in a smoker. If, however, the average nicotine content is less than 25 milligrams, the user is relatively safe. Suppose that you are a habitual smoker and are willing to risk your life; you should certainly try to find a brand of cigarettes whose average nicotine content is less than 25 milligrams. In this case you should formulate your hypotheses as follows:

H_0: $\mu \geq 25$, a_1: do not buy the brand;

H_1: $\mu < 25$, a_2: buy the brand.

The third type of test is called the *upper-tail test,* or *right-tail test.* Here, the hypotheses are usually expressed as

$$H_0: \theta \leq \theta_0; \qquad H_1: \theta > \theta_0.$$

We use this type of test when we are in doubt whether the value of a parameter is large enough for some predetermined goal. For the purpose of building a bridge, for example, a construction firm needs steel cables that have a mean breaking strength of more than 10,000 pounds. To decide whether a given make of steel cables should be purchased, the following hypotheses would be appropriate:

H_0: $\mu \leq 10,000$, a_1: do not buy the make;

H_1: $\mu > 10,000$, a_2: buy the make.

From our discussion so far we see that a hypothesis does not just come "out of the blue", unconnected to anything else. It is related to an action you might take, a theory you might verify, or a belief you might adopt. There are practical actions or beliefs about which a decision is

TABLE 12.1 Common Forms of Statistical Hypothesis Testing

Name (1)	Form of H_0 (2)	Form of H_1 (3)
Two-tail test	$H_0: \theta = \theta_0$	$H_1: \theta \neq \theta_0$
Upper-tail test	$H_0: \theta \leq \theta_0$	$H_1: \theta > \theta_0$
Lower-tail test	$H_0: \theta \geq \theta_0$	$H_1: \theta < \theta_0$

needed, and these practical actions or beliefs are translated into statistical hypotheses. Then, after the sample evidence has been analyzed, the appropriate practical action is engaged in, or the appropriate belief is adopted.

When we follow the conventional practice of testing H_0 against H_1, the two hypotheses must be such that, if one of them is true, it is logically impossible for the other one to be true also. In other words, the two hypotheses must be mutually exclusive in terms of the values of the parameter. For example, the hypotheses $\pi \geq 0.5$ and $\pi \leq 0.5$ could not be the null and alternative hypotheses because there is a value of the parameter (0.5) for which both are true; the hypotheses are not mutually exclusive in terms of the values of π.

In principle, there are no other restrictions on what the null and alternative hypotheses can be. In practice, the vast majority of statistical hypothesis tests are of one of the three forms presented before. For convenience, we summarize them in Table 12.1. As you can see in Table 12.1, a test is named by the form of H_1. The symbol θ stands for any parameter, such as μ, π, σ^2, etc. The notation θ_0 stands for a specific numerical value of the parameter, such as 0.25, $450, and so forth.

Type I and Type II Errors and Their Practical Consequences

The practice of testing a null hypothesis against an alternative on the basis of sample information will lead to two possible types of errors because of random fluctuations in sampling. In the one type, the null hypothesis is in fact true, but because sample data appear to be inconsistent with it, it is rejected. The error of rejecting a true H_0 is referred to as an *error of the first kind,* or a *type I error.* In the other type, H_0 is indeed false; yet, on the basis of sample information, we are led to accept it. The error of not rejecting a false H_0 is called an *error of the second kind,* or a *type II error.* Evidently, when we commit either type of error we are led to the selection of the wrong act. These comments are summarized in Table 12.2.

TABLE 12.2 Type I and Type II Errors and Decisions

Action taken on Basis of Sample Data	State of Nature	
	H_0 is true	H_1 is true
a_1: do not reject H_0	Correct act	Type II error
a_2: reject H_0	Type I error	Correct act

Note that the errors of testing are defined very abstractly. They are defined in terms of H_0 and H_1, no matter what these hypotheses may say and no matter what the practical actions may be that these statistical hypotheses are translated into. Note too that, at the time a decision is made from sample evidence, it is always thought that a correct decision is being made. No one deliberately makes a decision that one believes is a type I error or a type II error. Only with the aid of hindsight can a particular decision be known to be in error (or, for that matter, known to be correct). For example, suppose a new product must share more than 20% of the market in order to be financially successful. Then we have $H_0: \pi \leq 0.20$ and $H_1: \pi > 0.20$. Thus, H_0 states that the market share is too small to make a profit and H_1 states that the market share is large enough to make a profit, and if the sample results are encouraging, then H_0 is rejected. After a year or two of having the product on the market, it will be clear whether the new product is successful. If it is, rejecting H_0 was indeed a correct decision. If it is not, rejecting H_0 was a type I error.

It is helpful to state the practical consequences of type I and type II errors in any situation involving hypothesis testing. These statements are useful background in understanding the testing procedure. They are also useful, technically, in properly setting up the testing procedure. All of this will become clearer a little later; for the moment, let us illustrate what we mean by "stating the practical consequences" of type I and type II errors.

In the new-product example, where H_0 states essentially that the market does not like the product and H_1 states essentially that the market does like the product, what would a type I error be? By definition, a type I error is rejecting H_0 when you should not have. So the new product would be put on the market; it would fail, and the company would lose some money. Next, what would a type II error be? By definition, a type II error is not rejecting H_0 when you should have rejected it. So the product would be withheld from the market when it would have been a financial success, causing the company to miss some profit it could have earned.

It is also helpful to make a rough judgment about which type of error is the more serious or whether they are about equally serious. In the new-product example, which is worse: incurring a loss by marketing a product the public does not like, or missing a profit by not marketing a product the public would have liked? Many people jump immediately to the conclusion that an actual loss is much worse than a potential loss but this thinking may be deadly wrong. Consider the example of *Gone with the Wind*. It is said that Margaret Mitchell submitted her manuscript to scores of publishers before Macmillan pubished her novel in 1936. Despite the Great Depression of the 1930s, the book was an immediate huge success. By now, it has sold well over 10,000,000 copies, in 30 languages, in 40 countries. It has won a Pulitzer Prize. A classic movie has been made of it. The publishers who turned Margaret Mitchell down were certainly sorry when they saw how well Macmillan did with the book. Missing an opportunity to make a profit can be an extremely serious mistake indeed.

As another example of evaluating the consequences of type I and type II errors let us suppose a government agency wants to verify whether a particular brand of canned cat food actually delivers the 5 ounces of meat and meat products the label states as the weight each can contains. Of course, there are always random fluctuations of the weight from one can to another no matter how precisely the filling process is set. However, it is reasonable in a case such as this to insist the mean weight be at least 5 ounces. So we have $H_0: \mu \geq 5$ ounces and $H_1: \mu < 5$ ounces. Here H_0 essentially states that the cans have enough meat and meat products in them, and the alternative hypothesis states that they are short-filled. A type I error here involves the agency's believing the short-fill hypothesis, prosecuting for mislabeling, and almost certainly losing the case because the cans are really correctly filled. A type II error here involves thinking that the cans are all right when in fact they are short-filled and the agency should have prosecuted.

Which is more serious in this case, the type I error or the type II error? It is not easy to answer this question, but we urge the following argument. The type I error is more serious because it represents a complete waste of everybody's time and money, will lead to drastic changes in the government agency if it happens very often, tends to prevent the government agency from going after the clear cases of fraud it should be attacking, and puts the government in the position of harassing one of its own citizens when the citizen did nothing wrong. The government should be very sure it has a case before it acts, even if this means that slight amounts of short-filling are never prosecuted. You may argue differently, of course, and may reach a different conclusion.

Risks in Testing, and Decision Rules

The discussion of type I and type II errors leads us to consider the risks involved in hypothesis testing. First there is the *risk of type I error,* which is the probability of rejecting a true H_0. This probability, as noted before, is also called the *level of significance,* and it is universally denoted by α—hence the name α-*risk.* Second there is the *risk of type II error,* which is the probability of not rejecting a false H_0. This probability does not have a special name, but it is universally denoted by β—hence the name β-*risk.*

The possibilities of making type I and type II errors are ever-present; but the probabilities of making these errors can be held to low values. The fact that α and β can be held at reasonably low levels is one of the reasons why testing hypotheses is an attractive way of making decisions.

Let us turn our attention now to the notion of a decision rule. In testing hypotheses statistically, a *decision rule* should state (1) the type of sampling, (2) the sample size, (3) which values of the statistic lead to rejecting H_0, and (4) which values of the statistic lead to not rejecting H_0. Because SRS is assumed throughout our text and the sample size is explicitly stated in every example, we shall ignore (1) and (2) henceforth in our statements of decision rules. As for (3) and (4), we note that the critical values of the statistic are determined by the form of H_1 and the value of α. For example, we can state the decision rule for the coin-tossing example as follows, after recognizing that this is a two-side test and after setting α equal to 0.01.

H_0 will be rejected if and only if $\bar{P} < 0.4871$ or $\bar{P} > 0.5129$;

H_0 will not be rejected if and only if $0.4871 \leq \bar{P} \leq 0.5129$.

Is this a good decision rule? In general, what constitutes a good decision rule? This is not a simple question to answer. Roughly speaking for the time being, we may say that a good decision rule is one that will lead to a high probability of a correct decision, no matter what the value of the unknown parameter really is. Alternatively, a good decision rule is one for which both α-risk and β-risk are kept at very low levels.

At this point it may be pointed out that statistical testing can be conducted in two ways: in one the sample size is fixed, in the other the sample size is allowed to vary. With the first case, we can only specify the value of α and must let the value of β vary. For reasons to be stated shortly, this practice has its necessity as well as merits. Ideally, of course, we should specify both α-risk and β-risk at tolerable levels at each situation. To do this, we must find the sample size that can satisfy both specifications simultaneously. In this chapter we shall consider the fixed sample size only and the flexible sample size case will be introduced in the chapter that follows.

Choosing the Level of Significance

In our discussion of the practice of explicitly controlling α-risk alone, we should give a brief explanation of how the value of α should be determined for a given decision. Conventionally, α is often set equal to either 0.05 or 0.01. Being conventional values, both of them may be regarded as "safe" or "reasonable" values. However, this may overstate the appropriateness of setting α at 0.05 or 0.01. A much better practice than convention is comparison of the relative seriousness of type I and type II errors. If a type I error is definitely more serious than a type II error, then we should not commit it too often and then 0.01 is a more reasonable value for α. If a type II error is much more serious than a type I error then 0.05 is a more reasonable value for α.

It can happen that a type I error is about as serious as a type II error, but not more serious; then α should be set at 0.50 or near it. It can even happen that a type I error is definitely less serious than a type II error. Then α should be set at a value substantially above 0.50, say 0.75 or even 0.95 or 0.99.

The convention of setting α equal to 0.05 or 0.01 is often a good rule to follow, but not always. In general practice we often set α at a given level, such as 0.05 or 0.01, not at both levels. However, it may happen that, at the beginning, the decision maker is rather vague about the α-risk she is willing to assume. This being the case, it is quite proper to evaluate a test for both α-values and then decide, after the test is made, whether to act according to the test result for $\alpha = 0.05$ or for $\alpha = 0.01$.

12.3 A GENERAL PROCEDURE FOR TESTING

In the previous two sections, we relied heavily on the example of 5,070 heads out of 10,000 coin tosses to illustrate statistical hypothesis testing. We now restate the same ideas in a general and orderly way, so that they apply to many more situations than getting x heads in n tosses of a coin. There are six steps in statistical hypothesis testing.

(1) *State the hypotheses.* A hypothesis is any assertion about the numerical value of a parameter. Such an assertion is a translation from an existing theory, belief, or possible practical action into a statement about the numerical value of a parameter. Common practice is to state two hypotheses, H_0 and H_1. In principle, H_0 can be any assertion about the numerical value of parameter, in which case H_1 is the logical negation of H_0. In practice, H_0 is often an expression of the idea that the current procedure or belief is satisfactory, whereas H_1 expresses the idea that a new or experimental procedure or belief is better. In these cases, the null hypothesis often "nullifies a treatment," as when it asserts that a new drug is no better than an existing drug or that a new manufacturing procedure is no better than an existing manufacturing procedure. The null hypothesis is often not the hypothesis the investigator wants the sample evidence to support or believes that the sample evidence will support. Two conventions have arisen in statistical work for choosing which of two contradictory hypotheses should be regarded as H_0. If one of the hypotheses specifies a single value for the parameter, or a single sampling distribution for the statistic, make it H_0. If both hypotheses are of this character, or if neither is, choose H_0 in such a way that type I error is more serious than type II error.

(2) *Determine the level of significance.* Ideally, both α-risks and β-risks should be specified at appropriate levels for a statistical test. However, in this chapter, we adopt the practice of determining α, the level of significance, alone. This is often satisfactory in actual statistical applications, for two reasons. First, if a test is conducted by fixing both α and β at specific levels, the appropriate sample size must be found and used. However, limitations of time or money frequently determine the sample size, in which case it is reasonable to control the risk of type I error even though the risk of type II error is apparently not controlled. Second, as will be shown in Chapter 13, when α and n are fixed and when the true value of the parameter is very close to θ_0, β is very large. However, in such a case, the consequence of commiting type II error is not all serious. On the other hand, when the true parameter value differs from θ_0 by a great amount, to commit type II error is very serious, but then β will be very small.

Determining α requires at least a rough evaluation of the relative seriousness of type I and type II errors, and α should be selected in such a way that the more serious error has only a small probability of occurring. The conventional values of 0.05 and 0.01 for α are appropriate when type I error is the more serious. When both types of error are equally serious, setting α at 0.50 is suitable. When type II error is more serious, α should be set at very high values such as 0.95 or 0.99.

(3) *Select the test statistic.* The *test statistic* is the statistic for which the region of rejection will be calculated; alternatively it is the statistic whose sampling distribution is completely defined under the assumption that H_0 is true. If often turns out to be the estimator of the parameter stated in the null hypothesis. When the sampling distribution of the test statistic is normal, we always, for the sake of convenience, use the standard normal deviate of the statistic,

$$Z = \frac{\hat{\theta} - \theta_0}{\sigma_{\hat{\theta}}} \qquad (12.1\text{a})$$

as the *generalized test statistic.* If $\sigma_{\hat{\theta}}$ is unknown but $\hat{\theta}$ is normally distributed and n is sufficiently larger, we use

$$Z = \frac{\hat{\theta} - \theta_0}{S_{\hat{\theta}}} \qquad (12.1\text{b})$$

as the generalized test statistic. All the symbols in Equations (12.1) have the same meanings as in earlier definitions.

(4) *State the decision rule.* Given simple random sampling, the sample size, and the practice of using Z as the general test statistic, the decision rule for a test is stated in accordance with the type of test (the form of the alternative hypothesis) and the level of significance. For the three types of tests in Table 12.1 and for the two most frequently used levels of significance, the decision rules are as follows:

1. For a two-tail test, H_0 will be rejected at $\alpha = 0.05$ if and only if the computed Z-value is less than -1.96 or greater than 1.96. H_0 will be rejected at $\alpha = 0.01$ if and only if the computed Z-value is less than -2.58 or greater than 2.58.

2. For an upper-tail (or right-tail) test, H_0 will be rejected at $\alpha = 0.05$ if and only if the computed Z-value is greater than 1.64. H_0 will be rejected at $\alpha = 0.01$ if and only if the computed Z-value is greater than 2.33.

3. For a lower-tail (or left-tail) test, H_0 will be rejected at $\alpha = 0.05$ if and only if the computed Z-value is less than -1.64. H_0 will be rejected at $\alpha = 0.01$ if and only if the computed Z-value is less than -2.33.

The rejection regions for all of these cases are illustrated in Figure 12.2. Throughout Figure 12.2 it is assumed that H_0 is true and that $E(\hat{\theta})$ equals the θ_0 of Equation (12.1a). Critical Z-values for other

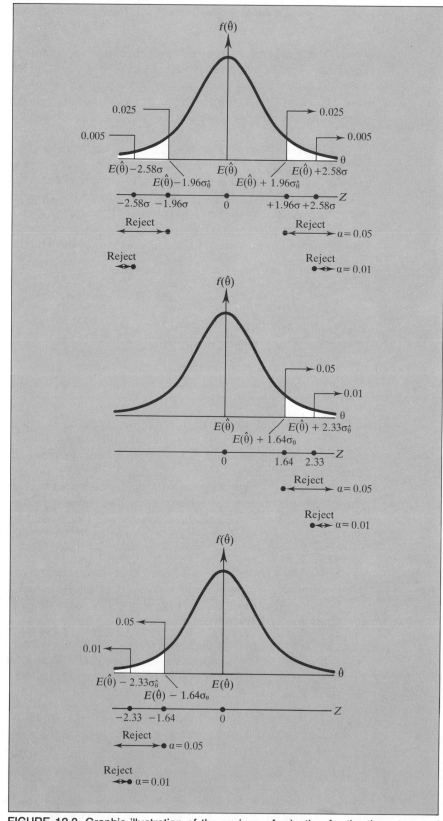

FIGURE 12.2 Graphic illustration of the regions of rejection for the three types of testing hypothesis at $\alpha = 0.05$ and $\alpha = 0.01$.

levels of significance can be found from the normal probability table in Appendix C.

(5) *Gather and analyze the sample evidence.* This is a routine but time-consuming step. Analyzing the sample evidence means making the calculations needed to see whether the test statistic is in the region of rejection.

(6) *Make a decision.* From the result in step (5) decide to reject or not to reject H_0 in accordance with the decision rule of the test, and then make a decision accordingly by selecting either a_1 or a_2.

Note that the foregoing procedure makes no provision for calculating whether β is satisfactorily low. If α is set equal to either conventional value, 0.05 or 0.01, not rejecting H_0 might be committing a serious type II error.

The rest of the chapter contains a series of illustrations of our general testing procedure, showing how to apply it to several common situations. We restrict ourselves to cases in which the normal distribution applies, just as we did in our discussion of confidence intervals in the last chapter. It may be noted now, however, that this same general procedure can also be applied to statistical tests in which the sampling distribution of the test statistic is not normal. We discuss such applications in later chapters.

Furthermore, our general procedure may be considered as an outline that should be followed when testing a statistical hypothesis. There are a number of obvious advantages in such a practice, especially for those who are not familiar with testing. It may even prove worthwhile for an experienced statistician, because others may wish to read and study his results. So it is best that you write out these steps clearly in each test at the beginning. When you become quite familiar with the procedure, you may merely do the computations and draw conclusion from them. Even then you should at least keep these steps in your mind all the time.

12.4 TESTING HYPOTHESES ABOUT μ

The population mean is a very important decision parameter. Often we wish to know whether a population mean has increased, or decreased, or remained unchanged. Or we may be interested in determining whether a population mean is different from some assumed value in a new situation. Can a new assembly procedure really reduce the mean time of assembling a certain mechanism? Has the real per capita income in the People's Republic of China increased at all since its modernization program beginning in the early 1980s? Has there been no change in the mean lifespan of American males during the past decade? Is the average number of recoveries from a certain disease with a new treatment really greater than that with the old? Is the mean tensile strength of a new make of steel wires significantly greater than that of the old? Each of these questions and many more can be answered by testing about μ. Let us turn to provide a few numerical examples.

Example 1 Two-tail Test

A floor-wax factory has nationwide selling outlets. In the past couple of years, its salesmen earned a mean commission of $600 per week with a standard deviation of $80. Recently, new brands of floor wax have entered the market. This factor tends to reduce the volume of sales per salesman and thus, to reduce the salesmen's income. Meanwhile, the list price of the firm's output has increased along with the general price inflation; this factor tends to increase the salesmen's commission per sale. The management of the firm is anxious to discover the net effect of these two factors on its thousands of salesmen's commission. To achieve this, the following decision procedure is adopted.

1. *Hypotheses.* H_0: $\mu = \$600$; H_1: $\mu \neq \$600$.

2. *Level of significance.* $\alpha = 0.05$. We use a conventional value of 0.05, realizing that it may not be fully justified until we know more about the practical consequences of type I and type II errors.

3. *Test statistic.* $Z = (\bar{X} - \mu_0)/\sigma_{\bar{X}}$, which is a standard normal variate under the assumption that H_0 is true.

4. *Decision criterion.* With $\alpha = 0.05$ for a two-tail test the decision rule becomes: Reject H_0 if and only if $|Z| > 1.96$. That is, reject H_0 if and only if $Z < -1.96$ or $Z > 1.96$.

5. *Computations.* Suppose that a sample of $n = 100$ is drawn from all the salesmen's commission accounts, (totaling over 3,000 units), and it is found that $\bar{x} = \$585$. Also, since $\sigma = \$80$, we have

$$\sigma_{\bar{X}} = \frac{80}{\sqrt{100}} = 8$$

and

$$z = \frac{585 - 600}{8} = -1.88.$$

In computing the standard error here we have ignored FPCF because $n \leq 0.05N$. Moreover, we have also assumed that σ has remained unchanged.

6. *Decisions.* $z = -1.88$, which falls in the acceptance region; therefore, H_0 cannot be rejected. This result indicates that the difference of $15 may be attributed to random fluctuations in the sample statistic and that it is not significant at an α-risk of 0.05. Since the sample result led us to conclude that the salesmen's monthly mean income has not changed, management need no longer be concerned with this problem for now.

It is perhaps more appropriate for this problem to state the alternative hypothesis as $\mu < \$600$, since management would have no trouble if the mean commission were greater than $600. Had the alternative hypothesis been so designated, we would reject H_0 for the same level of significance of 0.05 if and only if $Z < -1.64$. Recall that the computed z-value for the present test is -1.88, which is less than -1.64. Thus, the same difference that is insignificant for a two-tail test may become significant for a single-tail test. Further, had we decided to conduct a left-tail test, the managerial decision would be entirely different for the same sample results. Instead of choosing to do nothing (because H_0 was not rejected) management might (because of the acceptance of H_1) act in one or more ways to keep its sales force intact: step up its advertising campaign in order to increase its sales; increase the percentage of commission paid; or improve the quality of its output in order to improve its competitive strength.

These observations indicate the importance of formulating hypotheses and specifying the level of significance, thereby establishing the decision rule, before the collection and observation of data. Unless the required procedure is followed, we may be led to conduct a statistical test within the framework of a decision procedure that is both suggested by and tested by the same sample results, and this is improper.

Example 2 Lower-tail Test

The average distance for stopping a certain make of automobile while it is traveling 30 miles an hour is 60 feet. The engineering department of the company has designed a new brake system thought to be more effective. To test this invention, the new brake system is installed in 64 cars; tests show that the average distance for stopping a car at a speed of 30 miles an hour is 53.5 feet, with standard deviation of 4 feet. Does the difference of 6.5 feet indicate that the new brake system is more effective than the old?

Now, if the management wishes to avoid the mistake of adopting the new brake system if it really should not, the question can be answered by the following test.

1. *Hypotheses.* H_0: $\mu \geqslant 60$ feet; H_1: $\mu < 60$ feet.

2. *Level of significance.* $\alpha = 0.01$. We specify this value of α because we believe the investment for producing the new brake system is quite expensive and we do not want to reject H_0 too easily.

3. *Test statistic.* $Z = (\bar{X} - \mu_0)/\sigma_{\bar{X}}$.

4. *Decision criterion.* Reject H_0 if and only if $Z < -2.33$.

5. *Computations.* The sample mean, with $n = 64$, was given before as 53.5 feet. The standard deviation of the population is unknown in this case, but the sample is large enough for us to estimate it by s, which was given as 4 feet. Thus,

$$s_{\bar{X}} = \frac{s}{\sqrt{n}} = \frac{4}{\sqrt{64}} = 0.5$$

and

$$z = \frac{\bar{x} - \mu_0}{s_{\bar{x}}} = \frac{53.5 - 60}{0.5}$$

$$= -13.00.$$

6. *Decision.* Since $z = -13.00 < -2.33$ H_0 is rejected. The new brake system is more effective than the old. The management should seriously consider its adoption.

Example 3 Upper-tail Test

Suppose you are the purchasing agent of New York Subway Authority, and a lightbulb salesman calls on you, saying, "We now have a new long-life electric lightbulb that costs more but can save you money in the long run because your maintenance department spends less time replacing lightbulbs, you need fewer bulbs in your own inventory, and there are fewer accidents because of burned-out bulbs." His arguments sound attractive, so you ask the salesman for some hard data on the lives of the bulbs. He gives you a data sheet prepared by an independent testing laboratory that drew a random sample of 625 bulbs and measured the life of each bulb in the sample. You check with the lab and they verify that they prepared the data sheet. After some financial calculations of your own, you conclude that, if $\mu > 3,000$ hours, there will be savings compared with the bulbs you are now using; if $\mu = 3,000$ hours, there will be no savings but no extra cost, either, this being the economic break-even point; and if $\mu < 3,000$ hours, there will be extra cost instead of any savings. The sample results are $\bar{x} = 3,950$ hours and $s = 300.6$ hours. What should you do?

Here, we want convincing evidence in favor of the change to the new lightbulbs before making the change, because changing an existing procedure is always upsetting and costly. The hypotheses, therefore, should be stated as follows:

$$H_0: \mu \leq 3,000 \text{ hours} \quad \text{and} \quad H_1: \mu > 3,000 \text{ hours}.$$

A reasonable value for α in this situation is the conventional value of 0.05. The test statistic, as before, is Z and for this example,

$$z = \frac{\bar{x} - \mu_0}{s_{\bar{x}}} = \frac{3,950 - 3,000}{\dfrac{300.6}{\sqrt{625}}} = 79.01.$$

So $z = 79.01 > +1.64$. H_0 is rejected at $\alpha = 0.05$. (In this calculation, we have assumed the population is very large and so the FPCF is not needed to compute the standard error.)

We reject H_0 here. Does this mean we have proved that savings will follow from switching to the new bulb? The z-value of 79.01 is certainly impressive when all it takes to get into the region of rejection is 1.64. The impressiveness of the z-value means that a type I error is fantastically improbable. In that sense, we almost have logical proof that rejecting H_0 is a correct decision and, therefore, that savings will follow. There are other problems, though. We have trusted the independent lab's data sheet, and there is some chance that it has errors in it or even that it is fraudulent (a fake paid for with illegal bribes), despite the reputation of the lab. This would ordinarily seem to be a remote chance, though—not worth worrying about except for extremely important decisions. We have trusted our own financial calculations, which produced 3,000 hours as the financial break-even point. There may be mistakes in these calculations. Finally, we have assumed that the lightbulbs produced in the future will be of the same quality as those tested by the lab. if the manufacture has a good reputation, this problem is scarcely worth worrying about, either. We have good, solid evidence, almost logical proof, that the savings will occur.

12.5 TESTING HYPOTHESES ABOUT π

We have seen that situations often arise in which sampling is used to determine an attribute rather than the mean value of a population. In such a case, observations are qualitative in nature. Sampling attributes, as we already know, reveals information as to whether workers are males or females, whether products are defective or nondefective, and so forth. A population, of course, may contain more than two mutually exclusive categories. However, it is always possible to group the elementary units in a population into two mutually exclusive qualitative classes. For instance, voters may be Republican, Democratic, Liberal, or Independent, but all of those who are eligible to vote can be classified as being in favor or against a given candidate.

In any event, when we analyze qualitative data, we are interested in verifying an assumption made about the population proportion of success, π. Here, we would like to test the hypothesis about π with the sample proportion $\bar{P}$ as the testing statistic. (The standaridized test statistic here is $Z = (\bar{P} - \pi_0)/\sigma_{\bar{P}}$). Also, in such a test, we compute the standard error of $\bar{P}$ by using π_0 in the null hypothesis. This is a logical practice because in our test the sampling distribution of the testing statistic is determined under the assumption that the null hypothesis is true.

Example 1 Two-tail Test

The manufacturer of a patent medicine claims that its product is 70% effective in giving immediate relief from skin itches, from any cause. The American Medical Association, hoping to verify this claim, appoints a committee of seven skin specialists to evaluate the effectiveness of this medicine. Some members of the committee are confident that the manufacturer's claim could not be possibly true (owing to their past experience with similar drugs), but others suspect that the claim might be valid, so it is finally agreed that both alternatives should be considered. Also, after some thought, it is decided to set α at 0.01 and to try the medicine on 200 of all the patients who have skin disorders. In other words, the testing procedure is designed as follows.

1. *Hypotheses.* H_0: $\pi = 0.70$; H_1: $\pi \neq 0.70$.

2. *Level of significance.* $\alpha = 0.01$.

3. *Testing statistic.* $Z = (\bar{P} - \pi_0)/\sigma_{\bar{P}}$, which is a standard normal variate if H_0 is true.

4. *Decision rule.* Reject H_0 if and only if $Z < -2.58$ or $Z > 2.58$.

5. *Computations.* Suppose that among the 200 patients treated by this medicine, 125 experienced immediate relief; then $\bar{p} = 0.625$. Also, for this test,

$$\sigma_{\bar{P}} = \sqrt{\frac{\pi_0(1 - \pi_0)}{n}} = \sqrt{\frac{0.7(0.3)}{200}} = 0.0324;$$

$$z = \frac{0.625 - 0.700}{0.0324} = -2.31.$$

6. *Decisions.* Since $z = -2.31 > -2.58$, H_0 cannot be rejected. A difference of -0.075 between the sample proportion and the hypothetical value of π is not sufficient to disprove the manufacturer's claim. If the new drug does not have any undesirable side effects, it should be recommended for use.

Example 2 Lower-tail Test

A producer of 100% pasteurized pure orange juice claims that more than 30% of all orange juice drinkers prefer its product. To verify the plausibility of this claim, a competitor finds that in a sample of 150 orange drinkers only 39, or 26%, of those sampled preferred the said producer's brand. In view of this sample evidence, what conclusion can the competitor reach in terms of testing at, say, $\alpha = 0.05$?

In this case, the hypotheses should be stated as H_0: $\pi \geq 0.30$ and H_1: $\pi < 0.30$. This is a left-tail test. It is appropriate because the competitor is primarily interested in verifying the producer's claim against the alternative that its market share is not as large as claimed. Now, with data the competitor has gathered, we have

$$\bar{p} = 39/150 = 0.26;$$

$$\sigma_{\bar{P}} = \sqrt{\frac{0.3(0.7)}{150}} = 0.0374;$$

$$z = \frac{0.26 - 0.30}{0.0374} \doteq -1.07.$$

The computed $z = -1.07$ is greater than the critical z-value of -1.64. Hence, H_0 cannot be rejected at $\alpha = 0.05$ here. The competitor has to conclude that the claim made by the producer is not unfounded in terms of sample observations. There are, therefore, no grounds for the competitor to pursue this matter any further.

Example 3 Upper-tail Test

Suppose a television network has a policy of retaining a certain type of program without any changes at all if it is convincingly clear that at least 15% of all television viewers watch the program. Otherwise, the program will be considered for a shift to another time slot, for major changes in format and characters, or for outright cancellation. Suppose a national TV survey with $n = 1,600$ shows that 20% of the sample watched the program. Is it convincingly clear that more than 15% of all television viewers watched the program? To answer this question, we test $H_0: \pi \leqslant 0.15$ against $H_1: \pi > 0.15$. With the information given we have

$$z = \frac{\bar{P} - \pi}{\sigma_{\bar{P}}} = \frac{0.20 - 0.15}{\sqrt{\dfrac{0.15(0.05)}{1,600}}} = +5.60,$$

which is greater than $+1.64$ as well as greater than $+2.33$. H_0 is rejected at $\alpha = 0.05$ as well as at $\alpha = 0.01$. Note that the calculated value of z is so far into the region of rejection that rejecting H_0 is almost certainly a correct decision and not a type I error. This result would lead to the decision of retaining the program without any changes by the network.

12.6 TESTING HYPOTHESES ABOUT $\Delta\mu$

The evaluation of a possible difference between two population means is a type of decision situation that happen quite frequently. Is the mean income of carpenters really greater than that of college professors in the United States? Do two routes leading to an airport from a given location require the same mean travelling time? Could two manufacturing procedures produce auto tires with identical mean durability? If two makes of automobiles are sold at the same price, are their gasoline consumptions in terms of miles traveled per gallon also the same? If one drug more efficient than another so far the mean numbers of recovery of patients are concerned? The questions stated here are but a few of many of the cases in which a knowledge of the difference $\Delta\mu$ between two populations means can help us to find an answer.

Of course, to test a hypothesis about $\Delta\mu$, the test statistic is $Z = (\Delta\bar{X} - \Delta\mu_0)/\sigma_{\Delta\bar{X}}$. Here, as in our discussion in the previous two chapters, we shall be only concerned with the case of independent samples. As a reminder, you may recall that two samples are said to be independent if a first sample is selected from one population and a second sample is selected from a different population and if they are drawn in such a way that the selection of the sample elements from one population has no effect on the selection of sample elements from the other population.

Example 1 Two-tail Test

An agricultural experimental station is trying to compare the yields of two types of corn. Each variety of corn is planted on 64 acres of land and both varieties are exposed to fairly uniform growing conditions. The results are: the average yield of variety A is 215 bushels per acre with a standard deviation of 10 bushels; the average yield of variety B is 200 bushels per acre with a standard deviation of 9 bushels. Let us now analyze these data by way of a two-tail test.

1. *Hypotheses*. In this case the hypotheses can be stated in either of the following two ways.

   (a) $\qquad H_0: \mu_1 - \mu_2 = 0; \qquad H_1: \mu_1 - \mu_2 \neq 0;$

   (b) $\qquad H_0: \Delta\mu = 0, \qquad H_1: \Delta\mu \neq 0.$

2. *Level of significance.* $\alpha = 0.05, 0.01$. We have set both of the two conventional levels of significance here because we assume that the management team of the experimental station have not quite made up their minds about the α-risk they are willing to assume in the recommendation of one variety over the other.

3. *Test statistic.* $Z = (\Delta\bar{X} - \Delta\mu_0)/\sigma_{\Delta\bar{x}}$, which is a standard normal deviate under the assumption that H_0 is true. The assumption of normality is quite appropriate here because we suspect that the yields are normally distributed and that the sample of 64 acres each is quite large even when σ_1 and σ_2 are unknown.

4. *Decision criterion.* Reject H_0 at $\alpha = 0.05$ if $Z < -1.96$ or $Z > +1.96$; reject H_0 at $\alpha = 0.01$ if $Z < -2.58$ or if $Z > +2.58$.

5. *Computations.* Since

$$n_1 = n_2 = 64;$$

$$\bar{x}_1 = 215, \qquad \bar{x}_2 = 200; \qquad s_1 = 10, \qquad s_2 = 9;$$

we have

$$\Delta\bar{x} = 215 - 200 = 15;$$

$$s_{\Delta\bar{x}} = \sqrt{\frac{10^2}{64} + \frac{9^2}{64}} \doteq 1.68.$$

With these results, we see that

$$z = \frac{15 - 0}{1.68} \doteq 8.93.$$

Note that in the calculation of the standard error, FPCF has not been used because we have assumed the samples have been selected from the thousands of acres of land the experimental station may have available for its use.

6. *Decision.* The computed z-value of $+8.93$ leads to the rejection of H_0 at both levels of significance of $\alpha = 0.05, 0.01$. In view of the fact that the z-value is positive, variety A's average yield is significantly greater than that of variety B.

Note also that for this test the two samples must be independent. Independence can be achieved in this case by, say, dividing the thousands of acres of land into two equal parts at random (each of the two parts may be considered as a different population), and then selecting an SRS from each part.

Example 2 Upper-tail Test

A savings bank is considering two potential sites, in a fast-growing new residential town that now consists of more than 30,000 families, on which to build a new branch. The price of site I is much higher than that of site II. However, if the annual mean family income in site I is \$3,500 more than that in site II, it still pays to build the branch on site I. Suppose the bank wishes to demonstrate this possibility by testing; the hypotheses may be stated as follows:

$$H_0: \Delta\mu \leqslant 3{,}500; \qquad H_1: \Delta\mu > 3{,}500.$$

Owing to the fact that income distributions are usually positively skewed, the bank takes a sample of size 250 from the families around each of the sites in order to be in no doubt that the sampling distribution of $\Delta\bar{X}$ is very close to a normal distribution. Furthermore, if the bank is willing to assume an α-risk of 0.05, then H_0 will be rejected if and only if the computed z-value is greater than $+1.64$.

Now, suppose, the bank's survey has yielded the data below:

$$n_1 = n_2 = 250;$$

$$\bar{x}_1 = 32{,}156, \qquad \bar{x}_2 = 28{,}180;$$

$$s_1^2 = 7{,}025{,}000, \qquad s_2^2 = 6{,}749{,}500.$$

With these preliminary findings we have

$$\Delta\bar{x} = 32{,}156 - 28{,}180 = \$3{,}976;$$

$$s_{\Delta\bar{x}} = \sqrt{\frac{7{,}025{,}000}{250} + \frac{6{,}749{,}500}{250}} \doteq 234.73;$$

$$z = \frac{\Delta\bar{X} - \Delta\mu_0}{s_{\Delta\bar{x}}} = \frac{3{,}976 - 3{,}500}{234.73} \doteq 2.03.$$

Since this computed z-value is greater than $+1.64$, H_0 is rejected at $\alpha = 0.05$. The bank may now decide to select site I to build its new branch in that town.

Example 3 Lower-tail Test

Suppose that in a single-industry town there are 22,000 machine operators in employment. Of this labor force, 19,950 are males and 2,050 are females. An economist has claimed the mean weekly wages of the male workers is at least $30 more than that of the female workers. A statistician engaged by the industry tried to find out whether the economist's claim is reasonable by selecting a sample from each sex of the workers and obtained the following results:

Male Workers	Female Workers
$N_1 = 19,950$	$N_2 = 2,050$
$n_1 = 120$	$n_2 = 120$
$\bar{x}_1 = \$265$	$\bar{x}_2 = \$226$
$s_1^2 = 195$	$s_2^2 = 121$

With these data he proceeded to test $H_0: \Delta\mu \geqslant 30$ against $H_1: \Delta\mu < 30$. With the preliminary information gathered above, we have

$$\Delta\bar{x} = 265 - 226 = \$34; \quad s_{\bar{X}_1}^2 = \frac{s_1^2}{n_1} = \frac{195}{120} \doteq 1.6250;$$

$$s_{\bar{X}_2}^2 = \left(\frac{s_2^2}{n_2}\right)\left(\frac{N_2 - n_2}{N_2 - 1}\right) = \left(\frac{121}{120}\right)\left(\frac{2,050 - 120}{2,050 - 1}\right) \doteq 0.9498;$$

$$s_{\Delta\bar{x}} = \sqrt{1.6250 + 0.9498} \doteq 1.6046.$$

Finally,

$$z = \frac{34 - 30}{1.6046} \doteq +2.49,$$

which leads to the nonrejection of H_0 at $\alpha = 0.05$ as well as at $\alpha = 0.01$. There is significant statistical evidence that the male workers indeed make more by $30 a week on the average than the female workers. However, you should not jump to the conclusion of the seeming implication of sex discrimination that might be practiced by the industry. There may be other factors more appropriate to explain the difference in mean wages in this case. For example, the male workers may be more experienced and may have been in employment longer on the average than the female workers, and so on. Here is an example of the fact that statistical significance may not necessary be of practical importance. Furthermore, you should realize by now that, very often, statistics must be used with other relevant considerations to solve problems in many decision situations.

12.7 TESTING HYPOTHESES ABOUT $\Delta\pi$

Is *Dynasty* a more popular TV program than *Dallas*? Which of the two potential candidates in a given political party is more visible among the potential voters? Is there a real difference in the fraction defective of a product produced by two different manufacturing process? When we conduct a mail survey, can we really receive a greater response when we include a dollar bill in the mailing than when we do not adopt such a practice? Are there today more people in their forties who cannot read or write than those in their fifties? These questions are examples of decision situations in which we are interested in finding out whether two populations differ with respect to some attribute. Problems of this kind can be treated by testing hypotheses about $\Delta\pi$ with $Z = (\Delta\bar{P} - \Delta\pi_0)/\sigma_{\Delta\bar{P}}$ as the test statistic.

Example 1 Two-tail Test

Suppose we wish to determine whether there is a regional difference in the preference for a particular TV program between northern and southern audiences in the East of the United States. For this, suppose a sample of 1,500 families has been selected from a small town in Maine with 25,000 families, and another sample of 1,500 families has been taken from a small town with 27,500 families in Florida. Both towns are considered as "typical" cities. Furthermore, suppose 213 families in the northern town and 252 families in the southern town, respectively, are found to be watching the program on one day. In view of these findings can we reject $H_0: \Delta\pi = 0$ against $H_1: \Delta\pi \neq 0$ at $\alpha = 0.05$?

With the information provided, we have

$$\bar{p}_1 = \frac{213}{1,500} = 0.142, \qquad \bar{p}_2 = \frac{252}{1,500} = 0.168;$$

$$\Delta\bar{p} = 0.142 - 0.168 = -0.026;$$

$$s^2_{\bar{P}_1} = \left(\frac{\bar{p}_1\bar{p}_1'}{n_1}\right)\left(\frac{N_1 - n_1}{N_1 - 1}\right)$$

$$= \left(\frac{0.142(0.858)}{1,500}\right)\left(\frac{25,000 - 1,500}{25,000 - 1}\right)$$

$$= 0.0000764,$$

$$s^2_{\bar{P}_2} = \left(\frac{\bar{p}_2\bar{p}_2'}{n_2}\right)\left(\frac{N_2 - n_2}{N_2 - 1}\right)$$

$$= \left(\frac{0.168(0.832)}{1,500}\right)\left(\frac{27,500 - 1,500}{27,500 - 1}\right)$$

$$= 0.0000881;$$

$$s_{\Delta\bar{P}} = \sqrt{s^2_{\bar{P}_1} + s^2_{\bar{P}_2}}$$

$$= \sqrt{0.0000764 + 0.0000881}$$

$$= 0.01283.$$

Finally, we have

$$z = \frac{\Delta\bar{p} - \Delta\pi_0}{s_{\Delta\bar{p}}} = \frac{-0.026 - 0}{0.01283}$$

$$\doteq -2.03.$$

Here, the critical z-value $= -1.96$. H_0 should be rejected in favor of H_1. There exists a northern preference for the TV program that cannot be explained by chance variation alone.

Example 2 Upper-tail Test

A major manufacturing company has two factories, both of which have identical facilities and production procedures. Each factory produces over 50,000 units of output per day. It has been suspected for quite a while that one of the factories has consistently produced products with a higher percentage of defectives than the other. To determine whether this suspicion is indeed founded, a sample of $n = 1,600$ is selected for testing from each of the factories from a certain day's output. It has been found that the fractions of defectives in the samples are $\bar{p}_1 = 0.079$ and $\bar{p}_2 = 0.064$, respectively. In view of the empirical evidence, can we reject H_0: $\Delta\pi \leqslant 0$ in favor of H_1: $\Delta\pi > 0$ at $\alpha = 0.05$?

To answer this question, we note that

$$\Delta\bar{p} = 0.079 - 0.064 = 0.015;$$

$$s_{\Delta\bar{p}} = \sqrt{\frac{0.064(0.936)}{1,600} + \frac{0.079(0.921)}{1,600}}$$

$$\doteq 0.0091.$$

Thus,

$$z = \frac{0.015 - 0}{0.0091} \doteq +1.65.$$

So, $z = +1.65 > +1.64$. It seems we should reject H_0 at $\alpha' = 0.05$. However, this test is actually inconclusive. The computed z-value of $+1.65$ is so close to $+1.64$—the critical z-value in this case—that it is not clear that any conclusion should be made at all.

Very often we find that the computed Z-value of the test statistic is very close to the critical Z-value. When this happens, the mathematical precision of hypothesis testing should not be allowed to overrule common sense. In the example here, the computed z-value of $+1.65$ is undoubtedly in the region of rejection. However, the region of rejection and that of nonrejection, given the form of H_1, is determined by the value of α. Had we selected a level of significance of 0.06, the computed z-value of $+1.65$ would unquestionably be in the region of nonrejection, since the critical z-value would then be $+1.55$. It is certainly unimaginable that we could compare the seriousness of committing type I and type II errors so carefully and precisely that the value of 0.05

should be used instead of 0.06 in all circumstances. It is primarily this vagueness of the value of α that leads us to say that the testing result in our current example is inconclusive. In this case, the management may perhaps conduct a supplementary investigation that would, in effect, increase the sample size before a more concrete conclusion could be made.

Example 3 Lower-tail Test

Social scientists have realized for a long time that per capita income alone does not measure the standard and quality of living. Many other intangible factors such as equitable distribution of income, sociopolitical and legal justice, freedom from pollution and crime, and so on, also contribute to the total welfare of a nation. To throw some light on the issue of crime, an economist has taken a sample of 1,200 people in the United States and another sample of same size has been taken in Canada. All were asked the question: "Are you afraid to walk on the streets in your neighborhood at night?" To this question, 34% in the American sample answered "Yes"; while only 29% in the Canadian sample yielded the same answer. In view of these results, can we conclude that there is a true positive difference between the proportions of Americans and Canadians so far as their fears of street crimes are concerned?

To answer this question, we may test $H_0: \Delta\pi \geq 0$ against $H_1: \Delta\pi < 0$. From the data given, we have

$$\bar{p}_1 = 0.34, \qquad \bar{p}_2 = 0.29, \qquad \Delta\bar{p} = 0.05;$$

$$s_{\Delta\bar{p}} = \sqrt{\frac{(0.34)(0.66)}{1,200} + \frac{(0.29)(0.71)}{1,200}} \doteq 0.0189;$$

$$z = \frac{0.05 - 0}{0.0189} \doteq +2.65.$$

Since the computed Z-value is greater than -2.33, H_0 cannot be rejected at $\alpha = 0.01$. The Americans do indeed have a greater fear of street crime than the Canadians.

12.8 THE CORRESPONDENCE BETWEEN CONFIDENCE INTERVAL AND HYPOTHESIS TESTING

If you have studied the first section of this chapter very carefully, you may have already detected that there is a close relationship between confidence interval and hypothesis testing. As a matter of fact the classical theories of interval estimation and testing are but two different methods for achieving the same goal of throwing some light on the true value of a constant but unknown parameter. In general, any null hypothesis is rejected at α if θ_0 falls outside of the confidence interval with $1 - \alpha$, since such a hypothesis is considered as implausible. On the other hand, any null hypothesis is considered as plausible and cannot be rejected at α if θ_0 falls within the confidence interval with $1 - \alpha$. These statements are intuitively clear if you simply recall what we mean by a composite hypothesis and a confidence interval. This understanding would also lead us to the realization that a confidence interval is in effect a set of plausible hypotheses. From this identity, and when a confidence interval is constructed with $1 - \alpha$, it is quite proper to say that a null hypothesis is being tested with a confidence interval with $1 - \alpha$. Traditionally, though, we usually speak of testing at a risk (percentage of error) of α. In both cases, however, the error level is α.

To be more specific and precise, let us relate each of the three types of hypothesis testing to a proper form of confidence interval with numerical examples. First of all, for a two-tail test with $H_0: \theta = \theta_0$ and $H_1: \theta \neq \theta_0$, the corresponding confidence interval is obviously of the symmetric form with which we are now quite familiar; that is,

$$L, U = \hat{\theta} \mp Z_{\alpha/2}\sigma_{\hat{\theta}}.$$

Consider, for instance, the first example of a two-tail test in Section 12.4 about the mean commission of salesmen for a floor-wax factory. In that example, the null hypothesis of $\mu = \$600$ was not rejected at $\alpha = 0.05$. Now, if we construct a 95% confidence interval for μ, we would have

$$L, U = \bar{x} \mp z_{0.025}\sigma_{\bar{X}} = 585 \mp 1.96(8) = 569.32 \text{ to } 600.68.$$

From this result, we see that $\mu = \$600$ is a plausible hypothesis, since it falls within the confidence interval.

If we are conducting single-tail tests, the corresponding confidence intervals should be single-sided. Such confidence intervals were not discussed in the preceding chapter. We present them now.

When we are interested in establishing that a parameter value is at most as large as a specified quantity, the correct procedure is to construct a one-sided confidence interval of the following form:

$$\theta < \hat{\theta} + Z_\alpha\sigma_{\hat{\theta}}, \tag{12.2}$$

where we put the total allowance of error, α, in one tail as in the single-tail test case. Furthermore (12.2) corresponds to a lower-tail test and, thus, it can be properly called as the *left-side confidence interval*.

As an illustration of the application of (12.2), consider the brake system example in Section 12.4. There, $H_0: \mu \geq 60$ feet was rejected at $\alpha = 0.01$. Now, with the same data, the 99% left-side confidence interval is

$$\bar{x} + z_{0.01}s_{\bar{X}} = 53.5 + 2.33(0.5) = 54.665.$$

This result is interpreted the following way. With $\bar{x} = 53.5$, we can say with 99% confidence that the true value of μ cannot be greater than 54.665. Since $\mu = 60 > 54.665$, H_0 in this case is not a plausible hypothesis and it should be rejected, as it was.

One unfortunate aspect of (12.2) is that it does not provide a unique lower bound explicitly. However, it can be reasoned that an arbitrary lower confidence limit can be determined once the parameter being estimated is specified. In the case of μ, for example, we know that it can assume any value between $-\infty$ to $+\infty$. Hence, we may use $-\infty$ as the arbitrary lower bound and our previous result can be written as

$$-\infty < \mu < 54.665.$$

which evidently does not include 60.

Occasions may arise when we seek to determine a parameter value that is at least as large as a given figure. For this purpose, the appropriate one-sided confidence interval takes the form

$$\theta > \hat{\theta} - Z_\alpha \sigma_{\hat{\theta}} \qquad (12.3)$$

This type of confidence interval corresponds to an upper-tail test and, therefore, we may name it as the *right-side confidence interval*.

For illustration, let us return to the TV program example in Section 12.6. In this case, $H_0: \pi \leq 0.15$ was rejected at $\alpha = 0.01$ with $\bar{p} = 0.20$. For the same problem the 99% right-side confidence interval is

$$\pi > \bar{p} - z_{0.01}\sigma_{\bar{p}} = 0.20 - 2.33(0.008927) \doteq 0.1792.$$

We interpret this result as follows. If $\bar{p} = 0.20$, we are 99% confident that the true value of π should be at least greater than 0.1792. So $\pi = 0.15$ is not a plausible hypothesis at $\alpha = 0.01$.

Note that (12.3) does not provide us with an explicit and unique upper bound. However, again, when the parameter in question is specified, an arbitrary upper confidence limit can be given. In our current discussion we are concerned with π—a parameter whose value ranges from 0 to 1. Thus, we can select 1 as the arbitrary upper bound and write our previous result as below:

$$0.1792 < \pi < 1.0000,$$

which does not contain 0.15, the null hypothetical value of π. So, 0.15 is not a member of the set of plausible hypotheses in $H_0: \pi \leq 0.15$.

In conclusion, we state that once a confidence interval is constructed, it can be used to determine whether a hypothesis is plausible or not and, therefore, the confidence interval can be used to test any hypothesis immediately. Indeed, you will see that the decision rules for testing taken up in the following chapter are but alternative versions of confidence intervals.

GLOSSARY OF FORMULAS

(12.1a) $Z = \dfrac{\hat{\theta} - \theta_0}{\sigma_\theta};$

(12.1b) $Z = \dfrac{\hat{\theta} - \theta_0}{S_{\hat{\theta}}}.$

If the test statistic $\hat{\theta}$ is normally distributed, then we can use the standard normal deviate as the *generalized test statistic*. Here, θ_0 is the assumed value of θ in the null hypothesis and $S_{\hat{\theta}}$, of course, is the estimator for $\sigma_{\hat{\theta}}$. When σ is unknown and when n is sufficiently large for the CLT to be operative, (12.1b) can be used without significant loss of accuracy.

(12.2) $\theta < \hat{\theta} + Z_\alpha \sigma_{\hat{\theta}}.$

This expression gives us the *left-side confidence interval*. It is used in estimation when we wish to find the parameter value that is at most as large as specified quantity. It corresponds to a lower-tail test.

(12.3) $\theta > \hat{\theta} - Z_\alpha \sigma_{\hat{\theta}}.$

When we wish to determine the value of a parameter that is at least as large as given figure, we use this *right-side confidence interval*. It corresponds to an upper-tail test.

REVIEW QUESTIONS

12.1 Carl W. Ackerman, the late Dean of the Columbia University Graduate School of Journalism, in an address made on September 26, 1931, said: "Facts, when combined with ideas, constitute the greatest force in the world. They are greater than armaments, greater than finance, greater than science, business and law because they are the common denominator of all of them." Now, what are "statistical facts"? What "statistical ideas" have you learned that can make such facts meaningful and powerful?

12.2 A statistical hypothesis can be defined in two different ways. What are they? Which version do we usually use in practice? Why?

12.3 Differentiate a simple hypothesis from a composite hypothesis? Give examples of your own for each kind.

12.4 How is a null hypothesis selected? Is the selection of a null hypothesis always unambiguous?

12.5 What are the requirements, if any, that should be observed in the formulation of H_0 and H_1 in a given test.

12.6 State the null and alternative hypotheses in each of the following situations.
   a. A quality control inspector wants to test whether the mean weight of canned tomatoes is 12 ounces.
   b. A production manager wants to know whether the mean life of a certain make of electronic tubes is at least 250 hours.
   c. A marketing manager for a toy manufacturing firm wants to find out whether a consumer group's contention that more than 25% of the fire trucks produced by her firm do not function as advertised.

12.7 In what sense do we say that the classical theory of testing is in fact the decision theory for two-action decision problems? Explain and illustrate with your own examples.

12.8 How are the three different kinds of test differentiated? Under what condition or conditions is each of the three types of test appropriate?

12.9 If H_0 and H_1 are interchanged in single-tail tests, H_0 will be rejected in one case but will not be rejected in the other case with the same sample data. Would this also change the final decision associated with testing? Why or why not?

12.10 Is there a difference between rejecting H_0 and proving H_0 is false? Between not rejecting H_0 and proving that H_0 is true? Explain your answer.

12.11 How are type I and type II errors defined? Give an illustration of each type of error.

12.12 What do we mean by the consequences of committing type I and type II errors, respectively. Use an example to illustrate your explanation.

12.13 What is an α-risk? a β-risk? What have these risks to do with our wish to control errors in testing?

12.14 Traditionally, α is usually set either at 0.05 or at 0.01. Under what condition or conditions should 0.05 or 0.01 be used, respectively? Should we consider other levels of significance to be used from time to time? Explain.

12.15 What is a test statistic? How should it be selected in a given test?

12.16 What is a decision rule in testing? How is such a rule determined?

12.17 In testing, what are some of the reasons for the common practice of specifying only α-risk, leaving β-risk apparently uncontrolled?

12.18 When do we need a left-side confidence interval?

12.19 When do we need a right-side confidence interval?

12.20 How do we go about determining an upper or lower confidence limit in the case of estimating μ, π, $\Delta\mu$, and $\Delta\pi$, respectively, for one-side confidence intervals?

12.21 Discuss in detail the correspondence between hypothesis testing and confidence intervals.

12.22 In view of your answer to the preceding question, do you have a preference for confidence intervals over hypothesis testing, or vice versa, as a decision procedure? Defend your answer.

PROBLEMS

12.1 In the production of a particular precision tool, a hole of 0.5000 inches in diameter must be bored in a metal plate. Since quality is so critical in this case, sample diameters are frequently inspected to ensure the proper functioning of the manufacturing process. In the most recent sample of 120 plates, the mean diameter was found to be 0.5025 inches with a standard deviation of 0.0120 inches. How should the null and alternative hypotheses be stated in this case? Can we conclude the process is in control at $\alpha = 0.01$?

12.2 According to the data gathered by U.S. Chamber of Commerce, American citizens returning from a vacation abroad of 28 days or less in 1970s indicated that they spent on the average $1,125 on souvenirs. A survey conducted in 1985 with a sample of 350 vacationers abroad by a national research institute resulted a sample mean of $1,305 and a sample standard deviation of $285. To verify whether there has been a change in spending habits for souvenirs of the American tourists, how should the hypotheses be stated? What conclusion can you reach if you are willing to assume an α-risk of 0.05?

12.3 Medical reports have linked cigarette smoking with lung cancer and other ill effects. Suppose the cigarette producers know that, before these reports came out, the adult smokers in this country smoked 10 cigarettes per day on the average. The producers are eager to evaluate the effects of the medical reports on the cigarette consumption of adult smokers. Suppose that, to do this, they have drawn a simple random sample of 576 adult smokers throughout the country and found the sample mean to be 8.5 cigarettes per day and the sample standard deviation to be 12 cigarettes per day. (Here, the standard deviation exceeds the mean; this happens for some kinds of data.) How should the null and alternative hypotheses be stated in this case? What conclusion can you draw at $\alpha = 0.01$?

12.4 The Transit Authority of New York City uses tens of thousands of lightbulbs every year. The brand that has been use until now has a mean life of 1,000 hours. A new brand is offered to the Transit Authority at a lower price. The Authority decides that the new brand should be bought now, unless there is convincing evidence that it has a life of less than 1,000 hours at a level of significance of 0.05. Subsequently 100 bulbs of the new brand are tested, yielding an average of 990 hours and a standard deviation of 90 hours. Assuming that the lives of the new brand are normally distributed, what should the decision of the Transit Authority be?

12.5 In order for a manufactured part to fit other parts, a certain critical dimension is designed to be 5 inches. The manufacturing process is known to produce normally distributed dimensions. If a given day's sample of 49 yields $\bar{x} = 5.05$ inches and $s^2 = 0.0064$ inches^2, what is the 95% confidence interval for μ? In view of this interval, should the null hypothesis $\mu = 5$ be rejected in favor of the alternative hypothesis $\mu \neq 5$, at $\alpha = 0.05$?

12.6 Certain steel pipes have normally distributed outside diameters and these diameters are supposed to average 10 inches. We wish to test $H_0: \mu = 10$ against $H: \mu \neq 10$. If $\bar{x} = 9.94$ and $s = 0.018$ for a given day's sample of 36 pipes, what is the 99% confidence interval for μ? Does this interval indicate rejection or nonrejection of the null hypothesis at $\alpha = 0.01$?

12.7 A manufacturer claimed that at least 90% of the machine parts that it supplied to a factory conformed to specifications. An examination of 500 such parts revealed that 425 parts were not faulty. Determine whether the manufacturer's claim is legitimate at the 1% level of significance.

12.8 A dairy is contemplating a change of its milk containers from glass to paper. The change will not be made unless it is clear that over 70% of all its customers want the change. A survey made of 200 of its customers reveals that 120 of them are in favor of the change. The dairy sets α equal to 0.05. Should it change to paper containers?

12.9 A man who plans to open a restaurant in a certain city tells his bank, from which he wishes to borrow the necessary capital, that over 50% of the residents in a nearby residential district will patronize his restaurant from time to time after it opens. Suppose you are the loan officer in the bank and wish to verify this claim at $\alpha = 0.05$. You are skeptical and believe that $\pi \leq 0.50$, unless there is convincing evidence to the contrary. Suppose that, in a random sample of 50 residents in the district, 56% indicate their intention to patronize the proposed restaurant.
   a. What conclusions would you draw from this result?
   b. Suppose the sample had been 200 instead of 50, and the sample proportion were still 0.56. Would you conclude differently?
   c. Discuss the limitations of statistical testing in the light of your answers to (a) and (b).

12.10 The Gamma Paper Company decides to purchase 5,000 bales of waste paper unless there is convincing evidence that the mean weight is under 125 pounds per bale. To help her make this decision, the purchasing agent of Gamma selects a simple random sample of 100 bales (with the seller's permission) and finds $\bar{x} = 120$ pounds and $s = 6.5$ pounds. If Gamma is willing to assume an α-risk of 0.05, what should the company decide to do?

12.11 Johnson Production Systems is being audited by the accounting firm of Smith and Jones. Johnson's books show that the mean value of its accounts receivable is $250. Smith and Jones selected a sample of 120 accounts receivable, audited them, and secured the following information: $\bar{x} = \$244$ and $s = \$82$. Smith and Jones would like to verify whether $\mu = \$250$ by hypothesis testing.
   a. Should a single-tail or a two-tail test be used in this case?
   b. State the hypotheses.
   c. If Johnson's accounting system has performed well in the past, should α equal 0.05 or 0.01? Why?
   d. Should H_0 be rejected?

12.12 Two different manufacturers of automobile tires, Alpha and Beta, both claim that their tires' lives are normally distributed with mean lives (or durabilities) of 50,000 miles. To determine whether $\mu_{Alpha} = \mu_{Beta}$, the following experimental data have been obtained by an independent research institute.

Alpha Company	Beta Company
$n_1 = 32$	$n_2 = 36$
$\bar{x} = 48,500$ miles	$\bar{x}_2 = 50,150$ miles
$s_1 = 1,600$ miles	$s_2 = 2,000$ miles

What conclusion can you reach at $\alpha = 0.05$?

12.13 It is often argued that women score differently from men on a particular aptitude test. A sample of 75 women taking the test yields a mean score of $\bar{x}_1 = 310$ with $s_1 = 85$. A sample of 100 men taking the test yields $\bar{x}_2 = 270$ and $s_2 = 78$. Would you agree that women score differently on this test at $\alpha = 0.05$?

12.14 An educator wants to determine whether the proportion of female professors in colleges and universities on the West Coast is different from that on the East Coast of the United States. He draws a random sample of 200 professors from West Coast schools and a random sample of 250 professors from East Coast schools, and he finds that 40 from the West Coast and 35 from the East Coast are female. How should H_0 and H_1 be stated? What conclusion can be reached at $\alpha = 0.05$? at $\alpha = 0.01$?

12.15 An economist is interested in determining whether the unemployment rates for minorities are different in different regions. To start his study, he singles out Illinois and Texas. In a sample of 500 minority workers from Texas, he finds 120 unemployed; in a sample of 500 from Illinois, he finds 95 unemployed. What conclusion can be reached at $\alpha = 0.02$?

12.16 A sample of 80 steel wires produced by factory A yields a mean breaking strength of 1,230 pounds, with a standard deviation of 120 pounds. A sample of 100 steel wires produced by factory B yields a mean breaking strength of 1,190 pounds, with a standard deviation of 90 pounds. Are the population mean breaking strengths the same or different?
   a. State H_0 and H_1, and explain how you chose what to assert as the null hypothesis and what to assert as the alternative hypothesis.
   b. State your final answer and explain how you arrived at it.

12.17 A firm's packaging machinery is known to pour dry cereal into economy-size boxes with a normal distribution of weights. Frequent checks are made of the net weights in the boxes in order to maintain the adjustment of the machinery that controls the net weight. Two samples taken on two different dates yield the following information.

First Sample	Second Sample
$n_1 = 30$	$n_2 = 35$
$\bar{x}_1 = 19.7$ ounces	$\bar{x}_2 = 20.2$ ounces
$s_1 = 0.602$ ounce	$s_2 = 0.600$ ounce

Use $\alpha = 0.05$ in answering the following questions.
   a. Test the hypothesis that, on the first date, the population mean weight was 20 ounces.
   b. Test the hypothesis that, on the second date, the population mean weight was 20 ounces.
   c. Test the hypothesis that there was no change in the population mean weight between the two dates.

12.18 A random sample of 200 men was selected from New York State in 1986, and 120 were found to be in favor of a "more modern" divorce law. A random sample of 200 women selected from the same state at the same time revealed that 80 were in favor of such a new law. Is the proportion of men favoring a new divorce law different from that of women in New York State, given that $\alpha = 0.05$? Given that $\alpha = 0.01$?

12.19 To determine whether a certain type of fertilizer is effective, 100 plants out of 500 are left unfertilized. Of these 100, 52 are found to have satisfactory growth, and out of 400 fertilized plants, 275 are found satisfactory. What conclusion can you draw at $\alpha = 0.05$? at $\alpha = 0.01$?

12.20 Two groups of certain types of patients, A and B, each consisting of 200 people, are used to test the effectiveness of a new serum. Both groups are treated identically, except that group A is given the serum while group B is not. It is found that 140 and 120 of groups A and B, respectively, recover from the disease. Is this observed result sufficient evidence for the conclusion that the new serum helps to cure the disease if we are willing to assume an α-risk of 0.01?

12.21 During the spring of 1987, students in one of the author's classes were instructed to conduct a survey in New York City of voters' reaction toward various policies of the national Republican administration. The following results were obtained.

Satisfied with the Policy Administration	Men $(n_1 = 500)$	Women $(n_2 = 400)$
Foreign policy	210	145
Civil rights policy	397	232
Space policy	311	227
Economic policy	278	189
Defense policy	386	292

Assuming that the samples are random, do you think there is a significant difference, at $\alpha = 0.05$, between the reactions of men and women toward each of the policies mentioned in the survey? Analyze each policy separately from all the other policies.

12.32 Construct an appropriate confidence interval for $\Delta \mu$ for each of the three examples in Section 12.6. Comment on your results.

12.23 Construct an appropriate confidence interval for $\Delta \pi$ for each of the three examples in Section 12.7. Comment on your results.

13* Classical Theory of Testing. II: The Varying Sample-Size Case

13.1 INTRODUCTION

The classical theory of testing presented in the last chapter was developed under the assumption that the consequences of committing type I errors are more serious than those of committing type II errors and that the sample size is fixed. Under these assumptions, it is quite appropriate as well as necessary to specify α-risk alone in a given test. However, it was also pointed out then that ideally both α- and β-risk should be specified in a given test after we have assessed the relative seriousness of the consequences of committing both type I and type II errors. In this chapter, as promised, we take up the topic of testing by evaluating both α- and β-risks in a decision situation involving testing hypotheses.

The evaluation of β-risk consists of but three related aspects. The first is to study β-risk under the conditions that both the sample size and α-risk are fixed. This would lead to a treatise of what are called "power," and "performance" or "operating characteristic" functions. The second is to show the effects with varying sample size, on the behavior of β-risk given that α-risk is held at a constant level. This would lead us directly to the third and most important aspect of evaluating β-risk—the determination of the appropriate sample size that can satisfy predetermined levels of α- and β-risks for selected values of a parameter.

It may be pointed out at the very outset, in order to avoid repetition in the discussion that follows, that the probabilities of committing both type I and type II errors can only be determined for simple hypotheses. Thus, when the null and the alternative hypotheses are composite in a given decision situation, we evaluate both α and β by first specifying each time a pair of simple hypotheses that are respectively members of the composite H_0 and H_1. The reader may also be reminded that the symbols R and A in subsequent discussions stand for "region of rejection" and "region of acceptance", respectively, in a sampling distribution. Finally, the notation $\in$ means "is a member of".

13.2 POWER AND OPERATING CHARACTERISTIC FUNCTIONS

Let us begin by making clear the nature of the power and the operating characteristic functions. For this task, it is instructive to observe that in the practice of testing an H_0 against an H_1 for two-action decision problems, one and only one of the following four results can occur in a given test:

1. We may reject a true H_0. The probability of this wrong decision is α.

2. We may accept a true H_0. The probability of this correct decision is $1 - \alpha$.

3. We may accept a false H_0. The probability of this wrong decision is β.

4. We may reject a false H_0. The probability of this correct decision is $1 - \beta$.

Here, $1 - \beta$ is called the *power* of the test, since it is the ability of the test to accept the alternative hypothesis when it is in fact true. The power of the test, as the probability of rejecting a false H_0 (or of accepting a true H_1), depends on the value of β. Thus, if we are testing

$$H_0: \theta = \theta_0 \qquad \text{against} \qquad H_1: \theta = \theta_1,$$

then

$$\text{power of the test} = P(\hat{\theta} \in R \mid \theta = \theta_1),$$

which is the probability of rejecting H_0 when H_1 is true.

However, when the null and the alternative hypotheses are composite, we do not have uniquely defined error sizes. The probability of rejecting H_0 when it should be rejected depends upon the value of θ. Precisely, the *power function* of a test is the probability of rejecting H_0 considered as a function of θ with α and n fixed.

Now, suppose we are evaluating the following pair of hypotheses:

$$H_0: \theta \in V; \quad H_1: \theta \in W, \quad V \cap W = \emptyset,$$

where V is the set of all possible values θ_i, for θ in H_0, and similarly for W in H_1. For this test, if H_0 is false—that is, if $\theta \in W$—the power function is defined in terms of a likelihood function:

$$\mathrm{PF}(\theta_i) = P(\hat{\theta} \in R \mid \theta = \theta_i \quad \text{and} \quad \theta_i \in W)$$

$$= 1 - \beta.$$

Namely, the power of the test for any value θ_i, in H_1, is the probability of rejecting H_0 given that $\theta = \theta_i$ is true. However, if H_0 is true, we then have

$$\mathrm{PF}(\theta_i) = P(\hat{\theta} \in R \mid \theta = \theta_i \quad \text{and} \quad \theta_i \in V)$$

$$= \alpha.$$

Note that for any value $\theta \in \{H_0 \cup H_1\}$, PF gives the probability of rejecting H_0. Here $1 - \beta$ and α are regarded as variable probabilities, not as maximum probabilities.

The complement of the power function is called the *operating characteristic (OC) function*. It is also defined in terms of a likelihood function. If H_0 is true, the OC function is given as

$$\mathrm{OC}(\theta_i) = P(\hat{\theta} \in A \mid \theta = \theta_i \quad \text{and} \quad \theta_i \in V)$$

$$= 1 - \alpha.$$

which is the probability of making the correct decision of accepting H_0, when it is true.

When H_0 is false, we have

$$\mathrm{OC}(\theta_i) = P(\hat{\theta} \in A \mid \theta = \theta_i \quad \text{and} \quad \theta_i \in W)$$

$$= \beta,$$

the probability of committing a type II error–accepting a false H_0 given that the true parameter value is covered by H_1. Again, $1 - \alpha$ and β are regarded as variables here.

We see that OC and PF are complementary functions:

$$\mathrm{OC}(\theta_i) = 1 - \mathrm{PF}(\theta_i).$$

Note that the power of a test equals α only when H_0 is true; otherwise, it equals $1 - \beta$. Furthermore, the OC function equals β only when H_1 is true; otherwise it equals $1 - \alpha$.

To clarify previous comments and to bring out the use of power and OC functions in testing, let us consider some examples.

13.3 POWER AND OC FUNCTIONS FOR TESTS ABOUT μ

Power and OC Functions for Single-tail Tests

Suppose that the purchasing agent of a department store is interested in buying a certain make of small cardboard containers that, according to the manufacturer's specifications, have a mean crushing strength of 30 pounds and a standard deviation of 3 pounds. These specifications are exactly what the purchasing agent desires. To decide whether or not to buy, he has two alternative approaches, depending upon his attitude toward the α-risks. First, he does not want to forego the opportunity to buy a useful product. According to this attitude, the appropriate designations for the null and the alternative hypotheses should be

$$H_0: \mu \geq 30 \text{ pounds};$$

$$H_1: \mu < 30 \text{ pounds}.$$

Second, the agent may wish to avoid the mistake of buying when he should not; that is, if the mean crushing strength may be less than 30 pounds, and he is fearful of buying a useless product. With this attitude, the set of hypotheses to be evaluated becomes

$$H_0: \mu \leq 30 \text{ pounds};$$

$$H_1: \mu > 30 \text{ pounds}.$$

We shall now evaluate these two approaches by assuming that $\alpha = 0.05$ and $n = 36$ in both cases.

This illustrates a problem that students often find vexing—which hypothesis should be the null and which should be the alternative? Here, there is a slight additional complication over the value $\mu = 30$, but it should be obvious that it does not really matter which hypothesis contains the value of *exactly* 30 pounds. The real problem is whether to use weak boxes for the null hypothesis or to use strong boxes for the null hypothesis. From the standpoint of pure logic, it does not matter. Either weak or strong boxes can be specified by the null hypothesis, with the other kind of boxes specified by the alternative hypothesis. From a practical standpoint, a convention has grown up to answer this problem. The convention is to form the null hypothesis in such a way that a type I error is more serious than a type II error. This then justifies the conventional values for α—values in the vicinity of 0.05 or 0.01. Here, the purchasing agent must decide whether buying weak boxes is more serious than refusing to buy strong boxes. It may seem obvious that buying weak boxes is the more serious error, in which case H_0 specifies weak boxes and H_1 specifies strong boxes, thus making buying weak boxes (thinking that they are strong) a type I error.

However, we really need more information about the costs of the two kinds of error. If this vendor's boxes offer substantial cost savings that management strongly wants to achieve, and if a few broken boxes in shipment can be tolerated, then H_0 should specify strong boxes and H_1 should specify weak boxes, thus making refusing to buy the cheap strong boxes (thinking that they are weak) a type I error.

The foregoing paragraph is likely to be very confusing the first time through. It is suggested that the reader try it a second time, keeping in mind the distinction between what is really true (which hypothesis is really true) and what is apparently convincing (which hypothesis is accepted because the sample evidence to be gathered points that way). One reason for confusion is that the paragraph talks entirely about misleading sample evidence. The discussion concentrates on type I and type II errors, and they both involve misleading sample evidence. Another way of phrasing the central issue here is: "Which way of being misled by sample evidence would be more serious?"

There is another possibility. The purchasing agent could decide that both ways of being misled are about equally serious. In this case, it does not matter which way he frames his null hypothesis, and he should set α equal to 0.50 regardless.

In the analysis that follows, we assume that one kind of error is definitely more serious than the other kind, and we analyze each of the two possibilities.

The first approach is to test the null hypothesis, $\mu \geq 30$, against the alternative, $\mu < 30$. For this test, the α and β-risks are as follows:

	State of Nature	
Act	$H_0: \mu \geq 30$	$H_1: \mu < 30$
a_1: Buy	Correct act	$\beta = P(a_1 \mid \mu < 30)$
a_2: Don't buy	$\alpha = P(a_2 \mid \mu \geq 30)$	Correct act

For a left-side test, the general decision rule may be stated as follows: Reject H_0 if and only if

$$\hat{\theta} < \hat{\theta}_c = \theta_0 - Z_\alpha \sigma_{\hat{\theta}}, \tag{13.1}$$

where $\hat{\theta}_c$ is called the *critical value of the test statistic*.

Now, for our current example, the logical test statistic is evidently the sample mean. At $\alpha = 0.05$ and by (13.1), H_0 will be rejected if and only if

$$\bar{x} < \bar{x}_c = \mu_0 - z_\alpha \sigma_{\bar{X}}$$

$$= 30 - 1.64(3/\sqrt{36})$$

$$= 29.18 \text{ pounds.}$$

The decision rule so established means that

if $\bar{x} \geq 29.18$ pounds, take a_1–buy the product;

if $\bar{x} < 29.18$ pounds, take a_2–don't buy the product.

Turning our attention to the evaluation of power and OC functions for this test, we note that these two functions are complementary to each other. In general, for a left-tailed test, we would accept H_0 if and only if $\hat{\theta} > \hat{\theta}_c$. Thus,

$$OC(\theta_i) = P(\hat{\theta} > \hat{\theta}_c \mid \theta_i)$$

$$= 1 - N\left(\frac{\hat{\theta}_c - \theta_i}{\sigma_{\hat{\theta}}}\right), \qquad (13.2)$$

where θ_i is any value of θ.

Returning to our example, if $\mu = 30$ pounds, then

$$OC(30) = 1 - \alpha = 1 - N\left(\frac{\bar{x}_c - \mu}{\sigma_{\bar{x}}}\right)$$

$$= 1 - N\left(\frac{29.18 - 30}{0.5}\right)$$

$$= 1 - N(-1.64)$$

$$= 1 - 0.05$$

$$= 0.95,$$

and

$$PF(30) = \alpha$$

$$= 1 - 0.95$$

$$= 0.05.$$

Now, suppose μ is set equal to 28.175; then

$$OC(28.175) = \beta = 1 - N\left(\frac{29.18 - 28.175}{0.5}\right)$$

$$= 1 - N(2.01)$$

$$\doteq 0.0222,$$

and

$$PF(28.175) = 1 - \beta = 1 - 0.0222$$

$$= 0.9778.$$

Table 13.1 contains the OC and the power functions of a few selected values of the parameter. The graphs of the OC and the power functions are called the *OC curve* and the *power curve*, respectively. The power and OC curves for our illustration, as suggested by the values in Table 13.1, are shown in Figure 13.1.

TABLE 13.1 Illustrative OC and Power Curve Heights for a
Lower-tail Test With $\mu \geqslant 30$ against $\mu < 30$

Hypothesis that is true	Values of μ	$OC(\mu)$	$PF(\mu)$
H_0	30.5	$1.00 = 1 - \alpha$	$0.00 = \alpha$
H_0	30.0	$0.95 = 1 - \alpha$	$0.05 = \alpha$
H_1	29.5	$0.74 = \beta$	$0.26 = 1 - \beta$
H_1	29.0	$0.36 = \beta$	$0.64 = 1 - \beta$
H_1	28.5	$0.09 = \beta$	$0.91 = 1 - \beta$
H_1	28.0	$0.01 = \beta$	$0.99 = 1 - \beta$
H_1	27.5	$0.00 = \beta$	$1.00 = 1 - \beta$

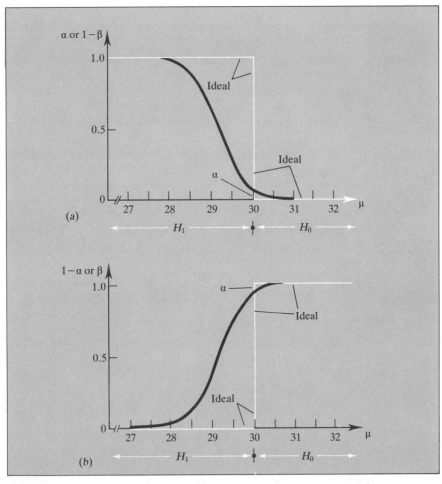

FIGURE 13.1 (a) Power and (b) OC curves for testing $\mu \geqslant 30$ against $\mu < 30$, drawn against the ideal power and OC functions.

It is important to note that the power curve is, as it should be, low over H_0 and high over H_1. This means the power of the test increases when the parameter value deviates more and more from the parameter values covered by H_0. An "ideal" power function for a lower-tailed test can be defined as

$$PF(\theta) = 0, \qquad \text{when } \theta \geqslant \theta_0;$$

$$PF(\theta) = 1, \qquad \text{when } \theta < \theta_0.$$

That is, if we had perfect information concerning θ, we will always reject H_0 if H_1 is true and never reject H_0 otherwise. Of course, in the absence of perfect information, such an ideal power function cannot be obtained.

It may also be observed that, given α and n, one decision rule is said to be better or more powerful than another if the power curve for the former is higher than that for the latter for all θ_i covered by H_1. In this connection, we say that a decision rule is the *uniformly most powerful test* if it yields the highest power curve possible, for all θ_i covered by H_1. It turns out, other things being equal, that the power of a test depends upon the selection of the rejection region (decision rule). If the rejection region is at one tail-end of the distribution of the test statistic (if the test is single-sided), then the test will be uniformly most powerful, since then β is the smallest possible given α and n. If, however, the critical region consists of any other portion of the area under the density curve of the test statistic, the test will be less powerful, since then we have a larger β than the minimum possible. These statements are demonstrated by Figure 13.2, which shows that

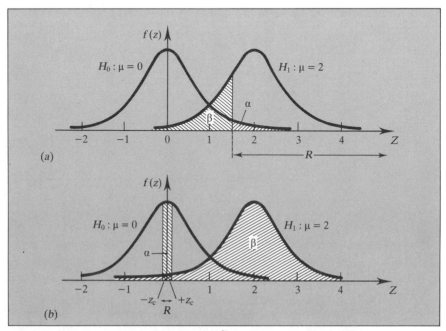

FIGURE 13.2 (a) Proper and (b) improper selection of critical region.

while α risks in (a) and (b) are identical, the critical region in (b) is unwisely chosen and the effect on β is disastrous.

The OC function, as the probability of accepting H_0, or as the complement of the power function, should be high over H_0 and low over H_1. Ideally, for a left-tailed test, we should have

$$OC(\theta) = 1, \quad \text{when } \theta \geq \theta_0;$$
$$OC(\theta) = 0, \quad \text{when } \theta < \theta_0.$$

Note that the actual power and OC curves for our illustrative test are drawn against the ideal power and OC curves in Figure 13.1.

To summarize, the decision rule established by the first approach is as follows.

1. Take a random sample of size $n = 36$ and compute the sample mean.

2. Set $\alpha = 0.05$.

3. Take a_1 (buy) if $\bar{x} \geq 29.18$; take a_2 (don't buy) if $\bar{x} < 29.18$.

Proceeding to evaluate the second approach for our illustrative example, we recall that by this approach the purchasing agent is anxious to avoid the mistake of buying when he should not. That is, we are testing $H_0: \mu \leq 30$ against $H_1: \mu > 30$. For this pair of hypotheses, the α-and β-risks are now as shown schematically below.

	State of Nature	
Act	$H_0: \mu \leq 30$	$H_1: \mu > 30$
a_1: Buy	$\alpha = P(a_1 \mid \mu \leq 30)$	Correct act
a_2: Don't buy	Correct act	$\beta = P(a_2 \mid \mu > 30)$

The general decision rule for an upper-tail test can be stated in this way: H_0 will be rejected if and only if

$$\hat{\theta} > \hat{\theta}_c = \theta_0 + Z_{1-\alpha}\sigma_{\hat{\theta}}. \tag{13.3}$$

For our current example, we see that the α-risk is the error of buying when the purchase should not be made. Now, with data given before and at $\alpha = 0.05$, H_0 will be rejected if and only if

$$\bar{x} > \bar{x}_c = \mu_0 + z_{1-\alpha}\sigma_{\bar{X}}$$
$$= 30 + 1.64(3/\sqrt{36})$$
$$= 30.82.$$

From this critical value, the decision rule now becomes:

take a_1: buy the product if $\bar{x} > 30.82$;

take a_2: don't buy the product if $\bar{x} \leq 30.82$.

TABLE 13.2 Illustrative OC and Power Curve Heights for an Upper-tail Test With $\mu \leqslant 30$ aganst $\mu > 30$

Hypothesis That is True	Values of μ	OC(μ)	PF(μ)
H_0	29.5	$1.00 = 1 - \alpha$	$0.00 = \alpha$
H_0	30.0	$0.95 = 1 - \alpha$	$0.05 = \alpha$
H_1	30.5	$0.74 = \beta$	$0.26 = 1 - \beta$
H_1	31.0	$0.36 = \beta$	$0.64 = 1 - \beta$
H_1	31.5	$0.09 = \beta$	$0.91 = 1 - \beta$
H_1	32.0	$0.01 = \beta$	$0.99 = 1 - \beta$
H_1	32.5	$0.00 = \beta$	$1.00 = 1 - \beta$

To calculate the OC curve for this test we note that, in general, when we conduct a right-tail test, H_0 will be accepted if and only if $\hat{\theta} \leqslant \hat{\theta}_c$. Hence,

$$\text{OC}(\theta_i) = P(\hat{\theta} \leqslant \hat{\theta}_c \mid \theta_i)$$

$$= N\left(\frac{\hat{\theta}_c - \theta_i}{\sigma_{\hat{\theta}}}\right). \qquad (13.4)$$

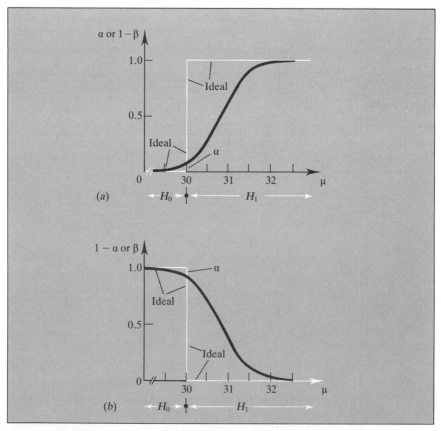

FIGURE 13.3 (a) Power and (b) OC curves for testing $\mu \leqslant 30$ against $\mu > 30$, drawn against the ideal power and OC functions for right-tail tests.

Now, applying this expression to our present case by assuming, say, $\mu = 30.5$, we have

$$\text{OC}(30.5) = N\left(\frac{\bar{x}_c - \mu}{\sigma_{\bar{X}}}\right)$$

$$= N\left(\frac{30.82 - 30.5}{0.5}\right) \doteq N(+0.64) = 0.738.$$

A few more OC-curve heights, calculated in similar fashion for this decision rule, are entered in Table 13.2. Power-curve heights corresponding to these OC-curve heights are also given in the same table. The power and OC curves for this test are shown in Figure 13.3. Note that these curves are drawn against the ideal forms of power and OC curves for a right-tail test.

Power and OC Functions for Double-tail Tests

The mean weekly family disposable income in a certain city was known to be $400 with a standard deviation of $50 during the late 1970s. The municipal government now wonders whether there has been a significant change in this average and plans to find out by taking a random sample of 100 families and testing the following pair of hypotheses at $\alpha = 0.05$:

$$H_0\colon \mu = 400; \qquad H_1\colon \mu \neq 400.$$

This decision situation is summarized schematically below:

	State of Nature		
Act	$H_0\colon \mu = 400$	$H_1\colon \mu < 400$ or	$\mu > 400$
a_1: Unchanged	Correct	β	β
a_2: Changed	α	Correct	Correct

Now, for a double-tail test, we would have two critical values of the test statistic in question. The general decision rule in this case becomes: Reject H_0 if and only if

$$\hat{\theta} < \hat{\theta}_{c_1} = \theta_0 - Z_{\alpha/2}\sigma_{\hat{\theta}} \tag{13.5a}$$

or

$$\hat{\theta} > \hat{\theta}_{c_1} = \theta_0 + Z_{1-\alpha/2}\sigma_{\hat{\theta}} \tag{13.5b}$$

For our current example and with the information provided, the decision rule is: Reject H_0 if and only if

$$\bar{x} < \bar{x}_{c_1} = \mu_0 - z_{\alpha/2}\sigma_{\bar{X}}$$
$$= 400 - 1.96(50/\sqrt{100})$$
$$= \$390.20,$$

or

$$\bar{x} > \bar{x}_{c_2} = \mu_0 + z_{1-\alpha/2}\sigma_{\bar{X}}$$
$$= 400 + 1.96(50/\sqrt{100})$$
$$= \$409.80.$$

Note that for a double-tail test, we would accept H_0 if and only if $\hat{\theta}_{c_1} \leq \hat{\theta} \leq \hat{\theta}_{c_2}$. Hence,

$$OC(\theta_i) = P(\hat{\theta}_{c_1} \leq \hat{\theta} \leq \hat{\theta}_{c_2} \mid \theta_i)$$
$$= N\left(\frac{\hat{\theta}_{c_2} - \theta_i}{\sigma_{\hat{\theta}}}\right) - N\left(\frac{\hat{\theta}_{c_1} - \theta_i}{\sigma_{\hat{\theta}}}\right), \qquad (13.6)$$

where θ_i refers to any value of θ. Now, for the present example, if $\mu = 395$, then

$$OC(395) = N\left(\frac{\bar{x}_{c_2} - \mu}{\sigma_{\bar{X}}}\right) - N\left(\frac{\bar{x}_{c_1} - \mu}{\sigma_{\bar{X}}}\right)$$
$$= N\left(\frac{409.8 - 395}{5}\right) - N\left(\frac{390.2 - 395}{5}\right)$$
$$= N(2.96) - N(-0.96)$$
$$\doteq 0.9985 - 0.1685 = 0.8300.$$

If $\mu = 415$, then

$$OC(415) = N\left(\frac{409.8 - 415}{5}\right) - N\left(\frac{390.2 - 415}{5}\right)$$
$$= N(-1.04) - N(-4.96) \doteq 0.1492.$$

Other values in Table 13.3 have been computed in the same fashion. The last column of this table contains values of the power function of this test.

Figure 13.4 has been designed to give the reader a feeling for β in terms of areas under the density curves of the distributions of $\bar{X}$ given alternative values of μ. Some observations on this point will be made shortly.

The power and the OC curves for the current test are shown by Figures 13.5 and 13.6, respectively. It is interesting to note that both

TABLE 13.3 Illustrative OC and Power Curve Heights for a Two-tail Test with $\mu = 400$ against $\mu \neq 400$

Hypothesis That is True	μ	$OC(\mu)$	$PF(\mu)$
H_1	375.0	$0.000 = \beta$	$1.000 = 1 - \beta$
H_1	382.5	$0.062 = \beta$	$0.938 = 1 - \beta$
H_1	387.5	$0.295 = \beta$	$0.705 = 1 - \beta$
H_1	392.5	$0.677 = \beta$	$0.323 = 1 - \beta$
H_1	397.5	$0.921 = \beta$	$0.079 = 1 - \beta$
H_0	400.0	$0.950 = 1 - \alpha$	$0.050 = \alpha$
H_1	402.5	$0.921 = \beta$	$0.079 = 1 - \beta$
H_1	407.5	$0.677 = \beta$	$0.323 = 1 - \beta$
H_1	412.5	$0.295 = \beta$	$0.705 = 1 - \beta$
H_1	417.5	$0.062 = \beta$	$0.938 = 1 - \beta$
H_1	425.0	$0.000 = \beta$	$1.000 = 1 - \beta$

curves are symmetric about μ_0 as should be for all double-tail tests. Ideally, for double-tail tests, we have

$$PF(\theta_i) = 0, \quad \text{when } \theta_i = \theta_0;$$

$$PF(\theta_i) = 1, \quad \text{when } \theta_i \neq \theta_0.$$

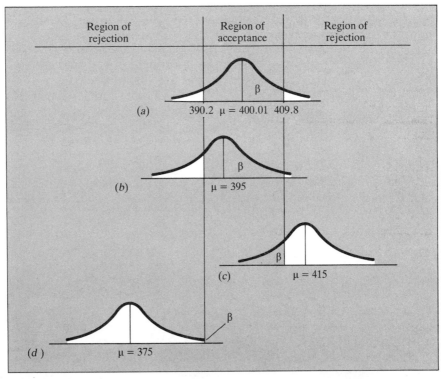

FIGURE 13.4 Probability of committing type II error in testing $\mu = 400$ against $\mu \neq 400$ at $\alpha = 0.05$ with $n = 100$, where white areas represent $1 - \beta$.

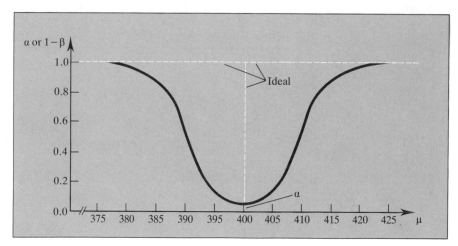

FIGURE 13.5 Power curve for $H_0: \mu = 400$ and $H_1: \mu \neq 400$, drawn against the ideal power curve.

These imply that an ideal OC function must satisfy

$$OC(\theta_i) = 1, \qquad \text{when } \theta_i = \theta_0;$$

$$OC(\theta_i) = 0, \qquad \text{when } \theta_i \neq \theta_0.$$

Note that the power and OC curves for our illustrative example in Figures 13.5 and 13.6 are drawn against their corresponding ideal forms.

Before proceeding further, let us make some additional comments on the three types of tests in the light of our discussion on β so far and point out the relation between α and β for fixed n. First, as we have already noted, single-tail tests are uniformly most powerful tests. There is no uniformly most powerful test in the case of double-tail tests.

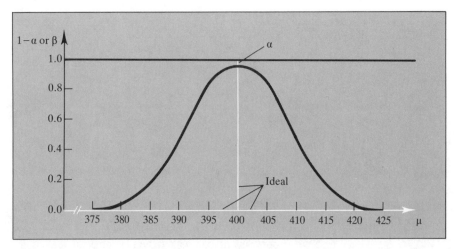

FIGURE 13.6 OC curve for $H_0: \mu = 400$ and $H_1: \mu \neq 400$, drawn against the ideal OC curve.

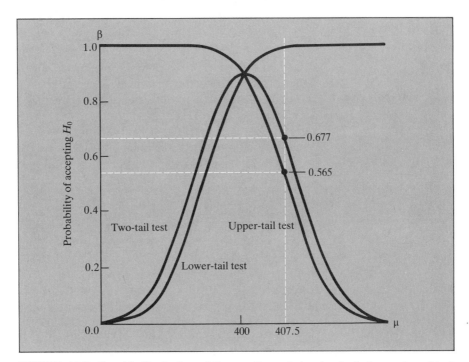

FIGURE 13.7 Graphic illustration of the merits and drawbacks between two-sided and one-sided tests with the family income example for which $H_0: \mu = 400$, $n = 100$, $\sigma_{\bar{x}} = 5$, and $\alpha = 0.05$.

However, a double-tail test is quite reasonable, even desirable, on many accounts in many situations. Had we conducted an upper-tail test as well as a lower-tail test for the current example, then we would have the OC curves in Figure 13.7. These curves show that a double-tail test is unbiased in the sense that the probability of accepting H_0 is the greatest at H_0. This property is not possessed by the single-tail tests. Also, as the same figure reveals, the two-tail test has some chance of detecting excesses of the true value of the parameter above μ_0, which is assumed to be 400 in the figure, though not as good as chance as the right-tail test. For instance, if the true value of μ is 407.5, the probability of accepting $\mu_0 = 400$ is only 0.565 with an upper-tail test, but the probability of accepting the null hypothesis is the much greater value of 0.677 with the double-tail test. However, as you can see from the figure, the double-tail test has a better chance of detecting deviations of the true value of μ below $\mu_0 = 400$ than the right-tail test. Similar comparisons can also be made between a left-tail test and a double-test by studying the figure carefully. Thus, in a given decision situation, the type of test to be selected should be the one whose OC curve comes nearest to giving the proper decisions for the possible values of the parameter that might prevail.

Next, let us summarize the important conclusions reached so far about the relationship between α and β for fixed n.

1. For a fixed n, the probability of committing a type I error is automatically determined once the level of significance is determined.

2. For a fixed n, if we reduce the size of the type I error, the size of the type II error is correspondingly increased.

3. For a fixed n, type I error is completely under control in a given test. Furthermore, the conventional practice of setting $\alpha = 0.05$ or 0.01 indicates that the error of rejecting a true null hypothesis is seldom made. A type II error is frequently made if the true parameter value is very close to the parameter value given in H_0. However, in such a case, the erroneous action of accepting a false H_0 is not at all serious. When the parameter value deviates from the parameter value in H_0 by a large amount, it is indeed a very serious matter to commit a type II error. Fortunately, in such a case, the probability of accepting a false H_0 is very slight. These comments should be intuitively clear and are revealed by Figure 13.4.

4. As already mentioned, if it is desired to fix both α and β at specific and appropriate levels in a given test, the test cannot be conducted with a fixed sample size. We must then determine the particular sample size that can satisfy these specifications simultaneously. The method of determining n, given the levels of α and β risks, is the main concern of this chapter and we take it up shortly.

13.4 POWER AND OC FUNCTIONS FOR TESTS ABOUT π

The discussion of the power and the OC functions with fixed n for tests on population proportions is identical with that for population means. We shall now work out an example to clarify this point.

During the last days preceding a political election, the campaign manager for a certain candidate wants to decide whether it is necessary to expend some extra effort. Toward this end, he decides that if at least 51% of the population of voters are for his candidate, then no extra effort need be contemplated; but if the percentage is 51 or less, extra effort should be made in order to ensure the election of his candidate. Furthermore, he decides to verify the population proportion by taking a random sample of 100 voters at an α-risk of 0.05. For this procedure, the α- and the β-risks are then as follows.

	State of Nature	
Action	$\pi_0 \leqslant 0.51$	$\pi_1 > 0.51$
a_1: Extra effort	Correct decision	$\beta = P(a_1 \mid \pi_1)$
a_2: No extra effort	$\alpha = P(a_2 \mid \pi_0)$	Correct decision

According to this decision framework and by (13.3), $H_0: \pi \leqslant 0.51$

will be rejected if and only if

$$\bar{p} > \bar{p}_c = \pi_0 + 1.64\sigma_{\bar{p}}$$

$$= 0.51 + 1.64\sqrt{\frac{(0.51)(0.49)}{100}}$$

$$= 0.51 + 1.64(0.05)$$

$$= 0.5920.$$

The OC function is now a function of π. Hence, we must identify the values of π; that is, the admissible simple hypotheses for π in order to compute the values of the OC function. Now, assuming $\pi_1 = 0.50$ and by (13.4), we have

$$OC(0.50) = \beta = P(\bar{p} < \bar{p}_c)$$

$$= N\left(\frac{\bar{p}_c + 1/2n - \pi_1}{\sigma_{\bar{p}}}\right)$$

$$= N\left(\frac{0.5920 + 0.005 - 0.50}{0.05}\right)$$

$$= N(+1.94) = 0.9738.$$

Note that the OC function has been introduced in the above computation. Also note that the OC curve, identified as $\bar{p} > 0.5920$ in Figure 13.8, gives high probabilities of accepting H_0 over H_0 and low probabilities of acceptance over H_1, as should be the case.

The campaign manager's decision rule, therefore, is as follows.

1. Take a sample 100 voters at random.

2. Set $\alpha = 0.05$.

3. Take a_1 (extra effort) if $\bar{p} \leq 0.5920$.

4. Take a_2 (no extra effort) if $\bar{p} > 0.5920$.

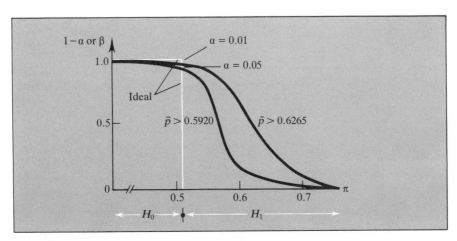

FIGURE 13.8 OC curves for the political campaign example at $\alpha = 0.05$, $\alpha = 0.01$, and $n = 100$.

Now if, for some reason, the campaign manager wishes to conduct this test with $\alpha = 0.01$, then H_0 would be rejected if and only if

$$\bar{p} > \bar{p}_c = 0.51 + 2.33(0.05) = 0.6265$$

Again, suppose $\pi_1 = 0.5$, then for this critical value,

$$\text{OC}(0.50) = \beta = N\left(\frac{0.6265 + 0.005 - 0.5}{0.05}\right) = N(2.63) = 0.9957$$

Thus, as observed before, given the sample size, in an attempt to reduce α, β is correspondingly increased. So that the whole OC curve for $\alpha = 0.01$ and $n = 100$, the one labeled as $\bar{p} > 0.6265$ in Figure 13.8, lies above that of the previous decision rule.

In the preceding example, if the campaign manager is more anxious not to make the extra effort because of the heavy costs it would entail, then the appropriate test becomes

$$H_0: \pi \geqslant 0.51; \qquad H_1: \pi < 0.51$$

The α- and β-risks are now as shown below.

	State of Nature	
Action	$\pi_0 > 0.51$	$\pi_1 < 0.51$
a_1: No extra effort	Correct act	$\beta = P(a_1 \mid \pi_1)$
a_2: Extra effort	$\alpha = P(a_2 \mid \pi_0)$	Correct act

According to this framework, the campaign manager will decide not to make the extra effort if there is evidence that more than 51% of the voters are in favor of his candidate. Set $\alpha = 0.05$ and $n = 100$ as before. H_0 will be rejected now if and only if

$$\bar{p} < \bar{p}_c = 0.51 - 1.64(0.05) = 0.418.$$

With the above result, the decision rule now becomes: If $\bar{p} < 0.418$, take a_2 (make extra effort), and if $\bar{p} \geqslant 0.418$, take a_1 (make no extra effort). For this decison rule, $\alpha = 0.05$ and the OC function is

$$\text{OC}(\pi_i) = \beta = P(\bar{p} \geqslant \bar{p}_c)$$

$$= 1 - N\left(\frac{0.418 + 0.005 - \pi_i}{0.05}\right),$$

where π_i stands for any value of π and whose graph is as shown by Figure 13.9. Note that this OC curve is the power curve for testing $H_0: \pi \leqslant 0.51$ against $H_1: \pi > 0.51$ for the same level of significance of 0.05 and the same sample size of 100.

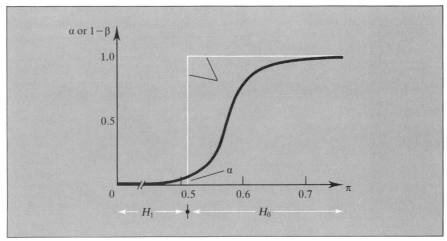

FIGURE 13.9 OC curve for the political campaign example with H_0: $\pi \geqslant 0.51$ at $\alpha = 0.05$ and $n = 100$.

13.5 TESTS WITH BOTH α AND β FIXED: DETERMINATION OF SAMPLE SIZE

Our evaluation of the power and the OC functions so far has been made by assuming that both α and n are fixed. Given the level of significance, how would the power and the OC functions of the test be affected by changes in n? In answering this question, we shall also provide a method of determining the appropriate sample size so that a given test can satisfy predetermined α- and β-risk.

Effects on β of Changing n

If the sample size is increased, the size of β-risk will be expected to remain constant or to decrease provided that α is held unchanged. It will usually decrease. The reason for this is obvious: the larger n is, the smaller the standard error of the test statistic which, in turn, generates a more compressed sampling distribution of the test statistic. That is, given a fixed α-risk, the area of the sampling distribution of the test statistic (with expectation μ) that measures β will become smaller when n is increased.

Let us illustrate this point by way of an example. Iron bars produced by a certain process are known to have a mean breaking strength of 300 pounds and a standard deviation of 24 pounds. To verify a belief that the mean breaking strength can be considerably increased by a newly developed manufacturing process, it seems appropriate to test the following pair of hypotheses:

$$H_0: \mu \leqslant 300 \text{ pounds};$$

$$H_1: \mu > 300 \text{ pounds}.$$

TABLE 13.4 Illustration of How Increasing n Affects the OC Curve with $\mu \leqslant 300$ against $\mu > 500$

Value of μ	OC function: β or $1 - \alpha$		
	$n = 10$	$n = 100$	$n = 500$
290	1.000	1.000	1.000
295	0.999	1.000	1.000
300	0.990	0.990	0.990
305	0.953	0.597	0.010
310	0.844	0.033	0.000
315	0.639	0.000	0.000
320	0.378	0.000	0.000

Now, suppose we arbitrarily set α at 0.01 for this test, and let n vary from 10 to 100 to 500 for the purpose of observing the effects upon β of changing n. If $n = 10$, then H_0 will be rejected if

$$\bar{x} > \bar{x}_c = 300 + 2.33\frac{24}{\sqrt{10}} \doteq 300 + 2.33(7.59) \doteq 317.68.$$

If $n = 100$, then H_0 will be rejected if

$$\bar{x} > \bar{x}_c = 300 + 2.33\frac{24}{\sqrt{100}} = 300 + 2.33(2.4) \doteq 305.59.$$

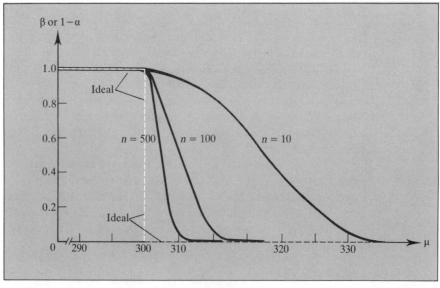

FIGURE 13.10 OC curves for testing $\mu \leqslant 300$ against $\mu > 300$ with $n = 10, 100,$ and 500.

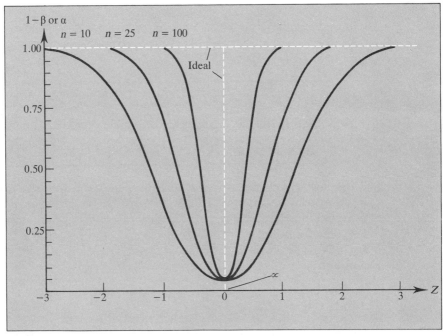

FIGURE 13.11 Power curves for testing $\mu = 0$ against $\mu \neq 0$ with $n = 10, 25$, and 100, drawn against the ideal power function with the horizontal scale in terms of $n(0, 1)$.

If $n = 500$, then H_0 will be rejected if

$$\bar{x} > \bar{x}_c = 300 + 2.33\frac{24}{\sqrt{500}} \doteq 300 + 2.33(1.073) \doteq 302.50.$$

The OC function can be computed with these critical values; see Table 13.4.

The OC curves of this test at $\alpha = 0.01$, with $n = 10, 100$, and 500 respectively, are given in Figure 13.10. This figure shows clearly how the OC curve approaches its ideal form as n increases. These curves reveal, in other words, that the largest sample gives the best test—the most nearly ideal test.

The effect of changing n on the power function for a two-sided test is illustrated by Figure 13.11. Again note how a power curve approaches its ideal form as n increases. (Note that this figure is drawn against the z-scale.)

Determining n for Fixed α and β

Having noted the effects upon β, of changing n, with α fixed, we can see why an appropriate sample size can be found so that prescribed α- and β-risks can be met. Suppose that in the salesmen's commission illustration evaluated in Chapter 12, management of the floor-wax factory decides that remedial actions are required if its salesmen's weekly mean commission is \$560 and that no remedial actions will be taken if the mean is \$600. Furthermore, suppose that management is willing to assume an α-risk of 0.05 for H_0 that $\mu = \$600$ and a β-risk of 0.10 for H_1 that $\mu = \$560$. Then the decision framework can be summarized as follows.

Act	State of Nature	
	$H_0: \mu = 600$	$H_1: \mu = 560$
a_1: No remedial action	Correct act	$\beta = 0.10$
a_2: Remedial action	$\alpha = 0.05$	Correct act

This decision framework can also be portrayed more revealingly by a graph such as Figure 13.12. Figure 13.12 is also instructive for establishing the decision rule for this case. First of all, according to the decision framework, we see that we are dealing with a lower-tail test here. Next, Figure 13.12 suggests that, given α, H_0 will be rejected if and only if

$$\hat{\theta} < \hat{\theta}_c = \theta_0 - Z_\alpha \sigma_{\hat{\theta}} \qquad (13.7a)$$

Next, recall that β is the probability of accepting H_0 given that H_1 is true. Now, given the specified β-risk and again as suggested by Figure 13.12, we see that H_0 will be accepted if and only if

$$\hat{\theta} > \hat{\theta}_c = \theta_1 + Z_{1-\beta} \sigma_{\hat{\theta}} \qquad (13.7b)$$

Returning to our current example and by equations (13.7a) and

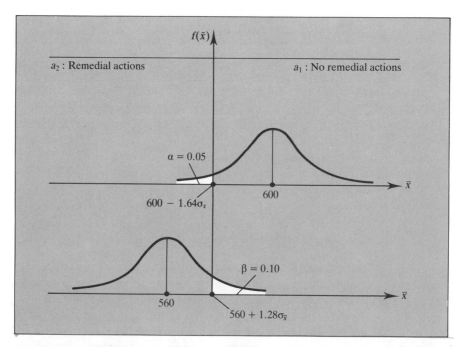

FIGURE 13.12 Graphic illustration of testing $\mu = 600$ against $\mu = 560$ with $\alpha = 0.05$ and $\beta = 0.10$.

(13.7b), we have that $H_0: \mu = 600$ will be rejected if and only if

(1)
$$\bar{x} < \bar{x}_c = \mu_0 + z_\alpha \sigma_{\bar{X}}$$

$$= 600 - 1.64 \frac{80}{\sqrt{n}}$$

$$= 600 - \frac{131.2}{\sqrt{n}}$$

and that $H_0: \mu = 600$ will be accepted if and only if

(2)
$$\bar{x} > \bar{x}_c = \mu_1 + z_{1-\beta} \sigma_{\bar{X}}$$

$$= 560 + 1.28 \frac{80}{\sqrt{n}}$$

$$= 560 + \frac{102.4}{\sqrt{n}}.$$

Finally, the values of n and $\bar{x}_c$ that will satisfy both of these two equations will furnish us with a basis for our decision rule. We can solve for n by equating both expressions for $\bar{x}_c$ as follows:

$$600 - \frac{131.2}{\sqrt{n}} = 560 + \frac{102.4}{\sqrt{n}},$$

$$40 = \frac{131.2 + 102.4}{\sqrt{n}},$$

$$\sqrt{n} = \frac{233.6}{40} = 5.84,$$

$$n \doteq 34.11 \text{ or } 35.$$

The critical value for $\bar{x}$ can now be found by substituting n into either of the two equations for $\bar{x}_c$. For example,

$$\bar{x}_c = 560 + \frac{102.4}{\sqrt{35}} \doteq 560 + \frac{102.4}{5.91608} \doteq 577.31.$$

Now, the decision rule may be stated: (1) take a random sample of size $n = 35$; (2) compute the sample mean; (3) if $\bar{x} \geq \$577.31$, take a_1: no remedial action is required (the probability that this action is the wrong one is $\beta = 0.10$); (4) if $\bar{x} < \$577.31$, take a_2: start remedial actions (the probability that this is the wrong decision is $\alpha = 0.05$).

To verify that n and $\bar{x}_c$, determined before, can satisfy the desired α- and β-risks, we note that

$$\alpha = P(\text{Reject } H_0 \text{ given that } H_0 \text{ is true}) = P(\bar{x} < 577.31 \,|\, \mu = 600)$$

$$= N\left(\frac{577.31 - 600}{80/\sqrt{35}}\right) \doteq N(-1.68) \doteq 0.0465 \doteq 0.05,$$

and that

$$\beta = P(\text{Accept } H_0 \text{ given that } H_1 \text{ is true}) = P(\bar{X} \geqslant 577.31 \mid \mu = 560)$$

$$= 1 - N\left(\frac{577.31 - 560}{80/\sqrt{35}}\right) \doteq 1 - N(1.28) \doteq 1 - 0.8997 \doteq 0.10.$$

This entire procedure used only two values of μ, 560 and 600. What is μ is some other value? That has implicitly been taken care of in the following way. If $\mu > 600$, there will be a probability of less than 0.05 of wrongly accepting H_1. Thus, if $\mu \geqslant 600$, there will be a maximum probability of 0.05 of wrongly accepting H_1. If $\mu < 560$, there will be a probability of less than 0.10 of wrongly accepting H_0. Thus, if $\mu \leqslant 560$, there will be a maximum probability of 0.10 of wrongly accepting H_0. So far, so good. The risks of type I and type II error have been kept within the desired bounds. If μ is between 560 and 600, the risks of type I and type II error will not have been kept within the desired bounds, however; it is assumed in this situation that management does not much care what it does if μ is one of these values. Management only cares that a reasonably high probability of making a right decision be guaranteed if μ is below 560 or above 600. If this correctly summarizes management's attitudes, this entire procedure should be used. Otherwise, of course, the procedure must be modified.

Consider now another example with an upper-tail test. In deciding whether a lot of 100,000 rifles should be accepted, the U.S. Army adopts the following quality standard: If only 1 percent of the lot is defective, accept. If 3% of the rifles in the lot are defective, reject. If the defective rifles comprise more than 1 percent but less than 3% of the lot, examine the type of defects before making a final decision. Now, suppose we focus our attention on acceptance or rejection of the lot only; then the pertinent hypotheses become

$$H_0: \pi \leqslant 0.01; \qquad H_1: \pi \geqslant 0.03.$$

Furthermore, if we assume that the Army is willing to take a risk of 0.01 of rejecting a lot with $\pi = 0.01$ and to take a risk of 0.05 of accepting a lot with $\pi = 0.03$, then the decision situation can be tabulated as follows.

	State of Nature	
Act	$H_0: \pi = 0.01$	$H_1: \pi = 0.03$
a_1: Accept	Correct act	$\beta = 0.05$
a_2: Reject	$\alpha = 0.01$	Correct act

The graphic representation of the α- and β-risks in this decision situation is as shown by Figure 13.13.

Here, we are concerned with an upper-tail test. A general decision rule can be established by studying Figure 13.13. From this figure, we

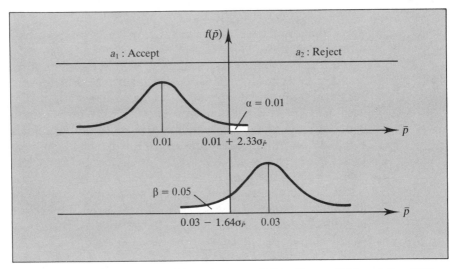

FIGURE 13.13 Testing $\pi = 0.01$ against $\pi = 0.03$ with $\alpha = 0.01$ and $\beta = 0.05$.

see that, with α and β specified, H_0 will be rejected if and only if

$$\hat{\theta} > \hat{\theta}_c = \theta_0 + Z_{1-\alpha}\sigma_{\hat{\theta}}, \tag{13.8a}$$

and H_0 will be accepted if and only if

$$\hat{\theta} \leq \hat{\theta}_c = \theta_1 - Z_{\beta}\sigma_{\hat{\theta}}. \tag{13.8b}$$

Returning to our example and recalling that $\alpha = 0.01$, so that H_0 will be rejected if and only if

$$\bar{p} > \bar{p}_c = \pi_0 + z_{1-\alpha}\sigma_{\bar{P}}$$

$$= 0.01 + 2.33\sqrt{\frac{(0.01)(0.99)}{n}}$$

$$\doteq 0.01 + \frac{0.2318}{\sqrt{n}}.$$

With $\beta = 0.05$, H_0 will be accepted if and only if

$$\bar{p} \leq \bar{p}_c = \pi_1 + z_{\beta}\sigma_{\bar{P}}$$

$$= 0.03 - 1.64\sqrt{\frac{(0.03)(0.97)}{n}}$$

$$\doteq 0.03 - \frac{0.2798}{\sqrt{n}}$$

Solving these two equations for $\bar{p}_c$ simultaneously, we find that

$$n \doteq 659, \qquad \bar{p}_c \doteq 0.019.$$

Thus, the stipulation that $\alpha = 0.01$ and $\beta = 0.05$ can be met by taking a random sample of size 659. With this rule, a_1 (accept the lot) should be taken if $\bar{p} \leqslant 0.019$; a_2 (reject the lot) should be taken if $\bar{p} > 0.019$.

Let us turn to consider a two-sided test. A process adjusted to fill seasoned tomatoes into cans is said to be in control if the net weight in each can is within the range of 16 ± 0.5 ounces. According to past experience, the standard deviation is quite stable and is equal to 0.5 ounce. When the process is in control, it is left alone; when the process is out of control, it is stopped for adjustments. To check from time to time whether the process is in control, how large a sample should be taken if management is willing to assume an α-risk of 0.01 of mistakenly stopping the process and a β-risk of 0.025 of mistakenly leaving the process alone when μ is "off" by 0.5 ounce?

First, let us summarize the decision framework as follows.

	State of Nature		
Act	$H_0: \mu_0 = 16$	$H_1: \mu_1 = 15.5;$	$\mu_2 = 16.5$
a_1: Leave the process alone	Correct	$\beta = 0.025$	$\beta = 0.025$
a_2: Stop the process	$\alpha = 0.01$	Correct	Correct

The α- and β-risks in this case are shown by Figure 13.14.

In general, to determine the sample size with α and β fixed for a double-tail test, as suggested by Figure 13.14 and given α, H_0 will be rejected if and only if

$$\hat{\theta} < \hat{\theta}_{c_1} = \theta_0 - Z_{\alpha/2}\sigma_{\hat{\theta}} \tag{13.9a}$$

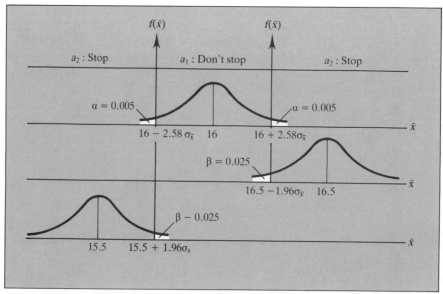

FIGURE 13.14 Testing $\mu = 16$ against $\mu \neq 16$ with $\alpha = 0.01$ and $\beta = 0.025$.

or

$$\hat{\theta} > \hat{\theta}_{c_2} = \theta_0 + Z_{1-\alpha/2}\sigma_{\hat{\theta}}. \tag{13.9b}$$

These are the realtionships among n, θ_{c_1} and θ_{c_2} that must be satisfied to meet the specified value of α-risk for rejecting H_0 (stopping the process in our current example). Now, for our example, reject H_0 if and only if

$$\bar{x} < \bar{x}_{c_1} = \mu_0 + z_{\alpha/2}\sigma_{\bar{X}}$$

$$= 16 - 2.58\frac{0.5}{\sqrt{n}}$$

$$\doteq 16 - \frac{1.29}{\sqrt{n}},$$

$$\bar{x} > \bar{x}_{c_2} = \mu_0 + z_{1-\alpha/2}\sigma_{\bar{X}}$$

$$= 16 + 2.58\frac{0.5}{\sqrt{n}}$$

$$\doteq 16 + \frac{1.29}{\sqrt{n}}.$$

A general decision rule in this case can also be formulated by focusing our attention on the fixed β-risk. Note that β is the probability of accepting H_0 either when the true parameter value is less than θ_1—the alternative parameter value which is less than θ_0—or when the true value of the parameter is greater than θ_2—the alternative parameter value which is greater than θ_0. Also note that type II error is only committed if H_0 is accepted when H_1 is true, and acceptance of H_0 requires that

$$\hat{\theta} \geq \hat{\theta}_{c_1} = \theta_1 + Z_{1-\beta}\sigma_{\hat{\theta}} \tag{13.9c}$$

and that

$$\hat{\theta} \leq \hat{\theta}_{c_2} = \theta_2 - Z_{\beta}\sigma_{\hat{\theta}}. \tag{13.9d}$$

Taking up our example again, $H_0: \mu = 16$ will be rejected if and only if

$$\bar{x} \geq \bar{x}_{c_1} = \mu_1 + z_{1-\beta}\sigma_{\bar{X}}$$

$$= 15.5 + 1.96\frac{0.5}{\sqrt{n}}$$

$$= 15.5 + \frac{0.98}{\sqrt{n}},$$

and

$$\bar{x} \leq \bar{x}_{c_2} = \mu_2 - z_\beta \sigma_{\bar{X}}$$

$$= 16.5 - 1.96\frac{0.5}{\sqrt{n}}$$

$$= 16.5 - \frac{0.98}{\sqrt{n}}.$$

We now have two equations for each of the two critical values. The required sample size can be obtained by equating either the pair of expressions for $\bar{x}_{c_1}$ or that for $\bar{x}_{c_2}$. Thus, for example, by equating the two statements for $\bar{x}_{c_1}$, we have

$$16 - \frac{1.29}{\sqrt{n}} = 15.5 + \frac{0.98}{\sqrt{n}}.$$

Solving for n,

$$\sqrt{n} \doteq 4.54 \quad \text{or} \quad n \doteq 21.$$

The critical values may be found as

$$\bar{x}_{c_1} = 15.5 + \frac{0.98}{\sqrt{21}} \doteq 15.5 + 0.21$$

$$= 15.71 \text{ ounces};$$

$$\bar{x}_{c_2} = 16.5 - \frac{0.98}{\sqrt{21}} \doteq 16.5 - 0.21$$

$$= 16.29 \text{ ounces}.$$

The decision rule for this example may now be summarized as follows. (1) Take a random sample of 21 cans from the production line, say, every hour, and determine the average weight of the contents; (2) leave the process alone if $15.71 \leq \bar{x} \leq 16.29$; (3) stop the process if $\bar{x} < 15.71$ or if $\bar{x} > 16.29$.

13.6 A NOTE ON SUSPENSION OF JUDGMENT

We have presented the classical theory of testing in this and the last chapter as a two-action decision problem. The impression given so far has been that classical statisticians would always make a terminal decision once sample evidence is made available. This is not true. As a matter of fact, a classical statistician may, under two conditions, decide to suspend judgment, delay the final decision so to speak, until additional information is made available. First is the case when a test is conducted with fixed values of α and n. With this procedure, if the sample size is smaller than what would have been drawn when both α- and β-risk are specified at acceptable levels, the probability of committing a type II error will be larger than desired. This becomes a concern, of course, when sample data lead to the rejection of H_0. When the consequence of committing a type II error is thought to be serious, a classical statistician often decides to delay the final selection between a_1 and a_2 until more sample evidence is obtained.

Second is the case when a classical statistician conducts a test without even specifying the α-risk in advance. That is, she may simply go ahead and observe the evidence provided by the sample with fixed size and then compute the probability of making the wrong decision for each act. If either risk is too large for the problem on hand, she may again suspend judgment until additional sample information is made available.

For example, if for a given test, the statistician uses the sample result $\hat{\theta}$ as the critical value $\hat{\theta}_c$, she can then determine the α-risk by computing the conditional probability of obtaining such a sample result given that the null hypothesis $\theta = \theta_0$ is true. Suppose that the resulting probability is 0.001; she may conclude that this risk is much smaller than she is willing to assume and, therefore, she may reject H_0 and take a_2. She reasons that her decision is justified since, if H_0 were true, the odds would be only 1 to 999 against the sample result. In other words, the sample result is extremely unlikely and her decision to reject H_0 is appropriate. However, if the computed α-risk is rather large, say, 0.25, then the odds against the sample result under the assumption of a true H_0 are now as large as 1 to 3. In view of this large α-risk, a classical statistician would usually conclude that the probability of committing a type 1 error is much larger than she is prepared to accept. Or, since the sample outcome is not so unlikely, she cannot reject H_0 and choose a_2. Should she then automatically reject H_1 in view of her acceptance of H_0? This evidently depends upon the level of β. If β also happens to be rather large, say, 0.30, then the probability of obtaining such a sample result given H_1 is true is 0.30. This is not an unlikely result either. As a consequence, she cannot justify the rejection of H_1 or the selection of a_1. This is a case in which she is confronted with the dilemma of being unable to reject either of the two hypotheses and, hence, being unable to make the choice between a_1 and a_2. She would then insist on delaying judgment until additional information is made available before a final decision.

To illustrate the previous discussion, let us consider the situation of a manager of a firm who has placed an ad for his new product in the current issue of a certain national monthly magazine. He decides that he will continue the ad in later issues if and only if 25 percent or more of the readers of the current issue have noticed the ad. In a telephone survey of 100 subscribers of the magazine, selected at random, 24 indicate that they have indeed read the ad. What should be his decision?

Here, the manager is concerned with testing H_0: $\pi \geqslant 0.25$ against

$H_1: \pi < 0.25$ with the sample result $\bar{p} = 24/100 = 0.24$. For this result and given that $\pi = 0.25$, we have

$$\alpha = P(\bar{p} \leqslant 0.24 \mid \pi_0 = 0.25)$$

$$= N\left(\frac{0.24 + 1/2(100) - 0.25}{\sqrt{\frac{(0.25)(0.75)}{100}}}\right)$$

$$\doteq N(-0.23) = 0.4090.$$

This implies that if the null hypothesis is true, the probability that the sample proportion will be 0.24 or smaller is greater than 0.40. Clearly, the sample outcome is highly likely and the manager should not reject H_0 or discontinue the ad. However, can he reject H_1 or decide to continue the ad? This now depends on how likely the sample outcome is given that H_1 is true. Since the alternative is stated as $\pi_1 < 0.25$, any value such as, say $\pi_1 = 0.249$ is member of H_1. For convenience, let us use $\pi_1 = 0.25$ to compute β.

$$\beta = P(\bar{p} > 0.25 \mid \pi_1 = 0.25)$$

$$= 1 - P(\bar{p} \leqslant 0.25 \mid \pi_1 = 0.25)$$

$$= 1 - 0.4090$$

$$= 0.5910.$$

This shows that the sample result is even more likely given that H_1 is true. The manager, therefore, cannot reject H_1 and select a_1. Given the manager's predetermined decision criterion, however arbitrary, as a classical statistician he would prefer to suspend judgment.

In practice, the manager often needs only to evaluate the α-risk. If any hypothesis is to be rejected, it should be the one that is inconsistent with the sample data. A sample proportion of 0.24 is a member of H_1 and thus it reinforces the validity of H_1. It is only the correctness of the null hypothesis that is in doubt. The results of our illustrative example may be summarized as follows. If a_2, the action "discontinue the ad" is taken; the act is consistent with sample evidence and the probability of erroneous action is at most 0.4090. In view of this large α-risk, judgment should be suspended until further information can be obtained.

GLOSSARY OF FORMULAS

(13.1) $\hat{\theta} < \hat{\theta}_c = \theta_0 - Z_\alpha \sigma_{\hat{\theta}}$.

This is the decision rule for a left-tail test. It says that H_0 will be rejected if and only if the test statistic $\hat{\theta}$ is less than the critical value $\hat{\theta}_c$ of the test statistic at α. Note also that this expression is nothing but an alternative form of the standard normal deviate $Z = (\hat{\theta} - \theta_0)/\sigma_{\hat{\theta}}$

introduced in the last chapter as the standardized test statistic that is normally or approximately normally distributed.

(13.2) $\quad \text{OC}(\theta_i) = P(\hat{\theta} < \hat{\theta}_c \mid \theta_i) = 1 - N\left(\dfrac{\hat{\theta}_c - \theta_i}{\sigma_{\hat{\theta}}}\right).$

The Operating Characteristic function is the probability of accepting H_0 for various admissible values of the parameter θ_i. In a left-tail test, H_0 can be accepted if and only if the test statistic $\hat{\theta}$ is greater than the critical value of the statistic. Note that $\text{OC}(\theta_i)$ is a conditional probability. Note also, $\text{OC}(\theta_i) = \beta$. Since OC and power functions are complementary to each other, we always have $\text{PF}(\theta_i) = 1 - \beta$ except when H_0 is true, in which case $\text{PF}(\theta_i) = \alpha$.

(13.3) $\quad \hat{\theta} > \hat{\theta}_c = \theta_0 + Z_{1-\alpha}\sigma_{\hat{\theta}}.$

This is the general decision rule for an upper-tail test. It says: Reject H_0 if and only if $\hat{\theta} > \hat{\theta}_c$.

(13.4) $\quad \text{OC}(\theta_i) = P(\hat{\theta} \leq \hat{\theta}_c \mid \theta_i) = N\left(\dfrac{\hat{\theta}_c + \theta_i}{\sigma_{\hat{\theta}}}\right).$

For an upper-tail test, H_0 can only be accepted if and only if $\hat{\theta} \leq \hat{\theta}_c$. Thus, $\text{OC}(\theta_i)$ is given by the conditional probability formula in this case.

(13.5a) $\quad \hat{\theta} < \hat{\theta}_{c_1} = \theta_0 - Z_\alpha \sigma_{\hat{\theta}};$

(13.5b) $\quad \hat{\theta} > \hat{\theta}_{c_1} = \theta_0 + Z_{1-\alpha}\sigma_{\hat{\theta}}.$

These two expressions constitute the decision rule for a double-tail test. As such, we have two critical values of the test statistic, $\hat{\theta}_{c_1}$ and $\hat{\theta}_{c_2}$. Here we have: Reject H_0 if and only if $\hat{\theta} < \hat{\theta}_{c_1}$ on $\hat{\theta} > \hat{\theta}_{c_2}$. These equations are also the alternative expressions of the standard normal deviate Z mentioned in (13.1).

(13.6) $\quad \text{OC}(\theta_i) = P(\hat{\theta}_{c_1} \leq \hat{\theta} \leq \hat{\theta}_{c_2} \mid \theta_i) = N\left(\dfrac{\hat{\theta}_{c_2} - \theta_i}{\sigma_{\hat{\theta}}}\right) - \left(\dfrac{\hat{\theta}_{c_1} - \theta_i}{\sigma_{\hat{\theta}}}\right).$

$\text{OC}(\theta_i) = \beta$ for a double-tail test is computed by this conditional probability formula because H_0 can now be accepted if and only if $\hat{\theta}_{c_1} \leq \hat{\theta} \leq \hat{\theta}_{c_2}$. Of course, in this case too $\text{PF}(\theta_i) = 1 - \beta$ except when H_0 is true.

(13.7a) $\quad \hat{\theta} < \hat{\theta}_c = \theta_0 - Z_\alpha \sigma_{\hat{\theta}};$

(13.7b) $\quad \hat{\theta} > \hat{\theta}_c = \theta_1 - Z_{1-\beta}\sigma_{\hat{\theta}}.$

When we wish to determine the appropriate sample size under the condition that both α- and β-risks are specified at given levels in advance for the case of a lower-tail test, we employ these two formulas as the general decision rule. In these equations, H_0 and H_1 are the specified simple hypotheses in composite H_0 and H_1, respectively. To obtain the n required that can satisfy both specified α and β, we equate these expressions and solve. After n is obtained, $\hat{\theta}_c$ can be found by substituting n in either of these two equations and solving for $\hat{\theta}_c$.

(13.8a) $\hat{\theta} > \hat{\theta}_c = \theta_0 + Z_{1-\alpha}\sigma_{\hat{\theta}};$

(13.8b) $\hat{\theta} < \hat{\theta}_c = \theta_1 - Z_\beta\sigma_{\hat{\theta}}.$

These two equations constitute the decision rule for an upper-tail test for the case of determining the sample size that can satisfy both α and β levels specified in advance. The application of the two equations is identical with those of (13.7).

(13.9a) $\hat{\theta} < \hat{\theta}_{c_1} = \theta_0 - Z_{\alpha/2}\sigma_{\hat{\theta}};$

(13.9b) $\hat{\theta} > \hat{\theta}_{c_2} = \theta_0 + Z_{1-\alpha}\sigma_{\hat{\theta}};$

(13.9c) $\hat{\theta} \geqslant \hat{\theta}_{c_1} = \theta_1 + Z_{1-\beta}\sigma_{\hat{\theta}};$

(13.9d) $\hat{\theta} \leqslant \hat{\theta}_{c_2} = \theta_1 - Z_\beta\sigma_{\hat{\theta}}.$

This group of equations constitutes two alternative decision rules for the case of double-tail tests when we wish to determine n so that both predetermined α- and β-risks can be satisfied. The first two equations concentrate on the null hypothetical value of the parameter and the level of significance; the last two equations concentrate on the specified parameter value in H_1 and the probability of committing type II error. In applicaton, we need only to use (13.9a) and (13.9b) or (13.9c) and (13.9d). The application of each decision rule is the same as the other. In each case, we find n first by equating the two equations on solving for n. Then we find $\hat{\theta}_{c_1}$ and $\hat{\theta}_{c_2}$ by substituting n in each of the two equations, respectively. One must observe though that the first pair of equations refers to the rejection of H_0 and the last two refer to the acceptance of H_0.

REVIEW QUESTIONS

13.1 There are four possible outcomes when we test an H_0 against an H_1 with α and n fixed in the two-action decision problems. What are they?

13.2 Why is "$1 - \beta$" called the power of the test?

13.3 What is an operating-characteristic function? What does it measure?

13.4 What is the relationship between the power and the OC functions?

13.5 Does the power of a test always equal the level of significance? If not, why not?

13.6 Does the OC function always equal β? If not, why not?

13.7 Equations (13.1), (13.3) and (13.5) can be considered as alternative forms of the standardized normal deviate $Z = (\hat{\theta} - \theta_0)/\sigma_{\hat{\theta}}$, which is used as the generalized test statistic when $\hat{\theta}$ is normally or approximately normally distributed. Explain why?

13.8 What are the shapes of the graphs of the ideal power curves for the three types of tests? What do the shapes imply? Can we ever have an ideal power curve with sampling?

13.9 What are the shapes of the ideal OC curves for the three types of tests? What do such curves mean? Can we ever have an ideal OC curve with sampling?

13.10 What is the uniformly most powerful test?

13.11 Since there is not a uniformly most powerful test in the case of double-tail tests, why do we still consider them to be reasonable and even desirable in many decision situations?

13.12 What are the important relationships between α and β when the sample size is fixed in a test?

13.13 How are the power and the OC functions affected by changes in sample size? Explain why.

13.14 Under what conditions may a classical statistician suspend judgment in a test?

PROBLEMS

13.1 The resistance of steel wires of a certain make is known to have a standard deviation of 0.02 ohms. A factory decides to buy this make of wire if the mean resitance per unit length is 0.4 ohms or more, and decides not to buy it if the mean resistance is less than 0.4 ohms. Furthermore, the factory management desires a decision rule such that $\alpha = 0.05$ and $n = 100$.
   a. State the appropriate hypotheses.
   b. Show the α and the β risks schematically.
   c. Establish the decision rule.
   d. Construct the power and the OC curves for this test.

13.2 A company manufactures cables whose breaking strengths have a mean of 100 pounds and a standard deviation of 6 pounds. A newly developed manufacturing process is believed to be both more efficient and capable of increasing the mean strength. The company wishes to adopt the new process if it is indeed more efficient, and decides to check—at the 1% level of significance—25 cables produced by the process.
   a. State the appropriate hypotheses.
   b. Show the α and the β risks schematically.
   c. Establish the decision rule.
   d. Construct the power and the OC curves for this test.

13.3 Rework the preceding problem on the basis of testing 100 cables. What conclusions can you draw regarding the power of this rest when sample sizes are increased?

13.4 In a manufactured part that is to fit other parts, a certain critical dimension is designed to be 4.6 inches. The variability in manufacturing is indicated by a variance of 0.25 in^2. The process is considered to be in control and is continued if it produces this part with a mean of 4.6 inches for the critical dimension. Otherwise, the process is considered out of control and it is stopped. To check whether the process is in control, the plant statistician is satisfied with $\alpha = 0.05$ and $n = 25$, taken every other hour.
   a. Formulate the appropriate hypotheses.
   b. Show the α and the β risks schematically.
   c. Establish the decision rule.
   d. Construct the power and the OC curves.

13.5 A manufacturer who produces flashlight batteries considers that his process is in control when the mean life of her product is 35 hours, and out of control when the mean life is not 35 hours. The process is known to have a variance of 36 hours^2. Establish a decision rule for checking this process with $\alpha = 0.05$ and $n = 36$, and construct the power and the OC curves for it.

13.6 A department store has set up this criterion for accepting or rejecting shipments of purchases: A shipment is accepted if 5% or less of the items are defective; otherwise, the shipment is rejected. The criteria also specify that α should be 0.05 and n should be 100.
   a. Formulate the appropriate hypotheses.
   b. Show the α and the β risks schematically.
   c. Establish the decision rule.
   d. Construct the power and the OC curves.

13.7 Rework the preceding problem by using $\alpha = 0.01$. Compare your results with those in the last problem in connection with the relationship between α and β when n is fixed.

13.8 The U.S. Navy decides to accept a shipment of 200,000 raincoats if the percentage of defectives in the lot is less than 10%. Furthermore, the Navy is anxious to accept the lot and is willing, by observing a random sample of 1,500 selected from the lot, to assume an α risk of 0.05 of rejecting a shipment that meets its specification. How should the hypotheses be stated in this case? What is the decision rule for this test? What are the values of the OC function for $\pi_1 = 0.12, 0.11, 0.10, 0.9, 0.08, 0.07$ or 0.05? Construct the OC and the power curves with the results.

13.9 To test the hypothesis that a coin is fair, the following decision rule is adopted: (1) Accept the hypothesis if the number of heads in 100 tosses is between 40 and 60 inclusive; (2) reject the hypothesis otherwise.
   a. What is the alternative hypothesis?
   b. What is the value of α for this test?
   c. What are the critical values for this decision rule in terms of a normal distribution?
   d. How should the β risks be calculated in this case?
   e. Calculate β for $\pi_1 = 0.1, 0.2, 0.3, 0.4, 0.5, 0.6, 0.7, 0.8,$ and 0.9.

13.10 Rework the last problem under the assumptions that $\alpha = 0.10$ and that critical values are to be determined.

13.11 In planning whether or not to have a branch in a certain city, the management of a department store has set up the following criteria: Build the branch if the mean weekly family income in that city is $500; do not build it if the mean weekly income is $450; $\alpha = 0.05$ and $\beta = 0.10$. Establish the decision rule (that is, find the critical value and sample size) for this case, assuming the standard deviation is $90.00.

13.12 The variability in manufacturing a certain part for wall clocks is indicated by a standard deviation of 0.02 inches, which, according to past experience, remains stable. This part is specified to have an outside diameter of 2.06 ± 0.01 inches. When this specification is not met, the production process is considered out of control, and it must be stopped for adjustment. If $\alpha = 0.01$ and $\beta = 0.10$, how large a sample is required for the purpose of checking whether the process is in control? What are the critical values for this decision rule?

13.13 A manufacturer who produces bolts considers this process in control if the average diameter is 12 centimeters and if the individual bolts do not deviate from this mean diameter by more than 1 centimeter. The standard deviation is known to be 0.25 centimeters. Given that $\alpha = 0.01$ and $\beta = 0.05$, what are the required sample size and critical values for checking whether the manufacturer's process is in control?

13.14 Suppose, with reference to a binomial population, we wish to test $\pi = 0.4$ against $\pi = 0.6$. Furthermore, suppose we would like to have $\alpha = 0.01$ and $\beta = 0.10$. How large should the sample be? What is the critical value?

13.15 Suppose that the President of the United States would introduce legislation for socialized medicine if sample results indicate that 70% of the voters desired it, and would not introduce such legislation if sample results indicated that 50% of the voters desired it. Furthermore, suppose that he would like to assume an α-risk of 0.01 and a β risk of 0.05. How large a sample is required? What is the critical value for this decision rule?

13.16 In testing $H_0: \Delta\mu = 0$ against $H_1: \Delta\mu = 2$ at $\alpha = 0.025$ with $n_1 = n_2 = 100$, what is the probability of committing a type II error, given that $\sigma_1^2 = 9$ and $\sigma_2^2 = 16$?

13.17 *A suggested research project.* You have now gone through half of this text. You have also learned all the procedures of computing various descriptive measures and the basic statistical theories for evaluting cross-section univariate data. In other words, you are now equipped with the fundamental statistical knowledge to conduct independent statistical studies in which only such data are utilized. Thus, you are advised to write a research paper on some business, economic, or sociopolitical problem that might be of interest to you by following all the six stages of a statistical investigation presented in Chapter 1. In doing this you are advised to observe the following points.

1. You should not try to be too ambitious in selecting your topic.

2. The topic you select should be one whose population can be identified easily; the adequate frame for it should be readily available to you.

3. Wherever graphs and computations are required, you should try to make good use of your home computer or the computer facilities at your school.

14* Statistical Quality Control

14.1 THE IMPORTANCE AND HISTORY OF QUALITY CONTROL

Statistical quality control, or simply *quality control,* refers to the continuous statistical surveillance of repetitive production processes. This branch of statistical analysis is quite simple and is widely employed for industrial as well as managerial operations. Quality control takes on an additional dimension of significance because all the principles of inductive statistics, such as those involving sampling designs, sampling distributions, and estimation and testing find their application in quality control procedures. In particular, the study of quality control serves excellently for the illustration of the classical decision procedures presented in the previous two chapters, since quality control problems can be viewed as two-action decision problems. Quality control, in other words, contains the main principles and ideas, such as formulation of decision rules, evaluation of α- and β-risk, and OC curves. Thus, its study will undoubtedly enable us to make the ideas about testing procedures more concrete.

The term *quality* refers to any property of the product, such as the breaking strength of yarn, the outside diameter of a ball bearing, the drained weight of a No. $2\frac{1}{2}$ can of meat, the amount of tension needed to produce a 1-inch deflection in a spring, the accuracy of clerical operations, or the safety records of factory workers.

In managing the various flows of industrial and business activities, one of the essential problems is to make certain that the quality of the products is up to the specified standard and that operations of all kinds are accurate to the desired degree. A manufacturer of, say, rivets, must know that the lengths of his products from various runs will continue to meet his customers' standards. The purchasing agent of a factory always wishes to make certain that incoming materials and equipment are not defective. An office manager has to be sure that clerical operations are accurate. And so on.

One obvious method—once widely used and still occasionally used today—of achieving such objectives is through 100% inspection. However, 100% inspection does not always mean 100% assurance: neither men nor machines are infallible. Moreover, this method is often expensive and time-consuming. To these drawbacks must be added the fact that 100% inspection is simply out of the question when tests of quality involve destroying the product.

The search for a more economical yet effective procedure for controlling output quality has led to the development and adoption of a method known as statistical quality control. This method can be simply thought of as an economical and effective system of maintaining and improving the quality of outputs throughout the whole operating process of specification, production, and inspection based on continuous surveillance with random samples.

The continuous surveillance of outputs by the use of samples is called *statistical quality control* for the reason that whenever sampling evidence indicates unsatisfactory outputs, these outputs are rejected, or corrective steps are called for in the maintenance or improvement of the production process. This explanation makes clear that quality control is not confined to the often-publicized function of cost savings in inspection. It also aids in making decisions concerning the specifications and actual production of outputs. In other words, it is a tool, as will be shown throughout this chapter, that is capable of influencing decisions related to acceptance or rejection of an existing lot or continuation or stoppage of the whole process of production. Therefore, we should think of output quality in terms of the three functions of specification, production, and inspection of products. For this reason, the most effective use of the techniques of quality control demands the cooperation of all those who are responsible for these different functions and requires the full understanding of these techniques by top management personnel.

The making of an excellent product with a high degree of uniformity is an old aspiration. For centuries, highly skilled artisans have striven to make products distinctive through superior quality and to minimize variations among different units of the same product. Standardization of parts of mass-produced items for the purpose of interchangeability was first attempted as early as 1789, when Eli Whitney, inventor of the cotton gin, introduced it into the production of firearms.

The idea of using statistical methods to control the quality of a product is quite new, however. It was not until the 1920s that the techniques of statistical quality control were developed and applied by Dr. W. A. Shewhart of the Bell Telephone Laboratories. The publication of Shewhart's classic in this field, *Economic Control of Quality of Manufactured Products,* in 1931 may be said to be the formal beginning of this important procedure. The Shewhart methods were immediately accepted by British industry, whereas throughout the whole 1930s only a small number of plants, mainly in the electrical and textile fields, adopted them in the United States.

World War II, with its vast demands for quickly produced goods and its more exacting specifications, accelerated the widespread adoption of statistical control techniques by military procurement agencies and industries in both Britain and the United States. As a result of the spectacular savings in materials and manpower that wartime applications made possible, as well as its acceptance by scientific societies, statistical quality control has come into its own in the United States. During the whole postwar era, statistical techniques have been widely used, not only in controlling the quality of industrial outputs but also in controlling inventories, sales, work safety, and many types of clerical and accounting operations. In spite of this rapid expansion, experts in the field are confident that in the near future, with the vast experience already gained and with further developments in methods, quality control procedures can be expected to make an increasing contribution to the economic goals of efficient decisions on rejecting or accepting existing lots of output and of continuous improvement in quality at lower costs.

There are two distinct aspects of statistical quality control: acceptance sampling and process control. *Acceptance sampling,* also called *acceptance inspection,* is concerned with the evaluation of a finite group of items, called the *inspection lot,* that is already in existence and about whose quality a decision must be made. This procedure is therefore aimed at the past performance of a production process. *Process control,* on the other hand, aims at evaluating future performance of a production process. It is thus concerned with an infinite population whose elements are all the possible units of output that can be conceivably produced by further repetitions of the process. We present these two procedures in the order mentioned.

14.2 THE NATURE OF ACCEPTANCE SAMPLING

The objective of acceptance sampling is to evaluate a specific lot of material or product that is already in existence and about whose quality a decision is made as to whether the lot should be accepted or rejected in accordance with some predetermined standards. The standards are not established, however, in terms of the inherent capacities of the production process. Instead, they are set according to what is required of the material or product of the lot.

Suppose a sample is drawn from a lot or a process. If the sample contains a specific proportion or less of defectives, the lot is accepted. Otherwise the lot is rejected. Such a decision process is actually the procedure of testing. As such, the decision rule is subjected to α- and, β-risk. Here, the α-risk is called the *producer's risk* because α in effect is the probability of rejecting a lot that actually conforms to the prescribed standard. The β-risk is called the *consumer's risk* because β can be viewed as the probability of accepting a lot that does not conform to the established standard. Let us make these points more obvious by a concrete example.

Consider a manufacturer who purchases certain goods from a supplier. The manufacturer will accept the lot if the fraction of defective items is 6% or less. She will reject the lot if it contains 9% or more defective items. So far, her decision rule amounts to testing

$$H_0: \pi \leqslant 0.06 \text{ against } H_1: \pi \geqslant 0.09.$$

In quality control terminology, a value such as 6% is called the *producer's risk point,* PRP, and the value such as 9% is called the *consumer's risk point,* CRP. These two points are the acceptable and rejectable quality levels, respectively. Observe that there is a zone of comparative indifference between these two quality levels. The probability of error for each of the two critical points can be calculated. In fact the probability for PRP is α and that for CRP is β. The probability of

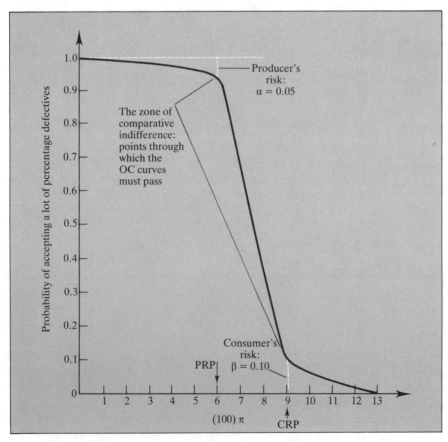

FIGURE 14.1 OC curve for an acceptance plan.

error for values in the zone of comparative indifference is uncontrolled; however, if PRP and CRP are (as they should be) fairly close to the economic break-even point, then for any value of π between PRP (π_0) and CRP (π_1), it would be of little, if any, importance whether H_0 is rejected or accepted.

Now, if our manufacturer also specifies in her decision rule that the producer's risk (α) should be 0.05 and the consumer's risk (β) should 0.10, then as you can easily verify with what you have learned in the last chapter, the whole decision rule would become: Take a sample with $n = 635$, accept the lot if and only if $\bar{p} \leq 0.0755$; i.e., accept the lot if and only if there are only 48 or fewer defective units in the lot. (Note that normal approximations of the binomial probabilities are employed for calculations because $n = 635$ is sufficiently large. You will undoubtedly gain additional insight about this decision rule as well as the various notions introduced in this section by studying reflectively the OC curve for our example in Figure 14.1. (Note that the horizontal scale of this figure is labeled as percentages.)

It should be noted that an OC curve gives the probability of accepting an isolated lot. With this interpretation, the buyer is thinking of the quality of isolated lots rather than the average quality of a stream of lots. We can also, however, interpret this probability as the proportion of lots that would be accepted in an infinite series of lots that are identical in quality defined in a certain way as in the lot in question.

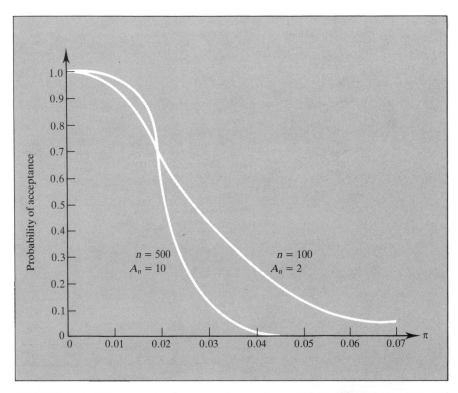

FIGURE 14.2 OC curves for two acceptance plans with different sample sizes and different acceptance numbers.

Consider, for example, an infinite series of lots of 10,000 items each taken from a process with an average fraction defective of 0.05. Because of random fluctuations, the defective fractions of the lots will vary in accordance with the binomial (or the hypergeometric) probability law. Some lots may contain, say, only 300 defective units and others may have 700 defective items. However, the mean number of defective items in a lot will remain at 500. In general, the OC curve at $\pi = 0.05$ is the proportion of these lots that will be accepted by the sampling plan on the average or in the long run. Thus, an OC curve may be thought to describe how a buyer is likely to view the operating characteristics of a sampling plan when he buys a steady stream of lots of material of the same kind and of identical quality from a given supplier.

The power of an OC curve to discriminate between good and bad lots depends upon the size of the sample and the prescribed acceptance number, A_n. This observation is vividly illustrated by Figures 14.2 and 14.3, respectively. Figure 14.2 presents two different acceptance sampling plans in which the proportions of the acceptance number to the sample sizes are both 2%. However, the OC curve for $n = 500$ and $A_n = 10$ is much closer to an ideal OC curve than that for $n = 100$ and $A_n = 2$. Figure 14.3 shows how the OC curve for a sampling plan varies with the acceptance number when n is fixed. As A_n decreases, the OC curve is moved downward, which indicates that the sampling plan is

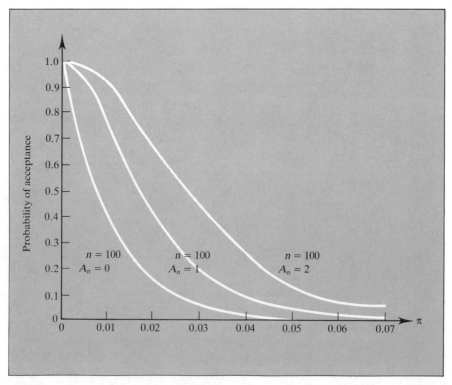

FIGURE 14.3 OC curves for three different acceptance plans with the same sample size but different acceptance numbers.

tightened up. When A_n increases, the OC curve is shifted upward, which has the effect of making the sampling plan more lax.

It must be observed that up to this point we have employed our familiar notation. However, as we proceed, we shall note that notation in quality control is often different from that used in other branches of statistics and from the standardized system of notation used in this text. No confusion should arise, though, since each symbol used here is carefully defined.

14.3 TYPICAL ACCEPTANCE SAMPLING PLANS

A typical acceptance sampling plan in statistical quality control usually specifies three different numbers: the sample size n, the number of acceptance A_n, and the number of rejection R_n. Also, there are four frequently employed sampling plans: the single-sample, the double-sample, the multiple-sample, and the sequential-sample sampling plans. The rationale for the latter three kinds of sampling or inspecting plans is that the choice between accepting and rejecting a lot can often be made on the basis of less than the full sample size of a single sample. For instance, in a given acceptance or inspection situation, we may adopt the following single-sampling plan:

> Take a random sample of 100 from the lot. If there are more than 5 defective items in the sample, the lot is rejected. If 5 or fewer items are defective in the sample, the lot is accepted.

In following such a decision rule, however, we may find that there are 5 defectives in the first 10 items inspected. It is then clearly unnecessary to examine the remaining 90 items. This possibility has led to *double sampling*—a process by which a small sample is observed first and a decision may be made to accept, or reject, or to take a second sample. For example, in double sampling, we may formulate this decision as:

> Select and examine a random sample of 40 items. If 1 or less defective item is found, accept the lot; if 3 or more defectives are found, reject the lot; if 2 defectives are found, take a second sample of 60 items (total now is 100). If the total number of defectives in the combined sample is 5 or less, accept the lot; if greater than 5 reject the lot.

If a decision can be made between accepting or rejecting a lot on the basis of a small first sample, costs will be considerably reduced, especially if the sampling is destructive. Thus, double sampling is better than single sampling in terms of costs. By the same reasoning, however, it is easy to see that double sampling is more expensive than triple sampling, which, in turn, is more costly than quadruple sampling. This philosophy has suggested what is called *multiple sampling*—a procedure that utilizes a series of small samples such that the cumulative number of defects is compared against an "accept" and a "reject" criterion after each sample is drawn until a decision can finally be made.

A logical extension of multiple sampling is to make an observation of one item at a time, deciding after each observation whether to accept or reject the lot or to continue sampling by comparing the accumulated number of defectives with acceptance and rejection numbers specified for each sample size. Such a technique, called *sequential sampling,* is especially appropriate for inspecting products that are very expensive and whose investigation results in their destruction.

It may be noted that single-acceptance sampling plans can be easily constructed on the basis of a table of binomial (or of hyper-geometric) probabilities for various sample sizes. Construction of double-, multiple-, and sequential-sampling plans is more difficult and complicated. In any event, risks of incorrect decisions in acceptance sampling can be specified at reasonably low levels of probability and the necessary sample size can be determined from these requirements. Furthermore, there are available numerous ready-made acceptance sampling plans based on several criteria: the *acceptance quality level* (AQL), the worst quality the buyer is prepared to accept in a lot with a stipulated high probability; the *lot tolerance percentage defective* (LTPD), the quality above which there is only a small probability that a lot will be accepted; and so on. Widely used catalogues of tabulated acceptance sampling plans include Dodge and Romig's *Sampling Inspection Tables: Single and Double Sampling*; Statistical Research Group, Columbia University, *Sampling Inspection*; and *Military Standards 105A: Sampling Procedures and Tables for Inspection by Attributes* (MIL-STD-105A).

Table 14.1 contains the single-, double-, and multiple-sampling plans that are frequently used when acceptable quality is defined as 0.5% or fewer defective items, and α- and β-risk are set at 0.05 and

TABLE 14.1 Three Acceptance Plans for Acceptance Quality Level of 0.5% with $\alpha = 0.5$ and $\beta = 0.10$

Type of sampling	Sample	Sample size	Combined samples		
			Size	Acceptance number	Rejection number
Single	First	75	75	1	2
Double	First	50	50	0	3
	Second	100	150	2	3
Multiple	First	20	20	*a*	2
	Second	20	40	*a*	2
	Third	20	60	0	2
	Fourth	20	80	1	3
	Fifth	20	100	1	3
	Sixth	20	120	1	3
	Seventh	20	140	2	3

a Acceptance not permitted until three samples have been inspected.
Source: Statistical Research Group, Columbia University; *Sampling Inspection* (New York: McGraw-Hill, 1948), p. 288.

TABLE 14.2 A Sequential Sampling Plan for Acceptance Quality Level of 0.5% with $\alpha = 0.05$ and $\beta = 0.10$

n	A_n	R	n	A_n	R	n	A_n	R	n	A_n	R
			19	a	2	37	0	3	55	0	4
2	a	2	20	a	3	38	0	3	56	0	4
3	a	2	21	a	3	39	0	3	57	0	4
4	a	2	22	a	3	40	0	3	58	0	4
5	a	2	23	a	3	41	0	3	59	0	4
6	a	2	24	a	3	42	0	3	60	0	4
7	a	2	25	a	3	43	0	3	61	1	4
8	a	2	26	a	3	44	0	3	62	1	4
9	a	2	27	a	3	45	0	3	63	1	4
10	a	2	28	a	3	46	0	3	64	1	4
11	a	2	29	a	3	47	0	3	65	1	4
12	a	2	30	a	3	48	0	3	66	1	4
13	a	2	31	0	3	49	0	4	67	1	4
14	a	2	32	0	3	50	0	4	68	1	4
15	a	2	33	0	3	51	0	4	69	1	4
16	a	2	34	0	3	52	0	4	70	1	4
17	a	2	35	0	3	53	0	4			
18	a	2	36	0	3	54	0	4			

a No acceptance until 31 items have been inspected.
Source: Table 8.4, Achoson J. Duncan, *Quality Control and Industrial Statistics,* 4th Ed., (Homewood, Illinois: Richard D. Irwin, Inc., 1974), p. 162.

0.10, respectively. Table 14.2 contains an example of a sequential sampling plan under the same specifications as for Table 14.1. These plans can be understood easily from just a glance at the tables.

The sequential plan was developed in 1943 by the American self-made statistician Abraham Wald (1902–1950), a refugee from Austria. Wald also developed a chart that simplifies the execution of a sequential plan. Such a chart consists of two parallel lines drawn according to the following equations:

$$A_n = -h_1 + sn; \qquad (14.1a)$$

$$R_n = h_2 + sn. \qquad (14.1b)$$

Here, h_1 and h_2, are the intercepts, and s stands for the slope. Values of these constants depend upon the specified values of the acceptable fraction defectives in the lot, and on the α- and β-risk. For example, if the quality level is 0.5%, defective, $\alpha = 0.05$, $\beta = 0.10$, then from Table 2.23 of Statistical Research Group, Columbia University, *Sequential Analysis of Statistical Data: Applications,* (New York, Columbia University Press, 1945), pp. 2.39–2.42, we have $h_1 = 0.9585$, $h_2 = 1.2305$, and $s = 0.01970$. Thus,

$$A_n = -0.9585 + 0.0197n;$$

$$R_n = +1.2305 + 0.0197n.$$

The graph for these two equations is as shown by Figure 14.4.

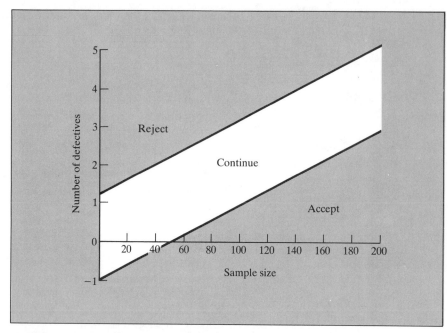

FIGURE 14.4 Graphic representation of a sequential sampling plan with $h_1 = -0.9585$, $h_2 = 1.2305$, and $s =$ slope $= 0.0197$.

In general, if such a graphic method is used in sequential sampling, the cumulated sample results are plotted successively on the chart. For each point the horizontal scale is the total number n of units drawn up to that time and the vertical scale is the total number of these units that are defective. If the plotted points fall within the two parallel lines, sampling is continued without a decision. The moment a point falls on or below the lower line, the lot is accepted. As soon as a point falls on or above the upper line, the lot is rejected. In the application of this method, it must be noted, that A_n is always rounded down to the next lower integer and, similarly, R_n is always rounded up to the next higher integer.

14.4 CHOICE AMONG THE FOUR SAMPLING PLANS

The four sampling plans as presented in Tables 14.1 and 14.2 have about the same discriminating power between good and bad lots. This is revealed by their OC curves drawn in Figure 14.5. The OC curve for the sequential-sampling plan is not plotted because it is practically identical with that for the multiple-sampling plan. Clearly, as far as decisions based upon them are concerned, they are interchangeable. Does this observation imply that we should feel indifferent among these plans so far as their applications are concerned?

The answer is clearly "No", from what we have already said before about these plans. A choice among them is often necessary for practical

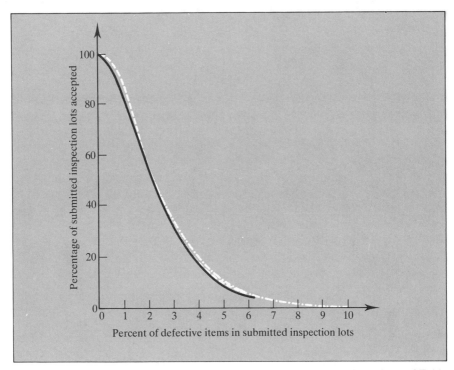

FIGURE 14.5 Operating-characteristic curves for the three sampling plans of Table 14.1. —•—, single sampling; ———, double sampling; —— sequential and multiple sampling. (*Source:* Same as for Table 14.1.)

reasons, mainly in terms of differences in costs of execution of the plan and actual inspection. Also, there is another criterion, which is even more important than cost consideration, in aiding us in choosing among the four plans. It is the average number of observations, denoted as $\bar{n}$, required to reach a decision. With the single-sampling plan, the sample size is fixed and the number of observations is known. Thus, if it is desired to minimize the variability in the number of units to be inspected, single sampling achieves this most effectively, since no consistent number prevails in any other plan. Next, if it is desired to minimize the maximum sample size to reach a decision, single sampling is the best, double sampling the second best, multiple sampling the third best, and sequential sampling the poorest. Finally, if it is desired to have the smallest average number of inspection for a decision, the pattern here is also obvious: sequential sampling requires the smallest average number, multiple sampling the next, and single and double sampling the most. As shown by Figure 14.6, sequential sampling usually requires about 33% to 50% fewer observations, on the average, than single sampling. Multiple sampling requires, on the average, about 10% to 30% fewer observations than single sampling. When the fraction defective in a lot is relatively low, double sampling may often require a higher average number of inspections for a decision than required by single sampling. However, at higher defective fractions in the lot, double sampling is better than single sampling.

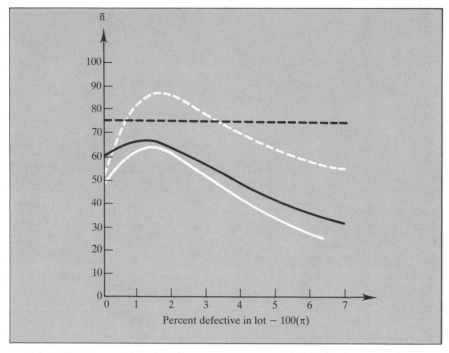

FIGURE 14.6 Average sample number $\bar{n}$ for four sampling plans having the equivalent operating-characteristic curves of Figure 14.5. –•–, single sampling; –––, double sampling; ----, multiple sampling; —— sequential sampling.
Source: Statistical Research Group, Columbia University, *Techniques of Statistical Analysis* (New York, McGraw-Hill, 1947), p. 240.

It should be pointed out that the values of the average sample numbers shown by the graphs in Figure 14.6 were calculated under the assumptions that the first samples in double and multiple sampling were inspected completely and that inspection of latter samples was curtailed the moment the rejection number was reached. However, the curtailing was not applied to accepted lots.

14.5 ADDITIONAL REMARKS ON ACCEPTANCE SAMPLING

There are at least three important applications of acceptance sampling. The first is one you are quite familiar with by now. That is, when a buyer receives a lot of material that has been delivered by a supplier, he has to determine by sampling inspection whether the lot is of acceptable quality. The second application is concerned with the decision of the supplier himself as to whether a lot is up to the standard required for shipment to a customer. The last application of inspection sampling is to determine whether a lot of partially finished material is of adequate quality to justify further processing. Hence, the terms "buyer" and "seller" used in connection with acceptance sampling are merely for the purpose of distinguishing the maker from the user of the product.

When a buyer has rejected a lot of shipment that is below standard, it may be returned to the supplier or it may be kept, depending upon previous arrangements with the supplier. If the lot is not of very bad quality and if the buyer needs the material quickly the buyer may keep the material with perhaps a price concession and other considerations. Very often a government purchasing agency has its own inspectors in the manufacturer's plant and each lot is inspected at the plant before it is shipped and therefore no rejection of a shipment would take place since a substandard lot would have already been rejected before the shipment is made.

It is also important to note that acceptance sampling is not aimed at controlling the quality of material; it merely accepts or rejects the lot according to some set standard. When all the lots are of the same quality, some lots will be accepted while others will be rejected owing to random variations in sampling. Thus, the quality of the accepted lots may not be of better quality than those that are rejected.

When acceptance sampling is conducted at various stages in a production process, it may have general beneficial effects upon the quality of production. This is because production personnel will become more quality-conscious, creating in them an interest in quality in terms of both production and inspection. However, this situation should not be considered as a procedure for "controlling" quality. Control of quality of outputs is a function of process control using the device known as a "control chart," a topic we take up immediately.

14.6 PROCESS CONTROL AND CONTROL CHARTS

Process control has the objective of evaluating the future performance of a production process. Hence, it is concerned with the infinite number of results of further repetition of the same process. The basic theoretical consideration of process control, furthermore, is that of distinguishing different sources of variations in the quality of outputs coming continuously from the production process.

The quality of a product, measured from unit to unit, sample to sample, or lot to lot, always shows variations. These variations exist no matter how well designed the process and how carefully controlled the operating conditions. This is so because the exact conditions existing at any given time can seldom be repeated, no matter how great an effort is made.

Variations in a manufacturing process, furthermore, are caused by two distinct types of forces. First, there are the inevitable chance, or random, forces inherent in the process. Random forces usually consist of a host of factors that are unidentifiable. The net effect of any one of them is so slight that its absence or its addition can hardly make any difference in the quality of outputs. These factors, however, in the aggregate would produce a certain amount of variation in the process, just as would be expected in repeated rolls of a pair of dice or in continuous tosses of a coin. This type of cause of variation is known by many different names: *common, chance, unassignable,* or *uncontrollable cause.*

Second, there are the forces that bring about changes in the inherent nature of the process. That is, the presence of this type of force will either change the average value or the dispersion, or both, of the quality of products produced by the process. Causes of this kind—tool wear, operator carelessness, variations in raw material, fluctuating power supply, and the like—are usually identifiable. Thus, they are often spoken of as *special, assignable,* or *controllable causes.*

Chance variations are uncontrollable, and there is no point in spending money and time attempting to control them. If variability of the process is confined to unassignable factors, the process is said to be operating within the limits of its inherent capacity. Thus, we would decide that the process is in a state of "statistical control." If, however, the behavior of the process is such that the presence of assignable causes is evident, the process is said to be "out of control." Steps must then be taken to remedy the difficulties. The main function of statistical quality control is to detect assignable variations when, or, if possible, before, they happen. To this end, the principal tool used is the *control chart.*

There are three main types of control charts whose applications depend upon how data are recorded. Data resulting from inspection of the quality properties may take any of the following forms.

1. The quality characteristics of the individual items may be recorded in actual measurements, say in inches or in pounds. If so, the quality of output is said to be expressed in terms of variables.

2. The quality properties may be said to be expressed in terms of attributes when the record of observations shows only the number of articles conforming to and the number of articles failing to conform to any specifications.

3. A record of inspection may be made to show the number of defects found in a sample (or more frequently in a single unit), when the possible number of defects per sample (or per unit) is very large compared with the average number of defects per sample (or per unit).

For purpose of control, variables are dealt with by the $\bar{X}$- (average) and R- (range) chart, or by the $\bar{X}$- and σ-chart. Attributes are handled by a control chart for fraction defectives or a control chart for the average number of defectives: the p- or the np-chart. For data of the third form, the control chart for the number of defects per unit, or the c-chart, is used.

All types of control charts have a general form that consists of a set of three horizontal lines drawn on graph paper from the vertical scale that contains the values of the statistic. The central line is the estimated or specified standard value, that is, the process average. The other two lines, which are customarily three sigmas (standard deviations) from the central line, are the *upper* and *lower control limits.*

Repeated samples are taken and a point is plotted on the chart for each sample. These points may be called *sample points*. Each sample point has the number of the sample for an abscissa (X value). The sample value is the corresponding ordinate (Y value). See Figures 14.7, 14.8, and 14.9.

A control chart is a quick visual aid for controlling the quality of a product. The process is said to be in statistical control as long as each sample point falls between the control limits. If the sample points lie outside or on the control limits, the process is considered out of control and the sources of trouble are identified and removed in order to restore control.

Starting with the next section, we shall present a broad outline of the construction, interpretation, and uses of the various types of control charts.

14.7 CONTROL CHARTS FOR VARIABLES

The quality chosen for variables of the control charts—the $\bar{X}$ and R-chart or the $\bar{X}$- and σ-chart—must be something that can be measured and expressed in terms of numbers. Examples are dimensions, hardness in Rockwell units, tensile strength in pounds per square inch, life in miles of an automobile tire, operating temperatures in degrees, weight in ounces of the contents of any container, time in seconds for the completion of an operation, and so forth.

Samples are often called *subgroups* in the work of statistical quality control. Subgroups for control charts should be so selected as to (1) make the differences among the individual items in the same subgroup as small as possible, and (2) reveal the possible or suspected differences among different subgroups. To achieve the first requirement, each subgroup should be selected from outputs produced during the same short interval of time or from outputs coming from one of the several distinct sources or locations. To secure differences in the process, subgroups should be taken at different time intervals or from different sources and locations.

The selection of subgroups in such a way as to minimize variations within each one implies that sample size should be small. Shewhart suggested 4 as the ideal size, since the distribution of $\bar{X}$ is nearly normal for subgroups of 4 or more even when the samples are from a nonnormal population. Sample size of 5 is also often used because the average can be so easily computed: the sum is multiplied by 2 and the decimal point is moved one place to the left. In general, if the subgroups represent some more or less continuous series involving order in time or location, they should be small but preferably not less than 4. But in a situation where cost of measurement is very high, subgroups of two or three may often be used to advantage. In any case, it is desirable that all subgroups be of the same size.

In quality control, the average quality of a manufacturing process is customarily checked by the use of the mean of the items in each subgroup. Either the range or the standard deviation is used to check on variability. Although the standard deviation is a more desirable measure of variations, the range is much easier to find. Moreover, for samples of size 10 or less the superiority of the standard deviation over the range is very slight, and when $n = 2$ there is no gain at all in the use of the former instead of the latter. Consequently, the $\bar{X}$-chart is usually accompanied by the R-chart when the subgroup size is 10 or less. On the other hand, if we wish to make the control chart more sensitive to small variaitons in the process average, larger samples of size 10 to 20 should be used: the larger the sample size, the narrower the control limits and the easier it is to discover small variations. This is, of course, true only if the subgroups are so chosen that greater variations in the process average occur among and not within subgroups. When n is larger than 10, the σ-chart is preferred to the R-chart for use with the $\bar{X}$-chart.

To be statistically reliable, the computation of control limits must be based on at least 25 subgroups. The frequency of drawing the subgroups may either be in terms of time, such as once every hour, or in terms of the proportion of outputs produced, such as 5 out of 100.

The procedure for setting up control charts is a relatively simple matter. For illustration, let us assume that a cannery that fills No. $2\frac{1}{2}$ cans of standard grade of tomatoes in purée by a machine process, wishes to set up the $\bar{X}$- and R-chart to control the drained weight and variability of canned tomatoes. To accomplish this, the following steps may be taken.

1. *Deciding on the selection, number, size and frequency of subgroups.* It is decided to start the control charts with 30 subgroups of 5 cans each. One subgroup is to be taken from the production line every hour.

2. *Measuring the items in the subgroups.* Each can is opened and the solid contents are emptied out and weighed. The measurements are recorded to the nearest half-ounce, as presented in Table 14.3.

3. *Computing the means and ranges of the subgroups.* These calculations are made by the following familiar formulas:

   $$\bar{X} = (x_1 + x_2 + \cdots + x_n)/n;$$

   $R = H - L$ (the difference between the highest
   and the lowest values in each subgroup).

   The average and range values for the present problems are recorded in the last two columns in Table 14.3.

4. *Computing the mean of the subgroup means.* This measure, denoted by $\bar{\bar{X}}$, is used as an estimate of the process or population mean, and will serve as the central line for the $\bar{X}$-chart. Generally, if there are k subgroups whose means are $\bar{X}_1, \bar{X}_2, \ldots, \bar{X}_k$, the mean

TABLE 14.3 Drained Weight of Contents of Size No. $2\frac{1}{2}$ Cans of Standard Grade of Tomatoes in Purée (Weight in ounces)

Sample	Weight in each of 5 cans per sample					Mean $\bar{X}$	Range R
1	22.5	24.5	21.5	21.0	24.5	22.8	3.5
2	22.5	22.0	22.0	19.5	20.5	21.3	3.0
3	22.0	21.0	21.0	20.5	21.0	21.1	1.5
4	23.5	21.0	23.5	21.5	23.0	22.5	2.5
5	21.5	24.0	22.0	22.0	18.5	21.6	4.5
6	22.0	22.5	22.5	24.0	23.5	22.9	2.0
7	22.5	19.0	20.5	21.0	20.5	20.7	3.5
8	24.5	21.5	21.5	22.5	22.5	22.5	3.0
9	21.5	24.5	20.5	20.0	22.0	21.6	4.0
10	21.0	24.5	21.0	23.0	22.5	22.4	3.5
11	20.5	22.5	22.5	23.0	21.5	22.0	2.5
12	20.5	21.5	21.0	19.0	21.0	20.5	2.0
13	19.0	20.0	22.0	20.5	22.5	20.8	3.5
14	20.0	20.5	23.0	22.0	21.5	21.4	3.0
15	21.5	20.5	20.0	19.5	21.0	20.3	2.0
16	19.0	21.0	21.0	21.0	20.5	20.5	2.0
17	21.5	20.5	22.0	21.5	23.5	21.8	3.0
18	22.0	20.5	21.0	22.5	20.0	21.2	2.5
19	21.5	24.0	21.5	21.5	22.5	22.2	2.5
20	22.5	19.5	21.5	20.5	20.0	20.8	3.0
21	22.0	23.5	24.0	22.0	22.0	22.7	2.0
22	25.0	20.0	20.0	20.5	22.5	21.6	5.0
23	23.5	24.5	23.0	20.5	21.5	22.6	4.0
24	21.0	20.5	19.5	22.0	21.0	20.8	2.5
25	22.5	21.5	22.0	22.0	19.5	21.5	3.0
26	22.5	22.0	23.0	22.0	23.5	22.6	1.5
27	21.0	22.0	22.0	23.0	22.0	22.0	2.0
28	20.0	23.5	24.0	20.5	21.5	21.9	4.0
29	21.0	20.5	19.5	22.0	21.0	20.8	2.5
30	22.5	21.0	20.0	19.5	19.5	20.5	3.0
Total						647.9	87.5

Source: Hypothetical.

of the subgroup means is obtained by the following equation:

$$\bar{\bar{X}} = \frac{\bar{X}_1 + \bar{X}_2 + \cdots + \bar{X}_k}{k}. \tag{14.2}$$

Substituting the subgroup means computed and recorded in Table 14.3, into this formula, we have

$$\bar{\bar{X}} = 647.9/30 = 21.6 \text{ ounces}$$

5. *Computing the mean of the ranges of the subgroups.* This measure, denoted by $\bar{R}$, will serve as the central line for the R-chart. Let R_1,

$R_2, \ldots R_k$ be the ranges of the k subgroups, then

$$\bar{R} = \frac{R_1 + R_2 + \cdots + R_k}{k}. \tag{14.3}$$

For our illustration,

$$\bar{R} = 87.5/30 = 2.9 \text{ ounces.}$$

6. *Deciding on control limits.* Common practice in quality control is to have 3-sigma control limits; that is, the control limits are three standard deviations above and below the central line. The 3-sigma control limits for the $\bar{X}$-chart are yielded by the

$$\bar{\bar{X}} \pm A_2 \bar{R}, \tag{14.4}$$

where A_2 is a constant factor that depends upon the size of the sample and can be looked up from a table for quality control chart constants, such as Table 14.4. Applying these formulas to our present example, we have

$$\text{upper control limit (UCL)} = \bar{\bar{X}} + A_2\bar{R} = 21.6 + 0.577(2.9),$$
$$= 23.3 \text{ ounces}$$

$$\text{lower control limit (LCL)} = \bar{\bar{X}} - A_2\bar{R} = 21.6 - 0.577(2.9).$$
$$= 19.9 \text{ ounces}$$

The 3-sigma control limits for the R-chart are obtained by the formulas

$$D_4\bar{R} \quad \text{and} \quad D_3\bar{R}$$

where both D_4 and D_3 are control chart constants. And for the problem at hand,

$$\text{UCL} = D_4\bar{R} = 2.115(2.9) = 6.1 \text{ ounces,}$$
$$\text{LCL} = D_3\bar{R} = 0(2.9) = 0.$$

7. *Drawing the control charts.* The central line on the $\bar{X}$-chart should be drawn as a solid line at $\bar{\bar{X}}$. The control limits should be drawn as dotted lines from the computed values.

The central line on the R-chart should also be drawn as a solid line from $\bar{R}$. For subgroups of size 7 or larger, both UCL and LCL for the R-chart should be drawn as dotted lines from the computed values. If, however, the subgroup size is less than 7, LCL for the R-chart is zero and should be drawn as a solid line.

8. *Plotting the sample points.* Finally, subgroup means and ranges are both plotted on the $\bar{X}$- and R-chart. These points may or may

TABLE 14.4 Control Chart Constants

Number of Observations in Sample, n	Chart for Averages			Chart for Standard Deviations					Chart for Ranges				
	Factors for Control Limits		Factor for Central Line	Factors for Control Limits				Factor for Central Line	Factors for Control Limits				
	A	A_1	A_2	c_2	B_1	B_2	B_3	B_4	d_2	D_1	D_2	D_3	D_4
2	2.121	3.760	1.880	0.5642	0	1.843	0	3.267	1.128	0	3.686	0	3.267
3	1.732	2.394	1.023	0.7236	0	1.858	0	2.568	1.693	0	4.358	0	2.575
4	1.500	1.880	1.729	0.7979	0	1.808	0	2.266	2.059	0	4.698	0	2.282
5	1.342	1.596	0.577	0.8407	0	1.756	0	2.089	2.326	0	4.918	0	2.115
6	1.225	1.410	0.483	0.8686	0.026	1.711	0.030	1.970	2.534	0	5.078	0	2.004
7	1.134	1.277	0.419	0.8882	0.105	1.672	0.118	1.882	2.704	0.205	5.203	0.076	1.924
8	1.061	1.175	0.373	0.9027	0.167	1.638	0.185	1.815	2.847	0.387	5.307	0.136	1.864
9	1.000	1.094	0.337	0.9139	0.219	1.609	0.239	1.761	2.970	0.546	5.394	0.184	1.816
10	0.949	1.028	0.308	0.9227	0.262	1.584	0.284	1.716	3.078	0.687	5.469	0.223	1.777
11	0.905	0.973	0.285	0.9300	0.299	1.561	0.321	1.679	3.173	0.812	5.534	0.256	1.744
12	0.866	0.925	0.266	0.9359	0.331	1.541	0.354	1.646	3.258	0.924	5.592	0.284	1.716
13	0.832	0.884	0.249	0.9410	0.359	1.523	0.382	1.618	3.336	1.026	5.646	0.308	1.692
14	0.802	0.848	0.235	0.9453	0.384	1.507	0.406	1.594	3.407	1.121	5.693	0.329	1.671
15	0.775	0.816	0.223	0.9490	0.406	1.492	0.428	1.572	3.472	1.207	5.737	0.348	1.652

Statistic	Standards Given		Analysis of Past Data	
	Central Line	Limits	Central Line	Limits
$\bar{X}$	$\bar{X}'$	$\bar{X}' \pm A\sigma'$	$\bar{\bar{X}}$	$\bar{\bar{X}} \pm A_1\bar{\sigma}$ or $\bar{\bar{X}} \pm A_2\bar{R}$
σ	$c_2\sigma'$	$B_1\sigma', B_2\sigma'$	$\bar{\sigma}$	$B_3\bar{\sigma}, B_4\bar{\sigma}$
R	$d_2\sigma'$	$D_1\sigma', D_2\sigma'$	$\bar{R}$	$D_3\bar{R}, D_4\bar{R}$

Source: This table is reproduced, by permission from the *ASTM Manual on Quality Control of Materials* (American Society for Testing and Materials, Philadelphia, Pa., 1951).

not be connected by straight lines. The $\bar{X}$- and R-chart for our illustrative problem is presented as Figure 14.7.

The procedure used to construct the $\bar{X}$- and σ-chart is the same as before. The only exception is that now standard deviations instead of ranges are employed to compute the control limits. In the symbolism of quality control, sample standard deviation is designated as σ and is obtained by the familiar expression $\sigma = \sqrt{\sum(x - \bar{X})^2/n}$.

If we have k subgroups whose standard deviations are $\sigma_1, \sigma_2, \ldots, \sigma_k$, then their arithmetic mean, denoted by $\bar{\sigma}$, is computed by

$$\bar{\sigma} = \frac{\sigma_1 + \sigma_2 + \cdots + \sigma_k}{k}, \tag{14.6}$$

In terms of standard deviations, the central line for the $\bar{X}$-chart, as before, is drawn at $\bar{\bar{X}}$ but its 3-sigma control limits become

$$\bar{\bar{X}} \pm A_1\bar{\sigma}, \tag{14.7}$$

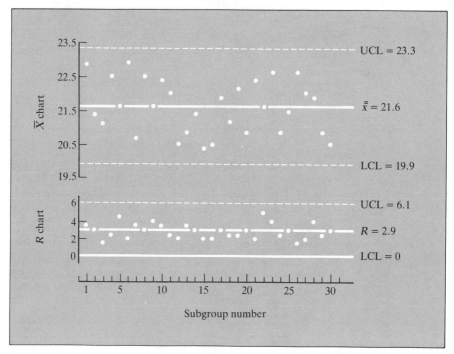

FIGURE 14.7 $\bar{X}$- and R-charts.

The σ-chart is used to control variability. It has $\bar{\sigma}$ as its central line and its 3-sigma control limits are computed by the formulas

$$B_4 \bar{\sigma} \quad \text{and} \quad B_3 \bar{\sigma}, \quad (14.8)$$

A_1, B_4, and B_3 are all control chart constants that can be obtained from Table 14.4. The construction of the $\bar{X}$- and σ-chart is left as an exercise for the student.

14.8 INTERPRETATIONS, USES, AND RISKS OF CONTROL CHARTS

Before taking up other types of control charts, we shall make some observations about the interpretation, uses, and risks of the $\bar{X}$- and R-chart or σ-chart. It may be noted, however, that most comments made in this section can also be applied to other types of control charts.

Joint use of the $\bar{X}$- and R-chart or σ-chart

As has already been pointed out, when a quality characteristic is expressed in terms of a variable, the mean may be used as a basis for action on a process. However, the mean alone is often insufficient to indicate the quality of a process, since in a process the sample means may remain in control while the sample variability has increased. The increase in variability indicates that individual items from the process may be either too large or too small, too heavy or too light, or too strong or too weak. Consequently, although the average quality may be satisfactory, many individual items may not be up to specification. It is therefore often necessary to use the $\bar{X}$-chart in conjunction with a control chart for the process variability.

There are, however, situations in which either the mean or the variability chart may be used to advantage without the other. The $\bar{X}$-chart may be used alone where experience with control charts for mean and range or standard deviation has revealed that instances of lack of control are almost always associated with causes that affect the average rather than the variability of the process. The R- or σ-chart may be used alone when, for technical reasons, the control of the mean is either unimportant or unjustifiably expensive.

Interpretation of control charts

In general, as has been briefly mentioned earlier, when all sample points fall between the control limits, we say that the process is in statistical control. That is, the variations among the sample values are caused by mere chance forces and the process should be left alone. When sample points fall outside the control limits, we conclude that the process is out of control. That is, the variations of the sample values cannot be attributed to chance but are caused by assignable forces. The causes that produce excessive variability must be sought out and corrected so that the process can be brought back into control.

One possible use of a control chart is that it aids in determining whether a process is in statistical control. The process in our previous illustration is in control. Had it not been in control, a check would have been made to discover the nature of the causes and ways of remedying them would have been developed. It would also be necessary to eliminate those sample points that are outside the control limits and recalculate the central value and control limits from the remaining subgroups. This point will be illustrated when we discuss the control chart for fraction defectives. It suffices to say here that the process must be in control before we can use the control chart for future action on it. Statistical theory aids us in predicting the future behavior of a process only if the process is a random variable, namely, a process whose variations are caused by uncontrollable random forces alone.

Use of control charts in establishing or changing specifications

Once evidence of the control charts indicates that the process is in control, control charts can be used to determine whether a given process can meet specifications. *Specifications,* or *tolerance limits,* refer to the extent of implied or expressed variability in the individual items. They are determined so that the products will be serviceable. A process that is in control will not necessarily produce products that will meet specifications. Although the variability of individual items may be caused by chance factors, it may nevertheless be too great to meet tolerance limits set for the products.

As an example, let us assume that the specification for the drained weight of contents of size No. $2\frac{1}{2}$ cans of standard grade tomatoes in purée is set at 21.6 ± 2 ounces. That is, the drained weight should be 21.6 ounces with about 10% deviation each way. The lower tolerance limit is to protect the consumer, while the upper tolerance limit is to avoid unnecessary waste for the cannery. Thus, any can whose drained weight is between 19.6 and 23.6 ounces may be considered as satisfactory or acceptable. From our previous calculations, we know that the process is in control in terms of both average and variability. But from Table 14.3 we find that 10 cans weigh more than 23.6 ounces and 12 cans weigh less than 19.6 ounces. In other words 22 of the 150 cans sampled fail to meet the specifications.

Three courses of action are open to the management when a process is in statistical control but a large number of its outputs are not up to standard. The first and natural course to take is to change the process itself. This action may require fundamental changes in methods, the purchase of new machines, the retraining of workers, and so forth. It may therefore be a very costly undertaking. It should not be followed unless other measures are considered unsatisfactory.

Second, 100% inspection may be employed to separate the unsatisfactory products from those that meet the specifications and to scrap or rework the bad products. This alternative, it may be repeated, is often unreliable and costly. Also, it is out of the question when inspection can be made only by destroying the products. There are situations, of course, in which 100% inspection is not to be ignored; for instance, imperfection in any part of, say, rifles used by soldiers is too great a risk to tolerate, and all units must be screened.

Third, if it is agreed that the established specifications are too tight and that a relaxation of tolerance limits will not reduce the serviceability of the product, then action may be taken to change the specifications in accordance with the capacity of the process. The *process capacity* refers to the variability of the individual items produced by a process. It can be determined by using the control chart data. It is determined by first estimating the true mean and standard deviation of the process. In quality control work, it is customary to denote the true process mean by $\bar{X}'$ which is estimated by the mean of the subgroup means, $\bar{\bar{X}}$. The true process standard deviation, represented by σ', is estimated by

$$\sigma' = \frac{\bar{R}}{d_2}, \tag{14.9}$$

where d_2 is another control chart constant given in Table 14.4. To use the drained weight of canned tomatoes as an example again, we have

$$\bar{X}' = \bar{\bar{X}} = 21.6 \text{ ounces};$$

$$\sigma' = \frac{\bar{R}}{d_2} = 2.9/2.326 = 1.247 \text{ ounces}.$$

Assuming that the drained weight of canned tomatoes produced by the given process is normally distributed with the above mean and standard deviation, we can then expect that about 99.7% of all the cans contain tomatoes whose drained weight will fall within the range of the mean plus and minus three standard deviations; that is, between 17.9 and 25.3 ounces. These figures are the capacity or the *natural tolerance limits* of the said process. Now, if the cannery resets its specifications to 21.6 ± 4 ounces, as it can be seen from Table 14.3, all its products will meet the new requirements as long as the process continues to be in statistical control.

Continuous Use of Control Charts

Once a process is brought into control and the average and dispersion are considered up to the specifications, the control charts may be expected to apply to future production. As more data accumulate, control limits as well as central values may be revised from time to time if it is deemed necessary.

The initial control limits reveal whether past operations were in control. Similarly, the continued use of the control chart shows whether current operations are in control. The process is let alone as long as it stays in control. Each sample point outside the control limits indicates that the variation is more than would be expected from chance variation if the process average has remained unchanged. It is thus used as a basis for hunting for an assignable cause or causes of variation, and taking action to remove them.

Sometimes a situation may develop in which sample points follow some peculiar trend. For example, we may find that although all points fall within the control limits, they continue to move to one side of the central line; or the successive sample points may follow a definite trend of leading towards either the upper or the lower control limit. Such patterns are danger signals that may indicate the need for changing the process. The common rule in dealing with situations like these is to consider the process out of control with runs of seven or more points in succession on the same side of the central line. The process must then be examined and the assignable cause found and eliminated. This point illustrates still another use of control charts: to bring the process back into control before its variability had made any serious damage to the quality of outputs.

Risks of Erroneous Inferences

The control chart represents a statistical decision rule that is no different from the decision rule of statistical testing. Indeed, the student may have already noticed that both rules are based upon the same set of principles. To use the control chart to decide whether to take on the process or to let it alone is the same as testing the null hypothesis that "the process remains in control" against the hypothesis that "the process is out of control," by continuous random sampling. This being so, conclusions reached in quality control are subject to the same two types of error that may be incurred when testing a hypothesis a single time:

> Type I error—the risk of taking action on a process that is actually in statistical control.

> Type II error—the risk of not taking action on a process that is actually out of control.

The first type of erroneous inference is determined by the control limits used. If, for example, a 5% level is used in the work, the control limits are 1.96 standard deviations away from the central value. As a result, the sample points will fall outside the control limits 5% of the time. That is, even if the process remains in control, we may stop the process and look for trouble that does not exist. Thus, we have rejected the hypothesis incorrectly and committed type I error.

When the process has actually changed but the method of control fails to reveal it, we can take the wrong action of not looking for the assignable causes when they actually exist. This is, of course, type II error. Given the frequency of type I error, the proportion of time for failing to recognize that the process is out of control depends upon the degree of maladjustment of the process. If the maladjustment is great and, therefore, current production deviates greatly from established standards, the risk of leaving the process alone is very slight. On the other hand, when the maladjustment is very small, the danger of committing type II error is considerably higher. It is important to observe, too, that a given degree of maladjustment is more likely to be discovered when the control limits are narrower than when they are wider.

Now, it becomes clear that if the control limits are, say, 1.96 standard deviations from the central value, the risk of taking the first kind of wrong action is great, whereas the risk of taking the second kind of wrong action is small. Conversely, if the control limits are, say, 3 standard deviations from the central line, the opposite will be true. Hence the actual control limits to be determined depend upon the seriousness of erroneously taking the respective types of wrong actions. When unnecessary stoppage is not very costly or readjustment of the process is not too arduous, narrower control limits may be set up. However, when it is expensive to have any kind of shutdown or when moderate deviations from specifications are not very serious, wider control limits may be used. Experience has shown that the 3-sigma limits seem to be an economically balanced selection. This is, indeed, the most frequently adopted standard in current quality control work.

14.9 CONTROL CHARTS FOR ATTRIBUTES

Control charts for variables are very powerful instruments in diagnosing quality problems and in detecting sources of trouble in the process;

their applications are nevertheless limited. In the first place, $\bar{X}$- and R-charts cannot be used when properties of products are not measurable; that is, when the differences are differences in kind rather than in degree. Textiles do or do not have the right color, bolts do or do not have heads, and, generally, products are merely divided into two classes as conforming to requirements or not meeting requirements: nondefective or defective items. Second, the fact that an $\bar{X}$- and R-chart is required for each characteristic makes their use economically impossible in many instances. For example, there are situations wherein literally tens of thousands of dimensions of a manufacturing process are to be inspected even though each dimension can be measured and therefore is a candidate for the $\bar{X}$- and R-chart.

Technical necessity and economic considerations account for the common use of two varieties of control charts for attributes: the control chart for *fraction* (or *proportion*) *defectives* (the p-chart), and that for the actual *number of defectives* (the np-chart). In quality control, a *defect* is defined as any failure to conform to specifications, and a *defective* refers to an item that has one or more defects. The application of the p- and the np-charts is not confined to quality properties that can only be observed as attributes; the charts can also be applied to characteristics that are measurable but are observed as attributes, such as dimensions checked by go and not-go gauges. One great advantage of charts for attributes is that a single chart can be used for any number of quality characteristics observed on one article, whereas a set of $\bar{X}$- and R-charts is necessary for each quality characteristic measured.

The choice between a p- and an np-chart is technical rather than theoretical in nature. The p-chart must be used whenever the subgroup size is not constant. Whenever the subgroup size is variable, the use of an np-chart is highly inconvenient, since in plotting the actual number of defectives both the central line and the control limits on the chart must be changed with every change in the subgroup size. However, when the subgroup size remains constant, either a p- or an np-chart may be used.

First, let us see how a control chart for fraction defectives is set up. Fraction defective, denoted by p, is the ratio between the number of defective articles and the total number of articles inspected. It is customary to express the fraction defective as a decimal fraction, which furnishes the basis for calculations. In presenting results and in charting, however, percent defective is often used. Percent defective is defined as $100p$.

The purpose of the p-chart is similar to that of the $\bar{X}$- and R-chart. It is mainly used to detect the presence of assignable causes of variation and to diagnosis of sources of trouble. On both accounts, it should be pointed out, the p-chart is not only less sensitive but inferior. For this reason, large subgroups are necessary if the p-chart is to be effective in detecting shifts in process level or process variability. It is generally recommended that the subgroup size be 50 or more. Moreover, in setting up the p-chart it is desirable, though not necessary, that all subgroups be of the same size. When different sample sizes are used, it becomes necessary to compute the control limits for each one.

To illustrate the steps involved in setting up the p-chart, let us suppose that a manufacturer of steel rods wishes to control the length and outside diameter of the rod. Qualities of performance, length, and outside diameter are checked by go and not-go gauges. For the length, two gauges are used: one has the minimum and the other the maximum length as specified. If a rod goes through both gauges or does not go through either, the rod is either too short or too long. A rod has the satisfactory length if it goes through the gauge for maximum length but not the one for minimum length. The outside diameter is checked by a single gauge with the maximum diameter at the head and the minimum diameter at the end. If a rod does not go into the gauge or goes all the way into the gauge, it is unsatisfactory because it is either too large or too small. A rod has the desired diameter if it will go halfway into the gauge. If either the length or the diameter is not proper, the rod is classified as a defective product. The company produces 2,000 steel rods each day and 500 units of a day's output, are inspected for 30 days in the month of May, 1988. The results of inspection are recorded in Table 14.5.

To construct a p-chart, we first find the fraction defective, p, for each subgroup by dividing the number of defective units by the total number of units in the subgroup. In our illustration a constant subgroup size of 500 is used, and the p-values are recorded in columns 3 and 6 in Table 14.5.

Next, the average fraction defective, designated as $\bar{p}$, is computed from

$$\bar{p} = \frac{\text{total number of defective units for all subgroups}}{\text{total number of items in all subgroups}} . \quad (14.10)$$

TABLE 14.5 Inspection Results for Steel Rods, May, 1988

Date	Number of defectives	Fraction defective	Date	Number of defectives	Fraction defective
May 1	11	0.022	May 16	21	0.042
2	20	0.040	17	10	0.020
3	18	0.036	18	23	0.046
4	16	0.032	19	14	0.028
5	21	0.042	20	18	0.036
6	20	0.040	21	33	0.066
7	15	0.030	22	25	0.050
8	22	0.044	23	23	0.046
9	21	0.042	24	16	0.002
10	19	0.038	25	21	0.042
11	35	0.070	26	23	0.046
12	40	0.080	27	15	0.030
13	22	0.044	28	19	0.038
14	11	0.022	29	20	0.040
15	16	0.032	30	12	0.024
Total				600	

Source: Hypothetical.

The value of $\bar{p}$ will serve as the central line of the p-chart. As before, it should be drawn as a solid line.

Third, control limits are calculated and placed. If the subgroups are of constant size, draw two horizontal lines across the chart at

$$\bar{p} \pm 3\sqrt{\bar{p}(1 - \bar{p})/n}, \tag{14.11}$$

where $\sqrt{\bar{p}(1 - \bar{p})/n}$ is the standard error for subgroups of size n. If subgroups are of varying sizes, that is, if n varies from subgroup to subgroup, draw horizontal dotted lines above and below each plotted sample point at $\bar{p} \pm 3\sqrt{\bar{p}(1 - \bar{p})/n}$, using the appropriate value of n for each subgroup.

For our illustration, subgroups are of the same size—500—and

$$\bar{p} = 600/15{,}000 = 0.040$$

Therefore, the corresponding values of control limits are

$$\text{UCL} = \bar{p} + 3\sqrt{\bar{p}(1 - \bar{p})/n} = 0.040 + 3\sqrt{(0.04)(0.96)/500}$$
$$= 0.066$$
$$\text{LCL} = \bar{p} - 3\sqrt{\bar{p}(1 - \bar{p})/n} = 0.040 - 3\sqrt{(0.04)(0.96)/500}$$
$$= 0.014.$$

Finally, as was mentioned earlier, in presenting results and in charting, it is generally preferable to use percent defective rather than fraction defective. Since percent defective is $100p$, from the previous calculations for our example we have $\bar{p} = 4\%$, UCL $= 6.6\%$, and LCL $= 1.4\%$. Also, the p-values in Table 14.5 are multiplied by 100 before they are plotted. The resulting p-chart for steel rods is shown in Figure 14.8.

The p-chart is interpreted in the same way as the $\bar{X}$- and R-chart. That is, if all sample points fall within the control limits, we say that the process variability is due to unassignable forces and we decide not to hunt for the trouble. In our illustration, as can be seen from Figure 14.8, the points representing fraction defectives of samples taken on May 11 and 12 fall above, and that on May 21 falls on, the upper control limits. These three sample points indicate the presence of assignable causes. Consequently, the control chart reveals that the process of steel rod production is not in statistic control. A check must be made to determine the nature of the special causes that seem to be affecting the process. For the sake of illustration, suppose it is found that during these out-of-control days, the cutting machine was not tight enough and caused the extra variations in the rod lengths. The operators of cutting machines are then duly warned to be more careful in future operations.

In order that the control chart may be used to control future production, it is necessary to drop the observations for the days when the process was out of control and to construct a new control chart on the basis of the remaining 27 subgroups. The student is advised to

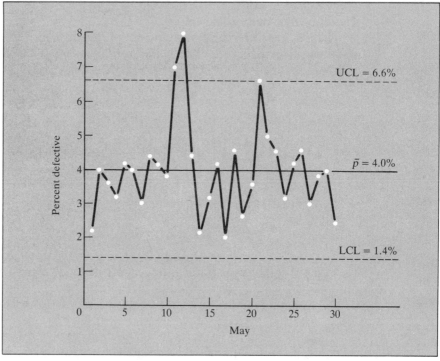

FIGURE 14.8 The p-chart.

verify that the new control chart will have the following values:

$$\bar{p} = 3.6\%, \qquad UCL = 6.1\%; \qquad LCL = 1.1\%.$$

It should also be seen that the remaining 27 sample points will all fall within these revised control limits, indicating that the process has been brought back into control.

Once the process is proved to be in control, the most important routine use of the p-chart, as usual, is as an aid for future action on the process. As long as the observed percent defective falls within the control limits, the process continues to be in control and is let alone. Whenever the observed percent defective falls outside the control limits, a possible lack of control is indicated and proper action is called for.

It is also interesting to note that out-of-control high spots indicate the presence of assignable causes that deteriorate quality and that must be identified and corrected. Conversely, out-of-control low spots may indicate either relaxed inspection standards or special adjustments introduced, causing quality improvement. If the former is discovered to be the case, inspection personnel must be warned to sharpen up their work. If the latter is true, these assignable causes may be incorporated in modifying the control chart for future use. These considerations illustrate how the p-chart can be used to bring to the attention of management any changes in the average quality level and its possible improvement.

Very often the correction of factors responsible for poor quality requires technical help in discovering the factors themselves. But the only clue the p-chart gives as to the cause of lack of control is the time at which the out-of-control spot is observed. Thus, the p-chart is much inferior to the $\bar{X}$- and R-chart, which is a very effective diagnostic tool to use when a product fails to meet requirements. Nevertheless, the p-chart has an important function: it suggests the place where the $\bar{X}$- and R-chart could be most tellingly used.

We may now turn to the np-chart. As was mentioned previously, when subgroups are of the same size, an np-chart is appropriate. It is established by drawing the central line at $n\bar{p}$, the average number of defectives and the 3-sigma control limits at

$$n\bar{p} \pm 3\sqrt{n\bar{p}(1 - \bar{p})}, \qquad (14.12)$$

where n stands for the subgroup size. It may be noted that the values of the np-chart are obtained by multiplying the corresponding values for the p-chart by n. The multiplication transforms the fraction defective into the number of defectives.

When subgroups are of the same size, there are two reasons for preferring the np-chart to the p-chart. In the first place, the np-chart saves one step in computation. The division of the number of defectives by the subgroup size to obtain the fraction defective p is eliminated. Second, the np-chart, with sample points being the actual numbers of defectives, can be understood more readily by many people. Often, however, many p-charts are used simultaneously because of varying sample size, whereas in the same situation only a few np-charts could be employed because of the rarity of a constant subgroup size. Then the use of two different types of charts may create a confusion that far outweighs the slight advantage of the np-chart. Consequently, it may prove more convenient to adopt the p-chart alone for all instances.

In quality control work, the true fraction or proportion defective is designated as p'. Once the process is brought into control, p' is estimated by $\bar{p}$. If p' is known or specified, both the p- and the np-chart can be constructed by using the same formulas (13.11) and (13.12), as before, with p' replacing $\bar{p}$.

The construction of an np-chart using the data in Table 14.5 is also left for the student as an exercise.

Before closing this section, let us note a common practice in quality control. Because of interest in extreme simplicity, it is customary to use the normal approximation even when such a practice seems theoretically unjustified. For example, in the construction of the p-chart with $p = 0.02$ or even smaller, a sample size of, say, 100, may be used. In such a case, clearly both p and n are too small to have normal approximations by binomial probabilities. Yet, in statistical quality control work, we still use normal approximations for simplicity even though the control limits are calculated somewhat inaccurately. This may not be of great importance in practice, however, since the appropriate risks usually cannot be determined with great precision. Again for these reasons, the CCF is almost never used in computations.

14.10 CONTROL CHARTS FOR NUMBER OF DEFECTS

There are some occasions when neither the combination of the $\bar{X}$- and R-chart nor the p-chart can be used as bases for decisions on a manufacturing process. These are quality control problems concerned with counting the number of defects when the subgroup is essentially unspecified, though presumably very large. This happens, for instance, when we inspect the defects on television cabinets: scratches, dents, nicks, unpainted portions, loose joints, and so forth. These defects can be counted but they cannot be measured and consequently cannot be handled by the $\bar{X}$- and R-chart. Yet the counted number of defects cannot be expressed in terms of fraction defectives because there is no method of determining the total number of opportunities for defects. In such a situation we must rely upon another type of control chart—the chart for the number of defects, or the c-chart—in order to control the production process.

It is important to keep in mind here the difference between the np- and the c-chart in application. For this purpose, it is worthwhile to recall the difference between a defect and a defective. A defect is a single instance in which an article fails to conform to specifications. A defective is an article that has one or more defects. The np-chart applies to the number of defectives in samples of constant size. The c-chart is used as a basis for decisions on the process using the number of defects in subgroups of constant size.

The application of the c-chart requires only that the subgroups are of the same size, but in most cases it is used for the number of defects observed in one unit of product. Thus, for instance, c may be the number of defective rivets in an airplane, or the number of "seeds" observed in a glass bottle, or the number of pinholes on a sheet of paper of a given size, or the number of imperfections discovered on a square yard of cloth. For this reason, the c-chart is sometimes called the control chart for defects per unit.

The sampling distribution of the total number c of defects can be approximated with a *Poisson* distribution—a distribution in which n is very large and p' is very small, so that np' is a very small positive number. The Poisson distribution is treated as a limit of the binomial distribution as n approaches infinity and np' remains constant. The theoretical justification for this can be found in our previous discussion on special discrete probability models. We are only interested in pointing out here that, since the true proportion and standard deviation for the binomial distribution (following the quality control symbolism), are np' and $\sqrt{np'(1 - p')}$, respectively, the limit of $1 - p'$ is obviously 1 as p' approaches 0. The average of the Poisson distribution is given as $c' = np'$. Its standard deviation, being the limit of $\sqrt{np'(1 - p')}$, becomes $\sqrt{np'}$ or $\sqrt{c'}$.

When c' is not known or specified, it is usually estimated by $\bar{c}$, the mean of the defects counted in several units (usually 25 or more) of the products used to construct the chart. The value of $\bar{c}$ will serve as the central line for the c-chart. The 3-sigma control limits for the c-chart then become

$$\bar{c} \pm 3\sqrt{\bar{c}}. \tag{14.13}$$

As a concrete illustration for setting up the control chart for the number of defects, we may assume that a woolen goods manufacturer wishes to control the quality of his products by means of the c-chart. For this purpose, 25 pieces of 100-yard bolts of woolen goods are checked and the defects counted include physical defects, finish irregularities, pinholes, flaws, and the like. Results of the inspection are recorded in Table 14.6.

From Table 14.6, the following values are computed:

$$\bar{c} = \frac{\text{total number of defects}}{\text{total number of units}} = \frac{100}{25} = 4;$$

$$\text{UCL} = \bar{c} + 3\sqrt{\bar{c}} = 4 + 6 = 10;$$

$$\text{LCL} = \bar{c} - 3\sqrt{\bar{c}} = 4 - 6 = 0.$$

(Whenever computations give a negative value of the lower control limit of a c-chart or p-chart, the limit is recorded as zero, since neither the number of defects nor the fraction defective can be negative.)

A c-chart constructed for these results plots the number of defects in as in Figure 14.9.

Note that all sample points in the c-chart fall within the control limits, indicating that the quality of the woolen goods is in statistical control. This initial c-chart can now be extended to check on the quality of future production. For illustration, suppose that the next ten pieces inspected, starting with piece No. 26, have numbers of defects of 12, 8, 5, 6, 4, 5, 6, 7, 6, and 9. These numbers are plotted in the extended

TABLE 14.6 Inspection Results of 25 Pieces of 100-Yard Bolts of Woolen Goods

Piece	Number of defects	Piece	Number of defects
1	2	14	4
2	3	15	3
3	6	16	3
4	3	17	2
5	1	18	7
6	8	19	4
7	2	20	3
8	5	21	9
9	2	22	1
10	4	23	2
11	5	24	6
12	9	25	3
13	3		

Source: Hypothetical.

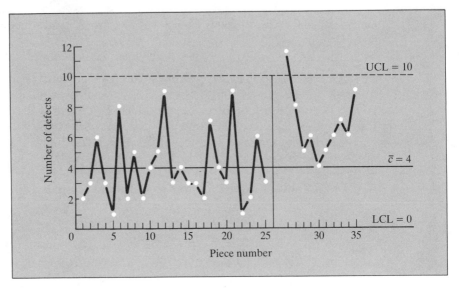

FIGURE 14.9 The c-chart.

c-chart in Figure 14.9. It can be seen that the number of defects for piece No. 26 falls above the UCL. This instance was investigated and whatever special cause existed for this extra variation was found and corrected. It can also be seen that all the remaining 9 points fall above the central line, having a trend toward the UCL. Does this trend indicate a deterioration of the process? A thorough examination revealed that since the initial control chart was established, inspectors had gained experience in discovering various types of defects. Thus the upward trend of defects is due to a tightening up of inspection standards and there is really no evidence that the quality has become poorer. This finding justifies an upward revision of the process average defects. Had it been discovered that this upward trend was due to the fact that less attention was being given to quality by production personnel, the previously established average would have to be continued but the production personnel would be warned to be more careful in order to arrest the continuation of quality deterioration.

14.11 APPLICABILITY OF CONTROL CHARTS IN AREAS OTHER THAN INDUSTRIAL QUALITY

Throughout this chapter, the discussion of process control has been confined to the applications of various types of control charts to industrial processes. As mentioned before, however, control chart techniques can also be applied with fruitful results to the control of the quality of clerical and other types of performance.

Indeed, the application of control charts to fields other than industrial quality is a broad and rapidly growing field. For instance, the $\bar{X}$- and R-chart has been used to control the amount of overtime work in plants and the amount of waste materials in accounting machine operations. The p-chart has been applied to marketing operations, such as those used by the Alden Mail Order House of Chicago, and to the methods used by air lines in recording plane reservations. The c-chart has been widely used in accident statistics and might be applied with advantage in epidemiological work. In these and many other fields, applications of control charts have either reduced errors in operations or improved quality of performance.

It is beyond the scope of a discussion in an elementary text such as this to describe any of these applications in detail. Nevertheless, it may be of interest to the student to know how control charts can be used in fields other than industrial process.

An industrial process may be considered as a process of machine operations. In contrast, the process of marketing, or any other kind of clerical work, is one of human operations. There are some basic similarities between these two types of process. First of all, a defective article produced by a machine operation has to be scrapped or reworked. Similarly, an error made by human operations, such as a wrong entry in a journal or a wrong price quoted in an invoice, has to be corrected. Second, a machine process can never produce outputs of uniform quality, but its variability could be expected to be within certain limits as long as only chance factors are present. Once the variability exceeds these limits, there must be present in the process special causes, such as improper setting of the machine, that must be adjusted. Likewise. human operations may produce unsatisfactory performance, but as long as that performance is caused by random forces, it could be expected not to exceed certain normal standards. Clerical errors, however, will certainly exceed such normal levels if some assignable cause is present. For instance, an inexperienced bookkeeper in an accounting office may cause the percentage of wrong entries to be greater than ordinary. This pattern of error may continue unless the said bookkeeper is given thorough instructions and close supervision or is replaced by an experienced worker.

These similarities between machine and human operations make possible the application of control charts to both types of processes without any special modifications. In either type of operation, control charts give evidence regarding the quality level, its variability, and the presence or absence of assignable causes of variations in the process. This, indeed, is the most important function of control charts.

GLOSSARY OF FORMULAS

(14.1a) $A_n = -h_1 + sn;$

(14.1b) $R_n = h_2 + sn.$

These two equations are employed to construct a sequential sampling chart. Here, h_1, h_2 and s can be found for specific values of quality level,

α and β for a given plan from Table 2.23 of Statistical Research Group, Columbia University, *Sequential Analysis of Statistical Data: Applications,* (New York: Columbia University Press, 1945), pp. 2.39–2.42.

(14.2) $\bar{\bar{X}} = \dfrac{\bar{X}_1 + \bar{X}_2 + \cdots + \bar{X}_k}{k}.$

The mean of sample (or group) means is computed by this formula and it is used as an estimate of the process mean $\bar{X}'$. This estimate serves as the central line of the $\bar{X}$-chart.

(14.3) $\bar{R} = \dfrac{R_1 + R_2 + \cdots + R_k}{k}.$

The mean of the sample ranges is obtained by dividing the sum of k subgroup ranges by k. This value is used as the central line of the R-chart.

(14.4) $\bar{\bar{X}} \pm A_2 \bar{R}.$

This expression yields the 3-sigma control limits for the $\bar{X}$-chart. A_2 is a constant whose value depends upon the sample size. It can be found in standard control chart tables such as Table 14.4.

(14.5) $D_4 \bar{R}$ and $D_3 \bar{R}.$

These two products serve as the upper and lower control limits, respectively, for the 3-σ R-chart. Again, D_4 and D_3 are two constants that can be found in Table 14.4.

(14.6) $\bar{\sigma} = \dfrac{\sigma_1 + \sigma_1 + \cdots + \sigma_k}{k}.$

This is the mean of the k subgroup-standard deviations. It serves as the central line for the 3-σ σ-chart. Note again, that in quality control literature, σ stands for sample standard deviation.

(14.7) $\bar{\bar{X}} \pm A_1 \bar{\sigma}.$

The 3-sigma control limits for the $\bar{X}$-chart in terms of standard deviations are determined by these formulas. As before, A_1 is a control chart constant depending upon the subgroup size.

(14.8) $B_4 \bar{\sigma}$ and $B_3 \bar{\sigma}.$

The 3-sigma upper ($B_4 \bar{\sigma}$) and lower ($B_3 \bar{\sigma}$) control limits for the σ-chart. B_4 and B_3 are again constant factors given in Table 14.4.

(14.9) $\sigma' = \bar{R}/d_2.$

This formula is used to estimate the process standard deviation σ' in quality control work. Here, d_2 is still another control chart constant given in Table 14.4. This estimate is needed in connection with determining the natural tolerance limits of the process.

(14.10) $\bar{p} = \dfrac{\text{total number of defective units for all subgroups}}{\text{total number of items in all subgroups}}.$

This formula gives the average fraction defective for the several subgroups used to construct the p-chart. The value of $\bar{p}$ is considered as an estimate of the process defective and serves as the central line of the control chart for fractions defective.

(14.11) $\bar{p} \pm 3\sqrt{\bar{p}(1 - \bar{p})/n}.$

These formulas are used to determine the 3-sigma control limits for the p-chart. Note that $\sqrt{\bar{p}(1 - \bar{p})/n}$ is the standard error for subgroups of a given size n. If subgroups are of varying sizes, control limits are drawn above and below each sample point by using the appropriate n in computations with equation 13.10.

(14.12) $n\bar{p} \pm 3\sqrt{n\bar{p}(1 - \bar{p})}.$

The 3-sigma limits for the chart for the number of defectives. The np chart has $n\bar{p}$, the average number of defectives as the central line. In both formulas 14.11 and 14.12, we estimate the true proportion defective, p', by $\bar{p}$ and the true number of defectives, np', by $n\bar{p}$. If p' were known or specified, we could construct appropriate limits and central lines with the same formulas but with p' replacing $\bar{p}$.

(14.13) $\bar{c} \pm 3\sqrt{\bar{c}}.$

In the construction of the c-chart, $\bar{c}$, the mean of the defects counted in several units of products, serves as the central lint. The 3-sigma control limits are selected by formula 14.13 in which $\sqrt{\bar{c}}$ is the estimated standard deviation of the sampling distribution of c, approximated by the Poisson distribution.

REVIEW QUESTIONS

14.1 What do we mean by *statistical quality control*?

14.2 Why is the study of quality control an important branch of statistical studies?

14.3 How is "product quality" defined?

14.4 What are the two theories of quality control? How do they differ from each other so far as their objectives are concerned?

14.5 What do PRP and CRP stand for? What are the corresponding notions for them, respectively, in terms of the theory of testing?

14.6 PRP is controlled by the probability of committing type I error and CRP is controlled by the probability of committing type II error. Explain why.

14.7 What are the producer's and consumer's risks in acceptance sampling? How are they controlled?

14.8 What do we mean by the "zone of indifference"? The probability of committing type II error within this zone is usually uncontrolled. Under what condition would this drawback be of little, if any, practical importance?

14.9 How should an acceptance sampling plan be specified?

14.10 The OC curve of an acceptance sampling plan can be interpreted in two different ways. What are they?

14.11 Given A_n as a constant proportion of n, how do the changes in n affect the OC curve of an acceptance sampling plan? Given a fixed n, how do the changes in A_n affect the OC curve of an acceptance sampling plan?

14.12 What is the basic reason for double, multiple, and sequential acceptance sampling plans? What are the criteria, in practice, that would enable us to choose among these plans in a given situation?

14.13 Acceptance sampling plans are only used by buyers to decide whether a lot of material should be rejected or accepted. Is this true? If not, why not?

14.14 Statistical quality control can never be as effective as 100% inspection. Is this true? Elaborate your answer.

14.15 What is the difference between random causes and assignable causes? What is the significance of this difference in quality control methods?

14.16 Give a general procedure of setting up a control chart.

14.17 What are the important functions of a control chart? Explain and illustrate.

14.18 What are the advantages and disadvantages of computing the control limits of the $\bar{X}$ chart from R and $\bar{\sigma}$? Which method is more common? Why?

14.19 Compare the $\bar{X}$-chart with the p-chart with regard to their respective strengths and limitations.

14.20 What is the difference between the p- and the np-chart? What advantages does the np-chart have over the p-chart?

14.21 How does the c-chart differ from the np-chart?

14.22 Statistical quality control is based on the laws of probability and the theory of sampling. Develop this statement.

14.23 Quality control charts can be applied to maintain quality of performance in marketing and general office work with the same effectiveness that they are applied to industrial process. Comment.

14.24 What type of control chart or charts would you recommend in each of the following situations? Give reasons.
  a. A factory wishes to maintain control of its accident rate.
  b. A cost accountant wishes to control the amount of waste material in a machine operation. The accounting department has 20 machines in use.
  c. A manufacturer of small relief valves used in instruments designed to test mechanical properties of metals, such as tension compression, bending, and shear, wishes to control the quality of his products.

PROBLEMS

14.1 The U.S. Navy must decide to reject or accept a lot of 100,000 rain coats. The purchasing agent is considering to choose between the following two plans.

  Plan I: Take a sample of $n = 50$, the lot is accepted if it contains one defective item or less; otherwise the lot is rejected.

  Plan II: Take a first sample of $n = 40$, if there is no defective item in it, the lot is accepted; if there are two or more defective items in it, it is rejected; if there is only 1 defective item in it, continue to take a second sample of $n = 20$; if there is no defective item in the second sample, the lot is accepted and it is rejected otherwise.

  Draw the OC curves for the two sampling plans. What comparative conclusions can you reach about the two plans?
  (Hint: OC curves here can be constructed with binomial probabilities for various values of π—the proportion defectives in the lot—directly from the computers. However, due to small π which may range from, say, 0.01 to 0.10, and rather large n, the binomial probabilities can be satisfactorily approximated by the Poisson probability law if you wish).

  Note: Table A-I in the Appendix is one that contains random digits. This table can be viewed as a lot of products that is 10% defective by counting 0s as defective items and the other numbers from 1 to 9 inclusive as nondefectives. So specified, an experiment of simulated sampling can be easily devised by using the successive digits in it. All the next four problems are to be worked out by simulated samples from this table—the lot. In doing this, you should avoid using the same random numbers in any two samples. This can be easily achieved by utilizing a fresh random start and reading the table in a different but systematic way for each of your samples.

14.2 Select 10 samples of 75 items each. Use the single sampling plan in Table 14.1. How many of your samples have led to rejection? What are the sizes of producer's and consumer's risks for this sampling plan?

14.3 Select 10 double samples by using the double sampling plan in Table 14.1. How many samples of yours have led to the rejection of the lot? What is the average sample size for your ten samples?

14.4 Select 10 multiple samples by following the instructions in Table 14.1. How many of your samples have led to rejection? What is the average sample size of the 10 samples?

14.5 Draw 10 sequential samples by using the sampling plan in Table 14.2. How often do your samples lead to rejection? What is the average number of the 10 samples?

14.6 Thirty samples of 5 items each were taken from the output of a process and a critical dimension was measured. The mean of the 30 samples was 0.6500 inch and $\bar{R}$ for the 30 samples was 0.0020 inch. Compute the 3-sigma control limits for the $\bar{X}$ and R-chart.

14.7 The true fraction defective p' of a process is 0.082. Calculate the 3-sigma control limits for the following subgroup sizes: 50, 200, and 500.

14.8 The results of inspecting 30 pieces (units) of glass show the average number $\bar{c}$ of defects (air bubbles) to be 2.5. Find the 3-sigma control limits for the c-chart.

14.9 In order to determine whether the average and variability of the length of life of the incandescent lamps manufactured by a certain plant is in control, 30 subgroups of 4 are taken. It is found that $\bar{X} = 1425$ hours and $\bar{R} = 25$ hours.
   a. Estimate the true standard deviation σ' of length of life.
   b. Assuming that the process is in control, compute the control limits for the $\bar{X}$- and $\bar{R}$-chart.
   c. Use the result in (a) to determine the process capacity (natural tolerance limits of the process).

14.10 It is desired to establish control over a machine that turns out a product whose critical dimension is measured to the nearest thousandth of an inch. For this purpose, 4 items are taken at half-hour intervals until 20 such subgroups are inspected. The resulting means, ranges, and standard deviations are as follows:

				Subgroup			
	1	2	3	4	5	6	7
$\bar{X}$	19.50	17.50	20.00	18.25	17.25	19.00	20.50
R	3	7	4	5	8	10	12
σ	1.1	1.6	2.7	3.3	1.9	3.9	5.4

	8	9	10	11	12	13	14
$\bar{X}$	19.25	18.75	19.75	17.25	20.25	19.25	20.00
R	6	7	6	7	6	3	4
σ	2.4	2.2	3.6	2.6	1.1	2.3	1.6

	15	16	17	18	19	20
$\bar{X}$	21.50	16.50	17.50	20.50	18.75	19.00
R	7	3	8	5	4	6
σ	3.2	1.1	3.0	1.8	1.7	2.4

   a. Compare the control limits for the $\bar{X}$- and R-chart and plot the data.
   b. Do the same for the $\bar{X}$- and σ-chart.
   c. Determine whether the process is in control.
   d. Which set of charts would you actually recommend for controlling the quality of the said output. Why?

14.11 Reconstruct the p-chart for the data in Table 14.5 after the out-of-control samples are eliminated.

14.12 Construct an np-chart for the data in Table 14.5. Comment on the results.

14.13 A nation-wide mail-order house desired to verify the accuracy of its clerical work in completing invoices. Subgroups of 200 are taken each day for 30 consecutive days for inspection. A defective is defined as an invoice containing at least one of a number of possible errors. The number of defectives found in each of these 30 groups is as follows:

$$2, 4, 3, 6, 8, 4, 10, 6, 5, 9, 3, 12, 5, 7,$$
$$6, 3, 4, 7, 8, 6, 5, 4, 3, 5, 7, 5, 9, 1, 1, 8.$$

Construct a control chart of data and comment on the state of control.

14.14 The following are numbers of pinholes discovered in the final inspection of 25 sheets of paper, 15 by 25 inches in size:

$$7, 8, 7, 5, 4, 10, 9, 17, 8, 5, 6, 18,$$
$$15, 8, 12, 4, 7, 6, 11, 9, 5, 8, 4, 7, 6.$$

    a. Construct an appropriate chart for the data.
    b. Is the process in statistical control?
    c. How can the control chart be employed for future use?

14.15   a. Construct a 3-σ chart for the individual values in Table 3.P6.
    b. With the aid of computer programming, construct 3-σ $\bar{X}$-chart with 50 SRSs and $n = 5$ selected from Table 3.P6.
    c. Comment on the results in (a) and (b) for this problem.

15 Inferences with t, χ^2, and F Distributions

15.1 SMALL-SAMPLE THEORY AND THE NUMBER OF DEGREES OF FREEDOM

So far we have been concerned with making inferences from large samples. The concept of a "large" sample is a relative one. It is related to the sampling distribution of the statistic under consideration. In general, *large-sample theory* refers to a class of situations wherein the probability distribution of a sample statistic is normal or approximately normal (either because the population under investigation is normal or because the sample size is sufficiently large for the Central Limit Theorem to be operative) and wherein the standard error of the statistic as estimated from the sample ($S_{\hat{\theta}}$) is close to the true standard error of the statistic ($\sigma_{\hat{\theta}}$).

Sometimes, however, we are called on to make inferences when the conditions for large-sample theory cannot be met. Although we do not have as much information from a "small" sample as we might like, we are not completely without resources. The proper course is to draw conclusions or to make decisions from the sample by taking into account the scanty nature of the evidence. A great contribution of modern statistics in the art of decision making is that it allows us to make good use of a small amount of data, an undertaking that used to be considered extremely hazardous or completely impossible. The main purpose and the unifying core of this chapter are to explain why and how strong conclusions can often be reached from small random samples. It may also be pointed out here that procedures for statistical inferences from small samples are the same as those presented in the preceding chapters, except that now we cannot apply the Central Limit Theorem, we cannot assume that sampling distributions are normal, and we cannot assume that $S_{\hat{\theta}}$ is close to $\sigma_{\hat{\theta}}$.

The study of statistical inference from small samples is called *small-sample theory* or *exact-sample theory,* because it is valid for small samples as well as for large samples. Large-sample theory, by contrast, is valid only for large samples. The main difference between large- and small-sample theories concerns sampling distributions. For large samples, sampling distributions are normal; for small samples, the sampling distribution differs from one case to another. In addition to the binomial and hypergeometric distributions, which have already been discussed, there are three nonnormal probability distributions that a statistic from a small sample often assumes: the t, χ^2, and F distributions. All three of these probability models are related to the standard normal probability model. We introduce these models and some of their applications in this chapter.

To begin with, the t, χ^2 and F distributions are sampling distributions; their *parameters* are *degrees of freedom,* often abbreviated df. Thus, one way of understanding what degrees of freedom are is to approach them as parameter values that distinguish one t distribution from another, one χ^2 distribution from another, or one F distribution from another. These sampling distributions are really families of sampling distributions, because there is one such distribution for each number, or pair of numbers, of degrees of freedom.

There is another way of understanding what degrees of freedom are, which is the relationships among observations in a sample. If you have had a substantial amount of college algebra, the following definition may be helpful: The *number of degrees of freedom* is the number of linearly independent observations occurring in a sum of squares. This definition is very abstract. The following discussion says the same thing in an easier and more intuitive way.

Suppose we try to estimate a population mean by a sample of size 1. The single value in the sample would constitute the estimate. A single observation provides some information about the population mean—not very much information, but some. Now suppose we try to estimate the population variance from the same sample. We cannot do it. A single observation provides no information at all on how much variation there is among the items in the population. To get any information about the population variance, we must have a sample size of at least 2. Let us modify our sample size so that it is n, where $n \geq 2$, and try to estimate the population variance. The first observation drawn into the sample provides no information at all about the population variance. Only the second and succeeding observations provide any information about the population variance. Because of the uselessness of the first observation in estimating the population variance, we say that we "lose 1 degree of freedom." We also say that "a sample of size n has $(n - 1)$ degrees of freedom" because, in such a sample, there are $(n - 1)$ observations that provide information about the population variance.

We can say the same thing in yet another way. When we calculate the sample variance using deviations from $\bar{X}$ we get a sum of n squared deviations, $\sum (x - \bar{X})^2$, which must obey the side-relation, or constraint, $\sum (x - \bar{X}) = 0$. This constraint is important. It implies that, if we know $\bar{X}$ and any $(n - 1)$ of the deviations, the remaining deviation is automatically determined. The remaining deviation is functionally dependent and is not "free" to vary at all. Had the deviations been calculated about a known μ, the remaining deviation would have been functionally independent and "free" to assume any value. Knowledge of μ and any $(n - 1)$ of the deviations is not enough to determine the value of the remaining deviation. The final result is that a sample of n squared deviations taken about $\bar{X}$ furnishes less information than the same number of squared deviations taken about μ.

To generalize: The number of degrees of freedom, denoted by δ (Greek lower-case delta, read aloud as "delta"), may be thought of as the number of elements that can be chosen freely, or as the number of variables that can vary freely, or as the number of functionally independent variables. Given the sample size, the number of degrees of freedom is $\delta = n - k$, where k is the number of constraints for the computation of a statistic $\hat{\theta}$ involving sums of squares. The constraints may be, for example, the number of estimators required to calculate the $\hat{\theta}$ in question.

15.2 STUDENT'S t DISTRIBUTIONS

If $X_0, X_1, X_2, \ldots, X_\delta$ are $\delta + 1$ independent standard normal variables, then the statistic

$$t_\delta = \frac{X_0}{\sqrt{\dfrac{1}{\delta}(X_1^2 + X_2^2 + \cdots + X_\delta^2)}} \tag{15.1}$$

is said to have a *Student's t*, or simply t, *distribution*. The t variable has a density function

$$f(t) = \left(\frac{1}{\sqrt{\delta\pi}}\right) \left[\frac{\Gamma\left(\dfrac{\delta + 1}{2}\right)}{\Gamma\left(\dfrac{\delta}{2}\right)} \right] \left(1 + \frac{t^2}{\delta}\right)^{-(\delta+1)/2}, \qquad -\infty \leqslant t \leqslant \infty. \tag{15.2}$$

Two density curves for t with $\delta = 2$ and $\delta = 20$ are drawn, respectively, against the density curve for the standard normal variable in Figure 15.1 for ready comparison between these two variables.

In (15.2), the quantity $\Gamma(\delta/2)$, "gamma function of $\delta/2$," refers to a value that is dependent on δ and is $[(\delta/2 - 1)!]$. This density function makes that for a normal variable look simple. Fortunately, a full understanding of it is required only for theoretical statistics. You, as a

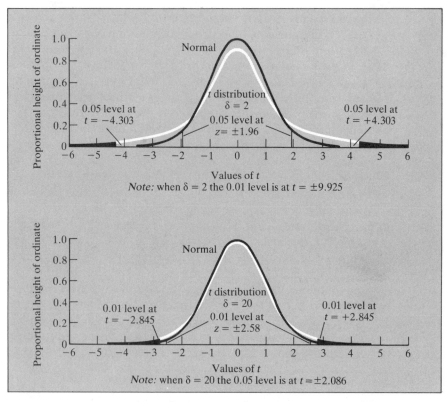

FIGURE 15.1 Comparison of *t* distributions with the standard normal distribution for
$\delta = 2$ and $\delta = 20$.

student of applied statistics, need to have little concern with it except to
take notice of the fact that the density function of *t* is completely defined
by δ—the number of degrees of freedom. Let us now take notice of some
of the interesting properties of the *t* variable.

1. Like a standard normal variable, a *t* variable is continuous and
   ranges in value from $-\infty$ to ∞.

2. Like a normal variable, the density curve for a *t* variable is
   symmetric and bell-shaped.

3. There is a *t* distribution for each degree of freedom (an integer).

4. A *t* variable is completely defined by δ—the single parameter of *t*.
   Thus, we have

$$E(t) = 0, \qquad \text{for } \delta > 1 ; \qquad (15.3)$$

and

$$V(t) = \frac{\delta}{\delta - 2}, \quad \text{for } \delta > 2. \qquad (15.4)$$

We see that a t distribution has no mean when $\delta = 1$ and it possesses no variance when $\delta \leq 2$.

5. A t distribution is similar to the standard normal distribution in that they both range in value from $-\infty$ to ∞, both are symmetric, and both have a mean of zero. They are only different from each other in the fact that a t distribution has a greater dispersion than the standard normal distribution. This property is revealed clearly by the standard deviation of t_δ, which is $\sqrt{\delta/(\delta - 2)}$. This quantity is always greater than 1 (the standard deviation of the standard normal distribution). However, it comes closer to 1 as δ becomes large. Thus, t approaches $n(0, 1)$ as a limit as δ approaches infinity. In practice, we can treat t_δ as $n(0, 1)$ when $\delta > 30$.

Table VII in Appendix C is a common way of presenting the PDF of t distributions. You must exercise some care when using this table. The diagram at the top of the table shows that it is a "two-tailed" table. This kind of table is different from Table VI for the normal distribution, which is a "lower-tail" table. Furthermore, Table VII is rather brief, since a large number of t distributions are given. It contains only a number of selected percentage points for each t distribution. Finally, the t-values in the cells could be negative or positive, depending upon whether it is below or above the zero mean of a distribution.

Let us try to use the table with a few examples. Suppose X is t_2, then

$$P(-4.303 \leq X \leq 4.303) = P(-4.303 \leq t_2 \leq 4.303)$$
$$= 0.05.$$

From this we see that

$$P(t_2 < -4.303) = 0.025 \quad \text{and} \quad P(t_2 > 4.303) = 0.025.$$

See Figure 15.1 for $\delta = 2$.

Likewise, if X is t_{20}, we have

$$P(-2.845 \leq t_{20} \leq 2.845) = 0.99$$
$$P(t_{20} < -2.845) = 0.005,$$
$$P(t_{20} > 2.845) = 0.005,$$
$$P(t_{20} > 2.528) = 0.01,$$
$$P(t_{20} < -1.725) = 0.05,$$

and so on. The column headings of Table VII are levels of significance for two-sided tests. Entries in the body are the critical values of t_δ for such tests. If we would like to have a single-tailed test with, say, $\alpha = 0.05$, the critical value is found in the column with $2\alpha = 0.10$ for the appropriate number of df. For example, for $P(t_{20} < -1.725) = 0.05$, the number -1.725 is found in the column headed by 0.10 corresponding to $\delta = 20$.

As another example of using the t table, let us try to find $P(-\infty < t_{60} < 2)$. Here, we want the whole area under the t curve except an upper-tail area. The t table shows that, for $t_{60} = \pm 2$, the combined tail area is 0.05. Hence the upper-tail area must be 0.025 and the answer we seek must be 0.975.

15.3 INFERENCES ABOUT μ WITH t DISTRIBUTIONS

One of the difficulties with using the normal distribution to analyze a sample is that the sample size must be large enough to justify using the normal distribution. When the population standard deviation is unknown, which is certainly the usual situation, the minimum sample size can pose a serious problem. A good way of looking at this situation is to start by comparing the following expressions:

$$(1) \quad \frac{\bar{X} - \mu}{\sigma_{\bar{X}}}, \quad \text{and} \quad (2) \quad \frac{\bar{X} - \mu}{S_{\bar{X}}}.$$

The first quotient contains only one variable, $\bar{X}$. When the population is normally distributed, it is equivalent to Z; that is, to $n(0, 1)$. The second quotient contains two random variables, $\bar{X}$ and $S_{\bar{X}}$; it can no longer be considered as $n(0, 1)$ even approximately unless n is greater than 30. It may be noted, though, if the numerical value of this quotient is computed for each sample in the sample space, some sampling distribution will result. As a matter of fact the numerator, $(\bar{X} - \mu)$, in the second expression is normally distributed with zero mean if the population is normally distributed. However, due to random fluctuations in $S_{\bar{X}}$, the standard deviation of the quotient must be greater than that for $n(0, 1)$. Hence, it seems reasonable to conclude that $(\bar{X} - \mu)/S_{\bar{X}}$ should follow a t distribution as stated in the following theorem.

THEOREM 15.1 SAMPLING DISTRIBUTION OF $(\bar{X} - \mu)/S_{\bar{X}}$ *If an SRS is drawn from a normal population with mean μ and an unknown standard deviation σ that is estimated by S, then the statistic*

$$t_{\delta} = \frac{\bar{X} - \mu}{S_{\bar{X}}} \tag{15.5}$$

has a t distribution with $\delta = n - 1$.

The use of this theorem requires that $n \geqslant 2$. The FPCF is not mentioned since $N = \infty$ for an exactly normal population. If sampling without replacement is conducted from an approximately normal but finite population, Theorem 15.1 is approximately true, provided FPCF is used. In other words, under these conditions the quotient

$$\frac{\bar{X} - \mu}{S_{\bar{X}} \sqrt{\dfrac{N - n}{N}}}$$

has an approximate t distribution with $\delta = n - 1$. As usual, the 5% rule applies here; that is, the FPCF can be omitted if $n \leq 0.05N$.

Equation (15.5) in Theorem 15.1 can be used as the test statistic about μ and as a method of producing confidence intervals for μ. Furthermore, the logic and procedures of testing hypotheses and constructing confidence intervals by using t distributions are identical with the general procedures developed for the large-sample case.

To illustrate the t test concerning μ, suppose a medical research center announced that it has developed a treatment for high blood pressure that can reduce a patient's blood pressure by more than 20 points. Learning about this, a doctor tries the treatment on ten of his patients who are suffering from high blood pressure. As a result, he finds that their blood pressure has been reduced by 21.5 points on the average, with $s = 1.5$ points. If the doctor is interested in finding out whether the new treatment is as effective as claimed by the research organization, by using the following t test he could determine this on the basis of the information he has obtained from his trials, assuming his patients are a random sample of all patients

1. *Hypotheses*. H_0: $\mu \leq 20$; H_1: $\mu > 20$.

2. *Level of significance*. $\alpha = 0.01$.

3. *Test statistic*. $t_\delta = (\bar{X} - \mu)/(S/\sqrt{n})$, which is distributed as t_9.

4. *Decision rule*. Since $P(t_9 \geq 2.821) = 0.01$, he would reject H_0 if $t > 2.821$. (*Note*: The critical value 2.821 is found from the column headed by 0.02 and the row headed by 9 df in the t table. The column under 0.02 is used for our upper-tailed test at $\alpha = 0.01$ because, as stated before, the t table is constructed with two-sided critical values.)

5. *Computations*.

$$n = 10, \qquad \bar{x} = 21.5, \qquad s = 1.5,$$

$$s_{\bar{X}} = \frac{1.5}{\sqrt{10}} \doteq 0.474, \qquad \text{and}$$

$$t_9 = \frac{\bar{x} - \mu}{s_{\bar{X}}} = \frac{21.5 - 20.0}{0.474} \doteq 3.165.$$

which is greater than 2.821.

6. *Decisions*. The difference of 1.5 between the sample mean and the hypothesized population mean is significant. H_0 is rejected in favor of H_1. If there are no undesirable side-effects from the use of the new treatment, the doctor may decide to use it exclusively henceforth.

In general, confidence intervals for μ based on the t distribution are given as

$$L, U = \bar{X} \mp t_{\alpha/2} S_{\bar{X}}. \tag{15.6}$$

where $t_{\alpha/2}$ is based on $\delta = n - 1$.

In this expression, $t_{\alpha/2}$ is based upon $\delta = n - 1$. Also, always keep in your mind that the t-table is two-sided.

As an illustration, suppose we wish to have an interval estimate of the mean tensile strength of malleable iron castings produced by a certain factory. We may first draw an SRS with, may, $n = 17$ castings for observation. Suppose, furthermore, we find that, for this sample,

$$\bar{x} = 57,000 \text{ psi} \quad \text{and} \quad s = 1,600 \text{ psi}.$$

With these data and by (15.6), a 95% confidence interval for μ becomes

$$L, U = \bar{x} \mp t_{.025}s_{\bar{x}}$$

$$= 57,000 \mp 2.120 \left(\frac{1600}{\sqrt{17}}\right)$$

$$= 56,177 \text{ to } 57,823.$$

It may be noted that the critical value of t, 2.120, in the above calculation is found in the column headed by 0.05 in the t table, corresponding to 16 df. In our example, the central 95% of the area is enclosed by ordinates erected at -2.120 and $+2.120$. Of course, if we wished to contruct a 99% confidence interval for a given δ, we would use the t values in the column headed by 0.01 corresponding to that δ.

Confidence intervals constructed with t distributions can be interpreted in the same way as those constructed with the normal distribution. It is important however, to note two points. First, the confidence interval constructed with a small sample is wider or less precise than that with a large sample. This is not only because a small sample has a large standard error but also because the t multiple is larger than the Z multiple. Second, if σ is known, confidence intervals for many different random samples of the same size would have the same width, even though they might have different midpoints, which are the different sample means. The reason here is that the standard error is a constant when the population standard deviation is known. When σ is unknown, the standard error is itself a random variable that varies in value from sample to sample. As a result, confidence intervals for different sample means, computed from samples of the same size, will have not only different midpoints but also unequal widths. This last observation, however, should not lead us to infer that confidence intervals constructed with estimated standard errors from small samples have a different meaning. They are still confidence statements and should be interpreted in the same way as those constructed under the assumption of normality.

15.4 INFERENCES ABOUT $\Delta\mu$ WITH t DISTRIBUTIONS

The Case of Independent Samples

Statistical inferences about the difference between two population means for independent samples can be made by the theorem stated below.

THEOREM 15.2 SAMPLING DISTRIBUTION OF $(\Delta\bar{X} - \Delta\mu)/S_{\Delta\bar{x}}$
If two SRSs of sizes n_1 and n_2 are independently drawn from normal populations with means μ_1 and μ_2, respectively, and identical but unknown variances, $\sigma_1^2 = \sigma_2^2$, then the statistic

$$t_\delta = \frac{\Delta\bar{X} - \Delta\mu}{S_{\Delta\bar{x}}} \qquad (15.7)$$

would have t distribution with $\delta = n_1 + n_2 - 2$.

The standard error in (15.7) is computed by the following formula

$$S_{\Delta\bar{x}} = S_w\sqrt{\frac{n_1 + n_2}{n_1 n_2}}, \qquad (15.8)$$

where S_w is the pooled, or weighted, estimator for the common population standard deviations and is defined as

$$S_w = \sqrt{\frac{(n_1 - 1)S_1^2 + (n_2 - 1)S_2^2}{n_1 + n_2 - 2}} \qquad (15.9)$$

which has $n_1 + n_2 - 2$ df.

As an example of testing by employing (15.7), let us consider the case where we wish to find out whether the compressive strength of bricks produced under standard conditions is different from that of bricks made under new conditions. First, we assume that both populations are normal and that $\sigma_1^2 = \sigma_2^2$. Next, we draw an SRS from each of the two populations to test H_0: $\mu_1 = \mu_2$ against H_1: $\mu_1 \neq \mu_2$ at, say, $\alpha = 0.01$. Let us also specify that the subscript 1 is for the standard conditions and the subscript 2 is for the new conditions. Suppose we have now obtained the following data:

$$n_1 = 12, \qquad n_2 = 10;$$
$$\bar{x}_1 = 11.6, \qquad \bar{x}_2 = 13.4;$$
$$s_1^2 = 1.25, \qquad s_2^2 = 1.30;$$
$$\Delta\bar{x} = 11.6 - 13.4 = -1.8.$$

From these primary results, we have

$$s_w = \sqrt{\frac{(12-1)1.25 + (10-1)1.30}{12 + 10 - 2}}$$

$$\doteq 1.27274;$$

$$S_{\Delta\bar{X}} = 1.27274\sqrt{\frac{12 + 10}{(12)(10)}} \doteq 0.545.$$

Finally,

$$t_{20} = \frac{-1.8 - 0}{0.545} \doteq -3.303.$$

This result leads to the rejection of H_0 since $P(t_{20} \leq -2.845) = 0.01$ and $-3.303 < -2.845$. Owing to the negative value of t, we may also conclude that the mean compressive strength of bricks produced under the standard conditions is significantly smaller than that obtained produced under the new conditions. If the costs of producing bricks under the two sets of conditions do not differ by much, bricks should be produced under the new conditions.

Confidence limits for $\Delta\mu$ can be constructed by

$$L, U = \Delta\bar{X} \mp t_{\alpha/2}(S_{\Delta\bar{X}}), \tag{15.10}$$

where $t_{\alpha/2}$ is based on $\delta = n_1 + n_2 - 2$. Thus, if we wish to construct a 99% confidence interval for $\Delta\mu$ with the example just given, with $\delta = 20$, we have

$$L, U = \Delta\bar{x} \mp t_{.005}S_{\Delta\bar{X}}$$

$$= -1.8 \mp 2.845(0.545)$$

$$= -3.35 \quad \text{to} \quad -0.25.$$

This result indicates that $\Delta\mu$ is negative and agrees with the conclusion reached by testing before. So, the correspondence between a test at α and an interval estimate with $1 - \alpha$ holds for t distributions as well. As a matter of fact, this correspondence between testing and interval estimation holds in all circumstances.

Our discussion of inferences concerning the difference between two population means has so far been presented under the assumption that the population variances are equal. If there is reason to believe that they are not equal, then the natural thing for us to do is to use the unbiased estimators S_1^2 and S_2^2 to replace σ_1^2 and σ_2^2 in the evaluation of the distribution of $\Delta\bar{X}$. Now, if two independent samples are drawn from two normally distributed populations that possess unequal variances, then the sampling distribution of $\Delta\bar{X}$ would have

$$S_{\Delta\bar{X}} = \sqrt{\frac{S_1^2}{n_1} + \frac{S_2^2}{n_2}}$$

as the estimator for the standard error of $\Delta\bar{X}$. However, the ratio

$$\frac{\Delta X - \Delta\mu}{S_{\Delta\bar{X}}}$$

would have only an approximate t distribution with δ as defined by

$$\delta = \left[\frac{S_1^2/n_1 + S_2^2/n_2}{\dfrac{S_1^2/n_1}{1/(n_1 + 1)} + \dfrac{S_2^2/n_2}{1/(n_2 + 1)}}\right] - 2.$$

With this modification, we may now test $\Delta\mu = 0$ against an appropriate alternative with the test statistic

$$t_\delta = \frac{\Delta\bar{X} - \Delta\mu}{S_{\Delta\bar{X}}}$$

in the usual way and calculate the confidence limits for $\Delta\mu$ in the familiar manner as

$$L, U = \Delta\bar{X} \mp t_{\alpha/2} S_{\Delta\bar{X}}.$$

It is important to remember, though, that in both cases δ is defined as just given above.

The Case of Dependent Variables

Two samples are said to be *dependent* (or *matched,* or *paired*) if each observation in one sample is associated with some particular observation in the other sample. An example would be a sample of households wherein the members' television viewing is observed during one week and then observed during a second week. Another example would be a sample of people who are observed once; then given some treatment such as a weight-reducing diet, a stop-smoking program, or a training couse; and then observed a second time to see how effective the treatment was. ("Treatment" is a very general word in statistical discussions and includes many more possibilities than medical treatment.)

Dependent samples can result from other arrangements besides before-and-after measurements of the same individuals. Two different groups of school children can be paired on the basis of IQ scores, or both IQ scores and sex, for example. Two different groups of plots of land can be paired and the basis of drainage, soil acidity, and any other factors considered relevant. The essential idea is the association of each observation in one sample with a particular observation in the other sample. Naturally, the two samples must be of the same size in order to be dependent.

The analysis of dependent samples is fundamentally different from the analysis of independent samples. When the samples are dependent, the first step is calculating the difference between the members of each pair of observations. Then all further analysis is done with these differences. in more detail, if the first sample's observations are $x_1, x_2, \ldots, x_n$ and the second sample's observations are $y_1, y_2, \ldots, y_n$, the first step is calculating the differences $d_1 = y_1 - x_1$, $d_2 = y_2 - x_2, \ldots, d_n = y_n - x_n$. All further analysis is done solely with the values of $d_1, d_2, \ldots, d_n$. Note that the sample size, n, refers to n pairs of observations or to n differences of the paired observations.

We restrict our discussion to the case in which the observed differences, d_i, are the values of an SRS from a population of differences and the population of differences is normally distributed with mean μ_D and standard deviation σ_D. However, we are not interested in whether population X or population Y is normally distributed. Even if both of them are normal variables, the population of d_i's can be nonnormal. Our requirement is strictly on the normality of the population of d's.

We estimate μ_D from the sample of d's in the usual way:

$$\bar{D} = \frac{\Sigma\, d}{n}$$

and we estimate σ_D from the sample of d's in the usual way:

$$S_D = \sqrt{\frac{\Sigma\, (d - \bar{D})^2}{n - 1}} = \sqrt{\frac{(\Sigma\, d^2) - (\Sigma\, d)^2/n}{n - 1}}.$$

Then the standard error of $\bar{D}$ can be estimated as

$$S_{\bar{D}} = \frac{S_D}{\sqrt{n}}.$$

If the population of d's is finite and only approximately normal, and if $n > 0.05N$, we should compute the estimate of $\sigma_{\bar{D}}$ with the FPCF as below:

$$S_{\bar{D}} = \left(\frac{S_D}{\sqrt{n}}\right) \sqrt{\frac{N - n}{N}}.$$

Finally, if the population of d's is normally distributed with μ_D, and if the differences d_i computed from two dependent samples are an SRS, then

$$t_\delta = \frac{\bar{D} - \mu_D}{S_{\bar{D}}} \tag{15.11}$$

has a t distribution with $\delta = n - 1$. Equation (15.11) is used as the test statistic for hypotheses about μ_D or for the construction of the confidence limits for the same.

As an illustration of using (15.11) for testing, suppose an efficiency expert believes that she has perfected a training program that can

TABLE 15.1 Time Required to Assemble a Certain Mechanism Before and After the Training Program

Worker	First Study (minutes)	Second Study (minutes)	d_i	d_i^2
1	7	8	+1	1
2	8	8	0	0
3	10	7	−3	9
4	11	6	−5	25
5	18	10	−8	64
6	16	9	−7	49
7	12	9	−3	9
8	12	8	−4	16
9	6	7	+1	1
10	12	10	−2	4
Total	112	81	−30	178

Source: Hypothetical.

considerably shorten workers' assembly times for a certain mechanism. To check this belief she plans to select 10 workers at random in a very large factory to make time and motion studies after they have gone through the training program. Suppose the results of her experiment are as shown in Table 15.1 where D is the time required in the second study minus the time required in the first study. Assuming the population is normal, what conclusion can she reach by testing H_0: $\mu_D \geqslant 0$ against H_1: $\mu_D < 0$?

With the data in Table 15.1, you can easily verify that

$$\bar{d} = -3 \text{ minutes};$$
$$S_D \doteq 3.1269 \text{ minutes};$$
$$S_{\bar{D}} = 0.9888 \text{ minutes}.$$

Thus, by (15.11), we have

$$t_9 = \frac{\bar{d} - 0}{s_{\bar{D}}} = \frac{-3 - 0}{0.9888} \doteq -3.034,$$

which is less than -2.821—the critical t value for $\delta = 9$ and $\alpha = 0.01$. Therefore H_0 is rejected and she may conclude that the training program is apparently of some help in reducing the average assembly time, as she thought.

The confidence limits for the true difference between population means in the dependent-sample case here can be computed in the usual way. For example, the 99% confidence limits for μ_D are

$$L, U = \bar{d} \mp t_{\alpha/2} S_{\bar{D}} = \bar{d} \mp t_{.005} S_{\bar{D}}$$
$$= -3 \mp 2.821(0.9888) \doteq -5.79 \text{ to } -0.21.$$

(Note: In this case, $t_{\alpha/2}$ is based on $\delta = n - 1$.)

15.5 CHI-SQUARE DISTRIBUTIONS

If $X_1, X_2, \ldots,$ and X_δ are independent standard normal variables, then the statistic

$$\chi_\delta^2 = X_1^2 + X_2^2 + \cdots + X_\delta^2 \qquad (15.12)$$

is said to be a chi-square variable, χ_δ^2, with δ degrees of freedom. This variable is defined by the following density:

$$f(\chi^2) = \frac{[(\chi^2)^{\delta/(2-1)}]e^{-(\chi^2/2)}}{(2^{\delta/2})\left[\Gamma\left(\dfrac{\delta}{2}\right)\right]}, \qquad 0 \leqslant \chi^2 \leqslant \infty. \qquad (15.13)$$

Again, there is no need for you to be intimidated by this rather forbidding expression. All what you have to know about this equation is that a chi-square variable is completely defined by its number of degrees of freedom and that there is a χ^2 variable for each positive integer.

We now state some of the important properties of chi-square distributions for later use. Some of these properties actually can be deduced from careful study of Figure 15.2, which gives the density curves of χ^2 variables for a few selected values of δ. The properties are listed below.

1. If X has a standard normal distribution, then X^2 has a χ^2 distribution with $\delta = 1$; that is, χ_1^2.

2. If X_1 is $\chi_{\delta_1}^2$ and X_2 is $\chi_{\delta_2}^2$ and if X_1 and X_2 are independent, then $X_1 + X_2$ is $\chi_{\delta_1+\delta_2}^2$. This is commonly called the *additivity property* of chi-square distributions.

3. If X is a standard normal variable and x_i, $i = 1, 2, \ldots, n$, are n observations constituting a random sample, each x_i being a value of X, then $\sum x^2$ is distributed as χ_n^2.

4. If X is a normal variable and if x_i are n observations constituting a random sample, each x_i being a value of X, then $\sum \{[(x - \mu)/\sigma]^2\}$ is distributed as χ_n^2.

Note that properties (3) and (4) are equivalent statements. In property (3) a random sample is selected from $n(0, 1)$; in property (4) a random sample is taken from $n(\mu, \sigma)$, and the operation of $(x_i - \mu)/\sigma$ transforms property (4) into property (3).

5. A chi-square variable ranges in value from 0 to ∞, since it is the sum of squared values.

6. A chi-square distribution is completely defined by the number of degrees of freedom. If X is χ_δ^2, its mean and variance, respectively,

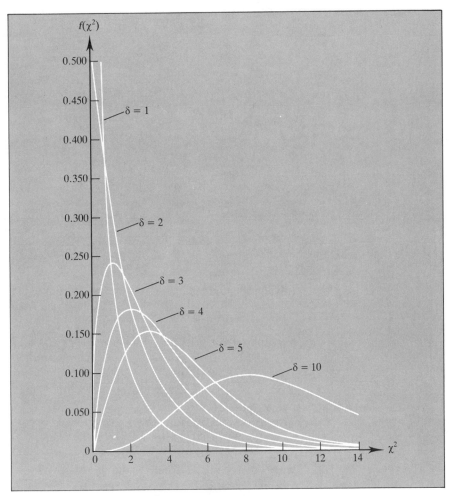

FIGURE 15.2 Graphs for χ^2 density functions for $\delta = 1, 2, \ldots, 10$.

are

$$E(\chi^2_\delta) = \mu = \delta; \qquad\qquad (15.14)$$

$$V(\chi^2_\delta) = \sigma^2 = 2\delta. \qquad\qquad (15.15)$$

7. Chi-square distributions are positively skewed. As δ gets large, however, χ^2_δ approaches the normal distribution $n(\delta, \sqrt{2\delta})$. In practice, chi-square probabilities, when $\delta > 30$, can be computed by employing normal approximations in the usual fashion.

Table VIII in Appendix C gives a few selected fractile points for chi-square distributions for $1 \leq \delta \leq 100$. Note that this table is in the cumulative form and gives upper-tail probabilities for chi-square distributions. Thus, we must exercise some care in using this table. This table is different from Table VI for the normal distribution, which is a "lower-tail" table, and from Table VII for the t distributions which is a "two-tail" table.

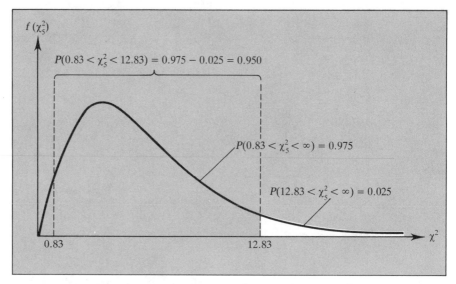

FIGURE 15.3 Examples of areas under a χ^2 probability density function.

As an example of using the χ^2 table, let us try to find $P(\chi_{16}^2 > 32)$. The table gives 0.01 as the answer. To obtain this answer, we start from the left-hand column and locate $\delta = 16$. Next, we move to the right until we locate the χ^2-value of 32. Finally, we go up and find the column heading, which gives us the probability value of 0.01.

If we seek a lower-tail area, the basic procedure is to look up the upper-tail area in the table and subtract it from 1. For instance, $P(\chi_{16}^2 \leq 32) = 1 - 0.01 = 0.99$.

When we want a central area, the basic procedure is to look up the upper-tail area in the table for the smaller value of χ^2 and then subtract the upper-tail area in the table for the smaller value of χ^2. For example, what is $P(0.83 < \chi_5^2 < 12.83)$? Figure 15.3 illustrates the problem. The table shows that $P(0.83 < \chi_5^2 < \infty) = 0.975$ and that $P(12.83 < \chi_5^2 < \infty) = 0.025$. The answer we seek then is $0.975 - 0.025 = 0.950$.

15.6 INFERENCES ABOUT σ^2 WITH χ^2 DISTRIBUTIONS

Often we wish to concentrate on the amount of variation in a population. Under suitable circumstances, the amount of variation in a random sample, as measured by S^2, can be used to cast light on the amount of variation in the population, as measured by σ^2. To conduct inferences about σ^2 on the basis of S^2 we need to know the sampling distribution of S^2. As was pointed out in Chapter 10, if an SRS is drawn from a normally distributed population and if $n \geq 100$, the sampling distribution of S^2 will be approximately normal by the Central Limit Theorem. But if the size of the sample is quite small, for practical reasons, what probability law will the distribution of S^2 obey? Of course, if S^2 is calculated for every sample in a sample space, *some* sampling distribution will emerge. However, such a procedure is conceivably very involved and time-consuming. Some simple and precise method is needed for finding the samping distribution of S^2. Towards this, we offer the following observations.

It can be shown that S^2 computed from an SRS drawn from a normal population can be defined as

$$S^2 = \chi_\delta^2 \left(\frac{\sigma^2}{\delta} \right),$$

where χ_δ^2 is a random variable and where the particular χ^2 has a distribution with $\delta = n - 1$. Next, it can also be verified that if the sample statistic that is distributed in accordance with χ^2 is $(\delta S^2)/\sigma^2$. Finally, substituting $\delta = n - 1$, we obtain

$$\frac{\delta S^2}{\sigma^2} = \frac{(n-1)S^2}{\sigma^2}.$$

It is important to note that the ratio on the right-hand side of this equation is the sum of squared deviations from a sample mean divided by the population variance, since $(n-1)S^2 = \sum (x - \bar{x})^2$. By property (4) of χ^2 distributions given above, the ratio $[(n-1)S^2]/\sigma^2$ qualifies as χ_δ^2 with $\delta = n - 1$. Let us summarize these arguments in the following theorem.

THEOREM 15.3 SAMPLING DISTRIBUTION OF $[(n-1)S^2]/\sigma^2$
If an SRS is drawn from a normally distributed population with σ^2, then the statistic

$$\chi_\delta^2 = \frac{(n-1)S^2}{\sigma^2} \tag{15.16}$$

has a χ^2 distribution with $\delta = n - 1$.

This theorem can be used to test hypotheses about σ^2 or to construct confidence intervals for σ^2.

In testing hypotheses about population variances, all the three types of tests can be used. However, in practice, we are usually concerned with the possibility that a population variance may be too large for a given situation and we are seldom worried about the possibility that σ^2 may be too small or may be different from a given quantity. As a result, we usually test σ^2 by an upper-tail test. This, incidentally, is why the table for χ^2 distributions is often given in terms of the upper-tail percentage points.

We now provide an example for the application of Theorem 15.3 to conducting inferences about σ^2.

Suppose that the Transit Authority of New York City plans to purchase light bulbs for its subway system. The Authority wishes to have bulbs that possess not only long life but also a high degree of uniformity. It decides, on the basis of past experience, that the variance should not exceed 250 hours^2. A test of 20 bulbs of a certain make yields a mean life of 1000 hours, which is considered to be satisfactory, but with a variance of 300 hours^2. Does this result indicate that the population variance exceeds 250?

Before proceeding to the analysis, a choice must be made in the way the hypotheses are formulated. The choice amounts to specifying either that the observed sample variance be consistent with at least one value of σ^2 that is less than or equal to 250, or that the observed sample variance be inconsistent with all values of σ^2 that are greater than 250. In other words, does the Transit Authority want reasonable assurance that the population variance *could* be 250 or less, or does it want reasonable assurance that the population variance *must* be 250 or less? If the latter, no analysis is necessary, because the sample result of 300 is obviously consistent with many values of the population variance over 250, so the sample evidence immediately rules out the conclusion that the population variance *must* be 250 or less. If, despite this reasoning, a formal analysis is desired, it would start by interchanging the hypotheses stated below. On the other hand, if the Transit Authority is content to specify only that the population variance *could* be 250 or less, the analysis below is needed before a conclusion can be reached from the sample evidence. Of course, the decision on which way to specify the population variance is a managerial decision, not a statistical decision. Assuming that the "loose" specification that the population variance *could* be 250 or less is the desired specification, the hypotheses should be stated as shown below (for any conventional value of α), and the analysis should proceed as shown below. This is another example of the often troublesome question: Which hypothesis should be the null and which the alternative?

Following the general procedure of testing developed in Chapter 12, we have the following test.

1. *Hypotheses.* H_0: $\sigma^2 \leqslant 250$; H_1: $\sigma^2 > 250$.

2. *Level of significance.* Arbitrarily set at 0.05.

3. *Test statistic.* $\chi_\delta^2 = (n - 1)s^2/\delta^2$, which has a chi-square distribution with $\delta = n - 1 = 19$.

4. *Decision rule.* Since $P(\chi_{19}^2 > 30.14) = 0.05$, H_0 cannot be rejected if and only if the observed chi-square value is greater than or equal to 30.14, and H_0 cannot be rejected if and only if the observed chi-square value is less than 30.14.

5. *Computations.*

$$\chi_{19}^2 = \frac{(20 - 1)300}{250} = 22.80.$$

6. *Decision.* Since the observed χ^2 falls in the acceptance region, H_0 cannot be rejected. This sample result, in other words, is not sufficient evidence for us to conclude that $\sigma^2 > 250$. The Authority

may, therefore, consider this make of light bulb satisfactory and decide on its purchase.

As observed before, tests on variances are typically of the upper-tail variety, since we are usually concerned with the fact that the variance may be too large. When we wish to conduct a two-sided test with chi-square distributions, we divide the region of rejection into two equal parts. For instance, if $\delta = 19$ and $\alpha = 0.05$ as in the previous test but the alternative is stated as $\sigma^2 \neq 250$, we would reject H_0 if $\chi^2 < 8.91$ or if $\chi^2 > 32.85$. In other words, we find the χ^2 value that has 97.5% of the area to the right of it (8.91) and the χ^2 value which has 2.5% of the area to the right of it (32.85). Note that $P(8.91 < \chi^2_{19} < 32.85) = 0.95$.

To have an internal estimate of σ^2, we try to construct a confidence interval such that it will contain σ^2 at a specified confidence level $1 - \alpha$. Such an interval may be made by using the information that if equation (15.16) is solved for σ^2, we have

$$\sigma^2 = \frac{(n - 1)S^2}{\chi^2_\delta}.$$

Now, inserting the values of $(n - 1)$, S^2, and χ^2, we can estimate the lower and upper confidence limits for σ^2 from

$$L = \frac{(n - 1)S^2}{\chi^2_{n-1;1-\alpha/2}} \quad \text{and} \quad U = \frac{(n - 1)S^2}{\chi^2_{n-1;\alpha/2}} \tag{15.17}$$

These chi-square values depend upon the number of degrees of freedom and the confidence level. These are indicated by the subscripts on χ^2 in the expression above. Note once more that the χ^2 table gives the probability that a given χ^2 value is exceeded. Thus, if we desire to have a 95% confidence interval, we should choose the value of $\chi^2_{\delta;.975}$ for the lower confidence limit and the value of $\chi^2_{\delta;.025}$ for the upper confidence limit. Similarly, if $1 - \alpha = 0.99$, then values of $\chi^2_{\delta;.995}$ and $\chi^2_{\delta;.005}$ should be used for the lower and upper confidence limits, respectively. It is interesting to observe that the larger chi-square value is used for L and the smaller chi-square value is used for U in constructing a confidence interval for σ^2 because χ^2 and σ^2 are inversely related. Our notation, $\chi^2_{\delta;\alpha}$, always refers to lower-tail values of χ^2, just as z_α refers to lower-tail values of Z.

As an example, let us now construct a 95% confidence interval for σ^2, using the illustrative material from the preceding test. Recalling that, in this instance, $n = 20$ and $s^2 = 300$, we have, therefore,

$$L = \frac{(20 - 1)(300)}{\chi^2_{19;.975}} = \frac{(19)(300)}{32.85} \doteq 173.5$$

and

$$U = \frac{(20 - 1)(300)}{\chi^2_{19;.025}} = \frac{(19)(300)}{8.91} \doteq 639.7,$$

or

$$173.5 \leqslant \sigma^2 \leqslant 639.7.$$

The confidence interval for the standard deviation can be derived directly from that for the variance. This is done by taking the square roots of the limits for σ^2. Thus, the corresponding 95% confidence interval for our illustrative problem is

$$\sqrt{173.5} \leqslant \sigma \leqslant \sqrt{639.7}; \quad \text{that is, } 13.2 < \sigma < 25.3.$$

Sometimes, especially in the case of estimating σ^2, we are concerned only with an upper confidence limit, not with the lower. In such a situation, we state that the variance is equal to or less than some specific value. Namely, we are interested in constructing a left-side confidence interval of the form $0 \leqslant \sigma^2 \leqslant U$ with a confidence probability of $1 - \alpha$. Here, U can be found from

$$U = \frac{(n-1)S^2}{\chi^2_{n-1;\alpha}}. \tag{15.18}$$

The 95% left-side confidence interval for the light-bulb illustration has as its upper confidence limit

$$U = \frac{(20-1)(300)}{\chi^2_{19;.05}}.$$

$$= \frac{(19)(300)}{10.12} = 563.$$

With this result we see that

$$0 \leqslant \sigma^2 \leqslant 563$$

contains the hypothetical value of 250 in the null hypothesis for the previous test. This explains once again why H_0 was not rejected before.

A corresponding confidence interval of the form $L \leqslant \sigma^2 \leqslant \infty$, which is obviously the right-side confidence interval for σ^2, can also be obtained easily. However, it is of little practical significance in this case.

15.7 *F* DISTRIBUTIONS

If $X_1, X_2, \ldots, X_{\delta_1}$ and $Y_1, Y_2, \ldots, Y_{\delta_2}$ are all independent standard normal variables, then the statistic

$$F = \frac{(X_1^2 + X_2^2 + \cdots + X_{\delta_1}^2)/\delta_1}{(Y_1^2 + Y_2^2 + \cdots + Y_{\delta_2}^2)/\delta_2} \tag{15.19}$$

is said to have an F distribution with (δ_1, δ_2) degrees of freedom. The numerator and denominator in (15.19) are independent. It turns out that an F variable is a ratio of two chi-square variables with δ_1 as df (the number of degrees of freedom) for the numerator and with δ_2 as df for the demoninator. Thus, an F distribution may be denoted as F_{δ_1, δ_2} and it is defined by the density

$$f(F) = \left[\frac{\Gamma\left(\frac{\delta_1 + \delta_2}{2}\right)}{\Gamma\left(\frac{\delta_1}{2}\right)\Gamma\left(\frac{\delta_2}{2}\right)} \right] \left(\frac{\delta_1}{\delta_2}\right)^{\delta_1/2} (F^{(\delta_1/2)-1})\left(1 + \frac{\delta_1 F}{\delta_2}\right)^{-(\delta_1+\delta_2)/2},$$

$$0 \leq F \leq \infty. \quad (15.20)$$

The only important thing for us to notice about this formidable expression is that an F distribution has the two parameters, δ_1 and δ_2. Density curves for a few selected F distributions are shown in Fig. 15.4.

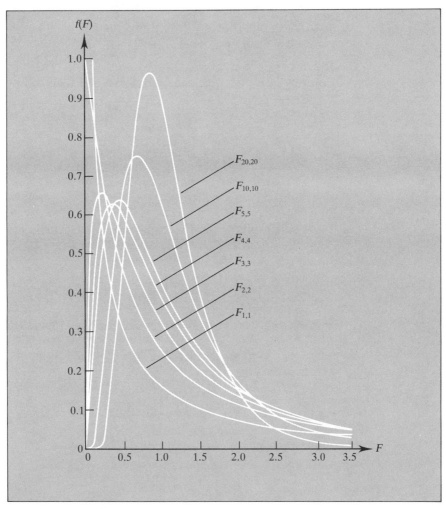

FIGURE 15.4 A few selected F density functions.

Some of the important properties of F distributions are enumerated below.

1. Being a ratio of two squared quantities, an F variable ranges in value from 0 to ∞.

2. There is an F distribution for each pair of positive integers, δ_1 and δ_2.

3. The mean and variance of F_{δ_1, δ_2}, respectively, are

$$E(F) = \frac{\delta_2}{\delta_2 - 2}, \qquad \text{for } \delta_2 > 2; \qquad (15.21)$$

$$V(F) = \frac{2\delta_2^2(\delta_1 + \delta_2 - 2)}{\delta_1(\delta_2 - 2)^2(\delta_2 - 4)}, \qquad \text{for } \delta_2 > 4. \qquad (15.22)$$

These equations imply that an F variable has no mean when $\delta_2 \leq 2$ and that it has no variance when $\delta_2 \leq 4$.

4. Like the chi-square distribution, an F distribution is positively skewed; but its skewness decreases with increases in δ_1 and δ_2.

5. If X if F_{δ_1, δ_2}, then $Y = 1/X$ is basically F_{δ_2, δ_1}. This is the *reciprocal property* of F distributions, and it can be expressed exactly as

$$F_{(1-\alpha); \delta_1, \delta_2} = \frac{1}{F_{\alpha; \delta_2, \delta_1}}, \qquad (15.23)$$

where both α and $1 - \alpha$ stand for lower-tail percentage points of an F distribution, analogous to z_α or $z_{1-\alpha}$ for the normal distribution.

Percentage points for the right-tail of several F distributions at 10%, 5%, 2%, 1% and 0.5% levels are given in Table IX of Appendix C. When X is, say, $F_{10,7}$, then

$$P(X > 3.64) = P(F_{10,7} > 3.64) = 0.05.$$

To say that $P(F_{10,7} > 3.64) = 0.05$ is the same as to say that

$$P(0 \leq X \leq 3.64) = P(0 \leq F_{10,7} \leq 3.64)$$
$$= 1 - 0.05 = 0.95,$$

and $F_{.95; 10.7} = 3.64$. See the graphic illustration of this relationship in Figure 15.5.

Similarly,

$$P(F_{10,7} > 6.62) = 0.01$$

and

$$P(0 \leq F_{10,7} \leq 6.62) = 0.99.$$

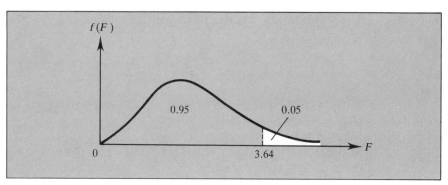

FIGURE 15.5 Upper-tail probability of $F_{10,7}$.

We can also use Table IX to find the left-tail percentage points of F distributions by following the reciprocal property as defined by (15.23). For example, suppose X is $F_{15,10}$; we may let Y be the $F_{10,15}$. From Table IX we find that

$$P(Y > 2.54) = P(F_{10,15} > 2.54) = 0.05.$$

Then, by reciprocal property,

$$P\!\left(\frac{1}{Y} \leq \frac{1}{2.54}\right) = 0.05.$$

Since $1/Y$ has the same distribution as X, we have then

$$P\!\left(X \leq \frac{1}{2.54}\right) \doteq P(F_{15,10} \leq 0.394)$$

$$= 0.05.$$

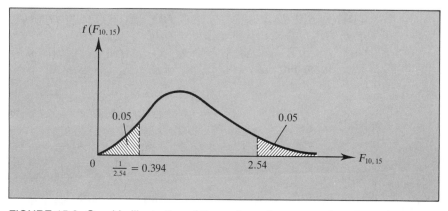

FIGURE 15.6 Graphic illustration of the reciprocal property of an F distribution.

The same result can also be obtained by using (15.23). Namely,

$$F_{.05;15,10} = \frac{1}{F_{.95;10,15}}$$

$$= \frac{1}{2.54} \doteq 0.394,$$

which says that $P(F_{15,10} \leq 0.394) = 0.05$. See the graphic illustration of this example in Figure 15.6.

15.8 INFERENCES ABOUT TWO POPULATION VARIANCES USING F DISTRIBUTIONS

Very often we are called upon to compare two population variances to see whether they are the same or different. Two different makes of auto tires, for example, may have the same mean durability, they should also have the same degree of dispersion, measured by variances, if they are to be considered comparable in quality.

The central core of the analysis here is to reach a conclusion that can be reached about the equality of two population variances on the basis of sample variances. For this task, as usual, we need to know the sampling distributions of S_1^2 and S_2^2. To begin with, we conceive the sample space as consisting of all the ways both samples, one selected from each of the two populations, could come out, so that each sample point in the sample space has a possible outcome for the first sample and also a possible outcome for the second sample. If we calculate both S_1^2 and S_2^2 for each sample point in the sample space, we must be able to obtain *some* sampling distribution for each of these two statistics. However, from a mathematical point of view, it is much more convenient to work with the ratio S_1^2/S_2^2 than to work with the two statistics separately. This is because the said ratio is one of two chi-square distributions and, thus, its distribution qualifies as an F distribution, as stated in the theorem below.

THEOREM 15.4 SAMPLING DISTRIBUTION OF $(S_1^2/\sigma_1^2)/(S_2^2/\sigma_2^2)$
If an SRS of size n_1 is drawn from one normally distributed population with σ_1^2 and an SRS of size n_2 is drawn from another normally distributed population with σ_2^2, and if the two samples are independent, then the static

$$F = \frac{S_1^2/\sigma_1^2}{S_2^2/\sigma_2^2} = \left(\frac{S_1^2}{S_2^2}\right)\left(\frac{\sigma_2^2}{\sigma_1^2}\right) \tag{15.24}$$

has the F distribution with $\delta_1 = n_1 - 1$ and $\delta_2 = n_2 - 1$.

This theorem is quite general, since its application does not require equality between the two population variances.

At this point, it is helpful to gain an intuitive understanding of (15.24). Since S_1^2 tends to equal σ_1^2, the ratio S_1^2/σ_1^2 tends to equal 1. Since S_2^2 tends to σ_2^2, the ratio S_2^2/σ_2^2 tends to 1. Hence, the statistic F as defined by (15.24) tends to equal 1. However, owing to random fluctuations in sampling, we would expect $(S_1^2/\sigma_1^2)/(S_2^2/\sigma_2^2)$ to be a little above or below 1 most of the time and to be substantially above or below 1 some of the time. Finding the probabilities of various extents of departure of this statistic from 1 is the main task of conducting inferences about equality between two population variances. These probabilities are found by using F distributions.

Before proceeding to the application of Theorem 15.4, let us make a few practical observations about conducting inferences on equality between two population variances. First of all, because of the way Theorem 15.4 is formulated, it is most convenient to state hypotheses in the form of a ratio, σ_1^2/σ_2^2. In testing about population variances, irrespective of the form of H_1, H_0 always states that σ_1^2 is equal to σ_2^2. Under the assumption that H_0 is true, then the right-hand side of (15.24) is reduced to S_1^2/S_2^2. This simplified ratio can then be used to test hypotheses as well as construct confidence limits for σ_1^2/σ_2^2.

Secondly, inasmuch as n_1 and n_2 are arbitrary designations, merely used to differentiate one sample from the other, the order of listing or of sampling is entirely immaterial to the analysis. For convenience, it is customary to designate the sample with larger variance as n_1, since then the ratio S_1^2/S_2^2 will necessarily be greater than 1 and values of $F \geq 1$ can readily be found in the F-table.

Finally, the common practice of setting $S_1^2/S_2^2 \geq 1$ also makes our life easier in hypothesis testing on the ratio of σ_1^2/σ_2^2 because, in this case, more often than not the test is usually of the upper-tail variety; that is, we often test H_0: $\sigma_1^2/\sigma_2^2 \leq 1$ against H_1: $\sigma_1^2/\sigma_2^2 > 1$. For this type of test, if S_1^2 is smaller than S_2^2, there is no need to continue the test because the test statistic S_1^2/S_2^2 would always be less than 1 and H_0 could never be rejected. In contrast, if this test statistic is greater than 1, then we must resolve the question whether it is significantly greater than the critical value of F at a given level of significance before a conclusion can be reached.

As an illustration of hypothesis testing, let us use the example presented in Section 5.6 of two makes of new machine, X and Y, that are designed to produce the same product. We were interested in Section 5.6 in the speeds per hour of the two makes of machine in producing the outputs. Data and results obtained before are now restated below:

$$n_X = n_Y = 10;$$

$$\bar{x} = 40.3 \text{ units}, \qquad \bar{y} = 40.8 \text{ units};$$

$$s_X^2 = 18.23, \qquad s_Y^2 = 135.11.$$

These data reveal, as can be easily verified, that the difference in mean speeds of the two makes of machines is not statistically significant. However, we may ask whether the sample variances indicate that there is a significant difference between the two population variances. To answer this question by testing, we may first formulate the hypotheses as

$$H_0: \sigma_Y^2/\sigma_X^2 \leqslant 1; \qquad H_1: \sigma_Y^2/\sigma_X^2 > 1.$$

Since $s_Y^2 > s_X^2$, the former is designated as the numerator and it becomes s_1^2. Furthermore, for this set of data, we have $\delta_1 = 10 - 1 = 9$ and $\delta_2 = 10 - 1 = 9$. Thus, the test statistic becomes

$$F_{9,9} = \frac{s_1^2}{s_2^2} = \frac{135.11}{18.23} \doteq 7.41.$$

This computed F-value leads us to reject H_0 at $\alpha = 0.05$ as well as at $\alpha = 0.01$. We reach this conclusion because from Table IX, we find $P(F_{9,9} > 3.18) = 0.05$ and $P(F_{9,9} > 5.35) = 0.01$. The computed F value is clearly greater than either of these critical F values.

Let us turn our attention now to the construction of an interval estimate for the ratio of two population variances with $1 - \alpha$. Evidently, we need an F value that has only $(\alpha/2)100\%$ of all values of F_{δ_1,δ_2} below it. This value is identified as the F value above which there are $(1 - \alpha/2)100\%$ of the F values. Of course, we also need an F value that has only $(\alpha/2)100\%$ of all values of F_{δ_1,δ_2} above it. This F value is usually the F value above which there are $(\alpha/2)100\%$ of the F values.

The general formulas for the computation of the confidence limits for σ_1^2/σ_2^2, given $1 - \alpha$, are

$$L = \left(\frac{1}{F_{\alpha/2;\delta_1,\delta_2}}\right)\left(\frac{S_1^2}{S_2^2}\right); \qquad (15.25a)$$

$$U = (F_{\alpha/2;\delta_2,\delta_1})\left(\frac{S_1^2}{S_2^2}\right). \qquad (15.25b)$$

It seems strange in these expressions that $F_{1-\alpha/2;\delta_1,\delta_2}$ does not appear in either. A moment's reflection, however, will convince you that such an F value is actually incorporated in the above expression—in disguise. If you still have doubt, just recall the fact that $F_{1-\alpha/2;\delta_1,\delta_2} = 1/(F_{\alpha/2;\delta_2,\delta_1})$. From this, we see that the reciprocal of the ratio on the right-hand side is equal to $F_{\alpha/2;\delta_2,\delta_1}$. Thus, in the derivation of (15.25b), the entire formula is inverted prior to its final form, thereby causing $F_{1-\alpha/2;\delta_1,\delta_2}$ to be "hidden" in its inverse, $F_{\alpha/2;\delta_2,\delta_1}$.

Another observation regarding (15.25b) is also of importance. That is, the reversal of δ_1 and δ_2 in obtaining the F-probabilities does not imply that we are dealing with two different distributions. However, the critical values of F needed to construct the confidence limits for σ_1^2/σ_2^2 must have the same number of degrees of freedom in the numerator as well as in the denominator.

Let us proceed to construct a 99% confidence interval for σ_Y^2/σ_X^2

with the machine data evaluated before. Here, we have

$$L = \left(\frac{1}{F_{.005;9,9}}\right)\left(\frac{s_1^2}{s_2^2}\right)$$
$$= (0.153)(7.41) \doteq 1.13;$$

$$U = (F_{.005;9,9})\left(\frac{s_1^2}{s_2^2}\right)$$
$$= (6.54)(7.41) \doteq 48.46.$$

With these results, we can write

$$1.13 \leqslant \sigma_Y^2/\sigma_X^2 \leqslant 48.46.$$

This interval does not include 1. So we reach the same conclusion as before in testing. The variance of speeds in producing outputs by machine Y is significantly greater than that by machine X. We have sufficient evidence to conclude that machine X is superior to Y so far as deviations in their speeds are concerned.

15.9 A NOTE ON THE HISTORY AND RELATIONSHIPS AMONG t, χ^2, AND F DISTRIBUTIONS

If you are a careful reader, you will have detected the fact that in this chapter we have deviated from our attempt to standardize statistical symbolism. For example, t is a statistic, yet we have used this lower-case letter for the variable as well as the individual values of the variable. We have denoted the statistic chi-square by the Greek letter χ with a superscript 2 attached to it; but, in general, we have reserved Greek letters to denote population parameters. Finally, we have used the capital letter F to stand for the variable S_1^2/S_2^2 as well as the realized values of the variable. We have done so for two related reasons. The first is that these notations are almost universally employed in all statistical literature. Second, these three notations were first introduced by the statisticians who discovered these three distributions and, out of respect, we continue to use them without any change.

In conducting inferences about population means when σ is unknown, it seems appropriate and necessary to make due allowance for the fact that the standard error of the mean is computed as $S/\sqrt{n}$, which is a statistic and is subject to sampling error. The method of making this technical allowance was introduced in 1908 by William Sealy Gosset (1876–1937), a research statistician for a famous Irish brewery—Guinness. Guinness did not then allow publication of research done by its staff. Gosset was able to obtain the relaxation of this rule only on condition that he used a pen name and the pseudonym he used was "Student." Thus, the name of "Student's t distribution" or simply the "t distribution" has been used ever since. Gosset (also spelled as Gossett by some authors) is little known today, but the name "Student" is one of the most celebrated in the history of statistics.

Chi-square distributions were first invented in 1876 by F. R. Helment (1843–1917), a German physicist. They were invented independently in 1900 by an English statistician Karl Pearson (1857–1936). Both happened to denote the sum of a set of squared independent standard normal variables by χ^2. Pearson has been called the "father of statistics" because he was the first, and perhaps the greatest, of the giants to whom statistics is indebted for virtually all the methods for large-sample theory. It is doubtful that a single year passed between 1890 and his death at the age of 79 in 1936, without some significant contribution to modern statistical theory emerging from his inventive and prolific mind.

As we have already noted, had the ratio S_1^2/S_2^2 been greater than 1, we would have faced the question whether the excess was more than could be attributed to chance variation alone. The answer to this question is given by the discovery of the F ratio, so named for honoring Sir Ronald A. Fisher. Just as Pearson was the man who perfected large-sample theory, Fisher, and Gosset to a lesser degree, were responsible for the full development of small-sample theory. With Fisher also began in 1935 the important and useful methods for the design of experiments, the theory of multivariate association analysis, and the analysis of variance. It is of great interest that, among the contributions to statistical methods made in the first half of the 20th century made by hundreds of original minds, at least half of them can be attributed to Fisher. Furthermore, Fisher is not only a giant in the history of statistics, but also one of the great figures in the history of scientific methods in general.

You may have noticed too that the three probability models introduced in this chapter are somehow related. As a matter of fact, as you may recall from Section 15.1, we have already pointed out that these three models are members of the same family. First t, χ^2, and F distributions are all sampling distributions derived from independent standard normal variables. Second, all of them are defined in terms of numbers of degrees of freedom. Finally, all three distributions can be defined in terms of each other as shown by the following simple mathematical argument.

The t statistic, as defined by (15.1), can be thought of as a ratio of a standard normal variable Z to the square root of the variable χ_δ^2/δ. That is

$$t = \frac{Z}{\sqrt{\chi_\delta^2/\delta}}.$$

To verify that this new expression for t is identical with (15.1), we first note that

$$t = \frac{\bar{X} - \mu}{\sqrt{S^2/n}} = \frac{(\bar{X} - \mu)/\sigma}{\sqrt{S^2/n\sigma^2}} = \frac{(\bar{X} - \mu)/(\sigma/\sqrt{n})}{\sqrt{S^2/\sigma^2}}.$$

The numerator of this expression is clearly a standard normal variable Z. Next, we know that

$$\frac{(n-1)S^2}{\sigma^2} = \chi^2_\delta, \quad \text{with } \delta = n - 1.$$

Also,

$$\frac{S^2}{\sigma^2} = \frac{\chi^2_{n-1}}{n-1} = \frac{\chi^2_\delta}{\delta}.$$

Hence, it follows that

$$t = \frac{Z}{\sqrt{\chi^2_\delta / \delta}}.$$

The relationship between t and F can easily be established by squaring both sides of this new expression for t. That is,

$$t^2 = \frac{Z^2}{\chi^2_\delta / \delta}.$$

By definition, the numerator of t^2 is χ^2_1. Again by definition, the denominator of t^2 is χ^2_δ with $\delta = n - 1$. Hence, t^2 qualifies as $F_{1,n-1}$. In general,

$$t^2_\delta = F_{1,\delta_2}, \quad \text{for } t^2_\delta, \delta = \delta_2 \text{ attached to } F.$$

Finally, we know that F is related to χ^2 directly, since F can be considered as a ratio of two independent χ^2 variables. Or, in symbols,

$$F = \frac{\chi^2_{\delta_1} / \delta_1}{\chi^2_{\delta_2} / \delta_2},$$

which clearly satisfies the requirement that

$$F = \frac{S^2_1}{S^2_2} = \frac{S^2_1 / \sigma^2_1}{S^2_2 / \sigma^2_2} = \frac{\chi^2_{\delta_1} / \delta_1}{\chi^2_{\delta_2} / \delta_2}.$$

Note that under the assumption that $\sigma^2_1 = \sigma^2_2$ in the above derivation for forming chi-square distributions, we automatically specify the null hypothesis that $\sigma^2_1 / \sigma^2_2 = 1$ in comparing the equality between two population variances.

In concluding this chapter, you should appreciate that t, χ^2, and F are all amazingly versatile statistics. In addition to their uses for the inferences covered by this chapter, as the remaining portion of this text will testify, they can be applied to many an inferential situation. As we proceed to the next chapter, for example, F tests are employed exclusively for all models of the "analysis of variance".

GLOSSARY OF FORMULAS

(15.1) $t_\delta = \dfrac{X_0}{\sqrt{\dfrac{1}{\delta}(X_1^2 + X_2^2 + \cdots + X_\delta^2)}};$

(15.2) $f(t) = \left(\dfrac{1}{\sqrt{\delta\pi}}\right)\left[\dfrac{\Gamma\left(\dfrac{\delta+1}{2}\right)}{\Gamma\left(\dfrac{\delta}{2}\right)}\right]\left(1 + \dfrac{t^2}{\delta}\right)^{-(\delta+1)/2}, \quad -\infty \leqslant t \leqslant \infty.$

A t variable is defined by (15.1) as a ratio of an $n(0, 1)$ to the square root of the mean of δ squared independent standard normal variables. Its density function, given by (15.2), shows that a t-distribution is completely defined by a single parameter δ—the number of degrees of freedom.

(15.3) $E(t) = 0, \quad$ for $\delta > 1;$

(15.4) $V(t) = \dfrac{\delta}{\delta - 2}, \quad$ for $\delta > 2.$

These two equations provide respectively the mean and variance for a t variable. Note that a t distribution has no mean if $\delta = 1$ and it has no variance if $\delta \leqslant 2$.

(15.5) $t_\delta = \dfrac{\bar{X} - \mu}{S_{\bar{X}}}.$

If an SRS is drawn from a normally distributed population, then this ratio is distributed as t with $\delta = n - 1$. This statistic can be used to test hypotheses about μ or to construct confidence limits for μ when σ is unknown and n is small.

(15.6) $L, U = \bar{X} \mp t_{\alpha/2}S_{\bar{X}}.$

This equation is employed to construct confidence limits for μ. Here, the critical t values depend upon $\delta = n - 1$ and $1 - \alpha$.

(15.7) $t_\delta = \dfrac{\Delta\bar{X} - \Delta\mu}{S_{\Delta\bar{X}}}$

(15.8) $S_{\Delta\bar{X}} = S_w\sqrt{\dfrac{n_1 + n_2}{n_1 n_2}}$

(15.9) $S_w = \sqrt{\dfrac{(n_1 - 1)S_1^2 + (n_2 - 1)S_2^2}{n_1 + n_2 - 2}}.$

This t ratio (15.17) is used as the test statistic for comparing two population means. Use of this test statistic requires that (1) the two samples are independent, (2) the parent populations are normally distributed with identical variances. Furthermore, for this ratio, $\delta = n_1 + n_2 - 2$. The unbiased estimator for the standard error of $\Delta\bar{X}$ is given by (15.8), where S_w is a pooled or weighted estimator for the common population standard deviation. It is computed by (15.9).

(15.10) $L, U = \Delta\bar{X} \mp t_{\alpha/2}S_{\Delta\bar{X}}$.

The confidence limits for $\Delta\mu$ under the two conditions stated immediately above are constructed using this expression. It is important to note that for this expression, too, $t_{\alpha/2}$ is based on $\delta = n_1 + n_2 - 1$.

(15.11) $t_\delta = \dfrac{\bar{D} - \mu_D}{S_{\bar{D}}}$.

This t ratio with $\delta = n - 1$ is employed to compare two population means when n_1 and n_1 are dependent samples. Use of this ratio requires that the observed differences d_i—the values of the variable D—are the values of an SRS drawn from a population of differences that is normally distributed with mean μ_D and standard deviation σ_D.

(15.12) $\chi^2_\delta = X_1^2 + X_2^2 + \cdots + X_\delta^2$;

(15.13) $f(\chi^2) = \dfrac{[(\chi^2)^{\delta/(2-1)}]e^{-(\chi^2/2)}}{(2^{\delta/2})\left[\Gamma\left(\dfrac{\delta}{2}\right)\right]}$, $\qquad 0 \leqslant \chi^2 \leqslant \infty$.

Equation (15.12) defines a χ^2 variable as the sum of δ squared independent standard normal variables. Its density function is given by (15.13). Again, we see that a χ^2 distribution is completely defined by the single parameter δ.

(15.14) $E(\chi^2_\delta) = \mu = \delta$;

(15.15) $V(\chi^2_\delta) = \sigma^2 = 2\delta$.

The mean of a chi-square variable is simply its number of degrees of freedom as shown by (15.14). The variance of a chi-square variable is twice its mean, as (15.15) indicates.

(15.16) $\chi^2_\delta = \dfrac{(n-1)S^2}{\sigma^2}$.

This χ^2 variable has $\delta = n - 1$. It is derived from the fact that if an SRS is drawn from a normally distributed population, $S^2 = \chi^2_\delta(\sigma^2/\delta)$. It is used to conduct inferences about σ^2.

(15.17) $L = \dfrac{(n-1)S^2}{\chi^2_{n-1;1-\alpha/2}}$;

$U = \dfrac{(n-1)S^2}{\chi^2_{n-1;\alpha/2}}$.

The two-sided confidence interval for σ^2 with $1 - \alpha$ has its lower and upper confidence limits defined by these expressions. You may be reminded that in these expressions the larger χ^2-value is used for L and the smaller χ^2-value for U, because χ^2 and σ^2 are inversely related.

$$(15.18) \quad U = \frac{(n-1)S^2}{\chi^2_{n-1;\alpha}}.$$

In constructing a left-side confidence interval for σ^2 of the form $0 \le \sigma^2 \le U$, we use this expression to obtain the upper confidence limit U. For this expression, χ^2_δ is the value that has $1 - \alpha$ of the area of its density curve to the right of it.

$$(15.19) \quad F = \frac{(X_1^2 + X_2^2 + \cdots + X_{\delta_1}^2)/\delta_1}{(Y_1^2 + Y_2^2 + \cdots + Y_{\delta_2}^2)/\delta_2};$$

$$(15.20) \quad f(F) = \left[\frac{\Gamma\left(\frac{\delta_1 + \delta_2}{2}\right)}{\Gamma\left(\frac{\delta_1}{2}\right)\Gamma\left(\frac{\delta_2}{2}\right)}\right]\left(\frac{\delta_1}{\delta_2}\right)^{\delta_1/2}(F^{(\delta_1/2)-1})\left(1 + \frac{\delta_1 F}{\delta_2}\right)^{-(\delta_1+\delta_2)/2},$$

$$0 \le F \le \infty.$$

If X_i, $i = 1, 2, 3, \ldots, \delta_1$, and Y_i, $i = 1, 2, 3, \ldots, \delta_2$, are all independent standard normal variables, the F variable with δ_1 and δ_2 is defined by (15.19). Note that F can also be thought as a ratio of two independent χ^2 variables. From the density function of F, (15.20), we see that an F distribution is completely defined by any pair of positive integers, δ_1 and δ_2.

$$(15.21) \quad E(F) = \frac{\delta_2}{\delta_2 - 2}, \quad \text{for } \delta_2 > 2;$$

$$(15.22) \quad V(F) = \frac{2\delta_2^2(\delta_1 + \delta_2 - 2)}{\delta_1(\delta_2 - 2)^2(\delta_2 - 4)}, \quad \text{for } \delta_2 > 4.$$

The mean (15.21) and the variance (15.22) of an F distribution are defined here. Note that both equations contain only the numbers of degrees of freedom that define an F variable. Also note that for $\delta_2 \le 2$, F possesses no mean and that for $\delta \le 4$, F possesses no variance.

$$(15.23) \quad F_{(1-\alpha);\delta_1,\delta_2} = \frac{1}{F_{\alpha;\delta_2,\delta_1}}.$$

This equation is the formal statement of the reciprocal property of F distributions. It says that if X is F_{δ_1,δ_2}, then $Y = 1/X$ is basically F_{δ_2,δ_1}. Be careful to observe that the reverse of δ_1 and δ_2 here does not imply that we are dealing with two different F distributions. This property simply enables us to obtain the lower-tail probability of any F_{δ_1,δ_2}.

(15.24) $F = \left(\dfrac{S_1^2}{S_2^2}\right)\left(\dfrac{\sigma_2^2}{\sigma_1^2}\right).$

For this F ratio, $\delta_1 = n_1 - 1$ and $\delta_2 = n_2 - 1$. Given that n_1 and n_2 are independent random samples drawn from normally distributed populations, F defined here can be used to conduct inferences with respect to the equality of two population variances. When we assume $\sigma_1^2 = \sigma_2^2$, then this F is reduced to S_1^2/S_2^2, which can be used as the test statistic in evaluating whether σ_1^2 is equal to σ_2^2. Furthermore, convention is to use the larger sample variance as S_1^2 in order to make it more convenient and easier to perform a test.

(15.25a) $L = \left(\dfrac{1}{F_{\alpha/2;\delta_1,\delta_2}}\right)\left(\dfrac{S_1^2}{S_2^2}\right);$

(15.25b) $U = (F_{\alpha/2;\delta_2,\delta_1})\left(\dfrac{S_1^2}{S_2^2}\right).$

These formulas are used to compute the lower and upper confidence limits for σ_1^2/σ_2^2 assumed to be 1.

REVIEW QUESTIONS

15.1 What is the difference between large-sample and small-sample theory?

15.2 Why do we refer to small-sample theory as exact-sample theory?

15.3 Provide at least two different explanations for the notion of "number of degrees of freedom".

15.4 Every statistic has a number of degrees of freedom, δ. How is δ determined for each statistic?

15.5 How is a "t variable" defined?

15.6 What are the important properties of t distributions?

15.7 If δ is a relatively large integer, say, greater than 30, then a t distribution can be approximated by the standard normal distribution. Why?

15.8 If certain conditions, or assumptions, are met, what distribution does the quotient $(\bar{X} - \mu)/S_{\bar{X}}$ have? What are the assumptions that must be met?

15.9 If certain assumptions are met, what distribution does the ratio $(\Delta\bar{X} - \Delta\mu)/S_{\Delta\bar{X}}$ have? What are the assumptions that must be met? How do you go about computing $S_{\Delta\bar{X}}$ in this case?

15.10 How do we define two dependent samples? Give illustrations of dependent samples.

15.11 If certain assumptions are met, what distribution does the statistic $(\bar{D} - \mu_D)/S_{\bar{D}}$ have? What are the conditions that must be met? What formula is used for $S_{\bar{D}}$?

15.12 How is the statistic χ^2 defined?

15.13 What are the important properties of χ^2 distributions?

15.14 Under what condition can we use normal probabilities to approximate the χ^2 probabilities?

15.15 If certain assumptions are met, what distribution does the quantity $(n - 1)S^2/\sigma^2$ have? What are the assumptions that must be met?

15.16 How is an F variable defined?

15.17 What are the important properties of F distributions?

15.18 What is the reciprocal property of F distributions? What is the main function of this property? Does the reverse of δ_1 and δ_2 in the application of this property mean that we are concerned with two different F distributions? Explain why or why not.

15.19 If certain assumptions are met, what distribution does the statistic $(S_1^2/\sigma_1^2)/(S_2^2/\sigma_2^2)$ have? What are the assumptions that must be met? Under what condition can this ratio be reduced to S_1^2/S_2^2?

15.20 By using the ratio S_1^2/S_2^2 in the evaluation of equality between two population variances, we often use the larger sample variance in the numerator. Why can we do this? What is the reason for doing this?

15.21 Why do we consider the t, χ^2, and F distributions as the members of the same family of distributions?

PROBLEMS

15.1 The observations in a sample can be used to decide whether the population from which they are drawn is approximately normal or definitely nonnormal. A simple method is graphing the data on a one-dimensional graph (by placing a dot on the horizontal axis for each observation) and then judging whether the visual pattern in the dots is approximately normal or definitely nonnormal. The first step is acquiring some understanding of how observations that are exactly normally distributed would graph, and that is the purpose of Problem 15.1(a).
   a. Using the normal table, find the nine values of z_0 for which $P(Z < z_0) = 0.1, 0.2, \ldots, 0.9$. Graph these nine values on a one-dimensional graph.
   b. Graph the following nine sample observations on a one-dimensional graph: 17, 18, 19, 21, 30, 40, 42, 43, 44. Is the visual pattern in the dots

approximately normal or definitely nonnormal? Why? (Hint: Look at the tails. If either tail has a heavy concentration of observations or an extreme outlier, the distribution is definitely nonnormal.)

c. Repeat part (b) for the following sample data: -10, 31, 50, 59, 64, 68, 71, 73, and 73. (Hint: Put two dots side-by-side near 73, so that each observation of 73 appears on the graph.)

d. Repeat part (b) for the following sample data: 0.06, 0.07, 0.07, 0.08, 0.09, 0.17, 0.24, 0.48, and 0.99.

e. Repeat part (b) for the following sample data: -11.9, -7.9, -5.1, -2.2, 0.1, 2.4, 4.9, 8.0, and 12.9.

15.2 a. Repeat Problem 15.1(a) for the four values of z_0 for which

$$P(Z < z_0) = 0.2, 0.4, 0.6, \text{ and } 0.8.$$

b. Repeat Problem 15.1(a) for the nineteen values of z_0 for which

$$P(Z < z_0) = 0.5, 0.10, \ldots, 0.95.$$

c. Using your answers to Problems 15.1(a), 15.2(a), and 15.2(b), graph the following sample data and discuss whether the visual pattern is approximately normal or definitely nonnormal: 91, 93, 95, and 98. (See the hint in Problem 15.1(b).)

d. Repeat part (c) for the following sample data: 91, 93, 95, and 118.

e. Repeat part (c) for the following sample data: 4, 16, 36, 64, 114, 148, 223, 298, 372, 455, 606, 750, 898, 1,074, 1,355, 1,642, 2,149, 2,706, and 3,841.

f. Repeat part (c) for the following sample data: 60, 720, 1,120, 1,420, 1,980, 2,280, 2,680, and 3,340. (No: one observation has not been forgotten; this sample has only eight observations.)

15.3 A serious limitation to the technique of Problem 15.1(a) is that it does not allow for sampling error. As an aid in remedying this, the RAND Corporation's table of 100,000 standard normal deviates (p. 75, line 3743, column 6, and the 26 succeeding table entries) provides the following z values, which would occur in repeatedly sampling from the standard normal distribution: Sample 1: -0.138, 0.047, 0.101, 0.529, 0.599, -0.794, -0.299, -0.919, and 1.663; Sample 2: 1.540, 0.831, 0.867, -0.811, 0.043, -1.782, -0.609, -0.205, and -0.115; Sample 3: -1.086, -2.067, 0.648, -1.697, 0.131, 0.474, 0.741, 1.482, and 0.090.

a. Graph each of these (simulated) samples from the standard normal distribution on a separate one-dimensional graph. Briefly, verbally compare them with one another and with the "perfectly normal" graph of Problem 15.1(a).

b. Review your answers to Problem 15.1(b) through 15.1(e) to see whether you would change any answers in the light of the graphs in Problem 15.3(a).

15.4 A serious limitation to the technique of Problems 15.2(a) and 15.2(b) is that the technique does not allow for sampling error. As an aid in remedying this, the RAND Corporation's table of 100,000 standard normal deviates (pp. 75–76, line 3746, column 3, and the 68 succeeding table entries) provides the z values in Problems 15.4(a) and 15.4(b) that would occur in repeatedly sampling from the standard normal distribution.

a. Sample 1: -0.358, -0.281, 0.736, and 1.473; Sample 2: 0.372, -0.292, -0.413, and -2.344; Sample 3: 0.603, -1.190, 0.851, and -1.405. Graph each of these (simulated) samples from the standard normal distribution on a separate one-dimensional graph. Briefly, verbally compare them with one another and with the "perfectly normal" graph of Problem 15.2(a).

b. Sample 1: 0.490, −0.771, −0.380, −0.569, 0.593, −0.553, −0.473, 1.021, −0.214, 0.281, −0.596, 0.465, 0.651, −1.547, −0.595, 0.444, −0.077, −0.802, and 1.281; Sample 2: −1.007, 0.840, −0.709, 0.189, 0.860, 0.638, −0.850, −0.404, −0.995, 0.345, 1.635, −0.423, −0.798, 2.587, −1.696, 0.093, 0.019, −1.371, and −0.617; Sample 3: 0.060, 1.069, −0.348, 0.011, 1.945, −0.484, −0.935, 2.257, −1.103, 1.222, −0.154, −1.704, −1.922, −1.799, −0.022, −1.103, 0.829, 1.161, and 2.074. Graph each of these (simulated) samples from the standard normal distribution on a separate one-dimensional graph. Briefly, verbally compare them with one another and with the "perfectly normal" graph of Problem 15.2(b).

c. Using all of your graphs for sampling from a distribution known to be the standard normal (Problems 15.1(a), 15.2(a), 15.2(b), 15.3(a), 15.4(a), and 15.4(b)), review your answers to Problems 15.2(c) through 15.2(f) to see whether you would change any answers in the light of your graphs based on the standard normal distribution.

15.5 The producer of a certain flashlight dry-cell battery claims that its output has a mean life of 750 minutes. A random sample of 15 such batteries has been tested, yielding a sample mean of 745 minutes and a sample standard deviation of 24 minutes. Test the null hypothesis that $\mu \geq 750$ against the alternative hypothesis that $\mu < 750$ at $\alpha = 0.01$.

15.6 The diameters of a random sample of 10 spheres have a mean of 4.08 inches and a standard deviation of 0.05 inch. Are these results consistent with the fact that the manufacturing process is adjusted to produce diameters with $\mu = 4$ inches at $\alpha = 0.05$?

15.7 What is the 95% confidence interval for μ with the data in the previous problem? Is $\mu = 4$ in the confidence interval? Should it be the confidence interval, in view of the preceding problem's results? Explain your answer.

15.8 A meat cannery has just installed a new filling machine. A random sample of 20 filled cans yields a mean weight of 16.05 ounces with a standard deviation of 1.5 ounces.

a. What is the 95% interval estimate for the true mean weight?

b. If the net content of each can is supposed to be 16 ounces, is the machine properly adjusted? Explain.

15.9 Construct a 99% confidence interval for the true mean with data in the preceding problem.

15.10 Repeat Problems 15.8 and 15.9 for a standard deviation of 0.08 ounce with the data (a) of Problem 15.1(b) and (b) of Problem 15.2(f).

15.11 Assuming N is very large, find the 95% confidence interval for μ for the sample data (a) of Problem 15.1(b) and (b) of Problem 15.1(e).

15.12 Assuming N is very large, find the 99% confidence interval for μ for the sample data (a) of Problem 15.2(e) and (b) of Problem 15.2(f).

15.13 Two working designs are under consideration for adoption in a plant. A time-and-motion study shows that 12 randomly selected workers using design A have a mean assembly time of 300 seconds with a standard deviation of 12 seconds and that 15 randomly selected workers using design B have a mean assembly time of 335 seconds with a standard deviation of 15 seconds. Test the null hypothesis that $\mu_A \geq \mu_B$ at $\alpha = 0.01$.

15.14 A labor union claims that a random sample of 30 employees in manufacturing industries in a certain city revealed a mean hourly wage rate of $6.25 and a standard deviation of $0.75. However, an employers' association claims that its own random sample of 28 employees showed that they earn $6.97 per hour with a standard deviation of $0.68. Are these results consistent with the hypothesis that $\mu_1 = \mu_2$ at $\alpha = 0.01$?

15.15 Two types of wheat are being compared for yields. A 25-acre plot is planted with each kind of wheat. The yield from each acre is considered to be one randomly selected observation. The results are as follows: variety A, $\bar{x}_1 = 35.8$ bushels per acre, $s_1 = 6$; variety B, $\bar{x}_2 = 32.9$ bushels per acre, $s_2 = 10$. Test H_0: $\Delta\mu = 0$ against H_1: $\Delta\mu \neq 0$ at $\alpha = 0.05$. Comment on whether the observations are really randomly selected and on what effect that has on your hypothesis test.

15.16 Construct a 95% confidence interval for $\Delta\mu$ with the data in the previous problem. Is $\Delta\mu = 0$ within the confidence interval? Should it be, in view of the preceding problem's results? If the observations are not really randomly selected, how should your confidence interval be interpreted?

15.17 To compare the efficiency of standard and electric typewriters, 8 typists are chosen at random and thoroughly familiarized with the operation of both kinds of typewriters. They are then asked to type on each kind of typewriter for 10 minutes. Their speeds, measured as average number of words typed per minute, are observed. The results of this experiment are shown in the last two columns of Table 15.P1.

TABLE 15.P1 Typing Test Results

	Average speed per minute	
Typist	Electric	Standard
1	75	79
2	89	62
3	66	54
4	85	67
5	102	81
6	115	78
7	97	66
8	77	73

Source: Hypothetical.

a. Are the two kinds of typewriters different at $\alpha = 0.01$?
b. Suppose that a big corporation will decide to buy standard typewriters unless the average speed of electric typewriters is 30 words per minute greater with a probability of 0.99. In view of the results obtained in part (a), what would the corporation decide?

15.18 Ten students selected at random earned the following final grades in physics and economics.

Student	1	2	3	4	5	6	7	8	9	10
Physics	66	72	50	81	62	73	55	90	77	85
Economics	75	70	65	88	59	85	60	97	82	90

Source: Hypothetical.

a. Can you conclude that the mean grades in these two subjects are different at $\alpha = 0.05$?
b. Construct a 95% confidence interval for the true mean difference.

15.19 What is the 95% confidence interval for σ^2 for the sample data (a) of Problem 15.1(b), and (b) of Problem 15.1(e).

15.20 What is the 99% confidence interval for σ^2 for the sample data (a) of Problem 15.2(e), and (b) of Problem 15.2(f).

15.21 Using SRS with $n = 3$ from an exactly normal population, find the "0.95 probabilistically reasonable" values for S^2 and for S under each of the following circumstances, where both tails of the sampling distribution of S^2 are ignored and each ignored tail has a probability of 0.025.
a. $\sigma^2 = 1$
b. $\sigma^2 = 500$
c. $\sigma^2 = 0.0025$

15.22 Repeat the preceding problem for $n = 30$ instead of $n = 3$.

15.23 A standard machine produces 1-inch bolts with a variance of 0.0006 inches^2. A random sample of 25 bolts produced by a new machine yields a sample variance of 0.0005 inches^2. The manufacturer is willing to buy the new machine if he can "prove" (using $\alpha = 0.05$) that it produces 1-inch bolts with smaller variance. Test H_0: $\sigma^2_{new} \leq 0.0006$, against H_1: $\sigma^2_{new} > 0.0006$.

15.24 Sixteen randomly selected wires of a certain make were tested for tensile strength and yielded a variance of 140 pounds^2. Is this sample result consistent with the belief that the population variance is equal to at most 125 pounds^2 at $\alpha = 0.05$?

15.25 In the preceding problem, what is the 95% left-side confidence interval for σ^2?

15.26 Diameters of a certain make of steel pipe are known to be approximately normally distributed. A random sample of 10 observations yielded a variance of 0.12 inches^2. In view of this evidence, test the null hypothesis that $\sigma^2 \leq 0.06$ at $\alpha = 0.01$. What is the 99% left-side confidence interval of σ^2?

15.27 Find the 95% confidence interval for σ^2_1/σ^2_2 for the sample data (a) of Problem 15.3(a), using samples 1 and 3; (b) of Problems 15.1(b) and 15.1(e).

15.28 Find the 99% confidence interval for σ^2_1/σ^2_2 for the sample data (a) of Problem 15.4(a), using Sample 3, and Problem 15.4(b), using Sample 3; (b) of Problems 15.2(c) and 15.2(e).

15.29 Using SRS with $n_1 = 3$ and $n_2 = 3$ and getting independent samples from exactly normal populations, find the "0.95 probabilistically reasonable" values for S_1^2/S_2^2 and for S_1/S_2 under each of the following circumstances, where both tails of the sampling distribution of S_1^2/S_2^2 are ignored and each ignored tail has a probability of 0.025.

a. $\sigma_1^2 = \sigma_2^2 = 1$
b. $\sigma_1^2 = \sigma_2^2 = 500$
c. $\sigma_1^2 = 2.25$ and $\sigma_2^2 = 0.0064$.

15.30 Repeat the preceding problem for $n_1 = 21$ and $n_2 = 31$ instead of $n_1 = n_2 = 3$.

15.31 It is known that two brands of tires have an average life of 45,000 miles. However, there may be some difference in the variability of mileage attained by the two brands. An experiment is conducted in which 16 randomly selected tires of each brand are used. The tires are run under similar conditions until they wear out. It is found that the two sample variances are $s^2 = 4{,}500$ miles^2 and $s^2 = 2{,}200$ miles^2. Should the null hypothesis $\sigma_1^2 \leq \sigma_2^2$ be rejected at $\alpha = 0.10$ and at $\alpha = 0.05$?

15.32 In the preceding problem, what is the 90% confidence interval for σ_1^2/σ_2^2? What is the 95% confidence interval?

15.33 Suppose there are two sources of raw materials under consideration. Both sources seem to have similar characteristics, but we are not sure about their respective uniformities. A random sample of 10 lots from source A yields a variance of 328, and a random sample of 11 lots from source B yields a variance of 134. Test H_0: $\sigma_A^2 = \sigma_B^2$ against H_A: $\sigma_A^2 \neq \sigma_B^2$, at $\alpha = 0.05$.

15.34 Would you reach the same conclusion with the data in the preceding exercise for the null hypothesis; $\sigma_A^2 \leq \sigma_B^2$?

Note: It is quite effortless conducting testing in all cases when the required sample statistics are given, as with all the illustrative examples in Chapters 12 and 13, and 15. However, when the required sample statistics have to be computed for the tests from raw data sets, more work is involved. Thus, you are instructed to solve the next two problems by computer.

15.35 To evaluate whether there is any difference between the means of starting wages between male and female MBA graduates in New York City, an SRS with $n_1 = 25$ is selected from the male MBA graduates of all universities and colleges in New York City, and an SRS with $n_2 = 20$ is selected from the female MBA graduates from the same schools for analysis. Sample observations are listed below:

Starting Wages of MBA Graduates in Thousands of Dollars, 1987

Males:	25, 28, 26, 25, 30, 29, 31, 27, 28, 26
	30, 24, 26, 29, 28, 25, 25, 28, 29, 28
	26, 27, 25, 24, 30.
Females:	31, 27, 21, 20, 33, 20, 23, 24, 25, 21,
	27, 20, 28, 29, 30, 21, 22, 23, 32, 35.

Assuming the popoulation variances are identical, and in view of the above data, can we conclude that $\mu_1 = \mu_2$, against $\mu_1 \neq \mu_2$ at $\alpha = 0.10$ and at 0.05?

15.36 The research department of American Chemicals, Inc., has just perfected a gasoline additive called the Booster. It is believed that this additive should increase the mileage of sedan cars by about two miles per gallon of gasoline on the average. To substantiate this belief, the following experiment is conducted. Twenty-five sedan cars of a certain make are selected; there cars are first driven with the Booster added to full tanks of gasoline until the tanks are dry; these cars are then driven under similar conditions without the Booster. Mileage-per-gallon data observed for both cases are as recorded in Table 15.P2 below.

TABLE 15.P2

Car	x_i (With Booster)	y_i (Without Booster)
1	12.25	11.84
2	16.12	13.55
3	17.16	14.49
4	15.00	15.00
5	16.70	14.25
6	14.10	13.95
7	16.84	13.55
8	16.25	14.14
9	14.00	13.06
10	15.22	15.97
11	16.47	15.05
12	19.98	16.45
13	15.19	14.10
14	13.33	13.43
15	17.78	14.24
16	17.25	14.11
17	16.95	13.00
18	18.85	14.21
19	16.99	13.12
20	18.55	14.73
21	14.95	11.22
22	16.77	12.17
23	18.00	14.50
24	17.44	14.27
25	16.50	13.95

In view of data above, what conclusion can the research staff reach by testing H_0: $\mu_D = 2$ against H_1: $\mu_D \neq 2$ at $\alpha = 0.05$ and at 0.01? Could the same conclusion be reached if the hypotheses were stated as H_0: $\mu_D \geq 2$ against H_1: $\mu_D < 2$, or if the hypotheses were formulated as H_0: $\mu_D \leq 2$ against H_1: $\mu_D \geq 2$? Which type of test should be used in this case if the result will be employed for promotional purposes?

16 Experimental Design and the Analysis of Variance

16.1 THE NATURE OF EXPERIMENTAL DESIGN

In 1935 Sir Ronald A. Fisher laid the foundation for the subject that has come to be known by the title of his book *The Design of Experiments*. Since then the theory of experimental design has been considerably developed and extended. Applications of this theory are found today in laboratories and research in natural sciences, engineering, and nearly all branches of social science.

An experiment was defined previously in connection with our discussion on probability theory as a repetitive process that results in any of a number of possible outcomes such that the particular outcome is determined by chance and cannot be predicted *a priori*. This definition implicitly assumed that the conditions of the experiment remained the same from trial to trial. However, in a more general sense, the objective of any experiment is to introduce changes into the experimental conditions to determine the effects of such changes upon the results obtained previously. Changes are thereby introduced into the experiment by changes in experimental conditions, so that the experimenter must determine the effects of such changes in results obtained in different sets of experimental conditions of the experiment.

Experimentation provides what is called experimental data, in contrast to observational data with which we have been mainly concerned up to this point. *Observational data* are represented by observations on the elementary units of a population or of a sample and are not changed or modified by any attempt on the part of an investigator during the course of observation. It is often difficult to assign cause and effect by studying observational data. If one is interested in establishing causal relationships, one should work with *experimental data,* data arising from observations on a universe or a segment thereof that has been "controlled" or modified by varying certain factors in order to determine what effect, if any, the factors have on the data. In other words, experimental data are the results from logically designed experiments that may provide evidence for or against theories of cause and effect.

A number of basic aspects of the theory of experimental design are worth noting at the very beginning. First of all, observations under one set of experimental conditions are called the *experimental unit.* Experimental conditions are usually grouped according to some common criteria, called *factors* or *treatments.* A *treatment* is a combination of conditions in a particular experimental unit. Many experiments are conducted to establish the effect of one or more (independent) variable on a response (the dependent variable). Here, the independent variables are treatments or factors, which are often qualitative in nature, such as different makes of machines, different advertisement channels, different ways of packaging merchandise, and so on. The values of a *response* are supposed to reflect the effects of different treatments. We have already indicated that the purpose of an experiment is to introduce changes in the experimental conditions to discover effects (responses) that such changes bring about. The responses themselves, however, are seldom of importance; we are rather interested in the differences among the effects. Hence, an experiment may also be viewed as a process that contrasts the effects of two or more treatments.

Second, in laboratory sciences, experimentation usually refers to "controlled" experiments in which one factor is varied while all other relevant factors are held "constant." In reality, however, it is often not possible to control any factor exactly except the one whose effect is being investigated. Hence, there always exists *experimental error,* the variation in the response due to the lack of precise control. The experimental error is measured by the variance of observations made under supposedly identical conditions. Experimental errors are of two types, random and systematic. Random errors cannot be eliminated. Systematic errors are due to consistent biases that can and should be avoided. This is done by randomization, as discussed later.

When one conducts "controlled" experiments in the real world, where innumerable forces are working with varying degrees of influence, results will be much more variable. In this case, it is convenient to think of all the variation that cannot be accounted for by the variation in the experimental treatments as experimental error, some of which might have been accounted for if the experiment had been conducted in a laboratory. Hence, real-world experiments tend to inflate experimental error, and they make it more difficult to assess the true effects of experimental factors. This limitation, however, does have the side benefit of enabling one to generalize the results to environments in which the experiment is conducted.

Third, the design of an experiment may assume a relatively simple form in which only one treatment variable is considered, or a quite complicated framework involving a number of factors may be used. In general, however, any experimental design would have as its foundation the four principles of replication, randomization, cross-classification, and experimentation with similar materials. *Replication* refers to the repetition of the same treatment on different experimental units. *Randomization* is the use of a random process to assign experimental units to treatments. *Cross-classification* involves a method of permitting each unit of experimental material to be employed for every treatment under test. The term "experimental material" has a broad interpretation and varies from one experiment to another. In any event, by *similar blocks of experimental materials* we mean that the characteristics of each experimental unit remain approximately constant from one trial to another. These concepts can perhaps be clarified via an example.

Suppose we consider evaluating the productivity in growing soybeans of four different kinds of chemical fertilizer, which we shall designate as F_1, F_2, F_3, and F_4. To do this, we may select four plots of land, say, L_1, L_2, L_3, and L_4, and assign them at random to each of the F_j in the cultivation of soybeans. Here, F_j would represent the treatment variable and L_i, the experimental material in our experiment. Experimental data observed may be given in terms of, say, pounds of soybeans produced. The results of this experiment will not be conclusive for at least three reasons. (1) Differences in yields may be caused by both treatments effects and land effects. When an effect can be attributed to two or more factors and the contribution due to each cannot be determined, we say that the effects have been *confounded*. In other words, with our experiment here, we cannot say for certain whether one fertilizer is more productive than another unless we can also assume the absence of "land effects." (2) The particular batches of fertilizer selected for the experiment may have unique characteristics that distinguish them from the makes they are presumed to represent. Namely, the batch of F_1 used may be different from other batches of the F_1 makes, and so on. (3) The plots of land may have characteristics that separate them from each other and from the class of all plots of land that can be employed to raise soybeans.

To overcome the first problem, that of confounding, we may consider the yield from each type of fertilizer as a single observation and apply the fertilizer to different plots of land. Such a repetition of experiments with various plots of land would tend to "average out" the possible land effects. In the process of replication, it is highly improbable that F_1 would be applied only to plots of land of a high quality, F_2 only to plots of land of an average quality, and so forth. Hence, the confounding of fertilizer effects and of land effects is reduced by an averaging process. Furthermore, it is easy to see that the greater is the variability among the pairs of replications, the larger is the number of pairs required to average or balance out the random differences. Hence, replication leaves in the clear the treatment effects which constitute the basis for inference.

One simple way to reduce the unrepresentativeness of a particular batch of fertilizer is to repeat the experiment with other batches of fertilizer of the same make using different plots of land. This will average out the batch-to-batch variations in fertilizer and will also provide an estimate of the variation among different batches of fertilizer of the same make.

To reduce the unrepresentativeness of a particular plot of land, we may again repeat the experiment with several plots of land applied with each batch of each make of fertilizer. If we also wish to generalize our results to the population of all plots of land, the plots of land should be chosen at random from the entire class of land and assigned at random to F_j. Randomization serves the double purpose in experimental design of eliminating an experimenter's biases and of furnishing us with an estimate of experimental error, since the principle of error estimation is based on the assumption of randomness.

It should be noted, too, that experimental errors usually tend to be correlated if the experimental units are adjacent in time or space. Randomization, without destroying the correlation pattern, gives any two factors an equal chance of being adjacent or nonadjacent, and thus the correlation between any two factors tends to cancel out with increased replication. Replications furnish an estimate of experimental errors and could be used as a test statistic for the true difference between treatment effects. On the other hand, randomizations are necessary requirements in the design of an experiment.

The fertilizer–land confounding can also be reduced by cross-classification and experimentation with similar units of experimental material. By these principles, we may subdivide each plot of land into segments and apply various makes of fertilizer to these segments. Or, we may permit each segmented plot of land to be applied with every make of fertilizer under test. Each of these devices has again the effect of averaging out the plot-to-plot variation.

Finally, a common method of analyzing experimental data is known as the *analysis of variance*. As the name implies, the analysis-of-variance procedure attemps to analyze the total variation of a response by decomposing it into independent and meaningful portions attributable to each of the independent variables and to chance variation. The "chance variation" category really includes the net effect of all variables not explicitly included in the analysis of variance. In other words, this procedure has the objective of identifying important independent variables in an experiment and determining how they interact and affect the response. This procedure can also be employed to analyze observational data, as exemplified in our first model of experimental design introduced in the next section.

It may now be noted that experimental design is a very broad and intensively investigated field. Entire books have been written on only limited phases of this subject. In this chapter we shall confine ourselves to the study of some of the simple but highly useful types of experimental design frequently employed in business and economic research.

The reader may be warned before he proceeds further that this chapter has the appearance of the most difficult one in this text up to now. The difficulty arises mainly from using rather involved summation signs and notation, and from the rather heavy computational labor with even the simple examples for various models introduced. To avoid confusion from the first source, the reader is advised to study with great care each of the definitions of various sums and statistics. He must be perfectly sure about each mathematical expression as he proceeds step by step. As to the second source of difficulty, problems involving the analysis of variance are usually solved with computer programs. However, as stated in the Preface, computers are no substitute for underlying principles. It is, therefore, necessary, although somewhat painful, for the reader to go through this chapter thoroughly before he can take advantage of computers as a computational aid.

16.2 COMPLETELY RANDOMIZED, ONE-VARIABLE CLASSIFICATION MODEL

As its name implies, the *completely randomized, one-variable classification model* involves only one treatment variable in the design. It is designed for the purpose of comparing three or more means. As such, it is simply an extension of the model of testing the significance of a difference between two sample means by the t ratio introduced in Chapter 15. This extension, however, is a very important one, since the t ratio can only be used to test the difference between two sample means.

Clearly, it would be grossly inefficient to compare several sample means by pairing them two at a time because, if there are, say, five samples, we would have $_5C_2 = 10$ different tests to perform. Furthermore, even if we have made ten such tests, we may still not be able to generalize about all of the five populations, from which the samples are drawn, at the same time. Worse still, it is easy to show that such a tedious and time-consuming procedure actually has a high probability of leading to wrong conclusions pairwise. If we were to have ten t tests on the ten possible pairs of the five sample means, where the data are such that t tests are valid, the probability of our arriving at a correct conclusion of no significant difference for any one test would be 0.95 given that $\alpha = 0.05$. Hence, the probability for our arriving at correct conclusions for all the ten t tests would be $(0.95)^{10}$; the probability of obtaining at least one wrong conclusion would be $1 - (0.95)^{10} \doteq 0.401$. That is, more than 40% of the time we would make at least one type I error when all ten null hypotheses were true. Needless to say, the larger the number of samples to be evaluated, the greater the probability of making wrong decisions when the population means are all equal. The value of the completely randomized, one-variable classification model, which furnishes us with a test of significance of differences among any number of sample means, is evident.

The model

This model assumes that there are c populations, $A_1, A_2, \ldots, A_c$, which are normally distributed, each with mean μ_j and all possessing the same variance σ^2. The common-variance assumption is reasonable when different treatment used for the same purpose may differ in central tendencies but differ at most only slightly in dispersion. Furthermore, we conceive that these c populations together constitute a *grand population* with mean μ, called the *grand population mean*, defined as

$$\mu = \frac{1}{c} \sum_{j=1}^{c} \mu_j.$$

Under the preceding two assumptions, we wish to test the null hypothesis that all of the treatment means are equal—namely,

$$\mu_1 = \mu_2 = \cdots = \mu_c = \mu.$$

If this H_0 is true, then we would expect $\mu_j = \mu$. Otherwise, we would expect μ_j to deviate from μ by a quanity, say, α_j—that is,

$$\alpha_j = \mu_j - \mu, \quad j = 1, 2, \ldots, c,$$

where the α_js, for obvious reasons, are called *treatment effects*. Furthermore, by the property of the arithmetic mean, we must have

$$\sum_j \alpha_j = \sum_j (\mu_j - \mu) = 0.$$

From these arguments we can deduce that

$$\mu_1 = \mu_2 = \cdots = \mu_c = \mu$$

and

$$\alpha_j = 0, \quad j = 1, 2, \ldots, c,$$

are equivalent statements, since, when we say that the treatment means are equal, we imply that the effects due to treatments are nil.

Now, let y_{ij} be the ith observation made from the jth treatment; then we have

$$y_{ij} = \mu_j + \epsilon_{ij},$$

where ϵ_{ij} are deviations of y_{ij} from μ_j due to chance fluctuations in random sampling. The ϵ_{ij} are the *error terms*, or *residuals*, which are assumed to be independent and normally distributed with zero expectation and a variance identical with the common variance σ^2 for the treatments.

Finally, noting that $\mu_j = \mu + \alpha_j$ and $\epsilon_{ij} = y_{ij} - \mu_j$, we have as the basic model for the completely randomized, one-variable classification experimental design the following linear form:

$$(y_{ij} - \mu) = (\mu_j - \mu) + (y_{ij} - \mu_j)$$
$$= \alpha_j + \epsilon_{ij}. \tag{16.1}$$

The Analysis

The central core of the analysis of an experimental design, irrespective of the type of model, lies in the partitioning of the total "sum of squares" (for the response) into meaningful and distinct portions. To see how this is done for our present model, let us first arrange the data obtained from the c samples, each with n_j ($j = 1, 2, \ldots, c$) observations into a general form as shown by Table 16.1. Note that in Table 16.1, n refers to the grand sample size and its is equal to the sum of n_j:

$$n = n_1 + n_2 + \cdots + n_c.$$

The dot notation is introduced for convenience in summing. Thus,

1. $t_{.j} = \displaystyle\sum_{i=1}^{n_j} y_{ij}$ = sum for the jth column

2. $\bar{y}_{.j} = \dfrac{1}{n_j} t_{.j}$ = sample mean for the jth column

3. $t_{..} = \displaystyle\sum_{j=1}^{c} t_{.j} = \sum_{j=1}^{c} \sum_{i=1}^{n_j} y_{ij}$ = sum for the grand sample

4. $\bar{y}_{..} = \dfrac{1}{n} t_{..}$ = grand sample mean

5. $S_j^2 = \dfrac{1}{n_j - 1} \displaystyle\sum_{i=1}^{n_j} (y_{ij} - \bar{y}_{.j})^2$

   = sample variance for the jth column

6. $S^2 = \dfrac{1}{n - 1} \displaystyle\sum_{j=1}^{c} \sum_{i=1}^{n_j} (y_{ij} - \bar{y}_{..})^2$

   = variance of the grand sample.

Turning our attention to the task of partitioning, we note that the corresponding sample identity for (16.1) is

$$(y_{ij} - \bar{y}_{..}) = (\bar{y}_{.j} - \bar{y}_{..}) + (y_{ij} - \bar{y}_{.j}). \tag{16.2}$$

TABLE 16.1 One-variable Classification Sample Data

	Sample				Grand total
Observation	1	2	$\cdots$	c	
1	y_{11}	y_{12}	$\cdots$	y_{1c}	
2	y_{21}	y_{22}	$\cdots$	y_{2c}	
$\vdots$	$\vdots$	$\vdots$		$\vdots$	
n_j	$y_{n_1 1}$	$y_{n_2 2}$	$\cdots$	$y_{n_c c}$	
Column total	$t_{.1}$	$t_{.2}$	$\cdots$	$t_{.c}$	$t_{..}$
Sample size	n_1	n_2	$\cdots$	n_c	n

In this expression, the three components are estimators for $(y_{ij} - \mu)$, α_j and ϵ_{ij}, respectively. Now, as can be shown quite easily, if we square the terms on both sides of (16.2) and sum these squared deviations over all individual observations i in all sample groups j, we obtain the various "sums of squares":

$$\sum_{j=1}^{c} \sum_{i=1}^{n_j} (y_{ij} - \bar{y}_{..})^2 \qquad \text{SST}$$

$$= \sum_{j=1}^{c} \sum_{i=1}^{n_j} (\bar{y}_{\cdot j} - \bar{y}_{..})^2 \qquad \text{SSC}$$

$$+ \sum_{j=1}^{c} \sum_{i=1}^{n_j} (y_{ij} - \bar{y}_{\cdot j})^2 \qquad \text{SSE}$$

or

$$\text{SST} = \text{SSC} + \text{SSE}.$$

Some comments on the result immediately above are now in order. First of all, SST (read total sum of squares) stands for the total variation of the response and, by definition (6) given before, SST = $(n - 1)S^2$. It is a measure of overall variation of the n observations. This variation arises from two different sources: (1) possible differences in treatments and (2) chance variations. Thus, this total sum of squares is partitioned into SSC and SSE.

The sum of squares between samples (columns), SSC, corresponds to the numerator of the variance for the column means, except for the weighting factor n_j, since

$$\text{SSC} = \sum_{j=1}^{c} n_j (\bar{y}_{\cdot j} - \bar{y}_{..})^2.$$

It, therefore, reflects the contribution of both different treatments and chance to intersample variability. Or, simply, SSC measures the variability of the c sample means. As such, if the c sample means were nearly identical, then SSC would be small, reflecting little contribution, if any, of the possible treatment differences to the total variation. However, if the c sample means differed greatly from one other, SSC would tend to be large, reflecting a considerable contribution of treatment differences to the total variation.

The sum of squares for error, SSE, is the error sum of squares *within* treatments. Since

$$\text{SSE} = \sum_{j=1}^{c} \sum_{i=1}^{n_j} (y_{ij} - \bar{y}_{\cdot j})^2$$

$$= \sum_{j=1}^{c} (n_j - 1)S_j^2$$

it is a measure of variation within the individual samples, or a measure of intrasample differences due to chance alone.

The sums of squares can be computed by expanding the binomials that define them and the results are as follows:

$$SST = \sum_j \sum_i (y_{ij} - \bar{y}_{..})^2$$

$$= \sum_j \sum_i y_{ij}^2 - n\bar{y}_{..}^2; \qquad (16.3)$$

$$SSC = \sum_j \sum_i (\bar{y}_{.j} - \bar{y}_{..})^2 = \sum_j n_j \bar{y}_{.j} - n\bar{y}_{..}^2; \qquad (16.4)$$

$$SSE = \sum_j \sum_i (y_{ij} - \bar{y}_{.j})^2 = \sum_j \sum_i y_{ij}^2 - \sum_j n_j \bar{y}_{.j}^2. \qquad (16.5)$$

Of course, SSE can also be computed as the difference between SST and SSC.

It may now be noted that, under the null hypothesis of no treatment effects, each of these sums of squares divided by the corresponding degrees of freedom would provide an estimator for the common variance for the treatment populations. Obviously, $\delta = n - 1$ for SST, since it is computed with a total of n observations by using the grand sample mean as an estimator of μ. For SSC, $\delta = c - 1$, since there are c column means to compare, and again the grand sample mean is employed as an estimator of μ for its determination. Finally, for SSE, $\delta = n - c$, since it is obtained from all the n observations with the c group means as estimators for the treatment population means. The estimators for σ^2, in the analysis-of-variance language, are called *mean squares*, MS. Here, we are especially interested in the mean square for error, MSE, and the mean square for column samples, MSC.

First, we see that MSE is always an unbiased estimator of σ^2 because the error term, as stated before, has the same variance as that for each of the treatment populations. Second, MSC is an unbiased estimator for σ^2 if and only if the treatment effects are nil, that is, if and only if $\alpha_j = 0$. Otherwise, MSC would reflect both chance fluctuations and the intersample variability—it would then be an upward biased estimator of σ^2.

From the nature of MSC and MSE, we can now readily design a test statistic for the null hypothesis of equal treatment population means. If this H_0 is true, then MSC and MSE would be equal; that is, the ratio MSC/MSE, which is an F-variable, would be unity or close to it. On the other hand, if this H_0 is false, or if the treatment effects are not nil, then the value of F defined here would be significantly greater than unity. Thus, we can use this F-ratio as the test statistic for this test and define the rejection regions as

$$\frac{MSC}{MSE} > F_{\delta_1, \delta_2; \alpha}, \qquad (16.6)$$

where $\delta_1 = c - 1$ and $\delta_2 = n - c$.

Our discussion in this subsection can now be summarized by an analysis-of-variance (ANOVA) table, Table 16.2. Note that the completely randomized, one-variable classification model is applicable for

TABLE 16.2 ANOVA Table for One-variable Classification

Source	SS	δ	MS
Between treatments	SSC	$c - 1$	$SSC/(c - 1)$
Within treatments: error	SSE	$n - c$	$SSE/(n - c)$
Total	SST	$n - 1$	—

both equal and unequal sample sizes. We shall consider an example for each case.

Example 1 Equal Sample Size

Suppose that a manufacturing company has purchased three new machines of different makes and wishes to determine whether one of them is faster than the others in producing a certain output. Five hourly production figures are observed at random from each machine, and the results are presented in Table 16.3. What conclusions can be drawn at $\alpha = 0.05$? At $\alpha = 0.01$?

Following our general procedure of testing, the foregoing questions can be answered by the following test, assuming the three populations are normally distributed and have a common variance.

1. *Hypotheses.* $H_0: \mu_1 = \mu_2 = \mu_3$; $H_1:$ Not all three μ_i are equal.

2. *Level of significance.* $\alpha = 0.05, 0.01$.

3. *Test statistic.* $F_{2,12} = MSC/MSE$. (*Note:* for this F, $\delta_1 = c - 1 = 3 - 1 = 2$, and $\delta_2 = n - c = 15 - 3 = 12$.)

4. *Decision rule.* Since $P(F_{2,12} > 3.89) = 0.05$ and $P(F_{2,12} > 6.93) = 0.01$, H_0 will be rejected at the 5% level if the observed F is greater than 3.89, and it will be rejected at the 1% level of significance if the observed F is greater than 6.93.

5. *Computations.* Suppose that sample data are as recorded in Table 16.3, then we may compute, quite conveniently, the column (or group)

TABLE 16.3 Hourly Output Volumes of Three Machines for Five Hours

Observations	A_1	A_2	A_3	Total
1	25	31	24	
2	30	39	30	
3	36	38	28	
4	38	42	25	
5	31	35	28	
Total	160	185	135	$t_{..} = 480$
n_j	5	5	5	$n = 15$
$\bar{y}_{.j}$	32	37	27	$\bar{y}_{..} = 32$

means and the grand sample mean first. These summary statistics may be placed at the bottom of the table that contains the original data.

Next, we should compute the sums of squares. We see that there are only three quantities, $\sum_j \sum_i y_{ij}^2$, $\sum_j n_j \bar{y}_{\cdot j}^2$, and $n\bar{y}^2_{\cdot\cdot}$, in the equations for the three sums of squares in this model; therefore it is advisable to compute them first before the sums of squares are obtained:

$$\sum_j \sum_i y_{ij}^2 = 25^2 + 30^2 + \cdots + 28^2 = 15{,}810;$$

$$\sum_j n_j \bar{y}_{\cdot j}^2 = 5(32^2) + 5(37^2) + 5(27^2) = 15{,}610;$$

$$n\bar{y}^2_{\cdot\cdot} = 15(32^2) = 15{,}360.$$

Finally, the three sums of squares are as follows:

SST = total variation

= $15{,}810 - 15{,}360 = 450;$

SSC = variation between columns (machines)

= $15{,}610 - 15{,}360 = 250;$

SSE = variation within columns (error)

= $15{,}810 - 15{,}610 = 200.$

We may now present these sums of squares, along with their degrees of freedom and mean squares, in a summary table, Table 16.4.

$$F_{2,12} = \frac{\text{MSC}}{\text{MSE}} = \frac{125.00}{16.67} \doteq 7.50.$$

6. *Decisions.* Since the computed value is greater than both 3.89 and 6.93, H_0 is rejected at both the 5% and 1% levels of significance. At least two of the three new machines are significantly different in their mean speeds; or, the machine effects are significant. However, this way of stating the conclusion is really shorthand for a more complicated idea, and the shorthand version must not be taken literally unless the requirements of the more complicated idea have been met. All we really know is that when we classified the data into three samples according to which machine produced the output, we got a statistically significant F value. From this evidence alone, we do not know whether the machine

TABLE 16.4 ANOVA Table for Machine Data

Source of Variation	SS	δ	MS
Machines (between columns)	250	$3 - 1 = 2$	125.00
Error (within columns)	200	$15 - 3 = 12$	16.67
Total	450	$15 - 1 = 14$	—

produced the significant F value or whether something associated with the machines, such as operator or raw material or electrical voltage or what-have-you, produced it. If all factors relevant to output volumes are known to be constant for all the data, except machine, then the conclusion that machine effects are significant can be taken literally. Otherwise, only the carefully phrased and weak statement: "When we classified the data into three samples according to which machines produced the output, we got a statistically significant F-value" is a justified conclusion.

Example 2 Unequal Sample Size

A big state university has more than 4,000 students taking the course of business and economic statistics each year. Almost without exception, the average grade of the students in this course has been the lowest among their average grades in all other business and economic subjects. The department of statistics of the said university attempts to improve the situation by appointing a committee to look into the problem. After considerable elaboration, the committee suggests that the course should be taught with four different methods to see if one method is more efficient than the others. These methods are

A_1 Statistics stressing underlying principles

A_2 Statistics stressing computations and interpretations

A_3 Statistics stressing a balance between principles and applications

A_4 Statistics stressing its usefulness and with humorous presentation

To evaluate whether the four methods are equally efficient, students of a given year are divided into four groups by a random process, with about the same number of students in each group. Each group is then taught by a different method. By the end of the course, a random sample is drawn from each group and the students' final grades are observed and are as recorded in Table 16.5. In view of these data, can we

TABLE 16.5 Final Examination Scores

| | Method | | | | |
	(1)	(2)	(3)	(4)	Total
	60	80	97	67	
	80	81	84	84	
	69	73	93	90	
	65	69	79	78	
		75	92	61	
		72			
Total	274	450	445	380	$t_{..} = 1,549$
n_j	4	6	5	5	$n = 20$
$\bar{y}._j$	68.5	75.0	89.0	76.0	$\bar{y}_{..} = 77.45$

conclude that the average grades of the students have been significantly affected by methods of teaching?

To answer the foregoing question, we may test

$$H_0: \mu_1 = \mu_2 = \mu_3 = \mu_4$$

against

H_1: At least two of the population means are different.

With data in Table 16.5, computations for this example are as follows.

$$\sum_j \sum_i y_{ij}^2 = 60^2 + 80^2 + \cdots + 61^2 = 122,115;$$

$$\sum_j n_j \bar{y}_{\cdot j}^2 = 4(68.5^2) + 6(75.0^2) + 5(89.0^2) + 5(76.0^2) = 121,004;$$

$$n\bar{y}_{\cdot\cdot}^2 = 20(77.45^2) = 119.970.$$

SST $= 122,115 - 119,970 = 2,145;$

SSC $= 121,004 - 119,970 = 1,034;$

SSE $= 122,115 - 121,004 = 1,111.$

From results presented in Table 16.6, we have

$$F_{3,16} = \frac{344.67}{69.44} \doteq 4.96.$$

Since $P(F_{3,16} > 3.24) = 0.05$ and $P(F_{3,16} > 5.29) = 0.01$, H_0 is rejected at $\alpha = 0.05$ but not at $\alpha = 0.01$. Different methods of teaching seem to have some statistically significant effects upon the average grades. This conclusion is only valid if the four samples are independent random samples. Even if this condition is met, we still have the same trouble as with the machine example. All we know here is that when we classify the data into four samples according to which method was used, we get a significant value of F at $\alpha = 0.05$. Other factors associated with a particular method may also affect students' grades, such as the differences among the instructors' personalities and competence and, most important of all, their attitudes toward the method they used. Until we know that these factors and other possible factors influencing students' grades apart from methods of instruction have been kept

TABLE 16.6 ANOVA Table for Method Data

Source of Variation	SS	δ	MS
Textbooks (between columns)	1,034	3	344.67
Error (within columns)	1,111	16	69.44
Total	2,145	19	—

constant, we cannot say that methods of teaching alone have caused the differences in grades.

The Least Significant Difference

The analysis of variance proper shows only whether or not there exists any significant difference among the treatment means. It does not reveal where the difference is. When the F-test leads to the rejection of H_0, we naturally wish to know which of the means causes the difference. There is a simple procedure, called the *least significant difference*, LSD, which can help us locate the significant differences between treatment-sample means. The LSD is defined as the smallest difference that could exist between two significantly different sample means. When we have equal sample size ($n_1 = n_2 = \cdots = n_c = n_0$), and when the F-test leads to the rejection of H_0, the formula for LSD is

$$\text{LSD} = \sqrt{\frac{2}{n_0}(\text{MSE})F_0}. \qquad (16.7a)$$

When the sample sizes are different, LSD is defined as

$$\text{LSD} = \sqrt{\left(\frac{1}{n_j} + \frac{1}{n_k}\right)(\text{MSE})(F_0)}. \qquad (16.7b)$$

In these two expressions, F_0 is such that $P(F_{1,\delta_2} > F_0) = \alpha$.

Any two sample means in ANOVA are said to be different from each other at a given level of significance if their absolute difference is greater than LSD as defined by (16.7). To apply (16.7a) to our first example of machine data, we note that $n_1 = n_2 = n_3 = 5$, MSE = 16.67, and, for $\alpha = 0.01$, $F_0 = F_{1,12} = 9.33$. Thus,

$$\text{LSD} = \sqrt{(2/5)(16.67)(9.33)} \doteq 7.89.$$

From calculations in Table 16.5, we find that

$$|\bar{y}_{.1} - \bar{y}_{.2}| = |32 - 37| = 5 < 7.89 \qquad \text{(not significant)},$$
$$|\bar{y}_{.1} - \bar{y}_{.3}| = |32 - 27| = 5 < 7.89 \qquad \text{(not significant)},$$
$$|\bar{y}_{.2} - \bar{y}_{.3}| = |37 - 27| = 10 > 7.89 \qquad \text{(significant)}.$$

Thus, among the three pairs of column means, only one pair ($\bar{y}_{.2}, \bar{y}_{.3}$) differs significantly. The management should probably decide to use the second make of machine exclusively, although the first make is not ruled out.

Now, let us illustrate the application of (16.7b) with data for the teaching-method example. For this example, MSE = 69.44. If we set $\alpha = 0.05$, $F_0 = F_{1,16} = 4.49$. For $n_1 = 4$ and $n_2 = 6$, we have

$$\text{LSD} = \sqrt{\left(\frac{1}{4} + \frac{1}{6}\right)(69.44)(4.49)} \doteq 11.40;$$

$$|\bar{y}_{.1} - \bar{y}_{.2}| = |68.5 - 75.0| = 6.5 < 11.40 \qquad \text{(not significant)}.$$

For $n_1 = 4$ and $n_3 = 5$; $n_1 = 4$ and $n_4 = 5$, we have

$$\text{LSD} = \sqrt{\left(\frac{1}{4} + \frac{1}{5}\right)(69.44)(4.99)} \doteq 13.43;$$

$|\bar{y}_{\cdot 1} - \bar{y}_{\cdot 3}| = |68.5 - 89.0| = 20.5 > 13.43 \qquad \text{(significant)};$

$|\bar{y}_{\cdot 1} - \bar{y}_{\cdot 4}| = |68.5 - 76.0| = 7.5 < 13.43 \qquad \text{(not significant)}.$

For $n_2 = 6$ and $n_3 = 5$; $n_2 = 6$ and $n_4 = 5$, we have

$$\text{LSD} = \sqrt{\left(\frac{1}{6} + \frac{1}{5}\right)(69.44)(4.99)} \doteq 11.27;$$

$|\bar{y}_{\cdot 2} - \bar{y}_{\cdot 3}| = |75.0 - 89.0| = 14.0 > 11.27 \qquad \text{(significant)};$

$|\bar{y}_{\cdot 2} - \bar{y}_{\cdot 4}| = |75.0 - 76.0| = 1.0 < 11.27 \qquad \text{(not significant)}.$

For $n_3 = n_4 = 5$, we have

$$\text{LSD} = \sqrt{\left(\frac{2}{5}\right)(69.44)(4.49)} \doteq 11.15;$$

$|\bar{y}_{\cdot 3} - \bar{y}_{\cdot 4}| = |89.0 - 76.0| = 13.0 > 11.15 \qquad \text{(significant)}.$

These results reveal that among the six pairs of means, three pairs $(\bar{y}_{\cdot 1}, \bar{y}_{\cdot 3})$, $(\bar{y}_{\cdot 2}, \bar{y}_{\cdot 3})$, and $(\bar{y}_{\cdot 3}, \bar{y}_{\cdot 4})$ differ significantly. We may also conclude from these results that the third method of teaching—statistics stressing a balance between principles and applications—seems to be more efficient than any of the other three methods.

It may be noted that LSD tests are also called *pairwise tests*. These tests should be employed if and only if the F-test has led to the rejection of H_0. When the LSD is erroneously employed in the case where the F-value is insignificant, it is quite possible to find that some pair or pairs of sample means differ by an amount greater than the value of LSD. However, such differences are still explained by chance variations in random sampling from the same population or populations with identical means. The LSD method of identifying significantly differing means has some undesirable properties. The rule just mentioned—do not use LSD at all unless the F-value is significant—removes some of the undesirable properties. There are other rules an investigator should consider using if she finds herself in this situation, but they are beyond the scope of this text.

Bartlett's Test of Homogeneity of Variances

It will be remembered that the application of ANOVA models requires that the population variances are equal. This assumption of homogeneity of variance is due the origin of experimental design in the field of agriculture, where such an assumption is usually satisfied. However, it is often not met in computer simulation, business and economics. Two-stage inferential procedures have been developed recently that do not require the homogeneity of variances for analyzing experimental data, but such methods are usually quite involved and are beyond the scope of an introductory text. It seems appropriate, though, when we apply ANOVA to business and economic data, that we should first evaluate whether the c population variances are equal for appropriateness.

There are several procedures available for testing

$$H_0: \sigma_1^2 = \sigma_2^2 = \cdots = \sigma_c^2$$

against

$$H_1: \text{At least two variances are unequal.}$$

For the purpose of testing this H_0, we shall select the method called *Bartlett's test*, developed by M. S. Bartlett in 1937. We make this selection because Bartlett's test is not at all difficult and it has the additional advantage that it can be employed whether the sample sizes are equal or unequal.

THEOREM 16.1 BARTLETT'S TEST OF HOMOGENEITY OF VARIANCES *If random samples of size $n_1, n_2, \ldots, n_c$ are drawn from c normally distributed populations and if the null hypothesis (all variances are equal) is true, then the statistic*

$$\chi_\delta^2 = \frac{2.3026[\log S_w^2 \, \Sigma \, (n_j - 1) - \Sigma \, (n_j - 1) \log S_j^2]}{1 + \dfrac{1}{3(c-1)} \left[\Sigma \left(\dfrac{1}{n_j - 1} \right) - \dfrac{1}{\Sigma \, (n_j - 1)} \right]} \qquad (16.8)$$

has a χ^2 distribution with $\delta = c - 1$.

In (16.8), S_w^2 stands for the pooled, or weighted, estimator for the common variance σ^2. It is computed in the same way as in the two-sample case presented in the previous chapter, where the weights used are the respective degrees of freedom for S_j^2, namely,

$$S_w^2 = \frac{\Sigma \, (n_j - 1)S_j^2}{\Sigma \, (n_j - 1)}.$$

To illustrate the application of (16.8), let us use the example for the machine data just evaluated. Here, we wish to test the following pair of hypotheses:

$$H_0: \sigma_1^2 = \sigma_2^2 = \sigma_3^2;$$

$$H_1: \text{At least two variances are unequal.}$$

Since $c = 3$, we have $\delta = 2$ for χ_δ^2 as defined by (16.8) in our example. Thus, H_0 will be rejected at $\alpha = 0.05$ if the computed value of χ^2 is greater than 5.99 and it will be rejected at $\alpha = 0.01$ if the computed χ_2^2

value is greater than 7.33. Now, as you can easily verify from data in Table 16.3, we have

$$s_1^2 = 26.5, \qquad s_2^2 = 17.5 \qquad \text{and} \qquad s_3^2 = 6.25.$$

With these quantities, we see that

$$
\begin{aligned}
s_w^2 &= \frac{(n_1 - 1)s_1^2 + (n_2 - 1)s_2^2 + (n_3 - 1)s_3^2}{n_1 + n_2 + n_3 - 3} \\
&= \frac{4(26.5) + 4(17.5) + 4(6.25)}{5 + 5 + 5 - 3} \\
&= 16.75.
\end{aligned}
$$

Finally, by (16.8), we have

$$\chi_2^2 = \frac{2.3026\{[(\log 16.75)12] - [4(\log 26.5) + 4(\log 17.5) + 4(\log 6.25)]\}}{1 + \dfrac{1}{3(3 - 1)} - \left(\dfrac{3}{4} - \dfrac{1}{12}\right)}$$

$$\doteq 1.74.$$

This result indicates that the null hypothesis of equal population variances cannot be rejected either at $\alpha = 0.05$ or at $\alpha = 0.01$. In other words, the differences of the three sample variances can be explained by chance variations in random sampling alone. Our application of the ANOVA procedure to the machine data is clearly justified.

16.3* RANDOMIZED-BLOCKS, ONE-VARIABLE CLASSIFICATION MODEL

The term *randomized-blocks experiment* stems from agricultural research, in which several levels of a treatment variable are all applied to each of several blocks of land. Each block of land is homogeneous, although there are differences from block to block. The blocks are subdivided, each subdivision receiving one level of the treatment variable. The main objective here is to establish significant differences among treatment effects, such as yields of different types of soybeans. But differences in crop yield may be attributed not only to different kinds of soybeans but also to differences in quality of the blocks of land. To reduce such confounding, or to isolate the "block effects," randomization is employed in the following way: within each block, subdivisions are created so that the number of subdivisions equals the number of treatment levels, and then subdivisions are assigned at random to each treatment level, making sure that each treatment level is used exactly in that block. The blocks may or may not be selected at random.

Despite its agricultural origin, the randomized-blocks design is widely used in many types of studies today. For instance, to determine the differences in productivity of, say, c makes of machines (treatments), we may isolate the possible effects due to differences in efficiency among operators (blocks) by randomly selecting operators and then randomly rotating machine assignments in such a way that each operator works all the machines. The basic idea here is to compare treatment levels (the different machines) within a block of relatively homogeneous experimental material (the same operator), then repeat the comparison on another block (another operator), and so on for additional repetitions of the comparison. The primary difference between the preceding model and the present one lies in the manner in which various experimental units are assigned. In the completely randomized design there are no blocks that each must receive every treatment level; there are no restrictions on assigning experimental units to treatment levels. In the randomized-blocks model the subdivisions of blocks of experimental units are randomly assigned to the treatments after the blocks have been deliberately arranged to be homogeneous.

The Model

Suppose we have r blocks, $B_i, i = 1, 2, \ldots, r$, and c treatments, $A_j, j = 1, 2, \ldots, c$; then we have rc populations, one for each block–treatment combination, each with a mean μ_{ij}. To derive a mathematical model for this case, let us first note that

$$\mu_{i\cdot} = \frac{1}{c} \sum_{j=1}^{c} \mu_{ij} \qquad = \text{block population mean;}$$

$$\mu_{\cdot j} = \frac{1}{r} \sum_{i=1}^{r} \mu_{ij} \qquad = \text{treatment population mean;}$$

$$\mu_{\cdot\cdot} = \frac{1}{rc} \sum_{i=1}^{r} \sum_{j=1}^{c} \mu_{ij} = \text{grand population mean.}$$

Then our model may be stated as

$$\mu_{ij} - \mu_{\cdot\cdot} = (\mu_{j\cdot} - \mu_{\cdot\cdot}) + (\mu_{\cdot j} - \mu_{\cdot\cdot}) + (\mu_{ij} - \mu_{i\cdot} - \mu_{\cdot j} + \mu_{\cdot\cdot}). \quad (16.9a)$$

Now, let us define

$$\beta_i = \mu_{i\cdot} - \mu_{\cdot\cdot} \qquad \text{as the block effect,}$$

$$\alpha_j = \mu_{\cdot j} - \mu_{\cdot\cdot} \qquad \text{as the treatment effect,}$$

and

$$\mu_{ij} - \mu_{i\cdot} - \mu_{\cdot j} + \mu_{\cdot\cdot} \qquad \text{as the interaction effect.}$$

The interaction effect is set at zero when it is assumed not to exist. Thus, (16.9a) is reduced to

$$\mu_{ij} - \mu_{\cdot\cdot} = \beta_i + \alpha_j$$

or, equivalently,

$$y_{ij} = \mu_{..} + \beta_i + \alpha_j + \epsilon_{ij}, \qquad (16.9b)$$

where y_{ij} is the single observation made from a population with μ_{ij}, and $\epsilon_{ij} = y_{ij} - \mu_{ij}$ is the "error" term.

For the preceding model, the following assumptions are made:

1. All rc populations are normally distributed with equal variances σ^2.

2. A random sample of size one is drawn from each of the rc populations; thus, the sample mean of y_{ij} is y_{ij} itself.

3. There is no "interaction" between blocks and treatments; namely, the block and treatment effects are additive, and there is no joint effect between β_i and α_j, except the sum of their simple effects.

4. The errors ϵ_{ij}, as before, are assumed to be independent and distributed as $n(0, \sigma^2)$.

5. $\sum_i \beta_i = \sum_j \alpha_j = 0$. This assumption is made for the convenience of solution for this model.

The Analysis

The analysis of this model begins, again, with partitioning the total sum of squares into nonoverlapping and meaningful components. As an aid for this purpose, we shall work out a tabular presentation of the sample data for this model as shown by Table 16.7.

We see that, for the randomized-blocks design, the subclasses arrange themselves naturally into rows and columns; the blocks may be referred to as *rows* and the treatments as *columns*.

Now, the corresponding sample quantities for model (16.9a) can be

TABLE 16.7 Summary of Sample Data for the Randomized-blocks, One-variable Classification Model

Block		Treatments 1	2	$\cdots$	c	Block Total	Block Mean
	1	y_{11}	y_{12}	$\cdots$	y_{1c}	$t_{1.}$	$\bar{y}_{1.}$
	2	y_{21}	y_{22}	$\cdots$	y_{2c}	$t_{2.}$	$\bar{y}_{2.}$
	$\vdots$	$\vdots$	$\vdots$		$\vdots$	$\vdots$	$\vdots$
	r	y_{r1}	y_{r2}	$\cdots$	y_{rc}	$t_{r.}$	$\bar{y}_{r.}$
Treatment total		$t_{.1}$	$t_{.2}$	$\cdots$	$t_{.c}$	$t_{..} = $ grand total	
Treatment mean		$\bar{y}_{.1}$	$\bar{y}_{.2}$	$\cdots$	$\bar{y}_{.c}$	$\bar{y}_{..} = $ grand mean	

written as

$$(y_{ij} - \bar{y}_{..}) = (\bar{y}_{i.} - \bar{y}_{..}) + (\bar{y}_{.j} - \bar{y}_{..}) + (y_{ij} - \bar{y}_{i.} - \bar{y}_{.j} + \bar{y}_{..}). \quad (16.10)$$

This formulation suggests that the total sum of squares in the response can be decomposed into three separate portions: due to blocks, treatments, and errors. It is interesting to note that blocking is in effect a device of local control whereby the within-treatment sum of squares is decomposed into two parts: block differences and chance variations. In so doing, the probability is increased of MSE being smaller than the mean square within. Thus, it is more likely that the significant differences among the treatments will be detected.

It can be shown that if we square both sides of (16.10) and sum with respect to i and j, we obtain

$$\sum_{i=1}^{r} \sum_{j=1}^{c} (y_{ij} - \bar{y}_{..})^2 \qquad \text{SST}$$

$$= \sum_{i=1}^{r} \sum_{j=1}^{c} (\bar{y}_{i.} - \bar{y}_{..})^2 \qquad \text{SSB}$$

$$+ \sum_{i=1}^{r} \sum_{j=1}^{c} (\bar{y}_{.j} - \bar{y}_{..})^2 \qquad \text{SSC}$$

$$+ \sum_{i=1}^{r} \sum_{j=1}^{c} (y_{ij} - \bar{y}_{i.} - \bar{y}_{.j} + \bar{y}_{..})^2 \qquad \text{SSE}$$

or

$$\text{SST} = \text{SSB} + \text{SSC} + \text{SSE}.$$

Let us pause a moment here to inform the reader that at this level of discussion, he is neither expected to be able to find these SS decomposions himself nor required to really understand whence they arise. It should be sufficient if he knows the meaning of each of these sums of squares. Now, in the above identity, SSB measures both block effects and error variations, since it reflects dispersion of row means from the grand sample mean. For SSB, $\delta = r - 1$. Similarly, SSC measures both chance variations and variations in treatment effects. For SSC, $\delta = c - 1$. Finally, the sum of squares for error, SSE, is based on deviations from both row and column means for all individuals that are treated in exactly the same way; therefore, the only possible contribution to this sum of squares should be chance variation due to random sampling. For SSE, $\delta = (r - 1)(c - 1)$. These observations lead to the following conclusions.

First, the mean square for error,

$$\text{MSE} = \frac{\text{SSE}}{(r - 1)(c - 1)},$$

is always an unbiased estimator for σ^2. Second, the mean square for blocks,

$$MSB = \frac{SSB}{r-1},$$

is an unbiased estimator for σ^2 if and only if the block effects are nil. Third, the mean square for treatments (columns),

$$MSC = \frac{SSC}{c-1},$$

is an unbiased estimator for σ^2 if and only if the treatment effects are nil.

Note also that for SST in this model, $\delta = rc - 1$, and that $(rc - 1) = (r - 1) + (c - 1) + (r - 1)(c - 1)$. The sums of squares for this model can be computed as follows:

$$C = \text{correction factor} = \frac{1}{rc} t_{..}^2; \qquad (16.11)$$

$$SST = \sum_{i=1}^{r} \sum_{j=1}^{c} y_{ij}^2 - C; \qquad (16.12)$$

$$SSB = \frac{1}{c} \sum_{i=1}^{r} t_{i.}^2 - C; \qquad (16.13)$$

$$SSC = \frac{1}{r} \sum_{j=1}^{c} t_{.j}^2 - C; \qquad (16.14)$$

$$SST = SST - (SSB + SSC). \qquad (16.15)$$

Table 16.8 summarizes what has been discussed in this subsection.

Finally, we come to the problem of testing with the current model. There seem to be two sets of hypotheses to be evaluated:

1. Block-effects test:
   $H_0: \beta_i = 0, \quad i = 1, 2, \ldots, r;$
   $H_1: \beta_i \neq 0, \quad$ for some i.

2. Treatment-effects test:
   $H_0: \alpha_j = 0, \quad j = 1, 2, \ldots, c;$
   $H_1: \alpha_j \neq 0, \quad$ for some j.

TABLE 16.8 ANOVA Table for Randomized-blocks, One-variable Classification Model

Source of Variation	SS	δ	MS
Between blocks	SSB	$r - 1$	$SSB/(r - 1)$
Between treatments	SSC	$c - 1$	$SSC/(c - 1)$
Error	SSE	$(r - 1)(c - 1)$	$SSE/(r - 1)(c - 1)$
Total	SST	$rc - 1$	—

In reality, however, we are interested in testing only the second set of hypotheses. We are not concerned with the problem of whether block effects are nil here, since the block means, under the randomized-blocks assumption, are merely indicative of the differences in blocks of experimental material. In a different context the first test is a meaningful one, as we shall see in the completely randomized two-variable classification model in the next section.

To make the test on treatment effects, we recall that MSE is an unbiased estimator of σ^2 whether or not $\alpha_j = 0$ (for all j) is true, while MSC is an unbiased estimator for σ^2 only if $\alpha_j = 0$ (for all j) is true. Thus, we will accept the null hypothesis that the treatment effects are nil if and only if MSC/MSE = 1 or is close to 1. The rejection region is then defined as

$$\frac{\text{MSC}}{\text{MSE}} > F_{\delta_1, \delta_2; \alpha}, \tag{16.16}$$

where $\delta_1 = c - 1$ and $\delta_2 = (r - 1)(c - 1)$.

Example

A motion study is to be conducted for determining the best work design for assembling wall clocks; five designs are under investigation. Four assemblers are selected at random from all assemblers in the plant and are thoroughly taught to work with all five designs. Then each worker follows each design for a day, his design for that day having been selected at random from the various designs, and the number of clocks assembled is recorded. The data are shown in Table 16.9. For this problem, the present model is appropriate. Here, the treatments are the different work designs, and the blocks are the assemblers. The test for this experiment is made as follows:

1. *Hypotheses.* $H_0: \alpha_j = 0, \quad j = 1, 2, 3, 4, 5; \quad H_1: \alpha_j \neq 0, \quad$ for some j.

2. *Level of significance.* $\alpha = 0.05; \alpha = 0.01$.

3. *Test statistic.* $F_{4,12} = \text{MSC/MSE}$. For this experiment, $c = 5$ and $r = 4$.

TABLE 16.9 Sample Data for Work-designs Experiment

Assembler	Work Design					$t_i.$	$\bar{y}_i.$
	1	2	3	4	5		
1	10	13	9	14	11	57	11.4
2	5	10	5	10	6	36	7.2
3	6	12	5	10	6	39	7.8
4	4	8	4	11	5	32	6.4
$t_{.j}$	25	43	23	45	28	$t_{..} = 164$	
$\bar{y}_{.j}$	6.25	10.75	5.75	11.25	7.00	$\bar{y}_{..} = 8.2$	

4. *Decision rule.* Since $P(F_{4,12} > 3.26) = 0.05$ and $P(F_{4,12} > 5.41) = 0.01$, H_0 will be rejected at $\alpha = 0.05$ if the computed value of F is greater than 3.26, and it will be rejected at $\alpha = 0.01$ if the computed F value is greater than 5.41.

5. *Computations.*

$$C = \frac{1}{rc} t_{..}^2 = \frac{1}{(4)(5)} 164^2 = 1344.8;$$

$$\text{SST} = \sum_{i=1}^{4} \sum_{j=1}^{5} y_{ij}^2 - C = (10^2 + 5^2 + \cdots + 5^2) - 1344.8 = 191.2;$$

$$\text{SSC} = \frac{1}{r} \sum_{j=1}^{5} t_{.j}^2 - C$$

$$= \tfrac{1}{4}(25^2 + 43^2 + 23^2 + 45^2 + 28^2) - 1344.8 = 108.2;$$

$$\text{SSB} = \frac{1}{c} \sum_{i=1}^{4} t_{i.}^2 - C$$

$$= \tfrac{1}{5}(57^2 + 36^2 + 39^2 + 32^2) - 1344.8 = 73.2;$$

$$\text{SSE} = \text{SST} - (\text{SSC} + \text{SSB}) = 191.2 - (108.2 + 73.2) = 9.8.$$

The sums of squares, together with their df and mean squares, are summarized in Table 16.10.

$$F_{4,12} = \frac{\text{MSC}}{\text{MSE}} \doteq \frac{27.05}{0.817} \doteq 33.11,$$

which is highly significant.

For this problem, if $\alpha = 0.05$,

$$\text{LSD} = \sqrt{\frac{2}{r} (\text{MSE}) F_0} = \sqrt{\frac{2}{4} (0.817)(4.75)} \doteq 1.39,$$

and for $\alpha = 0.01$,

$$\text{LSD} = \sqrt{\frac{2}{4} (0.817)(9.33)} \doteq 1.95.$$

TABLE 16.10 ANOVA Table for Work Designs Data

Source of Variation	SS	δ	MS
Between assemblers	73.2	$4 - 1 = 3$	24.40
Between designs	108.2	$5 - 1 = 4$	27.05
Error	9.8	$(4 - 1)(5 - 1) = 12$	0.817
Total	191.2	$20 - 1 = 19$	—

Let us present the absolute values of the differences between the possible pairs of means in tabular form, and indicate significant differences at $\alpha = 0.05$ by * and significant differences at $\alpha = 0.01$ by ** as follows:

	6.25	10.75	5.75	11.25	7.00
6.25	—				
10.75	4.50**	—			
5.75	0.50	5.00**	—		
11.25	5.00**	0.50	5.50**	—	
7.00	0.75	3.75**	1.25	4.25**	—

6. *Conclusions.* The null hypothesis is rejected at both 5% and 1% levels of significance. Among the ten pairs of treatments means, six pairs are found to be significantly different at $\alpha = 0.01$. Design 2 and Design 4 are by far the most efficient assembling methods.

16.4* COMPLETELY RANDOMIZED, TWO-VARIABLE CLASSIFICATION WITHOUT REPLICATION MODEL

This model refers to a *completely randomized design* in which sample data are classified in terms of two independent random variables and in which there is only one observation in each cell. The framework of this model is exactly the same as that for the model just discussed, except for the interpretation of data, and the lack of random assignments of one variable's levels to subdivisions of the other variable's levels.

In the randomized-blocks, one-variable classification model, we were interested in investigating only treatment effects—the independent variable A_j. The blocks were considered merely experimental material. In our present two-variable classification model, both treatments and blocks are independent variables and are evaluated simultaneously. Consequently, while A_j are treatments in the one-variable classification case, the treatments in the two variable-classification designs are really treatment combinations B_iA_j. Furthermore, in the two-variable classification without replication model, we select samples of size 1 from each treatment combination, and sample data may be presented as follows:

Treatment Combination	B_1A_1	B_1B_2	$\cdots$	B_2A_1	$\cdots$	B_rA_c
Observation	y_{11}	y_{12}	$\cdots$	y_{21}	$\cdots$	y_{rc}

Expressed in a two-way table, it becomes

	A_1	A_2	$\cdots$	A_c
B_1	y_{11}	y_{12}	$\cdots$	y_{1c}
B_2	y_{21}	y_{22}	$\cdots$	y_{2c}
$\vdots$	$\vdots$	$\vdots$	$\vdots$	$\vdots$
B_r	y_{r1}	y_{r2}	$\cdots$	y_{rc}

The second presentation is identical with the scheme for the randomized-blocks, one-variable classification model. This same scheme, however has two completely different interpretations. The first is as a one-variable classification with randomized blocks in which A_j constitute the independent variable and B_i are blocks within which A_j are assigned at random. The second is as a completely randomized, two-variable classification model in which both A_j and B_i are independent variables, and y_{ij} are each a sample of size 1 drawn from a population corresponding to B_iA_j.

For example, in our analysis of the work-design study earlier, we took the assemblers as blocks. The differences in efficiency among the five work designs were then compared. Now, if we wished to analyze the same data by our current model, we would investigate the possible differences in productivity among the assemblers as well as those among the work designs. No longer is each row merely a block that has no effect on the number of clocks assembled, except for the possible differences in work-design efficiency. The observation, say, $y_{11} = 10$ should now be interpreted as one level of output of the first-assembler-and-the-first-work-design combination. Furthermore, y_{11} has been drawn from a population of output levels corresponding to B_1A_1 whose mean is μ_{11}. Clearly, with this interpretation, y_{11} is now thought to be affected by both β_1 and α_1.

The analysis-of-variance table and testing procedures for this model are exactly the same as for the previous one, except that, in the present case, both tests, $\beta_i = 0$, and $\alpha_j = 0$, are now meaningful and should be conducted.

To conduct the additional test, $\beta_i = 0$ for all i against $\beta_i \neq 0$ for at least some i, we compare MSB and MSE; that is, the rejection region is defined as

$$\frac{\text{MSB}}{\text{MSE}} > F_{\delta_1, \delta_2; \alpha}, \tag{16.17}$$

where $\delta_1 = r - 1$ and $\delta_2 = (r - 1)(c - 1)$.

As an illustration, let us use the data in Table 16.10 to test whether there are any significant difference between work designs and between assemblers.

1. For work designs A_j:

$$F_{4,12} = \frac{\text{MSC}}{\text{MSE}} \doteq \frac{27.05}{0.817} \doteq 33.11,$$

$$P(F_{4,12} > 5.41) = 0.01;$$

2. For assemblers B_i:

$$F_{3,12} = \frac{\text{MSR}}{\text{MSE}} \doteq \frac{24.40}{0.817} \doteq 29.87,$$

$$P(F_{3,12} > 5.95) = 0.01.$$

Thus both tests are significant at $\alpha = 0.01$. The work designs are different in efficiency and the assemblers are different in productivity.

The pairwise tests for A_j conducted earlier indicated that six out of the ten pairs of column treatment means were significantly different at $\alpha = 0.01$. For B_i now, we have

$$\text{LSD} = \sqrt{\frac{2}{c} \text{MSE}(F_0)} = \sqrt{\frac{2}{5}(0.817)(4.75)} \doteq 1.25;$$

$$\text{LSD} = \sqrt{\frac{2}{c} \text{MSE}(F_0)} = \sqrt{\frac{2}{5}(0.817)(9.33)} \doteq 1.75.$$

From the row treatment sample means in Table 16.9, we note that

	11.4	7.2	7.8	6.4
11.4	—			
7.2	4.2**	—		
7.8	3.6**	0.6	—	
6.4	5.0**	0.8	1.4*	—

Thus, three out of the six pairs of row means are significantly different at the 1% level of significance and one pair is significantly different at the 5% level of significance. The first assembler is by far the most productive worker. These conclusions are justified only if we are willing to regard the data as coming from the model whose assumptions were listed before for the last model.

16.5* COMPLETELY RANDOMIZED, TWO-VARIABLE CLASSIFICATION WITH REPLICATION MODEL

The Model

Like the preceding one, the completely randomized, two variable classification with replication is concerned with two independent treatment variables, or "factors." We have, however, two new points to consider. First, instead of a single observation for each combination of treatment levels, we have for this model two or more observations for each combination of treatment levels; namely, each cell in the table of data contains a sample of size $n_{ij} \geqslant 2$ selected from the treatment–combination population B_iA_j. Second, in the previous model, the column and row effects were assumed to be additive or independent; now we assume them to be possibly dependent and to possibly "interact" upon each other. The *interaction effect* is a type of effect produced by factors A and B jointly; it cannot be attributed to either factor alone.

In pharmacology the interaction effect is usually called a *synergistic effect*. An example is the lethal combination of barbiturate sleeping pills and alcoholic liquor. Each of these is a drug, and each reduces the number of heartbeats per minute. Their combined effect, however, is a much more severe reduction than one would expect, knowing their individual effects. This is actually a failure of the two treatments to be additive—their combined effect is much more than the sum of their individual effects. Another way of phrasing the synergistic effect is the following: the effect of one treatment differs, depending on the level of the other treatment. That is, the reduction in pulse due to alcohol is different, depending on whether barbiturates are in the person's system or not.

Another example of an interaction effect is an experiment on additives to pigs' diets presented by George W. Snedecor and William G. Cochran, in their *Statistical Methods,* Sixth Edition (Ames, Iowa, The Iowa State University Press, 1967). The farmer wants to know whether pigs will gain weight so much faster with these additives that it is worth their cost. The additives are an antibiotic and vitamin B_{12}. The results are rather strange: the "control group" of pigs receiving neither additive gain 1.19 pounds per day; the pigs receiving only the antibiotic gain 1.03 pounds per day, which is worse than the control group; the pigs receiving only the vitamin gain 1.22 pounds per day, which is about the same as the control group; the pigs receiving both the additives gain 1.54 pounds per day, which is better than the control group.

An F test for interaction, which is explained below, shows that interaction is significant at the 1% level. This means that the effect of one treatment differs, depending on the level of the other treatment. For example, what effect does feeding antibiotics have on pigs' weight gains? Without the vitamin, antibiotics reduce the weight gains from 1.19 pounds per day to 1.03 pounds per day—a reduction of 0.16 pound per day. With the vitamin, antibiotics increase the weight gains from 1.22 pounds per day to 1.54 pounds per day—an increase of 0.32 pound per day. In short, antibiotics either reduce weight gains by 0.16 pound per day or increase weight gains by 0.32 pound per day, depending on whether vitamin B_{12} is also given.

Sometimes there is an explanation for an interaction effect, and sometimes there is not. For the pigs' weight gains, it is speculated that the rather strange results are caused by organisms that live in the pigs' intestines. If only the vitamin is given, the organisms use it instead of the pigs. If only the antibiotic is given, the organisms are killed but the pigs suffer from a vitamin B_{12} deficiency. If both additives are given, the organisms are killed, which benefits the pigs, and the vitamin B_{12} fills the nutritional gap caused by the absence of the organisms.

Interaction is important because, if it is present, the effects of two treatments cannot be discussed separately. Interaction means that the effect of one treatment depends on the level of the other treatment.

Thus, the interaction of factors is a property in its own right that can be examined. Hypotheses concerning it can be tested. The evaluation of interaction effects has two important advantages in experimental design. The first is that two separate experiments with one variable in each are generally more expensive than one experiment with two factors. The second is that statistical inferences drawn from an experiment with more than one variable are usually more conclusive and broader in their applications, a major reason for this being the ability to test for interaction effects when replication is present.

The two-way classification model we are now introducing may be regarded as an extension of the randomized-blocks design already studied. Indeed, the current model is defined by exactly the same identity as (16.9a) under the assumption that a random sample of size n is drawn from each of the rc populations, all of which are normally distributed with equal variance σ^2. The same identity, however, does have a new interpretation owing to the inclusion of the interaction effect. Let us restate the identity for convenience.

$$(\mu_{ij} - \mu_{...}) = (\mu_{i.} - \mu_{...}) + (\mu_{.j} - \mu_{...}) + (\mu_{ij} - \mu_{i.} - \mu_{.j} + \mu_{...}).$$
(16.18a)

Again, let $\alpha_j = \mu_{.j} - \mu_{..}$ and $\beta_i = \mu_{i.} - \mu_{..}$ as column and row effects, respectively. Defining

$$I_{ij} = \mu_{ij} - \mu_{i.} - \mu_{.j} + \mu_{...}$$

as the interaction effect and

$$\epsilon_{ijk} = y_{ijk} - \mu_{ij}$$

as the error term, or the deviation of the kth observation from the mean of the treatment-combination population $B_i A_j$, then (16.18a) becomes

$$\mu_{ij} - \mu_{..} = \beta_i + \alpha_j + I_{ij}.$$

Or, equivalently,

$$y_{ijk} = \mu_{...} + \beta_i + \alpha_j + I_{ij} + \epsilon_{ijk},$$
(16.18b)

where the ϵ_{ijk} as before, are assumed to be independent and distributed as $n(0, \sigma^2)$. Furthermore, for convenience of solution without loss of generality, we also assume that

$$\sum_i \beta_i = \sum_j \alpha_j = \sum_i \sum_j I_{ij} = 0.$$

The Analysis

Table 16.11 gives the general presentation of sample data for the *completely randomized, two-variable classification with replication model*. One "cell" consists of the individual observations for a particular combination of values of A_j and B_i. One "row" is considered to be all the cells pertaining to one value of B_i. Careful study of this table will assist the reader's understanding of the partitioning of the total sum of squares and computation of the sums of squares for this model. It is assumed that each cell contains the same number of observations, n. Note that, in this table,

TABLE 16.11 Sample Data for the Completely Randomized, Two-variable Classification with Replication Model Having n Observations Per Cell

Row treatment	Column treatment				Total (or mean) of row-cell sums (or means)
	A_1	A_2	$\cdots$	A_c	
B_1	y_{111}	y_{121}	$\cdots$	y_{1c1}	
	y_{112}	y_{122}	$\cdots$	y_{1c2}	
	$\vdots$	$\vdots$		$\vdots$	
	y_{11n}	y_{12n}	$\cdots$	y_{1cn}	
Cell sum	$t_{11\cdot}$	$t_{12\cdot}$	$\cdots$	$t_{1c\cdot}$	$t_{1\cdot\cdot}$
Cell mean	$\bar{y}_{11\cdot}$	$\bar{y}_{12\cdot}$	$\cdots$	$\bar{y}_{1c\cdot}$	$\bar{y}_{1\cdot\cdot}$
B_2	y_{211}	y_{221}	$\cdots$	y_{2c1}	
	y_{212}	y_{222}	$\cdots$	y_{2c2}	
	$\vdots$	$\vdots$		$\vdots$	
	y_{21n}	y_{22n}	$\cdots$	y_{2cn}	
Cell sum	$t_{21\cdot}$	$t_{22\cdot}$	$\cdots$	$t_{2c\cdot}$	$t_{2\cdot\cdot}$
Cell mean	$\bar{y}_{21\cdot}$	$\bar{y}_{22\cdot}$	$\cdots$	$\bar{y}_{2c\cdot}$	$\bar{y}_{2\cdot\cdot}$
	$\cdot$	$\cdot$	$\cdots$	$\cdot$	$\cdot$
B_r	y_{r11}	y_{r21}	$\cdots$	y_{rc1}	
	y_{r12}	y_{r22}	$\cdots$	y_{rc2}	
	$\vdots$	$\vdots$		$\vdots$	
	y_{r1n}	y_{r2n}	$\cdots$	y_{rcn}	
Cell sum	$t_{r1\cdot}$	$t_{r2\cdot}$	$\cdots$	$t_{rc\cdot}$	$t_{r\cdot\cdot}$
Cell mean	$\bar{y}_{r1\cdot}$	$\bar{y}_{r2\cdot}$	$\cdots$	$\bar{y}_{rc\cdot}$	$\bar{y}_{r\cdot\cdot}$
Total of column-cell sums	$t_{\cdot1\cdot}$	$t_{\cdot2\cdot}$	$\cdots$	$t_{\cdot c\cdot}$	Grand sum $= t_{\cdots}$
Mean of column-cell means	$\bar{y}_{\cdot1\cdot}$	$\bar{y}_{\cdot2\cdot}$	$\cdots$	$\bar{y}_{\cdot c\cdot}$	Grand mean $= \bar{y}_{\cdots}$

1. $t_{ij.}$ stands for the cell sum—for example,

$$t_{11.} = y_{111} + y_{112} + \cdots + y_{11n};$$

2. $\bar{y}_{ij.}$ stands for the cell mean—for example,

$$\bar{y}_{21.} = \frac{1}{n} t_{21.},$$

which is an unbiased estimator for μ_{21};

3. $t_{..}$ stands for the row total—for example,

$$t_{1..} = t_{11.} + t_{12.} + \cdots + t_{1c.} = \sum_{j} \sum_{k} y_{1jk};$$

4. $\bar{y}_{i..}$ stands for the row mean—for example, $\bar{y}_{1..}$ is the mean for all observations for B_1 and it is defined as

$$\bar{y}_{1..} = \frac{1}{c}(\bar{y}_{11.} + \bar{y}_{12.} + \cdots + \bar{y}_{1c.})$$

$$= \frac{1}{cn} t_{1..};$$

5. $t_{.j.}$ stands for the column sum—for example,

$$t_{.2.} = t_{12.} + t_{22.} + \cdots + t_{r2.} = \sum_{i} \sum_{k} y_{i2k};$$

6. $\bar{y}_{.j.}$ stands for the column mean—for example, $\bar{y}_{.2.}$ is the mean for all observations for the second column, or A_2, and it is defined as

$$\bar{y}_{.2.} = \frac{1}{r}(\bar{y}_{12.} + \bar{y}_{22.} + \cdots + \bar{y}_{r2.})$$

$$= \frac{1}{rn} t_{.2.};$$

7. $t_{...}$ stands for the grand sum, equal to

$$\sum_{i=1}^{r} \sum_{j=1}^{c} \sum_{k=1}^{n} y_{ijk}.$$

8. $\bar{y}_{...}$ stands for the grand mean, defined as

$$\bar{y}_{...} = \frac{1}{rcn} t_{...}.$$

With the foregoing notation, we now have the sample model corresponding to (16.18a) and (16.18b) as follows:

$$(y_{ijk} - \bar{y}_{...}) = (\bar{y}_{i..} - \bar{y}_{...}) + (\bar{y}_{.j.} - \bar{y}_{...})$$

$$+ (\bar{y}_{ij.} - \bar{y}_{i..} - \bar{y}_{.j.} + \bar{y}_{...}) + (y_{ijk} - \bar{y}_{ij.}). \quad (16.19)$$

As can be shown, if we square both sides of (16.19) and sum over i, j, and k, the total sum of squares is decomposed into four portions as follows:

$$\sum_{i=1}^{r} \sum_{j=1}^{c} \sum_{k=1}^{n} (y_{ijk} - \bar{y}...)^2 \qquad \text{SST}$$

$$= \sum_{i=1}^{r} \sum_{j=1}^{c} \sum_{k=1}^{n} (\bar{y}_{i..} - \bar{y}...)^2 \qquad \text{SSR}$$

$$+ \sum_{i=1}^{r} \sum_{j=1}^{c} \sum_{k=1}^{n} (\bar{y}_{.j.} - \bar{y}...)^2 \qquad \text{SSC}$$

$$+ \sum_{i=1}^{r} \sum_{j=1}^{c} \sum_{k=1}^{n} (\bar{y}_{ij.} - \bar{y}_{i..} - \bar{y}_{.j.} + \bar{y}...)^2 \qquad \text{SSI}$$

$$+ \sum_{i=1}^{r} \sum_{j=1}^{c} \sum_{k=1}^{n} (y_{ijk} - \bar{y}_{ij.})^2, \qquad \text{SSE}$$

or

$$\text{SST} = \text{SSR} + \text{SSC} + \text{SSI} + \text{SSE}.$$

The foregoing sums of squares can be computed by the following formulas:

$$C = \text{correction factor} = \frac{1}{rcn} t_{...}^2; \qquad (16.20)$$

$$\text{SST} = \sum_{i=1}^{r} \sum_{j=1}^{c} \sum_{k=1}^{n} y_{ijk}^2 - C; \qquad (16.21)$$

$$\text{SSR} = \frac{1}{cn} \sum_{i=1}^{r} t_{i..}^2 - C; \qquad (16.22)$$

$$\text{SSC} = \frac{1}{rn} \sum_{j=1}^{c} t_{.j.}^2 - C; \qquad (16.23)$$

$$\text{SSE} = \sum_{i=1}^{r} \sum_{j=1}^{c} \sum_{k=1}^{n} y_{ijk}^2 - \frac{1}{n} \sum_{i=1}^{r} \sum_{j=1}^{c} t_{ij.}^2; \qquad (16.24)$$

$$\text{SSI} = \text{SST} - (\text{SSR} + \text{SSC} + \text{SSE}). \qquad (16.25)$$

These sums of squares, together with their respective degrees of freedom and mean squares, are given in Table 16.12. Again, we take

TABLE 16.12 ANOVA Table for the Completely Randomized Two-variable Classification with Replication Model Having n Observations Per Cell

Source of variation	SS	δ	MS
Between rows, B_i	SSR	$(r-1)$	$\text{MSR} = \text{SSR}/(r-1)$
Between columns, A_j	SSC	$(c-1)$	$\text{MSC} = \text{SSC}/(c-1)$
Interaction, I_{ij}	SSI	$(r-1)(c-1)$	$\text{MSI} = \text{SSI}/(r-1)(c-1)$
Error, ϵ_{ijk}	SSE	$rc(n-1)$	$\text{MSE} = \text{SSE}/rc(n-1)$
Total	SST	$rcn-1$	—

notice that all the mean squares are estimators of the population variance σ^2 when the null hypothesis is true. No matter which hypothesis is true, their expectations, as can be shown, are

$$E(\text{MSR}) = \sigma^2 + \frac{cn}{r-1} \sum_i \beta_i^2;$$

$$E(\text{MSC}) = \sigma^2 + \frac{rn}{c-1} \sum_j \alpha_j^2;$$

$$E(\text{MSI}) = \sigma^2 + \frac{n}{(r-1)(c-1)} \sum_i \sum_j I_{ij}^2;$$

$E(\text{MSE}) = \sigma^2$, provided all the levels of both treatments are set by the investigator rather than being chosen at random.

Thus, we see that all these estimators, except MSE, will estimate some quantity greater than σ^2, unless $\beta_i = 0$ for all i (for MSR); $\alpha_j = 0$ for all j (for MSC), or $I_{ij} = 0$ for all i and j (for MSI).

Finally, for this model, we obviously have three sets of hypotheses to consider. They are as follows.

1. Test on the interaction effects of both factors:

$$H_0: I_{ij} = 0, \qquad i = j, 2, \ldots, r,$$

$$j = 1, 2, \ldots, c;$$

$$H_1: I_{ij} \neq 0, \qquad \text{for some } i \text{ and } j.$$

The rejection for this test is:

$$\frac{\text{MSI}}{\text{MSE}} > F_{(r-1)(c-1), rc(n-1); \alpha}. \qquad (16.26)$$

2. Test on the row treatment (factor) effects:

$$H_0: \beta_i = 0, \qquad i = 1, 2, \ldots, r;$$

$$H_1: \beta_i \neq 0, \qquad \text{for some } i.$$

The rejection region for this test is

$$\frac{\text{MSR}}{\text{MSE}} > F_{(r-1), rc(n-1); \alpha}. \qquad (16.27)$$

3. Test on the column treatment (factor) effects:

$$H_0: \alpha_j = 0, \qquad j = 1, 2, \ldots, c;$$

$$H_1: \alpha_j \neq 0, \qquad \text{for some } j.$$

The rejection region for this test is

$$\frac{\text{MSC}}{\text{MSE}} > F_{(c-1),rc(n-1);\alpha}.$$ (16.28)

It is important to note that for this model, or any two-or-more-variables classification design, where an interaction effect is to be evaluated, we begin with the test of interaction. The reason here is that if we find interaction to be significant, then it becomes pointless to test the main effects. The fact that there is interaction means that both main effects are significant, in the special sense of interaction. If one were to test a main effect, the null hypothesis would be that it has no effect. Since, in the presence of significant interaction, we already know it has some effect, we do not (usually) test the main effects when interaction is significant. Naturally, when interaction is not significant, we then go ahead and test the main effects separately.

Example

Suppose a firm has available three machines of different makes, $B_i, i = 1, 2, 3$, and four different sources of raw material, $A_j, j = 1, 2, 3, 4$, for production of a new product. It is known that all three makes of machines are equally productive in terms of speed—the number of items produced per hour—but it is not known if they perform equally well in terms of the number of defectives produced among the hourly outputs. In addition, it is unknown to the firm whether there are any differences in quality for the raw materials from the four different sources. Finally, it is suspected that the raw material from one source may have some particular effect on a particular type of machine, or vice versa. Thus, it is desired to establish whether B_i are different, whether A_j are different, and whether there exists any joint effect, (B_iA_j).

To answer these questions, each make of machine is operated under identical conditions with each source of material for two hours, and the number of defective units for each hour is recorded. The results of this experiment are shown in Table 16.13. In view of the experimental results, what conclusions can be drawn? What make of machine and which source of raw material should the firm purchase?

The three sets of hypotheses to be evaluated for this example are:

1. Interaction between machines and raw materials is nil; namely, all $I_{ij} = 0$, against not all I_{ij} are zero.

2. Mean numbers of defectives per hour for all three makes of machine are equal; that is, all $\beta_i = 0$ against not all β_i are zero.

3. Mean numbers of defectives per hour for raw materials from all the four sources are equal; namely, all $\alpha_j = 0$, against not all α_j are zero.

TABLE 16.13 Data for the Machines and Raw Materials Example

	A_1	A_2	A_3	A_4	Total
B_1	9	6	8	5	
	5	6	4	7	
Cell totals	14	12	12	12	50
B_2	4	5	2	1	
	2	3	6	5	
Cell totals	6	8	8	6	28
B_3	10	8	7	9	
	6	9	8	5	
Cell totals	16	17	15	14	62
Total	36	37	35	32	140

For the data in Table 16.13, we have

$$C = \frac{1}{rcn} t_{...}^2 = \frac{1}{(3)(4)(2)} (140)^2 \doteq 816.667;$$

$$SST = \sum_i \sum_j \sum_k y_{ijk}^2 - C$$

$$= (9^2 + 5^2 + \cdots + 5^2) - 816.667 = 952 - 816.667 = 135.333;$$

$$SSR = \frac{1}{cn} \sum_i t_{i..}^2 - C$$

$$= \frac{1}{(4)(2)} (50^2 + 28^2 + 62^2) - 816.667 = 74.333;$$

$$SSC = \frac{1}{rn} \sum_j t_{.j.}^2 - C$$

$$= \frac{1}{(3)(2)} (36^2 + 37^2 + 35^2 + 32^2) - 816.667 = 2.333;$$

$$SSE = \sum_i \sum_j \sum_k y_{ijk}^2 - \frac{1}{n} \sum_i \sum_j t_{ij.}^2$$

$$= 952 - \tfrac{1}{2} (14^2 + 12^2 + \cdots + 6^2 + \cdots + 14^2)$$

$$= 55;$$

$$SSI = SST - (SSB + SSC + SSE)$$

$$= 135.333 - (74.333 + 2.333 + 55) = 3.667.$$

With these sums of squares, the ANOVA table for our example is as shown by Table 16.14.

TABLE 16.14 ANOVA Table for Machines and Raw Materials Data

Source of Variation	SS	δ	MS
Rows: machines	74.333	$3 - 1 = 2$	37.167
Columns: raw materials	2.333	$4 - 1 = 3$	0.778
Interaction: $(B_i A_j)$	3.667	$(3 - 1)(4 - 1) = 6$	0.611
Error	55	$(3)(4)(1) = 12$	4.583
Total	135.333	$(3)(4)(2) - 1 = 23$	—

From the results in Table 16.14, we have the following.

1. For whether $I_{ij} = 0$,

$$F = \frac{\text{MSI}}{\text{MSE}} = \frac{0.611}{4.583} \doteq 0.13, \text{ which is insignificant.}$$

2. For whether $\beta_i = 0$,

$$F = \frac{\text{MSR}}{\text{MSE}} = \frac{37.167}{4.583} \doteq 8.11 > F_{2,12;0.01} = 6.93.$$

3. For whether $\alpha_j = 0$,

$$F = \frac{\text{MSC}}{\text{MSE}} = \frac{0.778}{4.583} \doteq 0.17, \text{ which is insignificant.}$$

Thus we see there are neither significant column (raw materials) treatment effects nor joint effects between column and block treatments. There exist, however, highly significant differences between machines of different makes. These conclusions indicate that the firm should purchase the second make of machine, B_2 (the reader may try to explain why this should be), and that it can select any of the four sources of raw materials if their prices are the same. The validity of these conclusions depends on random sampling and on meeting assumptions 1 and 4 in the list just after (16.9b).

These methods must be modified when the cells have unequal numbers of observations, but the modifications are beyond the scope of this book.

16.6 ADDITIONAL GENERAL OBSERVATIONS

The aim of this chapter has been to introduce the reader to the basic principles of the analysis of variance and to impress upon him the power of this tool. Because a number of aspects of this amazingly versatile technique have been left untouched, it seems appropriate to make a few general remarks here about those things that have been omitted.

First, by now the reader may have gained the impression that the analysis of variance, especially for the two-way classification models, is mainly concerned with the generation of a series of F tests on the same set of data, while the partitioning of the total sum of squares into meaningful components is only a means to this end. This, however, would be a superficial viewpoint. The essence of the analysis of variance is that it permits the decomposition of all potential information in the data into exclusive and distinct parts, each reflecting only some specific aspect of the experiment. In the one-way classification model, for example, the mean square between groups reflects variations in both systematic experimental manipulations and chance phenomena, but the mean square within groups measures only the unsystematic random variations that are attributable to any chance experiment. These two statistics are two independent ways of summarizing data—the information provided by one is not redundant to the other. Therefore, they furnish the researcher with a basis on which to decide whether significant treatment effects exist.

Similarly, in the two-way classification models, the mean squares for both treatment factors are independent of each other and are not redundant to the mean square for error or for interaction. The analysis of variance enables us to separate and to identify the factors contributing to total variation. Thus, the process of partitioning, not the F ratios, is the heart of the analysis of variance.

In short, the analysis of variance sorts the information yielded by an experiment into neat, exclusive, and meaningful portions and helps us to judge the experimental treatments easily—however large the number of treatment factors is. This is exactly the reason that the multiple t tests are useless in comparing more than two populations. In other words, multiple t tests do not provide the nonredundant feature— the various differences between pairs of means do overlap in the information they give. As a result, one cannot assess the evidence for the overall existence of treatment effects from a complete set of such differences derived from multiple t tests.

Next we note that, in this chapter, we have introduced models for the analysis of variance up to two experimental variables. In experiments with three or more factors, the basic ideas of partition, means of squares, and F tests are the same, but the models become much more involved. For example, for a three-factor model, in addition to mean squares representing the joint effects of particular pairs of the classification variables, there is also a mean square that measures the simultaneous interaction among all three factors. Of course, experiments with many factors are very difficult, in terms of time and labor, to perform.

In addition to the practical difficulty mentioned above, there is also a theoretical limitation for complicated models. That is, in the analysis of variance, we have assumed that the F tests are independent. In reality, however, the F ratios are dependent chiefly because all F ratios in the same model share the same denominator—the mean square for error. It can be shown that if the assumption of independence holds, and if there are only three F tests, then we should expect about $3(0.01)$ or 0.03 of these tests to show significance at $\alpha = 0.01$ by chance alone. Moreover the probability is $1 - (0.99)^3$ or about 0.03 that at least one of these tests will show spurious significances when the null hypothesis is true. However, when (as is generally true) these F tests are not independent, we have no accepted standards for calculating the number expected by chance; we know only that the probability is between 0.01 and 0.03 for at least one spuriously significant result. For really complicated models, where many F tests are made with the same data, the probability that at least one spuriously significant result will occur may be very large; what is worse, this probability and that for a Type I error cannot be determined in a simple and routine manner.

Owing to practical difficulty and theoretical limitation, we must not yield to the temptation to include too many treatment factors in our analysis when sample data seem easy or cheap to obtain, or when we desire to have a model that is impressive. In business and economic research, as in any type of scientific investigation, we should be interested in obtaining meaningful results by simple designs if situations permit, rather than in the elegance or complexity of experiments that may furnish only results that have no clear interpretation.

All the models introduced in this chapter are *fixed-effects* models, since in these models the different levels of each factor are chosen in advance of the experiment and the treatments actually administered were thought of as exhausting all treatments of interest. For these models, therefore, the only conclusions that can be drawn are concerned with the particular levels and treatments or treatment combinations. By far, the most frequently encountered experiments are of this kind.

In addition to fixed-effects models, there are two other types of models: random-effects and mixed models. A *random-effects* model is one in which inferences are made about an entire set of distinct treatments on the basis of a random sample selected from such a treatments population. Thus, in the fixed-effects models, treatments actually observed are considered as populations. Such treatments, however, consititute only a random sample in the random-effects models. From a computational point of view, fixed-effects and random-effects models are the same. They differ from each other mainly in the inferences that are drawn.

A *mixed* model, as the name indicates, is a mixture of both fixed-effects and random-effects models. In such a model, one or more treatments have fixed effects and the remaining factors are sampled. Also, each observation now results in a score that is a sum of both fixed and random effects. Obviously, in mixed models, there must be at least two factors under investigation. For the simple two-factor design of mixed models, the computational procedure requires no change from the fixed-effects models, but there is an important difference in the F ratios used to test the different effects.

The analysis of variance has been developed under a set of rigid assumptions: (1) treatments or treatment combinations are normally distributed with common variance; (2) the treatment effects are additive; and (3) the experimental errors are independent and distributed as $n(0, \sigma^2)$. Whenever any of these assumptions is not met, the F tests cannot be employed to yield valid inferences. It is indeed fortunate that many economic and business experiments do conform, at least approximately, to these premises. It is not uncommon, however, to encounter experimental work where departures from these assumptions exist. In such a situation, the analysis of variance can sometimes still be applied after a transformation of the data. *Transformation* refers to a process of transforming the original data into some other form, such as square roots, reciprocals, inverse sines, or logarithms, before the analysis is made. The assumptions of normality, additivity, and homogeneity of variances are often violated together; hence, a single transformation that corrects one of these will usually also result in the improvement of data in other respects.

The procedures of analysis of variance with transformed data are identical to those for original data, but the results obtained must be converted back into the original units before intelligent and appropriate interpretations can be given. While transformation techniques are quite simple and straightforward, the selection of an appropriate form of transformation for a particular set of data requires considerable theoretical knowledge in the field of statistics.

GLOSSARY OF FORMULAS

(16.1) $(y_{ij} - \mu) = \alpha_j + \epsilon_{ij}.$

This expression represents the completely randomized, one-variable classification model of ANOVA. For this model, we have c populations (treatments) that are normally distributed with μ_j and a common variance σ^2. In this equation, y_{ij} is the ith observation drawn at random from the jth population; $\alpha_j(= \mu_j - \mu)$ is called the treatment effect since it measures the possible effects of treatments on the response y_{ij}; $\epsilon_{ij}(= y_{ij} - \mu_j)$ is the error term, the deviation of y_{ij} from μ_j due to random variations. In this model, we test $H_0: \alpha_j = 0$ against H_1: not all α_j are zero. This model is designed to test equality among three or more means with equal or unequal sample sizes.

(16.2) $(y_{ij} - \bar{y}_{..}) = (\bar{y}_{..} - \bar{y}_{.i}) + (y_{ij} - \bar{y}_{.j}).$

This expression is the sample model corresponding to (16.1). The three components are estimators for $(y_{ij} - \mu_{..})$, α_j, and ϵ_{ij}, respectively. It also reveals how total variation of y_{ij} from the grand population mean μ is decomposed into two mutually exclusive and independent components: those due to possible treatment effects and those due to chance variations alone.

(16.3) $\text{SST} = \sum_j \sum_i y_{ij}^2 - n\bar{y}_{..}^2;$

(16.4) $\text{SSC} = \sum_j n_j \bar{y}_{.j}^2 - n\bar{y}_{..}^2;$

(16.5) $\text{SSE} = \sum_j \sum_i y_{ij}^2 - \sum_j n_j \bar{y}_{.j}^2.$

These are the computational equations for the sample sums of squares for model (16.2). For this model, the total sum of squares, defined as $\text{SST} = \sum_j \sum_i (y_{ij} - \bar{y}_{..})^2$, is partitioned into the sum of squares between (among columns), defined as $\text{SSC} = \sum_j \sum_i (\bar{y}_{.j} - \bar{y}_{..})^2$, and the sum of squares within (error) defined as $\sum_j \sum_i (y_{ij} - \bar{y}_{.j})^2$. The number of degrees of freedom for these three sums are $n - 1$ for SST, $c - 1$ for SSC, and $n - c$ for SSE. Each of these sums divided by its number of degrees of freedom is an estimator for the common variance σ^2 and they are called mean squares and are denoted as MS.

(16.6) $$\frac{\text{MSC}}{\text{MSE}} > F_{\delta_1, \delta_2; \alpha}.$$

Since the test statistic for $\alpha_j = 0$ in model (16.1) is $F = \text{MSC}/\text{MSE}$, so the region of rejection for this test is as defined by (16.6). Note that if treatment effects are nil, then MSC/MSE will be close to 1; otherwise it will be significantly greater than 1.

(16.7a) $$\text{LSD} = \sqrt{\frac{2}{n_0}(\text{MSE})(F_0)};$$

(16.7b) $$\text{LSD} = \sqrt{\left(\frac{1}{n_j} + \frac{1}{n_k}\right)(\text{MSE})(F_0)}.$$

Each of these two equations defines what is called the least significant difference in pairwise tests. Equation (16.7a) is for the case of equal sample sizes; (16.7b) is for unequal sample sizes. Two sample means are said to be significantly different at a given level of significance if their absolute difference is greater than LSD. In both expressions, F_0 is such that $P(F_{1, \delta_2} > F_0) = \alpha$. LSD can be employed to locate where the difference is only when the null hypothesis of equal treatment means has been rejected. Pairwise tests by using LSD can also be employed for randomized-blocks, one-variable classification, and completely randomized two-variable classification without replication models.

(16.8) $$\chi_\delta^2 = \frac{2.3026[\log S_w^2 \sum (n_j - 1) - \sum (n_j - 1) \log S_j^2]}{1 + \frac{1}{3(c - 1)}\left[\sum\left(\frac{1}{n_j - 1}\right) - \frac{1}{\sum (n_j - 1)}\right]}.$$

This statistic with $\delta = c - 1$, developed by Bartlett, is used to test the null hypothesis that three or more population variances are equal. The use of this test statistic requires that the samples are independent, that the populations are normally distributed, and that the population variances are equal. In this expression, S_w^2 stands for the weighted estimator for the common population variance σ^2, and the weights used are the numbers of degrees of freedom for S_j^2.

(16.9a) $\mu_{ij} - \mu_{..} = (\mu_{i.} - \mu_{..}) + (\mu_{ij} - \mu_{i.} - \mu_{.j} + \mu_{..})$;

(16.9b) $y_{ij} = \mu_{..} + \beta_i + \alpha_j + \epsilon_{ij}$.

These two equations are the alternative expressions for both the randomized-blocks, one-variable classification model and the two-variable classification without replication model. In both cases, we assume the grand population mean, $\mu_{..}$, is located at a position such that $\sum \alpha_j = 0$ and $\sum \beta_i = 0$. Furthermore, we also assume that the rc populations are normally distributed with a common variance σ^2, that the column (α_j) as well as block (β_i) effects are additive, so that there is no interaction effects, and that the errors are independent and normally distributed with zero mean and a variance identical to the common variance of the rc populations. In the randomized-blocks design we are only interested in the column effects and blocks are treated merely as experimental material to which column treatments have been assigned at random. In the randomized, two-variable classification model, however, we consider both A_j and B_i as independent variables and evaluate them simultaneously.

(16.10) Identical with (16.9a). See earlier comments.

(16.11) $C = \dfrac{1}{rc} t_{..}^2$.

(16.12) $\text{SST} = \displaystyle\sum_i^r \sum_j^c y_{ij}^2 - C$;

(16.13) $\text{SSB} = \dfrac{1}{c} \displaystyle\sum_i t_{i.}^2 - C$;

(16.14) $\text{SSC} = \dfrac{1}{r} \displaystyle\sum_j t_{.j}^2 - C$;

(16.15) $\text{SSE} = \text{SST} - (\text{SSB} + \text{SSC})$.

The equations in this group are the computational formulas for the sums of squares for the two models discussed above for (16.9). Here, C is the correction factor. It is important to recall that for SSB, $\delta = r - 1$; for SSC, $\delta = c - 1$; for SSE, $\delta = (r - 1)(c - 1)$; for SST, $\delta = rc - 1$. Again, each of these sums divided by its δ is an estimator of the common variance of the rc populations.

(16.16) $\dfrac{\text{MSC}}{\text{MSE}} > F_{\delta_1, \delta_2; \alpha}$.

To test $\alpha_j = 0$ in the randomized-blocks one-variable classification model, we use $F = \text{MSC}/\text{MSE}$ as the test statistic. Here, $\delta_1 = c - 1$ and $\delta_2 = (r - 1)(c - 1)$. Thus, the rejection region for this test is defined by (16.16).

(16.17) $\dfrac{\text{MSB}}{\text{MSE}} > F_{\delta_1, \delta_2; \alpha}.$

In the completely randomized two-variable classification mode, in addition to testing $\alpha_j = 0$ by (16.16), we would also wish to test $\beta_i = 0$ with $F = \text{MSB}/\text{MSE}$ as the test statistic. For this F, $\delta_1 = r - 1$ and $\delta_2 = (r - 1)(c - 1)$.

(16.18a) $(\mu_{ij} - \mu_{...}) = (\mu_{i\cdot} - \mu_{...}) + (\mu_{\cdot j} - \mu_{...}) + (\mu_{ij} - \mu_{i\cdot} - \mu_{\cdot j} + \mu_{...});$

(16.18b) $y_{ijk} = \mu_{...} + \beta_i + \alpha_j + I_{ij} + \epsilon_{ijk}.$

These are the alternative expressions for the completely randomized, two-variable classification with replication model. This model can be considered as an extension of the model defined by (16.9) under the assumptions that a random sample of size n, $n \geq 2$, is drawn from each of the rc populations, all of which are normally distributed with common variance σ^2. However, the current identity does have a new interpretation because of the inclusion of the interaction term I_{ij} as shown by (16.18b). In (16.18b), I_{ij} is defined by the last term on the right-hand side of (16.18a). Furthermore, in (16.18b), the ϵ_{ijk} are assumed to be independent and are $n(0, \sigma^2)$.

(16.19) $(y_{ijk} - \bar{y}_{...}) = (\bar{y}_{i\cdot\cdot} - \bar{y}_{...}) + (\bar{y}_{\cdot j\cdot} - \bar{y}_{...})$
$$+ (\bar{y}_{ij\cdot} - \bar{y}_{i\cdot\cdot} - \bar{y}_{\cdot j\cdot} + \bar{y}_{...}) + (y_{ijk} - \bar{y}_{ij\cdot}).$$

This is the sample model equation corresponding to (16.18a). It also suggests that the total sum of squares in this model, SST, is partitioned into the four components SSR, SSC, SSI, and SSE. The computation formulas for these sums of squares are given by next group of equations.

(16.20) $C = \dfrac{1}{rcn} t^2_{...};$

(16.21) $\text{SST} = \displaystyle\sum_i^r \sum_j^c \sum_k^n y^2_{ijk} - C;$

(16.22) $\text{SSR} = \dfrac{1}{cn} \displaystyle\sum_i t^2_{i\cdot\cdot} - C;$

(16.23) $\text{SSC} = \dfrac{1}{rn} \displaystyle\sum_j t^2_{\cdot j\cdot} - C;$

(16.24) $\text{SSE} = \displaystyle\sum_i^r \sum_j^c \sum_k^n y^2_{ijk} - \dfrac{1}{n} \sum_i^r \sum_j^c t^2_{ij\cdot};$

These computational formulas are for the model of completely randomized two-variable classification ANOVA. Be sure to recall that for SST, $\delta = rcn - 1$; for SSR, $\delta = r - 1$; for SSC, $\delta = c - 1$; for SSI,

$\delta = (r - 1)(c - 1)$; for SSE, $\delta = rc(n - 1)$. Again, each of these sums of squares divided by its number of degrees of freedom is an estimator for σ^2—the common variance of the rc populations.

(16.26) $$\frac{MSI}{MSE} > F_{(r-1)(c-1),rc(n-1);\alpha};$$

(16.27) $$\frac{MSR}{MSE} > F_{(r-1),rc(n-1);\alpha};$$

(16.28) $$\frac{MSC}{MSE} > F_{(c-1),rc(n-1);\alpha}.$$

These three espressions define the regions of rejection for testing $I_{ij} = 0$, $\beta_i = 0$, and $\alpha_j = 0$, respectively, for the model defined by (16.18). Note that for any ANOVA models with two-or-more-variables classification design, where an interaction effect is to be evaluated, we usually begin with the test of interaction. This is so if we find that interaction is significant, it becomes pointless to test the main effects.

REVIEW QUESTIONS

16.1 What is the difference between "observational data" and "experimental data"?

16.2 Try to explain why, in ANOVA, it is possible to reach conclusions about the possible differences among three or more population means by analyzing sums of squares.

16.3 Why is the completely randomized one-variable classification model of ANOVA just an extension of the t test for the equality between two population means? What are the advantages of this ANOVA model over a possible series of t test when we wish to evaluate three or more population means?

16.4 What are the assumptions for the completely randomized one-variable classification model?

16.5 In ANOVA models, variables are classified as independent and dependent variables. What is (are) the independent variable(s) and what is *the* dependent variable?

16.6 Use the first model for ANOVA introduced in this chapter to explain that the numbers of degrees of freedom for the various sums of squares are additive just as the sums of squares themselves.

16.7 Use the first model introduced in this chapter to explain in your own words the facts that MSE is always an unbiased estimator for the common population variance and that MSC may or may not be an unbiased estimator for the same parameter.

16.8 What is the "least significant difference"? What is it used for? Under what conditions can it be used?

16.9 Explain the rationale behind the testing procedure of the randomized-blocks, one-variable classification model? How does this model differ from the completely randomized two-variable classification without replication model?

16.10 Explain, in your own words, the rationale of the testing procedure of the completely randomized, two-variable classification with replication model.

16.11 What are the basic and common assumptions made for all the ANOVA models introduced in this chapter?

16.12 What is the most important feature in analyzing experimental data irrespective of the model under consideration?

16.13 How are fixed effects, random effects, and mixed effects models in ANOVA differentiated?

16.14 What are the difficulties involved in the analysis of variance for complicated models?

16.15 In Section 16.1, it was pointed out that results of an experiment would not be conclusive for at least three reasons? What are they? How can they be overcome? Now, with the completion of this chapter, do you think you can use a concrete example of your own to answer these two questions?

PROBLEMS

Note: All the problems for this chapter involve small samples and relatively simple numbers, so they can all be solved manually without much effort. When we are concerned with real problems for analysis of variance, computations may become highly tedious or even simply not feasible without the aid of computers. Packaged computer programs are readily available for ANOVA. It must be observed, however, that packaged ANOVA programs are usually keyed to specific designs; a program for each ANOVA model. You are recommended to work out problems 16.1, 16.8, and 16.11 by hand and all the rest by computer if you wish. Also in some packages there are separate programs for ANOVA proper, the LSD, and the test of homogeneity of population variances.

16.1 An experiment on the behavior of small random samples produced the data in Table 16.P1 from normal population with a common mean of 10 and common variance of 1.

TABLE 16.P1

Sample 1: A_1	Sample 2: A_2	Sample 3: A_3
12.9	9.5	9.1
13.2	11.2	10.7
11.3	9.0	10.8
9.0	9.0	10.5
10.6	10.5	9.6

Run an analysis of variance on these data at $\alpha = 0.05$. Can the LSD be used in this situation? Explain why or why not. If it can, use it to determine which pairs of sample means are significantly different.

16.2 An experiment on the behavior of small random samples produced the data in Table 16.P2 from normal populations for which the means are 5, 10, and 15, respectively, and which have a common variance of 1.

TABLE 16.P2

Sample 1: A_1	Sample 2: A_2	Sample 3: A_3
3.7	10.2	13.8
3.5	8.9	13.9
6.8	11.5	15.1
5.5	8.5	13.9
4.4	10.7	15.5

Run an analysis of variance on these data at $\alpha = 0.05$. Can the LSD be used in this situation? Explain why or why not? If it can, use it to decide which pairs of sample means are significantly different.

16.3 Four different makes of "gasoline-saving" cars were tested for gas consumption. Four cars of each make were selected at random. Each was driven over the same 500-mile course with the results shown in Table 16.P3.

TABLE 16.P3

A_1	A_2	A_3	A_4
30	20	25	17
29	22	24	20
31	19	20	18
24	23	26	17

a. Are the mean miles per gallon of the four makes of cars the same at $\alpha = 0.05$?
b. If H_0 is rejected, what is LSD at $\alpha = 0.05$? Specify the pairs of means, if any, that are significantly different.
c. Name some factors besides makes that could affect the data of Table 16.P3 and thereby produce the appearance of differences among the makes, judging from the quantitative data, even though such an appearance might be seriously misleading.

16.4 An agricultural experimental station wishes to determine the yields of five varieties of corn. Each type of corn is planted on four plots of land with equal fertility, and the yields, in units of 100 bushels, are as in Table 16.P4.

TABLE 16.P4

A_1	A_2	A_3	A_4	A_5
4	7	5	11	4
6	13	4	10	8
4	10	4	9	6
10	12	9	14	10

a. In view of these results, can we conclude that the mean yields of the five varieties of corn are the same at the 5% level of significance?
b. Apply the pairwise test to the results if appropriate.

16.5 Miss Smith, supervisor of a secretarial pool, has four typists under her supervision. She is concerned with the length of their coffee break, so she times them. Her observations, recorded in minutes, for each girl are as in Table 16.P5. Can the differences in average time that the four typists spent on coffee breaks be explained by chance variation at 5% and 10% levels of significance, respectively. Apply the pairwise test to the result if appropriate.

TABLE 16.P5

A_1	A_2	A_3	A_4
27	20	24	20
35	22	22	18
18	30	25	26
24	27	25	19
28	22	20	26
32	24	21	24
16	28	34	26
18	21	18	──
25	23	32	159
──	18	23	
223	30	22	
	32	──	
	──	266	
	322		

16.6 We wish to test whether there are any differences in the durability of three makes of computers. A random sample of size 5 is selected from each make, and the frequency of repair during the first year of purchase is observed. The results are as in Table 16.P6.

TABLE 16.P6

A_1	A_2	A_3
10	6	5
11	7	3
9	8	4
9	6	2
8	5	1

From the above data, what conclusion can you draw as to whether a significant difference exists between A_j? Which treatment means seems to have produced the difference? Answer both questions at $\alpha = 0.05$ and $\alpha = 0.01$.

16.7 Four different makes of machines are used to produce a certain kind of cotton piece goods. Samples of size 4, with each unit as 100 square yards, are selected from outputs of the machines at random, and the number of flaws in each 100 square yards are counted with the results in Table 16.P7.

TABLE 16.P7

A_1	A_2	A_3	A_4
20	13	8	9
24	17	10	5
19	15	12	7
21	14	9	4

From the above data, can the null hypothesis of equal means be rejected at the 5% level of significance? At the 1% level of significance? Which pairs of means are significantly different at $\alpha = 0.05$? At $\alpha = 0.01$?

16.8 A random sample is selected from each of three makes of ropes, and their breaking strengths (in pounds) are measured, with results in Table 16.P8.

TABLE 16.P8

A_1	A_2	A_3
95	121	82
87	130	73
90	99	76
88	119	70
101	125	81
	127	71
	120	

Test whether there are any differences in the mean breaking strengths of the ropes at $\alpha = 0.05$. Which pairs of means are significantly different at 5% level of significance?

16.9 Conduct a test of homogeneity of population variances for the data in Problem 16.2 at 5% and 1% levels of significance.

16.10 Conduct a test of homogeneity of population variances for data in Problem 16.5 at 5% and 1% levels of significance.

16.11 Conduct a test of homogeneity of population variances for data in Problem 16.8 at 5% and 1% levels of significance.

16.12 A time-and-motion study is conducted to determine the best method of assembling a simple mechanism; three methods are under evaluation. Five assemblers are selected at random from all the assemblers in the factory. After they are given training to familiarize them with the particular methods chosen for the experiment, a test is conducted; and number of assemblies completed in one hour is recorded, with the results in Table 16.P9.

TABLE 16.P9

Assembler	Method			Total
	A_1	A_2	A_3	
1	2	4	5	11
2	3	4	6	13
3	5	7	8	20
4	7	9	11	27
5	6	5	9	20
Total	23	29	39	91

a. Make an analysis of variance of the above data at $\alpha = 0.05$.
b. Perform the pairwise test at $\alpha = 0.05$.
c. What is the population about which this test is generalized?
d. What is the importance of the random selection of the assemblers?

16.13 Suppose that we are interested in establishing the yield-producing ability of four types of soybeans. We have three blocks of land that may be different in fertility. Each block of land is divided into four plots, and the types of soybeans are assigned to the plots in each block by a random procedure. The results obtained are shown in Table 16.P10.

TABLE 16.P10

	Soybeans			
Land	A_1	A_2	A_3	A_4
B_1	5	9	11	10
B_2	4	7	8	10
B_3	3	5	8	9

a. Test whether A_j are significantly different at $\alpha = 0.05$ and $\alpha = 0.01$.
b. Perform the pairwise test for A_j at $\alpha = 0.05$ and at $\alpha = 0.01$.

16.14 A chemist is interested in determining the effects of storage temperature on the preservation of apples. The variable under consideration is the number of apples that are rotten after a month of storage. He decides to use five lots of applies as the blocks of experimental material. He selectes 120 apples from each lot, divides them into four portions of equal size, and assigns the treatments at random to the portions. The treatments are arbitrarily set as follows:

A_1 = storage with temperature at 50°,

A_2 = storage with temperature at 55°,

A_3 = storage with temperature at 60°,

A_4 = storage with temperature at 70°.

This experiment yields the results in Table 16.P11 in terms of the number of rotten apples.

TABLE 16.P11

	Temperature Treatment				
Lots	A_1	A_2	A_3	A_4	Total
1	8	5	7	10	30
2	14	10	3	5	32
3	12	8	6	5	31
4	9	8	5	7	29
5	12	9	4	8	33
Total	55	40	25	35	155

a. Test whether or not here is any significant difference due to storage temperature at $\alpha = 0.05$.
b. Perform the pairwise test for A_j at $\alpha = 0.05$.

16.15 Four different drugs have been developed for a certain disease. These drugs are used in three different hospitals, and the results given in Table 16.P12 show the number of cases of recovery from the disease per 100 people who have taken the drugs. The randomized-blocks design has been employed to eliminate the effects of the different hospitals.

TABLE 16.P12

	A_1	A_2	A_3	A_4
B_1	10	11	12	10
B_2	19	9	18	7
B_3	11	8	23	5

What conclusion can you draw at $\alpha = 0.05$?

16.16 Make an analysis of variance for data in Problem 16.15 according to the completely randomized, two-variable classification model. Also, perform the pairwise tests for A_j and B_i. Do both with $\alpha = 0.05$.

16.17 Suppose that there are four types of corn and three types of fertilizer, and we wish to test the difference between the corns and between the fertilizers. Using the completely randomized, two-variable classification model, we obtain the yields in Table 16.P13.

TABLE 16.P13

Fertilizer	Corn			
	A_1	A_2	A_3	A_4
B_1	12	11	13	15
B_2	6	8	5	9
B_3	4	3	2	4

a. Does there exist a significant difference between the types of corn at $\alpha = 0.05$?
b. Does there exist a significant difference between fertilizers at $\alpha = 0.05$?
c. Perform the pairwise test for A_j and for B_i at $\alpha = 0.05$.

16.18 Are the block effects for data in Problem 16.14 nil, assuming completely randomized design?

16.19 Suppose that the data in Problem 16.15 are designed for the completely randomized, two-variable classification model.
a. Test whether there is a significant difference in recoveries owing to different drugs.
b. Test whether there is a significant difference in recoveries owing to different hospitals.
c. If the answer to (b) is yes, what factors could have contributed to these "block effects"?

16.20 There are two machines of different makes and three operators of different skills for the production of a certain product. We are interested in testing whether there is a difference in the machines A_j, in the operators B_i and if there is any interaction I_{ij}. Each combination of A_j, B_i produces the items for a number of hours, and $n_{ij} = 2$ hourly output figures are selected at random; the results are in Table 16.P14.

TABLE 16.P14

	A_1	A_2
B_1	9	16
	10	15
B_2	6	12
	8	10
B_3	2	11
	3	10

a. Test whether there is a significant difference between machines.
b. Test whether there is a significant difference between operators.
c. Test whether there is a joint effect, or interaction.

16.21 An experiment is conducted on the life of cutting tools in which variables of interest are the type of metal A_j, $j = 1, 2, 3$, and speed of the lathes B_i, $i = 1, 2, 3$. Suppose that the following data in Table 16.P15, given in hundreds of hours of effective use of the tools, are obtained.

TABLE 16.P15

Speed	Type of Metal		
	A_1	A_2	A_3
High: B_1	6	9	10
	4	8	9
	7	6	5
Medium: B_2	11	13	14
	10	10	12
	9	11	15
Low: B_3	9	8	10
	7	10	9
	6	9	12

a. Test whether there is a significant difference between metals A_j.
b. Test whether there is a significant difference between speeds B_i.
c. Test whether there is an interaction effect, I_{ij}. (For all three tests, set $\alpha = 0.05$ and $\alpha = 0.01$.)

17 Linear Bivariate Analyses

17.1 ASSOCIATION BETWEEN VARIABLES

Our study of statistical methods so far has been mainly concerned with cross-section univariate data. In this and the next two chapters we shall present statistical analyses of bivariate and multivariate populations. You may recall that a *bivariate population* is one that contains two measurements on each elementary unit. For instance, we may observe the height and weight of each individual in a population of adult men. All measured heights would be the values of a variable, say, X; all the weights, values of another variable, say, Y. We would then have a set of *bivariate data*. When each element of a population can yield three or more measurements, each referring to a specific characteristic, we would have what is called *multivariate data*. For example, for each household in the United States, we may observe its consumption expenditures, disposable income, level of liquid assets, and the number of people; as a result, we would have four variables with which to work.

The main objective of analyzing bivariate and multivariate data is to discover and measure the association or covariation between the variables; that is, to determine how the variables change *together*. When the average relationship between variables can be established mathematically in some functional form, we will be able to estimate quite accurately, on the average, the value of one variable on the basis of the value(s) of the other variable(s). Such a procedure may be called *estimation by association*.

There are two related but distinct aspects of the study of

657

estimation by association. The first is *regression analysis*, which attempts to establish the "nature or type of relationship" between variables; that is, to study the functional relationship between the variables and thereby to provide a mechanism of prediction or forecasting. Hence, regression analysis is quite sophisticated and very useful, since prediction is the central function of all sciences. The main task of any scientific investigation is to discover the general relationships between observed variables and to express the nature of such relationships precisely in mathematical terms in order to make useful predictions.

A word of caution is in order here. When the relationship between variables is sharp and precise, ordinary mathematical methods suffice. Algebraic and trigonometric relationships have been successfully studied for centuries. The bulk of conventional business and economic theories, whether expressed in diagrammatic or algebraic forms, postulate exact functional relationships between variables. However, the most elementary acquaintance with business and economic data indicates that points do not lie precisely on straight lines or other smooth functions. Thus, in reality, business and economic relationships are blurred and imprecise. Given this, ordinary mathematical methods are not very helpful, but statistical methods are. The special contribution of statistics in this context is that of handling vague, blurred, or imprecise relationships between variables. With statistical methods we can measure whether the vagueness is so great that there is no useful relationship at all. If there is only a moderate amount of imprecision, we can calculate statistically what the best prediction would be and also qualify the prediction to take into account the imprecision of the relationship.

The second aspect of association study is *correlation analysis*, which has the objective of determining the "degree or strength of the relationship" between variables. From a practical point of view, correlation analysis is not as important as regression study. However, correlation analysis does provide two useful side benefits. First, it helps to interpret some of the regression results more precisely. Second, it enables us to select the most important variables to be included in a multiple regression study. Accordingly, our discussion of association will stress regression analysis and will take up correlation analysis in a supporting role.

Association analysis can also be distinguished as *simple* and *multiple*: the former is concerned with only two variables; the latter with three or more variables. Furthermore, there is also the differentiation between *linear* and *nonlinear* association studies, according to the types of relationship that the variables have.

Bivariate analysis of the linear type will be the topic for discussion in this chapter. Multivariate linear association studies will be taken up in the next chapter. In Chapter 19, we present nonlinear association analyses, simple and multiple, and some other aspects of regression analysis. It is important to appreciate that a thorough understanding of simple linear association analyses is essential to successful learning of multiple and nonlinear relationships.

17.2 THE LINEAR BIVARIATE REGRESSION MODEL

The linear bivariate regression model is also called the *classical simple linear regression model*. The assumptions that specify this model and the implications of the assumptions are stated below.

(1) **LINEARITY** *A dependent, or explained, variable Y is linearly related to an independent, or explanatory, variable, X, by*

$$y_i = \beta_1 + \beta_2 x_i + u_i. \tag{17.1}$$

This expression is called the *population model equation* for the simple linear regression model. In this expression, y_i and x_i are the individual values of Y and X, respectively; β_1 and β_2 are the unknown regression parameters called the *population regression coefficients*; u_i stands for an individual value of U, the *random disturbance,* or *error term*.

Note that the simple linear dependence relationship defined by (17.1) consists of two parts: the *systematic* part identified by $\beta_1 + \beta_2 x_i$ and the *stochastic* part identified by u_i. This decomposition reminds us that (17.1) is a probabilistic instead of a deterministic model.

The stochastic nature of the regression model implies that the value of Y can never be predicted exactly as it can in a deterministic model. The uncertainty concerning Y is attributable to the presence of the error term u_i. There are three possible, though not mutually exclusive, reasons for the presence of u_i. First, U is a random variable that imparts randomness to Y. For example, children of the same age can never be expected to have the same weights, owing to the influence of many "random" forces, most of which cannot even be identified. Hence, we can interpret the error term as an inherent randomness in behavior. Second, U can arise because of the exclusion of other important and relevant explanatory variables in the model. For example, if we are studying the influence of disposable income on consumption expenditure, we can never expect families with the same disposable income to have the same consumption expenditure. This is due to the fact that, in addition to disposable income, many other factors, such as the number of people in the family, the ages of the parents and children, and so on, would also influence a family's consumption expenditure. Indeed, this is the main reason that leads to multiple regression analysis. The third source of error lies in errors of observation or measurement of the values of Y. In a particular application of regression analysis, any one of these reasons could furnish a proper interpretation for U, or any pair of these reasons, or all three reasons together.

(2) **NONSTOCHASTIC X** *While Y is a random variable, X is a nonstochastic one with values fixed in repeated samples such that, for any sample size, the variance of X is finite and is different from zero.*

This assumption confines us to consider only those situations in which the values x_i of X are "fixed in repeated samples". The notion of "fixed

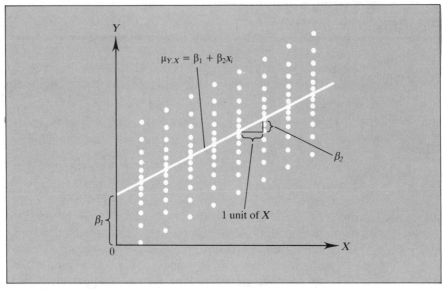

FIGURE 17.1 Distribution of subpopulations, Y's, associated with X values.

values of X" means that X has values selected or predetermined by the investigator. As such, x_i are either controllable or fully predictable. This assumption is equivalent to assuming that in an experimental framework we can choose a set of X values and hold them constant in repeated samples. Alternatively, we may think of establishing the properties of the estimators for the regression coefficients, β_1 and β_2, conditional upon given values of X and then, if in some applications we think it more appropriate to consider X as a random variable, see how these properties hold up for this change of assumption about X. Finally, the requirement that the variance of X be a finite number different from zero means that the values of X in the sample must not be all equal to the same number, and that they cannot change without limit as the sample size increases.

Now, the first and the second assumptions lead us to the conclusion that for each fixed value x_i of X, there is a probability distribution of Y values, where the Y values may be viewed as a *subpopulation* of Y. This is illustrated by Figure 17.1.

(3) NORMALITY *The error term associated with each value x_i of X is normally distributed with zero mean and an unknown but finite variance, σ_U^2.*

Since there are many forces working on the random residuals, U, and these forces are likely to be independent, an appeal to the Central Limit Theorem would justify a normal distribution for U. Furthermore, the numerous factors affecting the values of the dependent variable must be pulling in opposing directions, we would never expect small values of U to occur more frequently than large values, or vice versa. Thus, we can think of U as a variable with a probability distribution that has a zero mean and finite variance.

It is interesting to note that the normality of U imparts normality to the Y values. This means the Y values have a normal distribution on the condition that X has some specified value. Also, owing to the fact that $E(U) = 0$, we can deduce that the mean of y_i associated with x_i must be the systematic part in (17.1); that is, $\beta_1 + \beta_2 x_i$. Indeed, the conditional expectation of y_i given x_i is simply

$$
\begin{aligned}
E(y_i \mid x_i) = \mu_{Y.X} &= E(\beta_1 + \beta_2 x_i + u_i) \\
&= \beta_1 + \beta_2 E(x_i) + 0 \\
&= \beta_1 + \beta_2 x_i.
\end{aligned}
\tag{17.2}
$$

This newly derived result is called the *population regression equation of Y on X*. It gives us the mean value of Y given a fixed value of X, hence the notation $\mu_{Y.X}$. In (17.2), β_1 is the mean value of Y when $X = 0$; β_2 measures the change in the mean value of Y per unit change in the value of X. The graph of (17.2) is called the *population regression line*. If the assumption of linearity is met, the conditional means of Y values associated with all fixed values must fall on the straight population regression line. See Figure 7.1 again. Graphically, β_1 is the Y-intercept and β_2 is the slope of the regression line.

(4) HOMOSCEDASTICITY *This assumption states that the conditional variance of each of the normally distributed subpopulations of Y given X has the same numerical value for all x_i. Furthermore, this constant conditional variance of Y, denoted as $\sigma^2_{Y.X}$, is identical with the variance of the error term; that is, $\sigma^2_{Y.X} \equiv \sigma^2_U$.*

The identity between $\sigma^2_{Y.X}$ and σ^2_U is quite easy to verify. Refer to (17.1) and for any value of X we have

$$
\begin{aligned}
V(y_i \mid x_i) = \sigma^2_{Y.X} &= E(y_i - \mu_{Y.X})^2 \\
&= E[\beta_1 + \beta_2 x_i + u_i - E(\beta_1 + \beta_2 x_i + u_i)]^2 \\
&= E(\beta_1 + \beta_2 x_i + u_i - \beta_1 - \beta_2 x_i)^2 \\
&= E(u_i)^2 = \sigma^2_U.
\end{aligned}
$$

The square root of $V(y_i \mid x_i)$ is the *population standard deviation of the regression* and it is denoted as $\sigma_{Y.X}$, or σ_U. Clearly, $\sigma_{Y.X}$ also has the same value for each of the x_i.

(5) NONAUTOREGRESSION *The random disturbances should be nonautoregressive; namely, they should not be serially correlated. Alternatively, this assumption means that the covariance of the successive terms of U should be zero; that is,*

$$
E(u_i u_j) = 0, \quad i \neq j.
$$

This assumption implies that the random disturbances are independent in the probability sense. This would be the case if a positive or negative value of u_1 would not in any way influence the values of $u_2, u_3, \ldots, u_n$.

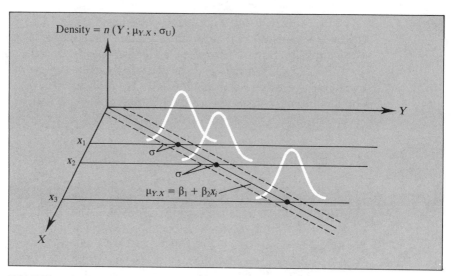

FIGURE 17.2 The classical normal linear regression model.

When this assumption is met, then the random character of U would be insured. The interpretation of nonautoregression as independence in the probability sense is quite justified because, as pointed out by A. S. Goldberger in his *Econometric Theory,* for normally distributed random variables, such as U here, uncorrelatedness implies independence.

The foregoing five assumptions completely specify the classical simple linear regression model. A graphic presentation of this model is given by Figure 17.2, which incorporates all these assumptions. The assumptions underlying this model are used in deriving estimators of the regression parameters. This model, as described by the five assumptions, involves three unknown parameters, the regression coefficients β_1, β_2, and σ_U^2 or $\sigma_{Y.X}^2$. We would also wish to conduct inferences about these parameters when the estimators have been established with sample data. It must be stressed here, however, that one or more of these assumptions is often violated in practice. Mild failures to meet all these assumptions are not particularly upsetting, but strong failures are. It is a good practice to check the sample data at least cursorily to see whether each of the assumptions is reasonable for that sample. A major portion of econometric theory is concerned with estimation problems of regression parameters when one or more of these assumptions are violated. Some of these problems will also be commented on later in this chapter.

17.3 ESTIMATION OF THE REGRESSION PARAMETERS

Alternative Estimation Procedures

Suppose that a simple random sample has been selected from a bivariate population of interest, and the investigator has predetermined each value of X; we would have a set of observations (x_i, y_i), $i = 1, 2, 3, \ldots, n$. Here, the sampling procedure is such that at least one value of Y must be selected at random for each x_i. Very often two or more observations of Y are made for each x_i. in any event, given the sample data set, the *sample linear regression model* becomes

$$y_i = B_1 + B_2 x_i + e_i \qquad (17.3)$$

and the *sample regression equation of Y on X* is given as

$$\hat{y}_i = B_1 + B_2 x_i. \qquad (17.4)$$

In these two equations, y_i and $\hat{y}_i$ denote the individual value of Y and the computed value (the estimated mean value) of Y, respectively. Also, B_1, B_2, and e_i are estimators for β_1, β_2, and u_i, respectively. Finally, in (17.4), B_1 is the *sample Y-intersect*, the mean value of Y given that $X = 0$, and B_2 is the *sample regression slope*, the change in the mean value of Y per unit change in the value of X.

From the previous two equations we see that

$$e_i = y_i - (B_1 + B_2 x_i)$$
$$= y_i - \hat{y}_i.$$

Thus, e_i is an individual deviation from a mean. As such, we have

$$\sum e_i = 0.$$

Now we come to the practical problem of how to obtain the values of B_1 and B_2. Three methods can be employed to obtain B_1 and B_2 from sample data. The first is the *method of least squares*. This method of estimation involves minimizing the sum of the observed values from their mean. The second method, the *best linear unbiased estimation* (BLUE), requires that the estimator be a linear combination of sample observations, that it be unbiased, and that its variance be smaller than that of any other linear unbiased estimator. Thus, by this method, one can derive the best linear unbiased estimators for β_1 and β_2. The third method that can be applied here is the *maximum likelihood method*. As you may recall, this method generates the maximum likelihood estimators, MLEs, of the parameters of a given population, considered to be those values of the parameters that would yield the observed sample results most often.

In practice, the method of least squares is almost universally employed for the estimation of regression parameters. There is ample motivation and justification of the popularity of this method. First of all, under the same set of assumptions, the least-squares estimators (LSEs) of β_1 and β_2 are identical as those obtained by the method of best linear unbiased estimation. Thus, LSEs are also BLUE. Secondly, the maximum likelihood estimators of β_1 and β_2 are also the same as the least-squares estimators. In addition, the least-squares method has reasonable and yet simple mathematical tractability that the other two methods do not possess.

In our discussion that follows we drop the subscripts attached to all quantities, since our summation will include all the individual values of the variables. However, you should keep in mind all the time that capital letters stand for variables and their individual values are denoted by the corresponding lower case letters.

The Method of Least Squares

The method of least squares has the nature of curve fitting. Given the linear dependence between X and Y and the n pairs of sample observations (x, y), this method produces estimators B_1 and B_2 in such a way that

$$\sum e^2 = \sum (y - \hat{y})^2 = \sum [y - (B_1 + B_2 x)]^2$$

is a minimum. Here, the e values are, as shown by the scatter diagram in Figure 17.3, the vertical deviations from the least-squares regression line fitted to scattered Y values. The rationale of the least-squares criterion is that it selects values for B_1 and B_2 that would minimize the differences between the actual observed values y and the computed values $\hat{y}$. It can be shown that this criterion is satisfied if B_1

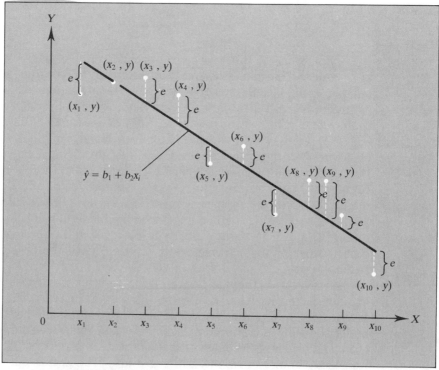

FIGURE 17.3 Graphic illustrations of residual errors as vertical deviations of Y values from the fitted sample regression line.

and B_2 are computed from the following two simultaneous equations, called *least-squares normal equations*:

(1)
$$\sum y = nB_1 + B_2 \sum x;$$

(2)
$$\sum xy = B_1 \sum x + B_2 \sum x^2.$$

Now, if we divide (1) by n and rearrange terms, we obtain

$$B_1 = \bar{Y} - B_2\bar{X}. \tag{17.5}$$

Next, if we multiply (1) by $\sum x$ and (2) by n and then subtract the first result from the second, we get

$$B_2 = \frac{n \sum xy - \sum x \sum y}{n \sum x^2 - (\sum x)^2}$$

$$= \frac{\sum (x - \bar{X})(y - \bar{Y})}{\sum (x - \bar{X})^2}. \tag{17.6a}$$

For reasons of computational and notational convenience, various measures in regression and correlation analyses can be computed on the deviations of the individual values of the variables from the respective means of the variables. In terms of deviations from sample means, the sums of squares and cross products can be defined as follows:

$$m_{11} = \sum (y - \bar{Y})^2 = \sum y^2 - n(\bar{Y})^2; \tag{17.7}$$

$$m_{22} = \sum (x - \bar{X})^2 = \sum x^2 - n(\bar{X})^2; \tag{17.8}$$

$$m_{12} = \sum (x - \bar{X})(y - \bar{Y}) = \sum xy - n(\bar{X})(\bar{Y}). \tag{17.9}$$

(Note that the subscripts 1 and 2 attached to the m values stand for Y and X, respectively.) With these definitions, for example, (17.6a) can be rewritten compactly as

$$B_2 = \frac{m_{12}}{m_{22}}. \tag{17.6b}$$

Consider now a numerical example of obtaining the LSEs B_1 and B_2 in (17.4) from a set of sample data. An economist wishes to study the effect of family disposable income X on family consumption expenditure Y of the the middle-income families in a certain city. For this investigation, she has predetermined 12 values of X ranging from \$25,000 to \$36,000 with intervals of \$1,000. These X values are as shown in column (1) of Table 17.1. Next, she has decided to select at random one family from each subpopulation of all families having a specific value of X. These Y values are recorded in column (2) of Table 17.1.

TABLE 17.1 Work Sheet for Computing Regression Coefficients of Consumption Expenditure on Disposal Income (in Thousands of Dollars)

(1) x	(2) y	(3) x^2	(4) y^2	(5) xy	(6) $\hat{y}$
25	26	625	676	650	24.54
26	25	676	625	650	25.30
27	24	729	576	648	26.07
28	28	784	784	784	26.86
29	27	841	729	783	27.60
30	30	900	900	900	28.37
31	28	961	784	868	29.13
32	30	1,024	900	960	29.90
33	30	1,089	900	990	30.66
34	32	1,156	1,024	1,088	31.43
35	33	1,225	1,089	1,155	32.20
36	32	1,296	1,024	1,152	32.96
Sum 366	345	11,306	10,011	10,628	345.00

$$\bar{x} = 366/12 = 30.5; \quad \bar{y} = 345/12 = 28.75$$

Source: Hypothetical.

With the sample data made available, the first step in regression analysis is to construct a *scatter diagram* of the sample data to see whether or not the dependent variable does depend to some extent upon the independent variable, whether the average relationship between them can reasonably be expressed by a straight line, and whether the assumptions of linear regression are reasonably met. In a scatter diagram, each point corresponds to a pair of values (x, y). The scatter digram for our illustrative data is shown by Figure 17.4. Examining this figure, we obtain some distinct impressions. First, there is a clear positive relationship between family consumption expenditure and family disposable income: the former, on the average, increases with an increase in the latter. Second, the points scatter somewhat from one another, but they also seem to have roughly a linear relationship; that is, the average relationship can be described adequately by a straight line. Third, the assumption of homoscedasticity seems to be reasonably met, since there is only a very mild impression of decreasing vertical scatter among the dots as X increases. At least, the data are not obviously heteroscedastic. Fourth, the assumption of normal subpopulations for Y canot be examined at all, since we have only one Y value for each X value; the best we can do is to speculate that, for any fixed disposable income, it is reasonable to have approximately a normal distribution of consumption expenditures. These observations strengthen our belief that linear regression analysis might fruitfully be applied to the sample data on hand.

The next step is to fit a straight line through the points in the scatter diagram—that is, to compute the values of the sample regression coefficients. To do this, and for later calculations, we need the sums as cumulated in columns (3), (4), and (5) of Table 17.1. With these sums,

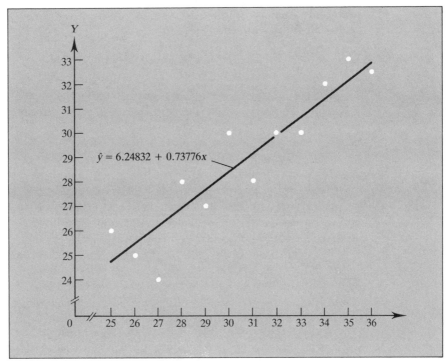

FIGURE 17.4 Scatter diagram and the fitted regression line of consumption expenditure on disposable income. Vertical scale, family consumption expenditures in thousands of dollars; horizontal scale, family disposable incomes in thousands of dollars. (*Source:* Table 17.1.)

the corresponding sums of deviations from the sample means are then derived as shown below.

$$m_{11} = \sum y^2 - n(\bar{y})^2 = 10{,}011 - 12(28.75)^2$$

$$= 92.25;$$

$$m_{22} = \sum x^2 - n(\bar{x})^2 = 11{,}306 - 12(30.5)^2$$

$$= 143.00;$$

$$m_{12} = \sum xy - n(\bar{x})(\bar{y}) = 10{,}628 - 12(30.5)(28.75)$$

$$= 105.50.$$

Now, within the above results, our economist finally has

$$b_2 = \frac{m_{12}}{m_{22}} = \frac{105.50}{143.00}$$

$$\doteq 0.73776 \quad \text{thousand-dollar increase in consumption per thousand-dollar increase in income;}$$

and

$$b_1 = \bar{y} - b_2\bar{x} = 28.75 - 0.73776(30.5)$$

$$\doteq 6.24832 \quad \text{thousands of dollars.}$$

Hence, she has the sample regression equation for consumption expenditures on family incomes as follows:

$$\hat{y} = b_1 + b_2 x = 6.24832 + 0.73776x.$$

The computed values of Y are presented in the last column of Table 17.1. Note that $\sum \hat{y}$ must be equal to $\sum y$ except for rounding. This observation serves a dual purpose: as a check on computational accuracy and as the verification that $\sum e = 0$.

The previous sample regression equation may be considered as an estimated consumption function for the middle-class families in our hypothetical city. The graph of this consumption function is the straight line fitted through the scattered points in Figure 17.4. To draw this sample regression line, we need to plot only two $\hat{y}$ values. As a check, the fitted line should go through the point $(\bar{x}, \bar{y})$.

The value of $b_1 = 6.24832$ in the sample regression equation means that the estimated annual average family consumption expenditure is \$6,248.32 when the family disposable income is zero. This could actually happen because of welfare payments not counted as income or because of families living on past savings. Mathematically, the value of B_1 is always important because it, together with B_2, determines the value of $\hat{y}$ for any specific value of X. However, very often the value of B_1 has no practical meaning at all. For instance, when we are regressing the height Y of oak trees on the age X of oak trees, where X ranges in value from 1 year to 10 years, we may obtain a negative value of B_1. Evidently, such a value is impossible in practice, although the negative B_1 still serves its mathematical purpose.

Next, the value of $b_2 = 0.73776$ in our example means that as one considers families with higher and higher disposal incomes, there is on the average an increase in consumption expenditures of \$737.76 for every increase of \$1,000.00 in family disposable income. The b_2 value in this example is called by economists the "marginal propensity to consume." In general, the B_2 value is always important from both mathematical and practical viewpoints. Mathematically, it is the estimated amount of change in the mean value of Y given X. Practically, there is always interest in what happens to Y when X changes.

17.4 SAMPLE VARIANCE AND STANDARD DEVIATION OF THE REGRESSION

The sample regression equation is called the *predictive equation* because its main function is to predict the mean value of $\mu_{Y.X}$ of Y, or an individual value y of Y, for a given value of X. But how good is it as a predictive device? Also, is the regression analysis really an improvement in predicting the value of Y on the basis of the value of X over univariate analysis where we would predict (estimate) an individual value of Y by the mean $\bar{Y}$ of Y? To answer the first question we need a measure for the scatter around the fitted regression line. This measure is the sample variance of the regression, or the sample variance of the random residuals. The second question is answered by comparing the values of sample variance of the regression and the sample variance of Y. The *sample variance of the regression,* denoted by $S_{Y.X}^2$, is defined by

$$S_{Y.X}^2 = S_U^2 = \frac{\sum (y - \hat{y})^2}{n - 2}$$

$$= \frac{m_{11} - (m_{12}^2/m_{22})}{n - 2}. \tag{17.10}$$

Note that this statistic has $n - 2$ *df* because $\hat{y}$ is computed with two sample statistics, B_1 and B_2, in the sample regression equation. The square root of S_U^2 is the *sample standard deviation of the regression* and it is denoted as $S_{Y.X}$, or S_U.

For our current example, we have

$$s_U^2 = \frac{92.25 - (105.50)^2/143.00))}{12 - 2}$$

$$\doteq 1.44161$$

and

$$s_U = \sqrt{1.44161} \doteq 1.20067.$$

In general, both S_U^2 and S_U measure variation or dispersion of the dots around the regression line in the scatter diagram. If all the dots are on the fitted line, then $S_U^2 = S_U = 0$. Then we say the fit is perfect. The farther the dots are from the regression, the larger these two measures are. Therefore, large values of S_U^2 and S_U would indicate poor fit and the sample regression equation would be a poor predictive device. These statements are very vague because they say nothing about how small S_U^2 or S_U should be before the sample regression equation becomes a useful predictive device. We shall provide a more obvious measure for the closeness of fit shortly. In the meantime, let us move to answer the second question posed earlier by comparing S_U and S_Y. For our example,

$$S_Y = \sqrt{\frac{\sum (y - \bar{y})^2}{n - 1}} = \sqrt{\frac{m_{11}}{n - 1}}$$

$$= \sqrt{\frac{92.25}{12 - 1}} \doteq 2.90.$$

By comparison, we see that s_Y here is more than three times as large as s_U.

The difference between these two values is a measure of how helpful it is to know the value of X before attempting to predict the value of Y. Suppose you knew the twelve values of Y in Table 17.1 and then were asked, "If a thirteenth family from this population were selected at random, what would its consumption expenditure be?" A reasonable guess would be $\bar{y} = \$28{,}750$. Predicting consumption expenditure in this way involves an average error of $s_Y = 2.90$, or about $\$2{,}900$. The related question is whether knowing the family's income would improve our prediction of its consumption expenditure. The number $s_U = 1.20067$, or $\$1{,}200.67$, is a measure of the average error in using the regression equation plus knowledge of X to predict Y. So, in our example, regression analysis is indeed a big improvement over the univariate analysis. In general, when $S_U < S_Y$, the knowledge of the value of the independent variable is helpful in predicting the value of the dependent variable. It happens, though, that S_U is always less than S_Y, except for a few rare cases where $S_U = S_Y$.

17.5 INFERENCES ABOUT REGRESSION COEFFICIENTS

Having obtained the sample regression equation and having concluded that it may be a useful one on the basis of comparing S_U with S_Y, we are still not ready to use it as the predictive device. This is because a sample regression equation is subject to sampling error. It can happen that a sample regression equation may suggest a predictive relationship even though the population does not have such a relationship at all. Hence, before we use the sample regression equation for predictive purpose, we must conduct statistical inferences to determine whether the sample results are significant or whether they can be explained by chance variations alone. Procedures of estimation and testing in regression analysis are identical in principle to those for univariate data. However, in regression analysis the sample size is usually less than 30 and the population regression variance is nearly always unknown. As a result, our discussion on inferences about regression parameters employs small-sample theory only. Of course, inferential procedures for small samples are also applicable to large samples.

To conduct inferences about β_1 and β_2, we follow the same procedures as for univariate data by using our knowledge of the properties of the appropriate sampling distributions. Sampling distributions for B_1 and B_2 are quite easily deduced by recalling the BLUE properties of LSE and by remembering that both B_1 and B_2 are mean values. With these reminders, the following two theorems, which give the distributions of B_1 and B_2, are quite straightforward.

THEOREM 17.1 SAMPLING DISTRIBUTION OF B_1 *If B_1 is an LSE derived from an SRS selected from a bivariate population for which all the assumptions of the fixed-X model are met, then $E(B_1) = \beta_1$. When σ_U^2 is unknown, the estimated standard error of B_1 is defined by*

$$S_{B_1} = S_U \sqrt{\frac{\sum x^2}{n \sum (x - \bar{X})^2}}$$

$$= S_U \sqrt{\frac{\sum x^2}{(n)m_{22}}}. \qquad (17.11)$$

Furthermore, if $n \leq 30$, the quantity

$$t_\delta = \frac{B_1 - \beta_1}{S_{B_1}} \tag{17.12}$$

has the t distribution with $\delta = n - 2$.

Equation (17.12) can be used as the test statistic for $H_0 : \beta_1 = 0$ against an appropriate H_1. It can also be employed to construct the confidence limits for β_1 by using

$$L, U = B_1 \mp t_{\alpha/2} S_{B_1}, \tag{17.13}$$

where $\alpha/2$ is based on $\delta = n - 2$ in this case.

THEOREM 17.2 SAMPLING DISTRIBUTION OF B_2 *If B_2 is an LSE derived from an SRS selected from a bivariate population for which all the assumptions of the fixed-X model are met, then $E(B_2) = \beta_2$. When σ_U^2 is unknown, the estimated standard error of B_2 is defined by*

$$S_{B_2} = S_U \sqrt{\frac{1}{\sum (x - \bar{X})^2}}$$

$$= S_U \sqrt{\frac{1}{m_{22}}}. \tag{17.14}$$

Furthermore, when $n \leq 30$, the quantity

$$t_\delta = \frac{B_2 - \beta_2}{S_{B_2}} \tag{17.15}$$

has the t distribution with $\delta = n - 2$.

Equation (17.15) can be used as the test statistic for testing $H_0 : \beta_2 = 0$ against some appropriate M_1. It can also be employed to construct the confidence limits for β_2 by using

$$L, U = B_2 \mp t_{\alpha/2}(S_{B_2}), \tag{17.16}$$

where $t_{\alpha/2}$ is based on $\delta = n - 2$.

Now, to apply Theorem 17.1 to conduct inferences about β_1 with our example, let us first test $H_0 : \beta_1 = 0$ against $H_1 : \beta_1 \neq 0$. Recall, from previous calculation, that we have $s_U = 1.20067$, thus, by (17.11), we have

$$s_{B_1} = 1.20067 \sqrt{\frac{11{,}306}{12(143)}} \doteq 3.0819.$$

With this result,

$$t_{10} = \frac{b_1 - 0}{s_{B_1}} = \frac{6.24832}{3.0819}$$

$$\doteq 2.027 > t_{10;.05} = 1.812.$$

Thus, $\beta_1 = 0$ can only be rejected at $\alpha = 0.10$ but not at $\alpha = 0.05$ since $t_{10;.025} = 2.228$.

Next, if we wish to construct a 95% confidence interval for β_1, we would have, by (17.13),

$$L, U = b_1 \mp t_{10;.025}(s_{B_1})$$

$$= 6.24832 \mp 2.228(3.0819)$$

$$\doteq -0.618 \text{ to } 13.115$$

which does include 0. It agrees with the previous testing result that b_1 is not significant at $\alpha = 0.05$.

Moving now to test H_0: $\beta_2 = 0$ against H_1: $\beta_2 \neq 0$, we have, by (17.14),

$$s_{B_2} = 1.20067\sqrt{\frac{1}{143}} \doteq 0.1004$$

and

$$t_{10} = \frac{b_2 - 0}{s_{B_2}} = \frac{0.73776}{0.1004} \doteq 7.348.$$

This large value of t leads to the rejection of $\beta_2 = 0$ at $\alpha = 0.05$ as well as at $\alpha = 0.01$. Here, since b_2 is a positive value, it would be more appropriate for us to test the alternative of $\beta_2 > 0$. Even when we do this, H_0 will be rejected at $\alpha = 0.01$ since $P(t_{10}) \geq 2.764) = 0.01$.

Finally, suppose we wish to construct a 95% confidence interval for β_2, we have

$$L, U = b_2 \mp t_{10;.025}(s_{B_2})$$

$$= 0.73776 \mp 2.228(0.1004) \doteq 0.514 \text{ to } 0.961.$$

Ordinarily, the regression analysis should continue when B_2 is significant even if B_1 is not. Our test indicates that $b_2 = 0.73776$ is highly significant, so we can proceed to use the sample regression obtained for predictive purposes. Also, in simple regression analysis, we shall adopt a rough rule: Continute the regression analysis if and only if $\beta_2 = 0$ is rejected at $\alpha = 0.10$.

Before ending this section, it may be pointed out that the interpretation of confidence intervals for β_i is identical to that in the univariate case. Thus, from the values of confidence limits just obtained for β_2, we may state that we have established with a 0.95 confidence probability that the population regression slope is positive. Also, we can write the above results as follows:

$$0.514 \leq \beta_2 \leq 0.961.$$

17.6 A NOTE ON INFERENCES FOR $\sigma_{Y.X}^2$ OR σ_U^2

The estimator for the variance of the population regression or that for the regression residuals plays a very important role in regression analysis, since this estimator is required for the computation of every standard error of estimators in regression analysis. It seems, therefore, appropriate for us to see whether S_U^2 obtained in a given case is merely a result of chance variations.

It can be shown that if all the assumptions in the fixed-X model are true, then the quantity

$$\chi_\delta^2 = \frac{(n-2)S_U^2}{\sigma_U^2} \tag{17.17}$$

has a χ^2 distribution with $\delta = n - 2$. Equation (17.17) can then be used as the test statistic for H_0: σ_U^2 is equal to some specified value.

Equation (17.17) can also be used to construct the confidence limits for a $100(1 - \alpha)\%$ confidence interval. Here, the confidence probability can be stated as

$$P\left[\chi_{\delta;.1-\alpha/2}^2 < \frac{(n-2)S_U^2}{\sigma_U^2} < \chi_{\delta;\alpha/2}^2\right] = 1 - \alpha,$$

which gives $(1 - \alpha)$ confidence limits for σ_U^2 with

$$L = \frac{(n-2)S_U^2}{\chi_{\delta;\alpha/2}^2} \quad \text{and} \quad U = \frac{(n-2)S_U^2}{\chi_{\alpha/1-\alpha/2}^2}. \tag{17.18}$$

17.7 PREDICTION AND FORECASTING

It has been stated at the very outset that the ultimate objective of regression analysis is estimation by association. To this end, we differentiate two cases: estimating the mean value $\mu_{Y.X}$, of Y, and estimating an individual value y of Y. For lack of better or standard terminology and for the sake of convenience in distinction, in this text we call the first case *prediction* and the second *forecasting*. We shall also denote the estimator of $\mu_{Y.X}$ associated with a specific value x_0 of X, by $\hat{\hat{y}}_0$ and called it *predictor*. We shall call the projection of a single value of Y, associated with x_0, as a *forecaster* and denote it as $\hat{y}_0$. Whether it is for prediction or for forecasting, the same sample regression is employed; that is, we have

$$\hat{\hat{Y}}_0 = \hat{Y}_0 = B_1 + B_2x_0. \tag{17.19}$$

Thus, for a given x_0, the predictor and the forecaster have the same

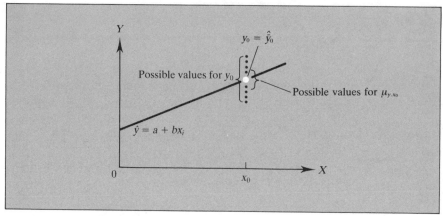

FIGURE 17.5 Predicting $\mu_{Y.x_0}$ versus forecasting an individual value y_0 of Y given $X = x_0$.

numerical value. However, as revealed by Figure 17.5, the projected values of $\overset{\circ}{Y}_0$ and $\hat{Y}_0$ are very different conceptually.

Prediction

"Prediction," as we are using the term, being a procedure of estimating $\mu_{Y.X}$, is concerned with the precision of the entire sample regression line. For this purpose, as usual, we must know the properties of the distribution of the predictor $\overset{\circ}{y}_0$. It turns out the task of finding these is quite easy. First, we know that $(B_1 + B_2x_0)$ is an unbiased linear estimator of $(\beta_1 + \beta_2x_0)$, so $E(\overset{\circ}{y}_0) = \mu_{Y.x_0}$. Second, $(B_1 + B_2x_0)$, being a linear combination of normally distributed random variables, must also be normally distributed. Third, to conduct inferences about any point on the regression line, we must have a standard error of the predictor. To derive this measure, we note that the error in determining the value of Y conditional on x_0 arises from two sources—chance variations in B_1 and chance variations in B_2. Thus, giving β_1 and β_2, the error in prediction, denoted as e_P, is clearly

$$e_P = \beta_1 + \beta_2x_0 - (B_1 + B_2x_0)$$
$$= (\beta_1 - B_1) + (\beta_2 - B_2)x_0.$$

Squaring this result and taking its expectation, we obtain the variance of the predictor, denoted σ_P^2, as

$$\sigma_P^2 = \sigma_U^2\left[\frac{1}{n} + \frac{(x_0 - \bar{X})^2}{\sum(x - \bar{X})^2}\right].$$

Now, when σ_U^2 is unknown, we replace it by S_U^2 in the above expression, which becomes the unbiased estimator for σ_P^2, denoted S_P^2. Taking the square for S_P^2, we have the estimator of the standard error of the predictor as follows:

$$S_P = S_U \sqrt{\frac{1}{n} + \frac{(x_0 - \bar{X})^2}{\sum (x - \bar{X})^2}}$$

$$= S_U \sqrt{\frac{1}{n} + \frac{(x_0 - \bar{X})^2}{m_{22}}}, \tag{17.20}$$

which is slightly biased, or asymptotically unbiased.

Finally, from the arguments given before, when $n \leq 30$, we see that the ratio

$$t_\delta = \frac{\hat{\overset{\circ}{y}}_0 - (\beta_1 + \beta_2 x_0)}{S_P} \tag{17.21}$$

has the t distribution with $\delta = n - 2$. Equation (17.21) can be used as the test statistic for H_0: $\mu_{Y.x_0}$ = some specified value against some appropriate alternative. It also allows us to construct confidence intervals for $\mu_{Y.x_0}$ via the following familiar expression:

$$L, U = \hat{\overset{\circ}{Y}}_0 \mp t_{\alpha/2}(S_P), \tag{17.22}$$

where $t_{\alpha/2}$ is based on $\delta = n - 2$.

As an illustration, let us continue the analysis of the consumption–income example. First, suppose we wish to test H_0: $\mu_{Y.x_0=30.5} = 29.00$ against H_1: $\mu_{Y.x_0=30.5} \neq 29.00$. (Here, 29.00 is the mean consumption expenditure for the two income levels of 30 and 31.) We have

$$\hat{y}_{30.5} = 6.24832 + 0.73776(30.5) \doteq 28.75;$$

$$s_P = \sqrt{\frac{1}{n} + \frac{(x_0 - \bar{x})^2}{m_{22}}}$$

$$= 1.20067 \sqrt{\frac{1}{12} + \frac{(30.5 - 30.5)^2}{143}}$$

$$\doteq 0.3466;$$

$$t_{10} = \frac{28.75 - 29.0}{0.3466} \doteq -0.7213.$$

Thus, H_0: $\mu_{Y.x_0=30.5} = 29.00$ cannot be rejected at $\alpha = 0.05$.

As a matter of fact, so far as prediction and forecasting are concerned, it is much more meaningful and useful to construct confidence intervals rather than to conduct hypothesis testing. For the construction of confidence interval for $\mu_{Y.x_0}$, we can restrict our attention to just one specified value of x_0, in which case (17.22) produces an ordinary confidence interval for the said parameter. Alternatively, we can specify each of several values of x_0, in which case repeated applications of (17.22) produce a confidence band for $\mu_{Y.x_0}$. The

TABLE 17.2 Interval Estimates for $\mu_{Y.x_0}$ and Y_0 for the Construction of the 95% Confidence Band for $\mu_{Y.x_0}$ and the 95% Forecasting Band for Y_0

(1) x_0	(2) $\hat{\hat{y}}_0$ or $\hat{y}_0$	(3) s_P	(4) $L,U = \hat{\hat{y}}_0 \mp 2.228s_P$	(5) s_F	(6) $L,U = \hat{y}_0 \mp 2.228s_F$
25.0	24.69	0.652	23.24 to 26.14	1.3663	21.65 to 27.73
27.0	26.17	0.4936	25.07 to 27.27	1.2982	23.28 to 29.06
29.0	27.64	0.3779	26.80 to 28.48	1.2587	24.84 to 30.44
30.5	28.75	0.3466	27.98 to 29.52	1.2497	25.97 to 31.53
32.0	29.86	0.3779	29.02 to 30.70	1.2587	27.06 to 32.66
34.0	31.33	0.4936	30.23 to 32.43	1.2982	28.44 to 34.22
36.0	32.81	0.652	31.36 to 34.26	1.3663	29.77 to 35.85

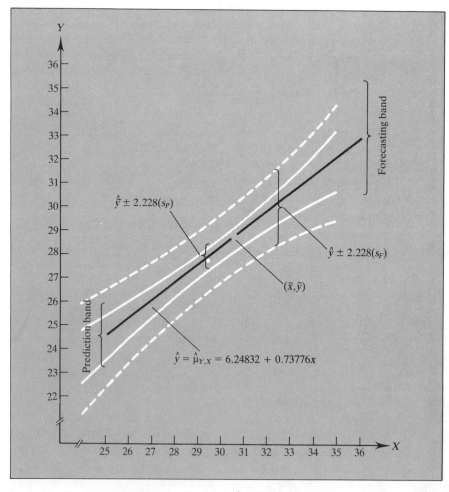

FIGURE 17.6 95% prediction and forecasting bands for the consumption–income data. (*Source:* Table 17.2.)

confidence band shows, for any specified x_0, what the confidence interval for $\mu_{Y \cdot x_0}$ is.

Now, with the values of $\hat{y}_{30.5} = 28.75$ and $s_U = 0.3466$, the 95% confidence limits for $\mu_{Y \cdot x_0 = 30.5}$ are

$$L, U = \hat{y}_{30.5} \mp t_{10; .025}(s_P) = 28.75 \mp 2.228(0.3466)$$
$$\doteq 27.98 \text{ to } 29.52.$$

Note that this interval includes the null hypothetical value of $\mu_{Y \cdot x_0 = 30.5} = 29.0$.

To gain additional insight into the behavior of confidence intervals for $\mu_{Y \cdot x_0}$ when the value of x_0 changes, we construct a confidence band. For this purpose, the values of $x_0 = 25.0, 27.0, 29.0, 30.5, 32.0, 34.0$, and 36.0 have been selected. The computations of 95% confidence intervals are made in Table 17.2 with the final results given in column (4) of that table. Note that the values of x_0 selected are symmetrical with respect to $\bar{x} = 30.5$. By this means, computations needed for the lower half of the table duplicate those of the upper half. The values of L and U in column (4) of the table are plotted in Figure 17.6, where they are connected by freehand lines. The solid lines in the figure present graphically the 95% confidence band for the individual heights of the population regression line. The result here should be interpreted as follows: We are 95% confident that the population regression line will fall within this band. The confidence band for our example is quite good in the sense that it is not wide enough to include any line with a negative slope. The confidence band is also indicative of the fact that the confidence interval widens as heights are farther removed from the point $x_0 = \bar{x}$, where it is the narrowest, or the most precise. The reason for this behavior is that errors in the slope of the line are magnified when projections are made at considerable distances from the mean of X.

Forecasting

Very often we may be interested in knowing an individual value y_0 of Y associated with x_0. For example, given that a student's I.Q. is 105, what is his forecast performance at the college? Here, we are not asking for the mean performance of all students whose I.Q. is 105. More generally, we may think about forecasting with regression in terms of what would happen if a new observation were made for which $X = x_0$; the basic question is often phrased as "forecasting the value of a new observation." We use the first n sample observations to make inferences about what the value of Y would be if an $(n + 1)$th observation were drawn for which $X = x_0$.

We note that "forecasting Y_0" is a more appropriate choice of words than "estimating Y_0" because "estimating" suggests a parameter whose value is to be estimated. There is no parameter here, since Y_0 is a random variable rather than a parameter. Hence, we speak of a forecaster of Y_0 instead of estimator of Y_0, and we speak of forecasting interval and *forecasting band* instead of confidence interval and confidence band in making inferences with a new observation of Y.

Turning our attention to the task of inferences, we observe that given a specified x_0, the forecaster $\hat{Y}_0$ is a random variable with its values scattered about the point on the regression line corresponding to x_0. As such, we can never know its value prior to the experiment. Here, the difference between the actual value of Y_0 and the value of the forecaster $\hat{Y}_0$ is called the *forecasting error*, which is a linear combination of normally distributed random variables—the random disturbances. It can be verified that the expectation of the forecasting error is zero; that is,

$$E(Y_0 - \hat{Y}_0) = 0.$$

Furthermore, the variance of the forecasting error, denoted by σ_F^2, as suggested by Figure 17.5, consists of two parts: (1) the prediction error, or variation due to random sampling, σ_P^2, and (2) the random disturbances measured by σ_U^2. Thus,

$$\sigma_F^2 = \sigma_P^2 + \sigma_U^2.$$

When σ_U^2 is unknown, we have the unbiased estimator for σ_F^2 as

$$S_F^2 = S_P^2 + S_U^2.$$

The square root of this quantity is a slightly biased, or asymptotically unbiased, estimator for the standard error of the forecaster, as given below:

$$S_F = S_U \sqrt{1 + \frac{1}{n} + \frac{(x_0 - \bar{X})^2}{\sum (x - \bar{X})^2}}$$

$$= S_U \sqrt{1 + \frac{1}{n} + \frac{(x_0 - \bar{X})^2}{m_{22}}}. \qquad (17.23)$$

As in the case of the predictor, the forecasting error is normally distributed. When σ_U^2 is unknown and when $n \leq 30$, the ratio $(\hat{Y}_0 - Y_0)/S_F$ is distributed as t_{n-2}. This result enables us to write

$$L, U = \hat{Y}_0 \mp t_{\alpha/2}(S_F), \qquad (17.24)$$

where, as in (17.17), $t_{\alpha/2}$ is based on $\delta = n - 2$.

Again, suppose we wish to construct a 95% forecasting interval for Y_0 with $x_0 = 30.5$, we would have

$$\hat{y}_{30.5} = \hat{\tilde{y}}_{30.5} = 28.75;$$

$$s_F = 1.20067 \sqrt{1 + \frac{1}{12} + \frac{(30.5 - 30.5)^2}{143}}$$

$$\doteq 1.2499;$$

$$L, U = \hat{y}_{30.5} \mp t_{10; .025}(s_F)$$

$$= 28.75 \pm 2.228(1.2499)$$

$$\doteq 25.97 \text{ to } 31.53.$$

The last result, of course, can also be written as

$$25.97 < Y_{30.5} < 31.53.$$

A series of forecasting intervals have been computed and the final results are as entered in the last column in Table 17.2 for the purpose of constructing a forecasting band for Y_0. The dashed lines in Figure 17.6 graphically represent the 95% forecasting band for a new observation. Observe that the 95% forecasting band is substantially wider than the corresponding 95% confidence band, reflecting the fact that the forecasting error is much greater than the predicting error. It is also interesting to note that the forecasting band behaves in the same way as the confidence band—it becomes wider as x_0 deviates more from $\bar{x}$.

Before ending our discussion on prediction and forecasting, two additional comments are in order. First, the larger the sample size, the narrower, on the average, will be the confidence interval for the conditional mean of Y at a given x_0. Increasing the sample size will also tend to narrow the forecasting interval for a new observation, but only in so far as it reduces the confidence interval of the regression line. Even for $n = \infty$, the width would not be zero; instead, for a 95% forecasting interval, for instance, it would be $2(1.96\sigma_U)$. This lower limit on the width of the forecasting interval is set because the individual values of Y vary for a given x_0, and even complete knowledge of the population distribution of Y at a given x_0 will not make possible exact forecasting of individual Y values associated with a given value x_0 of X.

The second point to note is that the use of the sample regression for prediction or forecasting does not permit extrapolation either below or above all the observed values of X. This restriction is based on two reasons. The first derives from what we have already learned. That is, the intervals are most precise at $x_0 = \bar{x}$. When x_0 deviates more and more from $\bar{x}$, the intervals become more and more imprecise and less and less useful as a result. The second reason is that the linear dependence between X and Y may not hold with a wider range of data. For example, suppose the actual observed data are for an automobile's gasoline consumption Y in miles per gallon at various speeds X in miles per hour, but that the only values of X for which test runs are made are 30, 40, 50, and 60 mph. Suppose also that the scatter diagram of the sample data suggests that the assumptions of our model have been met. Can we then put any faith in inferences for $\mu_{Y.x_0}$ with $x_0 = 20$ or 70 mph? The answer is clearly "No!" Gas mileage might be low either at 20 mph or at 70 mph; the former because the car is not in high gear; the latter because of greatly increased wind resistance. Whatever the reasons might be for a departure from the pattern for 30–60 mph when we infer about speeds below 30 mph or above 60 mph, it is evident that we have no data at all on whether the assumptions of our model still hold when we go below the lowest observed X value or above the highest observed X value.

17.8 A NOTE ON VIOLATION OF THE ASSUMPTIONS

The classical simple normal linear regression model has been developed under a set of assumptions. Given these assumptions, we have been able to state that the least-squares estimators of regression parameters have all the desirable properties. The objective of this section is to point out, in a summary fashion, how these properties of LSEs are affected when any one of these assumptions is violated in accordance with the most recent published research on the theory of statistics and econometrics.

First of all, the assumption of linearity is of only practical importance. When we find that the relationship of linear dependence does not hold for a given set of data, we simply use an appropriate nonlinear model for the analysis. The method of least squares can also be applied to nonlinear models, as will be shown in Chapter 19, to yield estimators that are BLUE, provided other assumptions still hold.

Next, the assumption of fixed X or the requirement that X be nonstochastic has two implications. Statistically, this assumption is made to set a framework for the sampling distributions of the least-squares estimators. That is, if we drew an infinite number of samples of the same size for a fixed set of X values, the sampling distributions of the LSEs, would possess the properties we have asserted. From the viewpoint of data-gathering processes, this assumption can be thought of as a condition that the investigator, in obtaining his data, must be able to hold one variable constant at predetermined levels. Unless data have been gathered in this fashion, the usual inferential procedure do not hold. However, since experimental control over variables is usually impossible in the social sciences, this assumption is often violated in practice.

The violation of the fixed X assumption is, however, not at all crucial. In practice we can consider both X and Y as random variables. With X as a random variable, provided all the assumptions for the error term are satisfied, we can then apply the method of maximum likelihood for the estimation. But it has already been pointed out that MLEs are identical with LSEs. Thus, relaxing the fixed X assumption and replacing it by the assumption that X is stochastic does not change the desirable properties and the feasibility of least-squares estimation. It must be noted, though, that there are some differences in interpretations of some measures related to correlation analyses between fixed-X and random-X models. These differences will be pointed out shortly.

Third, as can be verified, the application of least-squares estimation does not require the specification of the distribution form of the parent population. Hence, even if the assumption of normality of the disturbances or of the subpopulations, the Ys, is violated, LSEs are still BLUE owing to the independence of this property from the form of the parent population. When the assumption of normality is not met, the LSEs are not normally distributed in small samples and the inferential procedures presented before, strictly speaking, no longer hold. Fortunately, if the distribution of the error term is not radically different from normality, the estimation and testing procedures are not too badly affected and can be used as reasonable approximations.

Fourth, when the assumption of homoscedasticity is violated, then we have a case of *heteroscedastic* disturbances, for which $\sigma_{Y \cdot X}^2$ or σ_U^2 changes with the changes in the values of X. With the presence of heteroscedasticity, LSEs are no longer BLUE and the inferential procedures established no longer apply. It must be noted in this connection that the assumption of homoscedasticity is quite plausible in two frequently encountered situations. The first is when we describe economic and business aggregates through time, such as when we are regressing aggregate consumption expenditures on disposable national income or when we are regressing gross national product on the index of industrial production. The second is the case where regression analysis is applied to cross-section data by confining the X values to an interval, instead of the whole range of all possible values of X; examples include regressing total output with labor inputs by confining labor inputs from, say, two hundred to three hundred man-hours, or regressing family consumption expenditures on family disposable income by confining incomes to those of the middle class families only. Of course, when homoscedasticity is violated, methods other than the ordinary least-squares method (OLM) that as we have introduced must be used. Alternative methods for estimation can be found in any standard text on econometrics.

Finally, when we are dealing with cross-section data, and when the sample is truly a random sample the assumption of nonautoregression—the absence of serial correlation of the error term—is usually met. However, when we are dealing with time series data, random disturbances are nearly always autoregressive in nature. When disturbances are serially correlated, LSEs are no longer BLUE and S_U^2 would be either negatively or positively biased estimators for σ_U^2. As a consequence, the computational formulas for conducting testing on β_i or constructing confidence intervals for β_i would lead to incorrect statements. That is, the calculated rejection regions or confidence intervals will be either narrower or wider than the correct ones. A test for the presence of autoregression and a method for its correction will be presented in Chapter 19.

In closing this section, the reader may be informed that comments made here apply also to violations of similar assumptions for the multiple linear regression model to be taken up in the chapter that follows.

17.9 CORRELATION ANALYSIS

Population Correlation Coefficient

Up to now, we have discussed the *type* and *degree* of relationship that exists between two variables. In some situations, however, we may be interested only in the *degree* of relationship between two variables. For example, the federal government, in deciding on educational grants to a state or city government, may wish to know per capita income as a measure of the latter's ability to finance its own schools. Thus, the federal government may decide that per capita income is an appropriate criterion for the decision, because there is a high degree of relationship between per capita income and expenditures per student in each locality. Otherwise, another decision criterion should be chosen.

In regression analysis, the value of Y is assumed to be dependent in some degree upon that of X. The greater is the dependence, the smaller the dispersion around the regression line. Now we give our attention to a situation in which both X and Y are random variables. As such, they need not be designated as dependent and independent; either designation will yield the same result. In other words, we are here confronted with a bivariate normal population: One in which X is normally distributed with mean μ_X and standard deviation σ_X, and Y is normally distributed with mean μ_Y and standard deviation σ_Y. The two distributions, however, need not to be independent. Namely, high values of one variable may be associated with high values of the other variable, or high values of one may be associated with low values of the other. A bivariate normal population has a density function given by

$$f(x, y) = \frac{1}{2\pi\sigma_X\sigma_Y\sqrt{1 - \rho^2}} \exp\left\{-\frac{1}{2(1 - \rho^2)}\left[\frac{(X - \mu_X)^2}{\sigma_X^2}\right.\right.$$
$$\left.\left. - \frac{2\rho(X - \mu_X)(Y - \mu_Y)}{\sigma_X\sigma_Y} + \frac{(Y - \mu_Y)^2}{\sigma_U^2}\right]\right\}. \quad (17.25)$$

The beginning student need not be expected to understand the imposing expression here, except to note that this function is defined by five parameters: μ_X, μ_Y, σ_X, σ_Y, and ρ. The last parameter, ρ, is called the *coefficient of correlation* for the bivariate normal population. Here, ρ is the measure for the degree, or strength, of association between X and Y in the population.

It is convenient to think of the bivariate normal distribution as a three-dimensional surface. Figure 17.7 is a generalized portrait of the density of a bivariate normal distribution. This figure reveals that our

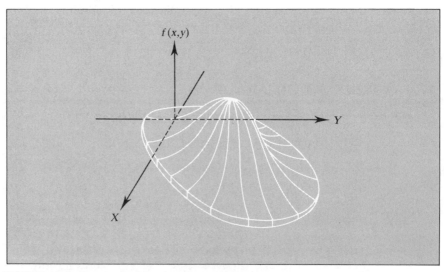

FIGURE 17.7 Graph of a bivariate normal distribution.

particular bivariate normal surface has some degree of covariability, since the mound-shaped surface resembles a long ridge that is not parallel to either the Y axis or the X axis. If we slice this population surface at a given X value, we have a density curve giving the density of Y at that X value. That is, we have the distribution of the subpopulation Y that corresponds to the selected X value. Similarly, if we slice the population surface at a selected Y value, there emerges a subpopulation of X associated with this particular Y. Now, if we take any cross section of the surface parallel to the XY plane, this cross section will be an ellipse. Furthermore, this cross section will be a circle when $\rho = 0$ (indicating no correlation), a straight line when $\rho = \pm 1$ (indicating perfect correlation), and some in-between shape when imperfect correlation exists. These cases are illustrated by the shapes in Figure 17.8.

From (17.25), we see that the *population coefficient of correlation* can be defined in terms of the covariance between X and Y as

$$\rho = \frac{\text{cov}(X, Y)}{\sigma_X \sigma_Y}. \tag{17.26}$$

A number of things may be observed about this definition. First, it is an equation involving the five parameters of the bivariate normal population: μ_X, σ_X, μ_Y, σ_Y, and ρ. The last, as mentioned before, is the correlation coefficient for the bivariate normal population. Second, ρ is symmetric with respect to Y and X; that is, interchanging X and Y does not change ρ. In other words, ρ is a pure number, because it is defined as the ratio of the covariance between Y and X to the product of their respective standard deviations. As such, when $\text{cov}(Y, X) = 0$, ρ is 0, indicating that there is no relationship between the two variables. When there is perfect covariability between Y and X, and Y and X vary in the same direction, $\rho = 1$. Similarly, when there is perfect covariability but Y and X vary in opposite directions, $\rho = -1$. When some degree

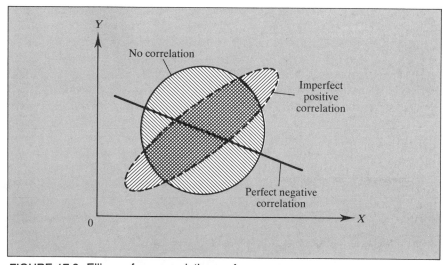

FIGURE 17.8 Ellipses from correlation surfaces.

of covariability exists between Y and X, we have $-1 < \rho < 0$ or $0 < \rho < 1$.

Sample Correlation Coeffieient

When a sample of n pairs of values is drawn, each Y value is a random observation from population Y, and each value of X is a random observation from population X; but the two are not necessarily independent. In addition, when the assumption of a bivariate normal population is met, the maximum likelihood estimator of ρ, usually denoted as r, is obtained by the following expression:

$$r = \frac{\sum (y - \bar{Y})(x - \bar{X})}{\sqrt{\sum (y - \bar{Y})^2][\sum (x - \bar{X})^2]}}$$

$$= \frac{m_{12}}{\sqrt{m_{11}m_{22}}}, \tag{17.27}$$

which may vary, as ρ, from -1 through 0 to $+1$. Again as for ρ, when $r = -1$ or $+1$, Y and X are said to be perfectly correlated negatively or positively. When $r = 0$, the two variables are said to be independent or uncorrelated; strictly speaking, X and Y are independent if and only if $\rho = 0$ rather than $r = 0$, and it is well to keep this in mind. Also, it is well to realize that if X and Y are allowed to have any joint distribution at all, then their independence implies that their covariance is zero and hence their correlation coefficient is zero, but the converse is not true, since dependent variables can have zero covariances. However, if X and Y are restricted to the bivariate normal distribution, then their independence implies that their covariance is zero and hence their (population) correlation coefficient is zero; and the converse is true, since dependent bivariate normal variables cannot have zero covariances. Other values of r are interpreted in terms of the coefficient of determination, to be discussed later.

It may be pointed out that r is a biased estimator of ρ (except that if $\rho = 0$ then r is unbiased), but it is generally used because of its relative simplicity and because the bias is negligible for large samples. For the consumption–income data example, we cannot compute r at all because X is not a random variable and hence the bivariate normal model does not fit. However, if we imagine a different data-gathering procedure, then computing r makes sense. The different data-gathering procedure is not to predetermine any values of X, but simply to take a random sample of 12 families and observe whatever values of X and Y happens to be for each of the 12 families. Assuming that all of the assumptions of the bivariate normal model are at least approximately met, we can then proceed to calculate r and interpret the results as follows. Assuming that the numerical values of the data just happen to come out exactly as already shown in Table 17.1, then, by (17.27), we have

$$r = \frac{105.50}{\sqrt{(92.25)(143.00)}} \doteq +0.9185$$

which indicates a very high degree of correlation between X and Y. (Note that we have used r to stand for the variable as well the realized values of the variable here because this usage is an almost universal practice.)

Inferences Concerning the Coefficient of Correlation

The r value just obtained is quite close to 1 and thus it might indicate significant relationship between consumption and income. However, we are not sure, because n is quite small. So, as usual, we should conduct a test on $\rho = 0$ to see whether $r = 0.9185$ might be due to chance variation alone.

To make inferences from r, we must begin with some observations about its sampling distribution. As illustrated in Figure 17.9, the distribution of r is symmetric when $\rho = 0$ and it is skewed when $\rho \neq 0$. For a normal bivariate population, the distribution of r approaches a normal distribution when n approaches infinity. When $\rho = 0$ there is a transformation for which the transformed values of r are distributed as t_{n-2}:

$$t_\delta = \frac{r\sqrt{n-2}}{\sqrt{1-r^2}}. \tag{17.28}$$

Since this transformation applies only to the case in which $\rho = 0$, it cannot be employed for interval estimation. It can be used, however, as the test statistic for testing the null hypothesis that $\rho = 0$ against an appropriate alternative.

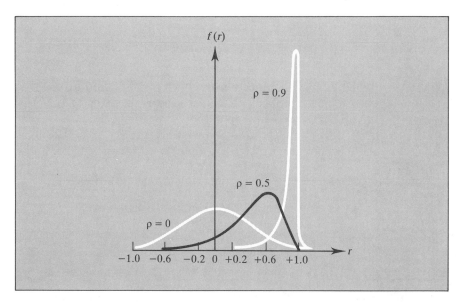

FIGURE 17.9 Sampling distributions of the sample coefficient of correlation for $\rho = 0$, 0.5, and 0.9.

Applying such a test to our current example,

$$t_{10} = \frac{0.9185\sqrt{12 - 2}}{\sqrt{1 - (0.9185)^2}} \doteq 7.346,$$

which leads to the rejection of $\rho = 0$ at $\alpha = 0.01$ for either H_1: $\rho \neq 0$ or H_1: $\rho > 0$. Thus, the correlation between consumption and income is highly significant.

Note that the null hypotheses $\rho = 0$ and $\beta = 0$ are equivalent, since, as can be shown, $\beta_2 = \rho(\sigma_Y/\sigma_X)$ and $B_2 = r(S_Y/S_X)$. As a result, the t tests in both cases should yield the same value. The t values are slightly different in our example owing to rounding errors.

With the t test just introduced, we cannot state explicitly the relationship between the two variables when the null hypothesis is rejected. If we desire to test a hypothesis that ρ has some value other than 0, or if we desire to construct a confidence interval for ρ, we may employ what is called the z transformation. That is, we may make a transformation of the distribution of r into an approximately normal distribution as follows:

$$z_r = \frac{1}{2}\ln\frac{1 + r}{1 - r}. \tag{17.29}$$

It can be shown that z_r is approximately normally distributed with $E(z_r) = z_\rho$, and the estimated standard error is

$$S_z = \frac{1}{\sqrt{n - 3}}. \tag{17.30}$$

To test a hypothesis about ρ by r, we have now the test statistic

$$Z = \frac{z_r - z_\rho}{S_z}, \tag{17.31}$$

which is approximately $n(0, 1)$. To avoid computations with logarithms, we employ a table of values for z_r corresponding to various values of r as given by Table X in Appendix C.

Now, suppose that we wish to test H_0: $\rho = 0.90$ against H_1: $\rho \neq 0.90$ for our illustrative example; we refer to Table X and find

$$z_\rho = 1.472 \quad \text{for } \rho = 0.90,$$

$$z_r = 1.589 \quad \text{for } r = 0.92.$$

Hence

$$z = \frac{1.589 - 1.472}{1/\sqrt{12 - 3}} \doteq 0.351.$$

Since the computed z value is less than 2.58, H_0 is accepted at $\alpha = 0.01$.

Confidence limits may be computed for z_ρ as follows:

$$L,U = z_r \mp \bar{z}_{1-\alpha}(S_z). \qquad (17.32)$$

We can convert z_r in this expression into r by looking at the entries in Table X for the value of z_r and then checking the stub and column headings to find the corresponding value of r. Owing to rounding and/or limited entries in the table, the conversion may be only an approximation.

Let us now construct a 99% confidence interval for ρ with the problem on hand, by noting that $s_z \doteq 0.333$.

$$U,L = z_r \mp z_{0.99}(s_z)$$

$$= 1.589 \mp 2.58(0.333) = 0.730 \text{ to } 2.448,$$

or

$$0.730 \leqslant z_\rho \leqslant 2.448.$$

From Table X, we find

z_ρ or z_r	ρ or r
0.730	0.625
2.448	0.985

Hence, the 99% confidence interval for ρ becomes

$$0.625 \leqslant \rho \leqslant 0.985$$

which includes $\rho = 0.90$.

Regression with Random *X*

If the bivariate population is one in which X is fixed, then we can only have a regression line of Y on X. With a bivariate normal population in which both X and Y are random variables that are linearly related we can have two linear regression lines. The assumption of linearity between X and Y here implies that all the means of the Ys associated with X values, $\mu_{Y.X}$, fall on a straight line—which is the regression line of Y on X with the following regression equation

(1) $$\mu_{Y.X} = \beta_1 + \beta_2 x.$$

Also, all the means of the Xs associated with Y values, $\mu_{X.Y}$, fall on a straight line—which is the regression line of X on Y with a regression equation

(2) $$\mu_{X.Y} = B'_1 + \beta'_2 y.$$

It is important to note that the two population regression lines given by these two equations are the same if and only if the relationship between X and Y is perfect, that is, if and only if $\rho = \pm 1$. Otherwise, with Y as the dependent variable, the intercept and slope will differ from the regression equation with X as the dependent variable.

The corresponding sample regression equation of X on Y is clearly

$$\hat{x} = B_1' + B_2'y,$$

where

$$B_2' = \frac{m_{12}}{m_{11}}$$

and

$$B_1' = \bar{x} - B_2'(\bar{y}).$$

Here, as before, the subscript 1 stands for Y and the subscript 2 stands for X.

The fact that we can have two regression equations when X is random implies that we can predict Y with X and vice versa. For example, if X and Y are the grades in mathematics and physics of students, respectively, there is reason to believe that not only can we predict students' grades in mathematics on the basis of their grades in physics, we can also do the reverse.

17.10 ANALYSIS OF VARIANCE IN REGRESSION

The application of the ANOVA procedure to regression studies achieves three objectives. It provides a clearer explanation of the relationship between correlation and regression, a more obvious and precise measure of the closeness of fit, and an alternative test on $\beta_2 = 0$.

Explained and Unexplained Variation

The analysis of variance in regression begins with the decomposition of the total variation in Y into two meaningful and distinct components by regression. For this task we will employ Figure 17.10 as an aid. From this figure we see that the following relationship holds:

$$(y - \bar{y}) = (\hat{y} - \bar{y}) + (y - \hat{y}).$$

This identity applies to a single observation. To have a summary measure for all sample observations, we may square both sides of this identity and sum over all sample observations to obtain

$$\sum (y - \bar{y})^2 = \sum (\hat{y} - \bar{y})^2 + \sum (y - \hat{y})^2, \quad \text{or}$$

$$\text{SST} \quad = \quad \text{SSR} \quad + \quad \text{SSE}$$

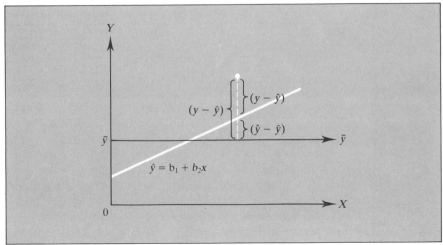

FIGURE 17.10 Decomposing the total variation of Y.

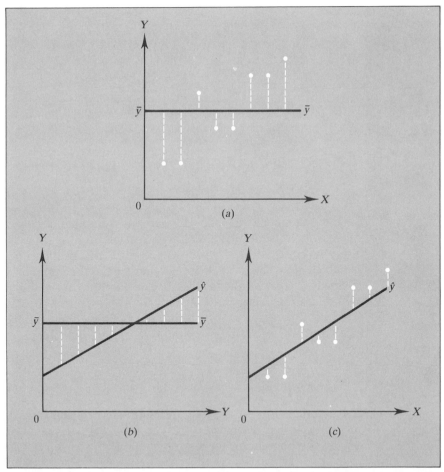

FIGURE 17.11 Graphic illustration of decomposing the total variation of Y in the regression of Y on X. (a) Total variation in Y before regression. (b) Explained variation due to regression. (c) Unexplained variation after regression.

TABLE 17.3 Anova Table for Regressing Consumption on Income

Source of Variation	SS	δ	MS
Regression	77.8334	$k = 1$	MSR $= 77.8334/1 = 77.8334$
Residual	14.4166	$n - c = 10$	MSE $= 14.4166/10 \doteq 1.44166$
Total	92.25	$n - 1 = 11$	MST $= 92.25/11 = 8.39$

The above result states that the total variability in Y is measured by the *total sum of squares* SST. Furthermore, because of regression of Y on X, SST can be decomposed into two parts: the *sum of squares due to regression* SSR, measuring the portion of total variability (total error) in Y which has been *explained* by the variability in X; and the *sum of squares for error* SSE, measuring the portion of the total variability in Y which has *not been explained* by the variability in X. Figure 17.11 provides a graphic illustration of this decomposition.

For calculating these sums of squares, we have

$$\text{SST} = m_{11}; \tag{17.33}$$

$$\text{SSR} = B_2^2(m_{22}) \tag{17.34}$$

$$\text{SSE} = \text{SST} - \text{SSR}. \tag{17.35}$$

Thus, for our consumption–income data, we have

$$\text{SST} = m_{11} = 92.25;$$

$$\text{SSR} = b_2^2(m_{22}) = (0.73776)^2(143.00) \doteq 77.8334;$$

$$\text{SSE} = \text{SST} - \text{SSR} = 92.25 - 77.8334 \doteq 14.4166.$$

Each of the sums of squares divided by its number of degrees of freedom yields a mean square MS. With regression analysis in general, for SST, $\delta = n - 1$; for SSR, $\delta = k$, where k is the number of independent variables; for SSE, $\delta = n - c$, where c is the number of regression coefficients. These calculations for our example are made and presented in Table 17.3. Note that MSE $= S_U^2$. This is indeed the case in our example. However, owing to rounding errors, the numerical values of MSE and S_U^2 may differ from each other slightly in practice; also, MST $= S_Y^2$.

F Test on $\beta_2 = 0$

The decomposition of SST into explained variation (measured by SSR) and unexplained variation (measured by SSE) leads to an alternative test on the population regression slope. If the null hypothesis $\beta_2 = 0$ is true, then the variations in Y from one observation to another will not be affected by variations in X but must be attributed to random disturbances alone. This means that SSR departs from zero only because of sampling error. Thus, if there is significant regression between X and Y, the ratio SSR/SSE would be different from zero, because of the effects of X on Y. A moment's relection will indicate that this statement can be applied equally well to the ratio MSR/MSE which, being a ratio of two chi-square variables, has an F distribution with $\delta_1 = 1$ and $\delta_2 = n - 2$ in the simple linear regression case. Using this F as the test statistic for $\beta_2 = 0$ against $\beta_2 \neq 0$, the rejection region would again be defined as

$$\frac{\text{MSR}}{\text{MSE}} > F_{1, n-2; \alpha} \tag{17.36}$$

Applying the F test to our current example, we have

$$F_{1,10} = \frac{\text{MSR}}{\text{MSE}} = \frac{77.8334}{1.44166} \doteq 53.99 > F_{1,10;.01} = 10.04.$$

which is a highly significant result.

Note that the F test here is equivalent to the t test on β_2, in that both tests give the same answer for the same level of significance and the same set of sample data. This should not be a surprise result if you recall that $F_{1,\delta_2} = t_\delta^2$, where δ for t^2 is equal to δ_2 for F. However, there is a difference, as you will see in the following chapter, between these two tests. That is, while the F test can be generalized to cover more than one explanatory variable, the t test can only be used for one regression coefficient at a time.

Coefficient of Determination

It has been mentioned before that S_U^2, as a measure of closeness-of-fit, does not have an obvious and exact meaning and that values of r, other than -1, 0, and $+1$, cannot be interpreted readily. It seems desirable and necessary to have a standard and unit-free measure of closeness-of-fit and a measure via which values of r can be easily interpreted. The measure that can serve both purposes is called the "coefficient of determination".

The *coefficient of determination* is simply defined as the ratio of explained sum of squares (explained error) to the total sum of squares (total error). The *sample coefficient of determination*, denoted by r^2, is given by the following expression:

$$r^2 = 1 - \frac{\text{SSE}}{\text{SST}}$$

$$= \frac{\text{SSR}}{\text{SST}}. \tag{17.37}$$

This is an MLE for the *population coefficient of determination* which is denoted by ρ^2.

From the definition for r^2, we see that the value of r^2 ranges from 0 to 1 because SSR $\leq$ SST. If SSE $= 0$, then SSR $=$ SST; hence $r^2 = 1$.

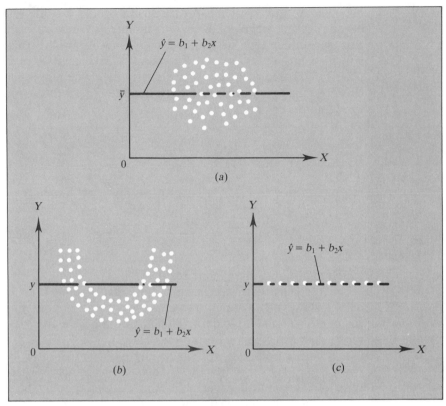

FIGURE 17.12 Different cases in which $b = 0$ and $r^2 = 0$.

When $r^2 = 1$, $y = \hat{y}$, or $e = 0$, indicating that all points in the scatter diagram fall on the sample regression line. If SSR = 0, then SSE = SST; hence, $r^2 = 0$. A necessary condition for $r^2 = 0$ is that the regression slope be zero. This can happen, however, for different reasons, as illustrated by Figure 17.12. The sample regression line could be horizontal (a) if the observations scatter around $\bar{y}$ in a random manner, (b) if the observations scatter around a curve such that the best-fitted line is a horizontal straight line, and (c) if all observations have the same value regardless of the value of X. Case (a) is obvious. Case (b) reflects a very poor fit because of the highly nonlinear relationship between the two variables. In case (c), with all values of Y being the same, or with $y = \bar{y}$, there is no variation in Y to be explained; therefore, the question of decomposition of the total variation SST is irrelevant. Alternatively, for this case, the difficulty is that the subpopulations of Y's do not have any variation since SST = 0. If SST = 0, SSR = 0 and SSE = 0. As a consequence, both the numerator and the denominator in (17.37) are zero and, thus, r^2 is indeterminate.

It may be noted now that r^2 may be interpreted from three viewpoints. First, it may be thought of as a measure of the amount of improvement due to the regression line. Next, it may be interpreted as measuring the closeness-of-fit of the regression line to the points in the scatter diagrams. Finally, it may be thought as measuring the degree of linearity of the scatter of the points.

Viewed as a measure of improvement due to regression, r^2 gives us the relative reduction in the total sum of squares (total error) when a regression line is fitted. For instance, with our illustrative example,

$$r^2 = \frac{\text{SSR}}{\text{SST}} = \frac{77.8334}{92.25}$$

$$\doteq 0.8437.$$

This result means that almost 85% of the total variation in consumption expenditure has been explained by the variations in family disposable income. There remains only about 15% of the variation in consumption that is unexplained by variations in disposable income.

When $r^2 = 0$, we say there is no reduction in SST; that is, there is no improvement due to fitting the regression line. This means that

$$\text{explained error} = \sum (\hat{y} - \bar{y})^2 = 0.$$

Graphically, this implies that the regression line is horizontal and coincides with $\bar{y}$. When $r^2 = 1$, we say that there has been a 100% reduction in the total error, or

$$\sum e^2 = \sum (y - \hat{y})^2 = 0.$$

Graphically, all the points in the scatter diagram fall on the non-horizontal regression line in this case.

As a measure of closeness-of-fit, we note that if $r^2 = 1$, then the points y all fall on the regression line, and that if $r^2 = 0$, the points y are scattered and the regression line becomes horizontal. Thus, we may say the closer the fit of the regression line to the points, the closer r^2 is to 1. For our illustrative data, $r^2 = 0.8437$, which is close to 1; hence the fit is considered as very close.

To interpret the value of r^2 as a measure of linearity, we focus our attention on the shape of the scatter of the points. When r^2 is close to 1, we see that the scatter of the points closely resembles a straight line. However, if r^2 is close to 0, it would indicate the opposite from resembling a straight line. From these observations, we may conclude that the closer the value of r^2 is to 1, the higher the degree of linearity of the points.

It is important to observe that all three of the different interpretations of r^2 are merely different aspects of the same result. Furthermore, r^2 as a measure showing the improvement in terms of reducing the total error should not be considered as a measure of the covariability of the two variables if the independent variable X assumes fixed values. However, if both X and Y are random variables, r^2 can then also be interpreted as a measure of the degree of covariability. Finally, it may be pointed out that the square root of r^2 is the sample correlation coefficient:

$$\sqrt{r^2} = \pm r, \tag{17.38}$$

where the sign of r is the same as that for the regression slope B_2. For our illustrative data, we have

$$r = \sqrt{0.8437} \doteq +0.9185,$$

as obtained before by (17.27).

In concluding our discussion on r^2, it is interesting to note the relationship

$$S_U^2 = (1 - r^2)S_Y^2, \tag{17.39}$$

where $(1 - r^2)$ is called the *coefficient of indetermination*. This expression states that the disturbance (unexplained) variance S_U^2 is simply a fraction of the original total variance S_Y^2. For instance, if $r^2 = 0.75$,

$$s_U^2 = (1 - 0.75)s_Y^2$$
$$= 0.25s_Y^2.$$

That is, 25% of the total variance of Y is unexplained by variations in the values of X. It may be noted that, in the application of (17.39), rounding errors must be allowed.

17.11 CONCLUDING REMARKS

In this chapter we have discussed, in a rather detailed fashion, the simple linear regression and correlation models by presenting the measure of coefficient of determination as the link between the two. Because these two models are constructed under different assumptions, they furnish different types of information, and it is not always clear to a student starting out which measure should be used in given problem situations. It may be useful, then, to compare the two models again.

First, the same type of relationship holds for both regression analysis and correlation analysis, as indicated by the fact that r takes the same sign as B_2. Also, if the value of B_2 is significant at a given level of significance, r is also significant at that level.

Second, r, via r^2, may be considered as a measure of the closeness-of-fit of the regression line. In general, the greater the value of r^2, the better is the fit and the more useful the regression equation as a predictive device. (Note that the greater the value of r^2 is, the closer r is to $+1$ or -1.)

Given the first two observations, we must realize that the main objective of regression analysis is to establish statistical dependence between the dependent and independent variables so that the former can be predicted by the latter; the correlation coefficient is a measure of the closeness-of-fit of the regression line and a measure of the degree of covariability between Y and X.

Third, a given value of the correlation coefficient is consistent with an infinite number of regression lines. For instance, in the case of perfect correlation, when all points are shifted upward or downward by an equal amount, the value of the correlation coefficient will remain as 1 but a different Y intercept will result. Similarly, if all points are rotated at a given point so that they all fall precisely on a different straight line, the slope, and perhaps the Y intercept, will change, while the correlation coefficient will still assume the value of $+1$ or -1 (or become indeterminate for a vertical or horizontal straight line).

Theoretically, therefore, regression is a directional method but correlation is not. The former should be used if one variable is clearly dependent upon the other. The latter is appropriate when neither of the two variables can be considered as being a consequence of the other.

Practically, on the other hand, the purpose of the investigation is perhaps the most important consideration in selecting between regression and correlation techniques. The choice depends, in other words, on whether we want to have a predictive equation or merely wish to determine the degree of association. As a matter of fact, in practical situations we are often more interested in finding out the nature of the relationship for the objective of prediction. In this connection, the reason for our interest in the degree of relationship may be only to select the most useful independent variable, among several possible independent variables, for regression analysis with the dependent variable that has been chosen.

As we have mentioned before, regression analysis is not restricted to the fixed X model. It is perfectly valid to use regression analysis with the bivariate normal model, including estimating the population regression line after choosing which variable to regard as the dependent variable, and doing all the computations and interpretations that were done for the fixed X model. We are not restricted, in the bivariate normal model, merely to doing a correlation analysis.

A point we have not mentioned before is that correlation analysis is not always restricted to the bivariate normal model. If we wish to test $\rho = 0$ and have a fixed X problem, we can validly compute r and test it just as if our data fitted the bivariate normal model. We cannot, however, work with any other values of ρ in this way, so hypotheses about them cannot be validly tested using the fixed X model nor can any confidence intervals be validly constructed. We will not justify this procedure but merely point out that it is mathematically sound.

Association analysis, while a very useful device, often opens up many opportunities for misinterpretation. The most unwarranted interpretation stems from the confusion between association and causation, arising chiefly from the conventional designation of dependent and independent variables. Many people take the independent variable to be the cause and the dependent variable to be the effect in a given situation, but this need not be so.

The link between association and causation can be stated thus: the presence of association does not imply causation; but the existence of causation always implies association. Statistical evidence can only establish the presence or absence of association between variables. Whether causation exists or not depends purely on reasoning. For example, there is reason to believe that high family income "causes" high family consumption expenditures; hence these two variables should be positively associated. There is also reason to support the premise that the high price of prime cuts of beef "causes" low quantities of this beef to be sold; hence these two variables should be negatively associated. That good weather is associated with high death rates in areas favored by retired people clearly does not mean that good weather "causes" high death rates.

Why is it that association need not imply causation? One reason is that the association between two variables may be the result of pure chance, such as soil erosion in Alaska and the amount of alcohol consumed in South America. Another reason is that association between two variables may be due to the influence of a third common factor. Since 1945, for example, it has been found that there is a close relationship between teachers' salaries and liquor consumption in the United States. Can we say that the increase in liquor consumption is the effect of the increase in teachers' salaries? Certainly not. Indeed, a more plausible explanation is that both variables have been influenced by the continuous increase in national income during the same period. A third possibility is that in a real relationship we may be unable to determine which variable is the cause and which is the effect; we often find that both variables may be the cause and the effect at the same time. It may also happen that cause and effect exchange places from time to time. The association between per capita income and per capita expenditures for education, for example, may be of this kind. The higher the per capita income is in a state, the more money can be spent for each student; the more money the state spends for education, the higher will be the per capita income in that state; we cannot be sure, however, that one has produced the other or vice versa.

Association observed between variables that could not conceivably be causally related are called *spurious*, or *nonsense, correlations*. More appropriately, however, we should remember that it is the *interpretation* of the degree of association that is spurious, not the degree of association itself.

GLOSSARY OF FORMULAS

(17.1) $y_i = \beta_1 + \beta_2 x_i + u_i$.

This is the population model equation for the simple linear regression model. Here, y_i, x_i, and u_i are the ith observations of dependent variable Y, the independent variable X, and the random disturbance or residual error U. β_1 and β_2 are the regression coefficients. The presence of the error term indicates that (17.1) is a probabilistic, rather than a deterministic, model.

(17.2) $\mu_{Y.X} = \beta_1 + \beta_2 x_i$.

The population regression equation is defined as the conditional expectation of Y given X. Here, β_1 is the Y-intercept, the mean value of

Y given $X = 0$; β_2, the regression slope, is the change in the value of $\mu_{Y.X}$ per unit change in X.

(17.3) $y_i = B_1 + B_2 x_i + e_i$;

(17.4) $\hat{y}_i = B_1 + B_2 x_i$.

These are the sample model and sample regression equations of Y on X. B_1 and B_2 are interpreted in the same way as are β_1 and β_2, the former being estimators for the latter. From these equations we see that $e_i = y_i - \hat{y}_i$ and that $\sum e_i = 0$.

(17.5) $B_1 = \bar{Y} - B_2\bar{X}$;

(17.6a) $B_2 = \dfrac{\sum (x - \bar{X})(y - \bar{Y})}{\sum (x - \bar{X})^2}$

These are the least-squares estimators for β_1 and β_2, respectively. They are derived in such a way that $\sum e^2$ = minimum. The LSEs are BLUE.

(17.7) $m_{11} = \sum y^2 - n(\bar{Y})^2$;

(17.8) $m_{22} = \sum x^2 - n(\bar{X})^2$;

(17.9) $m_{12} = \sum xy - n(\bar{X})(\bar{Y})$;

(17.6b) $B_2 = m_{12}/m_{22}$.

This set of m values, (17.7) to (17.9) are the sums of squares and cross products of the individual deviations from the respective means of the variables. They have been designed to facilitate computations and simplify notations for various measures in regression and correlation analyses. For example, equation (17.6a) can now be written as (17.6b).

(17.10) $S_U^2 = \dfrac{m_{11} - (m_{12}^2/m_{22})}{n - 2}$.

This expression is the computational equation for the unbiased estimator of σ_U^2—the variance of the error term. Equation (17.10) is originally defined in terms of the regression residuals $\sum (y - \hat{y})^2$. This statistic is identical with the common variance of the regression $S_{Y.X}^2$. It has $n - 2$ degrees of freedom because $\hat{y}$ is computed from the sample regression equation, which involves two statistics, B_1 and B_2. The square root of this statistic is the common standard deviation of the regression, denoted as S_U, which is sometimes rather misleadingly called the *standard error of estimate* in some texts. Finally, this statistic measures the closeness-of-fit but, unfortunately, it does not have a clearly intuitive meaning in this connection.

(17.11) $S_{B_1} = S_U\sqrt{\dfrac{\sum x^2}{(n)(m_{22})}}$;

(17.12) $t_\delta = \dfrac{B_1 - \beta_1}{S_{B_1}};$

(17.13) $L,U = B_1 \mp t_{\alpha/2}(S_{B_1}).$

This group of equations is related to the sampling distribution of B_1. Equation (17.11) is the estimator for the standard error of B_1. S_U in this expression is the estimator for the standard deviation of the regression. Equation (17.12) says that the ratio $(B_1 - \beta_1)/S_{B_1}$ is the t distribution with $\delta = n - 2$. It is used as the test statistic for $\beta_1 = 0$. This ratio also suggests the way to compute the confidence limits for β_1 as given by (17.13), where $t_{\alpha/2}$ is based on $\delta = n - 2$.

(17.14) $S_{B_2} = S_U \sqrt{\dfrac{1}{m_{22}}};$

(17.15) $t_\delta = \dfrac{B_2 - \beta_2}{S_{B_1}};$

(17.16) $L,U = B_2 \mp t_{\alpha/2}(S_{B_1})$

This group of formulas is related to the sampling distribution of B_2. Equation (17.14) is the estimator for the standard error of B_2. Equation (17.15) states that the ratio $(B_2 - \beta_2)/S_{B_2}$ is distributed as t with $\delta = n - 2$. It is used as a test statistic for $\beta_2 = 0$. It also suggests how the confidence limits for β_2 are constructed as shown by (17.16).

(17.17) $\chi_\delta^2 = \dfrac{(n - 2)S_U^2}{\sigma_U^2};$

(17.18) $L = \dfrac{(n - 2)S_U^2}{\chi_{\delta;1-\alpha/2}^2};$

$U = \dfrac{(n - 2)S_U^2}{\chi_{\delta;\alpha/2}^2}.$

Here, for (17.17), χ^2 has $\delta = n - 2$. It is used as the test statistic for the null hypothesis that σ_U^2 has some specified value. The confidence limits for σ_U^2 are given by (17.18).

(17.19) $\overset{\ast}{Y}_0 = \hat{Y}_0 = B_1 + B_2 x_0.$

$\overset{\ast}{Y}_0$ and $\hat{Y}_0$ here are called the predictor and forecaster, respectively. Both are obtained by the same sample regression equation. Thus, for a given x_0, they are identical in value. $\hat{Y}_0$ is an estimator for $\mu_{Y.X}$ and $\overset{\ast}{Y}_0$ is a forecast value of a new individual observation of Y given that $X = x_0$.

(17.20) $S_P = S_U \sqrt{\dfrac{1}{n} + \dfrac{(x_0 - \bar{X})^2}{m_{22}}}$

(17.21) $t_\delta = \dfrac{\hat{\hat{Y}}_0 - (\beta_1 + \beta_2 x_0)}{S_P};$

(17.22) $L, U = \hat{\hat{Y}}_0 \mp t_{\alpha/2}(S_P).$

This group of expressions is related to the sampling distribution of the predictor. Equation (17.20) is the estimator for the standard error of the predictor. The ratio $(\hat{\hat{Y}}_0 - (\beta_1 + \beta_2 x_0))/S_P$ is distributed as t with $\delta = n - 2$. It is used as the test statistic for the null hypothesis that $\mu_{Y.x_0}$ is equal to some specified value. It also enables us to construct confidence intervals and confidence bands for $\mu_{Y.x_0}$ by using (17.22). The confidence band may be thought as the space within which the sample regression line may vary at a given level of confidence $1 - \alpha$.

(17.23) $S_F = S_U \sqrt{1 + \dfrac{1}{n} + \dfrac{(x_0 - X)^2}{m_{22}}};$

(17.24) $L, U = \hat{Y}_0 \mp t_{\alpha/2}(S_F).$

Equation (17.23) is the estimator of the standard error for the forecaster, which is a forecast value of a new observation of Y given x_0. Note that this quantity is much greater than the estimator for the standard error of the predictor owing to the fact the former consists of variation in random sampling as well as random disturbances measured by the standard deviation of the regression. Equation (17.24) is the expression for constructing confidence limits for Y_0. The t multiple is used here because the ratio $(\hat{Y} - Y_0)/S_F$ is distributed as t with $\delta = n - 2$.

(17.25) $f(x, y) = \dfrac{1}{2\pi\sigma_X\sigma_Y\sqrt{1 - \rho^2}} \exp\left\{ -\dfrac{1}{2(1 - \rho^2)} \left[\dfrac{(X - \mu_X)^2}{\sigma_X^2} \right. \right.$

$$\left. \left. - \dfrac{2\rho(X - \mu_X)(Y - \mu_Y)}{\sigma_X\sigma_Y} + \dfrac{(Y - \mu_Y)^2}{\sigma_Y^2} \right] \right\}.$$

This is the density function of a bivariate normal population. It is defined by five parameters, μ_X, μ_Y, σ_X^2, σ_Y, and ρ. The last parameter ρ is called the population coefficient of correlation.

(17.26) $\rho = \dfrac{\text{cov}(X, Y)}{\sigma_X\sigma_Y};$

(17.27) $r = \dfrac{m_{12}}{\sqrt{m_{11}m_{22}}}.$

The first equation here defines the population coefficient of correlation as the ratio of the covariance between X and Y to the product of the standard deviations of X and Y. The sample coefficient is defined in the same way and (17.27) is computational formula for it. The coefficient of correlation measures the degree or strength of association between X

and Y. It is a pure number that ranges in value from -1 through 0 to $+1$. When it equals -1 or $+1$, we say there is perfect negative or positive correlation between X and Y. When it equals 0, we say there is no correlation between X and Y. Precise interpretations of other values of ρ or r are given by the coefficient of determination.

$$(17.28) \quad t_\delta = \frac{r\sqrt{n-2}}{\sqrt{1-r^2}}.$$

This expression says that if $\rho = 0$, the values of r transformed via the ratio $(r\sqrt{n-2})/\sqrt{1-r^2}$ have a t distribution with $\delta = n - 2$. This ratio can be used as the test statistic for $\rho = 0$ against some appropriate alternative. Owing to the fact that $B_2 = r(S_Y/S_X)$, the test on $\rho = 0$ should have the same t value as the t test on $\beta_2 = 0$.

$$(17.29) \quad z_r = \frac{1}{2}\ln\frac{1+r}{1-r};$$

$$(17.30) \quad S_z = \frac{1}{\sqrt{n-3}};$$

$$(17.31) \quad Z = \frac{z_r - z_\rho}{S_z};$$

$$(17.32) \quad L,U = z_r \mp Z_{1-\alpha/2}(S_z).$$

Equation (17.29) defines the normal transformation of r into z_r; z_r is approximately normal with $E(z_r) = z_\rho$. Equation (17.30) gives the estimator for the standard error of z_r. With this normal transformation of r, we can now test whether ρ assumes some specific value. For such a test, we use Z as defined by (17.31) as the test statistic in the usual way. To compute the confidence limits for z_r we use (17.32). Values of z_r corresponding to r are given by Table X in Appendix C. Results obtained by (17.32) should be converted back into values of r via entries in Table X.

$$(17.33) \quad \text{SST} = m_{11};$$

$$(17.34) \quad \text{SSR} = B_2^2(m_{22});$$

$$(17.35) \quad \text{SSE} = \text{SST} - \text{SSR}.$$

The total variations among individual values of Y, $\text{SST} = \sum(\hat{y} - \bar{y})^2$ is decomposed into explained variations, $\text{SSR} = \sum(\hat{y} - \bar{y})^2$ and unexplained variation, $\text{SSE} = \sum(y - \hat{y})^2$. Equations (17.33), (17.34), and (17.35) are the computational formulas for these three sums of squares. Each of these sums of squares divided by its number of degrees of freedom yields a mean square MS, or sample variance. For SST, $\delta = n - 1$; for SSR, $\delta = k$, where k is the number of independent variables in the regression equation; for SSE, $\delta = n - c$, where c is the number of regression coefficients in the regression equation. Note that $MST = S_Y^2$ and that $MSE = S_U^2$.

(17.36) $\dfrac{MSR}{MSE} > F_{1,n-2;\alpha}.$

This ratio defines the region of rejection when we use $F_{1,\delta_2} = (MSR/MSE)$ as the test statistic for H_0: $\beta_2 = 0$. This F test and the t test on $\beta_2 = 0$ should yield identical conclusions for the same set of sample data because $F_{1,\delta_2} = t_{\delta_2}^2$.

(17.37) $r^2 = SSR/SST.$

This formula defines the sample coefficient of determination as the ratio between the explained error (SSR) and the total error (SST). It is the estimator for ρ^2. Its value ranges from 0 to 1. The usual interpretation of r^2 is to consider it as the proportion of total variability in Y that has been explained by regressing Y on X. It also furnishes an interpretation of r. Thus, if $r = 0.5$, we say that only 25% of the variation in Y is accounted for by the variation in the value of X.

(17.38) $\sqrt{r^2} = \pm r.$

The square root of the coefficient of determination is the coefficient of correlation. The sign of r is the same as that for B_2.

(17.39) $S_U^2 = (1 - r^2)S_Y^2.$

This expression shows that the residual (unexplained) variance S_U^2 is just a fraction of the original total variance S_Y^2, with the fraction being the coefficient of indetermination $(1 - r^2)$. Thus, r^2 is related to variances as well as variations.

REVIEW QUESTIONS

17.1 What is the essence of association analysis?

17.2 What are the different ways to classify association studies?

17.3 List the assumptions for the classical simple linear regression model. Explain in your own words the meaning of each of these assumptions.

17.4 In the population regression equation of Y on X, $\mu_{Y.X} = \beta_1 + \beta_2 x_i$, what is the graphic interpretation of β_1, of β_2, and of $\mu_{Y.X}$?

17.5 How do we define the residual error e_i from the simple sample regression model and the sample regression equation of Y on X? Explain why $\Sigma e = 0$.

17.6 What do we mean by the method of least squares? What are the desirable properties of least-squares estimators?

17.7 What is the value of a scatter diagram for sample data in regression analysis?

17.8 Can you explain why $S_{Y.X}^2 = S_U^2$? What is the defect of S_U^2 as a measure of closeness-of-fit?

17.9 How do we go about determining that regression analysis is an improvement over univariate analysis by comparing S_U with S_Y?

17.10 What is main objective of testing $\beta_i = 0$ against $\beta_i \neq 0$ with $i = 1, 2$?

17.11 What is the difference between prediction and forecasting as the terms are used in this text?

17.12 What is a confidence band? What is it used for? What is the general shape of such a band? What is the reason for this general shape?

17.13 What is a forecasting band? What is it used for? Why is a forecasting band wider than a confidence band with the same sample data and at the same level confidence?

17.14 How is the coefficient of correlation defined? What does it measure? What is the range of its values?

17.15 What is the meaning of r when it equals -1, or 0, or $+1$?

17.16 The t tests on $\beta_2 = 0$ and $\rho = 0$ should yield the same result. Why?

17.17 In studying the correlation between lung cancer and cigarette smoking, a student obtains the result $r = +1.25$. Discuss.

17.18 Why do we generally not calculate r when X is fixed?

17.19 When X is random, we can regress Y on X and also regress X on Y. This being the case, can we conclude that $B_1 = B_1'$ and $B_2 = B_2'$? Why or why not?

17.20 How is the coefficient of determination defined? What is the range of values of r^2? What are the three possible interpretations of r^2?

17.21 Sample standard deviations of regression for two different regression problems are 100 pounds and 50 pounds, respectively. From these results can you conclude that the degree of relationship in the first is weaker than that in the second? Why or why not?

17.22 Why do B_2 and r take the same sign?

17.23 Given that B_2 and B_2' are the slopes of two sample regression lines, can you explain why the relationship $r^2 = b_2 b_2'$ holds?

17.24 How should the following r values -0.50, -0.90, $+0.75$, and $+0.95$ be interpreted?

17.25 How are the simple linear regression model and the simple linear correlation model related? Explain as fully as you can.

17.26 Why is the simple linear regression model the most important among all possible regression models?

17.27 Why can we not use the sample regression equation for prediction or forecasting with X values which are beyond the range of X values employed to establish the sample regression equation?

17.28 Why can we not take the presence of significant association as positive proof of causation between the two variables? Cite a few examples of your own to show that the existence of significant correlation between two variables may not indicate one is the cause of the other.

PROBLEMS

Note: Problems in this chapter can all be solved manually without much effort. However, if you wish and if your instructor approves, you may do all the calculations required for this set of problems on the computer. With the results in the printouts, you should be able to supply answers to most of the essay questions.

Instructions for problems 17.1 to 17.8: Do the following in each case.

a. Identify whether X is fixed or random, or something else.

b. Draw a scatter diagram for the sample data and judge whether it meets the requirements of linearity, homoscedasticity, and conditional normality. Irrespective of your answer here, continue with the problem.

c. Compute a least-squares sample regression of Y on X.

d. Interpret the values of B_1 and B_2 carefully and explain why the value of B_1 in the equation has or has not a practical meaning.

e. Compute $\hat{y}$ values.

f. Compute $S_{Y.X}$ and S_Y and comment on the implications of their difference.

g. Test the significance of B_1 and B_2 at $\alpha = 0.05$ and 0.01. For tests on β_2 use both double-tail and appropriate single-tail tests.

h. Construct 95% and 99% intervals for β_2. Comment on your results here compared with those in part g.

17.1 Suppose a firm intends to market an Elvis Presley memorial album, containing a phonograph record and an illustrated brochure about Elvis. To decide on the price it should charge, it conducts a market test in twelve U.S. cities selected at random from all small cities. It charges different prices in these cities, giving the Table 17.P1.

TABLE 17.P1

City	Price (X)	Sales (Y)
Mobile, Alabama	$7.98	622
Worcester, Massachusetts	7.98	733
Montgomery, Alabama	7.98	423
Rockford, Illinois	7.98	713
Peoria, Illinois	9.98	521
Huntsville, Alabama	9.98	401
Fresno, California	9.98	436
Rochester, New York	9.98	524
Sacramento, California	11.98	381
Jersey City, New Jersey	11.98	429
Raleigh, North Carolina	11.98	483
Evansville, Indiana	11.98	304

17.2 The number of defective items Y produced per unit of time by a certain machine is thought to vary directly with the speed X of the machine measured in rpm. Observations for 12 hours selected at random from a month yield the results in Table 17.P2.

TABLE 17.P2

x	y	x	y	x	y
13.2	9.4	13.1	9.6	13.8	9.2
14.9	12.2	10.8	7.5	10.2	7.0
8.1	6.0	10.9	5.7	15.8	9.0
16.4	11.4	17.4	12.3	12.0	7.0

17.3. The president of a chain retailing organization believes there is a positive relationship between the sales of his company's product and per capita income in the year just past. He decides to associate 1985 sales with 1984 per capita income in a random sample of 15 cities from among the many cities where his company has branches. The data are as given in Table 17.P3, where X is 1984 per capita income in thousands of dollars and Y is 1985 per capita sales in dollars.

TABLE 17.P3

x	y	x	y	x	y
6.0	15	6.6	23	5.4	12
6.3	25	7.5	25	6.9	22
6.0	17	6.6	16	6.6	18
6.9	23	6.3	18	6.0	18
8.1	12	4.8	11	4.5	10

17.4 The sample in Table 17.P4 contains the price and the quantity of a commodity supplied to a market over the last $3\frac{1}{2}$ years (14 quarters); X is price and Y is quantity.

TABLE 17.P4

x	y	x	y	x	y
$25	60	$55	160	$40	115
20	85	45	80	50	120
35	110	15	40	70	180
40	95	20	55	45	95
60	140	30	90		

17.5 Table 17.P5 gives the number X of hours of study for and grades Y on an examination in elementary statistics for a random sample of twelve students.

TABLE 17.P5

x	3	3	3	4	4	5	5	5	6	6	7	8
y	45	60	55	60	75	70	80	75	90	80	75	85

17.6 The marketing department of a firm wishes to determine whether sales Y of big department stores are functionally related to advertising expenditures X spent on television commercials. It first selected 12 cities, and from each city it selected at random one store among those whose annual sales were over $2,000,000; the data in Table 17.P6 were obtained.

TABLE 17.P6

City	X = TV commercial costs ($000's)	Y = Sales ($000,000's)	City	X = TV commercial costs ($000's)	Y = Sales ($000,000's)
1	42	2.5	7	90	7.7
2	75	6.0	8	100	9.0
3	120	9.5	9	105	7.4
4	55	4.5	10	97	8.2
5	84	5.5	11	80	5.5
6	50	3.1	12	115	9.1

17.7. The personnel manager of a big manufacturing firm wants to study the relation between the number X of years on the job of assembly line workers employed by the firm and their weekly salaries Y in dollars. His sample is as shown in Table 17.P7.

TABLE 17.P7

x	y	x	y	x	y	x	y
5	96	5	120	10	150	15	187
5	118	10	127	10	145	15	180
5	126	10	142	15	168	15	175
5	110	10	159	15	162		

17.8 The Gamma Co. is studying the problem of absenteeism in its assembly plant where management considers the amount of absenteeism Y excessive. Furthermore, among other factors, management suspects the age X of the workers might be a major factor. An SRS of ten employees selected yields the data in Table 17.P8.

TABLE 17.P8

Worker	x	y	Worker	x	y
A	35	2	F	40	4
B	25	7	G	57	0
C	34	4	H	53	1
D	46	2	I	43	3
E	37	3	J	26	5

Instructions for problems 17.9 to 17.16: Do the following for each.
a. Estimate $\mu_{Y \cdot x_0}$ and predict Y_0 for $x_0 = \bar{x} + 1.5$.
b. Compute S_P and S_F for $x_0 = \bar{x} + 1.5$.

c. Compute a 95% confidence interval for $\mu_{Y \cdot x_0}$ and a 95% forecasting interval for Y_0, for $x_0 = \bar{x} + 1.5$.

d. Construct a 95% confidence band for $\mu_{Y \cdot X}$ and a 95% forecasting band for Y_0. Graph them.

17.9 Use the data and results in Problem 17.1.

17.10 Use the data and results in Problem 17.2.

17.11 Use the data and results in Problem 17.3.

17.12 Use the data and results in Problem 17.4.

17.13 Use the data and results in Problem 17.5.

17.14 Use the data and results in Problem 17.6.

17.15 Use the data and results in Problem 17.7.

17.16 Use the data and results in Problem 17.8.

Instructions for problems 17.17 to 17.24: Do the following for each.

a. Compute r.

b. Say whether r is theoretically proper in this case? If not, why not? If so, test $\rho = 0$ against $\rho \neq 0$ at $\alpha = 0.05, 0.01$.

c. Compute r^2 and give it a precise interpretation.

d. If r^2 is rather low, say, less than 0.75, what variable or variables should be added to conduct a multiple regression analysis so that the predictive power of the regression can be improved? Explain your recommendations.

17.17 Use the data and results in Problem 17.1.

17.18 Use the data and results in Problem 17.2.

17.19 Use the data and results in Problem 17.3.

17.20 Use the data and results in Problem 17.4.

17.21 Use the data and results in Problem 17.5.

17.22 Use the data and results in Problem 17.6.

17.23 Use the data and results in Problem 17.7.

17.24 Use the data and results in Problem 17.8.

18 Linear Multivariate Analyses

18.1 INTRODUCTION

The regression model introduced in the previous chapter is applicable to relationships that include only one explanatory variable. The method of analyzing such a model is one of decomposing the total variability of the dependent variable into two distinct parts: systematic and random. The former refers to the changes in the mean value of the dependent variable Y with respect to the changes in the value of the independent variable X; the latter, with respect to the variability of Y that still remains unexplained by regressing Y on X and, thus, represents the error in prediction.

The relative systematic effect of X on Y is measured by r^2—the coefficient of determination. When the value of r^2 is relatively low, then only a small percentage of the total variability in Y is systematically related to the variations in X. This means the residual error is relatively large when we attempt to predict the mean value of Y on the basis of the value of X. We know, though, that one major source for the residual disturbance is due to the fact that some relevant explanatory variables may have been excluded from the regression analysis. There is reason to believe then that the systematic part in a regression can be increased, or the random disturbance can be decreased, by introducing additional relevant independent variables into the analysis. This practice leads us to multiple regression analysis with the objective of obtaining a more precise predictive device.

In reality, we can easily see that there is often more than one factor that would affect a certain outcome. Production of an output is usually a function of several input variables, such as labor, land, and capital. Not only the price of a commodity, but other factors, such as disposable income, advertising expenditure, and prices of closely related products will also have varying degrees of influences on the demand for that commodity. Clearly, multiple regression analysis is not only highly useful but also necessary in practice.

The multiple regression model, designed to describe the relationships between one explained variable and two or more explanatory variables, is a natural extension of the simple regression model. Most of the descriptive and inferential results derived for the bivariate case can easily be generalized so that they may apply to the multivariate case. However, the study of the multiple regression model does involve two practical problems when the number of independent variables is at all large. The first is that the computational formulas for various measures become very complex without the use of matrix notation. The second is that the computational labor becomes very heavy in any kind of notation.

To overcome the first difficulty, we shall in this chapter present the general linear multiple regression model in principle but shall confine our numerical examples to the trivariate case for which only two regressors are involved. The reason for this design of presentation is twofold. One is that all aspects of linear regression analysis are theoretically identical irrespective of the number of independent variables. The other is that we have the same set of descriptive and inferential measures and the interpretations of these measures are exactly the same whether there are only two or many independent variables.

The second difficulty has ceased to be an important consideration because of the availability of electronic computers. With the aid of computers today, sometimes as many as a dozen or more variables are considered with great ease in practical regression problems. In any event, when you have gained a full understanding of the material presented in this chapter, you will encounter no difficulty of a theoretical or practical nature in any linear multiple regression situation in the future.

18.2 THE POPULATION LINEAR MULTIPLE REGRESSION MODEL

This model is developed under the following set of assumptions.

(1) LINEARITY. *A dependent variable Y is linearly related to a set of independent variables X_j, $j = 2, 3, \ldots, J$, by the following model equation:*

$$y_i = \beta_1 + \beta_2 x_{i2} + \beta_3 x_{i3} + \cdots + \beta_j x_{ij} + u_i, \qquad (18.1)$$

where the subscript i refers to the ith observation of Y, the X's, and U, the last being a stochastic disturbance, or random error; the second subscript j used in describing the explanatory variables identifies the variable in question. The number of the explanatory variables, or regressors, is J − 1, so that when J = 2, (18.1) reduces to the simple linear regression model, and when J = 2, 3, we have the simplest case of multiple linear regression model in which Y is regressed with two X's as shown by

$$y_i = \beta_1 + \beta_2 x_{i2} + \beta_3 x_{i3} + u_i. \tag{18.2}$$

(2) NONSTOCHASTIC X'S. *Each of the regressors is nonstochastic with values fixed in repeated samples and such that, for any sample size, $\sigma^2_{X_j}$ is a finite number different from zero for every $j = 2, 3, \ldots, J$.*

(3) NORMALITY. *The error term associated with each set of fixed values of X is normally distributed with $E(U) = 0$ and an unknown but finite variance σ^2_U.*

With assumption (3), we see that the subpopulation of Y associated with each set of fixed values of the regressors would be normally distributed with a conditional expectations as

$$E(y_i \mid x_{ij}) = \mu_{1.23\cdots J}$$
$$= \beta_1 + \beta_2 x_{i2} + \beta_3 x_{i3} + \cdots + \beta_j x_{ij}. \tag{18.3}$$

This result is called the *linear multiple population regression equation of Y on X's*. In this expression,

β_1 = the mean value of y_i, when each of the regressors is equal to zero;

β_j = the change in $E(y_i)$ per unit change in the value of the jth explanatory variable when the values of other regressors are held constant.

Sometimes β_1 is called the *regression coefficient* or the *Y-intercept* and β_2, β_3, $\ldots$, β_J are called the *partial regression coefficients*. In the trivariate case, the linear population regression equation is given by

$$E(y_i \mid x_{i2}, x_{i3}) = \mu_{1.23}$$
$$= \beta_1 + \beta_2 x_{i2} + \beta_3 x_{i3}. \tag{18.4}$$

Graphically, this equation represents a regression plane fitted through an egg-shaped set of points y_i, in a three-dimensional space as shown by Figure 18.1. This graph is a simplification of the actual, more complicated linear trivariate model. In the actual model, there is a normal distribution for each set of possible values of the two independent variables. Thus, the points spread from $-\infty$ to $+\infty$, parallel to the Y-axis, for each set of possible values of X_2 and X_3. Each of these

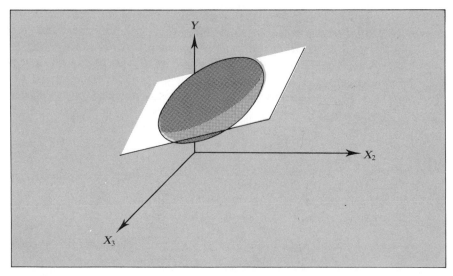

FIGURE 18.1 Regression plane fitted to a trivariate population in three-dimensional space.

normal distributions has a mean and a variance. In this case, the means lie on a plane rather than on a curved surface. Similar graphic interpretations can conceivably be made with the general case of $(J - 1)$ X's. However, such a task becomes practically impossible when we are concerned with regression graphs with four or higher dimensions.

(4) HOMOSCEDASTICITY. *The regression variance remains constant for each subpopulation of Y's and it is identical with the variance for the error terms; that is,*

$$V(y_i) = E(y_i - E(y_i)]^2$$
$$= \sigma^2_{1.23\cdots J} = \sigma^2_U.$$

(5) NONAUTOREGRESSION. $E(u_i, u_k) = 0, i \neq k.$

(6) SIZE OF n. *The number of observations exceeds the number of coefficients to be estimated.*

(7) *No exact linear relationship exists between any pair of the regressors.*

The foregoing set of assumptions constitutes the full specification of the *classical normal linear multiple regression model*. Note that the first five assumptions are identical with those for the classical normal simple linear regression model. Our earlier comments on these assumptions apply equally well here. However, an additional observation on assumption (2) is in order here. The provision of nonstochastic X's is principally a theoretical requirement for the application of the least-squares method for estimation. As a matter of fact, there are three linear multiple regression models: the fixed-X's model, the random-X's model, and the mixed X's model. In the last model, one or more explanatory varibles are fixed and one or more explantory variables are random. This last model is very rare in actual situations. By and large, the random-X's model is most frequently encountered in multivariate regression analysis. Because of comments already made on the fixed-X and random-X models, we may in practice treat both models as though they were the same so far as analyses are concerned.

Assumptions (6) and (7) are new. Assumption (6) makes a provision for a sufficient number of degrees of freedom in estimation. Of course, we can also include this assumption in the simple regression model. It is not explicitly given in such a case because we never conduct a regression analysis with $n \leq 2$ in reality. Assumption (7), says that none of the regressors should be perfectly correlated with any other regressor or with any linear combinations of other independent variables. This assumption, as we shall see later, is also necessary for estimation.

18.3 LEAST-SQUARES ESTIMATION OF REGRESSION COEFFICIENTS

Corresponding to (18.1) and (18.2), the sample linear multiple regression model and the sample multiple regression equation of Y on X's are, respectively,

$$y_i = B_1 + B_2 x_{i2} + B_3 x_{i3} + \cdots + B_j x_{ij} + e_i \tag{18.5}$$

and

$$\hat{y}_i = \hat{\mu}_{1.23\cdots J}$$
$$= B_1 + B_2 x_{i2} + B_3 x_{i3} + \cdots + B_j x_{ij}. \tag{18.6}$$

From these two equations, we see that

$$e_i = y_i - \hat{y}_i \quad \text{and} \quad \sum e_i = 0,$$

as in the simple regression model. Now, to apply the method of least squares to obtain B_i (and dropping the subscript i attached to all the individual values of the variables for slight simplication of notation), the sum of squares to be minimized is

$$S = \sum e^2 = \sum (y - B_1 - B_2 x_2 - B_3 x_3 - \cdots - B_j x_j)^2.$$

The values of B_i, the LSEs, can be found by solving the following set of least-squares normal equations:

(1) $$\sum y = nB_1 + B_2 \sum x_2 + B_3 \sum x_3 + \cdots + B_j \sum x_j,$$

(2) $$\sum x_2 y = B_1 \sum x_2 + B_2 \sum x_2^2 + B_3 \sum x_2 x_3 + \cdots + B_j \sum x_2 x_j,$$

(3) $$\sum x_3 y = B_1 \sum x_3 + B_2 \sum x_2 x_3 + B_3 \sum x_3^2 + \cdots + B_j \sum x_3 x_j,$$

$$\vdots$$

(J + 1) $$\sum x_j y = B_1 \sum x_j + B_2 \sum x_2 x_j + B_3 \sum x_3 x_j + \cdots + B_j \sum x_j^2.$$

The student with some knowledge in calculus can easily verify that, by differentiating S with respect to B_i, successively, and setting the resulting derivatives equal to zero, one obtains the above normal equations.

The nonmathematical student can easily understand the form of these equations in the following way. The first normal equation is found by summing the expression

$$y = B_1 + B_2 x_2 + B_3 x_3 + \cdots + B_j x_j.$$

The second normal equation is found by multiplying both sides of the expression by x_2 and summing. The third normal equation is found by multiplying both sides of the expression by x_3 and summing. This process is repeated for each regressor. With all the equations written, there is one for each of the regression coefficients, β_i, in (18.6).

As to the practical problem of solving these normal equations, we first note that the first normal equation can be written as

$$B_1 = \bar{Y} - B_2 \bar{X}_2 - B_3 \bar{X}_3 - \cdots - B_j \bar{X}_j. \tag{18.7}$$

Next, let

$$m_{1j} = \sum (y - \bar{Y})(x_j - \bar{X}_j) \tag{18.8a}$$

and

$$m_{kj} = \sum (x_j - \bar{X}_j)(x_k - \bar{X}_k), \qquad k, j = 2, 3, \ldots, J. \tag{18.8b}$$

Finally, substitution of (18.8) into the remaining equations, after some simplification, gives

(2)' $$m_{12} = m_{22}\beta_2 + m_{23}B_3 + \cdots + m_{2j}B_j,$$

(3)' $$m_{13} = m_{23}B_2 + m_{33}B_3 + \cdots + m_{3j}B_j,$$

$$\vdots$$

(J + 1)' $$m_{1j} = m_{2j}B_2 + m_{3j}B_3 + \cdots + m_{jj}B_j.$$

These equations can be solved for $B_2, B_3, \ldots, B_j$. However, such a task becomes tedious and quite laborious. When the number of regressors is at all large, we shall resort to electronic computers for the solutions. For the trivariate case (where $J = 3$), we have, as suggested by (18.7)

$$B_1 = \bar{Y} - B_2\bar{X}_2 - B_3\bar{X}_3. \tag{18.9}$$

Also, if we only consider the first two terms on the right-hand sides of both $(2)'$ and $(3)'$, then $(2)'$ and $(3)'$ would be the last two of the three least-squares normal equations written in terms of individual deviations from the respective means of the variables in the trivariate case. Thus, solving $(2)'$ and $(3)'$ for the trivariate case simultaneously, we have

$$B_2 = \frac{m_{12}m_{33} - m_{13}m_{23}}{m_{22}m_{33} - m_{23}^2} \tag{18.10}$$

and

$$B_3 = \frac{m_{13}m_{22} - m_{12}m_{23}}{m_{22}m_{33} - m_{23}^2}. \tag{18.11}$$

As our numerical illustration, let us consider the case of a toy manufacturer who sells his products in hundreds of sales districts throughout the United States. He introduced a new low-priced toy the previous year and he wishes to estimate the sales of this new toy in the coming year in terms of advertising expenditure and price. For this purpose he has selected an SRS of ten sales districts and their sales records on these three variables are observed and are as recorded in Table 18.1. In this table,

Y = sales in thousands of units;

X_2 = newspaper advertisement expenditure in hundreds of dollars;

X_3 = price in dollars.

TABLE 18.1 Sales Data of a New Toy

Sales District	x_2	x_3	y
1	11	6.55	12
2	14	7.00	13
3	12	6.50	12
4	20	6.75	17
5	15	6.50	16
6	23	6.25	25
7	32	5.75	36
8	28	6.25	34
9	30	5.50	45
10	35	5.00	45
Total	220	62.05	225

Source: Hypothetical.

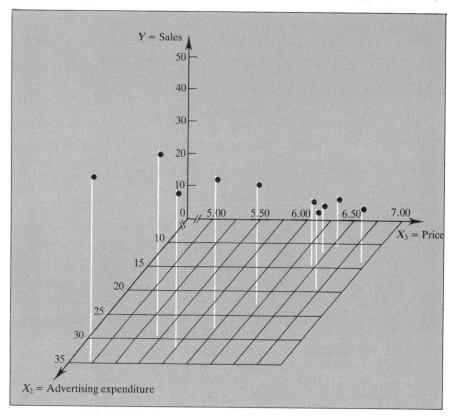

FIGURE 18.2 Scatter diagram for the sales of toys example. (*Source:* Table 18.1.)

A scatter diagram for data in Table 18.1 is given by Figure 18.2. Note that a plane will fit the dots in the three-dimensional space reasonably well and there seems to be approximately the same amount of variation in Y values throughout the graph. Namely, the assumptions of linearity, homoscedasticity, and nonautoregression are reasonably well satisfied. Of course, we cannot judge the normality of the error term; that is, the conditional normality of the subpopulations, the Y's, since there are not sufficient data for this purpose. We shall simply assume that the assumption of normality is justified in this case.

Proceeding with our example, the preliminary calculations are:

$$\bar{x}_2 = \sum x_2/n = 220/10 = 22.00,$$

$$\bar{x}_3 = \sum x_3/n = 62.05/10 = 6.205,$$

$$\bar{y} = \sum y/n = 255/10 = 25.50;$$

$$\sum x_2^2 = 5{,}548, \qquad \sum x_3^2 = 388.4025, \qquad \sum y^2 = 8{,}129;$$

$$\sum x_2 y = 6{,}642, \qquad \sum x_3 y = 1{,}514.60, \qquad \sum x_2 x_3 = 1{,}332.30;$$

$$m_{11} = \sum (y - \bar{y})^2 = \sum y^2 - n(\bar{y})^2$$
$$= 8{,}129 - 10(25.50)^2 = 1{,}626.50;$$

$$m_{22} = \sum (x_2 - \bar{x}_2)^2 = \sum x_2^2 - n(\bar{x}_2)^2$$
$$= 5{,}548 - 10(22)^2 = 708;$$

$$m_{33} = \sum (x_3 - \bar{x}_3)^2 = \sum x_3^2 - n(\bar{x}_3)^2$$
$$= 388.4025 - 10(6.205)^2 = 3.38225;$$

$$m_{12} = \sum (x_2 - \bar{x}_2)(y - \bar{y}) = \sum x_2 y - n\bar{x}_2 \bar{y}$$
$$= 6{,}642 - 10(25.50)(22) = 1{,}032;$$

$$m_{13} = \sum (x_3 - \bar{x}_3)(y - \bar{y}) = \sum x_3 y - n(\bar{x}_3)(\bar{y})$$
$$= 1{,}514.60 - 10(25.50)(6.025) = -67.675;$$

$$m_{23} = \sum (x_2 - \bar{x}_2)(x_3 - \bar{x}_3) = \sum x_2 x_3 - n(\bar{x}_2)(\bar{x}_3)$$
$$= 1{,}323.30 - 10(22)(6.205) = -41.8.$$

With these m values and by (18.10) and (18.11), we have

$$b_2 = \frac{(1{,}032)(3.38225) - (-67.675)(-41.8)}{(708)(3.38225) - (-41.8)^2}$$

$$\doteq 1.02205$$

and

$$b_3 = \frac{(-67.675)(780) - (1{,}032)(-41.8)}{(708)(3.38225) - (-41.8)^2}$$

$$\doteq -7.37774.$$

Now, by (18.9),

$$b_1 = 25.50 - 1.02205(22) - (-7.37774)(6.205)$$

$$= 48.79378.$$

Finally, the sample regression equation of sales Y on X_2 (advertisement expenditure), and X_3 (price) can be written as

$$\hat{y} = 48.79378 + 1.02205x_2 - 7.37774x_3.$$

The values of $\hat{y}$, or $\hat{\mu}_{1.23}$, can now be computed simply by replacing the pairs of values (x_2, x_3) in Table 18.1 into the foregoing equation and solving. As an exercise, you may compute these values. If you do so, you will find that when the $\hat{y}$ values are rounded to two decimal places, we have $\sum \hat{y} = \sum y = 255$, as should be the case.

The preceding sample regression equation substantiates economic theory or our intuitive belief that advertisement expenditure affects sales positively and that the quantity of toys sold varies inversely with price. Precisely, the value $b_2 = 1.02205$ means that in these data the mean sales increase by 1022.05 units per \$100 increase in advertisement expenditure when price is held constant; the value $b_3 = -7.37774$ means that in these data the mean sales decreases by almost 7377.74 units per dollar increase in price when advertisement expenditure is held constant. Clearly, the two values of the partial regression coefficients together would measure the total effect on the mean sales in these data when both X_2 and X_3 are increased by one unit each.

In the interpretation of our results, two additional observations must be made. First, the value $b_1 = 48.79378$ theoretically refers to the mean value of sales when both advertisement expenditure and price are zero. This obviously does not make any sense from a practical point of view here. Thus, just as in the simple regression case, whether the value of the Y intercept is practically meaningful depends on the nature of the variables considered. However, the value of B_1 does always have the mathematical importance of determining the value of Y together with B_2 and B_3, given that the values of X_2 and X_3 are specified.

Second, the absolute values of the partial regression coefficients do not indicate the relative importance of the effects of X's on Y. This is due to the fact that units of the independent variables may be different. For instance, in our current example, we cannot conclude that X_3 is much more influential upon the value of Y than X_2 since b_3 is almost 9 times as large absolutely as b_2. This is so because the units for X_2 are 100 times as large as the units for X_3. When units of the explanatory variables are different, evaluation of the relative weights of the partial regression coefficients can be made in terms of what are called β-coefficients—a topic we introduce immediately.

18.4 β COEFFICIENTS

To overcome, partially, the difficulty of direct comparison of the relative importance of the explanatory variables on the explained variable when different units of measurement are used, we may transform them into units of standard deviations. This is a rather simple procedure. It is easy to see that the population regression equation

$$\mu_{1.23\cdots J} = \beta_1 + \beta_2 x_2 + \beta_3 x_3 + \cdots + \beta_j x_j$$

is identical to the expression

$$\frac{\mu_{1.23\cdots J}}{\sigma_1} = \frac{\beta_1}{\sigma_1} + \frac{\beta_2 \sigma_2}{\sigma_1}\left(\frac{x_2}{\sigma_2}\right) + \frac{\beta_3 \sigma_3}{\sigma_1}\left(\frac{x_3}{\sigma_3}\right) + \cdots + \frac{\beta_J \sigma_J}{\sigma_1}\left(\frac{x_J}{\sigma_J}\right)$$

$$= \beta_1^* + \beta_2^*\left(\frac{x_2}{\sigma_2}\right) + \beta_3^*\left(\frac{x_3}{\sigma_3}\right) + \cdots + \beta_J^*\left(\frac{x_J}{\sigma_J}\right). \qquad (18.12)$$

In this newly derived equation, σ_1 stands for the standard deviation for

Y, σ_2, the standard deviation for X_2, etc., and β_i^*, $i = 1, 2, 3, \ldots, J$ are the β-coefficients, or the standardized regression coefficients.

Corresponding to (18.12), we have the sample multiple regression equation in terms of β-coefficients as follows:

$$\frac{\hat{y}}{S_1} = B_1^* + B_2^*\left(\frac{x_2}{S_2}\right) + B_3^*\left(\frac{x_3}{S_3}\right) + \cdots + B_J^*\left(\frac{x_J}{S_J}\right). \qquad (18.13)$$

Now, for our illustrative example,

$$s_1 = \sqrt{\frac{\sum (y - \bar{y})^2}{n - 1}} = \sqrt{\frac{m_{11}}{n - 1}} = \sqrt{\frac{1{,}626.50}{10 - 1}} \doteq 13.44;$$

$$s_2 = \sqrt{\frac{m_{22}}{n - 1}} = \sqrt{\frac{208}{10 - 1}} \doteq 8.87;$$

$$s_3 = \sqrt{\frac{m_{33}}{n - 1}} = \sqrt{\frac{3.38225}{10 - 1}} \doteq 0.613.$$

With these results, the sample β-coefficients are

$$b_1^* = \frac{b_1}{s_1} = \frac{48.79378}{13.44} \doteq 3.6305;$$

$$b_2^* = (b_2)\frac{s_2}{s_1} = 1.02205\left(\frac{8.87}{13.44}\right) \doteq 0.6745;$$

$$b_3^* = (b_3)\frac{s_3}{s_1} = (-7.37774)\left(\frac{0.613}{13.44}\right) \doteq -0.3365.$$

Finally, we write

$$\frac{\hat{y}}{13.44} = 3.6305 + 0.6745\left(\frac{x_2}{8.87}\right) - 0.3365\left(\frac{x_3}{0.613}\right).$$

The interpretations of the partial β-coefficients in this equation are as follows. On the average, in these data, a change of one standard deviation in X_2 (when X_3 is held constant) will produce a change of about 0.67 standard deviation in Y, and a change of one standard in X_3 (when X_2 is held constant) will produce a change of about 0.34 standard deviation in Y. Hence, it is clear that in this case advertisement expenditure is relative more important than price as far as the sales of the new toy are concerned. One reason for the relatively small effect of price on sales in our example may be that the new toy is a low-price commodity, as such, it tends to have a relatively inelastic demand with respect to price. In economic theory, a demand is said to be relatively inelastic if a 1% change in price will produce a less than 1% change in quantity bought.

However, the effects of the unexamined variables must be considered. Anything that affects sales (Y) and is definitely correlated with advertising (X_2) while being less correlated with price (X_3) will show up in this regression as an advertising effect. Similarly, anything that affects sales (Y) and is definitely correlated with price (X_3) while being less correlated with advertising (X_2) will show up in this regression as a price effect. In these data, the unexamined variables were free to vary in whatever way they wanted to. It is possible, for example, that as one considers first one sales territory and then another, as these data do, that the major competitor's toy price varied in the same direction as our toy manufacturer's advertising expenses. In that case, in those areas where advertising was heaviest, the competition was the most highly priced. If price is really the important determinant of sales of this toy, advertising will nevertheless show up in these data as the more important independent variable. Such things do happen in multiple regression, and one must be very careful in interpreting the results of a multiple regression computation.

Another way of looking at the difficulties in interpretation is the following. The statistical associations found in these data and measured by the regression computations are undeniably present in these data. But would deliberately increasing advertising expenses next year have the numerical effect on sales that these regression computations apparently suggest? Not necessarily. The unexamined variables may be powerful and may act in quite a different way next quarter from the way they acted for these data, which would make a very different regression equation the valid one for next year.

18.5 ESTIMATION OF POPULATION VARIANCE OF REGRESSION

The variances and covariances of the least-squares estimators of the regression coefficients all involve the common variance for the subpopulations, the Y's, associated with each set of values of the X's. This variance is identical with the variance of the error term and it has to be estimated. As can be shown, an unbiased estimator of $\sigma^2_{1.23\cdots J}$, or σ^2_U, is given by the following expression:

$$S^2_U = \frac{1}{n-c} \sum (y - B_1 - B_2 x_2 - B_3 x_3 - \cdots - B_J x_J)^2$$

$$= \frac{1}{1-c}(m_{11} - B_2 m_{12} - B_3 m_{13} - \cdots - B_J m_{1J}), \qquad (18.14)$$

where c stands for the number of regression coefficients, This statistic, as usual, measures the closeness-of-fit but, again as usual, does not have a precise intuitive interpretation.

Applying (18.14) to our example in which there are two independent variables and three regression coefficients, we see that

$$s_U^2 = s_{1.23}^2 = \frac{1}{n-3} \sum (y - b_1 - b_2 x_2 - b_3 x_3)^2$$

$$= \frac{1}{10-3} (m_{11} - b_2 m_{12} - b_3 m_{13})$$

$$= \frac{1}{7} [1{,}626.50 - 1.02205(1{,}032) - (-7.37774)(-67.675)]$$

$$\doteq 10.351.$$

The square root of this quantity is an estimate of the standard deviation of the regression. Thus

$$s_U = \sqrt{10.351} \doteq 3.2173.$$

Note that this result is much smaller than $s_1 = s_Y = 13.44$ obtained before. This indicates that regressing Y on X_2 and X_3 is an improvement over univariate analysis.

18.6 INFERENCES ABOUT MULTIPLE REGRESSION COEFFICIENTS

The coefficients in a sample multiple regression equation are subjected to sampling error. Before it can be used as a predictive device, we must first determine whether the sample regression coefficients are statistically significant. With respect to testing hypotheses, the multiple regression model offers to two kinds of test. The first is the test of the joint effect of X's on Y. In this case we test a rather comprehensive hypothesis that none of the independent variables has an influence on the mean of Y. That is, we test here the null hypothesis

$$H_0: \beta_2 = \beta_3 = \cdots = \beta_J = 0$$

against the alternative that H_0 is not true, namely, that at least one of the partial regression coefficients, regression slopes, is different from zero. The second method is to test the separate effect of each of the explanatory variables on the mean of Y. Here, we test the null hypothesis β_i equals zero, or some specific number, say, λ_i, that is,

$$H_0: \beta_i = 0, \quad \text{or} \quad H_0: \beta_i = \lambda_i.$$

We will consider the first type of test in this section and it can be done conveniently by the procedure of ANOVA. The second type of test will be taken up shortly. The application of ANOVA in the multiple regression model will also provide us a more obvious measure of closeness-of-fit in the statistic called "the coefficient of multiple determination."

Decomposition of Total Sample Variation of Y

Just as in the simple regression case, the total variation in Y can be decomposed into two distinct parts: the *explained variation*—the portion of total variation in Y that has been explained by regressing Y on X's and the *unexplained variation*—the portion of total variation in Y that has not been explained by regression. Thus, we see the following relationship holds:

$$\sum (y - \bar{Y})^2 = \sum (\hat{y} - \bar{Y})^2 + \sum (y - \hat{\mu}_{1.23\cdots J})^2.$$
$$\text{SST} \quad = \quad \text{SSR} \quad + \quad \text{SSE}$$

It may be noted that in the foregoing identity that

$$\text{SST} = m_{11}$$

which has $n - 1$ degrees of freedom. It can also be shown that for the case of $J - 1$ explanatory variables, we have

$$\text{SSR} = \sum_{j=2}^{J} B_j m_{1j}. \tag{18.15}$$

For SSR, $\delta = k$, where k is equal to the number of independent variables, that is $J - 1$, or the number of partial regression coefficients.
   Finally,

$$\text{SSE} = \text{SST} - \text{SSR}.$$

For SSE, $\delta = n - c$, where c is the number of regression coefficients in the multiple regression equation:

$$n - c = n - k - 1.$$

As usual, each of the sums of squares divided by the corresponding number of degrees of freedom yields a mean square—a sample variance. Furthermore, as in the bivariate case, we have $\text{MST} = S_Y^2$ and $\text{MSE} = S_U^2 = \text{SSE}/(n - c)$.
   The conclusions so far can be presented by an ANOVA table as Table 18.2.

TABLE 18.2 ANOVA Table for Multiple Regression

Source	SS	δ	MS
Regression	SSR	k	$\text{MSR} = \text{SSR}/k$
Residual error	SSE	$n - c$	$\text{MSE} = \text{SSE}/(n - c)$
Total	SST	$n - 1$	$\text{MST} = \text{SST}/(n - 1)$

F Test on the Joint Effect of *X*'s on Mean of *Y*

Now, turning our attention to testing the null hypothesis

$$H_0: \beta_2 = \beta_3 = \cdots = \beta_J = 0$$

against

$$H_1: \text{At least one of the } \beta_j \text{ is not zero,}$$

we note that if there is no significant regression of Y on any of the X's, then MSR would be close to zero and MSE would be close to MST in value. This is because, in the absence of significant regression, the explained portion of SST, represented by SSR, would be quite small. These observations lead us to consider the ratio MSR/MSE as the test statistic for the total regression effect of X's on Y. We see that MSC/MSE is a ratio of two chi-square variables; that is, an F statistic. Furthermore, if the null hypothesis that all the partial regression coefficients are zero is true, MSR/MSE will be closed to zero; if it is false, then the ratio will be significantly greater than zero. Hence, for this test, the rejection region is defined as

$$\frac{\text{MSR}}{\text{MSE}} > F_{\delta_1, \delta_2; \alpha}, \qquad (18.16)$$

where $\delta_1 = k$ and $\delta_2 = n - c$.

For our illustrative example, suppose we wish to test

$$H_0: \beta_2 = \beta_3 = 0$$

against

$$H_1: \text{At least one of the } \beta_i \text{ is not zero.}$$

From previous computations, we have

$$\text{SST} = m_{11} = 1{,}626.50.$$

By (18.15),

$$\begin{aligned}
\text{SSR} &= \sum_{j=2}^{3} b_j m_{1j} \\
&= b_2 m_{12} + b_3 m_{13} \\
&= (1.02205)(1{,}032) + (-7.37774)(-67.675) \\
&\doteq 1{,}554.044.
\end{aligned}$$

Finally,

$$\text{SSE} = \text{SST} - \text{SSR} = 1{,}626.50 - 1{,}554.044 = 72.456.$$

TABLE 18.3 ANOVA Table for Sales Data

Source	SS	β	MS	
Regression	1,554.044	$k = 2$	MSR = 1,554/2	= 777.022
Residual	72.456	$n - c = 7$	MSE = 72/7	$\doteq$ 10.351
Total	1,626.500	$n - 1 = 9$	MST = 1,626.5/9	= 180.722

These sums of squares can now be used to compute the mean squares as is done in Table 18.3.

From the results in the last column in Table 18.3, we have

$$F_{2,7} = \frac{\text{MSC}}{\text{MSE}} = \frac{777.022}{10.351} \doteq 75.07 > F_{2,7;.01} = 9.55.$$

This value of F leads to the rejection of H_0 at $\alpha = 0.01$. Hence, there is highly significant regression between sales, advertisement expenditure, and price.

18.7 FURTHER INFERENCES ABOUT MULTIPLE REGRESSION COEFFICIENTS

The F test just considered is an overall test on the joint effects of X's on the value of Y. Very often, we need to know the separate contribution of each of the independent variables on Y. This can be done by a "stepwise analysis" of decomposing SSR into $J - 1$ distinct parts to reflect the net regression effects of X's. However, such a procedure is not as obvious as we would like so far as interpretations are considered. Furthermore, the decomposition of SSR becomes quite involved and confusing when the number of explanatory variables is at all large. Finally, the ANOVA technique does not provide inferential procedures for β_1—the Y-intercept. To overcome all of these drawbacks, we proceed to conduct inferences on β_i via their sampling distributions.

The sampling distributions of B_i are quite easily established. As in the simple regression case, the method of least squares leads to precisely the same formulas as the methods of best linear unbiased estimation and maximum likelihood. This implication is that the least-squares estimators of the coefficients of a multiple regression model are BLUE. So, LSEs are unbiased, $E(B_i) = \beta_i$ with estimated standard errors defined as $S_{B_i} = S_U \sqrt{cn}$, where c are called Gauss multipliers and are the diagonal c values in the "inverse matrix" of the values of the variances and covariances of the LSEs. Finally, if the residual is normally distributed, B_i is also normally distributed. When σ_U^2 is unknown and $n \leq 30$, the quantity

$$t_\delta = \frac{B_i - \beta_i}{S_{B_i}} \tag{18.17}$$

is a t distribution with $\delta = n - c$. This ratio can be used as the test statistic for hypotheses of $\beta_i = 0$ and to construct confidence limits for β_i by the following expression:

$$L, U = B_i \mp t_{\alpha/2}(S_{B_i}), \tag{18.18}$$

where $t_{\alpha/2}$ is based on $\delta = n - c$ for t.

Now, in the trivariate case, we have

$$S_{B_1} = S_U \sqrt{\frac{1}{n} + \frac{\bar{X}_2^2 m_{33} + \bar{X}_3^2 m_{22} - 2\bar{X}_2\bar{X}_3 m_{23}}{m_{22}m_{33} - m_{23}^2}}, \tag{18.19}$$

$$S_{B_2} = S_U \sqrt{\frac{m_{33}}{m_{22}m_{33} - m_{23}^2}}, \tag{18.20}$$

and

$$S_{B_3} = S_U \sqrt{\frac{m_{22}}{m_{22}m_{33} - m_{23}^2}}. \tag{18.21}$$

For the sales data and from previous computations, we see that

$$S_{B_1} = 3.2173 \sqrt{\frac{1}{10} + \frac{(22)^2(3.38225) + (6.205)^2(708) - 2(22)(6.205)(-41.8)}{(708)(3.38225) - (-41.8)^2}}$$

$$\doteq 25.4071,$$

$$S_{B_2} = 3.2173 \sqrt{\frac{3.38225}{(708)(3.38225) - (-41.8)^2}} \doteq 0.2325,$$

and

$$S_{B_3} = 3.2173 \sqrt{\frac{708}{(708)(3.38225) - (-41.8)^2}} \doteq 3.3645.$$

To test H_0: $\beta_1 = 0$ against H_1: $\beta_1 \neq 0$,

$$t_\delta = \frac{b_1 - \beta_1}{s_{B_1}}$$

$$= \frac{48.79378 - 0}{25.4071} \doteq 1.9205 > t_{7;.05} = 1.895.$$

To test H_0: $\beta_2 = 0$ against H_1: $\beta_2 \neq 0$,

$$t_\delta = \frac{b_2 - \beta_2}{s_{B_2}}$$

$$= \frac{1.02205 - 0}{0.2325} \doteq 4.395 > t_{7;.005} = 3.499.$$

To test $H_0: \beta_3 = 0$ against $H_1: \beta_3 \neq 0$,

$$t_\delta = \frac{b_3 - \beta_3}{s_{B_3}}$$

$$= \frac{-7.37774 - 0}{3.3645} \doteq -2.1928 < t_{7;.05} = -1.895.$$

The above results reveal that only b_2 is significant at $\alpha = 0.01$ and that both b_1 and b_3 are merely significant at $\alpha = 0.10$. These conclusions are quite consistent with our previous observations that b_2 is by far much more influential on Y than b_3 is our example.

It is interesting and important to note that sometimes none of the B's is significant via t tests, yet the joint test on the partial regression coefficients via the F test may turn out to be highly significant. The reason for this is that the separate contributions of X's to the explanation of the variation in Y are weak; whereas their joint contribution, which cannot be decomposed, is quite strong. This may happen when any pair of the Xs is almost perfectly correlated, say, with their simple coefficient of correlation greater than 0.90. This is also the reason for assumption (7) in the multiple regression model that none of the regressors should be perfectly correlated with any other regressor.

Now, if it is desired to construct confidence intervals for β_i, we can do so easily by employing (18.18). For example, the 99% confidence interval for β_2 is

$$L, U = b_2 \mp t_{\delta;.005}(s_{B_2})$$

$$= 1.02205 \mp 3.499(0.2325)$$

$$\doteq 0.21 \text{ to } 1.84,$$

which does not contain zero as the previous test result dictated. This result illustrates once again the correspondence between a test at α and a confidence interval estimate with $1 - \alpha$. As the reader can verify himself if he constructs, say, a 95% interval estimate for either β_1 or β_3, the interval will contain the value of zero, since neigher b_1 nor b_3 is significant at $\alpha = 0.05$.

18.8 COEFFICIENT OF MULTIPLE DETERMINATION

Having obtained the sample multiple regression equation and established the varying degrees of significances of the regression coefficients, we still wish to know the closeness-of-fit of the regression. For example, in the trivariate case, we may wish to have some idea of the closeness-of-fit of the regression plane to a set of trivariate data—the actual points in the three-dimensional space. An obvious and clear-cut measure for this purpose is called "the coefficient of multiple determination."

The *sample coefficient of multiple determination*, denoted $R^2_{1.23\cdots J}$, or simply R^2, (irrespective of the size of J), is defined, as for r^2 in the simple regression case, as the ratio of the explained variation due to regression to the total variation in Y. Thus,

$$R^2 = \frac{\text{SSR}}{\text{SST}}. \tag{18.22}$$

So defined, R^2 can be interpreted as the proportion of the total variation in the explained variable that is associated with, or explained by, the regression of Y on X's. As a measure of closeness-of-fit, R^2 may be thought of as an indication of the spread of the Y values to the fitted regression. Hence, the closer the value of R^2 is to 1, the smaller is the scatter of the points about the fitted regression and the better is the fit.

For our illustrative data and with information in Table 18.3,

$$R^2_{1.23} = R^2 = \frac{1,554.044}{1,626.500} \doteq 0.9555.$$

Thus, about 96% of the variation in sales has been explained by variations in advertisement expenditure and price. There still remains only 4% of the variation in Y that can only be explained by factors that have not been taken into consideration in our analysis or by inherent randomness.

The square root of R^2, denoted as R, is called the *sample coefficient of multiple correlation*. This measure is seldom used today. However, when it is computed it should always take a positive sign, since the partial regression coefficients may take opposite signs, as in our illustrative example.

It is important to note that we have considered R^2 as a measure of closeness-of-fit, not a measure of covariability. As such, it is meaningful whether the independent variables are fixed or random. However, if the X's are random variables, then R^2 can also be considered as a measure of covariability between Y and its best linear unbiased estimate $\hat{y}$.

To test the null hypothesis that $\rho^2 = 0$, we employ the following ratio as the test statistic:

$$F_{k,n-c} = \frac{R^2/k}{(1 - R^2)/(n - c)}. \tag{18.23}$$

The test on $\rho^2 = 0$ is equivalent to the test on $\beta_2 = \beta_3 = \cdots = \beta_J = 0$. For the sales data on hand, we have

$$F_{2,7} = \frac{9555/2}{(1 - 0.9555)/(10 - 3)} \doteq 75.15.$$

Thus, R^2 is significant at $\alpha = 0.01$, as was the result of our test for $\beta_2 = \beta_3 = 0$ before. Furthermore, the computed values of F in both cases should be identical except for rounding errors.

The coefficient of multiple determination as defined by (18.22) is a MLE and it is asymptotically biased. To correct this bias, we may compute the *adjusted*, or *corrected*, *coefficient of multiple determination*, denoted as $\bar{R}^2$ and is defined as

$$\bar{R}^2 = 1 - \frac{\text{MSE}}{\text{MST}}. \tag{18.24}$$

Note that, since $\text{MSE} = \text{SSE}/(n-k)$ and $\text{MST} = \text{SST}/(n-1)$, the correction factor is $(n-1)/(n-k)$, which is greater than unity; hence, R^2 is adjusted downward. For our illustrative example,

$$\bar{R}^2 = -\frac{10.351}{180.722} \doteq 0.9427.$$

In practice, R^2 and $\bar{R}^2$ are asymptotically equal. Thus, when n is at all large, it does not make much difference which measure we should use. However, $\bar{R}^2$ does provide two convenient functions. First of all, it takes into account the number of independent variables in relation to the number of observations. It therefore facilitates comparisons of the "goodness-of-fit" of several regressions that may vary with respect to the number of explanatory variables and the number of observations.

Secondly, $\bar{R}^2$, being an unbiased estimator for ρ^2, can be employed to demonstrate more precisely the relationship between the unexplained error and total variation in Y by the following expression:

$$S_U^2 = (1 - \bar{R}^2)S_Y^2. \tag{18.25}$$

This equation says that the variance of regression residual is equal to the unexplained portion of the total variance. Thus, for data in Table 18.3, we see that

$$s_U^2 = (1 - 0.9427)(180.722) \doteq 10.355.$$

18.9 PREDICTION AND FORECASTING

When the sample multiple regression equation is judged to be useful from the various inferential results presented previously, it may then be employed as an estimation device. Again, following the same convention as in the bivariate case, the estimation of the mean value of Y we will call prediction and the projection of a specific, or a new observation, of Y we will call forecasting. We shall continue to denote the predictor as $\hat{Y}_0$ and the forecaster as $\hat{Y}_0$, respectively, corresponding to a set of fixed values of X's, denoted as x_{0j}, where $j = 2, 3, \ldots, J$.

As in the bivariate case, given a set of fixed values of X's, the predictor and forecaster are identical in value, since they are obtained from the same sample regression equation. Thus,

$$\hat{\hat{Y}}_0 = \hat{Y}_0 = B_1 + B_2 x_{02} + B_3 x_{03} + \cdots + B_j x_{0j}. \qquad (18.26)$$

In the application of this equation, the reader is reminded that $\hat{\hat{Y}}_0 = \hat{Y}_0$, but that these two statistics are different conceptually and have different sampling distributions and different interval estimates.

Prediction

Prediction of the expected value of Y is a problem of evaluating the precision of the estimated regression function as a whole. This is indicated by a confidence band that can be established, as in the bivariate case, by constructing a series of confidence intervals for $\mu_{1.23\cdots J}$. As in the bivariate case, also the predictor, $\hat{\hat{Y}}_0$ has the same sampling distribution as $\hat{y}$. Thus, we can simply state that the predictor is normally distributed with $E(\hat{\hat{Y}}_0) = \mu_{1.23\cdots J}$ and an unbiased estimator for its variance defined as follows:

$$S_P^2 = S_U^2 \left[\frac{1}{n} + \sum_j (x_{0j} - \bar{X}_j)^2 V(B_j) + 2 \sum_{k<j} (x_{0k} - \bar{X}_k)(x_{0j} - \bar{X}_j) \text{Cov}(B_k, B_j) \right],$$

$$k, j = 2, 3, \ldots, J; k < j. \qquad (18.27)$$

The square root of (18.27) is the slightly biased estimator of the standard error for the predictor and is denoted S_P. In particular, with the trivariate case, we have

$$S_P^2 = S_U^2 \left[\frac{1}{n} + (x_{02} - \bar{X}_2)^2 V(B_2) + (x_{03} - \bar{X}_3)^2 V(B_3) \right.$$

$$\left. + 2(x_{02} - \bar{X}_2)(x_{03} - \bar{X}_3) \text{Cov}(B_2, B_3) \right]$$

$$= S_U^2 \left[\frac{1}{n} + c_{22}(x_{02} - \bar{X}_2)^2 + c_{33}(x_{03} - \bar{X}_3)^2 \right.$$

$$\left. + 2c_{23}(x_{02} - \bar{X}_2)(x_{03} - \bar{X}_3) \right], \qquad (18.28)$$

where the c's are the *Gauss multipliers*, which can be computed by the formulas given below:

$$c_{22} = \frac{m_{33}}{m_{22}m_{33} - m_{23}^2}; \qquad (18.29a)$$

$$c_{33} = \frac{m_{22}}{m_{22}m_{33} - m_{23}^2}; \qquad (18.29b)$$

$$c_{23} = \frac{m_{23}}{m_{22}m_{33} - m_{23}^2}. \qquad (18.29c)$$

Having found the sampling distribution of the predictor, we can construct a confidence interval for the mean of Y for any set of specified values of the X's. We do so by noting that the ratio $[\hat{Y}_0 - E(\hat{Y}_0)]/S_P$ is a t distribution with $\delta = n - c$ for $J - 1$ explanatory variables. Hence, the confidence limits for the conditional mean of Y can be computed in the usual way:

$$L, U = \hat{Y}_0 \mp t_{\alpha/2}(S_P), \qquad (18.30)$$

where $t_{\alpha/2}$ is based on $\delta = n - c$.

Now, suppose our toy manufacturer would like to predict the mean sales in a given sales district that is attempting to spend \$3,000 for advertisement and to charge a price of \$6.00 for the coming year. Then we would have the point estimate for $\mu_{1.23}$, or the predictor, as follows:

$$\hat{y}_0 = b_1 + b_2 x_{02} + b_3 x_{03}$$

$$= 48.79378 + 1.02205(30) + (-7.37774)(6.00)$$

$$\doteq 35.18884 \text{ thousand units.}$$

Next, to construct a confidence interval for $\mu_{1.23}$, we need the following measures:

$$S_U^2 = 90.355;$$

$$(x_{02} - \bar{x}_2)^2 = 64, \qquad (x_{03} - \bar{x}_3)^2 = 0.042025;$$

$$c_{22} \doteq 0.00522, \qquad c_{33} \doteq 1.09362, \qquad c_{23} \doteq -0.06457.$$

With these basic results, we have

$$S_P^2 = 10.355\left[\frac{1}{10} + 0.00522(64) + 1.09326(0.042025)\right.$$

$$\left. + 2(-0.06457)(8)(-0.205)\right]$$

$$\doteq 7.164$$

and

$$s_P = \sqrt{7.164} \doteq 2.677.$$

Finally, if the manufacturer wishes to have a 99% interval estimate for the mean of Y, we have

$$L, U = \hat{y}_0 \mp t_{7;.005}(s_P)$$

$$= 35.18884 \mp 3.499(2.677)$$

$$\doteq 25.822 \text{ to } 44.556$$

or

$$25.822 < \mu_{30;6.00} < 44.566.$$

A confidence band can be constructed easily for the population regression plane for our example with a series of confidence intervals computed from a few selected pairs of fixed values of X_2 and X_3. It may be pointed out that the confidence band in the trivariate case, just as for the bivariate model, is the narrowest at $x_{02} = \bar{x}_2$ and $x_{03} = \bar{x}_3$. The confidence band becomes wider and wider as x_{02} and x_{03} deviate from the respective sample means, $\bar{x}_2$ and $\bar{x}_3$, more and more in both directions. This is one of the reasons why we usually do not attempt to make projections for Y with fixed values beyond the ranges of the values for the independent variables used to obtain the sample regression equation. Another reason for this restriction, of course, is that the relationship among the variables beyond the ranges may not be linear. These comments, of course, can be generalized to cover the case with $J - 1$ independent variables.

Forecasting

Turning our attention to the problem of forecasting an individual value of the dependent variable for a given set of values of the explanatory variables, we note that the best forecaster for Y_0 is $E(Y_0)$. This is because the sum of squared deviations around $E(Y_0)$ is smaller than around any other point. However, as in the bivariate case, Y_0 is a random variable rather than a parameter and $E(Y_0)$ is unknown; So in its place we use $\hat{Y}_0$, named the forecaster before—the least-squares fitted value of Y_0.

From our previous discussion, we know that $\hat{Y}_0$ is normally distributed with $E(\hat{Y}_0) = \mu_{1.23\cdots J}$. Our primary interest here is concerned with the *forecasting error* $(Y_0 - \hat{Y}_0)$. This error is normally distributed with zero as its expectation. Furthermore, the forecasting error would have as its estimated variance the estimated variance of the forecaster. That is,

$$S_F^2 = S_U^2 + S_P^2 \tag{18.31}$$

for the same reason as stated for the bivariate case. The square root of (18.31) is the estimator of the standard error for the forecasting error and it is denoted as S_F.

Take notice of the fact that the ratio

$$\frac{Y_0 - \hat{Y}_0}{S_F}$$

is a t distribution with $\delta = n - c$. This observation enables us to construct a forecasting interval that will contain the actual value of Y_0

with whatever probability we choose in the familiar manner:

$$L, U = \hat{Y}_0 \mp t_{\alpha/2}(S_F).\qquad(18.32)$$

Again, $t_{\alpha/2}$ here is based on $\delta = n - c$.

To continue with our numerical example, suppose the manufacturer is interested in projecting the specific sales in the said district at levels of advertisement expenditures and price as specified before. Then the point estimate of the specific sales is

$$\hat{y}_0 = \hat{\hat{y}}_0 = 35.18884.$$

If he also desires to have a 99% forecasting interval for Y_0, we then have

$$s_F^2 = 10.355 + 7.164 = 17.519;$$
$$s_F = \sqrt{17.519} \doteq 4.186;$$
$$L, U = \hat{y}_0 \mp t_{7;.005}(s_F)$$
$$= 35.18884 \mp 3.499(4.186)$$
$$\doteq 20.54 \text{ to } 49.84,$$

or

$$20.54 < Y_{30;6.00} < 49.84.$$

If a forecasting band is constructed, it should, as usual, be wider than the corresponding confidence band. All comments made on the similarities and differences between these two bands in the bivariate case apply equally well in the multivariate case.

18.10 PARTIAL CORRELATION COEFFICIENTS

We shall now introduce a new concept called the *partial correlation coefficient*, which exists only when there are two or more independent variables. For this purpose, we must first consider the *multivariate normal distribution*. This is an extension of the bivariate normal distribution. In the multivariate normal distribution, there are four or more variables. Each of the variables is normally distributed with its own mean and its own standard deviation; and each possible pair of variables has its own correlation coefficient. An observation from a multivariate normal distribution consists of one value for each variable. Sometimes one variable may be designated the dependent variable, the others being the independent variables. Then all the regression computations and interpretations just given for the fixed-X model are also valid for the current stochastic-X model. In addition, various correlation computations and interpretations can be made.

When we evaluate a multivariate normal distribution, we often wish to measure the covariability between the dependent variable and a particular independent variable by holding all other variables constant—that is, by removing the effects of other variables under the specification: "other things being equal." The quoted phrase here has a more restricted meaning in multiple regression analysis than it has in economics or in ordinary English. In multiple regression, only the variables explicitly considered in the calculations can ever be held equal or constant, so the other variables are never held constant no matter whether they should be or not in the practical problem one is solving. In ths so-called *controlled experiment,* variables not explicitly in the multiple regression can be held constant, at least approximately. In this case the experimental design has arranged for additional variables to be held constant, over and above what can be accomplished with multiple regression computations. Finally, in multiple regression, only the variables specified in the notation are held constant. This last is not a further restriction, however, since in sampling from the multivariate normal population, one can hold any variable or variables constant. The partial correlation coefficient helps us to answer questions such as this: Is the correlation between, say, Y and X_2 merely due to the fact that both are affected by X_3, or is there a net covariation between Y and X_2 over and above the association due to the common influence of X_3? Thus, in determining a partial correlation coefficient between Y and X_2, we attempt to remove the influence of X_3 from each of the two variables and to ascertain what net relationship exists between the "unexplained" residuals that remain.

It can be shown that partial correlation coefficients are closely related to partial regression coefficients and can be readily defined in terms of simple correlation coefficients. Thus, consider the trivariate case and let

$$r_{12} = \text{simple correlation between } Y \text{ and } X_2$$

$$= \frac{m_{12}}{\sqrt{m_{11}m_{22}}},$$

$$r_{13} = \text{simple correlation between } Y \text{ and } X_3$$

$$= \frac{m_{13}}{\sqrt{m_{11}m_{33}}},$$

and

$$r_{23} = \text{simple correlation between } X_2 \text{ and } X_3$$

$$= \frac{m_{23}}{\sqrt{m_{22}m_{33}}}.$$

From the simple correlations, we may define the following:

$$r_{12.3} = \text{partial correlation between } Y \text{ and } X_2 \text{ when } X_3 \text{ is held constant}$$

$$= \frac{r_{12} - r_{13}r_{23}}{\sqrt{(1 - r_{13}^2)(1 - r_{23}^2)}} \tag{18.33}$$

$r_{13.2}$ = partial correlation between Y and X_3 when X_2 is held constant

$$= \frac{r_{13} - r_{12}r_{23}}{\sqrt{(1 - r_{12}^2)(1 - r_{23}^2)}} \qquad (18.34)$$

and

$r_{23.1}$ = partial correlation between X_2 and X_3 when Y is held constant

$$= \frac{r_{23} - r_{12}r_{13}}{\sqrt{(1 - r_{12}^2)(1 - r_{13}^2)}} \qquad (18.35)$$

The simple correlation coefficients are called *zero-order* coefficients. Other zero-order coefficients are simple standard deviations and the regression coefficients in the bivariate case. The zero-order coefficients possess no secondary subscripts—that is, no subscripts after the point. The partial correlation coefficients for the triviate case as just defined are called *first-order* coefficients, since there is one secondary subscript after the point. The partial regression coefficients are also first-order, since B_2 can be written as $B_{12.3}$ and B_3 can be denoted as $B_{13.2}$. The Y-intercept and standard deviation of the regression in the bivariate case are both of first order, since they can be expressed as $B_{1.2}$ and $S_{1.2}$, respectively. By the same argument, the Y-intercept and standard deviation of the regression plane, written as $B_{1.23}$ and $S_{1.23}$, respectively, are *second-order* coefficients.

As a matter of fact, we have a hierarchy of coefficients, all identified as the number of the secondary subscripts after the point. Coefficients of a given order can generally be expressed in terms of the next lower order, such as defining partial correlations for the trivariate model in terms of simple correlations. This possibility often provides the simplest computational scheme for three or more independent variables. For example, our trivariate analysis may be built up for the four-variable case, with coefficients of second and third orders, which may, in turn, be defined in terms of zero- and first-order coefficients. This procedure, however, becomes excessively cumbersome and time-consuming, since the number of formulas grows exponentially and the formulas themselves become extremely complicated. These difficulties can be removed to a great extent if matrix algebra is employed, since then we need not be bothered with the subscripts, and the summation signs can be handled efficiently.

Returning once more to our illustrative example, the reader can easily verify that

$$r_{12} \doteq +0.9617, \qquad r_{12}^2 \doteq 0.9249;$$

$$r_{13} \doteq -0.9124, \qquad r_{13}^2 \doteq 0.8325;$$

$$r_{23} \doteq -0.8542, \qquad r_{23}^2 \doteq 0.7296.$$

From these computations, we have

$$r_{12.3} = \frac{0.9617 - (-0.9124)(-0.8542)}{\sqrt{(1 - 0.8325)(1 - 0.7296)}} \doteq +0.8579,$$

$$r_{12.3}^2 = 0.7339;$$

$$r_{13.2} = \frac{-0.9124 - (0.9617)(-0.8542)}{\sqrt{(1 - 0.9249)(1 - 0.7296)}} \doteq -0.638,$$

$$r_{13.2}^2 = 0.407;$$

$$r_{23.1} = \frac{-0.8542 - (0.9617)(-0.9124)}{\sqrt{(1 - 0.9249)(1 - 0.8325)}} \doteq +0.2073,$$

$$r_{23.1}^2 \doteq 0.043.$$

Note that the squares of partial correlation coefficients are called *coefficients of partial determination*. As in the bivariate case, the former are interpreted more conveniently in terms of the latter. For example, in our illustration, $r_{12.3}^2 = 0.7339$ means that about 73% of the proportion of the variation in Y (sales) unaccounted for by X_3 (price) that is now explained by the addition of X_2 (advertisement expenditure). Similarly, $r_{13.2}^2 = 0.407$ means that about 40% of the unexplained variations in sales by advertisement expenditure has now been accounted for by the inclusion of price into the regression.

The t ratio used to test the significance of a simple correlation coefficient can be extended to test the significance of partial coefficients of correlation when the number of degrees of freedom is reduced by the number of regression coefficients (or variables) in the analysis. For example, in the trivariate case, we may test the null hypothesis that $\rho_{ij.k} = 0$ by using

$$t_{n-3} = r_{ij.k} \sqrt{\frac{n-3}{1 - r_{ij.k}^2}}, \qquad (i, j, k = 1, 2, 3; i \neq j) \qquad (18.36)$$

as the test statistic. Thus, returning to our numerical example, to test $\rho_{12.3} = 0$ against $\rho_{12.3} \neq 0$, we have

$$t_7 = 0.8567 \sqrt{\frac{10-3}{1 - (0.8567)^2}}$$

$$\doteq 4.396 > t_{7;.005} = 3.499.$$

Next, to test $\rho_{13.2} = 0$ against $\rho_{13.2} \neq 0$, we have

$$t_7 = -0.638 \sqrt{\frac{10-3}{1 - (-0.638)^2}}$$

$$\doteq -2.192 < t_{7;0.05} = -1.895.$$

Finally, to test $\rho_{23.1} = 0$ against $\rho_{23.1} \neq 0$, we have

$$t_7 = 0.2073 \sqrt{\frac{10 - 3}{1 - (0.2073)^2}}$$

$$\doteq 0.561 > t_{7;.30} = 0.549.$$

Therefore, $r_{12.3}$ is significant at $\alpha = 0.01$, $r_{13.2}$ is significant at $\alpha = 0.10$ and $r_{23.1}$ is only significant at $\alpha = 0.60$. Here, $r_{23.1}$ can be considered as insignificant. This is indeed a very desirable result.

In general, other things being equal, the lower the degree of covariability between the independent variables, the better is the regression result. It may also be noted that tests on $\rho_{12.3}$ and $\rho_{13.2}$ correspond to tests on β_2 and β_3, respectively. This is exactly the same as in the case of bivariate linear analysis, where the test on the regression slope β_2 and that on ρ_{12} would yield the same result.

18.11 LINEAR BIVARIATE AND MULTIVARIATE REGRESSIONS COMPARED

Before concluding this chapter, let us compare briefly some of the basic results obtained from linear bivariate and multivariate regression analyses. Such a comparison will not only bring out clearly why multivariate analysis might be an improvement over bivariate analysis for the objective of prediction; it will also enable us to interpret more precisely the important measures for both models. It is clearly more direct and convenient for us to perform this task by comparing the bivariate model with the simplest multivariate model; that is with the case of two independent variables.

Let us begin by noting that, for our illustrative data, as the reader can easily verify, the simple linear regression of Y on X_2 is

$$\hat{y} = -6.56780 + 1.45763x_2$$

and that of Y on X_3 is

$$\hat{y} = 151.77733 - 20.43326x_3.$$

Hence,

$$b_{12} = 1.456783 \quad \text{in contrast to } b_{12.3} = 1.02205;$$
$$b_{13} = -20.43326 \quad \text{in contrast to } b_{13.2} = -7.37774.$$

The partial coefficient of regression $b_{12.3}$, which measures the average change in Y produced by X_2 while the effect of X_3 is held unchanged (or remains constant), is smaller than the corresponding simple regression coefficient, b_{12}, which measures the gross regression relationship between Y and X_2 without considering X_3 at all. A similar observation can also be made on the relationship between the absolute values of $b_{13.2}$ and b_{13}. In the trivariate analysis, estimates of Y are made with the specified values of two independent variables and, therefore, partial regression coefficients are expected to be different from the corresponding bivariate regression coefficients, where, in each case, estimates for Y are made with the fixed value of only one independent variable. The difference can be anything from slight to great. Also, b_{12} and $b_{12.3}$ can have different signs.

There are a number of ways to determine whether the trivariate analysis constitutes an improvement over a bivariate analysis in a given situation. The simplest method is to compare $S_{1.23}^2$ with $S_{1.2}^2$ and $S_{1.3}^2$. If the variance based on trivariate regression is smaller than each of the two bivariate regressional results, we then conclude that the inclusion of an additional independent variable into the analysis does constitute an improvement. This conclusion is obvious, since the reduction in variance in the trivariate regression means an improvement in the precision of estimating the value of Y, or in the reduction in residual error in estimation.

The foregoing improvement can always be expected under two conditions. First, the independent variables must not be perfectly correlated; otherwise, the addition of X_3 will not reduce the residual error in estimation, since the variations of X_2 and X_3 are, in effect, identical. Second, the addition of an independent variable should reduce the residual variation sufficiently so that the loss of one more degree of freedom can be more than compensated. When this condition is not met, trivariate regression will not aid in making more precise estimates of Y. This condition may not be met when the number of degrees of freedom is rather small and the independent variables are highly correlated.

For our illustrative data, we note that

$$s_{1.23}^2 = s_U^2 = 10.355.$$

You can also verify that for data in Table 18.1, the variances of the regressions of Y on X_2 and Y on X_3 are, respectively,

$$s_{1.2}^2 = 15.279 \qquad \text{and} \qquad s_{1.3}^2 = 34.05.$$

Clearly, $s_{1.23}^2$ is much smaller than both $s_{1.2}^2$ and $s_{1.3}^2$. This is indicative that trivariate analysis is an improvement over the bivariate regressions. Furthermore, by virtue of the fact that $s_{1.2}^2 < s_{1.3}^2$, we see that X_2 has a greater influence on Y than does X_3.

Finally, we may note that there is a close relationship among the coefficient of multiple determination, the coefficient of simple determination, and the coefficient of partial determination. Let us recall that

$R_{1.23}^2$ measures the proportion of the total variation in Y associated with (explained by) the variations in X_2 and X_3;

r_{12}^2 measures the proportion of the total variation in Y associated with (explained by) the variation in X_2;

$1 - r_{12}^2$ measures the proportion of total variation in Y not associated with (unexplained by) the variation in X_2;

$r_{13.2}^2$ measures the proportion of the total variation in Y not associated with (unexplained by) X_2 that is associated with (explained by) the varition in X_3.

From the above interpretations, we see that the following relationship must hold:

$$R_{1.23}^2 = r_{12}^2 + (1 - r_{12}^2)(r_{13.2}^2). \tag{18.37}$$

Applying this result to our example,

$$R^2 = 0.9249 + (1 - 0.9249)(0.407) = 0.9555,$$

which is identical to the R^2 computed before except for rounding errors.
Again, it is easy to see the logic for

$$R_{1.23}^2 = r_{13}^2 + (1 - r_{13}^2)(r_{12.3}^2). \tag{18.38}$$

For our illustrative data,

$$R^2 = 0.8325 + (1 - 0.8325)(0.7339) = 0.9554$$

which is again identical to the previous result except for rounding errors.

It is interesting to observe that R^2 represents the joint regression of Y on X_2 and X_3, while coefficients of partial determination reflect the sequence in which the variables are regressed. However, as the previous results indicate, the order used in regressing the variables has no effect on the value of R^2.

In concluding our discussion on multiple linear regression analysis, it may be pointed out that another simple way to determine whether, say, a trivariate regression is an improvement over a bivariate analysis is to compare $R_{1.23}^2$ with r_{12}^2 and r_{13}^2. If $R_{1.23}^2 > r_{12}^2, r_{13}^2$, then we say that trivariate analysis is an improvement over a regression of Y with either X_2 or X_3 alone since a greater proportion of the total error is reduced by regressing Y with both X_2 and X_3. At this point the reader must be informed that, in general, the value of R^2 can usually be increased with the increase in the number of independent variables. However, no statistical significance may be attached to some of the added independent variables. In addition to this limitation, there are two more aspects that must be appreciated when we attempt to include a large number of independent variables in a regression analysis.

First, when the number of independent variables becomes large, say, six or more, the practical interpretation of the partial regression coefficients becomes difficult. Hence, in a regression analysis we should not yield to the temptation, for the purpose of increasing the value of R^2, of including too many independent variables. Instead, we should limit the number of independent variables to a range that leads to clear interpretation of the problem under investigation.

The second problem is concerned with the selection of the independent variables for a regression analysis. This problem is more difficult unless we are guided by some well-established and clear-cut theory. In the absence of such a theory, regression analysis can still come to our aid when we are selecting the independent variables. Suppose, according to our common sense or some logical reasoning, a dependent variable Y is linearly related to, say, seven independent variables and we wish to limit our study to only three independent variables. Which three should we select?

From our understanding of the method of regression analysis so far, one obvious procedure is to establish first the simple regression of Y on each of the seven independent variables under consideration, to find r^2 for all seven cases, and then to select the X that has the highest r^2. Suppose it is X_3; we then denote this selection by Y and $X_2' = X_3$. Here, X_2' stands for the first independent variable in our proposed multiple regression study.

We now have six variables remaining, X_2, X_4, X_5, X_6, X_7, and X_8. The next step will be to conduct the trivariate regressions of Y on X_2' and X_2, Y on X_2' and X_4, and so on. We compute then $R_{1.3i}^2$ for all six cases and select the variable that gives the highest $R_{1.3i}^2$, which becomes the second independent variable. Suppose it is X_5; then denote this by $X_3' = X_5$.

The third step is to establish the regression of Y on X_2', X_3' and X_2, Y on X_2', X_3' and X_4, and so on for all remaining combinations of X_2', X_3', and all the remaining variables. Then select the variable that yields the highest $R_{1.35i}^2$ as the third and final independent variable in the analysis.

Since we have already decided to limit the number of independent variables to three, we stop here. However, if we wish to include more independent variables, we continue the process until $R_{1.35...}^2$, reaches a level that we deem satisfactory, or until the largest possible reduction in R_2 from adding another variable is too small to justify adding another variable. The procedure of finding independent variables one by one until a desired level is reached is called *stepwise regression*. With the aid of computers, the computational labor is not so prohibitive as the procedure suggests. It is in fact a simple matter to conduct a stepwise regression analysis with computers.

A stepwise regression analysis can also be conducted in terms of the results of t tests on the regression coefficients. Most computer programs for this procedure are based on this practice. Let us briefly discuss stepwise regression analysis by using the criterion of t tests for the selection of the best variables into the analysis.

Once the dependent and independent variables are identified and the data set is made available, the stepwise regression procedure would involve the following three steps.

STEP I. *Given Y and X_j, $j = 2, 3, \cdots, J$, Y is regressed with each and every one of the k independent variables of the form: $\hat{y} = A + Bx_i$. For* each of the regression results, we test $H_0: \beta = 0$ against $H_1: \beta \neq 0$. The independent variable whose regression coefficient has the highest t-value is the best one-variable for the prediction of Y and it is selected as the first independent variable and denoted X_2. (Note that the variable with the highest t-value will also be the one with the highest value of the coefficient of correlation, r, with Y.)

STEP II. *Next, we begin to search among the $(k-1)$ independent variables for the best two-independent-variable model of the form $\hat{y} = B_1 + B_2 x_2 + B_3 x_i$. This is accomplished by conducting a trivariate analysis by regressing Y with X_2 selected in the first step and each and every one of the remaining $(k-1)$ independent variables. As in step I, we conduct a t test on $H_0: \beta_3 = 0$ against $\beta_3 \neq 0$ for each of the $(k-1)$ regression results. The variable whose partial regression coefficient has the highest t value is retained as the second independent variable and is denoted as X_3.*

At this point, we may either go to Step III or do some additional analysis before we do so. It is better though to adopt the latter practice. This additional analysis involves going back to check for B_2 after $B_3 x_3$ has been added to the regression. If the t value becomes insignificant for some specified level of significance, say, at $\alpha = 0.10$, the variable X_2 selected at the first step is dropped and a search is made for the independent variable with a β parameter that will yield the most significant t-value in the presence of $B_3 x_3$.

This back-checking is of great value because the best fitted plane may yield a different value for B_2 than that obtained in the first step. This happens when X_2 and X_3 are highly correlated. Hence, both the value of B_2 and thereby its level of significance will usually change from the first to the second step. For this reason, a computer program with a feature of rechecking the t values at each step is preferred.

STEP III. *Now, we search for the third independent variable to be included into the regression analysis. Here, we seek the best regression sample model of the form with three independent variables; namely, we wish to include in the regression with X_2 and X_3 a third independent variable, resulting in the best regression of the form $\hat{y} = B_1 + B_2 x_2 + B_3 x_3 + B_4 x_i$. To accomplish this, we fit all the $(k-2)$ regressions with X_2, X_3, and each of the $(k-2)$ remaining variables, x_i as a possible X_4. The procedure again is to select the independent variable with the highest t value as the third independent variable X_4.*

Again, we recheck the t values corresponding to the coefficients for X_2 and X_3, replacing the variable(s) that have t values that have become insignificant. This procedure is continued until no further independent variable(s) can be found that yields significant t values at the specified α-level in the presence of the variables already included into the analysis.

The foregoing stepwise regression procedure results a regression equation containing only the main effects with t values that are significant at the specified α-level. Thus, in most practical situations, we often find that only three or four of the large number of independent variables will be retained. It is important to be warned that this procedure does not always provide us with a final regression model that has included all the important variables or that has eliminated all the unimportant ones. This is mainly due to the fact of sampling fluctuations. It is quite probable that we have committed type I error by including one or more unimportant independent variables or that we have committed type II errors by eliminating one or more important variables. Furthermore, the resulting regression equation may not be the best for the predictive purposes, because the stepwise regression analysis often ignores the high-order terms, such as interactions between the variables included and quadratic terms. What we should recognize is the fact that the stepwise regression analysis is merely an objective screening procedure. Subjective judgment on the importance, in terms of theory or logic, of the independent variables included in a regression study plays a very important role in using the regression results.

GLOSSARY OF FORMULAS

(18.1) $y_i = \beta_1 + \beta_2 x_{i2} + \beta_3 x_{i3} + \cdots + \beta_j x_{ij} + u_i$;

(18.2) $y_i = \beta_1 + \beta_2 x_{i2} + \beta_3 x_{i3} + u_i$.

Equation (18.1) is the expression for the general multiple linear regression model. It says that an explained variable Y is linearly dependent upon $J - 1$ explanatory variables, the X's. The u_i are observations on a random variable—stochastic disturbances or residual errors—that are independent of the X's. The β's are the parameters called regression coefficients that are to be estimated. When $J = 2$, (18.1) reduces to the simple linear regression model and when $J = 2, 3$, we have the simplest multiple linear regression model as given by (18.2).

(18.3) $E(y_i \mid x_{ij}) = \mu_{1.23\ldots J} = \beta_1 + \beta_2 x_{i2} + \beta_3 x_{i3} + \cdots + \beta_j x_{ij}$;

(18.4) $E(y_i \mid x_{i2}, x_{i3}) = \mu_{1.23} = \beta_1 + \beta_2 x_{i2} + \beta_3 x_{i3}$.

Since $E(U) = 0$ in (18.1) as well as in (18.2), the conditional expectation of y_i given a set of fixed values of X's of each of these two equations would yield (18.3) and (18.4), respectively. Equation (18.3) is called the multiple linear regression equation of Y on X's. In this equation, β_1 stands for the Y-intercept and the rest of the β's are called regression slopes or partial regression coefficients. β_1 is the mean value of y_i when each of the explanatory variables is equal to zero; β_j, the jth partial regression coefficient, measures the change in $E(y_i)$ corresponding to one unit change in the jth independent variable, holding the remaining explanatory variables constant. Equation (18.4) is the population multiple linear regression equation for the trivariate case. Graphically, this equation represents a plane fitted to the scatter of subpopulations, the Y's. Here, β_1 is the mean value of y_i at the origin in a three-dimensional space; i.e., the Y-intercept; β_2 is the slope of the fitted plane alone the X_2 axis, measuring the change of $E(y_i)$ per unit change in X_2 when X_3 is held constant; β_3 is the slope of the fitted plane along the X_3 axis, measuring the change in $E(y_i)$ per unit change in X_3 when X_2 is held constant.

(18.5) $\quad y_i = B_1 + B_2 x_{i2} + B_3 x_{i3} + \cdots + B_j x_{ij} + e_i;$

(18.6) $\quad \hat{y}_i = B_1 + B_2 x_{i2} + B_3 x_{i3} + \cdots + B_j x_{ij}.$

These two equations are the sample multiple linear regression model and sample regression equation of Y on X's, respectively. The interpretations of B_1 and B_j are identical with those for the corresponding population equations (18.1) and (18.3). Note that from these two equations we have $e_i = y - \hat{y}$ and $\sum e_i = 0$.

(18.7) $\quad B_1 = \bar{Y} - B_2 \bar{X}_2 - B_3 \bar{X}_3 - \cdots - B_j \bar{X}_j.$

This is the formula for computing the Y-intercept. It is obtained for solving the first least-squares normal equation with $J - 1$ regressors.

(18.8a) $\quad m_{1j} = \sum (y - \bar{Y})(x_j - \bar{X}_j)$

(18.8b) $\quad m_{kj} = \sum (x_j - \bar{X}_j)(x_k - \bar{X}_k), \qquad k, j = 2, 3, \ldots, J.$

These two equations are for the computations of sums of squares and sums of cross products of the individual deviations from the means of the respective variables in the sample multiple linear regression equation.

(18.9) $\quad B_1 = \bar{Y} - B_2 \bar{X}_2 - B_3 \bar{X};$

(18.10) $\quad B_2 = \dfrac{m_{12} m_{33} - m_{13} m_{23}}{m_{22} m_{33} - m_{23}^2};$

(18.11) $\quad B_3 = \dfrac{m_{13} m_{22} - m_{12} m_{23}}{m_{22} m_{33} - m_{23}^2}.$

This group of equations gives the LSEs for β_1, β_2, and β_3 in the trivariate case. Equation (18.9) is suggested by (18.7). The equations for B_2 and B_3 are obtained by solving simultaneously the second and the third least-squares normal equations, which are given in terms of the individual deviations from the means of the respective variables in the trivariate sample regression equation.

(18.12) $\quad \dfrac{\mu_{1.23\cdots J}}{\sigma_1} = \dfrac{\beta_1}{\sigma_1} + \dfrac{\beta_2 \sigma_2}{\sigma_1}\left(\dfrac{x_2}{\sigma_2}\right) + \dfrac{\beta_3 \sigma_3}{\sigma_1}\left(\dfrac{x_3}{\sigma_3}\right) + \cdots + \dfrac{\beta_J \sigma_J}{\sigma_1}\left(\dfrac{x_J}{\sigma_J}\right);$

$\qquad\qquad = \beta_1^* + \beta_2^*\left(\dfrac{x_2}{\sigma_2}\right) + \beta_3^*\left(\dfrac{x_3}{\sigma_3}\right) + \cdots + \beta_J^*\left(\dfrac{x_J}{\sigma_J}\right);$

(18.13) $\dfrac{\hat{y}}{S_1} = B_1^* + B_2^*\left(\dfrac{x_2}{S_2}\right) + \beta_3^*\left(\dfrac{x_3}{S_3}\right) + \cdots + \beta_J^*\left(\dfrac{x_J}{S_j}\right).$

These two expressions are the population and sample multiple linear regression equations, respectively, given in terms of β-coefficients. Population or sample β-coefficients for the partial coefficients are simply the products of each coefficient multiplied by the ratio of the standard deviation of X_j to that of Y. They are designed for the purpose of more precise interpretation of the regression coefficients so far as the relative effects of each of the X's on Y is concerned when the X's have different units of measurements. For example, if $b_3^* = 1.5$, then we say that if there is a change in the value of X_3 by one standard deviation (holding remaining independent variables constant), there will be a change of one and half standard deviations in the value of Y.

(18.14) $S_U^2 = \dfrac{1}{1-c}(m_{11} - B_2 m_{12} - b_3 m_{13} - \cdots - B_J m_{1J}).$

This is the computational formula for the variance of random disturbances. It is originally defined in temrs of the least-squares residuals, $S_U^2 = \Sigma e^2/(n - c)$, where c is the number of regression coefficients in the regression equation. Note that S_U^2 is identical with the common variance of the subpopulations of Y's, which is denoted $S_{1.23\cdots J}^2$. The square root of (18.14) is the standard deviation of the regression. S_U^2 is clearly a measure of the dispersion of the Y values from the fitted regression, or a measure of "closeness-of-fit". However, its value provides no clear interpretation on this score. Its basic importance rests on the fact that it is required to compute the standard errors associated with the various measures in the regression analysis.

(18.15) $\mathrm{SSR} = \displaystyle\sum_{j=2}^{J} B_j m_{1j}.$

As in the simple regression case, the total variability in Y in multivariate analysis, SST ($= m_{11}$), is decomposed into two distinct parts: the proportion of SST that is explained by regressing Y on X's, measured by SSR and computed by (18.15), and the proportion of SST that remains unexplained, measured by SSE ($=$SST $-$ SSR).

(18.16) $\dfrac{\mathrm{MSR}}{\mathrm{MSE}} > F_{\delta_1\delta_2;\alpha}$

When we test H_0: $\beta_2 = \beta_3 = \cdots = \beta_J = 0$, at α, the test statistic to be used is $F_{\delta_1,\delta_2} = \mathrm{MSR/MSR}$. Hence the rejection region for this test is defined by (18.16). For this F ratio, $\delta_1 = k$, the number of independent variables, and $\delta_2 = n - c$, where c stands for the number of regression coefficients. Note that if H_0 is true, then the value of F here will be close to zero; otherwise, it will be significantly greater than zero.

(18.17) $t_\delta = \dfrac{B_i - \beta_i}{S_{B_i}}$

(18.18) $L, U = B_i \mp t_{\alpha/2}(S_{B_i})$

When σ_U^2 is unknown and when $n \leqslant 30$, then the ratio as defined by (18.17) is distributed as t with $\delta = n - c$. This ratio can be used as the test statistic for $H_0 : \beta_i = 0$, $i = 1, 2, \ldots, J$ in the multivariate case. It also serves for the determination of the confidence limits for β_i as given by the expression (18.18). Here, $S_{B_i} = S_U \sqrt{c_{ii} n}$, where c_{ii} are called Gauss multipliers—the diagonal c values in the "inverse matrix" of the matrix of variances and covariances of LSEs.

(18.19) $S_{B_1} = S_U \sqrt{\dfrac{1}{n} + \dfrac{\bar{X}_2^2 m_{33} + \bar{X}_3^2 m_{22} - 2\bar{X}_2 \bar{X}_3 m_{23}}{m_{22}m_{33} - m_{23}^2}}$;

(18.20) $S_{B_2} = S_U \sqrt{\dfrac{m_{33}}{m_{22}m_{33} - m_{23}^2}}$;

(18.21) $S_{B_3} = S_U \sqrt{\dfrac{m_{22}}{m_{22}m_{33} - m_{23}^2}}$.

This group of equations are the computational formulas for the standard errors of B_1, B_2, and B_3 in the trivariate case.

(18.22) $R^2 = R_{1.23\cdots J}^2 = \dfrac{\text{SSR}}{\text{SST}}$;

(18.23) $F_{k, n-c} = \dfrac{R^2/k}{(1 - R^2)/(n - c)}$

$R_{1.23\cdots J}^2$ as defined by (18.22) is called the sample coefficient of multiple determination and it is a slightly biased estimator for $\rho_{1.23\cdots J}^2$. As it is defined, R^2 may be interpreted as the proportion of the total variation in Y associated with or explained by the regression of Y on X's. As such, it is a measure of closeness-of-fit. If the X's are also random variables, R^2 may be considered as a measure of the covariability between Y and X's. The F ratio defined by (18.23) is the test statistic for the null hypothesis that $\beta = 0$. This test is equivalent to the overall test that $\beta_2 = \beta_3 = \cdots = B_J = 0$.

(18.24) $\bar{R}^2 = 1 - \dfrac{\text{MSE}}{\text{MST}}$;

(18.25) $S_U^2 = (1 - \bar{R}^2)S_Y^2$.

R^2 defined by (18.22) is slightly positively biased. This bias is corrected by computing the adjusted coefficient of multiple determination as defined by (18.24). Note that $\bar{R}^2 < R^2$ because the correction factor $(n - 1)/(n - k)$ is greater than unity. $\bar{R}^2$, being an unbiased estimator, would make the relationship given by (18.25) more precise, since both S_U^2 and S_Y^2 are unbiased estimators.

(18.26) $\hat{\hat{Y}}_0 = \hat{Y}_0 = B_1 + B_2 x_{02} + B_3 x_{03} + \cdots + B_j x_{0j}$.

As in the simple regression case, the predicted (estimated) value of the mean of Y, the predictor, and the forecast value of an individual value of Y, the forecaster, associated with a given set of the values of the independent variables in the multivariate case are identical, since they are computed from the same sample regression equation.

(18.27) $S_P^2 = S_U^2 \left[\dfrac{1}{n} + \sum_j (x_{0j} - \bar{X}_j)^2 V(B_j) + 2 \sum_{k<j} (x_{0k} - \bar{X}_k)(x_{0j} - \bar{X}_j) \text{Cov}(B_k B_j) \right]$,

$$k, j = 2, 3, \ldots, J; k < j.$$

This is the unbiased estimator for the variance of the predictor with $J - 1$ independent variables. The square root of (18.27) is the standard error of the predictor and it is denoted as S_P.

(18.28) $S_P^2 = S_U^2 \left[\dfrac{1}{n} + (x_{02} - \bar{X}_2)^2 V(B_2) + (x_{03} - \bar{X}_3)^2 V(B_3) \right.$

$$+ 2(x_{02} - \bar{X}_2)(x_{03} - \bar{X}_3) \text{Cov}(B_2 B_3)$$

$$\left. = S_U^2 \left[\dfrac{1}{n} + c_{22}(x_{02} - \bar{X}_2)^2 + c_{33}(x_{03} - \bar{X}_3)^2 + 2c_{23}(x_{02} - \bar{X}_2)(x_{03} - \bar{X}_3) \right] \right.;$$

(18.29a) $c_{22} = \dfrac{m_{33}}{m_{22}m_{33} - m_{23}^2}$;

(18.29b) $c_{33} = \dfrac{m_{22}}{m_{22}m_{33} - m_{23}^2}$;

(18.29c) $c_{23} = \dfrac{m_{23}}{m_{22}m_{33} - m_{23}^2}$.

Equation (18.28) defines the variance of the predictor when there are only two independent variables. The c values in this equation are the Gauss multipliers, which are determined by formulas (18.29).

(18.30) $L, U = \hat{\hat{Y}}_0 \mp t_{\alpha/2}(S_P)$.

We use this formula to compute the confidence limits of a $(1 - \alpha)\%$ interval estimate for the mean of Y given a set of values for X's. This expression is suggested by the fact that when σ_U^2 is unknown and when $n \leqslant 30$, the ratio $[\hat{\hat{Y}}_0 - E(\hat{\hat{Y}}_0)]/S_P$ is distributed as t with $\delta = n - c$.

(18.31) $S_F^2 = S_U^2 + S_P^2$;

(18.32) $L, U = \hat{\hat{Y}}_0 \mp t_{\alpha/2}(S_F)$

The variance of the forecasting error is also the variance of the forecaster. It is the sum of the variance of the residual error and the variance of the predictor. The square root of (18.31), denoted as S_F, is the estimator for the standard error of the forecaster. Equation (18.32) provides the confidence limits for the forecasting interval with $1 - \alpha$. This expression is suggested by the fact that when σ_U^2 is unknown and $n \leq 30$, the ratio $(Y_0 - \hat{Y}_0)/S_F$ has a t distribution with $\delta = n - c$.

$$(18.33) \quad r_{12.3} = \frac{r_{12} - r_{13}r_{23}}{\sqrt{(1 - r_{13}^2)(1 - r_{23}^2)}};$$

$$(18.34) \quad r_{13.2} = \frac{r_{13} - r_{12}r_{23}}{\sqrt{(1 - r_{12}^2)(1 - r_{23}^2)}};$$

$$(18.35) \quad r_{23.1} = \frac{r_{23} - r_{12}r_{13}}{\sqrt{(1 - r_{12}^2)(1 - r_{13}^2)}}.$$

This set of equations define the partial correlation coefficients for the trivariate case. In general, a partial correlation coefficient is interpreted in terms of its square, called the coefficient of partial determination. The degree to which the random disturbance of a dependent variable is correlated with the variation of an independent variable can be expressed by $r_{ij.k}^2$. For instance, $r_{13.2}^2$ means the percentage of the proportion of unexplained variation in Y that is not accounted for by X_2 has now been explained by the inclusion of X_3 into the analysis.

$$(18.36) \quad t_{n-3} = r_{ij.k}\sqrt{\frac{n-3}{1 - r_{i,j.k}^2}}, \qquad i, j, k = 1, 2, 3; i \neq j.$$

This is the test statistic for H_0: $\rho_{ij.k} = 0$ in the trivariate case. It can be easily generalized to test that the population partial correlation of coefficient is zero when the number of degrees of freedom is reduced by the number of regression coefficients, c.

$$(18.37) \quad R_{1.23}^2 = r_{12}^2 + (1 - r_{12}^2)r_{13.2}^2;$$

$$(18.38) \quad R_{1.23}^2 = r_{13}^2 + (1 - r_{13}^2)r_{12.3}^2.$$

These two equations provide the same information about the relationship among the coefficient of multiple determination, the coefficient of simple determination, and the coefficient of partial determination. The truism of each of these two identities can easily be understood by recalling the meaning of each of the measures in it.

REVIEW QUESTIONS

18.1 What is the most important reason for multiple regression analyses?

18.2 What are the assumptions for the classical normal multiple linear regression model? What are the new assumptions for this model as compared with the classical normal simple linear regression model? What are the reasons for these new assumptions?

18.3 Given the sample multiple linear regression equation:

$$\hat{y}_i = B_1 + B_2 x_{i2} + B_3 x_{i3} + B_4 x_{i4}$$

provide a brief description for each of the terms in it.

18.4 Write out the set of least-squares normal equations required to estimate the regression coefficients in the regression equation given in the preceding equation.

18.5 Write out the set of normal equations in the answer to the preceding problem in terms of individual deviations from the means of the respective variables and give the computational formulas for B_i, $i = 1, 2, 3, 4$.

18.6 Since the variance of the regression, or of the regression residual, S_U^2, is not a very clear-cut measure of closeness-of-fit, why do we still consider it as a very basic and important statistic in any regression analysis?

18.7 Suppose we have computed a confidence band for $\mu_{1.23}$, what would be its shape in the three-dimensional space? Explain your answer precisely.

18.8 When the X's have different units, we usually determine their relative influences on Y by β-coefficients. There is another way to achieve the same objectives: Transform the values of each variable into percentages before calculations are made. Can you explain the rationale behind this procedure?

18.9 When an F test on $\beta_2 = \beta_3 = \cdots = \beta_J = 0$ is rejected, say, at $\alpha = 0.01$, can we conclude that the t test on each of the partial regression coefficients must also be significant at $\alpha = 0.01$? Explain why or why not.

18.10 The first-order coefficients of correlation in trivariate case can also be defined as

$$r_{12.3}^2 = \frac{R_{1.23}^2 - r_{13}^2}{1 - r_{13}^2}$$

and

$$r_{13.2}^2 = \frac{R_{1.23}^2 - r_{12}^2}{1 - r_{12}^2}.$$

Can you explain why these two expressions are identical with (18.33) and (18.34), respectively?

18.11 When there are three independent variables, we have $R_{1.234}^2 = \text{SSR/SST}$. How should SSR be computed here?

18.12 In the four-variable case, the second-order partial determination for the fourth variable can be computed by

$$r^2_{14.23} = \frac{R^2_{1.234} - R^2_{1.23}}{1 - R^2_{1.23}}.$$

How should this measure by interpreted? Suppose $r^2_{14.23} = 0.15$; what does this result mean precisely?

18.13 It can be shown that

$$r_{12.34} = \frac{r_{12.4} - r_{13.4}r_{23.4}}{\sqrt{(1 - r^2_{13.2})(1 - r^2_{23.4})}}$$

and

$$r_{13.24} = \frac{r_{13.4} - r_{12.3}r_{23.4}}{\sqrt{(1 - r^2_{12.4})(1 - r^2_{23.4})}}.$$

Rewrite these expressions in terms of R and R^2.

18.14 Explain what does each of the following quantities measure?
a. $S^2_1(1 - r^2_{13})$
b. $S^2_1 r^2_{13}$
c. $S^2_1 R^2_{1.23}$
d. $S^2_1(R^2_{1.23} - r^2_{13})$

18.15 How can we determine whether a regression analysis with three independent variables is an improvement over a regression analysis with two independent variables?

18.16 Suppose it is known that an explained variable is linearly related to ten explanatory variables and the investigator would like to have only four of the ten variables in her regression study. How would she go about selecting the four most important variables?

PROBLEMS

Note: With the availability of electronic computers today, regression and correlation analyses, even in the bivariate case, are seldom done by hand. Nevertheless, manual exercises in this and other cases would enable you to have a deeper understanding of the statistical concepts and measures. Hence, you are advised to do all the assignments selected by your instructor for the first 12 problems by hand with your pocket calculator as an aid only.
Instructions for problems 18.1 to 18.4 inclusive.
a. Compute the sample regression equation.
b. Interpret the Y-intercept and partial regression coefficients carefully.
c. Decide whether the partial regression coefficients can be compared readily. If so, explain why. If not, compute the β-coefficients and interpret the results.

18.1 The sales manager of a certain firm believes that sales ability, among other factors, might be associated with salesmen's verbal reasoning ability and vocational interest. To verify this, ten salesmen are selected at random from his staff and given two tests, one for verbal reasoning ability and the other for vocational interest. The results are given in Table 18.P1, where

Y = monthly average sales of a salesman in thousands of units,

X_2 = score on verbal reasoning ability test, ranging from 1, very poor, to 5, excellent, and

X_3 = score on vocational interest test, ranging from 1, nil, to 6, exceedingly strong.

TABLE 18.P1

Observation	y	x_2	x_3
1	1	1	2
2	1	1	1
3	1	2	1
4	2	2	3
5	2	3	2
6	4	3	4
7	3	4	3
8	5	4	5
9	6	5	4
10	6	5	6

18.2 Ten branch stores of a national retailing company have been selected at random in order to evaluate the effects of population and income on sales in each sales district. Data obtained are recorded in Table 18.P2 below.

TABLE 18.P2

y: Weekly sales (in tens of thousands of dollars)	x_2: Population (in hundreds of thousands)	x_3: weekly family income (in millions of dollars)
7	6	15
5	7	12
11	9	18
9	10	16
6	11	10
10	12	15
13	13	17
9	14	10
12	15	12
10	16	11

18.3 In Table 18.P3,

Y = the number of units of a certain handicraft product produced;

X_2 = labor input in hours;

X_3 = total variable cost in tens of dollars.

TABLE 18.P3

y	x_2	x_3
7	6	24
5	4	23
11	8	20
10	9	25
8	7	23
6	6	26
3	4	23
9	7	20
5	3	22
11	8	23

18.4 An economist who believes that a nation's imports (Y in hundreds of millions of dollars) are linearly related to the ratio of an import price index to a domestic price index (X_2 in percentage points) and per capita income (X_3 in hundreds of dollars) has made observations from 12 nations selected at random, and the following sums of deviations from the sample means have been derived from his data:

$$m_{11} = 6300, \qquad m_{22} = 2250, \qquad m_{33} = 4.68;$$

$$m_{12} = -3550, \qquad m_{13} = 125.25, \qquad m_{23} = -54.$$

Also, the data provide

$$n = 12, \qquad \bar{y} = 100, \qquad \bar{x}_2 = 70, \qquad \text{and} \qquad \bar{x}_3 = 6.7.$$

Instructions for problems 18.5 to 18.8 inclusive.
a. Prepare an ANOVA table.
b. Test $H_0: \beta_2 = \beta_3 = 0$, at $\alpha = 0.05, 0.01$.
c. Test $H_0: \beta_i = 0$, $i = 1, 2, 3$, at $\alpha = 0.05, 0.01$.
d. Compute 15% confidence intervals for β_1.
e. Predict the mean value of Y and forecast an individual value of Y and compute 95% confidence and forecasting intervals for $\mu_{1.23}$ and Y_0, respectively, with x_{02} and x_{03} to be specified.

18.5 Use results in Problem 18.1. (Set $x_{02} = 3$ and $x_{03} = 5$.)

18.6 Use results in Problem 18.2. (Set $x_{02} = 12$ and $x_{03} = 10$.)

18.7 Use results in Problem 18.3. (Set $x_{02} = 9$ and $x_{03} = 20$.)

18.8 Use results in Problem 18.4. (Set $x_{02} = 80$ and $x_{03} = 7$.)

Instructions for problems 18.9 and 18.12 inclusive.
a. Compute R^2 and $\bar{R}^2$. Interpret the results.
b. Compute the coefficients of partial correlations and interpret the results.
c. Test $\rho_{1.23}^2 = 0$ at $\alpha = 0.01$, by the F-ratio.
d. Test $\rho_{ij.k} = 0$ at $\alpha = 0.10, 0.05, 0.01$, by t-ratios.
e. Show that the trivariate analysis is an improvement over the bivariate analyses.

18.9 Use results in Problems 18.1 and 18.5.

18.10 Use results in Problems 18.2 and 18.6.

18.11 Use results in Problems 18.3 and 18.7.

18.12 Use results in Problems 18.4 and 18.8.

Notes and instructions for the next three problems. You are instructed to do the next three problems on computers. Computer packages are readily available for performing multivariate analyses. A typical computer printout of a multiple regression and correlation analyses consists of five parts. Part I simply identifies the variables, giving the sample means and sample standard deviations of the variables. Part II provides a "correlation matrix", which is a table showing the simple correlation coefficients between each and every possible pair of variables. Part III of the printout displays the estimated regression coefficients, the standard errors of the coefficients, and t values for the tests of $\beta_i = 0$. Part IV gives the results of the analysis of variance with the value of the F ratio which is the testing result of the overall test of the null hypothesis that all the partial regression coefficients are equal to zero. The last part, V, presents the values of R and R^2. It may also contain the partial correlations. From the printout for each of the next three problems, do the following.

a. Write out the estimated regression equation explicitly.

b. Interpret the Y-intercept and regression slopes.

c. Determine whether $\beta_i = 0$ can be rejected at $\alpha = 0.05$ and at $\alpha = 0.01$, for all the regression coefficients.

d. Construct 95% confidence intervals for β_i, $i = 1, 2, 3, \ldots, c$.

e. Determine from the F value whether the null hypothesis that all the partial regression coefficients equal zero can be rejected at $\alpha = 0.05$ and at $\alpha = 0.01$.

f. Construct a 95% confidence interval for the conditional mean of Y and a 95% forecasting interval for an individual observation of Y given that $x_{0j} = \bar{x}_j - 1.5, j = 1, 2, \ldots, J$.

g. Interpret the value of R^2 and test if it is significant at $\alpha = 0.01$.

h. If the coefficients of partial correlation are also given in the computer printout, interpret them carefully. If they are not given and if there are only three regressors in the problem, compute $r_{12.34}$, $r_{13.24}$, and $r_{14.23}$ and interpret the results.

i. In your judgment, should all the independent variables be retained in the regression model? If so, why? If you think that one or more regressors should be dropped from the regression model, which regressor or regressors should be eliminated? Explain fully your decision. (Alternatively, you may conduct a stepwise regression analysis for this purpose.)

18.13 In a study of the achievement of top management personnel, the American Association of Manufacturers, aided by a consulting firm for management efficiency, administered three psychological tests to 20 randomly selected vice presidents in charge of various departments from firms with capitalization over $100 million in order to construct a multiple regression model. In this model, the explained variable is

  Y: current annual salary in thousands of dollars,
and the explanatory variables are

   X_2: score on vitality and drive test,
   X_3: score on numerical and verbal reasoning ability tests
   X_4: score on sociability and leadership test.

The results on the analysis are as given in Table 18.P4.

TABLE 18.P4

y	x_2	x_3	x_4
85	16	78	17
82	17	65	11
120	20	80	14
95	22	74	6
125	24	82	29
145	32	77	25
158	32	95	36
140	30	80	28
138	33	75	26
135	34	77	24
175	37	82	50
190	37	82	85
175	39	82	68
185	38	83	71
150	38	94	15
200	40	92	66
210	43	90	92
225	44	89	95
250	45	98	85
245	45	90	95

18.14 The American Bankers' Association attempts to build a multiple regression model to aid the banks in their selection of locations to build their branch offices. The economists of the Association, after considerable deliberation, finally decide that the model should be constructed with the following variables:

Y: total demand deposit in millions of dollars,

X_2: annual median family income in thousands of dollars in the branch area,

X_3: number of business enterprises in hundreds in the branch area,

X_4: number of families in thousands in the branch area, and

X_5: median value of residential units in thousands of dollars in the branch area.

TABLE 18P.5

y	x_2	x_3	x_4	x_5
50	25	8	10	59
45	25	5	9	59
75	30	9	14	65
50	30	5	11	63
40	27	4	12	55
95	35	7	18	65
40	26	6	11	52
65	31	12	12	60
120	35	14	16	58
35	24	4	9	67
35	26	5	8	55
25	20	4	8	42
75	29	7	18	48
80	33	13	15	71
65	30	9	13	61
75	32	16	10	64
65	30	10	16	68
45	28	7	15	55
55	26	5	18	53
50	27	4	18	50

An SRS of 20 branches currently in operation throughout the nation is selected and data for the most recent census year have been collected and recorded as shown in Table 18.P5.

18.15 A large real estate company in Queens, N.Y.C. has prepared three regression models for heating cost in winter months for detached individual houses: one with gas heating, one for oil heating, and one with electric heating. All models consist of the same variables, as defined below:

Y: monthly mean heating cost in dollars,
X_2: monthly mean outside temperature,
X_3: daily mean inside temperature,
X_4: number of rooms,
X_5: thickness of insulation of the attic in inches, and
X_6: age of furnace or electric heater in years.

Data obtained from an SRS with $n = 20$ houses with oil heating are as given in Table 18.P6.

TABLE 18.P6

y	x_2	x_3	x_4	x_5	x_6
235	39	70	8	5	7
320	22	67	11	5	11
149	40	65	7	6	4
90	65	63	7	6	9
110	65	65	7	4	7
184	33	66	9	9	6
336	14	70	9	8	8
300	10	72	10	8	10
218	23	68	8	6	12
132	58	65	7	5	7
91	57	60	7	6	8
186	43	66	7	5	2
405	20	72	10	6	15
331	40	75	11	7	8
90	62	65	7	6	6
295	25	70	9	5	7
101	60	62	7	3	2
234	35	68	10	4	11
245	30	68	9	5	7
138	40	70	11	5	5

19* Further Regression Studies

19.1 INTRODUCTION

In the preceding two chapters we were exclusively concerned with linear regression models. Furthermore, these models were developed especially with cross-section data in mind. In order to have a wider application of regression analysis we must now consider an extension of association studies to cover relationships between variables that are nonlinear in nature and to point out some of the special problems and their solutions when regression studies are applied to time series data.

From theory, we may know in advance that the relationship between two variables can be represented adequately only by some curvilinear mathematical function. For example, liquidity preference theory suggests that the demand for money to hold as cash balances is a decreasing function of the interest rate but that the rate of decrease is gradually tapering. Again, the law of diminishing returns dictates that total production is positively and nonlinearly related to the variable input or inputs. Occasions may also arise in which theoretical considerations enable us to judge whether an assoccation between two variables should be positive or negative but not whether it is linear or otherwise. The laws of demand and supply illustrate this possibility. The usual procedure is to inspect the scatter diagram constructed with sample data; the general pattern of the scatter may suggest an appropriate form of regression. This is a very useful procedure. Even if nonlinear regression is indicated by theory or by past data using large ranges for the independent variables, linear regression is still appropriate for restricted ranges in the independent variables.

A basic mathematical theorem is that any two-dimensional curve can be approximated by linear segments, and the approximation can be made as accurate as desired by using short enough segments. In three dimensions, the same theorem holds by using segments of planes to approximate curved surfaces. In four or more dimensions, the same theorem still holds, although it is virtually impossible to visualize the process. Therefore, for restricted range(s) of the independent variable(s), linear regression can be very appropriate no matter what the basic functional relationship between Y and the independent variable(s) may be. This is one powerful reason for the popularity of linear regression in solving practical problems.

On the other hand, occasions do arise when the assumption of linearity may be a very poor one, resulting in unimpressive measures of closeness-of-fit as revealed by a large value of S_U^2 or small value of R^2. Figure 19.1 explains why. In panels (a) and (b) of Figure 19.1, the average relationships between X and Y can be adequately described only by second-degree curves; in panel (c) the relationship between the

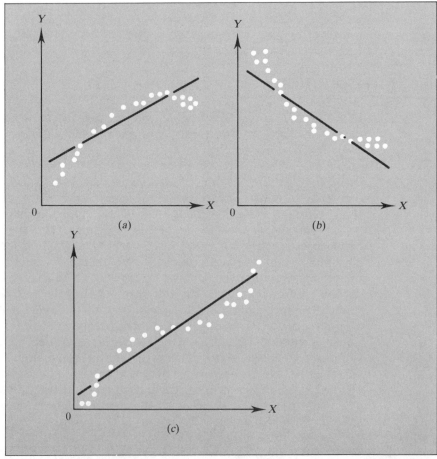

FIGURE 19.1 Graphic illustration of poor linear fits for nonlinear relationships between variables.

variables is cubic in nature. In each of these cases, a straight regression line is a poor fit not because of lack of systematic relationship between X and Y, because the relationship is not approximately linear. Thus, in addition to the linear regression models, we may encounter situations in which only some type of curvilinear description or presentation is appropriate. This leads us to the consideration of nonlinear regression models.

In the last two chapters, the regression models were developed under specific assumptions. Brief comments were made on those for the simple linear regression model. Such comments are also applicable to similar assumptions for the multiple linear model. In multivariate analysis, the only important new assumption is the independence among the explanatory variables. In this connection, the most important consideration for both models is that the regression results were interpreted under conditions satisfying these assumptions, especially those with reference to the error term. However, one or more of these assumptions may be violated from time to time even with simple random samples of cross-section data. This situation is greatly worsened by the fact that samples of business and economic data are often drawn from time series and predictive models are, as a rule, concerned with projections about future time-series values. Regression with time-series data usually introduces behavior patterns of error terms that limit our ability to use regression results as obtained in previous presentations with a high degree of reliability. This is due to the fact, as we shall see in later chapters, that time-series data are seldom free from autocorrelation, heteroscedasticity and multicollinearity. In order to draw useful conclusions from regression results when time-series data are employed, these undesirable properties must be identified, measured, and removed.

It is the objective of this chapter to introduce some of the most frequently encountered nonlinear regression models and to discuss the various aspects of autocorrelation, heteroscedasticity, and multicollinearity. The latter will be taken up with special reference to time-series data. Of course, our conclusions apply equally well to cross-section data when any of the assumptions about the error term is violated. We shall end this chapter with a discussion on "dummy variables," which are especially used in dealing with seasonal fluctuations in time-series data for the purpose of forecasting by regression.

19.2 NONLINEAR REGRESSION MODELS

In the discussion that follows, for the purpose of eliminating some of the subscripts attached to variables and regression coefficients, we shall use slightly different notations. Precisely, we will continue to use Y to denote the explained variable most of the time, but we will use letters V, W, X, and Z to represent the independent variables. Letters, such as A, B, C, D, etc., will be employed for the regression coefficients. Occasionally, we shall also use the first letter of the name of the variable, dependent or otherwise, to denote the variable.

Polynomial Functions

Very often we find that the most obvious nonlinear relationship between two variables is one in which the dependent variable Y, can be approximated by way of a simple polynomial in the independent variable X. A sample polynomial regression function is defined by the equation

$$y_i = A + Bx_i + Cx_i^2 + \cdots + Kx_i^k + u_i,$$

where the term involving the highest power of X is known as the *leading term,* and its coefficient is called the *leading coefficient.* The degree of the equation is the exponent k. While the relationship between two variables may assume a polynomial function of any degree, we generally seek to have as low a degree as possible. A commonly employed polynomial regression function is of the second degree, that is, a *parabola.* The sample regression equation in this case is given as

$$\hat{y} = A + Bx + Cx^2. \tag{19.1}$$

Of particular interest in this equation is the practical interpretation of the regression coefficient C. Here, C measures the curvature of a second-degree regression curve. When $C > 0$, slope of the parabola will increase with an increase in X; that is, the curve is concave from above as portrayed by Figure 19.2(a). When $C < 0$, slope of the parabola will decrease with the increase in X; i.e., the curve is concave from below as shown by Figure 19.2(b). Marginal or average cost functions and some types of production functions can often be approximated by parabolas.

To find the least-squares estimators for the parameters in a second-degree regression function, we first define

$$X = W \qquad \text{and} \qquad x = w;$$
$$X^2 = Z \qquad \text{and} \qquad x^2 = z.$$

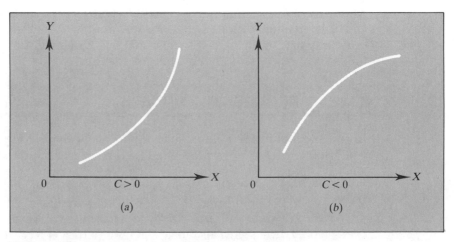

FIGURE 19.2 Curvatures of second-degree regression curves.

Here Z and z are just algebraic symbols, not standard normal variables. Substituting these transformations into (19.1), we have

$$\hat{y} = A + Bw + Cz. \qquad (19.2)$$

This result is formally identical with the trivariate multiple linear regression equation considered in the last chapter.

Note that in this case while Y is related to only one independent variable X, the fit involves regressing Y on two regressors, X (or W) and X^2 (or Z). Also, although W and Z are functionally dependent, they are not linearly dependent in the sense that one is, say, exactly twice the other. Thus, the linear model can be applied because there is no multicollinearity between W and Z.

The Exponential Function and Semilogarithmic Transformation

A highly useful nonlinear function that applies in situations that are incompatible with polynomial functions is the *exponential function.* When sample data can be fitted with an exponential curve, the sample regression equation can be written as

$$\hat{y} = AB^x. \qquad (19.3)$$

As the name exponential suggests, the independent variable X appears as an exponent. We shall restrict our consideration of this regression function to cases in which B is positive. If A is also positive, then the behavior of the function can be described as follows:

1. The ratio of the value of the function at any value of X to its value at $(X - 1)$ is always equal to B.

2. If $B > 1$, the function increases indefinitely as X increases to infinity and approaches zero asymptotically as X decreases to negative infinity.

3. If $B < 1$, the function approaches zero asymptotically as X increases to infinity and increases indefinitely as X decreases to negative infinity.

4. If $B = 1$, we have the mathematically trivial case that the function is constant at A.

(See Figure 19.3.) If A is negative, the function is always negative; its behavior is the mirror image of that stated above.

For theoretical necessity and practical convenience, take logarithms of both sides of (19.3), yielding

$$\log \hat{y} = \log A + x(\log B). \qquad (19.4)$$

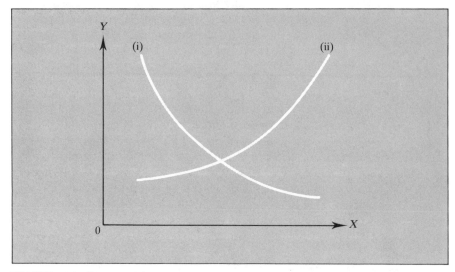

FIGURE 19.3 Exponential regression curves: (i) $A > 0$, $B < 1$; (ii) $A > 0$, $B > 1$.

Put $\log A = C$, and $\log B = D$, and this expression becomes

$$\log \hat{y} = C + Dx \qquad (19.5)$$

which is now in the form of a linear equation and is called a *semilog function*—for the obvious reason that one variable appears as its logarithm while the other appears as itself. For further simplification, we may put $\log \hat{y} = \hat{z}$ and obtain

$$\hat{z} = C + Dx \qquad (19.6)$$

which is the simple linear regression of Z on X. Here, Z and z are just algebraic symbols without the usual meaning of a standard normal variable. Hence, C and D can be found in the usual manner. To transform (19.6) back to the original form, we merely need to follow the equations

$$A = \text{antilog}\, C,$$
$$B = \text{antilog}\, D$$
$$\hat{y} = \text{antilog}\, \hat{z},$$

Note that in the employment of the semilog transformation, all we need to do is to take the logarithms of the values of Y before we proceed to do the usual computations.

The Power Function and Double-log Transformation

Sometimes we may find that a power function such as

$$\hat{y} = Ax^B, \qquad (19.7)$$

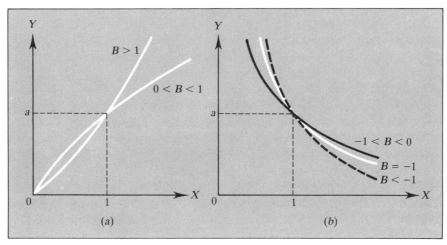

FIGURE 19.4 Power regression curves.

may represent the relationship between Y and X in the sample. Here, we would like to find the power B that is unknown. For this function, if $A > 0$ and $B > 1$, Y increases with an increasing rate of increase with the increase in X. If $A > 0$ and $0 < B < 1$, the function increases with a decreasing rate of increase. For either value of B, Y approaches infinity as X approaches infinity. When $A \neq 0$ and $B = -1$, this function is represented by a hyperbola—a curve for which the locus of points is such that the product XY is a constant. See Figure 19.4.

To facilitate the fitting of a power curve, we take logarithms of both sides of (19.7), obtaining

$$\log \hat{y} = \log A + B(\log x). \tag{19.8}$$

This result is a double-log transformation, since both variables are now expressed in terms of logarithms. If we set

$$\log \hat{y} = \hat{z},$$

$$\log A = C,$$

and

$$\log x = w,$$

we can rewrite the preceding regression equation as

$$\hat{z} = C + Bw. \tag{19.9}$$

which is a simple linear regression equation of Z on W. Hence, for actual computation, we first take logarithms of both Y and X values and then proceed as in simple linear regression.

The Reciprocal Function

Scatter diagrams for, say, sample data with reference to the demand for, or supply of, a commodity Y with respect to its price X, may indicate that the appropriate regression equations should be of the following forms, respectively:

$$\hat{y} = A + \frac{B}{x}, \qquad A, B, x > 0; \tag{19.10}$$

and

$$\hat{y} = A - \frac{B}{x}, \qquad A, B > 0 \quad \text{and} \quad x \geqslant \frac{B}{A}, \tag{19.11}$$

Note that in case (19.10), the slope of the function is everywhere negative and the function decreases as X increases. As X approaches zero, Y approaches infinity; as X approaches infinity, Y approaches A. For case (19.11), the function is everywhere positive. As X approaches infinity, Y approaches A and when $X = B/A$, $Y = 0$. In these expressions, the curvature the function will display is determined by the value of B. The larger B is, the flatter are the curves; the smaller B is, the more bent are the curves. (See Figure 19.5.)

For the regression functions above, the *reciprocal transformation* would make the determination of A and B quite simple. Namely, if we define a new variable $Z = 1/X$, then the foregoing equations would be transformed into

$$\hat{y} = A + Bz \tag{19.12}$$

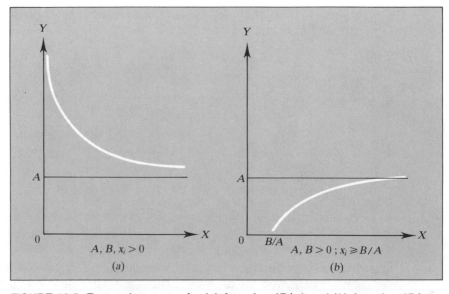

FIGURE 19.5 Regression curves for (a) $\hat{y}_i = A + (B/x_i)$ and (b) $\hat{y}_i = A - (B/x_i)$.

and

$$\hat{y} = A - Bz \qquad (19.13)$$

respectively. These are now simple linear regression equations of Y on Z. The least-squares estimators of A and B can be found in the routine manner. After A and B are found, we can convert the regression equation of Y on Z back to the original form by noting that $Z = 1/X$.

Multiple Curvilinear Regression: A Multiplicative Model

Just as with the linear models, nonlinear regressions may be simple or multiple in nature. Either theoretical considerations or empitical observations may, for example, suggest that the sample regression equation should be of the form, say,

$$\hat{y} = Ax_2^B x_3^C. \qquad (19.14)$$

This is evidently a trivariate regression function in which Y is related to the product of X_2 and X_3. To find the least-squares formulas for the regression coefficients, A, B, and C, we transform the original multiplicative relationship into an additive one as below:

$$\log \hat{y} = \log A + B(\log x_2) + C(\log x_3). \qquad (19.15)$$

Now, set

$$\log \hat{y} = \hat{z},$$
$$\log A = D,$$
$$\log x_2 = w_2,$$

and

$$\log x_3 = w_3;$$

then (19.15) becomes a linear regression equation of Z on W_2 and W_3 as

$$\hat{z} = D + Bw_2 + Cw_3. \qquad (19.16)$$

As a consequence, we can apply the linear methods developed previously to the logarithms of Y, X_2, and X_3 to find the least-squares values of the regression coefficients in (19.16). Once D, B, and C are found, we can convert the sample regression equation (19.16) back into (19.15) by noting the definitions for the transformations.

Double-log transformations are frequently used by economists because they correspond to the assumption of *constant elasticity* between the dependent and independent variables. The simple application of linear methods to logarithms of the variables gives a direct estimate of elasticities. In terms of the concept of "elasticities," the partial regression coefficient B is interpreted as the percentage change in the value of Y per one percent change in the value of X_2. Similarly, C refers to the percentage change in Y per one percent change in X_3.

Further Remarks

We see that in treating curvilinear regressions we usually search for an initial transformation of data, by way of either reciprocals or logarithms, in such a manner that the relationship between the transformed variables appears to be approximately linear. Transformations to linear regression are made mainly for two reasons. First, this procedure makes the calculations easier, since computational problems in nonlinear systems are quite formidable even for well versed mathematicians. Second, transformations to linear regression are desirable because statistical theory is especially well developed under the assumption of linearity.

To complete our discussion on curvilinear analysis, let us point out a few topics not discussed explicitly so far. First of all, just as with the linear models, a nonlinear analysis is conducted by decomposing the total variation in the dependent variable into a systematic part that is explained by the independent variable(s) and a random part, or the residual disturbance. The method of least squares has the function of minimizing the SSE or maximizing SSR.

Second, the unbiased estimator for the variance of the regression line (or plane), or the variance of disturbance, in each case is defined as MSE.

Third, the closeness-of-fit in each case is measured by r^2, or R^2, depending upon whether the nonlinear relationship is simple or multiple. In each case, also, the coefficient of determination (simple or multiple) is defined as the ratio of the sum of squares due to regression, SSR, to the total sum of squares, SST.

Fourth, simple or partial correlation coefficients in the nonlinear models are computed and interpreted in the same manner as in the linear cases. However, with nonlinear relationships, these relationships always take positive signs because the slope of a curvilinear regression line or plane can change signs at various points.

Finally, it is completely unnecessary nowadays to carry out regression analysis by hand; most library computer programs will not only run the regression, but will also transform variables beforehand and convert them back into nonlinear forms afterward. However, in order to show explicitly how these procedures work, simple numerical examples for some nonlinear regression problems are given in the problems to be solved by hand computations.

19.3 AUTOCORRELATION

A Note on the Nature of Time Series

As already mentioned, our discussion of the violations of the assumptions concerning the error terms in the classical linear regression models and their corrections will be made with special references to time-series data. It is important, then, that we should have a rough idea of the nature of time series at this point. A time series is thought to contain four distinct parts, which can be decomposed. The four components of a time series are the secular trend T, the cyclical fluctuations C, the seasonal variations S, and irregular movements I. *Secular trend* is the long-run average behavior of a time series and it can be considered as a regression line fitted to the series with time as the independent variable. *Cyclical fluctuations* are the wavelike movements with a duration (from one trough to another) longer than one year and less than approximately twleve years. The term *seasonal variations* refers to the changes in the values of a series from month (quarter) to month (quarter) with a span of one year and with roughly the same pattern of change year after year. *Irregular movements* are those changes in the values of the series that are produced by random forces or some "specific" factors, such as labor strikes, changes in public policies, sudden international tensions, etc.

There are many possible models so as far the composition of a time series is concerned. The two most popular ones, as we shall see in Chapter 21, are the *multiplicative* and *additive models*. The former treats a time series as the product of the four components, so that $Y = TCSI$; the latter considers a time series as the sum of the four components, so that $Y = T + C + S + I$. From the earlier definitions of T, C, S, and I, it can be understood easily that these four components will be all present in a series if it is one of quarterly or monthly data. In a series of annual data, however, there are only T and C. We often speak of *detrended data*, a case in which trend is eliminated from a series. For a series of annual data, detrended data may either mean the quotient $Y/T = C$ or the difference $Y - T = C$. For a series of monthly or quarterly data, detrended data is taken to mean $Y/T = CSI$ or $Y - T = C + S + I$.

With this much background on time series, we move on now to our present task on hand—a treatise on autocorrelation.

The Nature of Autocorrelation

Autocorrelation is also called serial correlation. While some authors make a distinction between these two terms, we shall use them here interchangeably. One assumption about the error term is of nonauto-regression—there should be no predictable pattern existing in the error term produced by the regression equation. That is, e_i should be independent. Autocorrelation, or serial correlation arise when this assumption is not met, namely, when there exists a significant pattern in the error term. A serially correlated error term contains a systematic trend such that knowledge of the value of e_{i-1} will improve our ability to predict the value of e_i.

To be more specific, let us consider a simple but quite common form of serial correlation called the *linear first-order serial correlation*, or just the *first-order serial correlation*. With reference to a sample, first-order serial correlation is present whenever the error term e_i is linearly dependent on the error term e_{i-1} in the following way:

$$e_i = re_{i-1} + v_i, \tag{19.17}$$

where v_i is an error term that is assumed to be statistically independent with zero mean and constant variance, and where r is the estimator for ρ, the *population coefficient of serial correlation,* and where r is defined as

$$r = \frac{\sum\limits_{i=2}^{n} e_i e_{i-1}}{\sum\limits_{i=2}^{n} e_{i-1}^2}. \tag{19.18}$$

When serial correlation exists, it may be either be positive or negative. *Positive serial correlation* results when the occurrence of a positive (negative) error term raises the probability above 0.5 that the next error term will have a positive (negative) value. Negative serial correlation emerges when the occurrence of a positive (negative) residual raises the probability above 0.5 that the next residual will be negative (positive). These two types of serial correlation are depicted graphically in Figure 19.6. Note that in this figure the observations in the scatter are numbered in the order of their occurrence. This is important in the evaluation of autocorrelation, since we are interested in determining whether the value of the error term is influenced by the order in which the sample points appear. Panel (a) of Figure 19.6 illustrates *positive serial correlation,* since the error term has positive values over the first six observations followed by negative values over the next five observations. Clearly, this pattern springs from fitting a linear regression line through data that is significantly nonlinear. The resulting autocorrelation is produced by this significant nonlinear trend and the value of r in (19.18) is positive and significant.

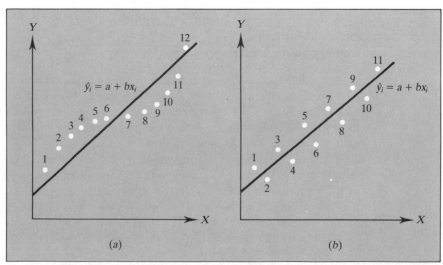

FIGURE 19.6 Illustrations of (a) positive serial correlation and (b) negative serial correlation.

Panel (*b*) in Figure 19.6 portrays *negative serial correlation,* where positive residuals are invariably followed by negative residuals, etc. This pattern implies a kind of *sine* wave variety in the data unaccounted for the variations in the values of the independent variable. In this case, the value of *r* in (19.17) is negative and significant.

Effects of Serial Correlation on Regression Results

The existence of autocorrelation in general makes regression results unreliable. First, serious serial correlation may adversely affect the properties of LSEs; that is, the estimates produced may not be the best linear unbiased estimators. This means that the fitted least-squares line or plane that results will not have the desirable properties we expect it to have. Second, the sample variances of the individual regression coefficients may fail to estimate the true values, resulting in possible spurious conclusions from *F* and *t* tests. Finally, autocorrelation tends to deflate the value of S_U^2 or to inflate the value of R^2, giving us the illusion of good closeness-of-fit statistics. That is, serial correlation produces more significant values of S_U^2 or R^2 than may be warranted.

The foregoing comments can again be illustrated by Figure 19.6(*a*). Let us consider the fitted heavy line in that figure as the "true" regression. Now, if the sample drawn consisted of only the first half of the data or only the second half, then as you can easily imagine, the regression line would be positioned either too high or too low. However, the proximity of the incomplete sample points to these sample regression lines would be likely to yield closeness-of-fit measures for the equation and for the regression coefficients that appear to be more significant than warranted. Furthermore, suppose the sample selected includes only the central six values, then a very poor regression equation will be calculated, one with poorly estimated regression coefficients and unpredictable measures for closeness-of-fit. Thus, when serial correlation is presented in realized residuals, our confidence in the regression results is shaken since we cannot rely on significant findings obtained from such results to buttress conclusions about the important business or economic relationships. We move on now to present a test on first-order serial correlation.

The Durbin–Watson Test for Serial Correlation

A convenient test for first-order serial correlation is based on the Durbin–Watson statistic *d* (a generalized von Neumann ratio), which is given by the expression:

$$d = \frac{\sum\limits_{i=2}^{n} (e_i - e_{i-1})^2}{\sum\limits_{i=1}^{n} e_i^2}.$$

(19.19)

Note that this D–W statistic relates directly with the sample coefficient of serial correlation as defined in (19.18). Approximately,

$$\sum_{i=1}^{n} e_i^2 \doteq \sum_{i=2}^{n} e_{i-1}^2 \doteq \sum_{i=2}^{n} e_i^2,$$

so that

$$d \doteq \frac{2 \sum_{i=2}^{n} e_i^2 - 2 \sum_{i=2}^{n} e_i e_{i-1}}{\sum_{i=1}^{n} e_i^2}$$

$$\doteq 2 - 2r$$

$$= 2(1 - r).$$

This result indicates that d varies in value from 0 to 4, since, as r approaches 1, d approaches 0; as r approaches -1, d approaches 4; as r approaches 0, d approaches 2.

It may also be pointed out that the exact distribution of d depends on the sample size n, the number of independent variables k in the regression analysis, and the particular values of the independent variable X (or independent variables X_i). However, given n and k, and assuming that e_i is distributed as $n(0, \sigma)$, the distribution of d always lies between the distributions of two other statistics, named d_L and d_U, as depicted by Figure 19.7. In this figure, $d_L^* = 4 - d_L$ and $d_U^* = 4 - d_U$. Critical values of d_L and d_U for both single-tail and two-sided

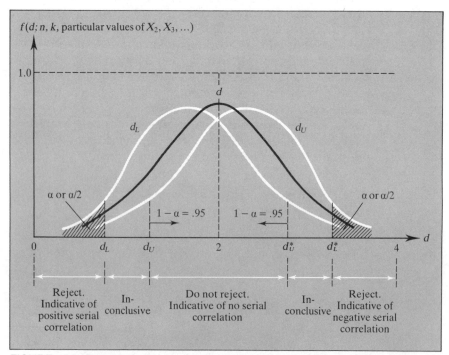

FIGURE 19.7 The relation between the sampling distributions of d, d_L, and d_U.

D–W tests at $\alpha = 0.05$ can be found in Table XI in Appendix C. It may be noted that Table XI is for single-tail tests. For a double-tail test, the levels of significance relate to each tail, so this value is doubled; namely, the correct 5% double-tail figures are as given in the 2.5% table.

Figure 19.7 also shows the rejection and nonrejection regions of a D–W test. It shows that if we are testing

$$H_0: \rho = 0 \quad \text{against} \quad H_1: \rho > 0,$$

the decision rules are:

1. Reject H_0 if $d < d_L$.

2. Do not reject H_0 if $d > d_U$.

3. The test is inconclusive if $d_L \leqslant d \leqslant d_U$.

Likewise, if we are testing $\rho = 0$ against $\rho < 0$, then H_0 will be rejected if the computed d value is greater than d_L^* [that is, if $d > (4 - d_L)$] and we conclude that there is significant negative autocorrelation. Finally, if the alternative is two-sided, the decision rules become:

1. Reject H_0 if $d < d_L$ or if $d > d_L^*(= 4 - d_L)$.

2. Do not reject H_0 if $d_U < d < d_U^* (= 4 - d_U)$.

3. The test is inconclusive if $d_L \leqslant d \leqslant d_U$, or if $d_U^* \leqslant d \leqslant d_L^*$.

Note that from these decision rules, and as suggested by Figure 19.7, there is at least one inconclusive region in each case. The reason is that it is practically impossible to tabulate all the exact distributions of d, so that only the extreme distributions of those for d_L and d_U are tabulated. Inconclusive tests often occur when n is small or when k is large or when both happen.

Suppose we are running a regression with $k = 3$ and $n = 30$ and we wish to test $\rho = 0$ against $\rho < 0$ at $\alpha = 0.05$. We find from Table XI that $d_L = 1.21$ and $d_U = 1.65$. Thus, H_0 will be rejected if $d < 1.21$; H_0 will be accepted if $d > 1.65$; the test is inconclusive if $d_L = 1.21 \leqslant d \leqslant d_U = 1.65$. Similarly, if the alternative is $\rho < 0$, then H_0 will be rejected if $d > d_L^* = 4 - d_L = 4 - 1.21 = 2.79$; H_0 will be accepted if $d < d_U^* = 4 - 1.65 = 2.35$; the test is inconclusive if $d_U^* = 2.35 \leqslant d \leqslant d_L^* = 2.79$. Finally, if a two-sided alternative, $\rho \neq 0$, is employed, then the critical points are found at the 2.5% entries in Table XI for $\alpha = 0.05$, and we find that $d_L = 1.12$ and $d_U = 1.54$. From these values, we have $d_L^* = 4 - d_L = 2.88$ and $d_U^* = 4 - d_U = 2.46$. Thus $\rho = 0$ will be rejected if $d < d_L = 1.12$ or if $d > d_L^* = 2.88$; $\rho = 0$ will be accepted if $d_U = 1.54 \leqslant d \leqslant d_U^* = 2.46$; the test is inconclusive if $d_L = 1.12 \leqslant d \leqslant d_U = 1.54$, or if $d_U^* = 2.46 \leqslant d \leqslant d_L^* = 2.88$. The reader may grasp the logic behind these results by studying Figure 19.7 carefully.

Methods of Correcting Serial Correlation

Having detected the existence of significant serial correlation, we naturally ask: Can it be corrected or removed? Several methods have been suggested in the literature on the problem of estimation in econometrics in connection with this issue. All of these methods are concerned with the transformation of observations. We shall discuss some of the simpler and more practical devices here.

Regression with Serially Correlated Terms

The first device is to conduct a regression with serially correlated terms. Under the assumption that there exists first-order serial correlation, then we have in a sample of size n,

$$e_i = re_{i-1} + v_i.$$

where, as has been explained before, e_i are serially correlated but v_i are independent. Thus, an efficient estimation procedure is one that minimizes the sum of squared error terms v_i. Namely, we wish now to apply the method of least squares to e_i such that

$$\sum_{i=2}^{n} v_i^2 = \sum_{i=2}^{n} (e_i - re_{i-1})^2 = \text{a minimum.}$$

Given, for example, the simple linear regression equation, with original observations, of series Y on series X as

$$\hat{y}_i = B_1 + B_2 x_i$$

then

$$e_i = y_i - \hat{y}_i$$
$$= re_{i-1} + v_i.$$

Next, employing r as determined by (19.18), we may transform Y and X into two new variables Y' and X' by transforming their original values as follows:

$$y_i' = y_i - ry_{i-1}; \qquad x_i' = x_i - rx_{i-1}.$$

These transformed values are then used to estimate the least-squares regression equation in the usual fashion. We have then

$$\hat{y}_i' = B_1' + B_2' x_i'. \tag{19.20}$$

It is interesting to note that under the appropriate assumptions about v_i, the transformed equation (19.20) will satisfy the usual assumptions of independence and constant variance for residual disturbances while the original equation does not. Furthermore, owing to the fact that $y_i' = y_i - ry_{i-1}$, $B_1'/(1 - r)$ and B_2' become the estimators for β_1

and β_2 in $\mu_{Y.X} = \beta_1 + \beta_2 x_i$, respectively. Hence, the original regression equation of the sample values is reduced to the form

$$\hat{y}_i = \frac{B_1'}{1 - r} + B_2' x_i. \tag{19.21}$$

The foregoing procedure can also be applied to situations in which more than one independent variable is involved. For example, given that

$$\hat{y}_i = B_1 + B_2 x_2 + B_3 x_3,$$

then the corresponding regression equation in terms of serially correlated error terms becomes

$$\hat{y}_i = \frac{B_1'}{1 - r} + B_2' x_2 + B_3' x_3. \tag{19.22}$$

Regression with Detrended Data

The second method of correcting autoregression is to conduct a regression analysis with detrended data. The reason for this procedure is that the presence of significant trend in time series introduces dependence between successive observations and tends to produce serially correlated regression residuals. This method is quite simple in principle, though rather time-consuming in execution. First the trends for the original series are determined (from a secular trend equation), and then trends are eliminated, either by division or by subtraction, from the original data set; finally the method of least squares is applied to the detrended data in establishing the regression equation.

A simpler way to achieve the same result is to work with the original observations, but with time as an additional explanatory variable. It can be verified that a multiple regression of one series on two or more series, all of which are deviations from linear trends, is identical with the regression function with original data when time is explicitly introduced into the analysis. Thus, given a sample regression equation of the form

$$\hat{y} = B_1 + B_2 x_2 + B_3 x_3, \tag{19.23}$$

whose residuals are dependent owing to trends, the dependence can be removed by introducing time T as an independent variable, resulting in

$$\hat{y} = B_1 + B_2 x_2 + B_3 x_3 + B_4 t, \tag{19.24}$$

where t denotes time periods with a defined origin and measured in appropriate units. One way to determine B_4 is to determine e_i for (19.23), plot e_i against time, and determine a time trend for e_i. This time trend is then incorporated into (19.23) to produce (19.24).

It should be noticed that with the inclusion of time as an additional explanatory variable, the original regression equation need not be linear in the variables, but the dependent variable is usually linear in T. Thus, we may have, for example,

$$\log \hat{y} = B_1 + B_2(\log x_2) + B_3(\log x_3) + B_4 t. \qquad (19.25)$$

In concluding our discussion on serial correlation, let us make a few additional remarks on the use of regression analysis for forecasting with time-series data. First, if serial correlation can be eliminated successfully by one of the methods introduced here, then the regression equation for the transformed variables is said to conform to the regression models; the standard deviation of regression and the standard errors of the regression coefficients are applicable and valid.

Second, detrended variables represent deviations from trends and, as such, the resulting regression equations can only be used for short-run forecasting. Precisely, if annual data are employed, then the forecasts would constitute year-to-year cyclical fluctuations in the dependent series. If quarterly or monthly data are employed, the forecasts constitute short-term forecasting for the cyclical and seasonal movements in the dependent series.

Third, theoretical correctness is one thing and accuracy in forecasting is another. If it is desired to do long-term forecasting, we may find that more accurate forecasts may be obtained by regressing original data, even though the resulting residuals may be dependent. The pitfall here is that any two series that have significant trend components or that are affected by the general business cycle will appear to be highly correlated whether or not there is any direct relationship between them. Thus, in employing original series we must be sure that theoretical or logical relationships exist among them and avoid relying merely on the coefficient of determination, which would be spuriously high.

Finally, it has been pointed out that for various reasons regression functions should not be applied beyond the range of data on which they are based. However, in using regression analysis with time-series data, our major objective is to provide estimates of the future, and these estimates usually involve extrapolation. Confronted with this dilemma, the advice is that a forecaster should be aware of the difficulties associated with extrapolation and should extrapolate only if he can support his statistical result with sound logical justification.

19.4 HETEROSCEDASTICITY

The Nature and Sources of Heteroscedasticity

One of the assumptions of the classical normal linear regression models is that $E(u_i^2) = \sigma_U^2$, for all i. This is the feature of constant error variance over all observations and it is known as *homoscedasticity* in contrast to the case of varying error variance called *heteroscedasticity*. When the assumption of homoscedasticity is violated, but when the other assumptions are not, the LSEs of the regression equation are still unbiased and consistent. However, they no longer have the minimum variances among the set of unbiased estimators and, hence, they are no longer efficient.

Many factors may give rise to heteroscedasticity. We shall mention here a few that are frequently encountered with economic and business data. Sometimes we may find that the nature of the data is such that the response, that is, the values of the subpopulation Ys associated with different levels of the independent variable(s), may exhibit various degrees of dispersion owing to economic reasons. Suppose, for example, that we are regressing family consumption expenditure on family income: the assumption of homoscedasticity is clearly not very plausible on *a priori* grounds. In this case, we would expect less variations in consumption expenditure for low income families: Consumption expenditures cannot fall far below the rather low level of average consumption expenditures without confronting starvation; they cannot rise too far above the average because the asset and credit positions of such families do not allow it. These constraints, however, are likely to be much less binding for families at higher levels of income and, hence, their expenditures for consumption may deviate from the mean to a much greater extent. Indeed, recent empirical studies reveal this pattern of heteroscedasticity when one regresses savings, vacation expenditures, and so on to income.

Heteroscedasticity often also arises when the dependent variable has a probability distribution whose variance is functionally related to its expectation or to its expectation as well as the sample size. For instance, if the dependent variable happened to be, say, the number of industrial accidents, observed per day, its probability distribution would obey the Poisson law and its variance would be identical with its mean which, in turn, is proportional to the size of the specified unit. Precisely, in such a case, $E(Y)$ increases as X increases and Y cannot then have a constant variance at all levels of X. Here, σ_U^2 increases with the increase of $E(Y)$ and the increase of X.

The few cases mentioned before all produces larger values of σ_U^2 at higher levels of the regressor(s). Furthermore, the reverse could also happen. Heteroscedasticity of the type of decreasing σ_U^2 with increasing in X (or X's) is often encountered with time series data. Various factors in business and economic time series can produce this condition in the variance of the error term. These factors may include (1) the maturity of certain economic patterns of the series over time, resulting more systematic and more predictable variables; (2) the improvement of data collecting and recording procedures over time, producing reductions in definitional and measuring errors; and (3) changes in structure and organization of business firms due to increases in assets and sales over time, initiating a trend toward more efficient programmed patterns.

Detecting Heteroscedasticity

The method of detecting the existence of heteroscedasticity, as usual, should be that of testing the null hypothesis that it exists. Such a test

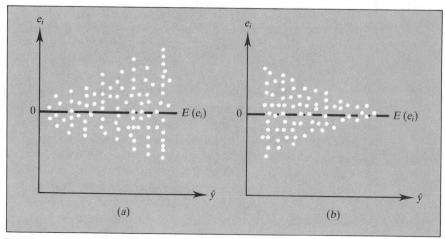

FIGURE 19.8 Residual plots for heteroscedasticity with (a) S_U increasing (b) S_U decreasing as X increases.

has indeed been made available by S. M. Goldfield and R. E. Quandt. However, we will not present the test here for two reasons. One is that this test is neither rigorous in theory nor universal in application. The other is that simple and effective methods are available for the discovery of significant heteroscedasticity by examining the patterns of the residual errors.

One way to discover non-constancy of variance of the error term is to plot the residuals against the computed values of Y, $\hat{y}$. If σ_U^2 is homoscedastic, then the residuals will fluctuate around the center line of zero in a random manner, without any systematic pattern. Otherwise, the scatter plot will indicate heteroscedasticity. These observations are illustrated by Figure 19.8. It may be mentioned in passing that many computer programs on regression studies also provide plots of regression residuals.

There is still another simple way for us to formulate a conclusion as to the extent to which σ_U^2 is heteroscedastic. This consists of studying the absolute values of the error term with rank-ordered independent variables, one at a time. Any systematic correspondence in the absolute size of the error term and the size of the independent variables would be produced by heteroscedasticity. As an illustration, let us consider the

TABLE 19.1 Partial Results of Regressing Y on X_2 and X_3

x_2	x_3	y	$\hat{y}$	$e = y - \hat{y}$
⋮	⋮	⋮	⋮	⋮
16	105	120	130	−10
19	60	100	95	+5
12	80	115	123	−8
15	92	124	134	−10
14	142	124	140	−16
20	148	139	156	+17
⋮	⋮	⋮	⋮	⋮

TABLE 19.2 Correspondence of the Absolute Values of the Error Term With Ranked Independent Variables

x_2	e	x_3	e
⋮	⋮	⋮	⋮
12	8	60	5
14	16	80	8
15	10	92	10
16	10	105	10
19	5	142	16
20	17	148	19
⋮	⋮	⋮	⋮

partial listing of a regression results of regressing Y on two independent variables X_2 and X_3, as given in Table 19.1.

Now, suppose the X values are ranked in ascending order along with the absolute values of the error term; we would have results as shown in Table 19.2. We see that there is no evident systematic pattern of any kind in the error term as the value of X_2 is increased. Hence, the error term seems to be homoscedastic with regard to X_2. However, it can also be clearly seen that there emerges a definite trend indicating that a particular value of X_3 is likely to affect the size of the error term. This observation means that X_3 is the source of heteroscedasticity.

Variance-Stabilizing Transformations

When the assumption of homoscedasticity is violated, it can usually be corrected by transformations of the variable or variables. Such transformations are called *variance-stabilizing transformations,* for obvious reasons. The particular type of stabilizing transformation to be used depends upon the source of heteroscedasticity. We shall here consider two simple but highly useful methods that are especially appropriate when business and economic data are used in regression analyses.

The Case When Y is a Poisson Variable
It has been found that if the dependent variable Y has a probability distribution that obeys the Poisson law, then the transformation of the type $Y^* = \sqrt{Y}$ not only stabilizes the error variance but also tends to improve normality of the error term. Specifically, if Y is a Poisson variable and if we let $Y^* = \sqrt{Y}$ and fit the model

$$y^* = \beta_1 + \beta_2 x_2 + \cdots \beta_J x_J + u, \tag{19.26}$$

we then satisfy at least approximately the least-squares assumption of homoscedasticity.

The Case When σ_U is Proportional to X
A frequently encountered situation in regression analysis with business and economic data, such as studies of consumption expenditures, savings, or vacation expenses with income, is one in which the error

variance is proportional to X^2 or the standard deviation of the error term is proportional to X. Here, we have a model of the form:

$$y = \beta_1 + \beta_2 x + u, \quad \text{where} \quad \sigma_U = dx. \tag{19.27}$$

The proper transformation required to obtain BLUE least-squares estimators for this model is simply to divide both sides of the heteroscedascity model by x. With this transformation, the homoscedastic value of d results:

$$d = \sigma_U/x.$$

Here, d is the constant standard deviation after transformation. This transformation is accomplished by dividing the original expression by x. By this, we have

$$\frac{y}{x} = \frac{\beta_1}{x} + \beta_2 + \frac{u}{x}.$$

Now, for convenience in application, defining $y' = y/x$ and $x' = 1/x$ and also let $\beta_1 = \beta_1'$, $\beta_2 = \beta_2'$ and $u/x = u'$, we can write the population model equation (29.27) in the form

$$y' = \beta_2' + \beta_2 x' + u'. \tag{19.28}$$

Notice that (19.28) is in the standard linear regression form. Furthermore, the variance of u' is now constant, since, from previous definitions, $u' = u/x$ and $d = \sigma_U/x$, where d is constant over all observations.

With transformed variables Y' ($=Y/X$) and X' ($=1/X$), the fitted sample regression equation so obtained is

$$\hat{y}' = B_1' + B_2' x', \tag{19.29}$$

where the primes on B_1 and B_2 remind us that the results are obtained from the transformed variables. To use (19.29) as a predictive equation, we must convert the transformed variables back into their original form. This is done by multiplying both sides of (19.29) by x, yielding

$$\hat{y} = B_1 + B_2 x, \tag{19.30}$$

where

$$B_1 = B_2' \quad \text{and} \quad B_2 = B_1'.$$

In closing this section, let us mention briefly two more cases that are also of interest to business and economics students. The first situation is one in which the dependent variables are proportions, or percentages whose variances are functions of both the mean and the sample size such that $V(Y) = \pi(1 - \pi)/n$ generated by, say, binomial experiments. Here, the error variance can be stabilized by what is called the *arc sine transformation* of the form $\sin^{-1}\sqrt{Y}$. Tables to facilitate this transformation can be found, for example, in *Handbook of Statistical Tables* by Donald B. Owen (Addison-Wesley Publishing Co., Inc., Reading, Mass., 1962).

The second situation that deserves brief mention is the fact that regression models are usually formulated with the error term to be additive: $y = E(Y) + u$. However, another highly useful model in business and economic analysis with regression studies is the *multiplicative model,* in which the explained variable is assumed to be the product of its mean and the regression residual: $y = [E(Y)]\sigma_U^2$. A moment's reflection will enable you to appreciate that data subject to multiplicative errors tend to produce heteroscedasticity with residual plots similar to that in Figure 19.8(a). In this case, the variance of the regression, or of the error term, can be stabilized to a great extent by the simple transformation of $y^* = \ln y$, where ln represents natural logarithms to the base e. That is, we attempt to stabilize the error variance by fitting the regression: $\ln \hat{y} = B_1 + B_2 x_2 + \cdots + B_j x_j$.

19.5 MULTICOLLINEARITY

The Nature of Multicollinearity and Its Indication

Multicollinearity is not concerned with any assumption of residual error given earlier. It is, instead, a violation of independence among the explanatory variables in a multivariate analysis. A unique assumption of the classical normal multiple linear regression model is that none of the regressors should be perfectly correlated with any other regressor or have any linear combination of other explanatory variables. We speak of *perfect multicollinearity* when this assumption is violated. We speak of *absence of multicollinearity* whenever all regressors are independent of each other. In reality, of course, neither of these two conditions can be found and the point is only of theoretical interest. In practice, we are always confronted with varying degrees of multicollinearity. Of special concern are cases of a *high degree of multicollinearity*; the case in which one regressor has a highly significant correlation with another regressor *or* has a linear combination with other regressors.

The values of simple and partial correlation coefficients provide us with indications of the extent and location of intercorrelation among explanatory variables. The simple correlation coefficient is the simplest indicator in this case, since it measures the covariance in the raw data series. It does not, however, inform us of the relationship between two variables in isolation. On this score, the coefficient of partial correlation is more useful by virtue of the fact that it measures the associated movement in two variables when the effects of all other variables have been held constant. Hence, we may adopt the convention that multicollinearity is presented in a regression equation whenever there exist high partial correlations between explanatory variables.

It must also be noticed now that multicollinearity visits empirical research habitually and that a relatively low degree of multicollinearity has little if any damaging results on regression studies. It is when multicollinearity is close to perfect correlation that serious concern arises. As a rule of thumb, when r_{ij}^2 or $r_{ij.k}^2$ is greater than 0.90, we should try to remove, if possible and useful, the bad effects of multicollinearity in multivariate analysis.

Effects of Multicollinearity and Procedures for its Removal

There are a number of undesirable effects on regression results when a high degree of multicollinearity is present. The first is that multicollinearity contributes redundant information and thereby produces confusing regression results. For example, suppose that in a trivariate regression the two independent variables are highly correlated; we may find that the t tests on both $\beta_2 = 0$ and $\beta_3 = 0$ are insignificant but the F test on $\beta_2 = \beta_3 = 0$ is highly significant. These seemingly contradictory results can be explained in two possible ways. One is that the t tests reveals that the contribution of one variable, say, X_2, is insignificant after the influence of the other variable, X_3, has been discounted because of its inclusion in the model. On the other hand, the significant F test implies that at least one of the variables has significant influence on the prediction of the value on Y. Indeed, the case may actually be that both X_2 and X_3 are influential, but the contribution of one overlaps that of the other. Another explanation for this seeming contradiction is that one may have a situation where the separate contribution of each of the explanatory variables is weak relative to their strong joint contribution on Y. This effect of multicollinearity is considered harmful only when all the influences of the regressors on Y cannot be disentangled.

Second, a high degree of multicollinearity produces highly imprecise estimates of the regression coefficients. This imprecision is due the large standard errors for the LSE of B_i. Thus, we cannot reliably make inferences about statistical importance under these circumstances. It must be observed in this connection, however, that the value of the overall regression equation may not be measurably impaired by the existence of multicollinearity. If the purpose of the regression study is merely to predict the value of Y and if whatever pattern of multicollinearity in the data remains unchanged into the forecast period, then the regression equation may provide reasonable forecasts despite the imprecision of the estimates of standard errors of the regression coefficients.

Finally, before ending this section, it might be useful to point out the effect of the presence of perfect multicollinearity as a point of reference. Perfect correlation between two independent variables makes it impossible to find a unique best-fitted plane; there will be an infinite number of best-fitted planes. Consequently, it is impossible to calculate the regression coefficients. Thus, the whole attempt to find the multiple regression equation fails completely. Figure 19.9 illustrates this situa-

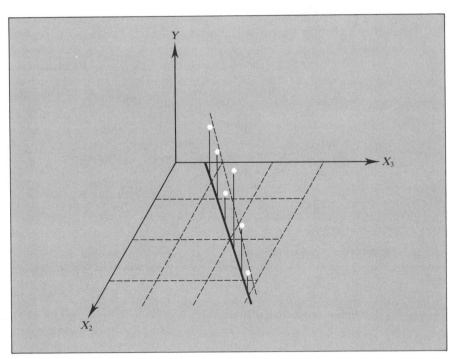

FIGURE 19.9 Graphic illustration of perfectly correlated independent variables in trivariate analysis.

tion. Graphically, the perfect correlation between X_2 and X_3 means that all the dots in the three-dimensional space (which are the raw data) are above the same straight line in the X_2–X_3 plane. This line is the heavy diagonal line in Figure 19.9. It should be obvious that, considering only the vertical plane (that is, a plane parallel to the Y axis) that goes through the solid diagonal line, a least-squares straight line can be uniquely determined that best fits the dots in the three-dimensional space. This line is the dashed line in Figure 19.9.

Next comes the essence of the problem in this discussion: there are an infinite number of planes in the three-dimensional space passing through the dashed line, and each one of them is a least-squares best-fitted plane, since the sum of the squared vertical deviations of the dots from the plane is a minimum. Considering the whole set of the best-fitting planes, one can have any number of slopes with respect to the X_2 axis (that is, any value for B_2), any number of slopes with respect to the X_3 axis (any value for B_3), and any intercept along the Y axis (any value for B_1). One cannot find a best-fitting plane with any desired combination of values for B_1, B_2, and B_3; but for any specific value of any one of the B's, one can find a best-fitting plane. In short, the best-fitting plane is not uniquely determined because the explanatory variables are perfectly correlated.

If the independent variables are not perfectly correlated but have a very high degree of correlation, Figure 19.9 would be modified so that all dots in the three-dimensional space fell above a narrow corridor in the X_2–X_3 plane. It should also be obvious intuitively, that the best-fitting plane can be uniquely determined, but inferences to the population plane are severely affected because of the comments made before.

Several methods have been developed as remedial measures for multicollinearity. Most of these methods can be applied without producing some bad side effects. The most effective method is also the most obvious device in handling multicollinearity. This procedure requires the elimination of all the multicollinear influences by deleting all highly correlated regressors except one. The selection should be done on *a priori* grounds and based on the expected influences exerted by the variables involved. This elimination will result in little, if any, reduction in the value of R^2, but it will produce changes in model structures and established hypotheses.

19.6 DUMMY VARIABLES

Another problem in regressing time-series data is the effect of heterogeneous historical influences on the interaction of the series. War, inflation, and recession, for example, may produce unusually large distortions in the relationship between two series. Consider, for example, the scatter diagram in Figure 19.10 of personal savings on personal income in the United States from 1935 to 1949. Wartime savings (circles in the diagram) are clearly at a much higher levels of personal income. This phenomenon is quite understandable: during wartime, because of rationing (which tends to reduce consumption) and patriotism (which tends to increase the purchase of government savings bonds), a greater proportion of personal income is saved. To isolate the

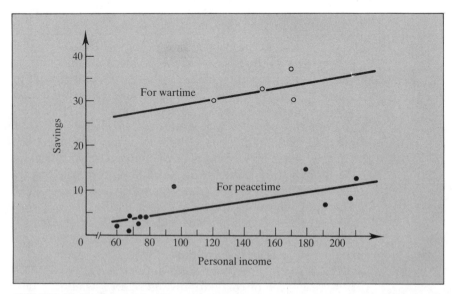

FIGURE 19.10 Regression lines of savings on personal income for conditions of peace and of war.

TABLE 19.3 Data for Regressing Personal Savings on Personal Income and War (in billions of dollars)

Year	Personal Savings, S	Personal Income, Y	War, W
1935	2	60	0
1936	4	69	0
1937	4	74	0
1938	1	68	0
1939	3	73	0
1940	4	78	0
1941	11	96	0
1942	28	123	1
1943	33	151	1
1944	37	165	1
1945	30	171	1
1946	15	179	0
1947	7	191	0
1948	13	210	0
1949	9	207	0

Source: Economic Report of the President, February 1970.

effect of nonhomogeneous influences and, therefore, to improve the forecast, one may apply regression analysis by using "dummy variables."

A *dummy variable* is a categorical or indicator variable. It can also be considered as a "switching" variable whose value can be switched "on" or "off" arbitrarily. With reference to the savings–consumption data, when the variable is switched on, indicating, say, wartime conditions, it assumes a value of 1; when it is off, indicating peacetime conditions, it assumes a value of 0. For the data in Table 19.3, to estimate the regression equation of personal savings S on personal income Y, we may introduce a dummy variable W. The resulting multiple linear regression equation becomes:

$$\hat{s} = a + by + cw$$
$$= -0.415022 + 0.059437y + 23.350885w.$$

(The regression coefficients are obtained in the usual fashion by the method of least squares.)

For convenience in forecasting, the foregoing multiple regression equation can be converted into two simple linear regression equations as follows:

for peacetime: $\hat{s} = -0.415022 + 0.059437y + 23.350885(0)$
$$= -0.415022 + 0.059437y;$$

for wartime: $\hat{s} = -0.415022 + 0.059437y + 23.350885(1)$
$$= 22.935863 + 0.059437y.$$

The first regression equation may be considered as an estimate of the *aggregate savings function.* The slope of this line, called the *marginal propensity to save* in economics, indicates that there is an increase in savings by an average amount of approximately 5.94 cents per dollar increase in personal income. When $W = 1$, then a increases by 23.350885 billions of dollars. This means that the savings function (regression line) shifts upward by an amount of $23.350885 billion, reflecting a general increase in savings due to rationing and patriotism. With the dummy-variable analysis, we note that there is a change in the Y-intercept but not in the slope of the regression. This may not be a realistic description, but it is a necessary consequence of the multiple linear regression model.

The device of introducing dummy variables can also be employed for cross-section data, for the same purpose of isolating the effect of heterogeneous influences, and for adjusting seasonal fluctuations. We shall consider an example of the latter. In Table 19.4, the first two columns contain a time series of sales S of a department store. The regression of S on time T for this series, as can be verified by the reader, is

$$\hat{s} = 14.758 + 0.4278t,$$

which, as is shown by Figure 19.11, is a very poor fit because of pronounced seasonal fluctuations, especially for the fourth quarter. This trend equation is therefore a very poor device for the purpose of

TABLE 19.4 Sales of a Department Store with Seasonal Dummy Variables

Year-Quarter	T	Sales (in $ million) S	Q_2	Q_3	Q_4	$\hat{s}$
1981	1	10	0	0	0	9.8
	2	15	1	0	0	14.8
	3	16	0	1	0	15.6
	4	30	0	0	1	30.4
1982	5	11	0	0	0	10.6
	6	15	1	0	0	15.6
	7	17	0	1	0	16.4
	8	31	0	0	1	31.2
1983	9	11	0	0	0	11.4
	10	17	1	0	0	16.4
	11	17	0	1	0	17.2
	12	31	0	0	1	32.0
1984	13	12	0	0	0	12.2
	14	17	1	0	0	17.2
	15	18	0	1	0	18.0
	16	33	0	0	1	32.8
1985	17	13	0	0	0	13.0
	18	18	1	0	0	18.0
	19	18	0	1	0	18.8
	20	35	0	0	1	33.6

Source: Fictitious data.

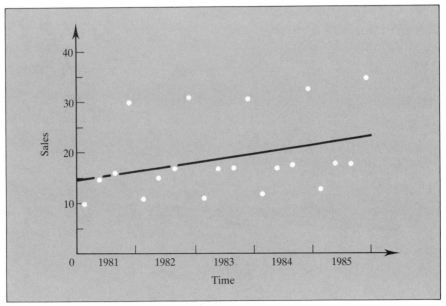

FIGURE 19.11 Department store sales.

forecasting. Now, to adjust for seasonal fluctuations, we may introduce three dummy variables, one for each of the three later quarters, Q_2, Q_3, and Q_4. No dummy variable is introduced for the first quarter because Q_2, Q_3, and Q_4 measure the shift in sales from a first-quarter base. The original data together with the three dummy variables are as shown in Table 19.4. By feeding these data into a computer program, the following multiple linear regression equation with four independent variables has been obtained:

$$\hat{s} = a + bt + cq_2 + dq_3 + eq_4$$
$$= 9.6 + 0.2t + 4.8q_2 + 5.4q_3 + 20.0q_4.$$

By substituting the values of the dummies into the foregoing multiple regression equation, we may obtain the forecasting equation for each quarter as follows:

for Q_1: $\hat{s} = 9.6 + 0.2t$;

for Q_2: $\hat{s} = 14.4 + 0.2t$;

for Q_3: $\hat{s} = 15.0 + 0.2t$;

for Q_4: $\hat{s} = 29.6 + 0.2t$.

From these regressions we see that the effect of trend alone on sales is 0.2 per quarter and that the seasonal shift coefficients, with the Y-intercept for the first quarter as the base, are reflected in the Y-intercepts for other quarters. Thus, the seasonal adjustment is exactly the same every year. The computed values of sales are given in

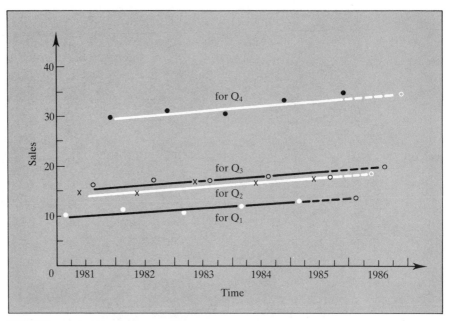

FIGURE 19.12 Regression of department store sales on time with dummies and projections.

the last column in Table 19.4. The least-squares fit is graphed in Figure 19.12 and the projected sales for the four quarters of 1986 are also shown there. In contrast to the simple regression of S on T, the fit with the introduction of dummies is almost perfect with small residual errors. Furthermore, in general, when the introduction of dummy variable(s) is appropriate, the slope of the simple regression equation without dummy variable(s) is biased because of heterogeneous influences.

GLOSSARY OF FORMULAS

(19.1) $\hat{y} = A + Bx + Cx^2$;

(19.2) $\hat{y} = A + Bw + Cz$.

Equation (19.1) defines the second-degree sample regression equation of Y on X. To facilitate computations, we define $X = W$ and $X^2 = Z$ and then (19.1) can be written as a multiple linear sample regression equation as (19.2).

(19.3) $\hat{y} = AB^x$;

(19.4) $\log y = \log A + x(\log B)$;

(19.5) $\log \hat{y} = C + Dx$;

(19.6) $\hat{z} = C + Dx$.

The first equation, (19.3), defines what is called the exponential regression function. It can be converted into the linear form by semilog transformation as shown by (19.4). Furthermore, if we let $\log A = C$ and $\log B = D$, then (19.5) results. Finally, let $\log \hat{y} = \hat{z}$ and we have transformed (19.3) into (19.6), which is a simple linear regression equation of Y on X. The regression coefficients C and D can be found in the usual way by working with the logarithms of Y and the original values of X.

(19.7) $\hat{y} = Ax^B$;

(19.8) $\log \hat{y} = \log A + B(\log x)$;

(19.9) $\hat{z} = C + Bw$.

A power sample regression equation such as (19.7) can be converted into a linear relationship by the double-log transformation as shown by (19.8). Moreover, if we let $\log \hat{y} = \hat{z}$, $\log A = C$, and $\log x = w$, then the linear regression equation in logarithms (19.8) can be reduced to the form as repressed by (19.9), which is a linear regression function in the usual form. The coefficients C and B can then be found in the usual manner by working with logarithms of Y and logarithms of X.

(19.10) $\hat{y} = A + (B/x)$, $\quad A, B, x > 0$;

(19.11) $\hat{y} = A - (B/x)$, $\quad A, B > 0$, and $x \geq B/A$;

(19.12) $\hat{y} = A + Bz$;

(19.13) $\hat{y} = A - Bz$.

When sample data can be adequately described by (19.10) or by (19.11), then these nonlinear relationships can be converted into linear regression models by the reciprocal transformation. This procedure is simply to define $Z = 1/X$ in order to obtain the linear regression equations of (19.12) and (19.13).

(19.14) $\hat{y} = Ax_2^B x_3^C$;

(19.15) $\log y = \log A + B(\log x_2) + C(\log x_3)$;

(19.16) $z_i = D + Bw_2 + Cw_3$.

Given a sample power regression equation of the form (19.14), a multiple linear regression equation of Y on X_2 and X_3 can be obtained via double-log transformation of all the variables as shown by (19.15). The last equation (19.16) is an alternative form of expression for (19.15) and you should be able to understand the transformation.

(19.17) $e_i = re_{i-1} + v_i$;

(19.18) $r = \sum_{i=2}^{n} e_i e_{i-1} \Big/ \sum_{i=2}^{n} e_{i-1}^2.$

Equation (19.17) here defines the first-order serial correlation of the error term—the residual disturbances. In this expression r is the estimator of the population coefficient of serial correlation, ρ, and is defined by (19.18). Note that r defined here is the first-order serial correlation of the error term, not the coefficient of correlation between the variables that measures the strength of association between the two variables.

(19.19) $d = \sum_{i=2}^{n} (e_i - e_{i-1})^2 \Big/ \sum_{i=2}^{n} e_i^2.$

This is the Durbin–Watson test statistic for testing the presence or absence of serial correlation. It is related to r as defined by (19.18) and it has been shown that $d \doteq 2(1 - r)$. Since r ranges in value from -1 through zero to $+1$, the value of d varies from 0 to 4. The critical values of d, denoted as d_L and d_U, for various sample sizes and the number of independent variables have been tabulated as given by Table X in Appendix C.

(19.20) $\hat{y}_i' = B_1' + B_2' x_i'$;

(19.21) $\hat{y}_i = \dfrac{B_i'}{(1 - r)} + B_2' x_i$;

(19.22) $\hat{y}_i = \dfrac{B_1'}{(1 - r)} + B_2' x_2 + B_3' x_3.$

Equation (19.20) is the result of correcting serial correlation by regressing serially corrected terms. This is done by defining X' and Y'—the individual values of the variables obtained by the transformations $y_i' = y_i - r y_{i-1}$ and $x_i' = x_i - r x_{i-1}$. Note that by these transformations, $B_1'/(1 - r)$ and B_2' become estimators of β_1 and β_2 in $\mu_{Y.X} = \beta_1 + \beta_2 x_i$. Hence, the original sample regression can finally be written as (19.21). The method of regressing with serially corrected error terms can also be applied to multiple regression for the correction of serial correlation. For the trivariate case, for example, the end result would be as shown by (19.22).

(19.23) $\hat{y} = B_1 + B_2 x_2 + B_3 x_3$;

(19.24) $\hat{y} = B_1 + B_2 x_2 + B_3 x_3 + B_4 t.$

Another method of removing serial correlation in regression with time series data is to conduct the regression study with detrended data for the variables. The same objective, however, can be achieved by regressing with the original data but considering time T as an additional independent variable. Thus, given a regression equation such as (19.23), for which significant serial correlation is found to exist and to be caused by trends, then the serial correlation can be removed by introducing time T as an additional independent variable and with the regression equation of the form (19.24) as a result. To determine the value B_4, we may determine e_i for (19.23) and plot them against time, and determine a time trend for e_i. We incorporate this time trend into (19.23) to produce (19.24).

(19.25) $\log \hat{y} = B_1 + B_2(\log x_2) + B_3(\log x_3) + B_4 t.$

In the application of the regression of form (19.24) for the corrected serial correlation, the original regression equation need not be linear in variables, except for T, as shown by this expression.

(19.26) $y^* = \beta_1 + \beta_2 x_2 + \cdots + \beta_J x_J + u.$

When heteroscedasticity is found to exist in a regression model and when it is found to be produced by the fact that the explained variable obeys the Poisson law, then the error variance can be stabilized by regressing Y^* to the independent variables. Here, $Y^* = \sqrt{Y}$.

(19.27) $y = \beta_1 + \beta_2 x + u,$ where $\sigma_U = dx;$

(19.28) $y' = \beta_1 + \beta_2 x' + u';$

(19.29) $\hat{y}' = B_1' + B_2' x';$

(19.30) $\hat{y} = B_1 + B_2 x.$

Heteroscedasticity is often produced by the fact that, for whatever reason, the error variance is proportional to X^2 or the standard deviation of the regression is proportional to X, as indicated by a regression model given by (19.27), where $d = \sigma_U/x$ is the stabilized (constant) standard deviation of the error term. Hence, let $y' = y/x$ and $x' = 1/x$, (19.27) may then be written as (19.28). Furthermore, with transformed variables Y' ($=Y/X$) and X' ($=1/X$), the fitted sample regression equation is now as written as (19.29). To use (19.29) as a predictive device, we multiply both sides of (19.29) by x in order to convert this equation back to the original form; (19.30) results. Be sure to note that in (19.30), $B_1 = B_2'$ and $B_2 = B_1'$.

REVIEW QUESTIONS

19.1 Given a set of bivariate or multivariate sample data, what is the simple and effective method by which we can determine an appropriate regression model for its analysis?

19.2 Throughout this chapter we have repeatedly spoken of "data transformation". What does this notion mean? What functions can such transformations perform?

19.3 If a set of sample data, in your judgment, can be analyzed by at least two different regression models, which model would you select for the final analysis? Explain your answer.

19.4 If the "true" relationship between Y and X can be adequately described by a cubic regression model of the form

$$y = a + bx + bx^2 + bx^3 + e,$$

it can be transformed into a straightforward multivariate regression as

$$y = a + bx + cv + dw + e$$

by letting $X^2 = V$ and $X^3 = W$. Here, X, X^2 and X^3, all explanatory variables are clearly related by definition. Would this fact produce damaging multicollinearity? Explain or why not?

19.5 What is the difference between exponential and power regression models? What are the respective mathematical properties of these two models.

19.6 Can you explain the fact that the specific curvature of the function defined either by (19.10) or by (19.11) would be determined by the regression slope B. Pay special attention to exactly how the value of B affects the curvature of the regression line.

19.7 The multiplicative power regression model as defined by (19.14) is often applied to describing a production function called the Cobb–Douglas production function. With two independent variables, say, labor denoted L, and capital denoted K, the Cobb–Douglas function is usually written as

$$Q = B_0 L^{B_1} K^{B_2},$$

where Q is quantity produced. This equation can be linearized either by common log or natural log transformation. In terms of natural log transformation, we have

$$\ln Q = \ln B_0 + B_1 (\ln L) + B_2 (\ln K).$$

Now suppose that from a set of sample data we have obtained the least-squares regression equation

$$\ln Q = 3.83 + 0.32 \ln L + 0.78 K.$$

Taking the antilog of this estimated intercept 3.83, we obtain

$$Q = 46.1 L^{0.32} K^{0.78}.$$

How should the estimated regression coefficients be interpreted in this case?

19.8 Think of a few types of business or economic data that may be fitted by the following.
a. A second-degree parabola regression line
b. An exponential regression curve

c. A power regression curve

d. A reciprocal regression line

e. A multiplicative power regression curve

19.9 Sometimes it is more convenient to work with natural logarithms than with common logarithms for the purposes of computation and interpretation. From Question 19.7, you can see that the transformations of variables or constants from their original values to logarithms are the same as those with common logarithms. Rewrite equations (19.4), (19.8), and (19.15) in terms of natural logarithms.

19.10 An exponential regression model, often called the *simple growth model,* that is fitted to a time series and is written as

$$\hat{y} = Ae^{Bx},$$

where y is an individual value of the response or dependent variable Y, x is that of the explanatory variable, which is often time, and e is the base of natural logarithms. With logarithmic transformation, the foregoing equation becomes a linear one and thus

$$\ln \hat{y} = \ln A + Bx.$$

After this regression is obtained in the usual way, it is preferable to leave it in its log form instead of converting it back to the exponential form. This is because logarithms have a simple and direct interpretation: "Change in $\ln Y \doteq$ relative change in Y itself".

The population growth Y in the United States, from 1850 to 1900, with X in units of decades, was estimated to be

$$\ln \hat{y} = \ln a + bx = 3.236 + 0.0223x.$$

Taking exponentials, we have

$$\hat{y} = e^{3.236}e^{0.0223x},$$

or

$$\hat{y} = 25.43e^{0.0223}.$$

From these results, what is the relative change in the American population from 1870 to 1880?

19.11 The supply function in economics can often be described by the model

$$\hat{q} = Ap^{B},$$

where Q is the quantity sold, P is the price, and A and B are regression constants. For computational ease, we convert the above equation into the following linear form:

$$\ln \hat{q} = \ln A + B(\ln p).$$

For this model, in general, we have the value of B as the *elasticity of supply,* which measures the relative change in quantity supply (sold) per 1% change in price. That is, if $\ln \hat{q} = \ln A + B(\ln p)$, then B = elasticity of supply. Now, suppose the supply function of a certain commodity is estimated to be

$$\ln \hat{q} = 10 + 1.8(\ln p),$$

what is the relative change in Q if there is a 1% increase in price?

19.12 The production manager of a manufacturing firm was constantly having trouble predicting his total production cost with any reasonable precision. He has hired a professional statistician to assist him in this task. With some research on the problem, the statistician has been able to build a model of multiple linear regression by regressing total cost C on material costs M per unit, hourly labor cost W per unit and the level of production Q. With a random sample of 25 production runs, she has obtained the following results:

$$\hat{c} = 35.45 + 15.32m + 0.69w - 12.44q$$
$$(3.785) \quad (3.600) \quad (0.385)$$

where the numbers in parentheses are computed t values for the partial regression coefficients. When presented with these results, the production manager thought the whole thing was a joke. "How could the total cost of production be negatively related to the level of production?" He feels a little better for the fact that the t value for the coefficient of production level is at least very small. Despite his misgivings about the model, he authorized its use for a short duration. However, when he read the report that contained the forecasting results for the five production points beyond the data period, the average error of prediction was only about 2%. His mind boggled. "By God," he said, "I have never come anywhere as close as this with any method I have used before. However, how can I justify a predictive device that implies that when production increases total cost of the production actually declines?" Can you help the manager about the justification of including Q in the model and the seemingly illogical behavior of its influence on C?

19.13 What are possible sources for and effects of autocorrelation on regression analyses?

19.14 How is the linear first-order serial correlation defined? How does positive or negative serial correlation result?

19.15 Describe briefly the methods introduced in this chapter for the removal of autocorrelation.

19.16 Suppose you have run a multivariate regression, resulting in a high R^2, and large t values for all the regression coefficients, but substantial serial correlation, and suppose you want to use the regression equation only for the purpose of forecasting, should you be concerned with autoregression? Explain why or why not.

19.17 What is the nature of heteroscedasticity? What are the possible reasons for its presence? How does it affect regression results?

19.18 What are the simple but efficient ways of detecting the existence of heteroscedasticity? Describe briefly the methods introduced for its removal.

19.19 What do we mean by multicollinearity? Under what condition would multicollinearity be truly damaging on regression studies? How can it be removed?

19.20 What do we mean by dummy variables? What are the important functions that can be performed by the introduction of dummy variables into regression analysis? Cite a few economic or business regression situations in which dummy variables can be fruitfully be introduced.

PROBLEMS

Instructions: All the problems here can be solved manually without much effort with the aid of a pocket calculator. However, if you wish, you may produce computer solutions for all the problems presented below. There are a number of canned computer programs for association analyses, simple or multiple, linear or nonlinear. These programs may differ from each other slightly in printouts, but all of them provide regression coefficients, variance of the error term, standard errors of regression coefficients, testing results in the values of t or F, and r^2 or R^2 values. Most programs also provide computed values of Y, $\hat{y}$, residual errors, and D–W test results. In any event, you should be able to answer nearly all the questions from the information contained in the computer printouts either straightforwardly or by a bit of effort and imagination of your own to fill in the possible missing points required to answer the problems completely.

For problems from 19.1 to 19.6 inclusive, do the following.

a. Draw a scatter diagram of the original data on arithmetic scales and from it judge which regression model is appropriate for their analyses.

b. Use the regression computer program available to you to conduct the desired regression study.

c. Write out the regression equation explicitly in the linear form and then convert it back to the original form. (You may round the regression coefficients to two or three decimal points.) Interpret the regression slope with reference to the units of the variables.

d. State whether the null hypothesis that the regression slope is zero can be rejected. If so, state at what level of significance.

e. Construct a 95% confidence interval for the mean of the explained variable with the value of the explanatory variable fixed at its mean plus 10% of this quantity.

f. If the same set of data has been fitted by two or more different regression equations (models), explain why or why not you might prefer one over the other(s).

g. Draw a scatter diagram of the transformed data and fit the linear regression equation obtained to it. By visual inspection alone, say whether you think the fit is proper and good.

19.1 A sample of eight observations of the total cost Y of production in hundreds of dollars and the number units an output produced in a manufacturing firm is drawn and the results are as presented below in Table 19.P1.

TABLE 19.P1

Observation	Total Cost	Total Output
1	$75	30
2	85	62
3	130	120
4	170	165
5	230	240
6	275	290
7	320	385
8	345	410

19.2 If you have fitted an exponential curve to data in Table 19.P1, go through the same sequence of analysis by fitting a reciprocal regression line to the same set of data. Fit an exponential regression line if you have already conducted a reciprocal regression analysis.

19.3 A small handicraft manufacturing company employs a very small labor force that ranges from two workers to ten workers from time to time throughout the year. Ms. Smart, the owner of the firm, wished to gain a clear idea about the total production function with respect to her working force. She did so by selecting two total weekly production levels Y at random from each of the 9 levels X of her working force in the previous year. The results are listed in Table 19.P2.

TABLE 19.P2

x:	2	2	3	3	4	4	5	5	6	6	7	7
y:	10	15	15	22	20	27	23	31	31	36	33	36

x:	8	8	9	9	10	10
y:	29	35	28	33	26	29

19.4 According to economic theory, the total net investment function for a nation as a whole is assumed to be of the form: $\hat{i} = Ar^B$, where i and r stand for individual quantities of investment and rate of interest, respectively. During the past ten years, the net total investment in billions of dollars and rates of interest in percentages of a developing nation are as shown in Table 19.P3.

i:	20	13	19	10	9	5	8	5	5	6
r:	9	12	9	15	18	24	21	21	27	24

19.5 According to the liquidity-preference theory of interest, the demand for money to hold as cash balances, for a given level of national income, is a decreasing function of the rate of interest. If we let M stand for money demanded and R for interest rate, then a regression model of the form: $\hat{m} = A + (B/r)$ would give a rather close approximation to the relationship dictated by the theory. A random sample of sixteen cities with population over one million throughout the world has been selected for observation. We have obtained data as shown by Table

19.P4, where m stands for individual amounts of average monthly money demanded in hundred of millions dollars and r stands for the average monthly rate of interest in percentages in the ten cities.

TABLE 19.P4

m:	14	23	13	12	11	17	18	14	13	11	13	10	12	13	10	11
r:	6	3	21	15	9	6	3	9	6	15	18	21	18	12	18	12

19.6 In Table 19.P5, we have a sample of the production level Q, labor inputs M, (in hundreds of man hours), and quantity of capital inputs K, (in tens of thousands of dollars), for the purpose of estimating the production function of the firm.

TABLE 19.P5

q:	120	180	190	235	285	290
m:	1	2	3	4	5	6
k	2.5	3.0	1.0	1.5	4.0	2.0

(*Note:* To answer part (g) for this problem, you might draw two scatter diagrams: one for Q against M and another for Q against K.)

19.7 The Republic of Utopia was almost exclusively an agricultural nation before 1980. In 1980, however, rich mineral deposits of great variety were discovered in that nation and an allout industrialization program was launched in the year that followed. The annual value of industrial outputs of all kinds during the period 1981–1990 in Utopia given in constant U.S. dollars in billions are as shown in Table 19.P6.

TABLE 19.P6

Year	Value	Year	Value
1981	2.0	1986	6.5
1982	2.4	1987	7.1
1983	3.1	1988	9.8
1984	3.8	1989	12.0
1985	5.0	1990	15.4

a. Draw a scatter diagram for the above data on arithmetic scales.
b. Draw a scatter diagram for the above data on semilog scales.
c. Fit a growth regression curve to the data of the form:

$$\hat{y} = Ae^{Bx},$$

or

$$\ln \hat{y} = \ln A + Bx.$$

d. What is the annual rate of growth of Utopia's industrial production during the decade?
(Hint: See review question 19.10.)

19.8 In Table 19.P7, Y stands for total output in thousands of units and X for labor inputs in hundreds of man-weeks, of a manufacturing firm during its first fifteen years in business. For data in this table, do the following.
   a. Write out the regression equation and calculate the regression residuals if your computer printout does not contain them.
   b. Describe the Durbin–Watson d-statistic? If it does not show on your computer printout, compute it yourself. In any event, with the d-statistic, can you rejected the null hypothesis that there is no serial correlation at $\alpha = 0.05$ for the two-sided alternative? For an appropriate single-tail alternative?
   c. If H_0 in (2) cannot be rejected, remove the serial correlation by regressing Y on X with transformed data and obtain the regression equation of the form: Equation (19.21).
   d. Remove the serial correlation by fitting a regression of the form $\hat{y} = B_1 + B_2 x + B_3 t$.
   e. Construct scatter diagrams for regression residuals from results obtained in this and the previous parts and determine whether one method seems to be better than the other for the task of removing serial correlation.

TABLE 19.P7

Year	y	x	Year	y	x	Year	y	x
1	18	4	6	5	3	11	47	14
2	14	3	7	27	7	12	66	16
3	26	8	8	29	10	13	63	15
4	24	6	9	33	12	14	49	13
5	18	5	10	43	14	15	78	18

19.9 Do the same as for the preceding problem using the data in Table 19.P8, where Y represents assembly-line workers' productivity scores and X represents bonus pay as percentages of the annual wages of the employees in a Japanese auto manufacturing firm during the past fifteen years.

TABLE 19.P8

Year	y	x	Year	y	x	Year	y	x
1	41	10	6	58	13	11	48	13
2	43	10	7	56	13	12	54	14
3	48	11	8	46	13	13	55	15
4	54	12	9	50	13	14	68	16
5	58	12	10	50	14	15	69	16

19.10 The Alpha construction company in Dallas wishes to predict the cost Y for the preparation of bids for contracts X in thousands of dollars, on the basis of the size of the bid in millions of dollars. For this objective a sample $n = 16$ bids have been selected from its files on bids during the past two years, yielding results as recorded in Table 19.P9.

TABLE 19.P9

x	y	x	y	x	y	x	y
3.2	17	1.8	12	16.5	65	16.0	50
7.2	39	8.4	27	10.4	31	10.0	30
4.4	17	5.0	35	15.6	46	18.0	65
1.7	11	6.9	22	12.0	51	20.0	73

a. What is the simple linear regression equation of Y on X from data in the table?

b. Make a residual analysis; that is, construct a scatter diagram against $E(e) = 0$ with respect to $\hat{y}$. Does this analysis lead to the conclusion that this set of data is heteroscedastic and that the standard deviation of the regression, or s_U, is approximately proportional to X?

c. Since in this case, the population model is such that $\sigma_U = dx$, the standard deviation can be stabilized by employing the population model defined by (19.28), for which the sample regression equation is given by (19.29). For (19.29), you may recall that we are dealing with transformed data of the forms $Y' = (Y/X)$ and $X' = (1/X)$. Obtain the sample regression equation from the transformed data and be sure to write the final results by recalling the $b_1 = b_2'$ and $b_2 = b_1'$.

d. Make a residual study of the newly obtained results. In your judgement, has s_U been stabilized? In any event, what is the stabilized s_U value?

19.11 The number of defects per 100 square yards of woolen piece goods follows approximately the Poisson probability law, and it is thought to be influenced by two major factors—the speed of the machine and the number of inexperienced operators. Let us denote the first factor as X_2, measured in rpm, and the second factor as X_3. To assist the anticipation of the quality of outputs, the quality control experts would like to find a regression model by an experiment designed as follows. (1) Run the machine at ten different speeds from 10.5 to 15.0 rpm with multiples of 0.5 rpm. (2) Run the machine for two hours at each speed; one to ten inexperienced operators are assigned to each two-hour period. (3) two 100-square-yard samples of finished woolen piece goods are to be inspected for the number of defects. Data from this experiment are recorded as shown in Table 19.P10.

TABLE 19.P10

x_2	x_3	y	x_2	x_3	y
10.5	1	2	13.0	6	7
10.5	2	3	13.0	7	13
11.0	2	3	13.5	6	16
11.0	1	2	13.5	5	11
11.5	3	4	14.0	8	19
11.5	3	5	14.0	7	13
12.0	4	4	14.5	8	18
12.0	5	6	14.5	9	23
12.5	6	11	15.0	10	19
12.5	5	8	15.0	10	26

a. Establish the regression equation of Y on X_2 and X_3 from data in the table.

b. Verify the existence of heteroscedasticity by residual analysis.

c. Establish the regression equation of Y^* on X_2 and X_3 using of the model as defined by (19.26).

d. Does the residual study with the regression calculated from the transformed data of $Y^* = \sqrt{Y}$ now approximately satisfy the least-squares assumption of homoscedasticity?

19.12 A professor of statistics believes that students' achievements Y in statistics are functionally related to their achievements X_2 in Freshman mathematics and X_3 in English composition. To verify this he selects at random ten students in their senior year and observes their grades in these courses. The results are presented in Table 19.P11.

TABLE 19.P11

x_2	x_3	y	x_2	x_3	y
98	92	80	60	75	60
70	75	61	95	89	85
73	80	66	78	84	70
85	88	78	82	80	72
86	84	75	90	90	79

a. Conduct a complete multiple linear regression analysis with data in Table 19.P11.
b. Does multicollinearity exist in this set of data? How do you come to your conclusion? Explain as fully as possible.
c. If you judge that a simple linear regression equation of either Y on X_2 or Y on X_3 is just as efficient as a multiple regression for the objective of prediction, which variable would you retain as explanatory variable? Give your reason(s).

19.13 Table 19.P12 contains consumption expenditures C, and disposable income Y, for the United States from 1935 to 1949.
   a. Draw a scatter diagram of C on Y. Explain why it is necessary to introduce a dummy variable W—for wartime conditions, in this case. If W is introduced as a dummy variable, should the values of the war years be 0 or 1? Explain.
   b. Write out the consumption function of C on Y and W.
   c. Draw the consumption function for wartime and peacetime, respectively; that is, fit regression lines to the points in the scatter diagram.

TABLE 19.P12 Consumption Expenditure and Personal Disposable Income for the United States, 1935–1949 (in billions of dollars)

Year	c_i	y_i	Year	c_i	y_i
1935	55.7	58.5	1943	99.3	135.3
1936	61.9	66.3	1944	108.3	146.3
1937	66.5	71.2	1945	119.7	150.2
1938	63.9	65.5	1946	143.4	160.6
1939	66.8	70.3	1947	160.7	169.8
1940	70.8	75.7	1948	173.6	189.1
1941	80.6	92.7	1949	176.8	188.6
1942	88.5	116.9			

Source: The President's Economic Report, February 1972.

19.14 A company that sells three lines of output, X_2, X_3, and X_3, hires its salesmen on the scores of their placement tests, X_5 and X_6. X_2, X_3, and X_4 are considered as dummy variables and

$X_2 = 1$ if the salesman is assigned to product line 1, equals zero otherwise;

$X_3 = 1$ if the salesman is assigned to product line 2, equals zero otherwise;

$X_4 = 1$ if the salesman is assigned to product
line 3, equals zero otherwise;

X_5 = score on test A;

X_6 = score on test B;

Y = average weekly sales in hundreds of dollars.

After a year, a random sample of $n = 15$ salesmen was selected for observation and the results are given in Table 19.P13.

TABLE 19.P13

Salesman	x_2	x_3	x_4	x_5	x_6	y
1	0	0	1	65	85	100
2	0	0	1	55	75	85
3	0	0	1	15	35	60
4	1	0	0	55	45	70
5	0	1	0	25	25	59
6	0	0	1	25	65	80
7	1	0	0	35	35	52
8	0	1	0	25	35	65
9	0	0	1	75	65	90
10	0	1	0	55	45	80
11	0	0	1	35	55	75
12	1	0	0	25	45	55
13	1	0	0	55	55	77
14	0	0	1	40	80	83
15	0	1	0	45	35	75

Conduct a comprehensive multiple regression analysis with the data in this table and write out explicitly all the measures with information provided by the computer printout.

19.15 *A suggested research project.* By this time you have learned most of the basic aspects of regression analysis, a method that is considered as the best friend of the economic or business forecasters, since it is the most powerful and most frequently used device for the purpose of forecasting. Now it is suggested that you write a research paper on the topic: "How to Forecast Gross National Product." You may do this by following roughly the outline below.
   a. State the fact that you attempt to build a regression model for the objective of forecasting GNP of the United States.
   b. Select eight to ten explanatory variables that in your judgment, are relevant to the determination of the size of GNP of the United States. If you are not very familiar with macroeconomics, you should consult a few standard text books on this topic to assist you in selecting the explanatory variables. Here, you should explain as well as you possibly can why and how each of the regressors is related to the explained variable in question.
   c. Obtain data for GNP and all the selected independent variables for the most recent 40 years. These data can be found from a number of sources given in the appendix to Chapter 2 of this text.
   d. Establish the multiple linear (predictive) equation with data you have obtained, by using a computer program.

e. Write out a full elaboration of your research up to this point from information provided by the computer printout. From this, you should utilize all you have learned from this and the previous two chapters on regression analysis.

f. Make an overall generalization about the possible effectiveness of the predictive equation you have constructed. In connection with this, you should conclude whether you are satisfied with the predictive equation or think some of the variables can be or should be eliminated for the ultimate objective of your paper. Your observations and statements here should follow logically from your discussion in (e).

g. If you have concluded that some of the explanatory variables can and should be eliminated in the final analysis, you should do it by following the procedure of stepwise regression analysis presented in the preceding chapter.

h. End your paper by a comparison between the original and the revised predictive equations on the following points:
   1. Satisfaction of the assumptions of least squares method.
   2. Accuracy in prediction.
   3. Convenience in application.

20 Index Numbers

20.1 THE NATURE AND TYPES OF INDEX NUMBERS

One of the most important problems in studying economics and business is how to measure the quantity of some heterogeneous aggregate. The aggregate may be one of physical quantity, such as stocks in the balance sheet or flows in the income statement. The aggregate may also be a list of prices, such as prices paid for the purchase of various types of input by a firm or prices received by a department store from its sales. In each case, the problem of measurement is to derive a single figure that is descriptive of the volume of, or change in, a given aggregate through time or from place to place. The statistical devices for such measurement are called index numbers. *Index numbers,* in effect, relate a variable or variables in a given period to the same variable or variables in another period, called the *base period.* An index, the simplified name for index numbers, that is computed from a single variable, is called a *univariate index,* whereas an index that is constructed from a group of variables is considered a *composite index.* A univariate index can be easily constructed and its meaning is readily apparent, but serious problems arise when we try to combine many variables in some meaningful way to present a composite index.

Even though the main concern of this chapter is to present the techniques and problems of constructing composite indices, we shall first give an illustration of a univariate index in order to bring out the

TABLE 20.1 Illustration of a Simple Production Index

Year	Production (thousand pounds)	Index A (1986 = 100)	Index B (1980–1981 = 100)
1980	8.5	63	81
1981	12.5	93	119
1982	9.4	70	90
1983	10.7	79	102
1984	13.6	101	130
1985	15.3	113	146
1986	13.5	100	129
1987	12.8	95	122
1988	14.7	109	140
1989	16.7	124	159
1990	18.0	133	171

basic nature and function of index numbers. Let us consider the hypothetical production data in Table 20.1. Index A is computed by selecting 1986 as the base period. The index numbers are then found by dividing each year's production by the production in 1986 and multiplying by 100. Thus, the index numbers are in the form of percentages. The index number for each year is interpreted in terms of the base period. For instance, the index number for 1990 means that production in 1990 is 133% of production in 1986. Index B is computed by using the average production of 1980 and 1981 (that is, 10.5 thousand pounds) as the base. This base is divided into each year's production and the result multiplied by 100 to form index B. Clearly, the main function of a univariate index number is to transform the absolute quantities of a variable into relative numbers so that comparisons of the changes in the variable through time can be readily made.

Composite indices are of many types and may be constructed in many ways. We shall be unable to cover the whole variety of indices in a single chapter. instead, we shall confine our discussion to some of the more frequently used indices in economics and business. These indices, in the order of their discussion here, are classified as follows:

1. Simple aggregative indices
   a. Simple aggregative price index
   b. Simple aggregative quantity index

2. Simple average-of-relatives indices
   a. Simple average-of-relatives price index
   b. Simple average-of-relatives quantity index

3. Weighted aggregative indices
   a. Weighted aggregative price index
   b. Weighted aggregative quantity index

4. Weighted average-of-relatives indices
   a. Weighted average-of-relatives price index
   b. Weighted average-of-relatives quantity index

5. Special indices
   a. Value index
   b. Productivity index

To avoid repetition we shall define here the basic symbols to be used in our discussion of indices:

p = price of a single commodity,

q = quantity of a single commodity,

p_0 = base-period price of a commodity,

q_0 = base-period quantity of a commodity,

p_n = given-period price of a commodity, where n refers to periods $\ldots, -3, -2, -1, 0, 1, 2, 3, \ldots,$

q_n = given-period quantity of a commodity,

i = a particular commodity, as in p_{0i} for the ith commodity in the base period,

k = the number of commodities included in the index number,

P = a price index,

Q = a quantity index,

P_b = a price index derived by using base-period quantities as weights,

P_n = a price index derived by using given-period quantities as weights,

Q_b = a quantity index derived by using base-period prices as weights,

Q_n = a quantity index derived by using given-period prices as weights,

V = a value index,

E = a productivity index.

To simplify our numerical illustrations, we shall use the hypothetical data of Table 20.2. We suppose that a manufacturing firm,

TABLE 20.2 Illustrative Price and Production Data, 1985–1987

Item	Unit	Price per unit			Quantity		
		1985	1986	1987	1985	1986	1987
A	ounce	$1.00	$1.25	$1.50	10,000	12,500	13,000
B	ton	10.00	11.75	13.50	1,000	1,100	1,250
C	pound	4.00	5.00	4.50	500	500	400

established in 1985, produces three types of products, A, B, and C. Price is defined as the annual average selling price, and production refers to annual total production in thousands. The firm wishes to measure the changes in its selling prices and in the physical volume of production in the aggregate from year to year.

20.2 SIMPLE AGGREGATIVE INDICES

The computation of a price index by the simple aggregative method is a very simple matter. We first add the various prices for each time unit to obtain $\sum p_n$ for each value of n. Next, the total of each given period is divided by the base-period total. Finally, the end result is presented in percentage form by multiplying the ratio obtained by 100. These computations are done in Table 20.3.

The general formula is

$$P = \frac{\sum p_n}{\sum p_0}(100).\qquad(20.1)$$

From Equation (20.1) we see that the simple aggregative price index attempts, in our example, to ascertain the total sales receipts in each year under the assumption of selling one unit of each commodity and to express this total as a percentage of the base-year revenue. As such, the simple aggregative index assigns equal importance to the absolute change of each price. This is where the main defect of this method rests, since it permits a commodity with a high price to dominate the index. As our illustrative data stand now, the price of B exerts much more influence than the price of C, which, in turn, dominates the price of A in the index numbers. These influences would be reversed if all the prices were quoted in the same units, say ounces. Thus, the unit by which each price happens to be quoted creeps into the simple aggregate of prices as a concealed weight that is often of no economic significance. This limits the practical usefulness of the simple aggregative price index.

TABLE 20.3 Computation of a Simple Aggregative Price Index (1985 = 100)

Item	1985 p_0	1986 p_1	1987 p_2
A	$ 1.00	$ 1.25	$ 1.50
B	10.00	11.75	13.50
C	4.00	5.00	4.50
Total	$15.00	$18.00	$19.50
Index number	1.00	1.20	1.30
or	100	120	130

The formula for the simple aggregative quantity index is

$$Q = \frac{\Sigma \, q_n}{\Sigma \, q_0}(100).$$ (20.2)

This formula, clearly, cannot be used for an aggregate in which the items are expressed in different units, since it would be meaningless when we add tons, pounds, and ounces together. If we used this formula to form an index for a group of, say, consumers' goods quoted in the same units, we would be comparing the quantities in a given year with the quantities in the base year for purchasing the goods actually bought in each year as if the price of each item each year were $1 per unit. This is a highly unrealistic assumption. Consequently, this formula is seldom employed to measure changes in quantity.

20.3 SIMPLE AVERAGE-OF-RELATIVES INDICES

As the name of the simple average-of-relatives index implies, it consists of averaging the price or quantity relatives. To compute a simple average-of-relatives price index, as illustrated by Table 20.4, we follow these steps. (1) We obtain the price relative by dividing the price of the ith item in a given period, p_{ni}, by its base-period price, p_{0i}. (2) We obtain the sums of the relatives of the years and divide each by the number k of items in the aggregate. The simple average of relatives is, in effect, an arithmetic mean of relatives. This method is summarized by the formula below:

$$P = \frac{\sum\limits_{i=1}^{k} \left(\frac{p_{ni}}{p_{0i}}\right) 100}{k}.$$ (20.3)

For example,

$$P_{1986} = \frac{3.675(100)}{3} = 122.5\%$$

TABLE 20.4 Computation of a Simple Average-of-relatives Price Index (1985 = 100)

Item i	1985 $\dfrac{p_{0i}}{p_{0i}}(100)$	1986 $\dfrac{p_{1i}}{p_{0i}}(100)$	1987 $\dfrac{p_{2i}}{p_{0i}}(100)$
A	$1.00(100)	$1.250(100)	$1.500(100)
B	1.00(100)	1.175(100)	1.350(100)
C	1.00(100)	1.250(100)	1.125(100)
Total	$300	$3,675	$3,975
Index number	100.0	122.5	132.5

TABLE 20.5 Computation of a Simple Average-of-Relatives Quantity Index

(1985 = 100)

Item i	1985 $\dfrac{q_{0i}}{q_{0i}}(100)$	1986 $\dfrac{q_{1i}}{q_{0i}}(100)$	1987 $\dfrac{q_{2i}}{q_{0i}}(100)$
A	1.00(100)	1.25(100)	1.30(100)
B	1.00(100)	1.10(100)	1.25(100)
C	1.00(100)	1.00(100)	0.80(100)
Total	300	335	335
Index number	100.0	111.7	111.7

The procedure for computing a simple average-of-relatives quantity index is the same as that for the corresponding price index. This is illustrated by Table 20.5. The analogous quantity index equation is

$$Q = \frac{\sum\limits_{i=1}^{k}\left(\dfrac{q_{ni}}{q_{0i}}\right)100}{k}. \qquad (20.4)$$

From the results obtained in Tables 20.4 and 20.5 by the method of simple averages of relatives, it may be said that the prices have increased, on the average, by 32.5% and that the quantities have increased, on the average, by 11.7% over the three-year period. What can be said about the simple average-of-relatives indices as compared with the simple aggregative indices?

First, it may be noted that the simple average of price relatives has avoided one difficulty encountered in the simple aggregative price index. The former is no longer influenced by the units in which prices are quoted or by the absolute level of individual prices. Relatives are pure numbers and are therefore divorced from the original units. Consequently, index numbers computed by the relative method would be the same regardless of the way in which the prices are quoted. This simple average of price relatives is said to meet what is called the *units test*. Also, it may be noted that the simple average-of-relatives method can now be used to compute a quantity index for an aggregate of items that are not quoted in the same units.

Despite these merits, the simple average of relatives is still a very unsatisfactory method, since it presents a serious difficulty in the selection of an appropriate average. The use of the arithmetic average is considered questionable sometimes because it has an upward bias. We shall comment indirectly on this point in Section 20.11. Meanwhile, it suffices to say here that this aspect of the difficulty is not a very serious one. The serious aspect is that the relatives are assumed to have equal importance. This is again a kind of concealed weighting system that is highly objectionable, since economically some relatives are more important than others. It is interesting to note that, in our example, the quantity relative for C exerts an influence in the 1987 quantity index that is possibly out of line with its practical importance. This is so because from the quantities and units of A, B, and C, we can see that C is the item of middle importance in the group; yet we assign to the quantity relative the same weight as those for A and B. As a consequence, the rather large absolute increases in the quantities of A and B may have been unduly offset by the rather small absolute (but large relative) decrease of the quantity of C.

In concluding this section, we should note that the main objection to both the simple aggregative and the simple average-of-relative indices is to the concealed weights that usually conflict with economic reality. Thus, improvements of an index rest with the introduction of appropriate weighting systems for its construction.

20.4 WEIGHTED AGGREGATIVE INDICES

In a later section we shall give a rather detailed discussion on weighting to suit the purpose of a given index. Here, we merely note that the most frequently used weights for aggregative price indices are base-year or given-year quantities of commodities and that the usual weights for aggregative quantity indices are either base-year or given-year prices of commodities.

The weighted aggregative price index with base-year quantities as weights is called the *Laspeyres index,* given by the formula

$$P_b = \frac{\sum\limits_{i=1}^{k} p_{ni}q_{0i}}{\sum\limits_{i=1}^{k} p_{0i}q_{0i}} (100) \tag{20.5}$$

The application of this formula, as shown by Table 20.6, involves the

TABLE 20.6 Construction of an Aggregative Price Index, Using Base-year Quantity Weights

	Value of 1985 quantities at given-year prices		
	1985	1986	1987
Item (i)	$p_{0i}q_{0i}$	$p_{1i}q_{0i}$	$p_{2i}q_{0i}$
A	(1)10,000 = 10,000	(1.25)10,000 = 12,500	(1.50)10,000 = 15,000
B	(10)1,000 = 10,000	(11.75)1,000 = 11,750	(13.50)1,000 = 13,500
C	(4)500 = 2,000	(5.00)500 = 2,500	(4.50)500 = 2,250
Total	22,000	26,750	30,750
Index number	100.0	121.6	139.8

following three simple steps:

1. Multiply the price of each item in each year by the base-year quantity of that item to obtain $p_{0i}q_{0i}$ for the base year and $p_{ni}q_{0i}$ for each given year.

2. Obtain the sums of the products computed in step 1.

3. Divide the total of each given year by the total of the base year and multiply it by 100.

In Table 20.6, the value of 121.6 for the Laspeyres index of 1986 may be interpreted in this way: "The list of products sold in 1985 would yield 21.6% more at 1986 selling prices than it actually did yield in 1985." In other words, according to this index, selling prices on the average rose 21.6% from 1985 to 1986. If the Laspeyres formula is used to compute a consumer's price index, the result would measure the difference between the cost in a given year and the cost in the base year of maintaining the standard of living of the base year. In general, the Laspeyres index attempts to answer the question, "What is the change in aggregate value of the base period's list of goods when valued at base-period and given-period prices?"

The weighted aggregative price index with given-period quantities as weights is sometimes referred to as the *Paasche index*. It is defined by the formula

$$P_n = \frac{\sum\limits_{i=1}^{k} p_{ni}q_{ni}}{\sum\limits_{i=1}^{k} p_{0i}q_{ni}}(100) \qquad (20.6)$$

The computation of the Paasche index is illustrated by Table 20.7. The index value of 140.9 for 1987 should now be interpreted thus: "The list of products sold in 1987 yielded 40.9% more than the same list of products would have yielded at 1985 prices." The Paasche formula,

TABLE 20.7 Construction of an Aggregative Price Index, Using Given-year Quantity Weights

Item (i)	Value of Given-year Quantities at Given-Year Prices			Value of Given-year Quantities at 1985 prices		
	1985	1986	1987	1985	1986	1987
	$p_{0i}q_{0i}$	$p_{1i}q_{1i}$	$p_{2i}q_{2i}$	$p_{0i}q_{0i}$	$p_{0i}q_{1i}$	$p_{0i}q_{2i}$
A	10,000	15,625	19,500	10,000	12,500	13,000
B	10,000	12,925	16,875	10,000	11,000	12,500
C	2,000	2,500	1,800	2,000	2,000	1,600
Total	22,000	31,050	38,175	22,000	25,500	27,100
Index number				100.0	121.8	140.9

when used to calculate a consumer price index, compares the cost in the given period with the cost in the base period of keeping the standard of living in the given period. In general, this formula answers the question, "What is the change in aggregate value of the given-period list of goods when values at base-period and given-period prices?"

A weighted aggregative quantity index is the counterpart of the analogous aggregative price index. The weights to be used are prices. The Laspeyres and Paasche aggregative quantity indices are given by the following formulas:

$$Q_b = \frac{\sum\limits_{i=1}^{k} p_{0i} q_{ni}}{\sum\limits_{i=1}^{k} p_{0i} q_{0i}} (100); \qquad (20.7)$$

$$Q_n = \frac{\sum\limits_{i=1}^{k} p_{ni} q_{ni}}{\sum\limits_{i=1}^{k} p_{ni} q_{0i}} (100). \qquad (20.8)$$

Note that all the sums of the products for these two formulas have already been obtained in Tables 20.6 and 20.7. Thus, by referring to these tables, the aggregative quantity index for 1987, by using base-year prices as weights and abbreviated notation in the formula, is

$$Q_b = \frac{\sum p_0 q_2}{\sum p_0 q_0}(100) = \frac{27,100}{22,000}(100) = 123.2\%.$$

The quantity index, by using given-period prices as weights for 1987, is

$$Q_n = \frac{\sum p_2 q_2}{\sum p_2 q_0}(100) = \frac{38,175}{30,750}(100) = 124.1\%.$$

The first result means that, at 1985 prices, the volume of output increased 23.2% between 1985 and 1987. The second result means that, at 1987 prices, the volume of output rose 24.1% between 1985 and 1987. Thus, generally speaking, a weighted aggregative quantity index answers the question, "If we buy (or sell) varying quantities of the same items in each of the two periods, but at the same prices, how much would be spent (or received) in the given period relative to the base period?"

An interesting observation may now be made. The Paasche and Laspeyres formulas employed to compute either the price or the quantity index usually yield different results. This is, of course, due to the differences in the weights. The difference, however, is not fortuitous. It does not make any particular sense to ask which formula is accurate or better. Each of them is meaningful in the sense that it has a simple and precise physical interpretation. In a way, we can actually consider the difference as a meaningful range of values. If, for instance, the price index computed by one method is 110 and by another method is 130, we may then say the price level has changed from 100 to between 110 and 130. This statement gives us useful, though not completely precise, information. It should be observed that this range becomes narrower, and therefore more precise, if the differences between base-year weights and given-year weights are smaller. During a short interval of time, say from two to five years, weights do not usually change by large amounts; as a result, it does not make much difference in theory whether the Laspeyres or the Paasche index is used. (In practice, however, there is a great deal of difference between these two formulas. For example, the use of the Paasche formula to construct a consumer price index requires an annual survey to determine current weights.)

20.5 WEIGHTED AVERAGE-OF-RELATIVES INDICES

Weighted average-of-relatives indices can be computed much as simple averages of relatives are, except that proper weights are introduced. Weights here are dollar values of items in the aggregate. Thus, if base-year values are used as weights, the weights are $p_{0i}q_{0i}$. If given-year values are employed, the weights are $p_{ni}q_{ni}$. If theoretical values are used as weights, the weights are $p_{ni}q_{0i}$ or $p_{0i}q_{ni}$. Values rather than quantities or prices are used in order to produce weighted relatives that are all in the same units. In the construction of weighted average-of-price relatives, for instance, if quantities are employed as weights, the product of relatives times the quantities quoted in different units would yield weighted price relatives in original units, and these could not be added together.

Like any weighted average, the weighted average of relatives is computed by multiplying each relative by its weight and dividing the sum of the products by the sum of the weights.

The Laspeyres average-of-relatives indices are:

$$P_b = \frac{\sum\limits_{i=1}^{k} (p_{0i}q_{0i})\left(\frac{p_{ni}}{p_{0i}}\right)(100)}{\sum\limits_{i=1}^{k} p_{0i}q_{0i}}, \qquad (20.9)$$

$$Q_b = \frac{\sum\limits_{i=1}^{k} (p_{0i}q_{0i})\left(\frac{q_{ni}}{q_{0i}}\right)(100)}{\sum\limits_{i=1}^{k} p_{0i}q_{0i}} \qquad (20.10)$$

The Paasche average-of-relatives indices are:

$$P_n = \frac{\sum\limits_{i=1}^{k} (p_{0i}q_{ni})\left(\frac{p_{ni}}{p_{0i}}\right)(100)}{\sum\limits_{i=1}^{k} p_{0i}q_{ni}} \tag{20.11}$$

$$Q_n = \frac{\sum\limits_{i=1}^{k} (p_{ni}q_{0i})\left(\frac{q_{ni}}{q_{0i}}\right)(100)}{\sum\limits_{i=1}^{k} p_{ni}q_{0i}} \tag{20.12}$$

Owing to cancellation in the numerators of each of (20.9) through (20.12), they are identical to weighted aggregative indices. That is, (20.9) is the same as (20.5), (20.10) is the same as (20.7), (20.11), is the same as (20.6), and (20.12) is the same as (20.8).

Since the procedures for constructing the four indices are similar, only one example is furnished here. A price index is constructed in Table 20.8 by using formula (20.9).

Several distinct advantages of weighted average-of-relatives indices over weighted aggregative indices must be observed.

1. The price or quantity relatives for each single item in the aggregate are, in effect, themselves a simple index that often yields valuable information for analysis.

2. When a new commodity is introduced to replace one formerly used, the relative for the new item may be spliced to the relative for the old one, using the former value weights.

3. When an index is computed by selecting one item from each of many subgroups of items, the values of each subgroup may be used as weights. Then only the method of weighted average of relatives

TABLE 20.8 Computation of a Weighted Average-of-relatives Price Index with Base-year Values As Weights

Item	Weights 1985 $p_{0i}q_{0i}$	price relatives 1986 $\frac{p_{1i}}{p_{0i}}(100)$	price relatives 1987 $\frac{p_{2i}}{p_{0i}}(100)$	Weighted price relatives 1986 $p_{0i}q_{0i}\frac{p_{1i}}{p_{0i}}(100)$	Weighted price relatives 1987 $p_{0i}q_{0i}\frac{p_{2i}}{p_{0i}}(100)$
A	10,000	125.0	150.0	1,250,000	1,500,000
B	10,000	171.5	135.0	1,175,000	1,350,000
C	2,000	125.0	112.0	250,000	224,000
Total	22,000			2,675,000	3,074,000
Index number	100.0			121.6	139.8

is appropriate, and the cancellation previously noted in (20.9) through (20.12) does not occur.

4. When different index numbers are constructed by the average-of-relatives method, all of which have the same base year but which involve different commodities, they can be combined to form a new index.

5. When index numbers are to be constructed with data that are not analogous to prices and quantities—ratios of profits to net worth, to median income, to cost of production; or ratios of defective items to output, to name a few—they can be made comparable by being expressed as percentages of some base.

20.6 VALUE INDICES: CONSISTENCY BETWEEN PRICE AND QUANTITY INDICES

The value of a single commodity is the product of its price and its quantity—that is, $v = pq$. Analogously, the value of an aggregate of commodities is the sum of individual values of the commodities—that is $\Sigma v = \Sigma pq$. The change in the value of an aggregate of values is measured by a *value index,* also called a *total cost index,* which is defined as

$$V = \frac{\sum\limits_{i=1}^{k} p_{ni}q_{ni}}{\sum\limits_{i=1}^{k} p_{0i}q_{0i}} (100). \tag{20.13}$$

In this formula, both given-period prices and quantities are variables in the numerator. It is not necessary to introduce any special weights; they are inherent in the value figures.

The value index is not in wide use, but because of the unsatisfactory nature of price and quantity indices it has occasionally been suggested that they be replaced by the value index. This temptation must be resisted, since the concepts of price level and quantity level answer questions that cannot be answered by the value level. Furthermore, an aggregate of values may be viewed as the product of a price level and a quantity level. The division of an aggregate of values into its price and quantity factors may be somewhat arbitrary, but this arbitrariness need not create confusion as long as our concepts of the two factors are consistent. The test of consistency is that the product of the price and quantity indices must produce the value index. This depends on appropriate weighting for the two indices. Following an abbreviated version of the notation used previously, we have two actual dollar values: Σp_0q_0 and Σp_nq_n; and two theoretical values: Σp_nq_0 and Σp_0q_n. With these quantities, four possible indices can be constructed:

$$P_b = \frac{\Sigma p_nq_0}{\Sigma p_0q_0}; \quad P_n = \frac{\Sigma p_nq_n}{p_0q_n}; \quad Q_b = \frac{\Sigma p_0q_n}{\Sigma p_0q_0}; \quad Q_n = \frac{\Sigma p_nq_n}{\Sigma p_nq_0}.$$

It can be readily seen that P_b and Q_n are consistent indices, since

$$P_b Q_n = \left(\frac{\sum p_n q_0}{\sum p_0 q_o}\right)\left(\frac{\sum p_n q_n}{\sum p_n q_0}\right) = \frac{\sum p_n q_n}{\sum p_0 q_0} = V.$$

The value index measures the change in actual values between the base and the given periods. Similarly, P_n and Q_b are consistent measures. However, P_b and Q_b, or P_n and Q_n, are not consistent. Thus a rule can be derived from these demonstrations: If the price index is constructed with base-period quantity weights, the quantity index must be constructed with given-period price weights, and vice versa, in order to make the price and quantity levels consistent. Finally, it may be pointed out that a value, or a total cost, index, in effect measures the combined influence of both price and quantity indices by seeing how much the total cost increases (due to changes in both price and quantity).

20.7 PRODUCTIVITY INDICES

Productivity means efficiency in production. It is measured in terms of the ratio of output to inputs. If this ratio rises—that is, if more units of output are produced with the same units of inputs—productivity increases. The measurement of changes in output is a relatively simple matter. If only one product is involved, changes in output are merely the changes in the number of units produced. If an aggregate of products is under consideration, changes in outputs can be readily measured by a "production index." The measurement of changes in inputs, however, presents very complicated problems: inputs are of great variety— different kinds of labor, various types of raw materials, investments in machines and equipment, management skill, and so on. Possibly, an index of some sort could be constructed to measure the changes in aggregate factors of production, but appropriate weighting for such an index is extremely difficult, even physically impossible in some cases. In practice, therefore, a productivity index is usually constructed on the basis of a single input that is judged as the most important factor. The input selected is often labor, since on the average, the wage bill consists of about two-thirds of the total costs of production in many types of operations. In addition, labor data are more readily available, and labor units—usually man-hours—can be defined and interpreted more precisely than other kinds of input data.

Labor productivity may be defined as man-hours per unit of output or as units of output per man-hour. A productivity index can be constructed by using either notion. The construction of a productivity index, using man-hours per unit of output and base-year quantities as weights, is illustrated in Table 20.9. The formula used is

$$E_b = \frac{\sum\limits_{i=1}^{k} r_{ni} q_{0i}}{\sum\limits_{i=1}^{k} r_{0i} q_{0i}} (100) \qquad (20.14)$$

TABLE 20.9 Construction of a Productivity Index, Using Base-year Quantity Weights

Items (i)	Units Produced in Base Year q_{0i}	Man-hours per unit 1985 r_{0i}	Man-hours per unit 1990 r_{ni}	Man-hours Required to Produce Base-year Quantity 1985 $r_{0i}q_{0i}$	Man-hours Required to Produce Base-year Quantity 1990 $r_{ni}q_{0i}$
A	10,000	$\frac{1}{2}$	$\frac{2}{5}$	5,000	4,000
B	1,000	5	$\frac{9}{2}$	5,000	4,500
C	500	$\frac{3}{2}$	$\frac{3}{2}$	750	750
Total				10,750	9,250
Index number				100	86

where r_{0i} and r_{ni} refer to man-hours per unit of output in the base and given periods respectively.

This index, by assuming that output remains constant, measures changes in man-hours per unit of output. Thus, the result in our example means that man-hours per unit of output have decreased by 14% between the two periods.

It is interesting to note that the ratio of input to output is the reciprocal of the ratio of output to input:

$$\frac{\text{input}}{\text{output}} = \frac{1}{\text{output/input}}.$$

It follows, therefore, that the result of taking the reciprocal of the previously computed index—that is, $1/0.86 \doteq 1.16$, or 116%—is an index that measures the change in output per man-hour.

What should also be noted is that the index of labor per unit of output, or of output per unit of labor, must not be considered as merely a labor productivity index: labor efficiency also depends upon the quality of investment and management. In other words, changes in labor required to produce a given quantity of output are often the joint effects of all factors of production.

20.8 SPECIAL TOPICS

In this section we shall introduce three special topics of considerable interest concerning index numbers. They are: shifting the base of an index, link-chain procedures, and splicing two overlapping index numbers.

Shifting the Base of an Index

Sometimes, we wish to shift the base of an index either to make the base more recent or to make two indices with different bases comparable. To shift the base of an index is a very simple matter. For instance, if an index number is constructed with 1988 = 100, as shown by index A below, and we wish to change the base to 1989, we simply divide all the index numbers of series A by the index of 1989 of that series to produce index B. Similarly, to shift the base from 1989 to 1990, we divide all the index numbers in B by that of 1990 in B. These results are:

Year	A 1988 = 100	B 1989 = 100	C 1990 = 100
1988	100	80	50.0
1989	125	100	62.5
1990	200	160	100.0

A glance at the above series shows that in each case, the ratios of index numbers are identical:

$$1.00:1.25:2.00.$$

Link-Chain Procedures

Old commodities may be withdrawn from and new ones may be introduced into the market continuously. It is, therefore, desirable to revise the list of items and the system of weights of index numbers from time to time. For this purpose, we employ what is called the *linking* procedure in which *link index numbers* are constructed with the previous period as the base of comparison.

The construction of link index numbers is a very simple matter. Suppose we have a series of four years with the following values:

$$1987 = a = 10,$$
$$1988 = b = 15,$$
$$1989 = c = 25,$$
$$1990 = d = 30;$$

and suppose we are interested in the series of changes from a to b, from b to c, and from c to d; we may then obtain the following link relatives:

$$I_{87-88} = \frac{b}{a} = \frac{15}{10} = 1.50 \text{ or } 150;$$

$$I_{88-89} = \frac{c}{b} = \frac{25}{15} \doteq 1.67 \text{ or } 167;$$

$$I_{89-90} = \frac{d}{c} = \frac{30}{25} = 1.20 \text{ or } 120.$$

Index numbers as obtained above clearly show the changes from the immediately previous period. These indices can also be chained back by a process of multiplication in order to produce an index with a fixed base. To do this, we note that, for example,

$$(I_{87-88})(I_{88-89}) = \left(\frac{b}{a}\right)\left(\frac{c}{b}\right) = \frac{c}{a} = I_{87-89}$$

which implies that the product of $(I_{87-88})(I_{88-89})$ becomes the index for 1989 with 1987 as the base; that is, $I_{87-89} = c/a$. Likewise,

$$(I_{87-88})(I_{88-89})(I_{89-90}) = \left(\frac{b}{a}\right)\left(\frac{c}{b}\right)\left(\frac{d}{c}\right) = \frac{d}{a} = I_{87-90}$$

Thus, the product of three link relatives gives us the index number for 1980 with 1987 as the base. In general, given a set of link index numbers which covers the period, say, 1980–1990, a series of index numbers with 1980 as the fixed base via the chain procedure becomes:

$$I_{80-81} = I_{80-81},$$

$$I_{80-82} = (I_{80-81})(I_{81-82}),$$

$$I_{80-83} = [(I_{80-81})(I_{81-82})]I_{82-83} = (I_{80-82})I_{82-83},$$

$$I_{80-84} = [(I_{80-81})(I_{80-82})(I_{82-83})]I_{83-84} = (I_{80-83})I_{83-84},$$

$$I_{80-85} = (I_{80-84})I_{84-85},$$
$$\vdots \qquad \vdots \qquad \vdots$$
$$I_{80-90} = (I_{80-89})I_{89-90}.$$

From the previous illustration, a general procedure for chaining emerges. A chain index number, I_{0-n}, for period n with period 0 as base, can be obtained by multiplying the chain index number for the previous period, $I_{0-(n-1)}$, by the link relative for period n, $I_{(n-1)-n}$. That is,

$$I_{0-n} = I_{0-(n-1)}[I_{(n-1)-n}]. \qquad (20.15)$$

Splicing Two Overlapping Indices

When the weights of an index number become out of date, we may construct another index with new weights. Thus, two indices result. On occasion, we may also wish to convert these two indices into a continuous series. The procedure employed for this conversion is called *splicing*, which is mainly a problem of finding proportions. To illustrate, suppose two prices indices—A, with q_{0i} as weights, and B, with q_{3i} as weights—are to be constructed with the values below:

$$1984: \quad \sum p_0 q_0 = \$10,$$

$$1985: \quad \sum p_1 q_0 = \$12,$$

1986: $\sum p_2 q_0 = \$15,$

1987: $\sum p_3 q_0 = \$20;$ $\sum p_3 q_3 = 25,$

1988: $\sum p_4 q_3 = 30,$

1989: $\sum p_5 q_3 = 40,$

1990: $\sum p_6 q_3 = 45.$

With these data, the following two Laspeyres price indices, A and B, result:

1984: $P_{84} = \dfrac{\sum p_0 q_0}{\sum p_0 q_0}(100) = \dfrac{10}{10}(100) = 100,$

1985: $P_{85} = \dfrac{\sum p_1 q_0}{\sum p_0 q_0}(100) = \dfrac{12}{10}(100) = 120,$

1986: $P_{86} = \dfrac{\sum p_2 q_0}{\sum p_0 q_0}(100) = \dfrac{15}{10}(100) = 150,$

1987: $P_{87} = \dfrac{\sum p_3 q_0}{\sum p_0 q_0}(100) = \dfrac{20}{10}(100) = 200;$ $P_{87} = \dfrac{\sum p_3 q_3}{\sum p_3 q_3}(100) \dfrac{25}{25}(100) = 100,$

1988: x_1 $P_{88} = \dfrac{\sum p_4 q_3}{\sum p_3 q_3}(100) = \dfrac{30}{25}(100) = 120,$

1989: x_2 $P_{89} = \dfrac{\sum p_5 q_3}{\sum p_3 q_3}(100) = \dfrac{40}{25}(100) = 160,$

1990: x_3 $P_{90} = \dfrac{\sum p_6 q_3}{\sum p_3 q_3}(100) = \dfrac{45}{25}(100) = 180.$

Now, we note that we can make indices A and B continuous either with A or with B. If we wish to make B continuous with A, we are attempting to find x_1, x_2, and x_3, via proportions:

$$\frac{2.0}{x_1} = \frac{1.0}{1.2} \quad x_1 = \frac{(2.0)(1.2)}{1.0} = 2.4, \text{ or } 240;$$

$$\frac{2.0}{x_2} = \frac{1.0}{1.6} \quad x_2 = \frac{(2.0)(1.6)}{1.0} = 3.2, \text{ or } 320;$$

$$\frac{2.0}{x_3} = \frac{1.0}{1.8} \quad x_3 = \frac{(2.0)(1.8)}{1.0} = 3.6, \text{ or } 360.$$

Thus, to make the new index continuous with the old, we in effect splice at the year that is base of the new index—1987 in our example. The x_i values can be obtained simply by multiplying the values in the

TABLE 20.10 Illustrations of spliced Indices

Year	A	B	Spliced Indices A': 1984 = 100	B': 1987 = 100
1984	100		100	50
1985	120		120	60
1986	150		150	75
1987	200	100	200	100
1988		120	240	120
1989		160	320	160
1990		180	360	180

new index by the index of the old at the year of splicing—2.0 in our example.

To make the old index, A, continuous with the new, B, is the same as to change the original base of the old index to the base of the new index. Thus, in our example, the base of A must be shifted from 1984 to 1987. This is done by dividing each value in the old by its value for the year of splicing—2.0 in 1987. These results are shown in Table 20.10.

Changing Weights with Splicing and Chain Techniques

It is interesting to note that the techniques of splicing and chaining procedures can be employed for the purpose of changing the weights of the index. From our previous discussion on splicing, we find that

$$\frac{P_{87}}{x_1} = \frac{100}{P'_{88}},$$

from which we have

$$x_1 = P_{87}(P'_{88})\frac{1}{100}$$

$$= P_{87}\left[\frac{\sum p_4 q_3}{\sum p_3 q_3}(100)\right]\frac{1}{100}$$

$$= P_{87}(I_{87-88})\frac{1}{100}$$

$$= 200(120)\frac{1}{100}$$

$$= 240.$$

In this calculation x_1 = the price index for 1988, or P_{88} and I_{87-88} is the link relative from 1987 to 1988. Thus, we have demonstrated that the price index for 1988 is found by multiplying the 1987 price index by the link relative I_{87-88}. This is a chain procedure. The result here differs from that obtained before in the fact that I_{87-88} uses q_{3i} as weights while the weights for P_{87} are q_{0i}. Clearly, q_{0i} and q_{3i} may very well be different from each other. Similarly,

$$\frac{x_1}{x_2} = \frac{P'_{88}}{P'_{89}},$$

$$x_2 = x_1\left(\frac{P'_{89}}{P'_{88}}\right)$$

$$= P_{88}\left(\frac{\sum p_5 q_3}{\sum p_3 q_3} \Big/ \frac{\sum p_4 q_3}{\sum p_3 q_3}\right)$$

$$= P_{88}\left(\frac{\sum p_5 q_3}{\sum p_4 q_3}\right),$$

where $(\sum p_5 q_3 / \sum p_4 q_3)(100)$ is the link relative $I_{88\text{-}89}$. Hence

$$x_2 = P_{88}(I_{88\text{-}89})\frac{1}{100}$$

$$= 240(133\tfrac{1}{3})\frac{1}{100}$$

$$= 320.$$

But $x_2 = P_{89}$. Thus, the price index for 1989 is found as the product of the price index for 1988 and the link relative $I_{88\text{-}89}$ whose weights are again q_{3i}.

Finally,

$$\frac{x_2}{x_3} = \frac{P'_{89}}{P'_{90}},$$

$$x_3 = P_{90} = P_{89}(I_{89\text{-}90})$$

$$= P_{89}\left(\frac{\sum p_6 q_3}{\sum p_5 q_3}\right)$$

$$= 320(112.5)\frac{1}{100}$$

$$= 360.$$

Thus, we see that two overlapping indices can be spliced by way of proportions which, in turn, leads to the technique of the chain-index. By using splicing and chaining, we can change the weights as frequently as desired.

In concluding this section, we may note that the link-chain procedure is useful in that it permits changes in the composition of the index from period to period. Its utility, however, should not be exaggerated. As a matter of fact, the strictest comparability is confined to chain index numbers that immediately follow one another. When outmoded commodities are continuously replaced by new ones, the meaning of chain index numbers becomes increasingly doubtful as more distant years are compared—we may often not be able to describe just what the comparison really means.

20.9 IMPORTANT CURRENT INDICES

The majority of published indices are price indices. The Wholesale Price Index and the Consumer Price Index constructed by the United States Bureau of Labor Statistics are by far the most important. An important quantity index currently available is the Federal Reserve Board's Index of Industrial Production. We shall present a brief description of these three indices in this section.

The BLS Wholesale Price Index

The BLS Wholesale Price Index was first calculated in 1920, but estimates have carried it back to 1890. Its main purpose is to show the general movements of prices at primary market levels. The price data used to construct it are drawn from those of sales in large lots in the primary markets—that is, prices prevailing at the first important commercial transaction for each commodity. Most of the prices included in the index are selling prices of representative manufacturers or producers or the prices quoted on organized exchanges or markets.

This index is based on a large sample of about 2000 commodity prices selected from 15 major groups and 88 subgroups of commodities classified by product. The purpose of such an extremely large sample is to provide sufficient data to compute price indices for commodity subgroups, such as indices of prices of wholesale processed food, textile products and apparel prices, and metal and metal product prices.

The Wholesale Price Index is constructed by a modified version of the Laspeyres formula. The weights employed are the total transactions as reported in the Census of Manufacturers. These weights are reviewed and revised each time complete census data become available. In between censuses, the weighting pattern may also be modified if it is considered desirable. The frequent changes in weighting patterns are accomplished by the link-chain procedure described in the last section.

The Wholesale Price Index, its components, and the individual price series are published monthly and can be found in the *Survey of Current Business*. Information furnished by these indices is invaluable to economists, managers, and government policy makers. These data enable the economist to study the general fluctuations in price level, to evaluate the imbalance between aggregate demand and supply, to analyze the price structure of the economy and the changes in relationships among individual commodities, and so on. Businessmen benefit from this information in determining production costs, in planning investment programs, in formulating production schedules and sales policies, in evaluating inventories, and in purchasing raw materials. Government planners find these data indispensable in formulating policies for economic stability as well as long-range policies for economic growth and other economic programs.

The BLS Consumer Price Index

As its full title—"Index of Change in Prices of Goods and Services Purchased by City Wage-Earner and Clerical Worker Families to Maintain Their Level of Living"—indicates, this index measures the average change in the price of a fixed "market basket" of commodities and services purchased by families of urban wage earners and salaried clerks.

The index was initiated during World War I under the demand for wage increases to meet rising costs of living, especially in the shipbuilding centers. It has been published regularly since 1921 with a few major revisions. A fully revised index, based on new expenditures and family income surveys for 1960–1961, was constructed in 1964. As now constituted, this index is constructed from a collection of approximately 400 carefully selected retail prices that include sales and excise taxes. These prices are reported regularly from 46 cities. Separate indices are published monthly for 20 large cities as is a single "all-item" index for the whole nation.

This index is also computed by a modified Laspeyres formula. In addition, as is true of the Wholesale Price Index, the link-chain procedure is used to offer freedom of substitution at intervals so that the indices may coincide with realities of consumption and markets. The CPI uses fixed quantities as weights. To accommodate the shifting importance of items, the weights are revised periodically. However, weight revisions do not necessarily occur at the same time as the shift of base. This is the reason why CPI is not strictly a Laspeyres index.

Of the thousands of statistics published by United States government agencies, the Consumer Price Index is probably the most important single statistic. As will be shown in the next section, it is used for a variety of purposes by private organizations as well as public agencies. However, we should remember that this index is calculated specifically to measure the average change in prices of goods consumed by families of urban wage earners and clerical workers. Severe limitations are encountered, therefore, in applying this index to the very rich or the very poor, or to groups whose living and spending patterns differ from those of typical urban worker families.

The FRB Index of Industrial Production

The Index of Industrial Production has been published by the Board of Governors of the Federal Reserve System since 1927. Its main purpose is to measure changes in the physical volume of manufacturing and mineral production and in the output of the gas and electricity industries.

This index was last revised in 1959. In its present form, it is a weighted average-of-relatives index of more than 200 different series, each of which represents the output of a particular product or industry or the man-hours worked in that industry. The data used are adjusted for the number of working days in the month, and the quantity relatives are weighted in proportion to the value added in production by each industry in the current base year. The total index and all its components are available with or without adjustment for seasonal variations in the *Federal Reserve Bulletin.*

The Federal Reserve Index has become one of the most quoted business indices now being published. Two factors are mainly responsible for its wide use. It is by far the best index available of the activity in a highly important sector of the economy, for it is comprehensive, well constructed, and up to date; moreover, it has symptomatic value. Manufacturing, mining, and utilities contribute about one-third to the total national income and account for about the same proportion of all nonagricultural employment. Furthermore, many other sectors of the economy are engaged in supplying materials to, or using the products of, manufacturing. Manufacturing and mining also are more cyclically sensitive than is any other type of business activity. All these factors make the Federal Reserve Index a widely used barometer of general business conditions, even though it is not an accurate measure of total business activity.

20.10 SOME APPLICATIONS OF PRICE INDICES

Early interest in indices came mainly from economists engaged in studying inflation and deflation, the structure of individual prices, the behavior and interrelationships of important economic variables, and the like. Through the years, however, indices, especially price indices, have come to play an increasingly important role in many decision-making problems for private enterprises, labor unions, and governments. This section will present some of the important applications of price indices.

Purchasing Power

It is the basic traditional function of a price index to measure the purchasing power, or value, of money. Since the value of money is the power of money over goods and services in exchange, we may deduce that the higher the level of prices, the lower the purchasing power of money—that is, the less a given income will buy in terms of goods and services. This is the same as saying that the purchasing power of money is the reciprocal of the price index. The general expression may be given thus:

$$\text{purchasing power of money} = \frac{1}{\text{price index}}.$$

For example, if the value of the Consumer Price Index in a given year is 124.5, then the purchasing power of the consumer dollar becomes $1/1.245 \doteq 0.80$, or 80 cents. The purchasing power of the consumer dollar has decreased by 20% from the base period to that year.

Real Wages

Real wages are simply wages expressed in terms of the purchasing power of money wages. Thus a real wage index can be constructed to show the changes in the purchasing power of the money wage income of the workers. This is done by constructing a money wage index with the same base as the Consumer Price Index and dividing the former by the latter:

$$\text{index of real wages} = \frac{\text{index of money wages}}{\text{Consumer Price Index}}.$$

In this formula the numerator may be either a city index or the national index. As an illustration, suppose that the index of money wages for a given type of worker in the United States, constructed with 1980 as the base, stood at 150 in January 1987, and that for the same month the Consumer Price Index had the value of 123.8; then the real wage index for these workers in that month would be

$$\frac{150}{123.8} \doteq 1.212, \text{ or } 121.2\%.$$

This means that these workers' real wages had increased by 21.2%, from 1980 to 1986, which is much less than what the money wage index indicates.

Escalator Clauses

The most widely publicized use of the Consumer Price Index is for the automatic adjustment of wages under "escalator clauses" in collective bargaining agreements. An escalator clause provides for an automatic amount of wage change, say, 50 cents an hour, with a given change in the percentage points of the Consumer Price Index, say, 0.8 point. Usually, no ceiling is placed on the extent that wages can increase, but the amount that wages can decline is limited so that they cannot fall very far below the wage rate at the time the escalator clause went into effect. The reason for such a clause, obviously, is to protect the workers' standard of living from price changes.

Terms of Exchange

Just as real wages are ratios of the money wage index to the Consumer Price Index, the terms of exchange for a commodity or a group of commodities are ratios of the price index of one commodity or a group of commodities to the price index of another commodity or group of commodities. The terms of exchange may thus be considered as an index of relative price that measures the change in the price of one in terms of the price of another. Or,

$$\begin{array}{c}\text{index of relative price}\\ \text{of A in terms of B}\end{array} = \frac{\text{price index of A}}{\text{price index of B}}.$$

If, for example, the price index for fuel, power, and lighting materials has increased from its base period by 80% but the Consumer Price Index has risen by 50%, then the prices of the first group of products have actually increased by 20% in terms of the latter. That is,

$$\text{index of relative prices of fuel, power and lighting materials} = \frac{180}{150} = 1.20 \text{ or } 120\%.$$

A special application of terms of exchange that is of interest to students of foreign trade is the concept of "terms of trade." By the "terms of trade" we mean the ratio at which commodities are traded internationally. When only two commodities are being traded, the terms of trade are the same as the ratio of their international prices. When many articles are entering trade, the terms of trade are defined as the ratio of the index of import prices to the index of export prices. As such, the terms of trade may be interpreted as the quantity of imports obtainable for one unit of exports. When the average price of a country's imports rises less rapidly than the average price it receives from exports, the nation's terms of trade are said to have become more favorable, since a greater amount of imports can now be obtained per unit of exports.

Another index ratio, important for the American economy, is the *parity ratio,* defined as:

$$\text{parity ratio} = \frac{\text{index of prices received by farmers}}{\text{index of prices paid by farmers}}.$$

The parity ratio, since the late 1920s, has been the basic guideline of American agricultural policy. Present laws stipulate that farmers who conform to certain requirements can sell most stable crops to the government at a price that is a given percentage of the parity.

From the above formula it is obvious that when the prices-received index is higher than the prices-paid index, agricultural prices are above parity. When the converse is true, agricultural prices are below parity. Suppose this parity ratio stood at 83, in a given year; this means that in that year the purchasing power of agricultural commodities with respect to what farmers buy was 83% of what it was in the base period.

The Constant Dollar

The value of an aggregate of goods is the product of price and quantity. Thus the value of an aggregate of goods may change because of changes in prices or in quantities or in both. Often we are interested only in the changes in the physical volume of goods and services: the changes in the value of an aggregate of items at constant dollars. In other words, we are interested in ascertaining what the value of goods and services would be if their prices had not changed or the value of money had remained constant. To achieve this, we employ what is called the procedure of *statistical deflation,* by which the effects of changes in prices upon the value of a list of commodities are removed. This procedure is defined by the following expression:

$$\text{physical volume in constant dollars} = \frac{\text{volume in current dollars}}{\text{appropriate price index}}.$$

Inasmuch as the denominator is a pure number, the quotient obtained in this formula is also in terms of dollars, which, however, by virtue of the division, have been transformed into constant dollars.

The price index used in statistical deflation is called the *deflator*. The deflator does not have to be constructed with all the prices of the items whose value is to be deflated. For instance, in deriving the real gross national product—that is, the GNP in constant dollars—the Department of Commerce uses deflators that are constructed on the basis of samples of prices that enter into the GNP. The actual procedure used is to break down the GNP into its main expenditure components—consumption, investment, and government expenditures—and deflate each component with a price index of a sample of prices specially constructed for the component. The deflated components are then added up to form the total GNP in constant dollars.

20.11 PROBLEMS OF CONSTRUCTING INDICES

Up to this point we have been concerned with some of the techniques of constructing indices and their possible applications. Now we turn our attention to some of the important theoretical and practical problems encountered in constructing indices.

The first problem is sampling. The most important thing to be noted here is that random sampling is seldom used. Typically, indices are constructed from samples deliberately selected. The representativeness of an index depends, therefore, on the fact that all or most of the prices or commodities judged to be important in the population are included in its construction. Clearly, the index maker's judgment and knowledge of the data under investigation are of paramount importance. He must select the commodities to be included in the index. He must decide, in the case of the price index, how the prices should be defined and where and when the price quotations should be collected.

The decision as to the number of items to be included in the sample is made with the primary objective of the index in mind. If our aim is to describe the movements of general business activity, for instance, we would want a broadly representative index, such as the Wholesale Price Index, which may behave rather sluggishly because it reflects the behavior of all types of business. If our purpose is to stress symptoms, we choose only a few series that we think to be particularly significant as indicators of the future course of business. The FRB Index of Industrial Production is an example of such an index that is more sensitive and can therefore be used as a business barometer or a forecasting index.

The second problem is concerned with the selection of the base period. Mathematically, of course, it does not matter at all which period is selected as the base period. However, it seems desirable in practice to follow a few guidelines on selecting the base period rather than leaving it completely arbitrary. The base period of an index is used for the computation of relatives and as a basis of reference both in describing the behavior of individual index numbers and in comparing them. Thus it must be carefully selected so that misleading results and interpretations may not arise. There are two simple rules to follow in choosing the base. One is that the base value should be judged as typical or "normal." It should be neither too high nor too low relative to values in other periods. When the base value is too high, the whole index would appear chronically depressed because most of the index numbers will fall well below it. If the base value is too low, distortions may be created in the opposite direction. A base value may be considered typical if it coincides with the trend rather than conforming to a cyclically high or low value. When it is difficult to select a single period as the base, the average value of a few periods—perhaps covering one complete cycle—may be used as the base.

The other rule to keep in mind for selecting the base period is that the base of an index should be relatively recent. This is desirable because we are usually more interested in comparing current fluctuations with some economic framework similar to the present.

The third is the problem of appropriate weighting. Assigning weight to the different variables according to their economic importance is always a troublesome task. The solution here relies heavily upon knowledge of economic theory. Fortunately, it may be noted, for an index to be useful in practice only approximate accuracy in weights is demanded. In addition to the weighting systems introduced previously in this chapter, many others can be used: "average quantities (or prices) of base and given years," "average quantities (or prices) of several years," "average quantities (or prices) of all years," and "hypothetical quantities (or prices)" are a few. Each of these weighting systems has its theoretical and practical merits as well as its drawbacks. Although the relative merits of these weighting systems are beyond the scope of our present discussion, it is important to note two points. (1) Changing the weights also changes the meaning of the index. Thus, the type of weights we want to use depends upon the question we seek to answer. (2) When two types of weights can yield similar information, we always select the one that involves less computational effort and permits more precise interpretation and greater theoretical consistency.

The fourth problem refers to the selection of the average. This problem has two aspects: Which average should be used? How representative is the index number as an average?

Theoretically, any measure of central tendency can be used as the average of the weighted aggregate quantities or weighted relatives. However, the arithmetic mean is the most frequently used average in constructing indices. This is so because no other indices have such a simple and apparent economic meaning as the weighted arithmetic indices. No other indices, either, are so easy to compute.

The question whether an index as an average is representative or meaningful depends upon the distrubition pattern of the relatives. It has been argued that an average is meaningful only if there is a real central tendency. To the extent that the values move together through time, the use of index numbers to describe their mass behavior is legitimate. However, if the values move very differently through time, the index number may lose its meaning. According to many studies made on this subject, it has been demonstrated that the frequency distribution of relatives computed from a base period in the recent past has a pronounced central tendency and the proportion of relatives in the modal class is rather large. However, the distribution of relatives with reference to a more remote base period becomes more dispersed and more negatively skewed, with a smaller proportion of relatives included in the modal class. These findings suggest that the index is more representative when its base is more recent. If we ignore the time element, we have also found a greater central tendency in a group of items that are more homogeneous, such as agricultural products, consumers' durable goods, or utilities, than exists in a group of greater heterogeneity. This indicates that an index is more meaningful if it is constructed from a group of items that have a greater tendency toward homogeneity.

Ideally, therefore, an index, like any other average, should be accompanied by a measure of dispersion. Unfortunately, indices are seldom so accompanied. Still, in using and interpreting index numbers we must keep the degree and type of dispersion in mind by analyzing the components of the index.

The fifth problem is that of changing products. In a dynamic economy old products are continuously being improved in quality or are replaced by new products. Since the significance of an index depends on the retention of the significance of the assortment of commodities comprising it, the comparison of either price levels or quantity levels from two widely separated points of time becomes difficult if not completely meaningless. Because of this, measurements of price levels over long periods of time are confined to staple commodity prices, such as grains and metals, that remain much the same from age to age. It is also for this reason that the link-chain procedure has been designed to cover the transition between periods of different product mixes in measuring price and quantity levels.

The sixth and last problem is that of the accuracy of formulas. Different formulas usually produce different results when applied to the same price or quantity data. There thus arises the question: "Which formula is accurate?" The accuracy of a formula, according to some theoretical statisticians, depends upon whether or not it meets certain mathematical tests. Of these tests, probably the most important are the time reversal test, the circular test, and the factor reversal test.

The *time reversal test* seeks to ascertain whether the index number for period 0 relative to period 1 is the reciprocal of the index number for period 1 relative to period 0. In other words, if the product of two index numbers computed by the same basic formula, with the time subscripts interchanged in the formula for the second index number, is equal to 1, we say that the formula meets the time reversal test. For example, if the formula meets this test, when the index for 1990, with 1980 as the base, is 2.0, then the index for 1980 with 1990 as the base must equal 0.5. Surprisingly enough, this seemingly important and desirable property of an index is not met by most formulas. It can be verified that among the numbered formulas introduced in this chapter, only the simple aggregate index—formulas (20.1) and (20.2)—the value index (20.13), and the chain link relative index (20.15) satisfy this requirement.

The *circular test* is an extension of the time reversal test. A formula is said to meet this test if, for example, the 1990 index, with 1985 as the base, is 2.0, and the 1985 index, with 1980 as the base, is again 2.0; then the 1990 index, with 1980 as the base, must be 4.0. In other words, we should be able to get a consistent index for 1990 relative to 1980 by multiplying the 1980 index relative to 1985 by the corresponding index for 1985 relative to 1980. Clearly, the desirability of this property is that it enables us to adjust the index values from period to period without referring each time to the original base. All the numbered index formulas so far discussed meet the circular test except the average of relatives—Equations (20.3) and (20.4)—and, on occasion, the weighted aggregative indices. Any weighted aggregative index— Equations (20.5) through (20.12) and Equation (20.14)—meets the circular test when the weights are the same for all computations using one numbered equation, but it fails the circular test if the weights differ from one computation to another using the same numbered equation.

The *factor reversal test* holds that the product of a price index and the quantity index should equal the corresponding value index. We have already discussed this property in Section 20.6 in some detail. What may be pointed out here is that none of the formulas so far discussed meets this test.

Attempts have been made, especially by Professor Irving Fisher, to design formulas that would meet most of these requirements. Of these, the most frequently noted is Fisher's "ideal index," which meets both the time reversal and the factor reversal tests but not the circular test (unless the weights are constant over time). The ideal index is given by the formula

$$\text{Fisher's ideal index} = \sqrt{(\text{Laspeyres index})(\text{Paasche index})}. \quad (20.16)$$

This formula, it may be noted, is the geometric mean of the Laspeyres and Paasche price (or quantity) indices. Since both indices are ratios, the geometric mean is the proper procedure for obtaining their average. One trouble with (20.16) is that it is laborious to apply. More serious is the objection that it is difficult to give a precise interpretation of what it actually attempts to measure. In any event, we see from (20.16) that Fisher's ideal price and quantity indices are simply $\sqrt{P_b P_n}$ and $\sqrt{Q_b Q_n}$, respectively.

The fact that most of the commonly used indices, especially the weighted indices, do not meet these tests does not necessarily mean that their usefulness is impaired. Failure to meet these tests does not mean that the index values do not have logically desirable properties. As has been mentioned before, both the Laspeyres and the Paasche formulas, inadequate as they may be in some sense of mathematical logic, do yield precise answers to specific questions. It has also been suggested that index values should be considered only as approximations but that they are all we are entitled to because of the nature of the problems inherent in measurements.

GLOSSARY OF FORMULAS

(20.1) $P = \left(\sum p_n / \sum p_0\right)(100).$

The simple aggregative price index is defined as a relative that is a ratio of the sum of prices in a given period to the sum of prices of the base period. The resulting proportion is multiplied by 100 in order to present the index number in the usual form of a percentage.

(20.2) $Q = \left(\sum q_n / \sum q_0\right)(100).$

The simple aggregative quantity index is defined as the ratio of the sum of quantities in a given period to the sum of quantities in the base period. This formula can only be used when the aggregates of physical quantities are given in the same units.

(20.3) $P = \sum_{i=1}^{k} \left(\frac{p_{ni}}{p_{0i}}\right) 100 \bigg/ k.$

The simple average-of-relatives price index is defined here as an arithmetic mean of price relatives. This index has the advantage over the index defined by (20.1) that it is not influenced by absolute prices. However, it has a defect that is equally undesirable, since it assigns equal weight (importance) to each of the relatives. Here, k stands for the number of items in the aggregate.

(20.4) $Q = \sum_{i=1}^{k} \left(\frac{q_{ni}}{q_{0i}}\right) 100 \bigg/ k.$

The simple average-of-relatives quantity index defined here can be used for an aggretate of items quoted in different units. However, it is still an unsatisfactory method of computing a quantity index because it has the the same problem of undesirable concealed weights as does the price index as defined by (20.3).

(20.5) $\left(\sum_{i=1}^{k} p_{ni} q_{0i} \bigg/ \sum_{i=1}^{k} p_{0i} q_{0i}\right)(100).$

This is the Laspeyres formula for an aggregative price index weighted by base-period quantities. It measures the change in the aggregate value of the base period's assortment of goods and services when valued at given-period prices.

$$(20.6) \quad P_n = \left(\sum_{i=1}^{k} p_{ni} q_{ni} \Big/ \sum_{i=1}^{k} p_{0i} q_{ni} \right) (100).$$

This is the Paasche formula for an aggregative price index weighted by base-period prices. Although this formula yields satisfactory results, due to several limitations, it is not as frequently employed in practice as (20.5). Its drawbacks, compared with (20.5), are that (1) current quantities are often difficult to obtain promptly; (2) computational labor is nearly doubled; (3) with changing weights, while comparison between a given period and the base period is clear and meaningful, comparisons between different periods are not entirely valid.

$$(20.7) \quad Q_b = \left(\sum_{i=1}^{k} p_{0i} q_{ni} \Big/ \sum_{i=1}^{k} p_{0i} q_{0i} \right) (100);$$

$$(20.8) \quad Q_n = \left(\sum_{i=1}^{k} p_{ni} q_{ni} \Big/ \sum_{i=1}^{k} p_{ni} q_{0i} \right) (100).$$

These are analogous Laspeyres and Paasche formulas for aggregative quantity indices corresponding to the price indices defined by (20.5) and (20.6), respectively. Note that prices are weights in these indices. In general, a weighted aggregative quantity index seeks to answer the question: If we buy (sell) varying quantities of the same items in each of the two periods, but at the same prices, how much would be spent (received) in the given period relative to the base period?

$$(20.9) \quad P_b = \sum_{i=1}^{k} [(p_{0i} q_{0i})(p_{ni}/p_{0i})](100) \Big/ \sum_{i=1}^{k} p_{0i} q_{0i}$$

$$(20.10) \quad Q_b = \sum_{i=1}^{k} [(p_{0i} q_{0i})(q_{ni}/q_{0i})](100) \Big/ \sum_{i=1}^{k} p_{0i} q_{0i} .$$

The Laspeyres price index (20.9) and the Laspeyres quantity index (20.10) can be computed as the weighted arighmetic means of price and quantity, respectively, the weights being base-year values.

$$(20.11) \quad P_n = \sum_{i=1}^{k} [(p_{0i} q_{0i})(p_{ni}/p_{0i})](100) \Big/ \sum_{i=1}^{k} p_{0i} q_{ni};$$

$$(20.12) \quad Q_n = \sum_{i=1}^{k} [(p_{ni} q_{0i})(q_{ni}/q_{0i})](100) \Big/ \sum_{i=1}^{k} p_{ni} q_{0i} .$$

The Paasche price (20.11) and quantity (20.12) indices can also be calculated as weighted arithmetic averages of price and quantity relatives, respectively; the weights are theoretical values—base-year price times given-year quantity for the price index, and the given-year price times the base-year quantity for the quantity index.

(20.13) $V = \left(\sum\limits_{i=1}^{k} p_{ni}q_{ni} \Big/ \sum\limits_{i=1}^{k} p_{0i}q_{0i} \right)(100).$

The value index defined here measures the change in actual values of an aggregate of goods and services. For this index, the weights are inherent in the value figures.

(20.14) $E_b = \left(\sum\limits_{i=1}^{k} r_{ni}q_{0i} \Big/ \sum\limits_{i=1}^{k} r_{0i}q_{0i} \right)(100).$

This equation defines a productivity index as labor inputs weighted with base-period quantity. Here, r may be considered either as units of output per man-hour or as man-hours per unit of output. Care must be taken to observe the definition of r in interpreting the value of the index.

(20.15) $I_{0-n} = I_{0-(n-1)}[I_{(n-1)-n}].$

This expression states that a chain index number for period n with period 0 as base, denoted as I_{0-n}, can be obtained by multiplying the chain index number for the previous period, $I_{0-(n-1)}$, by the link relative for period n, $I_{(n-1)-n}$.

(20.16) Fisher's ideal index $= \sqrt{\text{(Laspeyres index)(Paasche index)}}.$

Fisher's ideal index is defined here as the geometric mean of the Laspeyres and Paasche indices. It is called "ideal" because it can satisfy most of these tests of a good index. However, its application is of doubtful value because it does not possess a simple and intuitive meaning.

REVIEW QUESTIONS

20.1 Give a critical evaluation of each of the following statements:
    a. Neither the simple aggregative nor the simple average-of-relatives indices is weighted.
    b. When quantities in an aggregate are expressed in uniform units, both the simple aggregative and the simple relatives methods furnish satisfactory indices.
    c. The Laspeyres and the Paasche formulas not only provide meaningful results but also measure the same thing.
    d. Since the value of the base is always 100, it does not make any difference which period is selected as the base on which an index is constructed.
    e. The fact that none of the commonly used index formulas meets all the essential mathematical tests does not mean that no logically desirable results can be obtained.
    f. The Wholesale Price Index is a better measure than the Consumer Price Index if we wish to determine the general purchasing power of the American dollar.
    g. Since the 1960s, the average salary of college professors has nearly tripled. Clearly the professor's standard of living must have increased by about 200% since then.

h. A productivity index computed with man-hours per unit of output is actually a measure of labor efficiency alone.

20.2 What does each of the following indices measure?
a. Laspeyres price index
b. Paasche price index
c. Laspeyres quantity index
d. Paasche quantity index
e. Wholesale Price Index
f. Consumer Price Index
g. FRB Index of Industrial Production

20.3 If you wish to construct a price index by using a fixed quantity q_a for each price as weight, how would you state the formula? What would such a price index mean?

20.4 Suppose you are employed to construct a price index for a department store that sells thousands of items.
a. How would you decide on which items to include?
b. How would you define the prices?
c. What weights would you use?
d. Which formula would you select?

20.5 If the averages of the quantities for the first two periods, q_0 and q_1, is to be employed as weights, how should the formula for a Laspeyres price index be stated?

20.6 If the average of the prices of the first three periods, p_0, p_1, and p_2, is to be used as the base-period price, how should the Laspeyres quantity index be stated?

20.7 If the average of the prices for the first three periods is used as the base-period price and the average of the quantities of the first three periods is to be used as the weight, how should the Laspeyres index be stated?

20.8 What are the desirable properties an index is supposed to possess? Is there any index formula that can satisfy all these properties?

20.9 If a productivity index is computed with r to mean output per man-hour and the average of two years' quantities as weights, what would be the corresponding index value with r to mean man-hours per unit of output? Give a verbal interpretation of each index value.

20.10 A value index measures changes in actual values between two points of time. Can it be transformed into an index that measures the changes in physical volumes? If so, how? If not, why not?

20.11 What purposes can be served by studying the components of an index?

20.12 Why it is necessary to shift the base period of an index from time to time?

20.13 In your studies of economics or management, where do you think index numbers may be useful? Be specific.

20.14 Why is Fisher's index called the "ideal index"? What is the most important drawback of Fisher's ideal index?

PROBLEMS

20.1 A manufacturer purchases more than a thousand different types of raw material for production. He is interested in measuring changes in costs and physical volumes of purchases. Assume that it has been decided that five types of raw material, A, B, C, D, and E, are the important ones, and assume that the prices paid and quantities bought are as given in Table 20.P1.

TABLE 20.P1

Item	Unit	Unit Price 1984	Unit Price 1987	Quantity 1984	Quantity 1987
A	pound	$ 0.50	$ 0.65	4500	4000
B	ton	50.00	52.00	50	65
C	gallon	1.50	2.00	1250	1500
D	yard	4.00	5.50	400	350
E	ounce	0.25	0.15	80,000	120,000

a. Construct with 1984 as the base,
1. a simple aggregative price index;
2. a simple average-of-relatives price index;
3. a simple average-of-relatives quantity index;
4. a weighted aggregative price index with base-year quantities as weights;
5. a weighted aggregative price index with given-year quantities as weights;
6. a weighted aggregative quantity index with base-year prices as weights;
7. a weighted aggregative quantity index with given-year prices as weights;
8. a weighted average-of-relatives price index with base-year values as weights; and
9. a weighted average-of-relatives quantity index with base-year values as weights.
b. Construct, with 1987 as the base,
1. an aggregate price index weighted by base-year quantities; and
2. a weighted average-of-relatives quantity index with the Paasche formula.
c. Give an appropriate interpretation of each of the results you have obtained above.
d. Which index or indices constructed above would you actually recommend for the problem in hand?

20.2 Given the following index with 1980 as the base, shift the base to 1981 and then to 1983.

$$\begin{array}{ll} 1980: & 100 \\ 1981: & 110 \\ 1982: & 125 \\ 1983: & 115 \end{array}$$

20.3 How would you write the Laspeyres index if the chain index were applied to it? What would be the Laspeyres index for period $i + 1$ based on the period $i - 1$?

20.4 The BLS Consumer Price Index is computed by the Laspeyres formula. By applying the chain-index technique, we obtain

$$I_i = I_{i-1}\left[\frac{\sum\left(\frac{p_i}{p_{i-1}}\right)(p_{i-1}q_a)}{\sum p_{i-1}q_n}\right]$$

$$= I_{i-1}\left[\frac{\sum p_i q_a}{\sum p_{i-1}q_a}\right]$$

$$= (I_{i-1})I_{i-1,i}$$

where I_{i-1} is the price index for the previous month with 1987 = 100, and $I_{i-1,i}$ is the link relative for the months $i - 1$ and i, and q_a are fixed-quantity weights—the average quantity for 1980–1981. Now, let $i + 1$ = June 1989, $I_{i-1} = 150$, $I_{i-1,i} = 102$, and $I_{i,i+1} = 101$. What are the price indices for May and June? What is the meaning of the result?

20.5 Construct a productivity index by using man-hours per unit of output and base-year quantities as weights with the hypothetical data in Table 20.P2.

TABLE 20.P2

Items Produced, i	Units Produced in Base year q_{0i}	Man-hours per Unit	
		1985 r_{0i}	1990 r_{ni}
A	15,600	50	35
B	12,500	42	34
C	23,400	11	10
D	5,000	24	24

20.6 Splice the two indices shown in the accompanying table so that index A has the proper values for 1988, 1989, and 1990.

TABLE 20.P3

Year	Index A	Index B
1984	100	
1985	105	
1986	115	
1987	110	100
1988	x_1	110
1989	x_2	105
1990	x_3	115

20.7 Splice the two indices in the preceding problem by using the chain-index procedure.

20.8 Given the data as in Table 20.P4, find P_{88}, P_{89}, and P_{90}

TABLE 20.P4

Year	Index A	Link relatives
1985	100	
1986	110	
1987	125	
1988	x_1	$P_{87-88} = 95$
1989	x_2	$P_{88-89} = 105$
1990	x_3	$P_{89-90} = 115$

20.9 Consider the set of hypothetical data in Table 20.P5.

TABLE 20.P5

Commodity	Annual Price 0	1	2	q_a
A	$1.25	$1.45	$1.30	0.2
B	0.95	1.25	1.40	0.4
C	0.68	0.60	0.57	0.1
D	2.50	2.65	2.70	0.3

Using q_a as weights, do the computations included below.
a. Calculate chain price index numbers for period 0 through 2.
b. Compute an arithmetic mean of price relatives by using period $0 = 100$ and q_a as weights, and compare this result with the value of P_{0-2} obtained in (a).

20.10 Assume that one of the products selected for a price index has a substantial change in quality and suppose that you have the information in Table 20.P6. Calculate the index using the "linking method".

TABLE 20.P6

Reported Price	Base Period	Period 1	Period 2
Quality A	$10.00	$12.00	—
Quality B	—	20.00	22.00

20.11 Given a set of hypothetical data as in Table 20.P7, do the following.

TABLE 20.P7 Prices and Quantities of Three Dairy Products Consumed by a Family

Item	Unit	Price 1985	1990	Quantity 1985	1990
Milk	quart	$1.25	$2.70	350	205
Butter	pound	3.00	6.50	100	80
Eggs	dozen	2.40	6.15	90	120

    a. Construct a 1990 Laspeyres index.

    b. Construct a 1990 Paasche price index.

    c. Construct a 1990 Fisher price index.

    d. Order the three price indices just obtained in accordance with their magnitudes and explain why such an order emerges.

20.12 Use the same set of data in Table 20.P7 to do the following.

    a. Construct the three quantity indices for 1990 Laspeyres, Paasche, and Fisher.

    b. Order the results from (a) according to their magnitudes. Are they in the same order as your answer to (d) in Problem 20.11? Explain why or why not?

    c. From the results obtained in this and the previous problem, determine which of the three index numbers obtained in (a) passes the factor-reversal test.

21 The Nature and Trends of Time Series

21.1 REASONS FOR TIME SERIES ANALYSIS

Nations must plan for the future in order to survive and grow. Even installment purchases of a household involve plans for the future. Plans for sales, production, investment, marketing, and so on, are made daily by business firms in order to meet current competition and to maintain steady growth. The federal government must plan for future revenues and expenditures, not only for the sake of performing its routine functions efficiently but also for the purpose of influencing the aggregate business activity so that the economic progress of the nation may not be slowed by inflation or deflation.

A business or an economic action taken today is based on yesterday's plan and tomorrow's expectations. Plans for the future cannot be made without forecasting events and the relationships they will have. Forecasting can be made for a given line of activity independently or the forecast of one type of event can be made on the basis of other forecasts. Thus, the projection of population growth for the next decade is an element in the forecast of the future demand for steel which, in turn, is the basis for plans for expanding plant capacities. Similarly, forecasts of national income have been used by the government to estimate its future tax revenue, and by various industries to predict their relative shares of the national market. Needless to say, an individual firm can base its forecast of sales on the forecast of sales for the whole industry.

Business executives and government officials seem to have recognized the importance of forecasting as the basis of rational decisions and actions concerning the future. Hardly a single day goes by without reading some news in the financial columns about this kind of forward planning. Yet forecasting remains more an art than a science. Predictions about economic conditions always involve errors, and sometimes are simply seriously mistaken. Whatever misgivings there may be, the need for the forecast, be it implicit or explicit, is there. The question is not: "Forecast or no forecast?" Instead it is: "What kind of forecast?" It may also be mentioned here that the value of a forecast is not merely in its accuracy but in the fact that making it requires a balanced consideration of factors influencing future developments, which is of value in any planning for future actions.

Forecasting techniques vary from simple expert guesses to complex analyses of mass data. In any case, a forecast must be based upon what has happened in the past. The most promising method of knowing about the past so that inferences can be made for the future is the analysis of a time series. A *time series* may be defined as a collection of readings, belonging to different time periods, of some economic variable or composite of variables, such as per capita income, gross national product, price of tobacco, or index of industrial production. A time series then, portrays the variations of the variable quantity or price through time. Like all kinds of economic behavior, the movements of time series are generated by the systematic and stochastic logic of the economy. As such, if we find that a certain underlying and persistent trend of a series has continued for decades, we would be unwise to ignore the probability that it will continue. The belief that past behavior of a series may continue into the future forms a rational basis for statistical forecasting. Forecasting is also the main purpose of analyzing time series.

21.2 COMPOSITION AND ANALYSIS OF TIME SERIES

Types of Economic Change

The actual movements of a time series are caused by a variety of factors—some economic, some natural, and some institutional. Some tend to affect only the long-run movement of a series, others to produce its short-run fluctuations. Thus, a time series includes different types of change. Looking at Figure 21.1, we observe first that even though the movements of the original series seem quite irregular, on the average they tend to move continuously upward through time. This general movement, persisting over a long period, is called a *secular trend*. It is represented by the diagonal line drawn through the irregular curve.

Next, if we study the irregular curve year by year, we see that the curve starts with a low, reaches a high about the middle of the year, and then decreases again. This type of fluctuation, which completes a whole

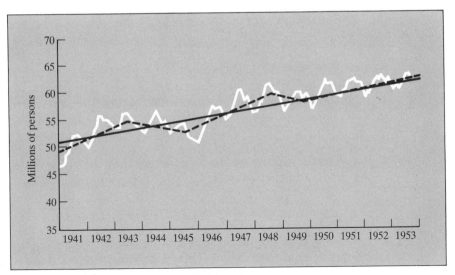

FIGURE 21.1 Employment in the United States, Bureau of Census Estimates, 1941–1953, by month: Curve (a), original data; Curve (b), secular trend; Curve (c), cylical fluctuations. (*Source: Federal Reserve Charts on Bank Credits, Money Rates, Business,* November, 1953.)

sequence within the span of a year and has about the same pattern year after year, is called *seasonal variation.*

Furthermore, looking at the broken curve superimposed on the original irregular curve, we find pronounced fluctuations moving up and down every few years throughout the length of the chart. These are known as *business cycles,* or *cyclical fluctuations*—so called because they comprise a series of repeated sequences, just as a wheel goes round and round.

Finally, the little sawtooth irregularities on the original curve represent what are referred to as *irregular movements.*

Time-Series Models and Methods of Analysis

Analysis of a time series, either to study one component in its own right or to eliminate one or more components from the original series, calls for decomposition of the series. To decompose a series, we must assume that some type of relationship exists among its four components. Usually we proceed on the assumption that a time series is made up of several additive or multiplicative components. Trends, cycles, and seasonals are in some sense considered as rather stable functions of time; the irregular movements are not.

The *additive model* assumes that the value of original data is the sum of the four components. Thus, let

Y = value of the original time series,

T = value of trend,

C = value of cycle,

I = value of irregular, and

S = value of seasonal;

then the additive model can be expressed as

$$Y = T + S + C + I. \tag{21.1}$$

The *multiplicative model* assumes that the value of original data is the product of the values of the four components. That is,

$$Y = TSCI. \tag{21.2}$$

Note that the additive model assumes the four components to be independent of each other. This means that the individual components are the outcomes of four independent sources of causation. Thus, for example, no matter how high or how low the trend value is, it will have no effect on the seasonal variation or the cyclical fluctuation. The trend of the level of employment since 1900 has been increasing continuously; the additive assumption implies that the seasonal variation in employment from year to year is in no way affected by the continuous growth in employment through time.

The multiplicative model is the one we shall use in our later discussion. This model assumes that the four components are due to different causes but also that they are related to each other. This assumption allows convenient isolation of the components by a series of divisions. It can also be argued that the outcomes of the four components are not due to different causes and cannot be isolated. Particularly, one may argue that both trend and cycles are often subjected to many common factors, such as national income, population, and changes in consumers' preferences.

There are available three common approaches to analysis of time series. One was offered by Warren M. Persons; another by the National Bureau of Economic Research. The Persons method is in common use, and we shall employ it in this text. Persons, in 1919, generalized and described a method of distinguishing trends from cycles that has long been extensively used. The idea is very simple one.

First of all, a simple type of linear function is often selected to represent the average long-run underlying movement of a time series. The main technieque used to fit the trend line is that of least squares. Next, an effort is made to discover whether the data contain seasonal variations. If they do, we eliminate them by dividing the original data by a seasonal index constructed for the purpose. Of course, if annual data are used, seasonals do not show up, and this step is unnecessary. Finally, the deseasonalized data are expressed as deviations, usually in percentage form, from the trend line. These relative deviations represent the cyclical fluctuations in the series. From these, the turning points and the amplitude of cycles in the series may then be examined.

The National Bureau of Economic Research has engaged in the

study of time series for more than half a century under the leadership of Wesley C. Mitchell and Arthur F. Burns. It has developed a method of its own for analyzing time series in order to study the behavior of cyclical fluctuations only. This method, for various reasons, has been used by a few investigators outside the bureau. Nevertheless, the bureau has made invaluable contributions to our understanding of the behavior of business cycles. Its findings are frequently quoted in writings on economic fluctuations and forecasting. They are also often used by firms in their planning and are a basis of many government policies. Thus, the student should gain at least a nodding acquaintance with the bureau's method by reading Burns and Mitchell, *Measuring Business Cycles*.

The method offered by Professors Box and Jenkins is the newest and is concerned with the building of stochastic models for discrete times series in the time-domain. This method attempts to use such models to bring out the nature of the system that generates time series, to obtain "optimal" forecasts of future values of time series, to represent dynamic relationships between two or more time series, and thus to estimate "transform functions" and to derive control policies. This method is highly sophisticated and attractive and is increasing in popularity in application, especially in forecasting. However, it is quite difficult conceptually as well as mathematically. It clearly does not belong to the level of an introductory text in statistics. For those students who might be interested in stochastic models of time series may consult *Time Series Analysis*: Forecasting and Control by George E. P. Box and Gwillym M. Jenkins (Holden–Day, San Francisco, 1970).

In the remaining space of this chapter, we shall present a discussion on secular trends and their measurements. Short-run fluctuations of time series data, that is, seasonal variations and cyclical movements, will be taken up in the chapter that follows. Also in the next chapter, we shall provide the salient features of forecasting with time series.

Before the measurement of any component of a time series is computed, we often find it necessary to make certain adjustments in the raw data. The usual adjustments to be made are for price changes, population changes, comparability, and calendar variations. We supply a brief explanation of these points via the topic of editing time series data.

21.3 EDITING TIME SERIES DATA

Raw data must be edited for price changes if we have a value series and if we are interested only in the quantity changes. The sales of a firm or of an industry may appear to have increased continuously for a number of years and thus show a positive trend. Yet this growth in sales may be due not to an increase in the physical volume of goods sold but to rising prices. If we are to have a more reliable picture of the growth of sales through time, the effects of price changes must be eliminated. Since value is the product of price and quantity, the effect of price changes can be eliminated by dividing each item in the value series by an appropriate price index. This, of course, is the familiar deflation process discussed in the preceding chapter.

The comparisons of production, income, consumption, and other series among nations or among regions in the same country require that raw data be adusted for population changes. For example, we may find that the national income of a country is rising but the per capita income of that nation is actually falling because of a faster growth in population. To avoid distortions in the figures and confusion in our comparative analysis, we should express the series on a per capita basis. This is done by dividing each value in the series by the appropriate total population figures.

Sometimes a series that covers a few decades may not be comparable with another, for a variety of reasons. First, figures for different periods of the series may be collected and reported by different agencies. Second, the definition of an item or the quality of a product may have changed through time. Changes in definitions have the same impact as changes in the limits of a population. The effects of changing quality are to produce noncomparable price quotations. Finally, a series may be reported in different manners at different time intervals. For instance, production figures may be reported as annual monthly averages for some years and, for others, as annual totals. Clearly, to edit data for comparability is a complicated task. It differs from series to series. What we must note here is that it is often difficult and sometimes impossible to get strictly comparable data and, therefore, comparability should not be taken for granted. Also, it must be remembered that comparability of data throughout the period under examination is necessary if meaningful results are to be obtained from analysis.

The use of the Gregorian calendar introduces an irregular yet consistent pattern of variations in monthly time series. Monthly data are skewed because of the fact that the months have varying numbers of days. For example, the month of February can be expected to be a special one in the statistical arrays. Again, national holidays and five-Sunday months produce the same sort of distortion. A series subjected to this kind of illogical and spurious fluctuation should be edited for calendar variations. Such an adjustment is made by a change that makes all months the same length. This is done in two simple steps. First, each monthly figure is divided by the number of days in that month (or by the number of working days in that month if this is appropriate) in order to obtain a daily average for each month. Next, each of the daily averages is multiplied by the average number of days in a month in order to obtain comparable monthly values. The average number of days in a month is the adjusting factor, which is 30.4167 for ordinary years and 30.5 for leap years.

21.4 NATURE OF SECULAR TREND

Secular trend, as a general and persistent movement, disregards the ups and downs of cyclical fluctuations. Short-lived phases of the business cycles pass, leaving a path that, when averaged, reflects the general drift of events over a long period of time. Like other representative measures, the secular trend summarizes the essentials of the life story of economic variables. It measures the average change or growth of time series per unit of time. As such, the secular trend is a sound index of vitality of the organism represented by the time series. Thus, the economic history of an industrialized nation can be told largely in terms of trends established for its major industries. Trends in the major industries are not only of importance to the owners, managers, and workers in these particular fields; they are also of significance as an indication of the economic life of the whole nation, which is mainly made up of these basic economic organs. For this reason, trend measurements today are used primarily to study growth itself in contrast to their principal use before the Great Depression for the study of business cycles.

To establish a trend line that is significant for a time series, the period must be sufficiently long. But the exact length of the period is undefined. It could be as short as 20 days, as in the growth of a population of yeast cells, or it could be as long as a few centuries, as in the growth of the human population of a nation. For most economic time series, the consensus is that the period must cover two or three complete cycles in order to produce any significant trend line.

The slope of a trend line for a given time series may be positive, such as the growth of gross national income of the United States, or negative, such as the ratio of agricultural employment to total labor force in any industrialized nation. It can also be linear or curvilinear. In any case, however, the trend is irreversible and smooth. As an irreversible movement, the trend line does not change direction as frequently as the cyclical fluctuation, although, through its gradual and smooth course, the rate of change may vary, or the direction may even change eventually, as the time series passes from its expansion phase into long-term saturation or decline.

Thus, different sets of time series data can assume a variety of patterns of long-run average behavior. The shapes and mathematical expression of some of the frequently encountered secular trends for business and economic data are as represented by Figure 21.2.

In selecting a method of trend fitting we must avoid the common fallacy of thinking that the facts will speak for themselves. They never do. Every method of observing them, every technique for analyzing them, is an implicit economic theory. Thus, instead of merely looking at the chart of a time series and concluding that a certain type of line would fit the data well, we must start *a priori* with some hypothesis that seems to describe the behavior of the series adequately. Usually, we have different trend hypotheses for the growth of an industry, the growth of the economy, and the growth of the individual firm.

First, what theory can we formulate for the growth of new industries? Empirical observations and theoretical considerations have produced some typical models for the growth of new industries. At the initial stage of a new industry there are only a few pioneering firms that are mainly concerned with exploring the market potential perfecting production techniques, and so on; thus its growth is slow. Then the new

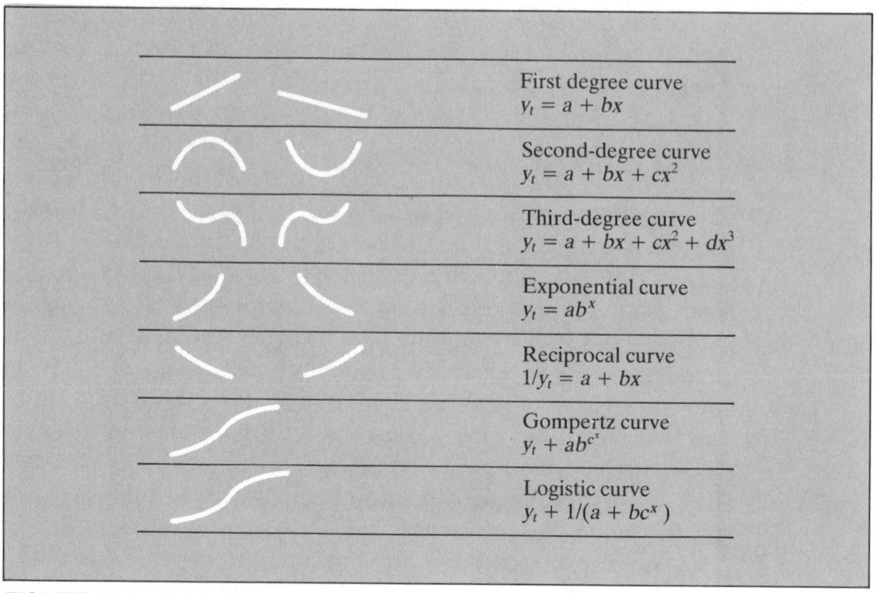

	First degree curve $y_t = a + bx$
	Second-degree curve $y_t = a + bx + cx^2$
	Third-degree curve $y_t = a + bx + cx^2 + dx^3$
	Exponential curve $y_t = ab^x$
	Reciprocal curve $1/y_t = a + bx$
	Gompertz curve $y_t + ab^{c^x}$
	Logistic curve $y_t + 1/(a + bc^x)$

FIGURE 21.2 Illustration of some typical forms of trends.

industry goes through a period of accelerating growth, when it provides the greatest stimulus to net new investment. As it approaches maturity, there is less need to expand capacity, and investment is mainly for replacement and modernization. Consequently, its growth rate continues to decline until the industry reaches a stage of saturation.

This typical behavior of single industries can be described by a number of mathematical curves, all of which trace out an S-shaped pattern of movement. Of these, the best-known and most frequently used is the Gompertz curve. The Gompertz curve, as shown by Figure 21.3 describes a trend in which the growth of increments of the logarithms declines at a constant rate. Therefore, the natural values of the trend show a declining ratio of increase, although by neither a constant amount nor a constant percentage. The curve has an upper and a lower asymptote. The lower asymptote of an upward trend is zero at negatively infinite time. The ordinate of the inflection point of the curve is about 37% of the upper asymptote. This curve is not symmetrical about its inflection point. Its first differences are skewed to the right. It may also be seen from this figure that the Gompertz trend a monotonic function of time; it moves either up or down but not in both directions for the same function. When it moves down, its curvature is convex to the origin, and when graphed on semilog paper it has a lower asymptote, usually not zero.

Another frequently used mathematical curve that may be fitted to a series to yield a declining percentage rate of growth is the "logistic" growth curve. As the Gompertz curve, the logistic trend may be fitted to data on arithmetic or semilog paper and their patterns of movement are approximately identical. It may be noted that the Gompertz and logistic curves, according to detailed studies by Kuznets and others, give a very

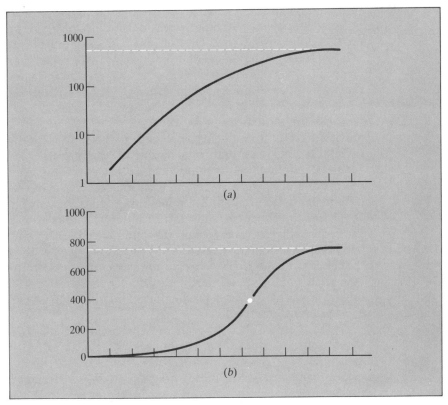

FIGURE 21.3 Gompertz curves drawn to (a) semilogarithmic and (b) arithmetic scales.

close approximation to the growth pattern of individual industries. These curves are often used to describe the "law of growth" of population and of production in certain industries, and are also used extensively in the field of biology. Two points must be kept in mind when we use and interpret the growth curves of individual industries. First, it may be necessary to give these curves an upward tilt in order to reflect the fact that a steady rising national income could lead to some corresponding rise in the saturation level for a particular industry. Second, because of many factors, such as changes in technology, discoveries of new sources of supply or exhaustion of old sources of raw materials, or the sudden emergence of new and strong competition, the growth trend of a particular industry may be subjected to shifts that are quite abrupt. Herein lies the potential danger of projecting the trend of an industry.

The economic growth of a whole nation is the result of the growth of all individual industries. For the economy as a whole, then, the trend should be measured most logically by the series of the Gross National Product. Other types of data, though less comprehensive, are also frequently used to reflect the nation's general economic activity. One method is to select one phenomenon so pervasive that it reveals the amount of activity in many different kinds of transactions. For instance, freight car loadings or the production of cardboard containers follows a pattern of change similar to the output of material products. Bank credit outside New York City is also a fairly accurate measure of the total volume of business of all kinds. A second method is to use a composite index of activities of the basic and vital industries. One of the most widely used indices for this purpose is the FRB Index of Industrial Production described in the last chapter.

On theoretical grounds, the growth of the aggregate economy is quite different from the typical pattern of individual industries. The inevitable and eventual retardation of the growth of an individual industry is influenced by many factors. The more important of these are discoveries of new processes, new products, new materials, changes in consumer tastes, and shifts in population distribution. The very factors that tend to retard old and mature industries, however, also stimulate the establishment of new ones. The stagnation of the coal industry has been more than compensated for by the emergence of the oil and power industries. The decline of textile industries that use cotton and silk as raw materials was primarily caused by discoveries of the synthetic fabrics and the growing production of rayon, nylon, and other chemically produced materials.

Thus, in a dynamic economy characterized by unceasing experimentation and innovation, the general drift of total production may be expected to continue upward. It is possible, furthermore, that this general upward drift could progress along a straight line, either indicating a constant amount of increase per year or reflecting a constant rate of increase annually as revealed by the first-degree and exponential curves.

Our theoretical considerations, however, do not rule out the possibility that the rate of change of the whole economy may vary from period to period. Many studies of American business experience during the past 180 years, for example, show a growth rate which fluctuates between 3% and 4% most of the time.

It may also be noted that, among the factors counted as critical for the long-run growth of the aggregate economy, the most significant is the rate of population growth. Not only does population growth generate continuous increase in the demand for consumer goods and investment expenditures; it also enlarges the labor force of a nation. Other principal aggregate growth factors include natural resources, capital formation, technological development, type of economic system, the sociopolitical fabric of the society, and the religious and psychological attributes of the population.

The growth of an individual enterprise may be reflected in its sales, its production, or its employment. Other things being equal, obviously the most important influence on the growth of individual concerns is the quality of management, which dictates the firm's long-term flexible adaptation to a changing economy. Keeping differences in the quality of management in mind, three possible generalizations can be made about the growth patterns of individual firms. In the first place, the most efficient firms may continue to grow when the industry is subject to retardation. Their continuous growth may be maintained by absorbing weak competitors or by controlling a progressively larger share of the market through shrewd marketing or other effective policies. This process may go on for such a long period as to give the individual concern a trend of apparent indefinite constant growth, as described either by the arithmetic lines or by geometric straight lines.

At the other extreme are the least efficient firms. Such firms may grow when the industry is advancing rapidly, but they face decline when the industry reaches maturity. Trend for this type of behavior, among others, can be described by a second-degree parabola curve.

Then there is the middle possibility. Firms of average efficiency may experience a growth pattern similar to that of the industry of which they are a part.

From our discussion of the nature of trends so far, you may have gained the understanding that, among all the trend patterns in Figure 21.2, the first-degree curve, the second degree curve, and the exponential curve are especially important because they can adequately characterize the growth or decline of many time series. Hence, we shall restrict our discussion to these types of trends.

Before taking on the measurements of secular trends, let us make a general comment on such measurements. Many methods are available for fitting trends to time-series data. In general, as in the regression case, when we fit a line to a set of data, we want the fit to be close, by which we mean that the deviations of the observations from the line will be small. One method that can achieve this is the familiar method of least squares. Recall that this method will yield unbiased and minimum-variance estimators of the trend parameters if the deviations, or residuals, are independent normal variables with constant variance. However, with time series data, these assumptions are nearly never met. For one thing, the raw data to which one fits the trend line have a cyclical component, so deviations from the trend contain cyclical as well as random fluctuations. Because of this, we cannot say that the least-squares trend line is necessarily better than any other trend line. As a descriptive measure, however, the least-squares trend line is just as good as any other and it does have the merit of objectivity, so that it is generally used in time-series analysis.

21.5 THE ARITHMETIC STRAIGHT-LINE TREND

The arithmetic straight line, or the first-degree curve, as shown in Figure 21.2, is certainly the simplest measure of secular trend among all the trend equations. This measure also happens to be one of the most useful, since from theoretical knowledge or practical experience, we have found that many business and economic time series tend to grow or decay by a constant amount per unit of time. The arithmetic straight-line trend equation is a first-degree polynomial as defined below:

$$y_t = A + Bx, \tag{21.3}$$

where

y_t = the computed trend value for time period t;

A = the trend value (in original units of Y) at the origin;

B = the slope of the trend line, measuring the constant amount of change per unit of time;

x = the value of the independent variable, time.

The computations for the least-squares estimators in (21.3) can be greatly simplified with time-series data if we use the middle of the series as the origin. We can do this because the time units in a series are usually of uniform duration and are consecutive numbers. When the middle period is taken as the origin, not only will the mean $\bar{X}$ of the time variable be zero but the sum $\sum x$ of time units will also be zero. Thus, with this practice, the least squares estimators, A and B, in (21.3) are simply

$$A = \frac{\sum y}{n}, \tag{21.4}$$

and

$$B = \frac{\sum xy}{\sum x^2}. \tag{21.5}$$

It will be recognized that (21.4) is the equation for the arithmetic mean of Y. Thus A, the trend value of Y at the origin, is the arithmetic mean of the Y variable. The value of B, of course, is the average and constant amount of change in the trend values per unit of time.

It is helpful to find and state the date of the origin when the middle of a series is used as the origin. In many series, each datum applies to a whole period of time. This being the case, if the series has an odd number of periods, the origin is the middle of middle period; if the series has an even number of the periods, the origin is between the two middle periods. Thus, if we have a series that extends, say, from 1976 to 1988, in years, the origin is taken as the end of June, 1982. On the other hand, if we have a series that covers a period from, say, 1976 to 1987, again in years, the origin then falls between 1981 and 1982—that is, midnight, December 31, 1981.

We may note that there is a practical problem in assigning coded numbers to the time units when we have an even number of time periods. In the example just cited, the origin falls between 1981 and 1982. This means that the middle of 1981 is six months to the left of the origin and the middle of 1982 is six months to the right of the origin. Furthermore, if we wish to keep the time unit at one year, then clearly the X value for 1981 is -0.5, that is half a time unit before the origin. The middle of 1980 is $1\frac{1}{2}$ time units before the origin and hence it has a value of -1.5, and so on. Likewise, consecutive positive values of 0.5, 1.5, 2.5, and so on should be assigned to every year more recent than the origin. There is an alternative method, which considers the time

TABLE 21.1 Computation of Least-squares Straight-line Trend for U.S. Annual Total Production of Anthracite in Thousands of Short Tons, 1972–1984

Year	x	x^2	y	xy	y_t
1972	−6	36	7,106	−42,636	7,092.29
1973	−5	25	6,880	−34,400	6,846.99
1974	−4	16	6,617	−26,468	6,601.70
1975	−3	9	6,203	−18,609	6,356.41
1976	−2	4	6,228	−12,456	6,111.12
1977	−1	1	5,861	−5,861	5,865.83
1978	0	0	5,097	0	5,620.54
1979	1	1	4,985	4,985	5,375.25
1980	2	4	6,056	12,112	5,129.96
1981	3	9	5,423	16,269	4,884.66
1982	4	16	4,588	18,352	4,639.37
1983	5	25	4,069	20,345	4,394.08
1984	6	36	3,954	23,724	4,148.79
Total	0.00	182	73,067	−44,643	—

Source: Business Statistics, 1984.

unit as six months, so that each year has two time units. With this practice, we see that for each year prior to the origin, negative values of −1, −3, −5, and so forth should be assigned. Similarly, for more recent years, the X values are 1, 3, 5, and so on, from the origin. Tables 21.1 and 21.3 are examples of fitting trends to an odd number of time periods and Table 21.2 is an example for the case of an even number of years.

The fitting of an arithmetic straight-line trend is illustrated by the data in Table 21.1. From the sums cumulated in that table, we have

$$\hat{a} = \frac{\Sigma y}{n} = \frac{73,067}{13} \doteq 5620.54;$$

$$b = \frac{\Sigma xy}{x^2} = \frac{-44,643}{182} \doteq -245.29.$$

Hence, the trend equation becomes

$$y_t = 5620.54 - 245.29x.$$

(Origin: 1978; $X = 1$ year; $Y =$ annual total of anthracite production in thousands of short tons, 1972–1984.)

To obtain the trend values we simply substitute the values x of X into the resulting trend equation. For example, the trend value for 1972 in our illustration is

$$y_{1972} = 5620.54 - 245.29(-6)$$

$$= 7092.29 \text{ short tons.}$$

Figure 21.4 is the graphic presentation of the secular trend fitted to the original data.

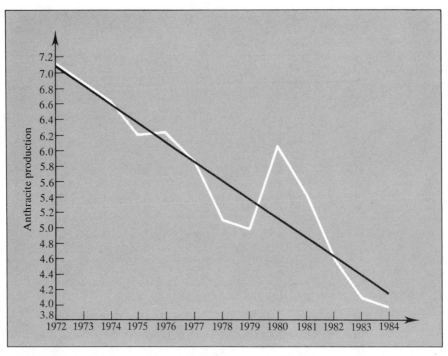

FIGURE 21.4 The least-squares arithmetic straight-line trend for U.S. annual total anthracite production in thousands of short tons, 1972–1984. (*Source:* Table 21.1.)

21.6 THE EXPONENTIAL TREND

As mentioned before, the *exponential trend* is an appropriate description for the underlying long-run drift of a time series if its growth is approximately at a constant rate of increase per unit of time, as might be the case for national product, population of a nation, or production of an industry. This trend is given by the equation

$$y_t = AB^x. \tag{21.6}$$

This expression is sometimes called a growth equation because it is often used to explain the phenomenon of the growth of a time series. In (21.6), A, as before, is the trend value of the series at the origin, and B, as will be shown and explained, is related to the average rate of change of the series.

Turning our attention to the practical problem of fitting an exponential curve to data, we note that if we take logarithms of both sides of (21.6), we obtain a linear function:

$$\log y_t = \log A + x(\log B), \tag{21.7}$$

which has been named the *geometric straight-line trend*. When we set the origin at the middle of the time series, the least-squares estimators

A (the Y-intercept) and B (the slope in (21.7)) are simply computed as follows:

$$\log A = \frac{\sum \log y}{n} \tag{21.8}$$

and

$$\log B = \frac{\sum x(\log y)}{\sum x^2}. \tag{21.9}$$

There is one mathematical restriction in the use of these two equations: Every value of Y in the data must be greater than zero. Otherwise, $\log y$ will not exist for every datum.

As an example of fitting a geometric straight-line trend, consider the data for the index of industrial output of the People's Republic of China from 1952 to 1975. The original data and the various preliminary computations are presented in Table 21.2. With the results in Table

TABLE 21.2 Computation of the Geometric Straight-line Trend for the Index of Chinese Industrial Output, 1952–1975, with 1952 = 100

Year (1)	x (2)	x^2 (3)	y (4)	$\log y$ (5)	$x(\log y)$ (6)	$\log y_t =$ $\log a +$ $x \log b$ (7)	y_t (8)
1952	−11.5	132.25	100	2.0000000	−23.00000	2.10143	126.3
1953	−10.5	110.25	126	2.1003705	−22.05389	2.14025	138.1
1954	−9.5	90.25	147	2.1673173	−20.58951	2.17907	151.0
1955	−8.5	72.25	151	2.1789769	−18.52130	2.21789	165.2
1956	−7.5	56.25	184	2.2648178	−16.98613	2.25671	180.6
1957	−6.5	42.25	208	2.3180633	−15.06741	2.29553	197.5
1958	−5.5	30.25	302	2.4800069	−13.64004	2.33435	215.9
1959	−4.5	20.25	369	2.5670264	−11.55162	2.37317	236.1
1960	−3.5	12.25	384	2.5843312	−9.04516	2.41199	258.2
1961	−2.5	6.25	225	2.3521825	−5.88046	2.45081	282.4
1962	−1.5	2.25	238	2.3765770	−3.56487	2.48963	308.8
1963	0.5	0.25	285	2.4548449	−1.22742	2.52845	337.6
1964	0.5	0.25	339	2.5301997	1.26510	2.56727	369.2
1965	1.5	2.25	415	2.6180481	3.92707	2.60609	403.7
1966	2.5	6.25	481	2.6821451	6.70536	2.64491	441.5
1967	3.5	12.25	421	2.6242821	9.18499	2.68373	482.8
1968	4.5	20.25	463	2.6655810	11.99511	2.72255	527.9
1969	5.5	30.25	551	2.7411516	15.07633	2.76137	577.3
1970	6.5	42.25	653	2.8149132	18.29694	2.80019	631.2
1971	7.5	56.25	711	2.8518696	21.38902	2.83901	690.3
1972	8.5	72.25	772	2.8876173	24.54475	2.87783	754.8
1973	9.5	90.25	866	2.9375179	27.90642	2.91665	825.4
1974	10.5	110.25	901	2.9547248	31.02461	2.95547	902.5
1975	11.5	132.25	991	2.9960737	34.45485	2.99429	986.9
Total	—	1150.00	10283	61.1486388	44.64274	—	—

Source: Derived from estimates compiled by Arthur G. Ashbrook, Jr., in U.S. Congress, Joint Economic Committee, *China: A Reassessment of the Economy* (Washington, D.C., GPO, 1975), pp. 42–43.

21.2, we have

$$\log a = \frac{\Sigma \log y}{n}$$

$$= \frac{61.1486388}{24} \doteq 2.54786,$$

$$a \doteq 353.07;$$

$$\log b = \frac{\Sigma x(\log y)}{\Sigma x^2}$$

$$= \frac{44.64274}{1150} \doteq 0.03882,$$

$$b \doteq 1.0935.$$

It should be noted that $(\log a)$ is the logarithm of the trend value at the origin and that $(\log b)$ is the average rate of change in $\log y_t$ per unit of time.

The geometric straight-line trend for our example, can now be written as

$$\log y_t = 2.54786 + 0.03882x$$

(Origin: December 31, 1963; time unit, 1 year; Y, Chinese industrial output index 1952–1975, with 1952 = 100.)

We may also present this result in exponential form as

$$y_t = 353.07(1.0935)^x.$$

For an exponential trend, the trend values are usually computed by first substituting x into the geometric straight-line trend equation and then converting them back into the original units. See columns (7) and (8) of Table 21.2 on this point.

Note that Figure 21.5 is constructed by plotting the uncoded data values on semilogarithmic paper, with the logarithmic scale extending along the Y axis.

In fitting an exponential trend, we satisfy the condition that the sum of the squares of the logarithmic deviations from the trend is a minimum. That is, the deviations to which the least-squares condition relates are the differences between logarithms of the original data values and the logarithms of the trend values. The geometric straight line, therefore, should not be thought of as the same as the least-squares arithmetic straight line for which the sum of the squares of natural-number deviations is a minimum.

There is a relationship between B and the average rate of growth, R. Namely, $R = B - 1$. For our example,

$$R = b - 1 \doteq 1.0935 - 1 = 0.0935.$$

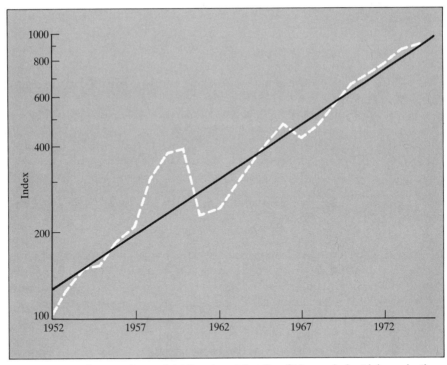

FIGURE 21.5 Geometric straight-line trend for the Chinese industrial production index, 1952–1975, with 1952 = 100. (*Source:* Table 21.2.)

Therefore $(B - 1)$ here can be interpreted as an average annual rate of growth of 9.35%.

This property of $(B - 1)$ for a geometric straight line is of considerable significance. When it has been transformed into a percentage, it defines the average annual rate of growth (or decline) of the series. Being a dimensionless measure, it permits comparisons of trends, all described by straight lines on ratio (semilog) graph paper, of series with different original units. Series, such as production of all kinds, population, or national income, become immediately comparable, and conclusions about the direction and magnitude of economic activities can readily be drawn. Consequently, this measure provides an effective device for the study of socioeconomic changes within a nation and among nations.

21.7 THE SECOND-DEGREE POLYNOMIAL TREND

The arithmetic straight-line trend introduced earlier belongs to a family of simple polynomials whose general formulation is

$$y_t = A + Bx + Cx^2 + Dx^3 + Ex^4 + \cdots,$$

where

A = the Y-intercept;

B = the slope, or the rate of change in Y, at the origin;

C = the rate of change of the slope at the origin—the degree to which the curve is bent;

D = the rate of change of the degree to which the curve is bent at the origin;

E = the rate of change in the rate of change of the degree . . . ; and so forth.

The straight line is the special and simple case in which all constants beyond B are zero. It is called a power curve of the first degree. A convenient way to remember the degree of a power curve is to relate it to the exponent of x in the last term of the equation. A power curve has the same degree as the exponent of x in the last term. The straight line has only the first two terms on the right of the equality sign in the above expression. With three terms on the right, we have a second-degree curve, and so on.

Although the straight line is not always an appropriate representation of trend, it is nevertheless generally the most useful member of the family of trends. Whenever a curve instead of a straight line is necessary to describe the general drift of a series, we must be careful not to fit a high-degree parabola to the data because, if we do, we are almost certain to mix trend with cycle. Moreover, observation of Figure 21.2 will show that none of polynomials of second or higher degrees can be projected very far without going off the page. We shall therefore give only an illustration of fitting a second-degree parabolic trend, and comment briefly on the nature of the third-degree polynomial. No more will be said about higher-degree polynomial trends, since they are not very useful in practice.

The general equation of the second-degree parabolic trend is

$$y_t = A + Bx + Cx^2 \qquad (21.10)$$

where A is still the Y intercept, B is the slope of the curve at the origin, and C is the rate of change in the slope. It should be noted that, just as B is a constant in the first-degree curve, C is a constant in the second-degree curve. Here, the C value determines whether the curve is concave or convex and the extent to which the curve departs from linearity. The second-degree curve, as shown in Figure 21.6 has curvilinearity without point of inflection and C determines the existence or nonexistence of curvilinearity under these conditions.

When the middle of the time series is taken as the origin, the constants in (21.10), as least-squares estimators, are computed by the

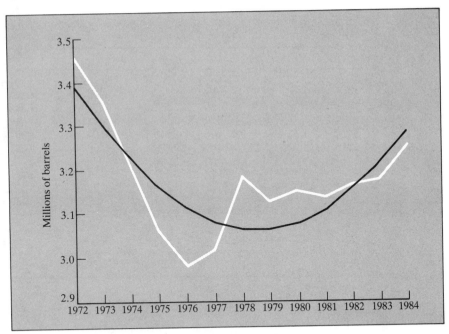

FIGURE 21.6 Second-degree polynomial trend for crude petroleum production in the United States, 1972–1984. (*Source:* Table 21.3.)

following formulas:

$$C = \frac{n \sum x^2 y - \sum x^2 \sum y}{n \sum x^4 - (\sum x^2)^2}, \qquad (21.11)$$

$$A = \frac{\sum y - \sum x^2}{n}, \qquad (21.12)$$

and

$$B = \frac{\sum xy}{x^2}. \qquad (21.13)$$

To obtain the coefficients for a second-degree parabolic trend, therefore, we need five sums, which are $\sum x^2$, $\sum x^4$, $\sum y$, $\sum xy$, and $\sum x^2 y$. Table 21.3 illustrates the procedure for obtaining these totals. For these series, we háve

$$c = \frac{13(592{,}752) - 182(41{,}215.6)}{13(4550) - (182^2)}$$

$$\doteq 7.859;$$

$$a = \frac{41{,}215.6 - 7.859(182)}{13}$$

$$\doteq 3060.405;$$

$$b = \frac{-169^2}{182} \doteq -9.297.$$

TABLE 21.3 Computation of the Least-squares Parabolic Trend for the Annual Volume of Crude Petroleum of the United States in Millions of Barrels, 1972–1984

Year	x	x^2	x^4	y	xy	x^2y	y_t
1972	−6	36	1,296	3,455.4	−20,732.4	124,394.4	3,399
1973	−5	25	625	3,360.9	−16,804.5	84,022.5	3,303
1974	−4	16	256	3,202.6	−12,810.4	51,241.6	3,223
1975	−3	9	81	3,056.8	−9,170.4	27,511.2	3,159
1976	−2	4	16	2,976.2	−5,952.4	11,904.8	3.110
1977	−1	1	1	3,009.8	−3,009.8	3,009.8	3,078
1978	0	0	0	3,178.2	0.0	0.0	3,060
1979	1	1	1	3,121.3	3,121.3	3,121.3	3,059
1980	2	4	16	3,146.4	6,292.8	12,585.6	3,073
1981	3	9	81	3,128.6	9,385.8	28,157.4	3103
1982	4	16	256	3,158.7	12,634.8	50,539.2	3,149
1983	5	25	625	3,171.0	15,855.0	79,275.0	3,210
1984	6	36	1,296	3,249.7	19,498.2	116,989.2	3,288
Total	—	182	4,550	41,215.6	−1,692	592,752	—

Source: Business Statistics, 1984.

With these results, the second degree least-squares trend equation for our example can then be written as

$$y_t = 3060.405 - 9.297x + 7.859x^2.$$

(Origin: 1978; $X = 1$ year; $Y =$ annual total in millions of barrels, 1972–1984.)

The trend values here are obtained by substituting the x and x^2 into the trend equation obtained. Thus, for example,

$$y_{1983} = 3060.405 - 9.297(5) + 7.859(25)$$

$$\doteq 3210 \text{ millions of barrels.}$$

To draw curvilinear trends, it is advisable to plot all the computed trend values on the chart. The trend drawn through the original data for our example is shown by Figure 21.8.

It may be pointed out that the value of B in a second-degree curve is identical with that in the straight-line trend for the same series if the second-degree curve is fitted from the middle of the series. In our present situation, furthermore, the positive value of C makes the curve convex to the X axis. Conversely, negative values of C will make the curve concave to the X axis.

When the value of x^2 becomes larger at the extremes of the series, the influence of C upon the trend increases, and the departure from linearity becomes quite marked. This limits somewhat the usefulness of this type of trend for the forecasting of trend values.

Now, a few words on the third-degree trend. As shown by the equation for this trend in Figure 21.2, this polynomial trend has four constants. The addition of the constant D reflects the fact that the concavity of the cubic curve changes from one point on the curve to another. Thus, it is quite possible for a curve of this type, by changing its concavity, to reverse the direction of the bend. It may actually assume an S shape. It is therefore a very flexible curve and provides a reasonably good description of some economic time series, especially if the period covered is relatively long. However, as has already been mentioned, the flexibility of higher-degree polynomials, such as this, is actually their weakness as well. This is so because when such a curve follows the data too closely it may fail to reveal the persisting and irreversible general drift of the series under the strong influences of cyclical fluctuations.

21.8 THE METHOD OF MOVING AVERAGES

A moving average may be considered as an artificially constructed time series in which each period's actual figure is replaced by the mean of the value of that period and those of a number of the preceding and succeeding periods. The properties and utility of moving averages can perhaps be brought out more vividly by a hypothetical illustration. The hypothetical data in Table 21.4 are assumed to have a uniform cyclical duration of 5 years and equal cyclical amplitudes of 2 units. Three-year and five-year moving averages are fitted to the data. The procedure for

TABLE 21.4 Computation of Three-year and Five-year Moving Averages for Hypothetical Data Having Five-year Cycles with Uniform Duration and Amplitude

Year (1)	Original Values (2)	Three-year mt (3)	Three-year ma (4)	Five-year mt (5)	Five-year ma (6)
1	1	—	—	—	—
2	2	6	2.0	—	—
3	3	7	2.3	9	1.8
4	2	6	2.0	10	2.0
5	1	5	1.7	11	2.2
6	2	6	2.0	12	2.4
7	3	9	3.0	13	2.6
8	4	10	3.3	14	2.8
9	3	9	3.0	15	3.0
10	2	8	2.7	16	3.2
11	3	9	3.0	17	3.4
12	4	12	4.0	18	3.6
13	5	13	4.3	19	3.8
14	4	12	4.0	20	4.0
15	3	11	3.7	21	4.2
16	4	12	4.0	22	4.4
17	5	15	5.0	23	4.6
18	6	16	5.3	24	4.8
19	5	15	5.0	—	—
20	4	—	—	—	—

calculating three-year moving averages is as follows:

1. Compute the three-year moving totals. This is done by adding up the values of the first three years and centering at the second year. This is the first three-year moving total. Then the value of the first year is dropped and the value of the fourth year is added to form the second three-year moving total, which is centered at the third year. And so the computation moves through the end of the series. The three-year moving totals are entered in column 3 of Table 21.4.

2. The three-year moving averages are obtained simply by dividing each of the three-year moving totals by 3. These values for our example are entered in column 4 of Table 21.4.

A similar procedure is used to compute the five-year moving averages. In a five-year moving average, the value of each year is replaced by the mean of the values of the five successive years of which two precede and two succeed the given year. Both five-year moving totals and moving averages are, of course, centered in the middle of the respective five-year period, with the first five-year moving total and the moving average centered in the third year. Columns 5 and 6 in Table 21.4 illustrate the computation of five-year moving averages. It may also be pointed out in passing that in computing moving averages for an even number of periods, the procedure becomes more complicated. Such a procedure will be discussed in the next chapter.

The results of our calculations are plotted with the original data in Figure 21.7. Both sets of moving averages may be considered as the statistical expression of secular movement of our hypothetical series.

By studying Table 21.4 and Figure 21.7, we can reach several

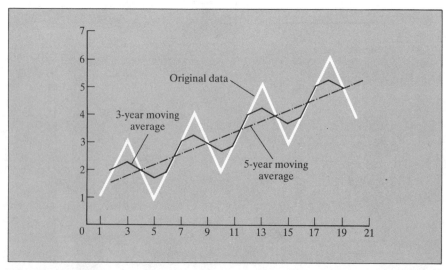

FIGURE 21.7 Three-year and five-year moving-average trends fitted to hypothetical data having five-year cycles with uniform duration and amplitude.

conclusions about the characteristics of moving averages:

1. If the data show a uniform periodic fluctuation, a moving average of length equal to the period will completely eliminate the periodic variations.

2. If the series changes on the average by a constant amount per time unit and its fluctuations are periodic, a moving average of length equal to the period will be linear.

3. Even if the data show a periodic fluctuation, a moving average of some length other than the length of the period, no matter how small the difference is between the duration of periodicity of the original series and the duration of the moving average, cannot obliterate completely the periodic variations in the original series. The averaging process then only tends to smooth out somewhat the short-run highs and lows.

With these properties in mind, we can see that the moving average may constitute a satisfactory trend for a series that is basically linear and whose cycles are regular in duration and amplitude. But these conditions are seldom met by any economic time series. The use of the moving average as a trend measure entails two disadvantages. First, in computing moving averages we lose some years at each end of the series. For instance, we lose two years at each end with the five-year moving average. Had we computed a seven-year moving average, we would have lost three years at each end.

A still more serious drawback is that the moving average is not represented by some particular mathematical function and, therefore, is usually not capable of objective projection into the future. Since one of the main objectives of trend analysis is that of forecasting, the moving average, lacking this desirable property, is no longer in wide use as a trend measure.

Nevertheless, the method of moving averages is a very useful technique in analyzing time series. First, in problems in which the trend of the time series is clearly not linear and in which we are concerned only with the general movements of the time series, be it trend, or a cycle, or possibly both, it is customary to study the smoothed behavior of the series by applying a moving average. Second, as we shall see in the following chapter, the moving average is the basis for the construction of a seasonal index.

21.9 SHIFTING THE TREND ORIGIN AND CHANGING THE TIME PERIOD

Shifting the Trend Origin

For simplicity and ease of computation, trends are usually fitted to annual data with the middle of the series as the origin. Very often we need to change the origin of the trend equation to some other point in the series. Annual trend values must be changed to quarterly or monthly values if we wish to study seasonal or cyclical patterns.

The shifting of the trend origin amounts to finding the new Y-intercept—that is, for an arithmetic straight line, the new value of a. The value of b remains unchanged, since the slope of the trend line is the same, irrespective of the origin. The procedure of shifting the origin may be generalized by the expression

$$y_t = A + B(x' + k), \tag{21.14}$$

where k is the number of time units shifted, x' is time measured from the new origin, and $x = x' + k$. If the origin is shifted forward in time, k is positive; if the converse, k is negative. Thus, to change the origin of the trend equation obtained from the anthracite data in Table 21.1 from 1978, for example, to 1984, we have

$$y_t = 5620.54 - 245.29(x' + 6)$$

$$= 4148.80 - 245.29x'.$$

(Oirigin: 1984)

Equation (21.14) can also be expanded to cover parabolic trend formulas. As an example, we may consider the following equation for the second-degree trend of data in Table 21.3: $y_t = 3060.405 - 9.297x + 7.859x^2$ with 1978 as its origin. Now, suppose we wish to shift this origin backward to, say, 1972, then we have

$$y_t = 3060.405 - 9.297(x' - 6) + 7.859(x' - 6)^2$$

$$= 3060.405 - 9.297x' + 55.782$$

$$+ 7.859(x'^2 - 12x' + 36)$$

$$= 3399 - 103.605x' + 7.297x'^2.$$

(Origin: 1972)

Reducing Annual Trend Values to Monthly Values

Monthly trend equations can be derived from annual trend equations without any loss in accuracy, except perhaps for rounding errors. When the Y units are annual totals, then an annual trend equation can be converted into an equation for monthly totals by dividing the computed constant A by 12 and the value of B by 144. (We divide A and B by 12 because the data are sums of 12 months, and we divide B by 12 again so that the time units, x will be in months as well.) If the annual trend equation is of second degree, the corresponding monthly trend equation is obtained by dividing A by 12, B by 144 and C by 1728, the last being identical to dividing C by 12 three times. Thus, for example, to reduce the second-degree trend equation for the data in Table 21.3 to monthly values, we have

$$y_t = \frac{3060.405}{12} - \frac{9.297}{144}(x) + \frac{7.859}{1728}(x)^2$$

$$\doteq 255.03375 - 0.064525x + 0.00458x^2.$$

(Origin: July 1, 1974)

The origin of this monthly trend equation may be shifted by half a month so that it will center at June 15, or at July 15, of 1974.

When data are given as monthly averages per year, the A value in the annual trend equation is already the arithmetic mean of the 12-month total. That is, A is already at the monthly level. The B value now represents the annual change in monthly magnitudes. Consequently, to convert an annual trend equation when annual data are expressed as monthly averages, A remains unchanged and B is divided by 12 only once. Of course, with a second-degree trend equation, the value of C now should be divided by 144.

A series of index numbers can be thought as data in the form of monthly averages per year. Thus, if we wish to convert the geometric straight-line trend for the Chinese industrial output index into monthly terms and to shift the origin half a month forward, we have then

$$\log y_t = 2.54786 + \frac{0.038820}{12}(x' + 0.5)$$

$$\doteq 2.54786 + 0.003235x'.$$

(Origin: July 15, 1964)

We may, on occasion, need to convert an annual trend equation into quarterly values. The procedure involved is similar to that which has just been explained. This is left as an exercise for you.

21.10 CHOICE OF PERIOD AND MATHEMATICAL EXPRESSION FOR TREND

Before concluding this chapter, we must take notice of two more analytical considerations in measuring trend: the choice of the period to be covered and the selection of the mathematical expression for the secular trend for the series.

Generally speaking, the longer the period covered the more significant the trend. Secular movements cannot be expected to reveal themselves clearly within a short span of time. When the period is too short, the general drift of the series may be unduly influenced by the cyclical fluctuations. This will make it difficult to separate the various

858 □ Statistical Analysis for Business and Economics

sources of variations in time series. As a minimum safety guard, it may be said that to compute trend the period must cover at least two or three complete cycles.

Furthermore, in order to produce more accurate values of the Y-intercept and the slope of the trend equation, the period must be so selected that the number of prosperous years must be about the same as the number of depressed years, and that the first and last years of the series must be on the opposite sides of the cycle, that is, if the series starts with an upswing it should end with a downswing. If the number of prosperous years is greater than the number of depressed years, the Y-intercept and, therefore, the level of the trend will be too high. If the situation is reversed, then the level of trend would be too low. If the series starts and ends with a cyclical upswing, the value of slope will be too large. If both the first and last years of the series coincide with a cyclical downswing, then the value of the slope will be too small. The correct value of the slope, therefore, can be derived only for a series that starts with an upswing and ends with a downswing, or vice versa. It may also be noted that usually bias in the slope is more damaging than bias in the level, since a trend becomes progressively worse as X increases if the slope is inaccurate.

The selection of the mathematical expression for a trend is always a difficult matter, because there is really no objective test than can be applied. In any case, in the selection of the mathematical expression to be employed in trend fitting for a given series, the very first thing to do is to establish a hypothesis or theory about the long-run average behavior of the series. Next, we should plot the data and subject them to economic analysis in accordance with the hypothesis we have formulated. If observation of the graph seems to support our hypothesis about the data, then a mathematical expression and the method of fitting it may be finally determined in conjunction with the following criteria.

1. Subject to modification in view of the other criteria, it must provide the best fit.

2. It must be able to provide reasonable extrapolated values.

3. It must be able to provide a trend that is free from cyclical and irregular influences.

The selection of a mathematical expression, therefore, cannot be defended by tests of goodness-of-fit alone. It is for this reason that more complex curves are avoided in applied work. Such curves may on occasion provide excellent fits, but they are neither free from cyclical influences nor capable of yielding reasonable extrapolated values.

Trend values are affected by a myriad of economic and social forces, legal framework, and natural phenomena; hence any attempt to express the aggregate impact of these by a simple formula is often fruitless and frustrating.

We may conclude our discussion by saying that trend fitting is at best an elusive process. It can contribute only an approximate concept of long-run forces. For this reason more time should be spent in studying the underlying socioeconomic, technological, and legal factors that contribute to the general drift than in attempting to improve the fit of a curve.

GLOSSARY OF FORMULAS

(21.1) $Y = T + S + C + I$;

(21.2) $Y = TSCI$.

A time series is hypothesized to be composed of four components: the secular trend T, the cyclical fluctuation C, the seasonal variations S, and the irregular movements I. There are many models for the composition of a time series, but the most popular ones are the two given here. Equation (21.1) defines what is called the *additive model,* which assumes the components are independent; that is, that the values of one are not affected and do not affect the values of any other component. Equation (21.2) defines the *multiplicative model,* which assumes that the four components are mutually dependent. This is the model we have adopted in this text for time series analysis.

(21.3) $y_t = A + Bx$;

(21.4) $A = \sum y/n$;

(21.5) $B = \sum xy / \sum x^2$.

The first equation here defines the arithmetic straight-line trend, where A is the trend value at the origin and B is the slope of the trend line. Here, the value of B measures the constant amount of change of the series per unit of time. When the origin is set at the middle of the time period, which is the independent variable, then the least-squares estimators for the parameters A and B are given by Equations (21.4) and (21.5), respectively.

(21.6) $y_t = AB^x$;

(21.7) $\log y_t = \log A + x(\log B)$;

(21.8) $\log A = \sum \log y/n$;

(21.9) $\log B = \sum x(\log y)/\sum x^2$.

If this set of formulas, (21.6) defines the exponential trend. For this equation, A, as usual, is the Y-intercept or the value of trend at the origin. The value of B, the slope of the trend line, has a special and significant meaning. Precisely, $R = B - 1$ and R here measures the average rate of change of the trend per unit of time. Being pure numbers (i.e. proportion or percentages), the values of R for different exponential trends can be compared readily. For computational purposes, (21.6) is converted into a geometric straight-line trend equation as shown by (21.7). Setting the origin of the series at the middle of time, $\log A$ and $\log B$ are LSEs in terms of logarithms, as given by equations (21.8) and (21.9) respectively.

(21.10) $y_t = A + Bx + Cx^2$;

(21.11) $C = (n \sum x^2 y - \sum x^2 \sum y)/[n \sum x^4 - (\sum x^2)^2]$;

(21.12) $A = (\sum y - \sum x^2)/n$;

(21.13) $B = \sum xy / \sum x^2$.

The first equation, (21.10), in this group defines the second-degree polynomial trend. In this equation, A = the Y-intercept or the trend value at the origin; B = the slope of the curve at the origin, and C = the rate of change in the slope, which determines whether the curve is concave or convex and the extent to which the curve departs from linearity. It is typical of trend of this type that the curve changes direction only once. Given the origin at the middle of the time periods, A, B, and C, as defined by the last three formulas, are LSEs.

(21.14) $y_t = A + B(x' + k)$.

This equation is designed for shifting the origin of a trend equation. In this expression, k = the number of time units shifted, x' = the time measured from the new origin, and $x = x' + k$. If the origin is shifted forward in time, k is positive; if the reverse, k is negative.

REVIEW QUESTIONS

21.1 What are the reasons for time-series analysis? Explain briefly the meaning of each of the four components of a time series.

21.2 What are the two most popular models for the composition of time series? What is the main difference between these two models?

21.3 Provide the essence of the Personian method of time series analysis.

21.4 What are the main points to be noted in editing time series data?

21.5 What are the general factors for secular trend of time series? Do you expect, generally, the trend of a firm to be different from that of the industry and that of the industry, in turn, to be different from that of the nation? If so, why? If not, why not?

21.6 How should the constants in the arithmetic straight-line trend be interpreted?

21.7 Under what condition is it appropriate to use the exponential trend? How should the slope B in such a trend equation be interpreted?

21.8 Why is it possible to compare two or more exponential trend equations readily?

21.9 What is the most important shortcoming of a second-degree trend equation?

21.10 It may be quite safe to project the trend value of a series to a number of time periods into future. Why?

21.11 What are moving averages? What are the important properties of moving averages?

21.12 Since moving averages are a poor measure of trend, why do we still consider them as an important device in time-series analysis?

21.13 What are the reasons for shifting the origin of a trend equation?

21.14 What are reasons of reducing annual trend values to monthly values?

21.15 What are the considerations in selecting a proper trend equation for a time series?

PROBLEMS

Note: Do those problems assigned by your instructor by hand and the rest on computer.

21.1 For the data in Table 21.P1, do the following:
   a. Graph the data and explain whether an arithmetic straight-line trend is appropriate.
   b. Determine the arithmetic straight-line trend.
   c. Calculate the trend values for each year in the data and fit the trend line to your graph.
   d. Calculate what the trend values would be for 1986 and 1987.

TABLE 21.P1 Annual Total U.S. Imports of Goods and Services (in billions of dollars), 1974–1985

Year	Y	Year	Y	Year	Y
1974	137.52	1978	230.32	1982	349.97
1975	133.00	1979	282.14	1983	365.55
1976	162.43	1980	333.54	1984	452.84
1977	194.17	1981	262.58	1985	470.50

Source: Adapted from *Survey of Current Business,* January 1987.

21.2 Do the same as for the preceding problem for the data in Table 21.P2.

TABLE 21.P2 Annual Total Hosiery Shipments in the United States (in million dozen pairs), 1971–1985

Year	Y	Year	Y	Year	Y
1971	211	1976	241	1981	303
1972	229	1977	248	1982	289
1973	228	1978	268	1983	308
1974	218	1979	290	1984	309
1975	226	1980	286	1985	309

Source: Adapted from *Survey of Current Business,* January 1987.

21.3 For the data in Table 21.P3, do the following.
   a. Plot the data on arithmetic-scale graph.
   b. Plot the data on semilog paper.
   c. Establish an arithmetic straight-line trend and compute the trend values. Fit the trend line to the original data on the arithmetic-scale graph.
   d. Establish a geometric straight-line trend and compute the trend values. Fit the trend line to the original data on the semi-log-scale graph.
   e. Plot the trend values of geometric straight-line trend on the same graph for the arithmetic straight-line trend. Which trend line seems to fit the data better in your judgment? Explain.
   f. What is the projected trend for 1987 by the arithmetic straight-line trend? By the geometric straight-line trend?

TABLE 21.P3 GNP of the United States (in billions of dollars), 1971–1985

Year	Y	Year	Y	Year	Y
1971	1049	1976	1620	1981	2876
1972	1142	1977	1835	1982	3026
1973	1284	1978	2032	1983	3174
1974	1388	1979	2366	1984	3553
1975	1480	1980	2573	1985	3889

Source: Adapted from *Survey of Current Business,* January 1987.

21.4 For the data in Table 21.P4, do the following:
   a. Compute a second-degree trend equation and fit it to the original data graphically.
   b. Comment as thoroughly as you can on the goodness-of-fit in this case.

TABLE 21.P4 International Operations of Air-Carriers (in millions of mail ton-miles), 1972–1985

Year	Y	Year	Y	Year	Y
1972	515	1977	397	1982	399
1973	522	1978	374	1983	415
1974	471	1979	372	1984	457
1975	426	1980	392	1985	433
1976	407	1981	376	—	

Source: Adapted from *Survey of Current Business,* January 1987.

21.5 Do the same as for the preceding problem with the data in Table 21.P5.

TABLE 21.P5 New Construction of Public Buildings (excluding military) in the United States (in millions of dollars) 1971–1985

Year	Y	Year	Y	Year	Y
1971	1136	1976	720	1981	1722
1972	874	1977	908	1982	1658
1973	941	1978	1053	1983	1700
1974	1006	1979	1211	1984	1636
1975	754	1980	1648	1985	1516

Source: Adapted from *Survey of Current Business,* January 1987.

21.6 Reduce all the annual trend equations obtained in the first five problems to monthly trend equations.

21.7 Shift the origin of each of the trend equations obtained in the last problem to the middle of December, 1985.

21.8 The series in Table 21.P6 represents for the Federal Reserve Board's Index of U.S. Industrial Production, not seasonally adjusted, 1967 = 100, for years 1966–1979.
   a. Graph the data and compute an appropriate trend equation according to your judgment.
   b. Fit the trend line to the original data in your graph.

TABLE 21.P6 Federal Reserve Board's Index of U.S. Industrial Production, 1966–1979 (1967 = 100)

Year	Jan.	Feb.	Mar.	Apr.	May	June	July	Aug.	Sept.	Oct.	Nov.	Dec.
1966	92.7	95.3	97.3	97.1	97.8	100.0	93.8	97.2	101.7	102.8	100.0	97.5
1967	98.1	99.1	99.0	99.6	98.7	100.9	94.3	99.6	102.7	103.4	103.1	101.4
1968	101.8	104.5	105.6	104.9	106.5	109.3	102.5	105.5	109.6	110.1	109.6	106.2
1969	107.3	110.4	111.6	110.6	110.5	114.0	107.3	111.6	115.1	115.1	112.0	108.3
1970	106.5	109.1	109.4	108.8	108.6	110.8	104.5	108.0	110.4	108.0	105.1	104.1
1971	105.5	108.3	108.6	108.8	109.5	112.5	105.4	108.8	113.5	113.9	111.6	108.5
1972	111.5	115.6	116.8	118.7	118.4	121.8	114.2	120.5	125.5	126.8	125.2	121.8
1973	122.7	128.1	128.8	128.6	129.6	133.0	126.4	130.3	134.8	135.3	132.9	126.7
1974	126.3	129.8	130.8	129.9	131.7	135.3	127.3	131.4	135.5	133.1	125.5	114.9
1975	111.8	113.0	111.8	113.0	113.8	119.2	114.5	121.4	125.9	125.4	123.8	119.8
1976	122.4	128.7	129.1	129.1	130.5	134.0	127.2	132.5	135.1	134.8	133.0	129.1
1977	130.0	134.7	136.6	137.1	138.3	142.6	135.3	139.6	143.5	143.9	140.4	135.8
1978	135.7	140.5	142.4	145.3	144.9	149.8	142.9	148.2	153.0	153.4	150.5	147.1
1979	146.9	152.7	154.5	151.3	152.8	156.9	149.0	152.7	157.1	156.2	152.4	147.7

Source: For 1966–1975, U.S. Board of Governors of the Federal Reserve System, *Industrial Production,* 1976 *Revision,* page S-144. For 1976–1978, Federal Reserve "Industrial Production" release G.12.3, August 16, 1979. For 1979, Federal Reserve "Industrial Production" release G.12.3, September 16, 1980.

22 Measures of Short-Run Fluctuations and Forecasting Techniques

22.1 INTRODUCTION

The measurement of long-run growth or decay is but one of the problems connected with time series analysis. Time series are also subjected to short-run fluctuations, seasonal and cyclical in nature, that are of great interest and importance to economic research and business policy formulation. Added to these, there are also irregular movements that require some consideration. We deal with short fluctuations in this chapter. We will also provide a discussion of business forecasting with stress on those forecasting methods that are used to predict the various components of time series data by the end of this chapter.

The Nature of Seasonal Variations

Seasonal variations follow a pattern of regular recurrence over time. The word "seasonal" has a broad meaning. A seasonal pattern may be a daily one (average temperatures for 24 hours), or a weekly one (store sales), or an annual one (employment). Nevertheless, seasonal patterns for many types of economic time series are related to the changing seasons of the year. Also, like the seasons, they tend to repeat themselves, even though the precise pattern may change through the passage of time.

Weather and social customs are the most important factors of seasonal variations. Variations in weather are clearly an important cause of seasonal patterns in agricultural production, construction work, logging and lumbering activities, and their related series. The relatively large seasonal variation experienced by the retail trade is the joint effect of customary buying seasons and weather-induced changes in consumer demand.

Seasonal variations generate problems for the individual firms as well as for the economy as a whole. They are expensive and wasteful because they necessitate surplus plant capacity and idle labor during seasonal slack periods. For the individual firm there is perhaps no other phase of time series analyses so vital to the day-to-day planning of business operations as seasonal analysis. Management must allow for seasonal variations in its purchases of raw materials and its employment of workers in order to offset these variations or to take advantage of them. Excess capacity in individual industries adds up to an enormous waste of resources for the entire economy. Whether or not a comprehensive solution for seasonal variation is possible, an understanding of its nature and an accurate method of measuring it are certainly a necessary first step toward a possible solution.

Our interest in seasonal analysis is not confined to its own significance only. If we are to succeed in studying business cycles, ability to analyze seasonal influences and to remove their effects on the raw data is essential. Unless seasonally adjusted data are used, the location of the turning points of cycles can never be precisely determined.

A technical problem exists for the students of business cycles because seasonal patterns tend to change through time. The change may be gradual, because of technological advancements or because of changes in weather, custom, consumer tastes, government policy, or business practices. The change may be abrupt, because of some powerful and rather prolonged irregular forces, such as World War II. With this changing characteristic, we may fail to measure the exact pattern of seasonal variations. Although methods are available to measure changing seasonals, these techniques are based on the rather unrealistic assumption that the seasonals are changing in some regular and systematic pattern. Fortunately, cyclical movements are usually so pronounced that they show up clearly when conventional methods, as presented shortly are used to eliminate seasonal variations. Difficulties do arise from time to time, however, when we attempt to trace the movement of cycles that are brief in duration and mild in intensity.

Nature of Cyclical and Irregular Movements

The term *business cycles* refers to cyclical fluctuations in the aggregate economic activity of a nation. They should be represented in series in the GNP or in other indices that reflect general business activity. Cyclical fluctuations in production or sales of an individual industry or firm are usually referred to as *specific cycles*. Methods used to measure business and specific cycles are the same.

Arthur F. Burns and Wesley C. Mitchell of the National Bureau of

Economic Research have written one of the most frequently quoted definitions of business cycles:

> Business cycles are a type of fluctuation found in the aggregate economic activity of nations that organize their work mainly in business enterprises: a cycle consists of expansions occurring at about the same time in many economic activities, followed by similarly general recessions, contractions, and revivals which merge into the expansion phase of the next cycle; this sequence of changes is recurrent but not periodic; in duration business cycles vary from more than one year to ten or twelve years; they are not divisible into shorter cycles of similar character with amplitudes approximating their own.—Arthur F. Burns and Wesley C. Mitchell, *Measuring Business Cycles*.

From the definition quoted above we may appreciate the complex nature of business cycles and the difficulty of studying them. There is in each cycle, following a period of decline, an upturn that gradually quickens its pace until it develops into a period of prosperity; then this reaches a limit; whereupon a downturn ensues that culminates in a depression. These four phases of a cycle are often termed *recovery, prosperity, recession,* and *depression.* The first two phases constitute a cumulative *upswing,* and the last two phases are the cumulative *downswing* of a cycle. The peak and trough of a cycle are often referred to as the *downturn* and *upturn,* respectively. A cycle is measured either from trough to trough or from peak to peak.

The most striking characteristic of cycles, general as well as specific, is that each cycle is a unique historical phenomenon. Each cycle differs from all the rest in duration, amplitude, and causes. This may account for the existence of more business cycle theories than the number of recorded cycles. Thus we shall not even attempt to mention here the main forces that lead to this type of fluctuation. The interested student may find the information in any standard textbook on business cycles.

Irregular movements are a type of fluctuation that is caused by random forces or specific and sporadic causes. A random movement, as its name implies, is completely unpredictable, though it does contribute to period-to-period variations. Random movements, fortunately, are relatively unimportant, so that in practice we may simply consider them merely as part of the total cyclical swing or as seasonal variations. Although it is impossible to identify or explain the random forces, their effects can be clearly seen. They appear as slight saw-tooth irregularities on cyclical movements in most monthly series.

Irregular movements caused by sporadic changes are more serious and their causes can usually be traced. For instance, strikes, earthquakes, floods, wars, and the like, produce sharp breaks in the underlying cyclical sweeps in most economic time series. Therefore, in measuring seasonals and cycles, these specific and sporadic causes must be recognized and due allowance must be made for them if possible.

22.2 ANALYSIS OF SEASONAL VARIATIONS

For business and economic data, a *seasonal index* usually contains twelve numbers, one for each month of a year, or for each of the months of a number of years, showing the relative amount of activity for a year, or a number of years, that has typically taken place in each month. Thus, a seasonal index may be specific or typical. A *specific seasonal index* refers to the seasonal changes during a particular year. A *typical seasonal index* is obtained by averaging a number of specific seasonals. It is thus a generalized expression of seasonal variations in a series.

By observing specific seasonals, one can determine whether the seasonal pattern of a series is stable or is changing gradually or abruptly. The representativeness of a typical seasonal index requires that the specific seasonals must be stable. With changing specific seasonals, the construction of a typical seasonal index is highly questionable and of little practical value.

There are available several methods of isolating seasonal variations from a time series, each having merits and drawbacks. Among these, the *method of ratio-to-moving-average* is by far superior, from a theoretical point of view as well as for practical reasons. We shall consider this method in detail before turning to have a look at the alternative procedures.

Construction of a Seasonal Index by the Method of Ratio-to-Moving-Average

The method of ratio-to-moving-average is very simple in principle. Its application, however, is very time-consuming and tedious without the aid of computers. This method starts with the multiplicative assumption for a time series; that is, $Y = TSCI$. It first attempts to estimate trend and cycle of the series, TC, by employing a 12-month moving average. After this, TC is eliminated, producing SI. This is done by dividing TC into the original data. Namely,

$$\frac{TSCI}{TC} = SI.$$

Finally, irregular movements, I, are eliminated from SI by an averaging process, producing S.

To illustrate the application of this method, we use the series for frozen vegetables (stocks, cold storage, end of month), 1952–1958; these data are entered in column (2) of Table 22.1.

To begin with, note that the first 12-month moving total—the 5204 in column (3)—is entered *between* June and July. This peculiarity is due, essentially, to the fact that an even number of time periods was used to produce the moving total; the data are for end-of-month dates, and the center of a 12-month period is not at the end of the sixth month or at the end of the seventh month, but between these dates. Similarly, the next 12-month moving total (the 5255) is between July and August.

TABLE 22.1 Frozen Vegetables, Stocks, Cold Storage, End of the Month, 1952–1958 (millions of pounds)

Computation of Ratios to Centered 12-month Moving Averages

Year and Month	Stock	12-Month Moving Total	12-Month Moving Average	Centered 12-Month Moving Average	Ratio-to-Moving-Average (%)
(1)	(2)	(3)	(4)	(5)	(6)
1952				—	
Jan.	444	—	—	—	—
Feb.	399	—	—	—	—
Mar.	348	—	—	—	—
Apr.	314	—	—	—	—
May	302	—	—	—	—
June	337	—	—	—	—
July	385	5204	433.67	435.80	88.3
Aug.	463	5255	437.92	440.05	105.2
Sept.	530	5306	442.17	445.17	119.1
Oct.	577	5378	448.17	451.09	127.9
Nov.	570	5448	454.00	456.46	124.9
Dec.	535	5507	458.92	460.88	116.1
		5554	462.83		
1953					
Jan.	495	5637	469.75	466.29	106.2
Feb.	450	5748	479.00	474.38	94.9
Mar.	420	5906	492.17	485.59	86.5
Apr.	384	6066	505.50	498.84	77.0
May	361	6218	518.17	511.84	70.5
June	384	6388	532.33	525.25	73.1
July	468	6524	543.67	538.00	87.0
Aug.	574	6638	553.17	548.42	104.7
Sept.	688	6731	560.92	557.05	123.5
Oct.	737	6817	568.08	564.50	130.6
Nov.	722	6902	575.17	571.63	126.3
Dec.	705	6962	580.17	577.67	122.0
1954					
Jan.	631	6987	582.25	581.21	108.6
Feb.	564	7015	584.58	583.42	96.7
Mar.	513	7025	585.42	585.00	87.7
Apr.	470	6998	583.17	584.30	80.4
May	446	6965	580.42	581.80	86.7
June	444	6909	575.75	578.09	76.8
July	493	6855	571.25	573.50	86.0
Aug.	602	6796	566.33	568.79	105.8
Sept.	698	6740	561.67	564.00	123.8
Oct.	710	6697	558.08	559.88	126.8
Nov.	689	6647	553.92	556.00	123.9
Dec.	649	6622	551.83	552.88	117.4
1955					
Jan.	577	6612	551.00	551.42	104.6
Feb.	505	6615	551.25	551.13	91.6
Mar.	457	6590	549.17	550.21	83.1
Apr.	427	6573	547.75	548.46	77.9
May	396	6547	545.58	546.67	72.4
June	419	6522	543.50	544.54	76.9
July	483	6503	541.92	542.71	89.0
Aug.	605	6494	541.17	541.55	111.7

continued

TABLE 22.1 (Continued)

		Computation of Ratios to Centered 12-month Moving Averages			
Year and Month	Stock	12-Month Moving Total	12-Month Moving Average	Centered 12-Month Moving Average	Ratio-to-Moving-Average (%)
(1)	(2)	(3)	(4)	(5)	(6)
1955					
Sept.	673			540.88	124.4
Oct.	693	6487	540.58	540.46	128.2
Nov.	663	6484	540.33	541.13	122.5
Dec.	624	6503	541.92	544.50	114.6
		6565	547.08		
1956					
Jan.	558	6670	555.83	551.46	101.2
Feb.	496	6816	568.00	561.92	88.3
Mar.	450	7012	584.33	576.17	78.1
Apr.	424	7234	602.83	593.58	71.4
May	415	7476	623.00	612.92	67.7
June	481	7710	642.50	632.75	76.0
July	588	7939	661.58	652.04	90.2
Aug.	751	8165	680.42	671.00	111.9
Sept.	869	8380	698.33	689.38	126.1
Oct.	915	8612	717.67	708.00	129.2
Nov.	905	8822	735.17	726.42	124.6
Dec.	858	8998	749.83	742.50	115.6
1957					
Jan.	787	9137	761.42	755.63	104.2
Feb.	722	9260	771.67	776.55	94.2
Mar.	665	9376	781.33	776.50	85.6
Apr.	656	9454	787.83	784.58	83.6
May	625	9506	792.17	790.00	79.1
June	657	9530	794.17	793.17	82.8
July	727	9524	793.67	793.92	91.6
Aug.	874	9500	791.67	792.67	110.3
Sept.	985	9457	788.08	789.88	124.7
Oct.	993	9378	781.50	784.79	126.5
Nov.	957	9289	774.08	777.79	123.0
Dec.	882	9182	765.17	769.63	114.6
1958					
Jan.	781	9106	758.83	762.00	102.5
Feb.	698	9025	752.08	755.46	92.4
Mar.	622	8901	741.75	746.92	83.3
Apr.	577	8812	734.33	738.04	78.2
May	536	8754	729.50	731.92	73.2
June	550	8719	726.58	728.04	75.5
July	651	—	—	—	—
Aug.	793	—	—	—	—
Sept.	861	—	—	—	—
Oct.	904	—	—	—	—
Nov.	899	—	—	—	—
Dec.	847	—	—	—	—

Source: Various issues of *Business Statistics.*

All the rest of the 12-month moving totals are similarly positioned between two months.

Next, the entries in column (4) are obtained by dividing the entries in column (3) by 12. Column (4)'s entries are between two months, just as column (3)'s entries are.

The entries in column (5) are obtained by taking pairs of entries from column (4), averaging them, and recentering the result. For example, the first entry in column (5) is 435.80 and is obtained by averaging column (4)'s entries of 433.67 and 437.92; the second entry in column (5) is 440.05 and is obtained by averaging column (4)'s entries of 437.92 and 442.17.

Finally, the entries in column (6) are obtained by dividing the observed datum in column (2) by the centered 12-month moving average in column (5). For example, the first entry in column (6) is 88.3 and is obtained by dividing column (2)'s entry of 385 by column (5)'s entry of 435.80 and then multiplying the quotient by 100.

Column (2)'s entries are regarded as values of $TSCI$, which can be rewritten as $TCSI$. Column (5)'s entries are regarded as values of TC. Column (6)'s entries are regarded as values of SI, because $TCSI/TC = SI$.

It is helpful to gather all the entries in columns (1) and (6) into a table by themselves, without other data. This is done in Table 22.2.

Of course, there are several entries for each month in Table 22.2—six entries, in fact. We want only one number for each month as the final result of the computation of seasonal indices. One of the acceptable methods of going from the several entries for each month in Table 22.2 to just one number for each month is illustrated in Table 22.3. Table 22.3 is regarded as containing values of SI. The purpose of Table 22.3 is to eliminate I from SI; the last row in Table 22.3 contains the values of S.

TABLE 22.2 Ratios-to-Moving-Averages for End-of-Month Stocks of Frozen Vegetables, 1952–1958

Month	Year						
	1952	1953	1954	1955	1956	1957	1958
Jan.		106.2	108.6	104.6	101.2	104.2	102.5
Feb.		94.9	96.7	91.6	88.3	94.2	92.4
Mar.		86.5	87.7	83.1	78.1	85.6	83.3
Apr.		77.0	80.4	77.9	71.4	83.6	78.2
May		70.5	76.7	72.4	67.7	79.1	73.2
June		73.1	76.8	76.9	76.0	82.8	75.5
July	88.3	87.0	86.0	89.0	90.2	91.6	
Aug.	105.2	104.7	105.8	111.7	111.9	110.3	
Sept.	119.1	123.5	123.8	124.4	126.1	124.7	
Oct.	127.9	130.6	126.8	128.2	129.2	126.5	
Nov.	124.9	126.3	123.9	122.5	124.6	123.0	
Dec.	116.1	122.0	117.4	114.6	115.6	114.6	

Source: Table 22.1.

TABLE 22.3 Computation of the Seasonal Index for the Stock of Frozen Vegetables, 1952–1958

Rank	Jan.	Feb.	Mar.	Apr.	May	June	July	Aug.	Sept.	Oct.	Nov.	Dec.
1	101.2	88.3	78.1	71.4	67.7	73.1	86.0	104.6	119.1	126.5	122.5	114.6
2	102.5	91.7	83.1	77.0	70.5	75.5	87.0	105.2	123.5	126.8	123.0	114.6
3	104.2	92.4	83.3	77.9	72.4	76.0	88.3	105.8	123.8	127.9	123.9	115.6
4	104.6	94.2	85.6	78.2	73.2	76.8	89.0	110.3	124.4	128.2	124.6	116.1
5	106.1	94.9	86.5	80.5	76.7	76.9	90.1	111.7	124.7	129.2	124.9	117.4
6	108.6	96.7	87.7	83.6	79.1	82.8	91.6	111.9	126.1	130.6	126.3	122.0
Total of four central items	417.4	373.1	338.5	313.5	292.8	305.2	354.4	433.0	496.4	512.1	496.5	463.7
Modified mean	104.4	93.3	84.6	78.4	73.2	76.3	88.6	108.2	124.1	128.0	124.1	115.9
Adjusted seasonal index	104.5	93.4	84.7	78.4	73.2	76.3	88.7	108.4	124.2	128.1	124.2	116.0

Source: Table 22.1.

The first six lines of Table 22.3 contain all of Table 22.2's entries, except that each month's entries are ranked from lowest to highest in Table 22.3. Then, in Table 22.3, the lowest and highest entries for each month are ignored, and the remaining four entries for each month are averaged. These averages could be regarded as the seasonal indices except for the fact that they add up to 1199.2 instead of 1200. The next step is to multiply these averages by a suitable constant to force their sum to equal 1200. Here the constant is

$$1200/1199.2 \doteq 1.00067.$$

Sometimes this step does not produce indices that add up to 1200. Here the indices add up to 1200.00 if each index is rounded to two decimal places, but they add up to 1200.3 if each index is rounded to one decimal place. Because we want one-decimal-place indices here, we adjust the rounding rule so that three of the answers that would ordinarily be rounded up are rounded down instead, thus forcing the sum to be exactly 1200. The three answers affected in this way are the indices for March, April, and June; these are the ones for which the least amount of rounding error is introduced by rounding down instead of up.

Interpreting a Seasonal Index

Intuitively, a month's seasonal index (such as 116.0 for December frozen vegetable stocks) is the average percentage for that month's activity when compared with the average of all the months in the data. For example, December frozen vegetable stocks are 116.0% of the average of all 84 months' frozen vegetable stocks in Table 22.3. Alternatively, December frozen vegetable stocks average 16.0% more than the average for all 84 months. (This is not exactly correct, because of the computational method used to get 116.0, but it is close enough to permit a correct intuitive understanding of seasonal indices.) Similarly, the January seasonal index of 104.5 means (intuitively though not exactly) that January frozen vegetable stocks are, on the average, 104.5% of the average of all 84 months' frozen vegetable stocks.

Now, suppose actual frozen vegetable stocks for December 1959 were 706 million pounds, and actual frozen vegetable stocks for January 1960 were 652 million pounds. These two data need to be *seasonally adjusted* or *deseasonalized, to allow for the seasonal pattern.*

Seasonally adjusted stocks for December 1959: $\dfrac{706}{1.160} \doteq 608.6.$

Seasonally adjusted stocks for January 1960: $\dfrac{652}{1.045} \doteq 623.9.$

A newspaper report would typically say, "The stocks declined from 706 to 652 million pounds, but on a seasonally adjusted basis they rose from 608.6 to 623.9." To understand this statement, start with the fact that stocks normally fall from 116.0% of the long-run monthly average to 104.5% of the long-run monthly average, when going from December to January. We can convert the actual data into implied long-run monthly averages by dividing the actual data by the seasonal indices. We get, of course, 608.6 and 623.9 as the implied long-run monthly averages. The increase from 608.6 to 623.9 says that stocks are increasing, after allowing for the usual seasonal pattern. Or, rephrasing this idea, the decline in actual stocks was less than the usual decline from December to January.

Seasonally adjusted data always give implied long-run averages, and changes in these averages are particularly important. Seasonally adjusted data reveal whether there are changes in the level of the trend or the business cycle, provided one is willing to judge that irregular forces are unimportant. In other words, seasonally adjusted data are estimates of *TCI*, because the actual data are assumed to represent *TCSI* and dividing by the seasonal index removes *S* from *TCSI*.

Verifying That the Model Is Appropriate

The concept of decomposing a time series of actual data *Y*, into the four components *T*, *C*, *S*, and *I*, where the components are related multiplicatively as *Y* = *TCSI*, is only a mathematical model. The model may or may not be appropriate to the actual data. The model's computations can be performed for any set of actual data; the issue we raise here is whether they *should* be performed. When computing seasonal indices, we recommend drawing several graphs as a check on whether the computations are appropriate for the actual data.

Figure 22.1 is the first of these graphs. It shows the actual data, or *TCSI*, from column (2) of Table 22.1, and the estimates of *TC* from column (5) of Table 22.1. The first issue is whether there appears to be a seasonal pattern in the actual data. Looking at each calendar year's actual data separately, it is apparent that a trough occurs early in the year and a peak later on in the same year. This graphical evidence of a definite seasonal pattern justifies the computation of seasonal indices.

The second issue is whether the 12-month moving average has removed *SI* from *TCSI*. It has, judging from Figure 22.1 because the

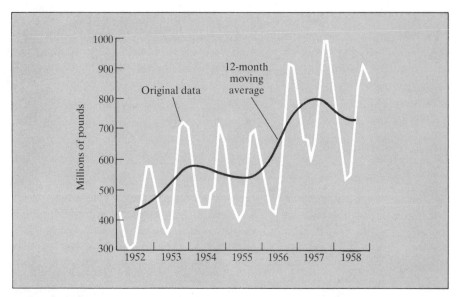

FIGURE 22.1 Stocks of frozen vegetables in the United States, 1952–1958, and 12-month moving average. (*Source:* Table 22.1.)

12-month moving average no longer follows the sharp peaks and troughs of the actual data. It can happen that a 12-month moving average will appear to follow some of the sharp lurches in the actual data, in which case there is graphical evidence that the 12-month moving average is not an estimate of TC but is, instead, an estimate of TC combined with substantial portions of S or I. The computations of Table 22.1 do not, in principle, have to remove all of the seasonal and irregular effects from the data, as when the peaks and troughs within a year are markedly more pronounced in some years than in other years, or when there are a few sharp spikes in the data at approximately equal amounts of time from one another.

Figure 22.2 is another useful graph. No vertical axis is shown, because it is a "tier graph" in which the vertical axis is moved downward for each year. To construct a tier graph for ratios-to-moving-averages, graph the ratios in the usual way for the first calendar year. Then move the vertical axis downward a little and graph the ratios for the next calendar year; continue by moving the vertical axis downward by the same amount for each succeeding calendar year. The issue is whether the ratios-to-moving-averages follow approximately the same pattern each year. Here they do, having troughs at May and peaks at October, and about the same pattern for other months too. This justifies the averaging process in Table 22.3.

If, by contrast, a tier graph shows quite different peaks and troughs or quite different shapes for the various years, then it does not make much sense to average the ratios in order to get seasonal indices. Incidentally, the averaging process of Table 20.3 involves dropping the most extreme entries for each month. It can be argued that no entries should be dropped, or that no entries should be dropped and that the

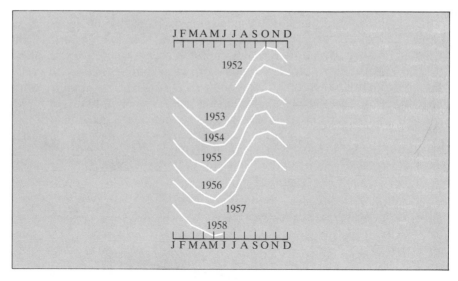

FIGURE 22.2 Tier graph showing ratios-to-moving-averages for end-of-month stocks of frozen vegetables in the United States, 1952–1958. (*Source:* Table 22.2.)

medians should be computed instead of the means, or that more than one highest and more than one lowest entry should be dropped. There is no single correct approach. Table 22.3 is only one of several acceptable procedures of going from several ratios for each month to a single seasonal index for each month.

Figure 22.3 shows the final results, the seasonal indices. For our illustrative data, the seasonal pattern is quite pronounced, having a seasonal low in May that is about 27% below 100 and a seasonal high in October that is about 28% above 100. After seeing what the average seasonal pattern is, in Figure 22.3, it is helpful if some explanation can

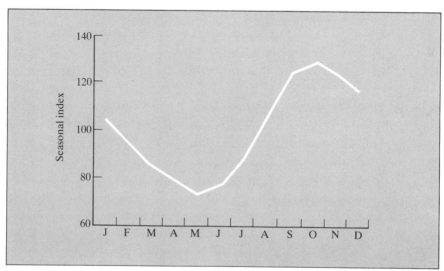

FIGURE 22.3 Seasonal indices for frozen vegetable stocks in the United States, 1952–1958. (*Source:* Table 22.3.)

be found for the seasonal pattern. Here it is obvious that vegetables are grown mostly in the spring and summer, whereas they are eaten throughout the year. Therefore, one would expect the inventory of frozen vegetables to grow rapidly when vegetables are harvested in the summer and fall and then to shrink rather steadily until next year's harvests come in. If there is no obvious explanation for the pattern in the calculated seasonal indices, one must consider the possibility that the calculated pattern is spurious—that there are no persistent natural causes for higher rates of activity in some months and lower rates in other months and that the calculated seasonal pattern is merely the result of random effects.

Alternative Methods of Measuring a Seasonal Index

Two other methods of computing the seasonal index merit mention, especially because one of them brings out indirectly the advantages of the ratio-to-moving average method.

The simplest possible method of computing a seasonal index is to calculate the average value for each month (for January, for February, and so on) and express averages as percentages so that the percentages of the average for all 12 months can add up to 1200, or average 100.

This method is indeed simple but very crude. It assumes there is no trend component in the series; that is, $Y = CSI$. This, however, is an unjustified assumption. most economic series have trends, and, therefore, the seasonal index computed by this method is actually an index of trends and seasonals. Furthermore, the effects of cycles on the original values may or may not be eliminated by the averaging process. This depends on the duration of the cycle and the term of the average—that is, on the number of months included in the average. Thus, this method is of little value and is seldom used.

The second alternative is the method of *ratio-to-trend*. This method assumes that seasonal variation for a given month is a constant fraction of trend. Starting with the model $Y = TSCI$, some argue that trend can be eliminated by dividing each observation by its corresponding trend value. The ratios resulting from this operation compose *SCI*. Each of these ratios to trend is a one-based relative—that is, a pure number with a unity base. Next, an average is computed for the ratios for each month. This averaging process eliminates cycle and random influences from the ratios to trend. Thus, the 12 averages of ratios to trend contain only the seasonal component. These averages, therefore, constitute the seasonal index. As with the method of ratio-to-moving-average, some slight corrections are necessary in order to adjust these ratios to average unity.

The ratio-to-trend method is certainly a more logical procedure than the crude measurement of seasonals mentioned above. It has an advantage over the moving-average procedure too, for it has a ratio-to-trend value for each month for which data are available. Thus, unlike the case of moving averages, no loss of data occurs. This is a distinct advantage, especially when the period covered by the time series is very short.

The main defect of the ratio-to-trend method is that if there are pronounced cyclical swings in the series, the trend—whether a straight line or a curve—can never follow the actual data as closely as a 12-month moving average does. As a result, the ratio to trend will tend to be more variable than the ratios to a 12-month moving average. Under these circumstances, it is likely that the averaging process will have a greater ability to remove irregular movements from the ratios to moving averages than it has in removing irregular and cyclical movements from the ratios to trend. This is another way of saying that a seasonal index computed by the ratio-to-moving-average method may be less biased than one calculated by the ratio-to-trend method.

In conclusion, because of its theoretical and practical advantages, the ratio-to-moving average method is probably the one most widely used. Its application is not confined to periodic fluctuations of 12-month duration. It can be used equally well for any periodic fluctuation, such as hourly variations of temperature within the day or daily variations in sales within the week.

A Note on Changing Seasonals

As mentioned before, the use of the conventional methods to measure typical variations is appropriate and significant only if the variations are stable from year to year. Unfortunately, seasonal patterns tend to change through time. Changes in seasonals may show up in the amplitude or—and this is more serious—in timing. These changes are sometimes abrupt and sometimes gradual. We are concerned here with the appropriate ways to measure such changing seasonals.

In certain situations the seasonal variations of a series may remain stable for a number of years and then change suddenly into patterns quite different from the old, which in turn may remain stable for years before they change again. Such changes are caused either by powerful sporadic factors or by deliberate managerial policies. During World War II, which necessitated an all-out effort in many lines of production, seasonals in these lines disappeared but reestablished themselves afterward. Changes in the seasonal variations of automobile sales were observed when the industry altered the design of cars to make them less dependent on changes in weather and when it changed the introduction of new models from early spring to fall.

A simple but satisfactory method of dealing with this kind of seasonal variation is to analyze the variations independently for the two periods separated by the abrupt change. The seasonal index for each separated period may be computed. When we use such indices in analysis, each index should be used for the period for which it is constructed.

Gradual changes in seasonals are fairly common. They are brought about by modifications of custom, technology, business practices, and other factors that change slowly but steadily. The emergence of air conditioning has increased the summer use of electricity. Changes in comsumers' tastes, encouraged by intensive advertising, have gradually eliminated the pronounced seasonal fluctuations in ice-cream production. An elastic credit supply and the central banking reserves of the federal reserve banks have progressively reduced seasonal swings in short-term interest rates almost to the vanishing point.

Gradual changes in seasonal patterns are usually secular in nature. In such cases, no average can be a typical representation of the seasonal pattern, since errors that run in one direction cannot be removed by averaging. When the change in a seasonal is gradual, instead of illogically deriving a typical seasonal index we study the steady and progressive change in the specific seasonal indices month by month and obtain a measure of change in the index for each month. When the specific seasonal indices—that is, ratios-to-moving-averages— have been obtained, the ratios of each month are plotted as an independent time-series graph. Twelve such graphs, with the X axis scaled in years, characterize the changes in seasonal pattern and therefore enable us to measure them. We reason that if there is a changing seasonal pattern, then progressive change will be reflected in the movements of the ratios for each month in the form of a discernible general drift from year to year. That is, the movement in the values of each month for the year can be appropriately defined by a trend line. The trend line here serves, as usual, the purpose of an average. The trend value for each month in each year is the first approximation of the seasonal index for that month in that year. We therefore end our analysis of gradually changing seasonal patterns with as many specific indices as there are years in the period under examination. These specific index values are trend values. The preliminary specific seasonal indices for each year, as before, must be adjusted to average 100. To adjust data for seasonal variations, each monthly original observation is divided by the adjusted seasonal index for that month in the same year. For forecasting, we use the projected trend values by extending the trend line for the desired month.

Whenever the values of the same month for the years tend to change gradually by a constant absolute amount, straight-line trends are appropriate. In many cases, however, values for each given month may not behave linearly. One frequently used device is to draw a freehand trend line through plotted points for a single month; the trend values are then read from the chart. This method is actually used by the Federal Reserve System in dealing with changing seasonals for the construction of its industrial production index. Another widely used method is to compute a moving average of five or seven terms. This procedure is used by the National Bureau of Economic Research. Here, as elsewhere in statistical analysis, the trend line to be determined depends upon the nature of the data and the judgment and experience of the investigator.

22.3 ANALYSIS OF CYCLICAL FLUCTUATIONS

Cyclical fluctuations do not repeat themselves periodically, as do seasonal variations. Neither do they behave fortuitously, as do irregular movements. The cycles of a specific series usually embrace a certain broad pattern that shows repetition but always contain some differences in duration and intensity. Because of this lack of uniformity in cycles, it is possible to isolate them but impossible to project them into the future. this, as will be seen later, constitutes the most difficult part of forecasting with time series.

A great deal of work in the analysis of cyclical fluctuations makes use of annual data, but this practice leaves much to be desired. Annual series obscure two of the most critical aspects of cycles: the location of the turning points and the measurement of the amplitude of fluctuations between the turning points. In order to bring out the relevant information on cycles, therefore, it is much more desirable to use quarterly or monthly data, especially the latter. However, as soon as data that record variations within the year are used, the distortions caused by seasonal and irregular movements enter the picture. Thus, to measure cycles from monthly data, we must attempt to remove seasonal variations in addition to removing the trend. That is, we are concerned mainly with the estimate of cyclical and irregular movements.

To estimate CI under the multiplicative assumption—that is, $Y = TSCI$—three methods are available, differing only in the sequences of eliminating T and S.

The first method starts with the division of the original data by trend values to obtain $CSI = TSCI/T$. Then we derive the estimate of CI by dividing the seasonal index into data that have been adjusted for trend: $CI = CSI/S$.

The second method is just the reverse, for original data are first adjusted for seasonal variation and then corrected for trend. Here, (1) $TSCI/S = TCI$, and (2) $TCI/T = CI$.

The third method begins with an estimate of TS, which is, of course, the product of trend and seasonal variations. Then we eliminate TS from the original data by dividing the latter by the former. That is, $CI = TSCI/TS$.

All three methods yield the same numerical results. The first one, however, is seldom employed because there is no practical use for CSI values. The second is convenient when we attempt to estimate CI with data that have already been deseasonalized. The third is often followed in measuring cycles from original data. It has two advantages over the first method, one of which is trifling: it is slightly less laborious to perform one multiplication and one division than to divide twice. The second advantage is more important: the division of original data by TS reveals more clearly that CI are deviations from statistical normal.

The procedures just described are appropriate whether the trend is an arithmetic straight-line, a geometric straight-line, or any other type of mathematical trend function. In each case, when the data have been adjusted for trend, the trend line of the adjusted data becomes a straight line parallel to the X axis. The percentage values on the Y axis express the cyclical influences.

In monthly data, the quantity TS is called *statistical normal* in the sense TS is an estimate of what the actual data would be if trend and seasonal were the only factors operating. The third method, using

TABLE 22.4 Cyclical-Irregular Movements for Frozen Vegetables, Stocks (Cold Storage, End of the Month) 1952–1958 (Y in millions of pounds)

Year and Month (1)	Actual Data[b] $Y = TCSI$ (2)	Trend[a] $y_t = T$ (3)	Seasonal Indices (as ratios)[b] $S/100$ (4)	Statistical Normal $TS/100$ (5)	Cyclical-Irregular Relatives %, $(Y/TS)(100)$ (6)
1952					
Jan.	444	406.819	1.045	425.126	104.4
Feb.	399	411.641	.934	384.473	103.8
Mar.	348	416.463	.846	352.328	98.8
Apr.	314	421.285	.784	330.287	95.1
May	302	426.107	.732	311.910	96.8
June	337	430.929	.763	328.799	102.5
July	385	435.751	.887	386.511	99.6
Aug.	463	440.573	1.084	477.581	96.9
Sept.	530	445.395	1.242	553.181	95.8
Oct.	577	450.217	1.281	576.728	100.0
Nov.	570	455.038	1.242	565.157	100.9
Dec.	535	459.860	1.160	533.438	100.3
1953					
Jan.	495	464.682	1.045	485.593	101.9
Feb.	450	469.504	.934	438.517	102.6
Mar.	420	474.326	.846	401.280	104.7
Apr.	384	479.148	.784	375.652	102.2
May	361	483.970	.732	354.266	101.9
June	384	488.792	.763	372.948	103.0
July	468	493.614	.887	437.836	106.9
Aug.	574	498.436	1.084	540.305	106.2
Sept.	688	503.258	1.242	625.046	110.1
Oct.	737	508.079	1.281	650.849	113.2
Nov.	722	512.901	1.242	637.023	113.3
Dec.	705	517.723	1.160	600.559	117.4

[a] $y_t = 606.92857 + 4.82190949x$ (Origin: July 15, 1955; time unit, 1 month; y_t, millions of pounds; arithmetic straight-line trend).
[b] *Source:* Tables 22.1 and 22.3.

$CI = Y/TS$, of isolating cyclical fluctuations can therefore be appropriately called the *method of ratio-to-statistical-normal*. This method is applied for stocks of frozen vegetables, as presented in Table 22.4. To save space, we present only the first 24 months; calculations for the remaining months are exactly analogous.

Columns (1) and (2) of Table 22.4 are copied from Table 22.1. Column (3) contains the trend values computed from an arithmetic straight-line trend and the trend equation is given as a footnote to column (3). Column (4) is copied from Table 22.3, except that they are now expressed as ratios, $S/100$. Each entry in column (5) is a product of the entries in columns (3) and (4). Each entry in column (6) is an estimate of CI for that month that is obtained by dividing the original data in column (2) by the statistical normal in column (5). Note that the quotient is multiplied by 100 so that the final result is a percentage instead of a ratio. This final result is called a *cyclical-irregular relative* since it shows the value of CI relative to Y. Figure 22.4 presents the

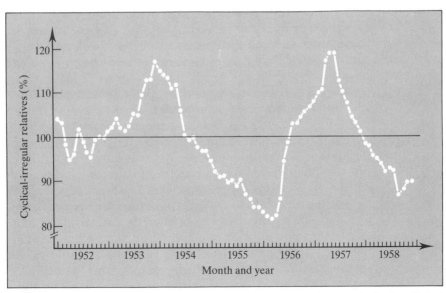

FIGURE 22.4 Cyclical-irregular relatives for frozen vegetable stocks in the United States, 1952–1958. (*Source:* Table 22.4 and supplementary calculations by the author.)

values of CI graphically for the entire period from 1952 to 1958. These cyclical-irregular relatives are often looked upon as deviations from normal—the values that could have been had there been no cyclical and irregular fluctuations.

Sometimes we wish to eliminate most of the irregular movements from the *CI* curve. This is often done by smoothing the curve with freehand drawing or by the calculation of a moving average. To estimate *C* by taking a moving average of *CI*, the terms used are often 3 months or 5 months. Odd terms make computation easier, and short durations avoid the tendency to smooth out too much of the cycles.

The isolation of cyclical fluctuations by a moving average is actually not a satisfactory method. A 3-month moving average may smooth out only a negligible part of the cycle, and the resulting curve may not be very smooth. A 5-month moving average may produce a smoother estimate of cycles, but the portion of cycles smoothed out may be considerable.

The fact that there is no satisfactory method of removing irregular movements, coupled with some theoretical considerations—on which we will here comment briefly—has led to the practice of analyzing cyclical and irregular fluctuations as a single entity. Irregular movements caused by random forces are relatively unimportant. Furthermore, random forces occur quite frequently, usually from unknown sources. Thus it is neither possible nor necessary to identify them: it is best to treat them as part of the cyclical swing that we actually observe. It seems reasonable to consider the slight sawtooth effect of cyclical movement as a part of the cycles, but can we also ignore the short-term sporadic changes that rise and fall with considerable magnitude just as the cycles do?

Part of the answer lies in the basic difference between these two types of variation. Two main properties of cycles are that they are cumulative and self-generating. Thus, if the fluctuations in the short run are such that they rise abruptly and then immediately fall back toward the previous level, then they are not cumulative and should be considered as irregular variations. Sometimes sporadic forces are quite capable of generating fluctuations that are cumulative for a number of months. Prolonged strikes, speculative booms, and war scares are examples of such irregular forces. Under these circumstances we may insist that, to be qualified as cycles, the cumulative expansions and contractions must last a minimum number of months, say longer than 12 as used by the National Bureau of Economic Research. Here we come to the realization that cyclical causes are diversified, complicated, and dynamic. They can never be expected to produce identical smooth cycles as portrayed by the sine and cosine functions of trigonometry. Irregular movements are part of the aggregate of factors that create the ragged cyclical course we observe in reality. Our attention to irregular movements should warn us that not every rise and fall comprises a cycle. When we mark off the turning points of cycles, we must be careful that they reveal faithfully the underlying cyclical forces at work.

Turning our attention back to our current example, we note that Figure 22.4 also enables us to determine the cyclical turning points of the series. A *cyclical turning point* is the date at which a cycle reaches its lowest point and a new cycle starts going upward, or the date at which a cycle reaches its highest point and then it goes downward. The former is called the *cyclical upturn* and the latter, *cyclical downturn*. A complete cycle consists of an upward cyclical movement and a downward cyclical movement.

In general terms, Figure 22.4 appears to show two complete cycles. One of them begins in the middle of 1952, peaks in December 1953, and ends in March 1956. The other complete cycle begins in March 1956, peaks in June 1957, and ends in September 1958. There is obviously a problem in dating the beginning of the first cycle: Is it April 1952 or September 1952? We evaded answering this question when we said that this cycle begins "in the middle of 1952," but evading a question is not a satisfactory solution! The fact is that there is no precise procedure of dating the beginning of the first cycle. Then we are back to the problem of dating the beginning of the 1952–1956 cycle, not knowing whether this date should be April 1952 or September 1952. We regard this problem as unsolvable except by a mathematically arbitrary process. This is typical of many actual time series. Judging from the results of computations like those of Table 22.4, the existence of cycles is beyond dispute but the turning points are open to some controversy that cannot be settled, even after all the data are available.

We said the last complete cycle in Figure 22.4 ended in September 1958. We do not really know this until we examine the 1959 data, because the little upturn at the end of 1958 could be merely another "minor blip" instead of the beginning of a new cycle. If we had to make some business decisions early in 1959 concerning frozen vegetables, and the only information about the cyclical component was that shown in

Figure 22.4, which ends with December 1958, we couldn't possibly know whether a strong upturn in the cyclical component or something quite different would occur in 1959. We would have a suggestion that a new cycle was beginning, but only that. This accounts for the vagueness in most economic forecasts: When examining the most recent months of a time series, we have no way of knowing whether these are a "minor blip" in a cycle or the beginning of a cyclical upturn or downturn.

In closing our discussion of cyclical-irregular relatives, let us take note of the following:

1. The cyclical turning points may never be exactly revealed because of problems with "minor blips" at the cyclical upturn or the cyclical downturn.

2. The cyclical turning points are never revealed at the time they occur but become apparent only after later data become available.

3. The cycles in either the raw data or the calculations of cyclical-irregular relatives are sometimes strikingly present but still meaningless because they are random effects, not naturally caused effects. This also sometimes happens with a trend—it can be undoubtedly present in the raw data or in the regression computations producing a trend, but meaningless because it is a random effect without a natural cause.

22.4* PRELIMINARY COMMENTS ON FORECASTING

It was repeatedly stated in the previous chapter that one of the basic aims of time series analysis is forecasting. However, forecasting, as should now be observed, is much more than projecting a series mechanically into the future. It involves making assumptions about the future course of business activity when economic planning is formulated by a firm, an industry, or a government. Assumptions regarding the future are made on the basis of observations of the past. Here lies the basic difficulty in attempting to forecast the future conditions of business. The future may be some sort of extension of the past, but it can hardly be expected to be an exact replica. Forces responsible for economic change are numerous and complex. They are often difficult to discover and to measure. They may appear in all kinds of combinations. Furthermore, they may be constantly changing. Even if the response mechanism of an industry or of the economy remains essentially the same through the passage of time, it is not always easy to know how business conditions will respond to new stimuli whose effects we have failed to observe before.

The basic difficulty—that the past can never be a perfect guide to the future—warns us that forecasting should not be thought of as a routine application of some techniques or theoretical ideas to a list of unchanging variables. Successful forecasting requires expert blending of economic theory, significant statistical expertise, and thorough familiarity with the relevant statistical data. It should utilize both quantitative and qualitative information. The forecaster must have the ability to distinguish between new facts that are important and those that are not. He must be competent to judge under what conditions past relationships can be relied upon and when they cannot. He must be able to appreciate the effects of nonmeasurable socioeconomic and political forces upon business activities. In other words, forecasting is, and probably will remain, more an art than a science.

Numerous forecasting techniques with varying degrees of complexity have been devised during the past few decades. Most of these fall into one of three broad categories: We shall cover these methods in remaining space of this chapter as outlined below.

1. Naïve methods:
   a. the economic rhythm method, or method of forecasting a series by itself;
   b. the method of exponential smoothing.

2. Barometric methods:
   a. statistical indicators;
   b. diffusion index.

3. Analytical methods:
   a. regression analysis;
   b. econometric models.

22.5* FORECASTING WITH NAIVE METHODS

A forecasting method is said to be naïve if it lacks a rigid theoretical basis. As a method of forecasting, it ranges from simple coin tossing to decide on an upward or a downward movement, to mechanical projection of a time series into the future. A frequently used naïve device is the simple but useful method of assuming that things will not change. Using this technique, plans are made on the assumption that, in so far as the particular events are concerned, the future will resemble the present. According to this type of forecasting, then, it is predicted that, for example, sales of the next quarter will be the same as those for this quarter or sales of the next quarter will increase by the same amount as they did in the last quarter. As a matter of fact, for most short-term decisions, this is exactly what is done. Of course, this type of naïve forecast becomes more questionable as the period of forecast becomes longer. The naïve method, in general, and time series analysis, in particular, assumes that the future is some kind of extension of the past. In the discussion that follows, we concentrate on the two more sophisticated methods.

The Economic Rhythm Method

This method is simply that of forecasting a time series by itself. As such, it is often used by an individual firm or industry to forecast sales, production, plant facilities, or the like. To forecast a time series by itself involves simply the projection into the future of its measurable components: the trend, the seasonal, and the cycle. In projecting a series we may have either one of two purposes in mind. Either we may merely wish to project each of the measurable components independently or we may wish to use these projections to arrive at a synthesis of the components as the forecast of the actual value. Forecasting by synthesis of trend, seasonal, and cycle is just the reverse of decomposing the time series. That is, we first forecast values of the three components for a given time period and then combine these projected values into a single forecast by a process of multiplication.

A firm or industry that is experiencing a steady and substantial rate of growth must make forecasts of future trends for planning the construction of costly facilities in anticipation of the future activity. A forecast of long-run growth will enable the business managers to avoid the common and unprofitable practice of basing a decision as to the expansion of plant capacity on the current demand for their product. This is so because such a forecast will help them to determine whether an increase in demand is permanent (secular) or temporary (cyclical). When a cyclical expansion is mistaken for a secular growth, unneeded capacity may be built. When secular growth is incorrectly interpreted as a temporary expansion, a share of the market may be lost forever to competitors. A forecast of secular trend serves long-range planning for fixed assets in two ways. It aids in the expansion of capacity in accordance with anticipation of the steady growth of demand and in the purchase or construction of equipment and plant at the most advantageous time, which is usually when the demand for the firm's output is below its peak or when the producers of fixed assets are temporarily in a depressed stage of their activity.

Needless to say, in the forecast of secular trend, the first step is the measurement of the trend in the immediate past. The forecasting of trend would be made by extrapolation, that is, projection of the fitted trend into the future. It may also be recalled that projecting a trend into the future assumes that forces producing the change in secular trend will continue to have the same effects in the future as in the past. This implies that the further a fitted trend is projected into the future the more questionable the forecast becomes. However, judging from the fact that secular trend is a type of change that is quite persistent, it is fairly safe to project a series several years into the future.

Forecasts of seasonals are necessary for such activities as budgeting and production scheduling, for example, which are planned on a monthly basis.

Where it is appropriate to construct a typical seasonal index, the seasonal index is an adequate forecast of the seasonal variations for the next year. If the seasonal is undergoing a gradual change, it is often sufficient to use the specific seasonal index of one year as the forecast for the seasonal of the year that follows. Or, if the seasonal changes assume a clearly defined trend, the projected monthly trend values may serve as the forecasts. With an abruptly changing seasonal, the seasonal index computed after the change should be used as the forecast. Forecasts based on seasonal indices are made by taking an annual forecast based on trend or some other device and combining it with seasonal indices, thus producing monthly forecasts that take account of seasonal fluctuations. For instance, if it is forecast that sales of a firm in the next year will be, say 1,200,000 units and if there were no seasonal variations in the firms sales, the monthly sales would be 100,000 units for each month. But if January is expected to be only 80% of the monthly average sales, then the forecast for January should be only 80,000 units. In other words, the forecast of total annual sales can be transformed into monthly forecasts by multiplying the average monthly forecasted sales by the appropriate monthly seasonal index values.

Sometimes a useful approximate forecast of actual value can be made by a synthesis of trend and seasonal variation. When the forecast is made on an annual basis, it is done by simply projecting the trend line. If the forecast is needed on a monthly basis, the projected monthly trend values are multiplied by the appropriate seasonal indices. A forecast of actual value merely on the extension of trend line and the seasonal indices may be adequate for many types of decisions. Nevertheless, we must recognize these limitations for such a forecast.

1. The type of trend equation selected may not be appropriate.

2. The trend constants and, therefore, the trend values are subject to sampling errors.

3. The forces influencing the trend may change after the trend equation has been selected.

4. The seasonal may not remain the same as it has been in the past, or it may have been changing and the change may not have been adequately described.

5. The forecast may have been made under the assumption that it is not influenced by cyclical and irregular effects.

Now, while nearly every time series contains cyclical and irregular components, it may be discovered that a large number of products, as shown by the demand for motor fuel, for shoes, and for paperboard for food packaging have been experiencing ever-expanding markets with only mild responses to cyclical forces. Except for irregular factors, such as wartime restrictions and strikes, these products have considerable regularity in their growth over time, even though there are shifts in their growth rates. For such products, projections of the statistical normal can be considered as useful forecasts for both short-term and long-term planning.

However, for those series, such as consumers' durable goods and investment goods, that are greatly affected by the cyclical factor, projecting the cyclical movement becomes the most important part of forecasting a series by itself. This is so because nearly all types of short-run activities of the firm—ordering supplies of raw materials, scheduling production, advertising, hiring workers, arranging for a line of credit, or the like—are influenced by cyclical fluctuations. Unfortunately, accurate forecasts of both cyclical turning points and amplitude are extremely difficult if not impossible because there is simply no objective way of extending cyclical relatives or residuals into the future. Nearly all the methods of forecasting discussed in this chapter are concerned with cycles, but they are primarily for predicting general business conditions rather than specific cycles.

Sometimes, in attempting to project cyclical movements mathematically, a cycle is fitted to data by some function of the sines or cosines of the time scale. Such procedures assume periodicities in both duration and amplitude of the cyclical pattern or that the pattern is changing in accordance with some known law. The trouble with them is that almost no economic time series can meet the required assumption.

One frequently used device of forecasting cyclical movement is the method of extending a cycle curve subjectively. With this method, the estimate of CI in the recent past is first smoothed by a moving average or freehand and both the CI values and the resulting C values are plotted in the same graph. By studying carefully the relationship between the CI and C curves, and the behavior of the C curve in the recent past, the C curve is extended into the future for a few months to a year by freehand. Projections of the C values are then read from the chart. It should be noted that projection of the cycle is no longer a mechanical procedure as in the case of trend and seasonal projections. It involves a great deal of subjective judgment. This method, therefore, can be used only by an investigator who is thoroughly familiar with the business under consideration and who can do it carefully and conscientiously.

Whatever method is used to project the cycle, the forecast of the actual value of a series is the product of the projected trend, seasonal, and cycle: the forecast of the actual value equals projected trend times projected seasonal times projected cycle.

Among recent developments, one of the most exciting methods of forecasting the cycle of a series by itself is the method of "exponential smoothing," which we shall present in the next section. Another promising device for this purpose is to forecast cyclical fluctuations of one series by those of another with regression analysis. Problems of applying resgresion analysis to time-series data will be discussed later.

The Method of Exponential Smoothing

This method for forecasting is an outgrowth of recent attempts to maintain the smoothing function of moving averages without their corresponding drawbacks and limitations as pointed out in the previous chapter. *Exponential smoothing,* a special kind of weighted moving average, is found to be useful in short-run forecasting for inventories and sales. The basic principle and the application of this device are both quite simple. If we wish to forecast the value of a time series for the period $t + 1$ on the information available just after period t, the forecast is best considered as a function of two components: the actual value y_t of the series for period t and the forecasted value S_{t-1} for the same period made in the previous period $t - 1$. The use of both realized and estimated values available now for predicting future values is better than the use of either alone, since the actual value in period t might have been unduly influenced by random factors, or because the conditions that led to the forecast for period t may not hold any longer.

The forecast of a time series for the period $t + 1$ via exponential smoothing is in effect a random variable with a specific probability distribution. As such, it seems appropriate to use the expected value of the random variable as the forecast. Unfortunately, the probability distribution of the forecast is unknown and, thus, all that we can do is to estimate its expectation and employ it as the actual forecast. This estimate is called the *smoothed value* for period $t + 1$, and it is obtained as a weighted average of y_t, the actual value of the series for period t, and S_{t-1}, the smoothed value (forecast) for period t, which is made of course in the previous period $t - 1$. The weights employed to compute this estimate are called *smoothing constants*, denoted as α and β, with $\alpha + \beta = 1$. Exponential smoothing can be applied to any power of y_t and S_{t-1}, but economic and business applications are usually for the first three degrees with simple exponential smoothing are by far the most popular. Our discussion will be confined to simple exponential smoothing, whose equation is given as follows:

$$S_t = \alpha y_t + \beta S_{t-1}, \qquad 0 < \alpha, \beta; \qquad \alpha + \beta = 1. \qquad (22.1)$$

Several things about the preceding exponential smoothing model are worth noting. First, the value of S_{t-1} represents the average experience of the series to date. In period t a new observation of the series becomes available, and it is then used together with S_{t-1} to determine S_t.

Second, the function S_t is a linear combination of all past observations (in terms of moving averages obtained with two terms at a time), with weights given to all past observations decreasing geometrically with the age of data; thus, the name "exponential smoothing." The speed at which remote values are dampened out depends upon the value of α as demonstrated below:

Time Period		Weight	
		$\alpha = 0.2$	$\alpha = 0.5$
t	$\alpha\beta^0 =$	0.2,	0.5;
$t - 1$	$\alpha\beta =$	0.16,	0.25;
$t - 2$	$\alpha\beta^2 =$	0.128,	0.125;
$t - 3$	$\alpha\beta^3 =$	0.1024,	0.0625;
$t - 4$	$\alpha\beta^4 =$	0.08192,	0.03125;
and so on.			

Finally, from the fact that the larger the value of α, the faster past responses are dampened out from the smoothed values, we may derive a rule of thumb for determining the value of α. When the magnitude of random variations in the series is large, we would like to average out the random effects quickly. This being the case, we should select a small α so that the smoothed value S_t will reflect S_{t-1} to a greater extent than it reflects the "noisy" y_t. When we have a moderately stable process, a large α should be selected. In practice, the value of α employed often falls within the range of 0.10–0.60, which is often determined by means of simulation with the purpose of minimizing the variance.

Let us note now that S_t as defined by (22.1) may be considered as the forecast of a series for the period $t + 1$. If there is a significant trend in the series, exponential smoothing, like any other moving average, lags behind the systematic trend. Such a trend must therefore be estimated and adjusted for S_t in order to provide a final forecast for period $t + 1$, S_t'. A convenient procedure is to use the differences between successive forecasts as trend estimates, which in turn are adjusted by the smoothing constants. The adjusted trend value is added to each new smoothed value to correct the forecast of trend. In this procedure, we take the following three steps:

1. Take the difference ΔS_t between the current smoothed value and the preceding one, which is

$$\Delta S_t = S_t - S_{t-1}. \tag{22.2}$$

2. Estimate the new trend as

$$T_t = \alpha \Delta S_t + \beta T_{t-1}. \tag{22.3}$$

3. Determine the forecast for $t + 1$, denoted as S_t', as below:

$$S_t' = S_t + \left(\frac{\beta}{\alpha}\right)T_t. \tag{22.4}$$

When annual data are involved, S_t' would constitute the final forecast for period $t + 1$. However, if the series investigated is of quarterly or monthly data, a further correction must be made for seasonal variability. Denoting the seasonally correct forecast for period $t + 1$ as S_t^* and the seasonal index for period $t + 1$ as I_{t+1}, we have then

$$S_t^* = S_t'(I_{t+1}). \tag{22.5}$$

In ordering to have some idea of the accuracy of our forecasts, we may compute the forecasting error as

$$e_{t+1} = S_t' - y_{t+1}. \tag{22.6}$$

for annual data; and

$$e_{t+1} = S_t^* - y_{t+1} \tag{22.7}$$

for quarterly or monthly data.

TABLE 22.5 Example of Simple Exponential Smoothing

Time Period t	Actual Value y_t	Smoothed Value S_t	Change in S_t ΔS_t	Trend Estimate T_t	Forecast S_t'	Forecasting Error e_{t+1}
Initial estimates	—	100.00	—	0.00	—	—
1981	110	104.00	4.00	1.60	106.4	+1.4
1982	105	104.40	0.40	1.12	106.1	−13.9
1983	120	110.64	6.24	3.17	115.4	−0.6
1984	116	112.78	2.14	2.76	116.9	−4.1
1985	121	116.07	3.29	2.97	120.5	−2.5
1986	123	118.84	2.77	2.89	123.2	+3.2
1987	120	119.30	0.46	1.92	122.2	−2.8
1988	125	121.58	2.28	2.06	124.7	−1.3
1989	126	123.35	1.77	1.94	126.3	+2.3
1990	124	123.61	0.26	1.27	125.5	—

$$\alpha = 0.4; \beta = 1 - \alpha = 0.6; \beta/\alpha = 1.5$$

To commence exponential smoothing we need two estimated initial values: the initial smoothed value and the initial trend value. For the first estimate, the practice is to use an average of a few past observations of the series. As for the initial trend value, we may use the slope of the trend equation obtained from past data, or we may simply start with a trend value of zero, or we may use the average of first differences of a few values.

Table 22.5 provides an example of simple exponential smoothing for a hypothetical series of annual sales with $\alpha = 0.4$, an initial smoothed value of 100, and an initial trend value of zero. Judging from the sizes of forecasting errors, the forecasts seem to be quite good except for 1983. The rather large forecasting error in S_{1982}' is clearly produced by the unusually large change in sales (more than 14%) from 1982 to 1983. It may also be noted that if a rather small value of α is used, or if an initial zero trend is employed when there exists a positive trend in the series, then exponential smoothing tends to underestimate the actual values at the beginning; but these downward biases would be corrected quickly after a few periods, as in our example. Also, smoothing with trend may give larger forecast errors than smoothing without trend when the underlying series has no trend.

Exponential smoothing for a hypothetical series in Table 22.5 begins with the forecast for 1982, and S_{1981}' is computed as follows:

1.
$$S_{1981} = \alpha y_{1981} + \beta S_{1980}$$
$$= 0.4(110) + 0.6(110) = 104;$$

2.
$$S_{1981} = S_{1981} - S_{1980}$$
$$= 104 - 100 = 4;$$

3.
$$T_{1981} = \alpha \, \Delta S_{1981} + \beta T_{1980}$$
$$= 0.4(4) + 0.6(0) = 1.6;$$

4.
$$S'_{1981} = S_{1981} + (\beta/\alpha)T_{1981}$$
$$= 104 + 1.5(1.6) = 106.4;$$

5.
$$e_{1982} = S'_{1981} - y_{1982}$$
$$= 106.4 - 105 = 1.4.$$

Forecasts for other years in Table 22.5 are computed in the same way.

It is interesting to note that exponential smoothing can also be employed for projections over long terms. This is done by using the smoothed series as a basis and making projections into the future with some mathematical trend function. However, this practice leads to very different extrapolated values when different values of the smoothing constant α are employed. This observation makes one rather doubtful about the usefulness of forecasts made too far into the future by exponential smoothing.

22.6* FORECASTING WITH BAROMETRIC METHODS

The *barometric method* implies that past historical patterns tend to repeat themselves in the future, and it embraces the idea that the future can be predicted from certain happenings of the present. Thus, past statistical behavior that seems to be associated regularly with fluctuations in a particular series of general business activity is discovered and used as the basis for forecasting. Foreshadowing series are searched to provide an advance reading of what is expected to follow in the series to be forecast.

The search for foreshadowing series is not based on the leads actually revealed by historical data alone. Theoretical considerations as to the leads and lags in various series are also employed. Cross-checking between empiricism and theory in the search for leading series is the best hope for establishing the thesis that the future does not represent a break from the past but that changes are largely determined by present conditions. The foreshadowing or leading series selected serve as barometers of future changes in specific series or general business conditions.

We have two barometric methods available: statistical indicators and diffusion index. We consider these two methods in that order.

The Method of Statistical Indicators

It is of great importance for government economists and business managers to predict the turning points of cyclical swings in the economy such as, for example, the advance and decline of GNP. In general, the determination and prediction of turning points are difficult tasks, mainly because a series such as GNP only consists not only of trends plus long swings, but also of many ups and downs of shorter durations and milder amplitudes that obscure the picture. This is especially true in this country since the 1940s, owing to institutional changes and more active government intervention in the private sector of the economy.

There has been continuous evidence since World War II that the amplitude of business cycles has been greatly reduced, and that a fairly smooth growth can be achieved. This means that the turning points in general business activity, as measured by GNP or the index of industrial production occur less frequently and are more difficult to define. For this reason, in recent years, turning points are effectively sought in changes in the growth rate rather than in the absolute level of general business activity; and the main forecasting strategy for detecting turning points is the use of "statistical indicators" based on a study of the lead-lag relationships among different time series.

The lead-lag approach attempts to determine the approximate lapse of time between the movement of one series and the movements of general business conditions. This approach, for a very natural reason, has received more attention in the history of forecasting than has any other. If one or more series can be found such that their turning points lead by a number of months with substantial regularity the turning points of general business in the past, it is only logical to use these leading series to predict what is going to happen to general business activity.

The most important list of statistical indicators in modern times originated during the 1937–1938 sharp business contraction. Henry Morgenthau, at that time Secretary of Treasury, requested the National Bureau of Economic Research (NBER) to devise a system that would signal when the depression was nearing an end. NBER economists, under the leadership of Wesley Mitchell and Arthur F. Burns, selected 21 series that, on their past performance, some dating as far back as 1854, promised to be fairly reliable indicators of business revival. Since then the Bureau has revised the list several times. Since its origin, series have been classified as leading, rough coincident, and lagging. In 1966, 72 indicators had been selected by NBER, 35 of which were claasified as leading, 25 as coincident, and 11 as lagging. The most recent list at this writing, issued in 1977, shows 111 indicators, classified under various economic headings. These indicators are published in *Business Condition Digest*.

Leading indicators are mainly those series that are concerned with business decisions to expand or to curtail output. Time is required to work out their effects, and so they tend to move ahead of turns in business cycles. Leading indicators signal in advance a change in the basic performance of the economy as a whole. Early warning signals provided by leading indicators aid in forecasting short-term trends in the coincident series. *Coincident indicators* are those whose movements coincide roughly with, and provide a measure of, the current performance of aggregate economic activity. Hence, they inform us whether the economy is currently experiencing a slowdown, a boom, or whatever. Movements of *lagging indicators* usually follow, rather than lead, those of the coincident indicators. In general, lagging indicators move in directions opposite to those of the leading indicators throughout various phases of business cycles.

The statistical-indicator approach to forecasting attempts to derive the broad general framework of what the whole economy is doing from what its sections are doing and then moves on to evaluate any particular segment within this framework. The use of this approach requires careful analysis of the underlying data, since the indicators are by themselves merely mechanical summaries. Furthermore, a good deal of confusion may arise from the fact that most indicators have behaved contrary to their usual fashion from time to time. A leading indicator, for example, may on occasion coincide with or even lag behind the turning points of general business cycles.

In 1963, the U.S. Department of Commerce, through its Office of Business Economics (renamed the Bureau of Economic Analysis in 1972), inaugurated the monthly publication, *Business Condition Digest,* which presented the data for cyclical indicators, including those NBER initiates. The large number of indicators actually furnishes an excess of information for the purpose of predicting turning points. Consequently the NBER specified a "short list" of 25 indicators to provide a convenient summary of the current situation. With the addition of "GNP in current dollars," one obtains the 26 series, 12 leading, 8 roughly coincident, and 6 lagging. Weekly plottings of these series, called SIA indicators, are made available to subscribers by Statistical Indicator Associates, North Edgremont, Mass. (See Figure 22.5).

Experience shows that "general business activity" from month to month cannot be found in any single statistical series. Gross national product comes closest, but even this series has limitations. From its investigation of hundreds of different series of business statistics and contemporary business records, the NBER decided upon those months when the weight of the various statistics and other information suggested that definite highs or lows in general business activity had been reached. It is these months, technically called "reference peaks" and "reference troughs," that the three groups of the 26 statistical indicators have been found to lead, coincide with, or lag.

No one indicator has had an invariable relationship to the reference months. Exceptions have occurred often enough to make dependence on one or even a few of these indicators especially hazardous. This danger is avoided by having recourse to all 26, where reinforcing movements permit the emergence of a more reliable picture. Moreover, analysis does not begin and end with looking at the 12 leading indicators. The dual role of the 6 laggers is indispensable: they help to substantiate a movement in the coincident indicators as something more than merely a temporary movement of the economy, and they set the stage for a subsequent reversal.

It must be realized that a turning point in a business cycle is an "event" only to the historian. At the time of its occurrence, it may be simply a temporary reversal of business activity. It is not until later, when we have witnessed the development characteristic of the period following a turning point, that we can be sure a major cyclical turn has occurred. These characteristic movements very definitely include the typical movements of the lagging indicators. Without them, substantiating a reversal as cyclical is tenuous.

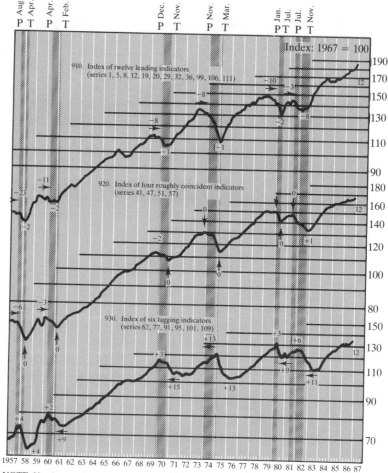

FIGURE 22.5 Composite indices and their components. (*Source:* Adapted from *Business Condition Analysis,* January, 1987.)

As to setting the stage for a subsequent turning point, the levels of interest rates, unit labor costs, and inventories (all lagging indicators) are vital. In a downturn (upturn), the eventual working down (up) of money rates, inventories, and unit labor costs is instrumental in evoking a subsequent recovery (recession). To overlook the extent of these downturns (upturns) in the belief that the lagging indicators are of value only after a business reversal is to ignore the full value of the indicator approach.

It is important to realize that these critical levels do not usually precede the actual turning point of activity. The primary value is to provide confirmation of the cyclical nature of a turn in business activity within a few months after the turn has occurred.

To facilitate the reading of statistical indicators, NBER has innovated a broader type of summary of the overall situation. This consists of constructing an index for each class of indicators. In the construction of these indices, indicators are weighted and adjusted in such a way that all the indicators have the same opportunity to influence the index irrespective of their differences in amplitude. The indices themselves are also adjusted in a similar fashion, with a resulting magnitude of 1% per month in their average swings. Thus, if the most recent monthly increase in an index is 1.5, it is increasing 50% faster than its historical average. The index for leading indicators is further adjusted to have the same trend as that of the index for the coincident series. Thus, the major difference that remains, as shown by Figure 22.5, is in cyclical timing, with fluctuations of the three indexes moving in their typical fashion of lead, coincident, and lag. These indexes are easy to read, and the magnitudes of their swings are readily compared. They are thus a superior type of indicator, but close study of the components is still essential for understanding and interpreting their movements.

For example, in Figure 22.5, we see that the index of leading indicators started an upswing 8 months before the last trough of the index of roughly coincident indicators in November, 1982. However, the index of lagging indicators did not begin its upward movement until December, 1983—a lag of 11 months. Throughout 1984–1986, both leading and lagging indicator indices sustained relatively strong upward movements. These readings suggest that the general business activity would probably continue its upswing throughout 1987 and maybe 1988.

These are of course tentative conclusions, and more careful study of the behavior of the components of these indices and other important indicators may provide a more positive forecast. Furthermore, the directions of all these indices may be modified or changed by federal economic policies concerning the heavy federal budget deficits, the huge import surpluses, the slowdown of inflationary rates, the reduction of interest rates, the rather abnormal stock market boom during the period 1983–1987, and so on. All these phenomena and many others are contradictory forces on the performance of the economy as a whole. The federal government would have a very difficult time in deciding what to do in, say, 1988. Thus, it is quite difficult for a forecaster to say anything with a high degree of certainty about the general business conditions for 1988 at the beginning of that year.

Note that the indices used in Figure 22.5 include twelve leading indicators, 4 coincident indicators, and 6 lagging indicators. Different series have been selected for the construction of these indices from time to time, and they can be identified in various issues of *Business Condition Digest*.

The indicators to be selected for the indices are evaluated according to six major characteristics: (1) economic significance, (2) statistical adequacy, (3) consistency of timing at business cycle peaks and troughs, (4) conformity to business expansion and contraction, (5) smoothness, and (6) prompt availability.

The record of the NBER indicators in forecasting turning points has been quite good. However, statistical indicators are of little help in forecasting cyclical amplitude, although they can be used to secure an early and approximate judgment of how intensive a recession is likely to be. For this, the magnitude of declines in the leading series during the first few months is taken to indicate the severity of the full contraction. Such a judgment, however, may be so speculative and rough as to be of hardly any value for decision making.

One limitation of the indicators is that they are selected mainly in accordance with their historical performance. Their relationship to aggregate economic activity is not causal, although there may be some logical basis as to why a series tends to lead or to lag. These relationships, therefore, cannot be considered as stable ones. Their timing patterns will change with changes in the structure of the economy, in consumer's preferences, in managerial decision procedures, and in the reactions of business and government to changing business conditions.

The Method of Diffusion Index

To deal with the problem of variability of the individual statistical indicators, the NBER has worked with the movements of broad groups of the series instead of with each separately. The device employed is called *diffusion index,* which shows the percentage of a given set of time series that is expanding from month to month or in any other time periods. The Bureau has constructed many indices of this type, and indices of this sort have also been developed by the Conference Board, Citibank, N.A. and others; a number of such indexes are published by *Business Condition Digest.*

The most comprehensive diffusion index, constructed by the NBER, includes some 400 series that are generally in conformity with business-cycle patterns. This index and the index for general business activity are shown by Figure 22.6. This figure, among other things, shows vividly the difference between the amplitudes of cycles before and after the 1940s, as mentioned earlier. Because of its broad coverage, the NBER diffusion index reveals the tendency of all sectors of the economy to respond to aggregate demand at different time sequences. At any given time, some series are expanding while others are contracting; some are reaching their peaks while others are moving toward their troughs. However, after an upswing of general business activity gets into full force, almost all sectors of the economy will be expanding with it. After a certain period of time, some sectors, and then more and more, will run into difficulties and thus start to contract.

The movement of the diffusion index is evidently related to that of general business activity. But it is important to note and to understand that the peaks and troughs of the diffusion index are not the peaks and troughs of business cycles. It is easy to see that as long as more than 50% of the series are expanding, the economy as a whole is in a process of expansion. Consequently, it is not until the diffusion index has crossed the 50% line from above that the peak of business cycle is reached. Similarly, as long as less than 50% of the series are expanding, general business must be in a state of contraction. As a result, the aggregate economy itself reaches its trough and starts to expand only when the diffusion index has crossed the 50% line from below.

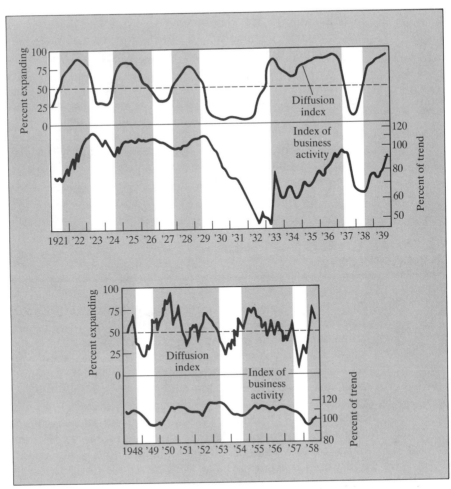

FIGURE 22.6 Diffusion index and the movement of business activity. (*Source:* G. H. Moore, "The 1957–58 Business Contraction: New Model or Old?", *American Economic Review,* Vol. 49, May 1959, p. 298.)

The shaded areas of Figure 22.6 are periods of business-cycle contractions. From the chart it can be seen that there is a lead and lag relationship between the movements of the diffusion index and those of business activity. When the diffusion index reaches its peak and begins to turn down, the whole economy continues to expand until the diffusion index, decreasing, crosses the 50% line. At this time, more sectors of the economy are contracting and the downswing of general business commences.

The diffusion index, comprising several hundred series, provides persistent leads, though of irregular durations, to the index of business activity. Thus, it seems to be an excellent device for forecasting the turns in business cycles. But the student should not rush to conclude that we have now discovered an infallible predicting device. The leads are by no means regular. There are occasional false signals, such as those in 1951 and 1956. Waiting to date the turns until the diffusion index has risen or fallen to the 50% line may involve important delays.

Further delays are also unavoidable because many of these series are not available for months. In forecasting we are not so much concerned with where the economy has been as with where the economy is and what its future course may be.

Despite these shortcomings, the diffusion-index approach to forecasting is now widely recognized as a supplementary device for observing the scope and vitality of cyclical movements. While diffusion indices are no substitute for more judgmental or less mechanical forecasting methods, they do furnish an interesting and informative continuing guard against the possibility that the forecaster's judgment may be carrying him away from the raw facts underlying trends in business data.

22.7* ANALYTICAL METHODS OF FORECASTING

An analytical method of forecasting entails detailed analyses of causative forces operating currently on the variable to be predicted. Relationships of cause and effect disclosed by analyzing current data are used to judge the future course of the causative forces and their effects on future behavior of the variable to be predicted. Analytical techniques may be nonmathematical—such as the rather naïve factor-listing procedure or the more sophisticated device of opinion polling—or mathematical—such as regression analysis and econometric models. In any event, such methods call for careful analyses of forces at work in order to establish useful relationships and their quantification. The analysis of current forces at work by no means excludes the employment of past statistical relationships to make a forecast. As a matter of fact, historical patterns are often used to estimate the constants contained in mathematical models.

In this section, we shall discuss the use of regression and econometric models as forecasting procedures.

Forecasting with Regression Models

Most of the forecasting techniques introduced so far have been presented in connection with broad economic forecasts. Such forecasts are of value to the businessman only indirectly, as a basis from which he can forecast the future demand for the output of his own industry or his own firm. Demand forecasting on the microeconomic level is the most important type of business forecasting, because it aids business management directly in planning for and scheduling additional plant capacity, in establishing employment policies, in setting up sales quotas and advertising budgets, in lining up sources of finance, and in purchasing raw material and supplies. Forecasts of sales for an industry or a firm can be made in some fashion by nearly every method introduced previously; however, the general procedure that has received increasing attention currently is regression analysis.

For the purpose of forecasting, regression analysis is usually applied to time-series data. As noted in Chapter 19 in a rather detailed fashion, while regressing with time-series presents no new computational problems, problems of theoretical and technical nature do arise. You are advised to review the sections in Chapter 19 which were concerned with the identification and correction of heteroscedasticity, serial correlation and multicollinearity at this time. We shall move on now to introduce a very useful regression model—the lead-and-lag regression model—and to comment on some of the special and practical problems of forecasts for the industry and the firm, where much use is made of regression analysis.

The Lead-and-Lag Regression Analysis

The application of regression models to time series data is essentially an approach of forecasting one series by another series. For this, the lead-and-lag relationship between two series can be used to our advantage in obtaining more accurate forecasts. This approach is to find a series that "leads" the series you want to forecast. For example, there are data suggesting that the cyclical turning points in the Dow–Jones Industrial Average (DJIA) for common-stock prices lead those of Gross National Product (GNP) by an average of about nine months. If you are willing to rely on this nine-month leading relationship and you wish to predict GNP, then all you do is to observe the DJIA and employ a "lagged regression" of past DJIA values on past GNP values to see what your prediction of GNP will be. Computationally, the only difference between a lagged regression and an ordinary regression is that the values of the variables entering into the regression calculation are offset by the amount of the lag instead of being for the same time periods. For instance, in a nine-month lagged regression of GNP on DJIA, the first data pair might be GNP for November 1980 and DJIA for February 1980; the second data pair would be GNP for December 1980 and DJIA for March 1980; the third would be GNP for January 1981 and DJIA for April 1980; and so on.

A question frequently encountered in the search for lead-and-lag relationship is whether the "lag" should be nine months, or eight, or ten, or some other figure. To solve this problem, a general procedure is to try varying amounts of lag, running a separate regression analysis. Then select the amount of lag that yields the highest value of the coefficient of determination as the final regression analysis. In any event, when the amount of lag is determined, the regression model applied is of the general form:

$$y_t = A + Bx_{t-1} + e_t. \qquad (22.8)$$

Forecast for the Industry and the Firm

The single most important variable to be forecast by an industry or a firm is sales. Here, the sales-level of an industry is usually forecast first, and then the firm's forecast is made on the basis of the predicted value of the whole industry.

The first step in forecasting the sales of an industry by regression analysis involves the selection of factors that are considered to affect the demand for the industry's output. The demand for a commodity often depends upon a multiplicity of aggregate economic variables, such as GNP, disposable income, population growth, employment level, prices, and so on. As a rule, the factors to be selected for analysis should be kept to a minimum, even to a single variable if it is believed to be adequate. This is because of the danger of imprecise and vague results when too many independent variables are included in the study. If, for example, a product is used by both consumers and producers, there is reason to believe that both real consumer disposable income and industrial production are the two most important independent variables. However, these two factors are highly correlated themselves. Consequently, it would be sufficient to use either one of them for analysis. The one to be chosen, of course, should be that which has the higher correlation with past sales of the product.

The second step involves the development of a guide for appraising the industry's prospects of future sales. This is done by regressing the industry's past sales on the selected demand factor. The regression equation thus obtained will serve as the first approximation of the forecasting equation for sales on the basis of the independent variable.

Very often, by employing the most important independent variable for analysis, a reasonably good fit is obtained. However, residuals unexplained by the independent variable may still remain for three reasons: inaccuracies may exist in the data used; erroneous regression curves, time-lag relationships, and other types of technical errors may have been introduced into the analysis; and, finally, other factors that affect sales may have been excluded. If the investigator is convinced that his analysis is basically free from the first two types of error and that the residuals are mainly attributable to the third one, then he can try to account for the omission of the other independent variables by employing a *net time trend* as a "catchall" variable. This is accomplished by plotting the residuals from the regression line as a time series and fitting to it a trend line. Such a trend is in effect a regression line, since "time" is treated as an additional independent variable that supposedly represents the combined effects of all demand factors not explicitly determined.

We say "supposedly" represents the omitted variables, because any omitted variable will have its effect through such explicit variables as it correlates with, or through the residuals. If X_2 and time are the only independent variables, then an omitted variable that correlates well with X_2 (in the sense of partial correlation, holding time constant) will affect the partial regression coefficient for X_2 and its standard error, even though time is "supposed" to handle all of the effect of the omitted variable. Whether we get a regression equation suitable for forecasting, using only one explicit independent variable plus a time variable, depends on the particular situation.

The estimated trend (regression) equation may now be used to improve the accuracy of prediction. This is done by incorporating in the regression equation both the explicit independent variable and time. This is the third step of the general procedure.

The use of a single independent variable and a time-trend factor is one of the simplest forms of multiple regression. Although there are many regressions where the estimates may be considerably improved by fitting a trend to the residuals from the basic regression line, this device should not be used without discrimination. A net time trend is properly used in situations where the omitted factors are themselves highly correlated and where it may not be possible to determine directly their particular effects upon demand. Otherwise, additional explicit independent variables may have to be used to explain and predict sales.

After the forecast for the whole industry is made, the forecast of the firm's sales may be based on the industry forecast. This involves the additional step of discovering the firm's position in relation to the industry of which it is a part. Once the firm has determined its sales as a percentage of the total market, it can apply this percentage to the forecast for the industry. Sometimes the company's sales may be forecast by relating them directly to national or regional economic variables. A firm may employ both methods in arriving at a final forecast for its sales.

The use of regression analysis for forecasting involves a number of additional considerations that must be observed in order to provide maximum reliability. First of all, time series employed in a given regression may need some prior adjustment or transformation in order to provide comparability, to avoid spurious correlation, and to improve the accuracy of forecasts. For example, if we are regressing the sales of beef on disposable income, we may note that both variables are positively correlated with the growth of population. When population increases, both sales of beef and disposable income will increase. Thus, a more realistic procedure should be the correlation of per capita beef consumption to per capita disposable income. Again, if we are dealing with value series, the original data should be deflated by appropriate price indices before regression is applied. This procedure would establish more accurately the underlying real relationship between the series. Occasionally, we may be concerned with time series that are measured in different units and which differ from each other greatly in terms of their absolute magnitudes. In such a case, it is best to regress the index number of the dependent variable with the index number(s) of the independent variable(s) in order to provide clearer results and easier interpretation.

Second, a firm or an industry may produce several different products whose sales are subject not only to the influences of different factors but also to differences in the shifts of their relationships with general economic activity over time. It is therefore often desirable to break down the industry's total sales into homogeneous groups of output and carry out a separate regression study for each group.

Third, the independent variable or variables selected are either those whose estimates are logically obtained at an earlier stage in the analysis or those that lead or lag in time with the variable to be predicted. The employment of leads and lags, however, must be confined only to cases where some clear-cut reason underlies the relationship. Furthermore, the leads or lags must be consistent from a logical or empirical point of view. We should not, for example, select a forecaster (the independent variable) as a variable that may lead another during the upswing of the cycle but lag it during the downswing. For instance, we should not select general business activity as the forecaster for the rate of interest, since the expansion of business activity may lead to a rise of interest, but a rise in interest may bring about a contraction in business activity. What should also be noticed here is that many lead and lag relationships often shift considerably beyond the initial period of observation.

Finally, in establishing the regression line for two time series, it is often desirable that it fit the more recent years better than it fits the whole range of data. It is also better to ignore irregular disturbances produced by wars or strikes that affect particular years. When these irregular influences are taken into the analysis, dummy variables must be introduced. In general, to establish the best relationship possible requires that information other than statistical considerations be brought to bear on the problem. It is important to realize that the final purpose of a regression function is to provide the best set of future estimates of the variable to be forecast, not to minimize the average error of estimate in the past.

Considerable space has been given to regression analysis because this approach offers many valuable contributions to forecasting problems. Regression is the device by which we select, from the many variables in our complex economic system, those that are useful for forecasting. With it, we make the giant step from intuitive evaluation of the relationships among variables to precise quantified knowledge. In many situations this is the most suitable and fruitful method of forecasting. As we shall see immediately, regression analysis is also the econometrician's standard tool in his research.

Forecasting with Econometric Models

Econometrics views the behavior of an economic system as guided by numerous economic magnitudes whose interrelationships can be expressed by a set of simultaneous equations. The variables in those equations are either endogenous or exogenous. Endogenous variables are determined within the economic system itself, and include, among others, income, production, money stock, employment, prices, rent, and interest. Exogenous variables are determined by such noneconomic forces as nature, politics, customs, or institutions. For the sake of simplicity and to avoid a vicious circle in which everything seems to depend upon everything else, the exogenous variables are first estimated on whatever information is available and these estimates are then used to determine the endogenous variables. Econometrics seeks to discover and measure the quantitative aspects of the actual operation of the economic system in order to forecast the course of certain economic magnitudes with a specific level of probability.

The appropriate procedure in forecasting by econometric methods starts with *model building,* or *specification.* It involves the theorizing of the interrelationships between the variables under investigation and expresses the theory in mathematical terms. A *model* is a set of mathematical relations (usually in the form of equations), each expressing an economic theory.

We may, for instance, construct a model for the gross national product (GNP) in the following manner. GNP, in any accounting period, is made up of three components; consumption, gross investment, and government expenditure. Let Y_t = GNP, C_t = consumption, I_t = gross investment, and G_t = government expenditure for a given period; we have then

$$(1) \qquad Y_t \equiv C_t + I_t + G_t,$$

where the subscript t identifies the accounting period for which the variables are evaluated. We shall assume that data are available for equal periods, say annually, and let t take on the values $1, 2, 3, \ldots$, denoting the first, the second, the third, $\ldots$, of these periods.

Equation (1) is a *definitional equation*. It is thus an identity; it is true by definition. Next, for the completion of our model, we must proceed to formulate a theory for each variable on the right side of equation (1), so that these variables can be related functionally. Mathematical expressions for these variables are called *behavior equations* because they describe the responses in these variables due to the stimuli from other variables.

For consumption, we may advance the simple theory that consumption in a given period depends on the GNP of the preceding period, Y_{t-1} (a lagged endogenous variable), in such a way that equal increments in GNP, irrespective of the level of GNP from which we start, always bring equal increments in consumption. This relationship may be called the *marginal propensity to consume*, denoted by m. Furthermore, we assume there is a minimum consumption even if the GNP is zero. We shall call this minimum a. The mathematical expression for such a consumption function may be written as

$$(2) \qquad C_t = a + mY_{t-1}.$$

Gross investment is the sum of induced private investment and autonomous investment. The former is that type of investment expenditure that is induced by consumption. There is reason to believe (according to the principle of acceleration) that induced private investment, in any given period, is proportional to the increase in consumption of that period over the preceding period. The constancy of proportionality is called the *relation* and may be denoted by i. Since the increase in consumption is given by $C_t - C_{t-1}$, the size of induced investment may be written as $i(C_t - C_{t-1})$. Autonomous investment refers to capital formation for replacement and the application of innovations. As such, it may be assumed to be independent of the consumption level. We shall designate it by k. The whole investment function can now be given as

$$(3) \qquad I_t = k + i(C_t - C_{t-1}).$$

Government expenditure is an exogenous variable that may be considered as a given known constant, G^*. Thus

(4) $$G_t = G^*.$$

This system of four equations constitutes our simple econometric model for GNP. With this we proceed to rearrange the system of equations into some convenient form so that it can be fed with information on exogenous variables and some economic variables that are usually known in advance of the period for which the forecast is desired. This often involves the derivation of a single equation for the variable that we intend to forecast. For our present example, we start with equation (1) and use the other relations to obtain

$$Y_t = (a + mY_{t-1}) + [k + i(C_t - C_{t-1})] + G^*$$
$$= a + mY_{t-1} + k + i[(a + mY_{t-1}) - (a + mY_{t-2})] + G^*$$
$$= a + mY_{t-1} + k + i(mY_{t-1} - mY_{t-2}) + G^*,$$

which may be simplified to produce the following forecasting equation for GNP:

(5) $$Y_t = m(1 + i)Y_{t-1} - imY_{t-2} + a + k + G^*.$$

After the forecasting equation has been derived, the next step is to estimate the parameters in the equation on the basis of past data so as to fill the formal equation with numerical values that are trustworthy. In Equation (5) for our example, there are four parameters: a and m, which are related to the consumption function, and k and i, which are contained in the investment function. We may associate consumption figures with the GNP of, say, the past twenty years, and obtain a regression equation that would provide estimates of the constants a and m. Similarly, by relating investment expenditures with changes in consumption in the past, estimates of k and i are made. Suppose the values of the estimates are $a = \$10$ billion, $m = 0.8$, $k = \$5$ billion, and $i = 0.9$; then we rewrite equation (5) as

$$Y_t = 0.8(1 + 0.9)Y_{t-1} - (0.9)(0.8)Y_{t-2} + 10 + 5 + G^*.$$

When the values of the predetermined variables are inserted into the model, estimated values of other variables in the system can be derived readily for the forecast period. For example, we know what the values of GNP are for the preceding two periods. Also, from the government's planned budget, we have the size of the government expenditure for a given period. Now, suppose $Y_{t-1} = \$950$ billion, $Y_{t-2} = \$960$ billion, and $G^* = \$240$ billion; then our forecast for the given period's GNP will be

$$Y_t = 0.8(1 + 0.9)950 - (0.9)(0.8)960 + 10 + 5 + 240 = \$1007.8 \text{ billion.}$$

A forecast made from an econometric model is not exact, because the estimates of the model parameters are subject to sampling errors. more serious is the possibility that the theoretical relationships in the model may not be correct. Furthermore, even if the relationships established among the variables may be valid for the past or the present, they are subject to change when strong and new forces come into play. These considerations point to the realization that if econometric methods are to yield useful forecasts, two important conditions must be met. First, criteria of success must be set up to test economic theories using the model and past data. Second, the models must be constructed with built-in flexibility in order to facilitate the absorption of shifting relationships. It may also be observed that, although econometrics, to a greater degree than any other forecasting method, is analytical in nature, its successful use still requires a great deal of skill, scientific knowledge, and personal judgment. It may also be said that the development of models has made possible the quantification of predictions that can be readily checked and that model building is the only logically suitable method with which to incorporate the best features of all forecasting techniques.

Econometric models may be macroeconomic in nature; that is, models may be constructed for the purpose of predicting future levels of some aggregate economic variables, such as national income, price level, or employment. They can also be employed at the microeconomic level for a particular industry or firm. The procedure used is the same. For instance, we may try to hypothesize that the demand for gasoline as a motor-vehicle fuel in the United States depends upon (1) the number of gasoline-consuming vehicles in use, which includes passenger cars, trucks, airplanes, buses, and so forth; (2) the average number of miles per consuming vehicle, which, in turn, depends on disposable income, prices of motor fuel, and so on; (3) the average number of miles driven per gallon; and (4) a time trend that is supposed to serve as a measure of the influence of other variables not included in the first three. On the basis of the empirical evidence available, we may then try to combine all these variables into a forecasting equation for the sales of gasoline used as motor fuel. To construct econometric models on the microeconomic level, the investigator, in addition to having technical competence, must also have experience with and knowledge of the particular industry or firm.

22.8* COMMENTS ON LONG-TERM ECONOMIC FORECASTING

Our previous discussion of forecasting for aggregate business activity was mainly concerned with cyclical fluctuations—that is, short-term forecasting. Before ending this chapter, we should comment briefly on long-term economic forecasting of economic aggregates. In many situations, projections of broad economic aggregates, such as GNP, for a decade or longer into the future are necessary. Long-term economic projection amounts to forecasts of aggregate supply or potential output at full employment capacity. Such projections serve a number of useful purposes in planning. In the first place, they indicate to us how fast aggregate demand has to grow in order to make possible a continuous high level of employment. They also suggest to us specific measures required to sustain the desired growth rate of aggregate demand. The measures may include, for instance, the stimulation of consumption or some particular type of investment. Finally, such projections are necessarily the first step in making a long-range projections for particular industries and firms by the regression technique described in the preceding section.

Real gross national product is the most important and comprehensive indicator of economic activity, and it is usually projected first over the long term. A working forecast of GNP can be simply made by assuming that the past trend will continue. Considering only peacetime years of a high level of employment, GNP has been growing, on the average, about 3.0% per annum during the past 30 years. The stability of this growth rate serves as an indicator of its reliability.

A more detailed projection of aggregate supply is often made, in addition to this stable statistical growth rate, on assumptions of population growth, the proportion of the population in the labor force and its distribution between civilian labor and the armed forces, estimates of unemployment, productivity, number of hours worked per year man, and so forth. Projected figures for these detailed factors are available from a variety of sources. Population and labor force projections are furnished by the Bureau of the Census and the Department of Health, Education, and Welfare. Other studies, such as *Potential Economic Growth of the United States During the Next Decade* by the Staff of the Joint Economic Committee and *Long-Range Economic Projection* by the Conference on Research in Income and Wealth, are available on trends in productivity and other factors. It may be noted that technological advances, more efficient use of raw materials, more efficient distribution methods, a more highly skilled labor force, and so on, have led to a continuous increase in labor productivity. During the past 50 years output per man-hour, in both manufacturing and agricultural output, has increased at an annual rate of about 2 to 3%.

GLOSSARY OF FORMULAS

(22.1) $S_t = \alpha y_t + \beta S_{t-1}, \qquad 0 < \alpha, \beta; \qquad \alpha + \beta = 1;$

(22.2) $\Delta S_t = S_t - S_{t-1};$

(22.3) $T_i = \alpha \Delta S_t + \beta T_{t-1};$

(22.4) $S'_t = S_t(\beta/\alpha)T_i;$

(22.5) $S^*_t = S'_t(I_{t+1});$

(22.6) $e_{t+1} = S'_t - y_{t+1}$;

(22.7) $e_{t+1} = S^*_t - y_{t+1}$.

This group of equations describes the method of forecasting by exponential smoothing with the simple model as defined by (22.1). In this model, the forecast S_t of time period t is defined as a weighted average of the actual value y_t of the series in period t and the smoothed or forecast value in period $t - 1$. The weights are the smoothing constants, α and β, with $\alpha + \beta = 1$. The value of α is usually set in the range 0.10–0.60. Note that S_t in (22.1) is considered as the forecast for the period $t + 1$ if there is no trend. To use this model we need only the initial smoothed value, which may be estimated as an average of a few past observations of the series. When there is significant trend, S_t must be adjusted for trend to get S'_t as the final forecast, as shown by (22.4). Now another initial value of trend is required for the application of (22.1). This value may take on the value of the slope of past trend equation, or a value of 0, or the average of first differences of a few values. Then we define T_i as the weighted average as shown by (22.3), where ΔS_t is defined by (22.2). The final forecast S'_t with adjusted trend is defined by (22.4). When monthly data are used in exponential smoothing, a seasonal factor may be present and it also must be adjusted to provide the final forecast S^*_t, which is obtained by (22.5) where I_{t+1} stands for the seasonal index for period $t + 1$. Equations (22.6) and (22.7) provide procedures for calculating the forecasting errors for annual and monthly data, respectively.

(22.8) $y_t = A + Bx_{t-1} + e_t$.

This equation provides a generalized lead-and-lag regression model for forecasting by regressing a lagged series Y with a leading series X. Note two things about this model: (1) the subscript t refers to time period, not trend value; (2) the time period refers to the average amount (in months) of lead and lag between the two series.

REVIEW QUESTIONS

22.1 What do we mean by seasonal variation?

22.2 What are the factors; that may produce seasonal variations in economic and business time-series data?

22.3 What are the reasons for the importance of seasonal variations of the activities of individual business enterprises?

22.4 Differentiate specific and typical seasonal indices.

22.5 What does a 12-month moving average measure? Explain your answer.

22.6 What are the steps involved for the construction of typical seasonal indices by the ratio-to-moving average method?

22.7 What do we meaning by changing seasonals? How do we usually handle such seasonals?

22.8 Why is the method of ratio-to-statistical-normal usually preferred over others in measuring cycles?

22.9 What is the difference between business cycles and specific cycles?

22.10 In what sense do we say that each cycle is a unique historical phenomenon?

22.11 Discuss briefly the difficulties involved in determining the turning points of cycles.

22.12 What is the basic difficulty in forecasting?

22.13 What are the forecasting methods introduced in this text? Explain briefly the logic and procedure of each of the methods.

22.14 What do we mean by "statistical normal?" Under what conditions would the statistical normal constitute a reasonably good forecast of the actual value of a time series? What are the limitations of such a forecast?

22.15 Provide an explanation of the difficulties involved in forecasting cyclical fluctuations by the economic rhythm method.

22.16 What do we mean by "exponential smoothing"? What is its function in forecasting? What are the merits and limitations of this method for forecasting?

22.17 How can time series be classified into leading, coincident, and lagging statistical indicators? Give a few examples for each type of indicator.

22.18 How are the statistical indicators organized in order to facilitate their reading so far as the determination of cyclical behaviors are concerned? What are the merits and limitations of using statistical indicators in forecasting?

22.19 What is a diffusion index? How can it be used as a forecasting device? What are the shortcomings of this method?

22.20 Comment on the nature of the regression model $y_t = A + Bx_{t-1} + e_t$. What is the function of this model?

22.21 State briefly the steps involved by forecasting sales-levels of an industry and firm by regression analysis.

22.22 What is an econometric model? What are the advantages and drawbacks of forecasting by this method?

22.23 "Regression analysis is the best friend for a forecaster." Why?

22.24 Comment briefly on the procedures of long-term economic forecasting.

PROBLEMS

Instruction: You may solve some or all the problems below by computer programs in part or in total. However, you should write out the specific answers from the computer printouts. When the printouts do not contain all the answers to the problems, you should supply them yourself.

22.1 Construct a seasonal index for the monthly data in Table 21.P6 by the ratio-to-moving-average method. (Use the original trend equation.) Analyze the results of the appropriateness of the model graphically by using the same type of graphs as Figures 22.3, 22.4, and 22.5.

22.2 For data in Table 21.P6, do the following.
   a. Compute the cyclical-irregular movements by the method used in this text.
   b. Graph your result and identify the cyclical turning points in these data.
   c. The NBER gives the peaks and troughs covering the period 1966–1980:

Peak:		Dec. '69	Nov. '73	Jan. '80
Trough:	Feb. '61	Nov. '70	Mar. '75	

   d. Compare these turning points with yours in (b). Explain why your turning points might differ substantially from NBER's.

22.3 From results in Problem 22.1 compute the monthly statistical-normal of 1985 as the monthly forecasts for that year's industrial production indices. Check the actual values for 1985 and calculate the forecasting errors. Comment on the "goodness" of your forecast.

22.4 For data in Table 21.P3, you have computed an arithmetic straight-line trend and a geometric straight-line trend. Now, forecast the value of GNP for the most recent year for which the actual GNP value is available by both trend equations. Compare your forecasts with the actual value. Which trend equation yields a better forecast? Explain why.

22.5 Table 22.P1 contains data on year-end values of inventory in hundreds of thousands of dollars at a certain manufacturing firm.
   a. Apply simple exponential smoothing to the series by using $\alpha = 0.25$, an initial smoothed value of 38, and an initial trend value of 1.
   b. Do the same as in (a) by using $\alpha = 0.50$, an initial smoothed value of 38, and an initial trend of zero.
   c. Compare the forecasting results and comment on the differences.

TABLE 22.P1

Year	y_t	Year	y_t
1976	40.5	1981	43.5
1977	42.6	1982	45.1
1978	39.8	1983	47.2
1979	42.9	1984	48.0
1980	44.7	1985	46.4

22.6 Table 22.P2 contains seasonally adjusted annual consumption expenditures Y, and personal disposable income X of the United States (in billions of dollars) from 1971 to 1985. For data in this table do the following.

b. Compute a linear regression of Y on X for the same set of data for the period of 1971–1982 by using model (22.8) with X leading Y by one year. Compute the regression residuals.

c. Compare the results in regression residuals obtained in (a) and (b). Do you think the lead-and-lag model is an improvement over the standard model? If so, why? If, not, why not?

d. Forecast the consumption expenditures for 1983 and 1984 by each regression. Comparing with the actual Y values, which equation yields better results? Do these observations agree with your comments for (c)?

TABLE 22.P2

Year	X	Y	Year	X	Y
1971	776.8	691.6	1979	1729.3	1566.8
1972	839.6	757.6	1980	1918.0	1732.6
1973	949.8	837.2	1981	2127.6	1915.1
1974	1038.4	916.5	1982	2261.4	2050.7
1975	1252.6	1129.3	1983	2425.4	2229.3
1977	1379.3	1257.2	1984	2670.2	2423.0
1978	1551.2	1403.5	1985	2801.1	2581.9

Source: Economic Report of the President, 1986, p. 282.

22.7 Consider the following econometric model of national income:

$$Y_t = C_t + I_t + G_t;$$

$$C_t = a_0 + a_1(Y_t - T_t), \qquad 0 < a_1 < 1;$$

$$I_t = b_1 Y_{t-1} + b_2 R_t, \qquad b_1, b_2 > 0.$$

Here

Y = national income,

C = consumption expenditures,

I = investment expenditures,

T = taxes on income, and

R = rediscount rate of Federal Reserve Banks.

a. Which are the endogenous and exogenous variables in this model, respectively?

b. What is the reduced predictive equation?

c. What is the value of Y_t given that $a_0 = 40$, $a_1 = 0.9$, $b_1 = 0.2$, $b_2 = -32$, $R_t = 5$, $Y_{t-1} = 1500$, $G_t = 400$, and $t_t = 370$?

23* Bayesian Inference

23.1 INTRODUCTION

In *The Devil's Dictionary* by Ambrose Bierce, we find the following entry:

> INDECISION, n. The chief element of success; "for whereas," said Sir Thomas Brewbold, "there is but one way to do nothing and divers ways to do something, whereof, to a surety, only one is the right way, it followeth that he who from indecision standeth still hath not so many chances of going astray as he who pusheth forwards"—a most clear and satisfactory exposition of the matter.

We trust you disagree with the assertion that indecision is the chief element of success, despite Bierce's conclusion that the quotation cited is "a most clear and satisfactory exposition of the matter." There are other ways of analyzing a decision problem! One of these ways is through *classical methods* of statistical inference, which treat population parameters as unknown but constant quantities. We have up to now been exclusively concerned with many of the results of the classical approach to statistics. Another of the ways of analyzing a decision problem is through *Bayesian methods,* which regard population parameters as random variables. This and the next two chapters present some results of the Bayesian approach to statistics. Each of these two approaches is appropriate to some situations. Neither is appropriate to all situations, and they both have some limitations. They are complementary rather than contradictory approaches.

The chief difference between classical methods and Bayesian methods lies in the role of personal judgment. Classical methods try to stress objective sample evidence to the exclusion of personal judgment. (It is saying too much to assert that classical methods succeed in excluding personal judgment. Such matters as deciding how large a sample to take, the degree of confidence for a confidence interval, or the specified probability of type I error in hypothesis testing are all partly matters of judgment in the usual applications of classical methods.) Bayesian methods, on the other hand, stress both objective sample evidence and the role of personal judgment.

There is a vital difference in the role of personal judgment when we are comparing the classical conception of a population parameter with the Bayesian conception of a population parameter. The classical conception is that of a fixed but unknown constant, and the purpose of sampling is to cast light on the values the constant might reasonably have in view of the sample evidence. The stress is all on the objective sample evidence; nothing is explicitly said about personal judgment.

The Bayesian conception is that a population parameter is itself a random variable! At first, this is a startling and apparently wrong-headed idea. How can the mean income μ of all Americans in 1987 for example, be a random varible? Does it not have to be a constant that could be calculated from a complete census of all American incomes? Bayesians say that μ would be known exactly after such a census had been taken, and so, with the aid of information derived from a complete census, μ is a constant. But with less information—a sample instead of a census, or no sample at all and just one's casual impressions of American incomes in 1987—we can if we wish regard μ as a random variable. This means that μ can assume any of several values, with a probability or probability density attached to each value.

The probability or probability density reflects our current judgment on how likely it is that μ equals that value. Our current judgment can be based on any amount of objective information, from none at all to an enormous amount of very accurate information. Our current judgment can be quite vague or diffuse, in which case all the possible values of μ in a wide range have roughly equal probabilities or probability densities. Alternatively, our current judgment can be quite strong, in which case only the values of μ in a narrow range have high probabilities or probability densities, and all the possible values outside this range have much lower probabilities or probability densities. In Bayesian statistics, therefore, the probability distribution of a population parameter describes one's current judgment about which values of the parameter are likely and which values are unlikely.

When there is little or no objective information available, different people will have different judgments about which values of the parameter are likely, so their *prior probability distributions* for the parameter, which are formed before a random sample is taken, will be quite different. After a random sample is taken, each person forms a *posterior probability distribution* for the parameter. The posterior probability distribution is influenced both by the prior probability distribution and by the objective information disclosed by the sample. One of the central issues in Bayesian analysis is just how these two influences should be blended to form a posterior probability distribution. We take up this topic shortly.

Within the broad category of Bayesian statistics there are two major subcategories. One is Bayesian inference and the other is Bayesian decision theory. The difference between them concerns "loss functions," which measure the costs of making wrong decisions. If the loss functions are not considered in the analysis (or, at least, not explicitly and quantitatively considered), the analysis uses *Bayesian inference*. Bayesian inference is used, as in the classical case, for estimating population parameters and for testing hypotheses about population parameters. If the loss functions are explicitly stated in quantitative form and are used in the analysis, then *Bayesian decision theory* is being applied. Bayesian decision theory is used to select the best act from among a set of possible acts, in view of the decision maker's prior probability distribution, the sample evidence (if a sample is taken), and the loss function.

It is generally agreed that bayesian decision theory is by far much more useful than Bayesian inference. Thus, in many elementary texts, Bayesian inference is often excluded from formal discussion. However, in this text we present both, for two reasons. First, most of the material for the discussion of Bayesian inference is also required for the development of Bayesian decision theory. So there is little loss in time and effort in our plan. Second, the presentation of Bayesian inference will provide a vivid connection between classical and Bayesian statistics. Indeed, in terms of the underlying logic and the explicit procedures of estimation and testing, the Bayesian methods can actually be considered as extension of the classical theory. Under certain conditions, as we shall see, both inferential procedures will lead to the same conclusions or to identical results, although these results are different in terms of interpretations. Furthermore, Bayesian decision theory may be considered as a further extension from Bayesian inference when we move from two-action to multi-action decision problems.

Before we take up Bayesian statistics proper, it may be noted that in regarding a parameter as a random variable in the Bayesian framework, we need a slight change in notation. In general, a parameter, being a random variable, will be denoted by $\tilde{\theta}$ and its individual values by θ_j. Also, in Bayesian terminology, the θ_j are called *state values,* or *states of nature,* or simply *states.* For instances, $\tilde{\mu}, \tilde{\pi}, \tilde{x}_m$, etc., will denote the state random variables, and μ, π, x_m, etc., will denote the realized values of these state random variables.

23.2 BAYES' THEOREM

It has been stated that a Bayesian inference or decision may be made on prior information alone or on both prior and sample information. When the latter is the case, these two types of information are integrated into what may be called posterior information. The device used for the integration, or for the revision of prior information into posterior information with sample data, is called Bayes' theorem. The name "Bayesian" employed to characterize the general methods introduced in this and the next two chapters is a consequence of this theorem. We shall introduce this all-important theorem now.

Bayes' theorem is a probability rule that is concerned with conditional probabilities. We shall develop this theorem here by following an example in detail. We are told that in an urn there is a large number of physically identical chips and that these chips may be all black, or half black and half white, or all white. Suppose one chip is drawn at random from the urn and it turns out to be black. In view of this sample outcome, what are the respective probabilities for the three possible propositions? To solve this problem, the three possible states of the state random variable, color of the chips, may be denoted as

θ_1 = all chips are black,

θ_2 = half of the chips are black and half of the chips are white,

θ_3 = all chips are white.

Next, we should assign a probability to each of these states according to our degrees of belief in these propositions. Since we have no information whatsoever about the distribution of color of the chips, we may assume all three states of nature are equally likely and assign equal probabilities to them. Namely,

$$P(\theta_1) = 1/3; \qquad P(\theta_2) = 1/3; \qquad P(\theta_3) = 1/3.$$

These values are called *prior probabilities,* forming the *prior probability distribution,* of the state random variable. They are so called because they are established prior to the empirical evidence about to be gathered.

Now, let X be the event that "the chip is black." Here, X stands for the experimental or sample result; it is the additional information we have obtained to help evaluate the probabilities for the three states of nature. From the content of the question posed initially, what we seek to find are the conditional probabilities

$$P(\theta_1 \,|\, X) = \frac{P(\theta_1 \cap X)}{P(X)},$$

$$P(\theta_2 \,|\, X) = \frac{P(\theta_2 \cap X)}{P(X)},$$

and

$$P(\theta_3 \,|\, X) = \frac{P(\theta_3 \cap X)}{P(X)}.$$

To obtain these probabilities we need, first of all, the probabilities for the joint events, $\theta_j \cap X, j = 1, 2, 3$. From information given by the problem and our solution so far, we must have

$$P(\theta_1 \cap X) = P(\theta_1)P(X \mid \theta_1)$$
$$= (1/3)(1) = 1/3;$$
$$P(\theta_2 \cap X) = P(\theta_2)P(X \mid \theta_2)$$
$$= (1/3)(1/2) = 1/6;$$
$$P(\theta_3 \cap X) = P(\theta_3)P(X \mid \theta_3)$$
$$= (1/3)(0) = 0.$$

In these computations, the terms $P(X \mid \theta_j)$ are called *likelihoods*, because they indicate how likely the sample result X under consideration is, given the possible states of nature, θ_j. Thus, for instance, in our example, $P(X \mid \theta_1) = 1$ means that the likelihood (probability) of selecting a black chip given that all chips are black is one.

After this, we need the probability of the event X, the denominator in the ratios for the desired conditional probabilities. This is the marginal probability of a sample or experimental result. It is simply the sum of the joint probabilities, $P(\theta_j \cap X)$. That is,

$$P(X) = P(\theta_1 \cap X) + P(\theta_2 \cap X) + P(\theta_3 \cap X)$$
$$= 1/3 + 1/6 + 0$$
$$= 1/2.$$

Finally, we have

$$P(\theta_1 \mid X) = \frac{P(\theta_1 \cap X)}{P(X)} = \frac{1/3}{1/2} = \frac{2}{3};$$
$$P(\theta_2 \mid X) = \frac{P(\theta_2 \cap X)}{P(X)} = \frac{1/6}{1/2} = \frac{1}{3};$$
$$P(\theta_3 \mid X) = \frac{P(\theta_3 \cap X)}{P(X)} = \frac{0}{1/2} = 0.$$

These results are called *posterior probabilities*, constituting the *posterior probability distribution*, of the state random variable. They are so named because they are determined after the sample results are known. Posterior probabilities are also called *revised probabilities* in the sense that they are obtained by revising the prior probabilities with sample information. It is interesting to note how the evidence provided by the outcome of a black chip is revealed in the high posterior probability for θ_1, low posterior probability for θ_2, and zero posterior probability for θ_3 in contrast to the uniform prior distribution. From our understanding of this example, we may state Bayes' theorem as follows:

THEOREM 23.1 BAYES' THEOREM *If $\theta_1, \theta_2, \ldots, \theta_n$ are the state values of a state random variable $\tilde{\theta}$ that are mutually exclusive and* *collectively exhaustive events with nonzero prior probabilities with respect to a random experiment, and if X is any sample outcome in the sample space of the said experiment such that $P(X) > 0$, then the posterior probability of an event θ_j given X is*

$$P(\theta_j \mid X) = \frac{P(\theta_j \cap X)}{P(\theta_1 \cap X) + P(\theta_2 \cap X) + \cdots + P(\theta_n \cap X)}$$

$$= \frac{P(\theta_j)P(X \mid \theta_j)}{\sum\limits_{j=1}^{n} P(\theta_j)P(X \mid \theta_j)}, \qquad j = 1, 2, \ldots, n, \qquad (23.1)$$

where the numerator is a specific term of the denominator and the denominator is the probability of the sample result, $P(X)$.

There are a number of interesting points about Bayes' theorem. First of all, while it deals with a conditional probability, its interpretation here is different from that of the general conditional probability theorem developed in Chapter 5. The general conditional probability theorem asks, "What is the probability of the sample or experimental result given the state value?" whereas Bayes' theorem here asks: "What is the probability of the state value given the sample or experimental result?" In this context, Bayes' theorem is unacceptable to a classical statistician, since he considers the probability of a state value to be meaningless. To him, a state value has some true but unknown value, and therefore the probability that the state value has a particular numerical value is either zero or one, but we do not know which. However, it is not Bayes' theorem itself that upsets the classical statistician but its application to probabilities for state values. If (23.1) is suitably reinterpreted, it becomes a theorem in probability, just as surely true as any other theorem in probability; this, of course, is entirely acceptable to the classical statistician. The "suitable reinterpretation" is the following: Let $\theta_1, \theta_2, \ldots, \theta_n$ be a partition of a sample space, and let X be any event defined over the same sample space; then (23.1) is true as a theorem of probability. In this interpretation, Bayes' theorem is useful and interesting because it "reverses the direction of the conditional probabilities." That is, in the left-hand side of (23.1) the condition is X, while in the right-hand side the conditions are all θ. Returning to our current topic, Bayes' theorem can be applied to probabilities for state values under the subjective interpretation of probability.

Second, the notions of "prior" and "posterior" in Bayes' theorem are relative to a given sample outcome. That is, if a posterior distribution has been determined from a particular sample, this posterior distribution would be considered the prior distribution relative to a new sample. Thus, for example, in the illustrative problem just considered, with the result of a black chip, the probability of θ_1 has been revised upward, the probability of θ_2 has been revised downward, and state θ_3 has become an impossible event and hence should be eliminated from further consideration. Now, suppose that another chip has been selected at

TABLE 23.1 Posterior Distribution After Second Black Chip

State of Nature θ_j	Prior Probability $P(\theta_j)$	Likelihood $P(X \mid \theta_j)$	Joint Probability $P(X \cap \theta_j)$	Posterior Probability $P(\theta_j \mid X)$
θ_1	2/3	1	2/3	4/5
θ_2	1/3	1/2	1/6	1/5
Total	3/3	—	$P(X) = 5/6$	5/5

random and, again, it turns out to be black; what should be the respective probabilities for the remaining two possible states? The answer to this question can be provided by applying Bayes' theorem in the usual way, except that we use the posterior probabilities obtained before as the prior probabilities now, as shown by Table 23.1.

As a matter of fact, when we have two independent samples available, we can revise a given prior distribution just once by using the combined information. The posterior distribution so obtained would be identical with that obtained by conducting the revision process twice, as we have done, once with the original prior distribution and the outcome of the first sample and once with the revised distribution and the outcome of the second sample. For our illustrative example, to combine the two samples in the revision process is to treat the two samples as a single sample of two chips (both black) selected with replacement. Table 23.2 shows that the application of Bayes' theorem to the outcome of the combined sample yields the same posterior distribution as that obtained in Table 23.1.

An important application of Bayes' theorem is in revising probabilities. That is, a decision maker is often confronted with a set of mutually exclusive and exhaustive states of nature in connection with a phenomenon that is subject to test by experiment. Before an experiment is performed, the decision maker may be nearly completely ignorant about the distribution of the state variable, and he often assumes that all states of nature are equally likely. If he has grounds for an educated guess, he should assign prior probabilities accordingly. Thus, different decision makers may assign different prior probabilities to the same set of states of nature.

For instance, to judge whether a coin is fair, one might initially assign equal probabilities to the occurrences of heads and tails. Another person, somehow believing that the coin is biased in favor of heads, may

TABLE 23.2 Posterior Distribution After Two Black Chips

State θ_j	Prior $P(\theta_j)$	Likelihood $P(X \mid \theta_j)$	Joint $P(X \cap \theta_j)$	Posterior $P(\theta_j \mid X)$
θ_1	1/3	$(1)(1) = 1$	1/3	4/5
θ_2	1/3	$(1/2)(1/2) = 1/4$	1/12	1/5
θ_3	1/3	$(0)(0) = 0$	0	0
Total	3/3	—	$P(X) = 5/12$	5/5

be inclined to give, say, 2/3 as the prior probability of heads and 1/3 as that of tails. Such initial differences, however, do not hinder the use of Bayes' theorem, since its very aim is to modify the prior probabilities $P(\theta_j)$ by experiment. After the experiment is performed, we replace $P(\theta_j)$, by $P(\theta_j \mid X)$. Furthermore, we may conduct a new experiment by using posterior probabilities of the preceding experiment as prior probabilities. As we proceed with repeated experiments, evidence accumulates and modifies the initial prior probabilities, thereby modifying the intensity of a decision maker's belief in various states of nature. In other words, the more evidence we accumulate, the less important are the prior probabilities. The only restrictions on the application of Bayes' theorem are that none of the states is assigned a prior probability of 0 or 1 and that the sum of probabilities assigned to all states must add up to 1.

It is convenient to restate Bayes' theorem to show more vividly how Equation (23.1) applies to $f_0(\theta_j)$ and $f_1(\theta_j)$ by using revised notation. The restatement is

$$f_1(\theta_j) = \frac{f_0(\theta_j)f(x \mid \theta_j)}{f(x)}, \qquad (23.2)$$

where

$f_1(\theta_j)$ = the posterior probability of the event $\tilde{\theta} = \theta_j$,

$f_0(\theta_j)$ = the prior probability of the event $\tilde{\theta} = \theta_j$,

x = the observed sample or experimental result; that is, the observed value of a statistic X—a sufficient statistic that summarizes the sample evidence,

$f(x \mid \theta_j)$ = the likelihood function in the Bayesian analysis—the probability of the event $X = x$ given that $\tilde{\theta} = \theta_j$, and

$f(x) = \Sigma f_0(\theta_j)f(x \mid \theta_j)$—the sum of probabilities of the sample result under the given prior probability distribution $f_0(\theta_j)$.

23.3 A FIRST LOOK AT BAYESIAN ESTIMATION

We shall now consider an example for the twofold purpose of illustrating the effects of the application of Bayes' theorem and the Bayesian estimation procedure. Suppose the purchasing agent of a firm must decide whether to accept an incoming lot of 10,000 units of a certain machine part. Suppose also that he adopts the quality standard that the lot is satisfactory if it contains less than 5% of defectives and it is unsatisfactory if it contains 5% defectives or more. One way to make the decision here is to adopt the decision rule stated as: If $E(\tilde{\pi}) < 0.05$, accept the lot; if $E(\tilde{\pi}) \geqslant 0.05$, reject the lot. Here, $\tilde{\pi}$ is the state random

TABLE 23.3 Posterior Distribution After a 100-Item Sample

State π_j	Prior $f_0(\pi_j)$	Likelihood $f(4 \mid \pi_j)$	Joint $f_0(\pi_j)f(4 \mid \pi_j)$	Posterior $f_1(\pi_j)$
0.02	0.10	0.09023	0.009	0.07
0.04	0.35	0.19537	0.069	0.53
0.06	0.30	0.13386	0.040	0.31
0.08	0.15	0.05725	0.009	0.07
0.10	0.10	0.01891	0.002	0.02
Total	1.00	—	$f(x) = 0.129$	1.00

variable and it is the fraction of defective units in the lot. It is not claimed here that this decisions rule is either good or bad. It is enough here that it specifies a way of making the decision. Later we shall go more deeply into this issue. Furthermore, this decision can be made on the prior information the purchasing agent may have about the lot or on his prior and sample information jointly.

Now suppose that, in accordance with his past experience with merchandise of this type, the purchasing agent believes the fraction defective of the lot would range from 0.02 to 0.10, as shown in the first column of Table 23.3. Also, based on his judgment, he is able to assign prior probabilities to the various values of the state random variable as given in the second column of the table. Having established the prior distribution of $\tilde{\pi}$, the purchasing agent, if he so desires, may now make his decision on prior information alone. This is done by computing the prior expected value of $\tilde{\pi}$, denoted as $E_0(\tilde{\pi})$, which is computed in the usual fashion:

$$E_0(\tilde{\pi}) = \sum_j \pi_j f_0(\pi_j)$$

$$= (0.02)(0.10) + (0.04)(0.35) + (0.06)(0.30)$$

$$+ (0.08)(0.15) + (0.10)(0.10)$$

$$= 0.056.$$

This is greater than 0.05; therefore, the lot should be rejected in accordance with this "prior analysis."

However, if the purchasing agent elects to make the decision with sample information together with his personal prior judgment on the state random variable, he may take a random sample of, say, 100 items from the lot for this purpose. Suppose that in the sample four units are found to be defective. How does this evidence influence his prior beliefs and thereby affect his final decision?

To answer this question, he must first revise the prior probabilities using the sample result. This is done by employing Bayes' theorem, as shown in Table 23.3. Here, if sampling is made without replacement, the likelihoods obey the hypergeometric probability law. However, owing to the smallness of the sample relative to the population size, the hypergeometric probabilities can be approximated by the binomial probabilities, which, in turn, owing to small π_j and large n, can be approximated by the Poisson probabilities. Thus, for example,

$$P(x = 4 \mid \pi = 0.02) \doteq f_b(4 \mid 100, 0.02)$$
$$\doteq f_P[4 \mid \mu = 100(0.02)]$$
$$= f_P(4 \mid 2)$$
$$\doteq 0.09023;$$

$$P(x = 4 \mid \pi = 0.04) \doteq f_b(4 \mid 100, 0.04)$$
$$\doteq f_P(4 \mid 4)$$
$$\doteq 0.19537;$$

and so on.

Of course, the exact hypergeometric probabilities can be easily obtained from the computer, but the approximations here are almost identical to the exact probabilities because of the very favorable conditions.

Let us make a few comments on the results contained in Table 23.3. Note that the value of $f(x) = 0.129$ is the probability under the prior distribution of the sample obtained. Once the sample result x is known, the posterior probability of each state can be determined as that proportion of the probability of the sample result contributed by each state. An interesting way to interpret the value of $f(x)$ is this: If, say, 1000 samples of size 100 were drawn from a situation described by the state variable and its corresponding prior distribution, there would be, on the average, 129 samples with four defective units. Of these 129 samples with $x = 4$, nine would result from the state $\pi_2 = 0.02$, 69 would result from the state $\pi_2 = 0.04$, and so on. Now, since 69 out of the 129 occurrences of the sample result are due to the state $\pi_2 = 0.04$, the probability to be assigned to state π_2, given $x = 4$, should be $69/129 \doteq 0.53$, the proportion of the total occurrences attributable to the state $\pi_2 = 0.04$. Posterior probabilities for other states can be interpreted in exactly the same manner.

A quick comparison between $f_0(\pi_j)$ and $f_1(\pi_j)$ shows that sampling has indeed modified the initial probabilities to a great extent. Since the sample outcome is 4% defective, it is not surprising that the prior probability for $\pi_2 = 0.04$ has been revised upward by more than 51%. Not anticipated on the basis of intuition, however, is the upward revision of the prior probability of the adjoining state $\pi_3 = 0.06$, although the change is quite small in our example. Meanwhile, as expected, the probabilities assigned to all the other states have been modified downward. Furthermore, the farther the state is from π_2 the greater is the percentage reduction. Thus, sampling has the effect of condensing the probabilities of the states around the state whose value is identical with that of the sample result. It is interesting to point out also that the largest posterior probability may still be attached to some other state, despite the sample result, if the prior probability of that other state is much larger than that for the state that is identical to the sample outcome. Finally, it should be clear that a different posterior distribution would emerge, given the same sample result, if a different prior distribution were assumed.

Returning to the problem of estimation, we note that when a posterior distribution is established, we may proceed to calculate the posterior expected value of the state random variable. Denote this as $E_1(\tilde{\pi})$, and for our illustrative problem we have

$$E_1(\tilde{\pi}) = \sum_j \pi_j f_1(\pi_j)$$

$$= (0.02)(0.07) + (0.04)(0.53) + (0.06)(0.31)$$

$$+ (0.08)(0.07) + (0.10)(0.02)$$

$$= 0.0488.$$

which is less than 0.05; the lot now should be accepted. Thus the decision is altered in view of sample information in this case.

We see that the Bayesian estimation procedure usually provides two distributions from which decisions can be made: the *prior distribution,* which is obtained from prior information alone, and the *posterior distribution,* which is derived from posterior information—the combined prior and sample information. This point is a decided advantage of the Bayesian procedure over the classical method. When sampling is very expensive or a decision must be made before sample information can be made available, the classical approach would be of no help to the decision maker, while the Bayesian method can still provide a solution. Granted that a decision based on prior information alone is inferior to one made on posterior information, it remains true that if a decision has to be made anyway, it is better to make it with some information, though scanty, than with no information at all!

23.4 COMMENTS ON THE SUBJECTIVE PRIOR PROBABILITY LAW

Prior probabilities for the state random variable are a prerequisite for the application of Bayes' theorem in Bayesian analysis. While Bayes' theorem itself is not controversial, many statisticians concerned with applications question Bayesian analysis because prior probabilities may be based on personal degrees of belief and, therefore, cannot be objectively evaluated. The Bayesians maintain, however, that subjective probabilities are the only kind obtainable in the real world, since relevant objective probabilities can never be known. In any problem situation, the relevant objective probabilities must be estimated on the basis of whatever information is available. Because sample information can never be perfect, probability assignments are inevitably subjective. Furthermore, if one admits the idea of subjective prior probabilities, then the posterior probabilities obtained with Bayes' theorem represent one's degree of belief in the alternative states that should be held after the empirical evidence bearing on the states has been obtained. Thus, the posterior probabilities are also subjective to the individual who establishes the subjective prior probabilities. This implies that another statistician with different prior probabilities would produce different posterior probabilities with the same sample evidence.

It may be noted here that the debate between subjective and objective interpretations of probability, or between the acceptance and rejection of the concept of prior probabilities, is more philosophical than practical. In practice, one may find that both positions are reasonable in different circumstances. The use of prior probability, for example, is quite appropriate in many business problems where, say, a manager often wants a systematic way to take into account his personal beliefs in the statistical decision process. In many other situations, however, the insistence on empirical evidence and the rejection of prior degrees of belief are also appropriate. For example, in medical research, a new drug should be evaluated without using the prior degrees of belief (or prejudices) of the physicians and drug firms that develop it.

In any event, if one accepts the subjective interpretation of probability and if one finds it appropriate to employ Bayesian procedures, the very first thing to do is to introduce a systematic method for assigning values to the prior probability law over the states in accordance with the degrees of belief held by the decision maker. One of these procedures, developed by L. J. Savage, is called the *lottery technique*. This procedure requires the decision maker to answer a series of yes-no questions phrased in terms of simple betting odds, and it was presented in Chapter 5.

Very often, subjective probabilities actually reflect empirical data or past experience but only to the extent that they are integrated with the degrees of rational belief held by the decision maker. Indeed, prior probabilities assigned to the state random variable may be directly equated to historical relative frequencies in many situations. For example, in the acceptance problem, the likelihoods of the various fractions defective of the machine parts may be equated to the relative frequencies of fractions defective of this and similar products according to past experience. However, great care must be taken in establishing a prior probability law on such a basis, since improvement or deterioration may have taken place in the production process, different raw materials may have been used, or some other factor may be present that has changed the quality of the output and thereby altered the relevance and usefulness of historical data in assessing the required probabilities.

In the absence of prior probabilities established by the lottery technique or past data it has been suggested that equal probabilities of states be employed. This position stems from Laplace (1749–1827), who was one of the first to adopt Bayes' theorem as the major method of statistical inference. Employment of equal priors has been criticized as unrealistic, since it implies that the state of belief prior to sampling is one of complete ignorance, a condition that rarely exists in practice. However, the use of a uniform prior probability law can be interpreted as resulting in final inferences that are not affected by the subjective elements of belief to which many statisticians object. Moreover, uniform priors may be an advantage, or at least a computational convenience, when sample information overwhelms prior information.

When the number of states is relatively small and when the statistician is quite patient and persistent, the lottery procedure may be useful in estimating prior probabilities. However, this procedure becomes almost impossible in terms of time and energy when the number of states is very large. The extreme case, of course, is when the state random variable is continuous and the appropriate prior probability law is a density function.

Thus, when the state set is large or continuous, different procedures are required in order to avoid the mathematical drudgery. Fortunately, as we shall see in the next two sections, if the general distribution pattern of a prior probability law is known to follow a certain special probability model, such as those introduced in Chapters 8 and 9, its parameters can usually be determined from historical data or from observing some simple facts about the functional form of the model. Very often, when the prior distribution can be approximated by a special probability law, the corresponding posterior distribution also obeys the same probability law. That is, certain prior probability laws lead directly to particular expressions for the revised probabilities and computational effort is reduced to a minimum.

In passing, it is interesting to note that the resurgence of Bayesian statistics owes much to applied statisticians in collegiate schools of business. The use of a probability distribution to express the degrees of belief in alternative states has great attractiveness in business decision making, where the attractiveness of each of the available courses of action can be measured on monetary or utility scales and where personal judgment is always present and important. Among those who have made important contributions to Bayesian inference and decision procedures are Bruno de Finetti, L. J. Savage, Howard Raiffa, Robert Schlaifer, Harold Jeffrey, J. J. Good, and Dennis V. Lindley.

23.5 BAYESIAN ESTIMATION WITH BETA PRIOR DENSITY FUNCTIONS

The acceptance sampling example cited earlier refers to a problem situation of using a binomial sampling process to revise the prior probabilities. In general, with binomial sampling, it is desired to estimate the probability of success of a Bernoulli variable. This being the case, the state random variable should be considered as continuous rather than discrete, since $\tilde{\pi}$, as a probability, is capable of assuming any real value between 0 and 1. In principle, any continuous probability distribution whose area is between 0 and 1 can be used as a prior distribution for $\tilde{\pi}$. In practice, it turns out to be convenient to use beta distributions as priors for $\tilde{\pi}$, because then the posterior distribution for $\tilde{\pi}$ will also be a beta distribution. When using a beta prior for $\tilde{\pi}$, the decision maker selects the beta parameters $\tilde{r}$ and $\tilde{n}$ so that the beta probability density curve assigns high densities to values of $\tilde{\pi}$ that the decision maker believes are likely, low densities to values of $\tilde{\pi}$ that the decision maker believes are unlikely, and so on for intermediate cases and extreme cases. While the decision maker is restricted to the family of all possible beta distributions, when he uses a beta prior for $\tilde{\pi}$, this restriction is not serious. There are a great many beta distributions, and the decision maker can usually expect to find one that approximates very closely his degrees of belief. The beta parameters $\tilde{r}$ and $\tilde{n}$ have a different interpretation here compared with that given in Chapter 7 in the context of theoretical probability. Here, the beta parameters for a prior distribution for $\tilde{\pi}$, can be regarded as meaningless; their numerical values merely choose the particular beta density curve from the family of all beta density curves that the decision maker finds closest to his degrees of belief concerning the possible values of $\tilde{\pi}$. In fact, fractional values for $\tilde{r}$ and $\tilde{n}$ are permitted. The only restrictions are $\tilde{r} > 0$ and $\tilde{n} > \tilde{r}$, where $\tilde{n}$ and $\tilde{r}$ are real numbers. With this much background, we may now formally state the Bayesian theorem of binomial sampling.

THEOREM 23.1 BAYESIAN THEOREM OF BINOMIAL SAMPLING WITH β PRIOR DENSITY FUNCTIONS *If an SRS with size n is selected from a binomial population whose prior distribution is assumed to obey the β probability law with parameters $\tilde{r}_0$ and $\tilde{n}_0$, whose values are assigned in accordance with the decision maker's degrees of belief, then we have for this prior β function, denoted $\beta_0(\tilde{\pi} \mid \tilde{r}_0, \tilde{n}_0)$, the following descriptive measures:*

$$E_0(\tilde{\pi}) = \tilde{\pi}_0 = \frac{\tilde{r}_0}{\tilde{n}_0}, \tag{23.3}$$

$$V_0(\tilde{\pi}) = \sigma_0^2(\tilde{\pi}) = \frac{\tilde{r}_0(\tilde{n}_0 - \tilde{r}_0)}{\tilde{n}_0^2(\tilde{n}_0 + 1)}, \tag{23.4}$$

and for $\tilde{r}_0 > 1$ and $(\tilde{n}_0 - \tilde{r}_0) > 1$,

$$\tilde{x}_{m_0}(\tilde{\pi}) = \frac{\tilde{r}_0 - 1}{\tilde{n}_0 - 2}. \tag{23.5}$$

Furthermore, with a prior β distribution for $\tilde{\pi}$ defined, the posterior distribution for $\tilde{\pi}$ would also be a β distribution with parameters $\tilde{r}_1 = \tilde{r}_0 + \tilde{r}$ and $\tilde{n}_1 = \tilde{n}_0 + \tilde{n}$. As a result, the posterior β distribution, denoted $\beta_1(\tilde{\pi} \mid \tilde{r}_1, \tilde{n}_1)$, would have the following descriptive measures:

$$E_1(\tilde{\pi}) = \tilde{\pi}_1 = \frac{\tilde{r}_1}{\tilde{n}_1}, \tag{23.6}$$

$$V_1(\tilde{\pi}) = \sigma_1^2(\tilde{\pi}) = \frac{\tilde{r}_1(\tilde{n}_1 - \tilde{r}_1)}{\tilde{n}_1^2(\tilde{n}_1 + 1)}, \tag{23.7}$$

and, when $\tilde{r}_1 > 1$ and $(\tilde{n}_1 - \tilde{r}_1) > 1$,

$$\tilde{x}_{m_1}(\tilde{\pi}) = \frac{\tilde{r}_1 - 1}{\tilde{n}_1 - 2}. \tag{23.8}$$

It may be noted that, in the above theorem, $\tilde{\pi}_0$ and $\tilde{\pi}_1$ are the prior and posterior estimators for the state random variable $\tilde{\pi}$, respectively.

Turning now to consider how a statistician can convert his personal degrees of belief into a specific beta distribution, let us consider three cases. First, if the decision maker thinks that a uniform distribution is appropriate as the prior probability law, then he can set $r_0 = 1$ and $n_0 = 2$. With a uniform prior distribution, the prior expectation of $\tilde{\pi}$ would be

$$\pi_0 = 1/2 = 0.5.$$

Also, the variance for a uniform prior is

$$\sigma_0^2(\pi) = \frac{1(2 - 1)}{2^2(2 + 1)} \doteq 0.083.$$

Now, suppose the purchasing agent in the previous example uses a uniform prior. In view of the sample results of $r = 4$ and $n = 100$, the posterior expectation of the fraction defective becomes

$$\pi_1 = \frac{1 + 4}{2 + 100} \doteq 0.049$$

with a posterior variance of

$$\sigma_1^2(\pi) = \frac{5(102 - 5)}{102^2(102 + 1)} \doteq 0.00045.$$

Next, if a uniform prior is judged to be inappropriate, but the decision maker wants a skewed prior distribution fitted to his judgment of the mean and mode, then the parameters of a prior beta distribution can be found by the decision maker's judgment on the approximate values of $E_0(\tilde{\pi})$ and $\tilde{x}_{m_0}(\tilde{\pi})$. Thus, for instance, if the purchasing agent in the previous example feels that the most probable value of $\tilde{\pi}$ is, say, 0.03, and that the mean value of $\tilde{\pi}$ is approximately, say, 0.05, then

$$\pi_0 = \frac{r_0}{n_0} = 0.05$$

and

$$x_{m_0}(\pi) = \frac{r_0 - 1}{n_0 - 2} = 0.03.$$

From the first equation, we obtain

$$r_0 = 0.05 n_0.$$

Substituting this result into the equation for $x_{m_0}(\pi)$ we have

$$\frac{0.05 n_0 - 1}{n_0 - 2} = 0.03.$$

Solving, this yields

$$n_0 = 47; \qquad r_0 = 2.35.$$

With these prior parameter vaues, we have $\pi_0 = 0.05$ and $\sigma_0^2(\pi) = 0.00099$.

Now, given the same sample results as before, the posterior expectation of the fraction defective becomes

$$\pi_1 = \frac{2.35 + 4}{47 + 100} \doteq 0.043$$

with

$$\sigma_1^2(\pi) = \frac{6.35(147 - 6.35)}{147^2(147 + 1)} \doteq 0.00028.$$

Before proceeding further, let us make some important observations on these results. First, the posterior expectations of $\tilde{\pi}$ are nearly identical and lead to the same decision of accepting the shipment even though two quite different prior densities, $\beta_0(\tilde{\pi} \mid 1, 2)$ and $\beta_0(\tilde{\pi} \mid 2.35, 47)$, have been assumed. This is an illustration of how large samples overwhelm "gentle" priors. A *gentle prior* is one whose density curve has a flat-topped appearance—that is, with no pronounced central tendency or with a high degree of dispersion. Thus, a gentle prior implies the lack of much prior information on the state variable. In this context, we see that a uniform prior can indicate a completely informationless state, although it turns out to be impossible to specify any particular prior as the one for complete ignorance—any gentle prior will do.

Furthermore, the larger the sample, the more important the sample information becomes in the process of revising the prior density function. In our example, $n = 100$ is very large and, as a result, the posterior expectations are much closer to the sample result of 0.04 than they are to the prior expectations of 0.5 and 0.05, respectively. It is, of course, possible for a posterior expectation to be closer to the prior expectation than it is to the sample result. This happens when the sample is small or when the prior variance is much smaller than the sample variance.

Finally, the posterior variance is usually smaller than the prior variance, since the sample provides additional information that tends to reduce our uncertainty about the state and, therefore, reduce the variations in the state variable. However, with beta densities, it is possible for the posterior variance to be larger than the prior variance in the case where sample evidence shifts the expectation of the posterior density very close to 0.5.

It may now be pointed out that the method of using guesses about the mean and the mode of a beta density for the determination of prior parameter values would break down if a symmetric prior density were employed, since then the mode and the mean would be identical. Hence, when $E_0(\tilde{\pi})$ is assumed to be 0.5, a rough estimate of $V_0(\tilde{\pi})$ is a way of establishing a prior beta density.

As an illustration, let us consider an example where, in a close election between two candidates, one candidate wishes to determine the probability of his winning—that is, $P(\tilde{\pi} > 0.5)$. Suppose that after careful consideration, the politician assigns the following parameter values to his prior beta density:

$$\pi_0 = \frac{r_0}{n_0} = 0.5$$

and

$$\sigma_0^2(\pi) = \frac{r_0(n_0 - r_0)}{n_0^2(n_0 + 1)} = 0.05;$$

then from the equation for π_0, we have

$$r_0 = 0.5n_0 \qquad \text{or} \qquad n_0 = 2r_0.$$

Substituting this result into the equation for $\sigma_0^2(\pi)$ and rearranging terms, we find that

$$r_0(2r_0 - r_0) = 0.05(2r_0)^2(2r_0 + 1).$$

or

$$r_0^2 = 0.2(r_0^2)(2r_0 + 1).$$

Dividing both sides of this result by r_0^2 yields

$$r_0 = 2,$$

and substituting this number into the expression for π_0 we see that

$$n_0 = 4.$$

Finally, suppose that in a sample of 22 voters, 13 are found to be in favor of the candidate in question; then we have

$$\pi_1 = \frac{2 + 13}{4 + 22} \doteq 0.5769.$$

That is, the candidate's expected majority should be about 58%. Using (9.12b), we have

$$F_\beta(\tilde{\pi} < 0.5 \mid 15, 26) = F_b(\tilde{r} < 26 - 15 \mid 26 - 1, 1 - 0.5)$$

$$\doteq 0.212.$$

Thus, the candidate should estimate his probability of winning at $1 - 0.212 = 0.788$.

From our discussion on revising beta distributions, we can conclude that a beta prior can conceptually be broken down into two parts: (1) the rectangular prior followed by (2) a fictitious sample with $r_0 - 1$ successes in $n_0 - 2$ trials. (Note, for a rectangular prior $r_0 = 1$ and

$n_0 = 2$.) For example, if one sets $r_0 = 3$ and $n_0 = 4$, it could be reasoned that his choice is the same as if he started with a rectangular prior distribution and found two successes ($r_0 - 1 = 2$) in two trials ($n_0 - 2 = 2$). This means that the statistician can establish his prior beta density on the basis of a fictitious sample.

So far, we have concentrated on the Bayesian point estimation of population proportions. Interval estimation can also be made within the Bayesian framework. Usually, Bayesian confidence intervals are constructed with reference to the posterior distributions of the state random variables. In general, when the posterior distribution of $\tilde{\theta}$ is normal or approximately normal, the Bayesian procedure here is analogous to that of the classical practice as given by the expression

$$L, U = \tilde{\theta}_1 \mp Z(\tilde{\sigma}_{\tilde{\theta}_1}). \tag{23.9}$$

To apply (23.9) to the case of proportions, it is required, similarly to the classical theory, that $\tilde{n}_1 \tilde{\pi}_1 \geq 5$ and that $\tilde{n}_1(1 - \tilde{\pi}_1) \geq 5$. Now suppose we wish to construct a 95% confidence interval for $\tilde{\pi}$ for the example of the politician just given; we would have

$$L, U = \pi_1 \mp 1.96\sqrt{V_1(\pi)}$$

$$= 0.5769 \mp 1.96\sqrt{\frac{13(26 - 13)}{26^2(26 + 1)}}$$

$$\doteq 0.5260 \text{ to } 0.6278.$$

(Observe that π_1 here refers to a realized posterior value of $\tilde{\pi}$.) Note, for this example, that $\bar{p} = 13/22 \doteq 0.5909$. Hence, the corresponding confidence limits for a 95% classical confidence interval are

$$L, U = \bar{p} \mp 1.96\sqrt{\frac{\bar{p}\bar{p}'}{n}}$$

$$= 0.5909 \mp 1.96\sqrt{\frac{(0.5909)(0.4091)}{22}}$$

$$\doteq 0.3854 \text{ to } 0.7964.$$

Thus, because it uses prior information, the Bayesian interval is centered better and is more precise than the classical interval.

23.6 BAYESIAN ESTIMATION WITH NORMAL PRIOR DENSITY FUNCTIONS

Natural Conjugate Prior Distributions

The beta density, according to the Bayesians, belongs to a group of probability models called "natural conjugate prior distributions." When the prior and posterior density functions are of the same form, the prior is referred to as the *natural conjugate of the conditional,* or *likelihood, function.* Thus, when a natural conjugate is used as the prior probability law, the computational burden in deriving the posterior distribution is eased. To quality as a natural conjugate, a probability distribution must be mathematically tractable, rich in its distribution patterns, and easy to interpret. The beta family of distributions clearly satisfies all these requirements. First of all, it is mathematically tractable in the sense that, given $\tilde{r}_0$ and $\tilde{n}_0$, it is an easy routine to determine the posterior beta distribution with any sample result. Second, the beta family satisfies the requirement of richness, since it includes a variety of distribution patterns. Finally, the beta density has the following relatively simple interpretation: the prior information is approximately equivalent to information provided by $\tilde{r}_0$ successes in a sample of $\tilde{n}_0$ trials from binomial sampling. In this connection, we also note that $\tilde{r}_0$ and $\tilde{n}_0$ are not required to take on integer values, since with a prior probability law the interpretation is made in terms of a "hypothetical" sample.

It may be noted now that a beta density can be used as the prior probability law only if the state random variable is limited in value to an interval between 0 and 1. Situations often arise, however, in which the state random variable is capable of assuming any value within a specified interval other than $(0, 1)$. Often the interval takes on the entire real line. If under such a situation a prior normal density function is appropriate for the state random variable, then the calculation of the posterior distribution is quite simple.

In this section, we first introduce a very important theorem in Bayesian statistics that is concerned with sampling from a population of measurements and the employment of a prior normal density function. Next, we comment on the properties of normal density functions as a family of conjugate prior distributions. Finally, we spell out the conditions under which the results derived from normal prior probability laws would still be valid even if a different prior from the normal prior were assumed.

Bayesian Estimation with Normal Sampling

Normal sampling refers to sampling from populations of magnitudes. The procedure is to assume first a normal prior distribution for the state random variable—the parameter to be estimated, with prior parameters whose values are given in accordance with the decision maker's degrees of belief or subjective judgment. Next, an SRS is selected from the population under consideration, yielding a likelihood function of the sample statistic given the unknown parameter and the standard error of the sample statistic. This likelihood function is of course a sampling distribution and it is also assumed to be normal either because the parent population is normal or because the sample is sufficiently large for the CLT to be operative. Finally, the prior normal distribution for the state random variable and the normal likelihood (sampling) distribution are incorporated to produce a posterior distribution that will also be normally distributed with posterior parameters defined in terms of the parameters for the prior and sampling distributions. Let us now state these features in a theorem.

THEOREM 23.2 BAYESIAN SAMPLING WITH NORMAL PRIOR DENSITY FUNCTIONS *Let X be a population of magnitudes with an unknown mean $\tilde{\mu}_X$ and a known variance $\tilde{\sigma}_X^2$; let the prior distribution of $\tilde{\mu}_X$ be normal with $\tilde{\mu}_0$ and $\tilde{\sigma}_0^2$ whose values reflect a decision maker's subjective judgment; and let the likelihood function $f(\bar{X} \mid \tilde{\mu}_X, \tilde{\sigma}_X^2)$, generated by an SRS drawn from the population under investigation, also be normal. Then the posterior distribution of $\tilde{\mu}_X$ will also be normal with its posterior mean and variance defined as follows:*

$$E_1(\tilde{\mu}_X) = \tilde{\mu}_1 = \frac{(\tilde{\mu}_0)\tilde{\sigma}_X^2 + (\bar{X})\tilde{\sigma}_0^2}{\tilde{\sigma}_0^2 + \tilde{\sigma}_X^2}; \tag{23.10}$$

$$V_1(\tilde{\mu}_X) = \tilde{\sigma}_1^2 = \frac{(\tilde{\sigma}_0^2)(\tilde{\sigma}_X^2)}{\tilde{\sigma}_0^2 + \tilde{\sigma}_X^2}. \tag{23.11}$$

Before we move on to provide a numerical example for the application of Theorem 23.1, let us make a couple of observations on this theorem. First of all, there is no relationship between $\tilde{\sigma}_X^2$ and $\tilde{\sigma}_0^2$. The value of $\tilde{\sigma}_0^2$ together with that of $\tilde{\mu}_0$ in the prior normal distribution reflect the statistician's subjective judgment on the state random variable $\tilde{\mu}_X$. More precisely, the confidence that one has in his judgment on the value of $\tilde{\mu}_0$ is expressed on his selection of $\tilde{\sigma}_0^2$. In general, the more vague one is about $\tilde{\mu}_0$, the greater is the value assigned to $\tilde{\sigma}_0^2$.

Secondly, it may be noted that the revised mean of the posterior distribution of $\tilde{\mu}_X$ is a weighted mean of the prior expectation and the sample mean. The weights are the reciprocals of the variances of the respective distributions. These weights are sometimes referred to as the *precision*, or *information content* of the respective estimates. From (23.11) we see that the information content of the posterior distribution is the sum of the information contents of the prior distribution and the sampling distribution, since (23.11) can be written as

$$\frac{1}{\tilde{\sigma}_1^2} = \frac{1}{\tilde{\sigma}_0^2} + \frac{1}{\tilde{\sigma}_X^2},$$

or

$$\frac{1}{\tilde{\sigma}_1^2} = \frac{1}{\tilde{\sigma}_0^2} + \frac{n}{\tilde{\sigma}_X^2},$$

which indicates that the revised variance is smaller than that of either the prior distribution or the distribution of the sample mean. Thus, the posterior distribution, which combines estimates from both sources (judgment and sample), has more information than either source separately.

Let us consider an example. The manufacturer of a new machine designed to produce product X claims that its performance is characterized by a normal distribution with a mean of 25 units of output per hour and a variance of 6. That is, the manufacturer claims that $f(x) = n(x \mid 25, \sqrt{6})$, where x is the actual hourly output.

Suppose the production manager of a certain firm would like to buy the machine if the mean output per hour is as claimed. After a thorough study of the machine's design and construction, he believes the chances are about 2 out of 3 that the mean output will fall within the range of 22 ± 3, the chances are about 96 out of 100 that the mean output will fall within the range of $22 \pm 2(3)$, and that the distribution of mean output is about normal. In other words, according to his judgment the prior distribution of $\tilde{\mu}_X$ is normal with $\mu_0 = 22$ and $\sigma_0^2 = 9$.

In order to revise his prior beliefs, the production manager observed four such machines in operation for an hour and obtained a sample mean $\bar{x} = 24$. Also, for $n = 4$, and assuming σ_X^2 is 6 as claimed by the manufacturer, we have

$$\sigma_{\bar{X}}^2 = \frac{\sigma_X^2}{n} = \frac{6}{4} = 1.5.$$

With the empirical results obtained, the revised, or posterior, mean and variance can now be computed using the prior information as follows:

$$\mu_1 = \frac{\mu_0 \sigma_{\bar{X}}^2 + (\bar{x})\sigma_0^2}{\sigma_0^2 + \sigma_{\bar{X}}^2}$$

$$= \frac{22(1.5) + 24(9)}{9 + 1.5}$$

$$\doteq 23.714$$

and

$$\sigma_1^2 = \frac{(\sigma_0^2)\sigma_{\bar{X}}^2}{\sigma_0^2 + \sigma_{\bar{X}}^2}$$

$$= \frac{9(1.5)}{9 + 1.5}$$

$$\doteq 1.286.$$

Hence, the posterior distribution becomes

$$f_1(\tilde{\mu}_X \mid \bar{x} = 24) = n_1(\tilde{\mu}_X \mid 23.714, \sqrt{1.286})$$

compared to the prior distribution,

$$f_0(\tilde{\mu}_X) = n_0(\tilde{\mu}_X \mid 22, \sqrt{9}).$$

Now, with the posterior distribution on hand and if a 95%

confidence interval is required by (23.9), we have

$$L, U = \mu_1 \mp 1.96\sigma_1 = 23.714 \mp 1.96\sqrt{1.286}$$

$$\doteq 23.714 \mp 2.223,$$

which does contain $\tilde{\mu}_X = 25$. If the production manager is willing to consider having his desired output within a 95% posterior interval estimate as enough proof, then the machine should be purchased.

It is interesting to note that if we accept σ^2 as 6 instead of estimating it from the sample, the classical maximum likelihood point estimate for μ in this example is $\bar{x} = 24$ and the corresponding 95% confidence interval is

$$L, U = \bar{x} \mp 1.96\sigma_{\bar{x}} = 24 \mp 1.96\sqrt{1.5}$$

$$\doteq 24 \mp 2.400,$$

which is less precise (wider) than the Bayesian interval, reflecting the fact that the classical procedure ignores the value of prior information.

Some interesting observations may be made from the results just obtained. First, since the sample mean is greater than the prior mean, the revised mean should reflect this by being larger than the prior mean. Next, in our example, the revised mean is closer to the sample mean than it is to the prior mean, reflecting the relatively smaller amount of information about the mean contained in the prior in this case. Precisely, $\sigma_{\bar{X}}^2$ is only about 17% of σ_0^2; or we note that the weight of the sample mean is $1/1.5$, in contrast to $1/9$ as the weight attached to the prior expectation. Finally, as noted before, since sample information provides additional information, the variance of the revised distribution of the mean is smaller than either the prior or sample variance taken alone. This is always true in normal sampling with normal priors and posteriors and known variance. (Recall that this may not be the case under certain conditions with binomial sampling.)

Now, it is important to note that the weight given to the sample mean increases with the increase in the sample size. Thus, for example, in the previous illustration, given the same prior information but given $\bar{x} = 24$ with $n = 25$, then we would have $\tilde{\mu}_1 \doteq 23.95$, which is nearly equal to the sample mean due to the reduction of $V(\bar{X})$ from 1.5 (with $n = 4$) to 0.24 (with $n = 25$). In the case of the larger n, the sample gives a great deal more information. In this connection, it may be noted, as can be verified by the reader, that if the information provided by sample evidence, measured by $1/V(\bar{X})$, is large relative to that furnished in the prior density function for $\tilde{\mu}_X$, measured by $1/\sigma_0^2$, even relatively large percentage changes in $\tilde{\mu}_0$ would have only a negligible effect on the revised density function. Similarly, a large percentage change in σ_0^2 would have only an insignificant effect on $\tilde{\mu}_1$ if the smallest possible (but reasonable) value of σ_0^2 is large relative to $V(\bar{X})$. These observations lead to the conclusion that when a large amount of sample information can be made available, irrespective of the parameters of the prior density function we would have

$$\tilde{\mu}_1 \doteq \bar{X}$$

and

$$\tilde{\sigma}_1^2 = \tilde{\sigma}_{\bar{X}}^2.$$

Thus, when a statistician is in a position where the amount of sample information obtainable is very large relative to prior information, the inference or decision will, in effect, be made on sample information alone and no weight is given to the prior degrees of belief concerning the values $\tilde{\mu}_X$ might have. This statement implies that a value of zero is assigned to $1/\tilde{\sigma}_0^2$; that is, $\tilde{\sigma}_0^2$ is infinity. This being the case, the prior density function can be ignored in the computation of the revised mean and variance. Here, the conclusion also implies that the Bayesian and classical procedures would produce identical results as n approaches infinity or $1/\tilde{\sigma}_0^2$ approaches zero.

Normal Priors as a Conjugate Distribution

The family of normal distributions also possess all the desirable properties of a conjugate family. In terms of mathematical tractability, the prior and posterior distributions are members of the same family of probability density functions. Furthermore, given the prior normal density and sample result, the posterior distribution is quite easily calculated from the established equations for posterior parameters, when σ^2 is known.

As to richness, the normal distribution, unlike the beta model, is always symmetric. However, for a normal distribution the mean is capable of assuming any real value, and the variance can take on any positive real value, so the normal probability law can still be employed to cover a large number of sets of beliefs. More important is the fact, as will be seen in the next subsection, that equations for posterior parameters derived under a normal probability prior law would still be valid under certain conditions even if a highly skewed prior distribution were assumed.

The interpretation of a normal prior density function, as in the beta case, can be made in terms of a fictitious sample; but in practice it is not so direct, since the employment of "equivalent sample information" in the normal case requires a different "parametrization" of the distribution.

We proceed by assuming that the fictitious sample information is provided by a sample size $\tilde{n}_0$, which is defined as

$$(1) \qquad \tilde{n}_0 = \frac{\sigma_X^2}{\tilde{\sigma}_0^2},$$

from which we have

$$(2) \qquad \tilde{\sigma}_0^2 = \frac{\sigma_X^2}{\tilde{n}_0}.$$

That is, we think of the prior variance as defined by the fictitious sample size and the population variance, and the prior distribution is $n(\tilde{u}_x; \tilde{u}_0, \sigma/\sqrt{n_0})$. Likewise, let us define the posterior sample size as

$$(3) \qquad\qquad \tilde{n}_1 = \frac{\sigma^2}{\sigma_1^2},$$

where

$$(4) \qquad\qquad n_1 = n_0 + n.$$

As a consequence of (4), the posterior mean can now be written as

$$(5) \qquad \tilde{\mu}_1 = \frac{(\sigma^2/n)\tilde{\mu}_0 + (\sigma^2/n_0)\bar{x}}{\sigma^2/n + \sigma^2/n_0} = \frac{n_0\tilde{\mu}_0 + n\bar{x}}{n_0 + n}.$$

With this new parametrization, we observe that the prior distribution is defined in terms of $\tilde{\mu}_0$ and n_0 instead of $\tilde{\mu}_0$ and $\tilde{\sigma}_0^2$. Thus, the prior distribution can be interpreted roughly as the information contained in a sample of size n_0 which happens to produce a sample mean $\tilde{\mu}_0$. So interpreted, μ_1, as defined by (5), can be thought of as a pooled mean based on two independent samples with the n_1, the pooled sample size, as defined by (4), one part from the prior distribution and one part from the sample. It must be stressed that the prior sample is fictitious and it represents the statistician's degrees of belief about the state random variable.

Definition (5) for the posterior mean can also be utilized to determine the relative weights of prior and sample information. Under the new parametrization, $\tilde{\mu}_1$ is a weighted mean with $n_0/(n_0 + n)$ and $n/(n_0 + n)$ as the weights, respectively. Hence, when $n_0 > n$, the prior mean would be given more weight and $\tilde{\mu}_1$ is closer to $\tilde{\mu}_0$ than to $\bar{x}$; and vice versa. Clearly, when $n_0 = n$, the posterior mean would be midway between $\tilde{\mu}_0$ and $\bar{x}$. Also, the case where $1/\sigma_0^2$ approaches zero or n approaches infinity is equivalent to having n_0 approach zero. This being true, then we have an "informationless" or a "diffused" prior state and an inference is in effect made on empirical evidence alone.

For the example used in this section before, we have

$$n_0 = \frac{\sigma^2}{\sigma_0^2} = \frac{6}{9} = \frac{2}{3}.$$

Since $n = 4$, then

$$n_1 = n_0 + n = \frac{2}{3} + 4 = \frac{14}{3}$$

and

$$\mu_1 = \frac{n_0\mu_0 + n(\bar{x})}{n_0 + n} = \frac{(\frac{2}{3})(22) + (4)(24)}{\frac{14}{3}} \doteq 23.714$$

as before with the original parametrization. Note that μ_1 is closer to $\bar{x}$ than to μ_0 since $n_0 < n$. Also note that n_0, being a fictitious sample size, need not be an integer.

Normal Prior Density Functions

Our discussion so far in this section has been made under two important assumptions: a prior normal probability law and a normal sampling distribution of $\bar{X}$. Under these two assumptions, the resulting posterior density for $\tilde{\mu}_X$ will also be normal. It is reasonable to ask now about the effects on the expectation and variance of the posterior distribution when these two assumptions are violated.

The normality assumption for the sampling distribution of $\bar{X}$ can be easily taken care of by recalling the Central Limit Theorem, by which we know that the distribution of $\bar{X}$ will be approximately normal, irrespective of the pattern of the population distribution, if the size of the sample is greater than 30. Furthermore, with a sufficiently large

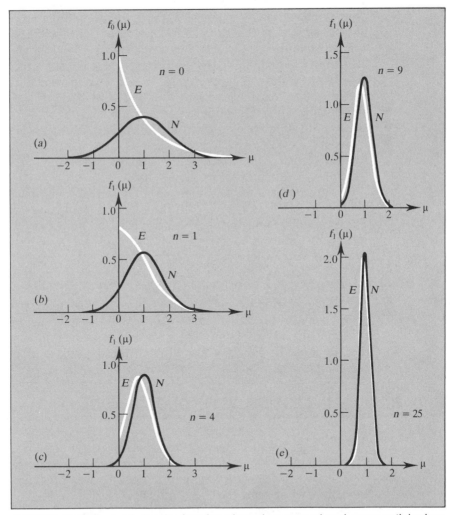

FIGURE 23.1 Revised density functions based on normal and exponential priors, each prior with an expectation and variance of unity, for samples of sizes 1, 4, 9, and 25. Each sample yields a sample mean and variance of unity. (*Source:* Reproduced from Robert Schlaifer, *Introduction to Statistics for Business Decisions* (New York, McGraw-Hill, 1961), by specific permission of the copyright holder, the President and Fellows of Harvard College.)

$n, n > 30$ or so, the population variance (if unknown) can be replaced by the sample variance to compute the variance of the sample mean without changing the sampling distribution of the sample mean significantly. It is also true, in Bayesian analysis, that if the best decision depends on $\tilde{\mu}_X$ but not on σ_X^2, the posterior distribution is insensitive to σ_X^2.

Next, if a prior probability law other than the normal density function is assumed, the posterior density function may still be normal with parameters as defined by (23.10) and (23.11) under certain conditions. These conditions are: (1) $n > 30$; (2) the prior density has the same mean and variance irrespective of its shape; (3) the prior density function is relatively smooth near the observed sample mean. These conditions are demonstrated by Figure 23.1. The graph for $n = 0$ in this figure refers to two different prior density functions, the normal (denoted N) and the exponential (denoted E) distributions. For both prior distributions, the same expectation of $\mu_0 = 1$ is assumed. Other graphs in the figure give the resulting revised density functions of $\tilde{\mu}_X$ for $n = 1, 4, 9,$ and 25, respectively. It is assumed that all these revised densities are obtained with $\bar{x} = \mu_0 = 1$ and $\sigma_X^2 = \sigma_0^2 = 1$. This figure shows that when the sample size is rather small, such as 1, 4, and 9, substantial differences remain in the revised densities. However, when a moderate sample size is used, such as 25, the differences between the revised density functions are so small that they can be ignored completely for nearly all practical purposes.

Thus, the results for a normal prior can be generalized to any prior density function as long as the three conditions stated before are met. This seemingly amazing conclusion is actually quite easy to understand. After all, the revised mean is a weighted average of the prior and sample means, where each is weighted by the reciprocal of its variance. With the increase in n, the variance of the sample mean will decrease; the sample mean will carry a greater weight in determining the revised mean. Thus, when the sample size is increased enough, the shape of the prior density function carries but little weight in producing the posterior density function. The meaning of "enough" refers to the fact that $\tilde{\sigma}_0^2$ must be substantially larger than $\tilde{\sigma}_X^2$ and, as a rule of thumb, the sample size must be greater than 30.

23.7 BAYESIAN TESTING WITH ODDS RATIOS

Recall that classical testing procedures were developed under the simplified but very useful framework of two-action decision problems. With such a framework, one is to choose between two acts or to select between two hypotheses. A null hypothesis is rejected when the probability of occurrence of the value of the test statistic is small, indicating the sample outcome is one of the extreme values of the sampling distribution of the test statistic under the assumption that the null hypothesis is true. Alternatively, in a Bayesian context, we say that a null hypothesis is rejected because the alternative has a higher probability of being true in view of the empirical evidence.

The Bayesian approach to testing with two-action problems is quite similar to the classical method. Now, the statistician is directed to reject a hypothesis if he believes its alternative is more likely to be true in the light of total evidence instead of just sample evidence. Thus, again, as with Bayesian estimation, if we can quantify our prior degrees of belief in the null and alternative hypotheses, Bayes' theorem can aid us in statistical testing.

We shall now consider a simple example for the double purpose of bringing out the salient features of the Bayesian testing procedure and of pointing out the similarities and differences between classical and Bayesian testing procedures.

During the 1972 Presidential election, both Republicans and Democrats were concerned with the registration of young voters. Republicans claimed that the young voters were about evenly divided so far as their registration by party was concerned. Democrats, however, claimed that the ratio was about 6:4 in favour of the Democratic Party in young voters' registrations. A political scientist, in order to find out which claim was more tenable, selected ten registered young voters at random and found that seven were registered as Democrats. What can we say in view of this sample outcome relative to the following pair of hypotheses?

$$H_N: \tilde{\pi} = 0.5; \qquad H_A: \tilde{\pi} = 0.6.$$

If the political scientist is to make a choice between the above hypotheses on sample information alone, as in the classical case, he may simply form what is called the *information odds ratio,* or the *likelihood ratio, LR*. This ratio is defined as the conditional probability of the sample result given the null hypothetical value divided by the conditional probability of the sample result given the alternative hypothetical value. For our example, we have

$$\text{LR} = \frac{P(x = 7 \mid \pi = 0.5)}{P(x = 7 \mid \pi = 0.6)}$$

$$= \frac{\binom{10}{7}(0.5)^7(0.5)^3}{\binom{10}{7}(0.6)^7(0.4)^3}$$

$$= \left(\frac{5}{6}\right)^7\left(\frac{5}{4}\right)^3$$

$$\doteq 0.545.$$

Thus, the sample outcome of seven Democratic registrations is 0.545 as likely to have been produced by a 50% Democratic registration population as by a 60% Democrat registration population. The Bayesians may say that odds on the state $\tilde{\pi} = 0.5$ relative to the state $\tilde{\pi} = 0.6$ are 545 to 1000. That is, if one uses sample evidence as the sole basis for his bet on $\tilde{\pi} = 0.5$ against $\tilde{\pi} = 0.6$, a fair bet should then have a return of $10.00 for each $5.45 successfully placed on the proposition that $\tilde{\pi} = 0.5$. Alternatively, one who would bet on $\tilde{\pi} = 0.5$ should be willing to pay up to $5.45 for a return of $10.00 should he win.

Turning to the Bayesian approach, we must first have numerical values of the scientist's prior degrees of belief on the two states of nature. Suppose he feels that the odds are about $3:7$ against H_N's being true. Then he can revise these prior values in view of the sample result and obtain his subjective posterior degrees of belief on the two states. The results, by the application of Bayes' theorem, are given below:

State π_j	Prior $f_0(\pi_j)$	Likelihood $f(7 \mid \pi_j)$	Joint $f_0(\pi_j)f(7 \mid \pi_j)$	Posterior $f_1(\pi_j)$
0.5	0.3	0.1172	0.03516	0.189
0.6	0.7	0.2150	0.15050	0.811
	1.0		$f(x) = 0.18566$	1.000

Note that the likelihoods above are binomial probabilities. Now, it may be noted, when there are only two states, Bayes' theorem can be expressed in terms of odds ratios as

$$\frac{f_1(H_N)}{f_1(H_A)} = \left[\frac{f_0(H_N)}{f_0(H_A)}\right]\left[\frac{f(x \mid H_N)}{f(x \mid H_A)}\right], \qquad (23.12)$$

which says that the *posterior odds ratio* is equal to the product of the *prior odds ratio* and the *information odds* (or *likelihood*) *ratio*. For our example, we have

$$\text{prior odds ratio} = \text{OR}_0 = \frac{f_0(H_N)}{f_0(H_A)}$$

$$= \frac{0.3}{0.7} \doteq \frac{0.4285}{1.0000},$$

$$\text{likelihood ratio} = \text{LR} = \frac{f(x \mid H_N)}{f(x \mid H_A)}$$

$$= \frac{0.1172}{0.2150} \doteq \frac{0.545}{1.000},$$

and

$$\text{posterior odds ratio} = \text{OR}_1 = \frac{f_1(H_N)}{f_1(H_A)}$$

$$= \frac{0.189}{0.811} \doteq \left(\frac{0.4285}{1.0000}\right)\left(\frac{0.545}{1.000}\right)$$

$$\doteq \frac{0.233}{1.000}.$$

It is interesting to note now that all the three odds ratios above are less than unity, indicating that H_A is more likely to be true than H_N. However, given the prior odds and sample information, the posterior odds are much smaller than either the prior or the likelihood odds ratios, implying that, in terms of posterior probabilities, the state $\tilde{\pi} = 0.5$ becomes less likely or the state $\tilde{\pi} = 0.6$ becomes more tenable, as compared to conclusions reached on sample information alone.

Next, it may be observed that, just as in the case of estimation, when more empirical evidence about the true state becomes available through increased sampling, the likelihood ratio comes to overwhelm the prior odds in the determination of the posterior odds. This occurs with even fairly modest sample sizes, and it will not matter much what the prior odds are. To demonstrate this effect, consider prior odds of $1:1$ versus $3:7$ on the states $\tilde{\pi} = 0.5$ and $\tilde{\pi} = 0.6$ in our example, and the sample results of 7 out of 10, 14 out of 20, and 35 out of 50.

When $n = 10$ and $x = 7$ we have, for a $1:1$ prior:

$$\text{OR}_1 = \left(\frac{1}{1}\right)\left(\frac{0.1172}{0.2150}\right) \doteq \frac{0.545}{1.000};$$

and for a $3:7$ prior:

$$\text{OR}_1 = \left(\frac{3}{7}\right)\left(\frac{0.1172}{0.2150}\right) \doteq \frac{0.234}{1.000}.$$

When $n = 20$ and $x = 14$ we have, for a $1:1$ prior:

$$\text{OR}_1 = \left(\frac{1}{1}\right)\left(\frac{0.0370}{0.1244}\right) \doteq \frac{0.297}{1.000};$$

and for a $3:7$ prior:

$$\text{OR}_1 = \left(\frac{3}{7}\right)\left(\frac{0.0370}{0.1244}\right) \doteq \frac{0.127}{1.000}.$$

When $n = 50$ and $x = 35$ we have for a $1:1$ prior:

$$\text{OR}_1 = \left(\frac{1}{1}\right)\left(\frac{0.00200}{0.04154}\right) \doteq \frac{0.0481}{1.0000};$$

and for a $3:7$ prior:

$$\text{OR}_1 = \left(\frac{3}{7}\right)\left(\frac{0.00200}{0.04154}\right) \doteq \frac{0.0206}{1.0000}.$$

The above calculations show that while the posterior odds in favor of $\tilde{\pi} = 0.5$ against $\tilde{\pi} = 0.6$ with $3:7$ priors are always about 43% of what they would be with $1:1$ priors, increasing the sample evidence makes us more and more confident with either prior odds that $\tilde{\pi} = 0.6$ is the true state.

It was mentioned before that the classical tests introduced previously are equivalent to the likelihood ratio approach; this is similar to the principle of maximum likelihood. The Bayesian approach is also related to the likelihood ratio, since it considers $OR_1 = (OR_0)(LR)$. This implies that the classical and the Bayesian testing procedures will yield the same result if the prior odds ratio is unity. If the prior odds ratio differs from unity, these two approaches will lead to the same result only if sample information overwhelms the prior information in determining the posterior odds. However, as will be pointed out in the next section, even when the same results are obtained by the two different methods, the results have different interpretations.

It may be noted that in our foregoing discussion we have denoted the null and alternative hypotheses as H_N and H_A, instead of H_0 and H_1, respectively, because we have reserved the set of subscripts "0" and "1" to denote "prior" and "posterior" quantities. For the same reason, we shall in our subsequent discussion employ the symbols θ_a and θ_b, instead of θ_0 and θ_1, to stand for the assumed values in the null and alternative hypotheses, respectively.

23.8 BAYESIAN TESTING FOR CONTINUOUS STATES

The example just given is concerned with two exact or simple hypotheses: the state random variable is assumed to be discrete and it can take on only two values, as stated in H_N and H_A. In many applied situations, however, at least one of the hypotheses is inexact, implying that the state random variable may be continuous. Classical solutions to such problems, as we have seen, often include an exact null hypothesis and an inexact alternative. However, with the Bayesian approach, we must determine the probability of each hypothesis in terms of the prior and posterior distributions, which are continuous under the assumption that the state random variable is continuous. If both the null and alternative hypotheses are exact, Bayesian analysis can easily handle the situation by substituting probability densities wherever probabilities are called for. If one hypothesis is exact and the other species some interval of real numbers, Bayesian analysis will always reject the exact hypothesis. This is because probabilities will be used in this situation rather than probability densities, and the probability that any continuous variable assumes a specific value is zero. Ordinarily, however, Bayesian analysis with a continuous state variable uses null and alternative hypotheses such that each hypothesis specifies some interval of real numbers.

In Bayesian analysis, if we are concerned with single-tailed tests, the hypothesis should be stated in the composite forms such as

$$H_N: \tilde{\theta} \leq \theta_a; \qquad H_A: \tilde{\theta} > \theta_a$$

for a right-tail test and

$$H_N: \tilde{\theta} \geq \theta_a; \qquad H_A: \tilde{\theta} < \theta_a$$

for a left-tail test. With these designations, one can then assign prior probabilities to the hypotheses in forms such as

$$P_0(H_N \text{ is true})$$

and

$$P_0(H_A \text{ is true}) = 1 - P_0(H_N \text{ is true}).$$

With such probabilities assigned, one can easily form the prior odds ratio and identify which hypothesis is more likely to be true as in the discrete case.

For a two-tail test, a classical null hypothesis is often exact, such as $\theta = \theta_a$. However, in the Bayesian case, it is always stated as an interval. Precisely, we now have

$$H_N: \ \theta_a \leq \tilde{\theta} \leq \theta_b.$$

This is to be tested against the alternative

$$H_A: \tilde{\theta} < \theta_a \quad \text{or} \quad \tilde{\theta} > \theta_b.$$

Given these hypotheses, the prior odds ratio can again be determined once prior probabilities, in the forms of

$$P_0(H_N) = P_0(\theta_a \leq \tilde{\theta} \leq \theta_b)$$

and

$$P_0(H_A) = P_0(\tilde{\theta} < \theta_a) + P_0(\tilde{\theta} > \theta_b) = 1 - P_0(H_N)$$

are assigned. Needless to say, these prior probabilities can be revised with the use of sample information, and the corresponding posterior odds ratios can be determined.

As an illustration of a left-tailed test, let us use the last example referring to a close election cited at the end of Section 23.5. To solve this problem by testing, we have

$$H_N: \tilde{\pi} \leq 0.5; \qquad H_A: \tilde{\pi} > 0.5.$$

Recall that the candidate's prior distribution is assumed to be a beta density with $r_0 = 2$ and $n_0 = 4$. This means that the prior beta density is symmetric about $\tilde{\pi} = 0.5$ and that $P_0(H_N) = P_0(H_A) = 0.5$. So, the prior odds ratio in this case is $OR_0 = 1$. Recall also that, for this example, a sample of $n = 22$ yields $r = 13$. This sample result produces a posterior beta density with $n_1 = 26$ and $r_1 = 15$. We have

$$
\begin{aligned}
P_1(H_N) &= P_1(\tilde{\pi} \leq 0.5) \\
&= P_{\beta_1}(\tilde{\pi} \leq 0.5 \,|\, r_1 = 15, n_1 = 26) \\
&= P_{b_1}[\tilde{r} < (26 - 15) \,|\, n = (26 - 1), \pi = 0.5] \\
&= 0.21218,
\end{aligned}
$$

and
$$P_1(H_A) = 1 - P_1(H_N) = 0.78782.$$

These results provide a posterior odds ratio of

$$OR_1 = \frac{0.21218}{0.78782} \doteq \frac{0.269}{1.000}.$$

Thus, in terms of posterior analysis, the alternative becomes about four times as likely as the null hypothesis. Hence, H_N should be rejected in favor of H_A, unless even more convincing evidence is demanded.

Consider now an example for a lower-tail test. A manufacturing firm is willing to install a new automated process on the assembly line if the mean number of man-hours saved per week is at least 1000. This process is known to have a variance of 220 hours^2. In other words, the decision in this case can be made by testing the following pair of hypotheses:

$$H_N: \tilde{\mu} \geqslant 1000; \qquad H_A: \tilde{\mu} < 1000.$$

To conduct this test, the manufacturer feels that a normal distribution with mean 900 and variance 256 would represent his prior degrees of belief about the process. Furthermore, he selects four firms among those which have adopted the process in their plants, and he observes that the mean number of man-hours saved per week is 1045; that is, $\bar{x} = 1045$ with $n = 4$ and $V(\bar{X}) = 220/4 = 55$. We assume random sampling, the same previous assembly-line method as our manufacturer now uses, and a normal sampling distribution for $\bar{X}$. With the sample information, his prior values can be revised to yield

$$\mu_1 = \frac{900(55) + (1045)(256)}{256 + 55} \doteq 1019.36;$$

$$\sigma_1^2 = \frac{256(55)}{256 + 55} \doteq 45.27;$$

$$\sigma_1 = \sqrt{45.27} \doteq 6.73.$$

In terms of the posterior density (which is normal), we have

$$
\begin{aligned}
P_1(H_N) &= P_1(\tilde{\mu} \geqslant 1000) \\
&= 1 - P_1(\tilde{\mu} < 1000) \\
&= 1 - N\left(\frac{1000 - \mu_1}{\sigma_1}\right) \\
&= 1 - N\left(\frac{1000 - 1019.36}{6.73}\right) \\
&\doteq 1 - N(-2.88) \\
&= 1 - 0.0020 \\
&= 0.9980;
\end{aligned}
$$

$$P_1(H_A) = 1 - P_1(H_N) = 0.0020.$$

Thus, under the manufacturer's posterior distribution, the alternative hypothesis appears to be extremely unlikely; H_N cannot be rejected and the automated assembly process should be installed.

Finally, let us consider an example of a two-tail test. The production process for high-breaking-strength ropes is considered to be in control if the mean breaking strength of ropes produced is within the range of 495 to 505 pounds. Otherwise, it is considered to be out of control. To check on the quality of the process, the production manager selects nine ropes for observation from time to time for the purpose of testing the following pair of hypotheses frequently:

$$H_N: 495 \leqslant \tilde{\mu} \leqslant 505; \qquad H_A: \tilde{\mu} < 495 \quad \text{or} \quad \tilde{\mu} > 505.$$

Suppose the process variance is 81 and the production manager's prior distribution is normal with mean 500 and variance 100. Furthermore, suppose a certain day's sample yields a sample mean of 490, with a normal sampling distribution. In view of these facts, is the process in control?

To answer the preceding question, we note that, in terms of the production manager's prior density together with the sample evidence, we would have $\mu_1 \doteq 490.83$ and $\sigma_1 \doteq 2.873$. With this posterior distribution,

$$P_1(H_N) = P_1(495 \leqslant \tilde{\mu} \leqslant 505)$$

$$= N\left(\frac{505 - 490.83}{2.873}\right) - N\left(\frac{495 - 490.83}{2.873}\right)$$

$$\doteq N(4.93) - N(1.45)$$

$$= 1 - 0.9265 = 0.0735$$

and

$$P_1(H_A) = 1 - P_1(H_N) = 0.9265.$$

These results indicate that it is unlikely that H_N is true; the process appears to be out of control.

It has been stated before that the classical and Bayesian testing procedures would yield identical results if the prior were such that H_N and H_A were considered equally likely. However, these results have different interpretations. Let us cite an example to amplify these statements.

Consider a normal population with an unknown mean and a known variance of 64. Now, we wish to test the following hypotheses:

$$H_N: \tilde{\mu} \geqslant 250; \qquad H_A: \tilde{\mu} < 250.$$

Suppose a random sample with $n = 16$ yields an $\bar{x} = 248$; we would have $\sigma_{\bar{x}} = 8/\sqrt{16} = 2$. By the classical procedure, we may simply compute the z value

$$z = \frac{248 - 250}{2} = -1.$$

Since we have here a lower-tail test, the observed z-value in effect means that

$$P(Z \leqslant -1) = N(-1) = 0.1587.$$

Had we been testing $\mu \leqslant 250$ against $\mu > 250$, then we would have

$$P(Z \geqslant -1) \doteq 1 - 0.1587 = 0.8413.$$

Now, for the same problem, if a Bayesian assumes a diffuse prior probability density, then we have

$$n_0 = 0; \qquad \mu_1 = \bar{x} = 248; \qquad \sigma_1 = \sigma_{\bar{X}} = 2.$$

With these posterior parameters, we have

$$P_1(H_N) = P(\tilde{\mu} \geqslant 250)$$

$$= 1 - N\left(\frac{250 - 248}{2}\right)$$

$$= 1 - N(1)$$

$$= 1 - 0.8413$$

$$= 0.1587;$$

$$P_1(H_A) = 0.8413.$$

We see that the posterior probability for H_N is identical with the classical result—the probability associated with the observed value of Z. However, as Figure 23.2 shows, these identical results cannot be interpreted identically. In the classical case, the value of 0.1587 is at the lower tail of the sampling distribution of $\bar{X}$ specified under the condition that $E(\bar{X}) = \mu = 250$. This area, a probability, measures the "extremeness" of the sample result. In the Bayesian case, the value of 0.1587 is at the upper tail of the posterior distribution of μ_X centered at $\mu_1 = 248$. This area is the posterior probability that H_N is true.

The foregoing comments hold true for hypotheses concerning parameters other than the population mean. Furthermore, the difference in interpretation between the classical and Bayesian results would also hold in the case where objective evidence overwhelms the prior information in the determination of the posterior distribution and, thereby, identical or nearly identical results are obtained.

Before closing this chapter, we may observe that our discussion of the Bayesian approach to testing, as of the classical approach, has been limited to two-action problems. It is entirely possible, however, that a statistician may have several hypotheses in mind, such as competing theories for a given phenomenon. The Bayesian approach to several hypotheses is identical with that for just two hypotheses. All one needs to do is to determine which hypotheses is most likely to be true, either in terms of prior probabilities or in terms of posterior probabilities.

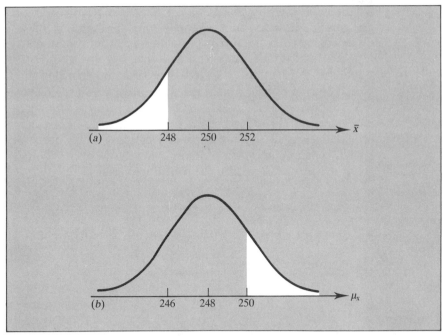

FIGURE 23.2 Distribution of $\bar{x}$ and μ_x showing, respectively, (a) the extremeness of the sample result and (b) the posterior probability that H_N is true.

It may also be noted that problems involving two or more hypotheses are essentially decision-oriented. Both probabilities of the states and losses due to erroneous decisions should be considered. We shall turn our attention to this topic in the following two chapters.

GLOSSARY OF FORMULAS

$$(23.1) \quad P(\theta_j \mid X) = \frac{P(\theta_j)P(X \mid \theta_j)}{\sum\limits_{j=1}^{n} P(\theta_j)P(X \mid \theta_j)}.$$

As defined here, Bayes' theorem attempts to answer the question: What is the particular state value of the state random variable given that the sample or experiment yields a result of X? The answer is the posterior probability of that particular state value that is obtained by dividing the product of the prior probability of that state value, $P(\theta_j)$, and the likelihood, which is the probability of obtaining the sample result given that state value, $P(X \mid \theta_j)$, by the sum of the joint probabilities of prior probabilities and likelihoods. Note that the numerator in (23.1) is a single term of the denominator.

$$(23.2) \quad f_1(\theta_j) = \frac{f_0(\theta_j)f(x \mid \theta_j)}{f(x)}.$$

This expression is thought to be an alternative statement of the Bayes' theorem. It says that the posterior probability of a state random variable, $f_1(\theta_j)$, given $\tilde{\theta} = \theta_j$, is derived from three inputs: (1) the prior probability of the state random variable given $\tilde{\theta} = \theta_j$, $f_0(\theta_j)$; (2) the likelihood function, $f(x \mid \theta_j)$, which is determined by the sampling distribution of the sample result X, evaluated at the observed value x of X; (3) the sum of the joint probabilities, $f(x)f(x \mid \theta_j)—f(x)$, which is sum of probabilities of the sample result obtained under the prior probability distribution, $f_0(\tilde{\theta})$. This general formula can be used for both discrete and continuous state random variables, even though you are not required to work with it for continuous cases.

(23.3) $E_0(\tilde{\pi}) = \tilde{\pi}_0 = \tilde{r}_0/\tilde{n}_0;$

(23.4) $V_0(\tilde{\pi}) = \sigma_0^2(\tilde{\pi})\tilde{r}_0(\tilde{n}_0 - \tilde{r}_0)/[\tilde{n}_0^2(\tilde{n}_0 + 1)];$

(23.5) $\tilde{x}_{m_0}(\tilde{\pi}) = (\tilde{r}_0 - 1)/(\tilde{n}_0 - 2);$

(23.6) $E_1(\tilde{\pi}) = \tilde{\pi}_1 = \tilde{r}_1/\tilde{n}_1;$

(23.7) $V_1(\tilde{\pi}) = \sigma_1^2(\tilde{\pi})\tilde{r}_1(\tilde{n}_1 - \tilde{r}_1)/[\tilde{n}_1^2(\tilde{n}_1 + 1)];$

(23.8) $\tilde{x}_{m_1}(\tilde{\pi}) = (\tilde{r}_1 - 1)/(\tilde{n}_1 - 2).$

If the state random variable $\tilde{\pi}$ can be assumed to have a prior β distribution, then its expectation, variance, and mode are defined by the first three equations in this group. In these three equations $\tilde{r}_0$ and $\tilde{n}_0$ are determined by the subjective judgment of the decision maker. The β prior distribution can be revised into a posterior distribution with an SRS of size n and number of successes $\tilde{r}$. The posterior distribution would also be a β distribution with posterior descriptive measures as defined by the last three equations in this group. Note that $\tilde{n}_1 = \tilde{n}_0 + n$ and $\tilde{r}_1 = \tilde{r}_0 + \tilde{r}$. Also, (23.5) is undefined unless $\tilde{r}_0 > 1$ and $(\tilde{n}_0 - \tilde{r}_0) > 1$. Similarly, (23.8) is defined under the restrictions of $\tilde{r}_1 > 1$ and $(\tilde{n}_1 - \tilde{r}_1) > 1$.

(23.9) $L, U = \tilde{\theta}_1 \mp Z\sigma_{\tilde{\theta}_1}.$

This is the general formula for computing the lower and upper confidence limits for a Bayesian interval estimation.

(23.10) $E_1(\tilde{\mu}_X) = \tilde{\mu}_1 = \dfrac{(\tilde{\mu}_0)\tilde{\sigma}_{\bar{X}}^2 + (\bar{X})\tilde{\sigma}_0^2}{\tilde{\sigma}_0^2 + \tilde{\sigma}_{\bar{X}}^2};$

(23.11) $V_1(\tilde{\mu}_X) = \tilde{\sigma}_1^2 = \dfrac{(\tilde{\sigma}_0^2)(\tilde{\sigma}_{\bar{X}}^2)}{\tilde{\sigma}_0^2 + \tilde{\sigma}_{\bar{X}}^2}.$

Given a prior normal distribution, $n_0(\tilde{\mu}_0, \tilde{\sigma}_0^2)$, for the state random variable $\tilde{\mu}_X$, the posterior distribution of $\tilde{\mu}_X$ is obtained by revising the normal prior by $\bar{X}$ computed from an SRS with size n. The posterior expected value and variance of $\tilde{\mu}_X$ are defined by (23.10) and (23.11), respectively. Note that $\tilde{\mu}_1$ is a weighted mean of $\tilde{\mu}_0$ and $\bar{X}$, the weights being the reciprocals of their variances, $1/\tilde{\sigma}_0^2$ and $1/\tilde{\sigma}_{\bar{X}}^2$, respectively. These reciprocals are sometimes called the *precision* or *information content* of the respective estimates.

$$(23.12) \quad \frac{f_1(H_N)}{f_1(H_A)} = \left[\frac{f_0(H_N)}{f_0(H_A)}\right]\left[\frac{f(x \mid H_N)}{f(x \mid H_A)}\right].$$

In this expression, H_N and H_A stand for the null and alternative hypotheses, respectively. In testing, Bayes' theorem can be stated as odds ratios. In words, the posterior odds ratio is equal to the product of prior odds ratio and the information odds (or likelihood) ratio.

REVIEW QUESTIONS

23.1 What are the similarities and differences between classical and Bayesian inferential procedures?

23.2 In what sense do we consider the Bayesian method as a continuation of the classical approach for conducting inferences?

23.3 How is Bayes' theorem defined? What is the question it attempts to answer? What are the unique features of this theorem?

23.4 What are the Bayesian prior and posterior estimators for a state random variable? How does the Bayesian estimation procedure differ from the classical practice?

23.5 From the Bayesian point of view, a posterior distribution is also subjective in nature even though it is obtained by revising the prior distribution with empirical evidence. What is the reason for this view?

23.6 In constructing a Bayesian confidence interval for population proportion, what are the conditions required in order to use normal approximations? Why is a Bayesian interval estimation more precise than a classical one in general?

23.7 How does a Bayesian go about to determine the values of $\tilde{r}_0$ and $\tilde{n}_0$ when he uses a β prior distribution for the state random variable $\tilde{\pi}$?

24.8 What is a conjugate prior distribution? What are the requirements for a probability model to be considered as a conjugate prior distribution? Give examples.

24.9 Give the essential features of the Bayesian theorem of sampling with normal prior density functions.

24.10 Under what conditions would we have approximate equalities between the posterior mean of the sample mean, and between the posterior variance and the variance of the sampling distribution of the sample mean? What is the implication of these results?

23.11 Why is it still often appropriate for us to employ the findings of Bayesian normal sampling even when other prior laws for the state random variable $\tilde{\mu}_X$ is assumed?

23.12 Describe the procedure of Bayesian testing in terms of odds ratios.

23.13 How should the null and alternative hypotheses be stated for continuous state random variables with the Bayesian approach? Explain your answer.

23.14 Explain and illustrate that the classical and Bayesian testing procedures would yield the same conclusion if the prior were such that H_N and H_A were considered equally likely? Do they differ in terms of interpretation? If so, how?

PROBLEMS

23.1 A coin is tossed. If it turns up heads, two balls will be drawn from urn I; otherwise, two balls will be selected from urn II. In both cases, the sampling is to be made with replacement. Urn I contains two black and six white balls. Urn II contains seven black balls and one white ball. Given that both balls drawn are black, what is the probability that the sample is selected from urn I? From urn II?

23.2 A manufacturing firm produces steel pipes in three plants with daily production volumes of 500, 1,000, and 2,000 units, respectively. According to past experience, it is known that the fraction of defectives produced by the three plants are, respectively, 0.05, 0.08, and 0.10. If one pipe is selected at random from a certain day's total production and is found to be defective, from which plant does that pipe come? Explain your answer fully.

23.3 Suppose for data in Table 23.3 that the prior probabilities for the four states are 0.15, 0.45, 0.25, and 0.05, respectively, but that all the other conditions remain as before, what would be the prior and posterior decisions of the purchasing agent now?

23.4 The executives of a national TV network are reviewing the possible proportions of the total viewing audience for a proposed new program. They assume that there are only three state values of interest: 0.2, 0.3, and 0.4. Furthermore, they judge the prior probabilities for these states to be 0.5, 0.3, and 0.2, respectively. Later, of 20 potential viewers questioned at random, 6 indicate interest in the proposed program. In view of this finding, what are the revised probabilities for the three states?

23.5 Suppose, for the preceding problem, an additional random sample of 20 yields 7 viewers in favor of the program, what are the posterior probabilities for the three state values now?

23.6 Suppose the prior probabilities in Problem 23.4 are revised by the combined sample results—13 successes in 40 trials, would the posterior probabilities be the same as obtained in Problem 23.5? Explain and verify.

23.7 What are the prior and posterior expected values of $\tilde{\pi}$ for the results obtained in Problem 23.4?

23.8 In view of the results in Problem 23.5, what are the prior and posterior expectations of $\tilde{\pi}$, respectively?

23.9 If the TV executives in Problem 23.3 assume a prior β function with $r_0 = 2$ and $n_0 = 10$, what is $E_1(\tilde{\pi})$, given 6 successes in a sample of 20?

23.10 For the preceding problem, given the same β prior density function and 13 successes in 40 trials, what would be $E_1(\tilde{\pi})$ now?

23.11 A statistician believes that the most likely value of $\tilde{\pi}$ is 1/4 and the expected value of $\tilde{\pi}$ is 1/3 for his prior β density function. What are the prior parameters $\tilde{r}_0$ and $\tilde{n}_0$?

23.12 According to the personal judgment of the owner of a women's clothing store, the prior expected proportion of customers who enter her store and make a purchase is 0.20 and the most likely prior proportion is 0.15. What are the parameters of her prior β density function for $\tilde{\pi}$?

23.13 Suppose the owner in the preceding problem observed that on a certain day, at random, of ten customers who had entered her store, three made purchases, what is her posterior expectation of $\tilde{\pi}$?

23.14 If a decision maker feels that, for the state random variable being considered, he can assume a prior density function as the β probability model with $E_0(\tilde{\pi}) = 0.5$ and $V_0(\tilde{\pi}) = 0.1$, what are the values of $\tilde{r}_0$ and $\tilde{n}_0$ for his prior distribution?

23.15 Construct a 95% confidence interval for $\tilde{\pi}$ with results in Problem 23.10. Comment on the appropriateness of using the normal approximation in this case.

23.16 A manufacturer is considering the introduction of a new product for which he believes it is reasonable to assume a normal prior density function for the mean sales μ_X, with $\mu_0 = 450$ and $\sigma_0^2 = 100$. The product is introduced in 25 randomly selected stores as a market test, resulting a mean sales of 475. If the distribution for similar products is known to be normal with $\sigma_X^2 = 900$, what is the posterior density function for $\tilde{\mu}_X$? What are its expectation and variance?

23.17 In the preceding problem, if $n = 65$ with a sample mean as before, what is $\tilde{\mu}_1$ now? Comment on the difference between the two posterior estimates for $\tilde{\mu}_X$. Construct a 95% confidence interval for $\tilde{\mu}_X$ with $n = 65$.

23.18 Carole tells Allan that she has extrasensory perception (ESP). She tells him that if he conceals a five-dollar bill in one hand and a ten-dollar bill in the other, she can tell at last 70% of the time which hand holds the ten-dollar bill. Allan does not believe this; he thinks she can do so only about 50% of the time by chance. He tries to settle the issue with her by testing H_N: $\tilde{\pi} = 0.5$ against H_A: $\tilde{\pi} = 0.7$. Furthermore, Allan's degrees of belief in Carole's ability are 0.95 to 0.05 for the null and alternative hypotheses, respectively. These values reflect that Allan is extremely skeptical of Carole's ESP ability. In 25 trials, Carole identifies Allan's hand that holds a ten-dollar bill 17 times. For this problem, what are Allan's prior and posterior odds ratios against Carole's having ESP?

23.19 Suppose Allan had used a 1:1 prior in the preceding problem, would the alternative hypothesis become more likely than the null hypothesis, given the same sample result? What does the prior odds ratio of 1 imply here?

23.20 If a beta prior density function with $r_0 = 2$ and $n_0 = 9$ has been assumed for testing the following hypotheses:

$$H_N: \tilde{\pi} \leq 0.3 \quad \text{and} \quad H_A: \tilde{\pi} > 0.3,$$

and if four successes have been observed in 12 trials, what are the probabilities for H_N and H_A to be true, respectively? What is the posterior odds ratio here?

23.21 A quality-control statistician has specified that the fraction defectives to be produced by the production to be 0.10 or less. In testing $\tilde{\pi} \leq 0.10$ against $\tilde{\pi} > 0.10$, he employs a prior β-density function with $r_0 = 1$ and $n_0 = 8$. Suppose in a sample of size 18, two defectives have been observed: can H_N be rejected?

23.22 The Principal of a secretarial school claims that the mean typing speed of her graduating students is 100 words per minute with a variance of 100. The director of an employment agency, however, believes that the mean speed can hardly be so high. His prior belief on the state random variable can be characterized by a normal density function with a mean of 90 and a variance of 120. Suppose in testing $\tilde{\mu} \leq 100$ against $\tilde{\mu} > 100$ the director observed the mean speed of ten graduating students to be 92. What are the posterior probabilities for the null and alternative hypotheses to be true, respectively? What is the posterior odds ratio in favor of H_N?

23.23 Suppose that in the previous problem all conditions remain the same except that the sample mean is now 104, what conclusion can you reach? Comment on your result.

23.24 Cartridge fuses produced by a certain firm are designed to last more than 3,000 hours on the average with a variance of 2,000 hours^2. An engineer believes, however, that the life of such a fuse is normal with a mean of 2,600 hours and a variance of 2,400 hours^2. In testing $\tilde{\mu} \geq 3,000$ against $\tilde{\mu} < 3,000$, a sample of 25 fuses yields a mean of 3,025 hours. Show that in terms of the posterior distribution, H_N should not be rejected.

23.25 For the preceding problem, if all the conditions remain the same, except that now the sample size is 100 and the sample mean is 3,000, what conclusions can be reached?

23.26 The manager of a supermarket chain will decide to carry a new make of canned tomatoes if the net mean weight is between 9.95 and 10.05 ounces. Furthermore, the manager's prior degrees of belief are that the net weight is normal with a mean of 10 and a variance of 4. Suppose in testing the hypothesis

$$H_N: 9.95 \leq \tilde{\mu} \leq 10.95$$

against

$$H_A: \tilde{\mu} < 0.95 \quad \text{or} \quad \tilde{\mu} > 10.05,$$

a sample of 64 cans yields a mean of 9.90 and a variance of 9. Should H_N be rejected?

23.27 Suppose a statistician, in evaluating the mean sales per store of a new product, believes the mean sales is normal with a mean of 500 and a variance of 1,000. The product is introduced initially to 36 stores and it is found that the sample mean is 510 and the sample variance is 625. In view of these facts, determine the posterior odds ratio for

$$H_N: 485 \leq \tilde{\mu} \leq 515;$$

$$H_A: \tilde{\mu} < 485 \quad \text{or} \quad \tilde{\mu} > 515.$$

24* Bayesian Decision Theory: Prior and Posterior Analyses

24.1 INTRODUCTION

It has been suggested that Bayesian inference can be considered as an extension of the classical approach, since both are engaged in making inferences about some uncertain quantity—a parameter or a whole probability, or density, function—and both utilize the concept of sampling distributions. Both methods are, furthermore, informal analyses because neither includes an explicit evaluation of payoff or loss functions associated with estimation and testing.

An inferential procedure that does not consider and weight a payoff or a loss function is essentially an incomplete theory, since it does not provide a unique standard for one to judge whether an estimator is "optimal" or whether an act (of rejecting or not rejecting a null hypothesis) is the "best". A classical statistician's selection of an estimator, for instance, may be a matter of deciding whether it possesses certain desirable properties or whether one property is more important than another in some situations. For example, we know that $\hat{S}^2$, computed with the divisor n, is an MLE that is biased and S^2, computed with the divisor $n - 1$, is not an MLE that is unbiased. However, which one should be used as an estimator for σ^2? The decision can only be made in accordance with one's subjective judgment. Likewise, subjective judgment is also present when a Bayesian selects among the posterior mean, median, or mode as an estimator of $\tilde{\mu}_X$ in different situations. In testing, too, when a classical statistician accepts or rejects a hypothesis in terms of likelihood functions, or when a

951

Bayesian does the same with prior or posterior odds ratios, the choice is somewhat arbitrary because the economic consequences of erroneous decisions are not integrated into the process of selecting the act.

Informal approaches to inference may be quite satisfactory if one merely desires a "rough-and-ready" idea of the uncertain quantity under consideration. However, where errors in estimation or testing may lead to serious consequences, a more formal and complete procedure is desirable. Such a procedure is provided by the Bayesian decision-theoretic framework called *Bayesian decision theory,* or simply *decision theory.*

Just as Bayesian inference is an extension of the classical, Bayesian decision theory may be considered as yet another extension of inferential statistics. In Bayesian decision theory, a decision maker is to select the "best" act from a set of alternative courses of actions given a set of payoffs or losses and a prior or posterior distribution of the state random variable. This method is quite similar to inference, since estimation and testing can also be thought of as decision making under uncertainty. With estimation, the actions correspond to the available estimates; with testing, the actions correspond to the stated hypotheses. In either case, one must select one of the acts. In either case, too, the likelihood function, the prior probability law, or the posterior distribution represent the decision maker's state of information, which is never perfect, and thus he must make a decision under uncertainty.

In the Bayesian decision-theoretic structure, a decision can be made on prior information alone or on posterior information, which is the combined prior and sample information—thus the distinction between prior and posterior analyses. While the general decision mechanisms for prior and posterior analyses are the same, with posterior analysis we shall also be concerned with optimal information gathering or the determination of the optimal sample size. The principle of optimal information gathering is the most important aspect of Bayesian decision theory: it is called *preposterior analysis.* To go one step further, the preposterior analysis will also lead to what is called the Bayesian *sequential analysis.* In this chapter we present a general decision-making process and the Bayesian decision theory of prior and posterior analyses. In the chapter that follows, preposterior and sequential analyses will be taken up.

24.2 THE STRUCTURE OF DECISIONS

The word "decision" has many meanings, including a referee's decision in a sporting event, a court's decision in a lawsuit, and a business firm's decision to introduce a new product. We are interested in business and economic decisions. In that context, the notion of a decision has four implications that must be clearly understood.

First, there must be two or more possible acts available to the decision maker, from which he must choose one act.

Second, when deciding on an act, the decision maker must consider the possible states of nature. A *state of nature* is any influence outside the control of the decision maker. Sometimes a state of nature is literally that, such as whether next winter's weather will be mild or severe or something in between. Sometimes a state of nature involves human activities, such as whether a new product will be purchased in large quantities in the next 5 years, or whether a business firm will suffer a serious strike next year.

If the state of nature that will actually occur *can be predicted exactly,* the decision is made *under certainty.* For example, suppose a savings institution offers a guaranteed interest rate of 7.75% a year for 5 years, provided at least $1,000 is deposited. If the interest is left on deposit too, the original deposit will grow at a compound annual interest rate of 8.17%. If you want to deposit enough money now to have $5,000 at the end of 5 years, how much should you deposit? The answer happens to be $3,376.26 and is arrived at by dividing $5,000 by $(1 + 0.0817)^5$, but the details of how to make this calculation are unimportant. The fact that it can be made, and made without any room for doubt, is important; it explains why the decision to deposit $3,376.26 is called a decision under certainty. Decision making under certainty may not be simple, and it often requires quite a bit of mathematical calculation. Some branches of mathematics, such as "linear programming," are especially suited to this kind of calculation. Many important business decisions require this kind of calculation.

If the state of nature that will actually occur *cannot be predicted exactly,* and hence two or more states of nature are possible, the decision is made *under uncertainty.* As an example of decision making under uncertainty, consider a variation on the preceding example. Instead of merely having $5,000 in the bank 5 years from now, your objective is to have $5,000 in the bank 5 years from now after allowing for inflation. For example, if prices are 50% higher 5 years from now than they are now, you want your deposit to grow to $7,500; if prices are 10% lower 5 years from now than they are now, you want your deposit to grow to $4,500. How much should you deposit?

There is no way of knowing for sure. The amount of change in the price level in the next 5 years cannot be predicted exactly, so any decision about how much to deposit is made under uncertainty. It may at first appear that no decision at all can be made about how much to deposit, but this is not true. If you are willing to assign a probability to each of the possible amounts of change in the price level over the next 5 years, and if you are willing to assign a cost to every possible failure of your deposit to grow to the correct amount in 5 years, you can use Bayesian decision theory to find out what the deposit should be. This will not guarantee the desired result after 5 years, but it will provide a rational way of allowing for changes in the price level. Decision making under uncertainty is by no means impossible. It often requires quite a bit of mathematical calculation, and it frequently results in an "educated guess" instead of an accurately known answer, but many business decisions benefit greatly from the approach provided by Bayesian decision theory.

A third implication of the term "decision" is that each combination of a possible act and a possible state of nature will produce an *outcome,* which can also be called a *consequence* or a *payoff.* To use Bayesian decision theory, we must measure every payoff before we can pick the best act. For business and economic decision problems, there are two units of measurement for payoffs. One is money (dollars, pounds, pesos, or whatever) and the other is utility (utiles).

Money can be used to measure not only the direct monetary gains and costs of an outcome but also such intangibles as convenience, goodwill, self-satisfaction, and peace of mind. One way to measure an intangible variable is to assign a monetary value to it by evaluating the relevant factors that contribute to its value. Thus, taking into consideration a firm's reputation, the loyalty of its customers, the advantageous competitive position of its products, and some other factors, an economist may assign, say, a value of $100,000 to the firm's goodwill.

Another way of converting an intangible into monetary values is to ask an introspective question such as "Would I be willing to stand in a line ten blocks long to buy a ticket to see a very popular musical group, or would I prefer to give up a quarter, fifty cents, a dollar, or two dollars to avoid standing in the line?" In answering a question of this sort, one can eventually determine the monetary value of the act of standing in the line.

It is also possible to convert time into monetary values, because people consciously or unconsciously value their time at so much money per hour or per day. For example, suppose it costs you $50 to have your apartment cleaned by a maid, or it costs you 5 hours to clean it yourself. If you decide to hire a maid, you must value your time at more than $10 per hour. Of course, in this example we have ignored many factors that may enter the decision situation. For example, you may consider cleaning to be valuable physical exercise.

Sometimes money is an inadequate measure of the payoffs, and a more personal, subjective, psychological measure is needed. There is such a measure and it is called "utility." While we shall restrict our discussion mainly to the case where money is an adequate measure of the payoffs, we shall also comment briefly on the nature of utility and the use of it for decision making in the appendix attached to this chapter.

A fourth implication of the term "decision" is that the decision maker must select some kind of rule to enable him to choose the best possible act in view of all the acts, states of nature, and payoffs available. The rule for selecting the best act is called a *decision rule* or a *decision criterion or a decision strategy.* A number of decision rules have been worked out by statisticians, and each is aimed at achieving a specific objective.

In summary, decision theory calls for the following.

1. A list of the possible acts.

2. A list of the possible states of nature.

3. A payoff or a loss for each combination of a possible act and a possible state of nature.

4. A decision rule for choosing the best act in view of the payoffs or losses.

Let us make some general comments on (3) and (4) before taking up Bayesian decision theory proper.

24.3 PAYOFF AND LOSS MATRICES

A matrix is nothing more than a rectangular array of numbers or symbols. A *payoff matrix,* or a *payoff table,* has a row for each possible act and a column for each possible state of nature, and each intersection of a row and a column gives the payoff for that act and that state of nature.

One cannot take literally the phrases "all possible acts" and "all possible states of nature," any more than one can take literally the phrase "all possible outcomes of an experiment" as the definition of a sample space. Instead, one must restrict oneself to relevant acts, relevant states of nature, and relevant outcomes of an experiment.

Consider a simple example of a payoff table. Suppose the manager of a manufacturing firm is considering whether or not to expand the plant capacity by purchasing one of two machines, one of which has twice the capacity of the other and costs over 50% more. The firm's existing plant capacity is not quite sufficient to meet the current demand for its output. Past experience suggests that the firm's sales have a high correlation with general economic conditions. If economic conditions improve in the near future, the high-capacity machine will be required. If conditions remain stable, the low-capacity machine will be adequate. If a recession is in the making, the current capacity will do. Thus, at the moment, the manager must choose among three possible acts:

a_1: purchase the high-capacity machine;

a_2: purchase the low-capacity machine;

a_3: purchase no machine.

In general, the *action set* can be denoted as

$$A = \{a_i\}, \quad i = 1, 2, 3, \ldots.$$

There are three possible states of nature of the state random variable "general economic conditions" for this comparatively simple decision situation:

θ_1: prosperity;

θ_2: stability;

θ_3: recession.

TABLE 24.1 Payoff Table for the New-machine Example (in millions of dollars)

Act	State of Nature		
	θ_1	θ_2	θ_3
a_1	2.5	1.5	-1.0
a_2	1.6	2.0	0.0
a_3	1.2	1.2	0.8

Source: Hypothetical.

The state set may be denoted in general as

$$\tilde{\theta} = \{\theta_j\}, \quad j = 1, 2, 3, \ldots .$$

The decision maker next calculates or estimates the payoffs on the basis of information currently available. These calculations, or estimates, can be quite complicated and they can use either money or utility. Suppose the manager uses money to measure these payoffs and suppose that, after due consideration of costs and revenues, the manager arrives at the estimates shown in Table 24.1. Note that making a payoff table is a good way of organizing and displaying the outcomes produced jointly by the acts and states of nature. It allows us to compare payoffs readily. For example, in Table 24.1 the relative merits of the three courses of action under the various states of nature are clearly evident. Suppose a_1 (purchasing the high-capacity machine) is taken. Then, if θ_1 (prosperity) emerges, the firm will make a net profit of $2.5 million; if θ_2 (stability) prevails, the firm will make a net profit of $1.5 million; and if θ_3 (recession) occurs, the firm will suffer a loss of $1 million. We interpret other rows of the table in exactly the same fashion.

The payoff matrix also enables us to see whether all acts in a decision situation are admissible. An act is *admissible* if it is not dominated by any other act. An act a_k is said to *dominate* another act a_r if, for each possible state of nature, a_k leads to a payoff that is at least as high as that for a_r and if, for at least one state of nature, a_k leads to a higher payoff than a_r. Our payoff matrix shows that all three acts are admissible. However, suppose the payoff of 0.8 (for a_3 and θ_3) were changed to -1.0. Then a_3 would be dominated by a_1, and it would also be dominated by a_2. Because a_3 would be dominated by at least one other act, it would be eliminated from all further consideration and could not possibly be the best act (under any decision rule).

It is often convenient to work with opportunity losses instead of payoffs. An *opportunity loss* is the difference between a payoff and the highest possible payoff, for the same state of nature. In Table 24.1, calculated opportunity losses starts with identifying the highest possible payoff for θ_1, then identifying the highest possible payoff for θ_2, and then identifying the highest possible payoff for θ_3. These payoffs are 2.5, 2.0, and 0.8, respectively. We convert the payoffs for θ_1 to

TABLE 24.2 Opportunity-Loss
Table for the New-machine Example (in millions of dollars)

	State of Nature		
Act	θ_1	θ_2	θ_3
a_1	0.0	0.5	1.8
a_2	0.9	0.0	0.8
a_3	1.3	0.8	0.0

Source: Table 24.1.

opportunity losses by subtracting each payoff from 2.5, producing 0.0, 0.9, and 1.3, as Table 24.2 shows. We convert the payoffs for θ_2 to opportunity losses by subtracting each payoff from 2.0, producing 0.5, 0.0, and 0.8, as Table 24.2 shows. We convert the payoffs for θ_3 to opportunity losses by subtracting each payoff from 0.8, producing 1.8, 0.8, and 0.0, as Table 24.2 shows.

The phrase "opportunity loss" is often shortened to the single word "loss" when it is clear from context that opportunity losses are involved and not economic losses or accounting losses. Tables showing opportunity losses are often called *loss tables* or *loss matrices*. Some authors use the word "regret" for the phrase "opportunity loss," and they call such tables as Table 24.2 *regret tables*.

An opportunity loss always has the following interpretation. It is the difference between the results from the *chosen act* for the state of nature that eventually occurs and the results the *best act* would have yielded (had it been known in advance that that state of nature would occur). For example, consider the loss of 0.0 in Table 24.2 for a_1 and θ_1. This is the (opportunity) loss resulting from buying the high-capacity machine and later having prosperity. If it were known in advance that prosperity would occur, the best act would be buying the high-capacity machine, so the (opportunity) loss is 0.

By contrast, consider the loss of 0.9 in Table 24.2 for a_2 and θ_1. This is the (opportunity) loss resulting from buying the low-capacity machine and later having prosperity. If it were known in advance that prosperity would occur, the best act would be buying the high-capacity machine, for a payoff of 2.5. The chosen act has a payoff of only 1.6 when prosperity occurs, so the manager has lost the opportunity of making an extra 0.9 million dollars. The opportunity loss is therefore 0.9. All the other entries in Table 24.2 are interpreted similarly. Note that, because managers cannot predict the state of the economy perfectly, they are likely to choose an act other than the best act. If they had perfect information about the future state of the economy, they would never incur an opportunity loss. With imperfect information, they are likely to incur an opportunity loss. Opportunity losses are a measure of the cost of imperfect information about the state of nature.

Keep in mind the sharp distinction between an opportunity loss and an accounting loss. Opportunity losses can be huge even though accounting profits are involved, and opportunity losses can be small or zero even though huge accounting losses are involved. The key concept in understanding an opportunity loss is that an opportunity loss always measures the difference between what you actually did and the best you could have done under the circumstances that eventually occurred. If you actually made a \$100,000,000 profit in 1988 but could have made a \$150,000,000 profit by spending another \$10,000,000 on aggressive advertising, you have incurred a large opportunity loss even though there are no accounting losses anywhere in this situation. If you actually incurred a \$25,000,000 accounting loss in 1988 but, through skilled management and some good luck, managed to hold the accounting loss to this figure when any other action would have resulted in an even larger accounting loss, then your opportunity loss is zero even though huge accounting losses are involved in this situation.

It is useful for later work to have general algebraic notation for the best act, for payoffs, and for (opportunity) losses. Let $a_\dagger$ (which is read aloud as "a sub dagger" or just as "a dagger") be the symbol for the best act for a particular state of nature. For example, in Tables 24.1 and 24.2, $a_\dagger = a_1$ if $\tilde{\theta} = \theta_1$, $a_\dagger = a_2$ if $\tilde{\theta} = \theta_2$, and $a_\dagger = a_3$ if $\tilde{\theta} = \theta_3$. (The subscript of a happens to equal the subscript of θ in these equations, but this is a coincidence and does not always happen.)

When money is used to measure payoffs, let $m(a_i, \theta_j)$ be the payoff for the ith act and the jth state of nature. This notation can be condensed to m_{ij}. In Table 24.1, $m_{11} = 2.5$, $m_{12} = 1.5$, $m_{21} = 1.6$, and so on. (If the payoff table is set up like Table 24.1, with acts as rows and states of nature as columns, the symbol m_{ij} follows the usual convention for referring to entries in a table having rows and columns, where the first subscript is a row and the second subscript is a column.)

In a loss table, let $l(a_i, \theta_j)$ be the (opportunity) loss for the ith act and the jth state of nature. This notation can be condensed to l_{ij}. In Table 24.2, $l_{11} = 0.0$, $l_{12} = 0.5$, $l_{21} = 0.9$, and so on. (If the loss table is set up like Table 24.2, with acts as rows and states of nature as columns, the symbol l_{ij} follows the usual convention for referring to entries in a table having rows and columns, where the first subscript is a row and the second subscript is a column.)

The computation of losses from payoffs can be expressed algebraically as follows:

$$l(a_i, \theta_j) = m(a_\dagger, \theta_j) - m(a_i, \theta_j), \tag{24.1}$$

where $m(a_\dagger, \theta_j)$ is the highest payoff for the state θ_j.

Equation (24.1) can be rewritten, using condensed notation, as

$$l_{ij} = m_{\dagger j} - m_{ij}, \tag{24.2}$$

where $m_{\dagger j}$ is the highest payoff for the state θ_j.

Having obtained a payoff table, or a loss table, we proceed to the next step in the analysis, applying a decision rule. As mentioned before, a number of decision rules have been worked out by statisticians, however, we shall confine ourselves within the Bayesian framework by using the decision rule called the *expected value criterion*, and we explain this rule next.

24.4 BAYESIAN PRIOR ANALYSIS

The Bayesian decision rule is called the *Bayesian measure,* which is simply the expected value of the payoffs or of the opportunity losses. It is thus often called the *expected value criterion.* Suppose the manager in the new-machine illustration believes, from whatever information is available, that the state of nature represented by θ_1 (prosperity) is twice as likely to occur as state θ_2 (stability) and that state θ_2, in turn, is twice as likely to occur as state θ_3 (recession). Let $f_0(\theta_j)$ be the probability of θ_j. From what has just been said, if $f_0(\theta_3) = A$, then $f_0(\theta_2) = 2A$ and $f_0(\theta_1) = 4A$. The sum of these three probabilities must equal 1, so we can obtain the value of A by solving the following equation:

$$A + 2A + 4A = 1;$$

$$7A = 1;$$

$$A = 1/7.$$

This implies that the probability distribution for the state variable $\tilde{\theta}$, is

$$f_0(\theta_j) = \begin{cases} 4/7, & \text{for } \tilde{\theta} = \theta_1; \\ 2/7, & \text{for } \tilde{\theta} = \theta_2; \\ 1/7, & \text{for } \tilde{\theta} = \theta_3. \end{cases}$$

Now, having a probability distribution for the state variable, we can calculate the expected value of the payoffs for each act (using Table 24.1) and then choose the act with the highest expected payoff. This is what is meant by using the expected-value criterion to choose the best act. In the following computations, the symbol EP_0 stands for "expected payoff calculated prior to taking a sample," or "prior expected payoff." Note that an expected payoff is calculated just like any other expected value—each of the values that the payoff can assume is multiplied by its probability of occurring, and then these products are added up.

$$EP_0(a_1) = 2.5(4/7) + 1.5(2/7) + (-1.0)(1/7) \doteq 1.7143;$$

$$EP_0(a_2) = 1.6(4/7) + 2.0(2/7) + 0.0(1/7) \doteq 1.4857;$$

$$EP_0(a_3) = 1.2(4/7) + 1.2(2/7) + 0.8(1/7) \doteq 1.1429.$$

The best act is a_1, because the expected value of its payoff is the greatest. We can, if we wish, add a star to a_1, making it a_1^*; to show that it is the best act.

If we were working with a loss table instead of a payoff table, we would calculate prior expected losses and then choose the act with the smallest prior expected loss. Using Table 24.2 and letting the symbol

EL_0 stand for "prior expected loss," we would have

$$EL_0(a_1^*) = 0.0(4/7) + 0.5(2/7) + 1.8(1/7) = 0.4000;$$

$$EL_0(a_2) = 0.9(4/7) + 0.0(2/7) + 0.8(1/7) = 0.6286;$$

$$EL_0(a_3) = 1.3(4/7) + 0.8(2/7) + 0.0(1/7) = 0.9174.$$

The best act is a_1 because it has the lowest expected (opportunity) loss. It can be proved that the best act will always have the highest expected payoff and the lowest expected loss, just as a_1 does in this example.

We see that a Bayesian, essentially, looks at the average payoff for each act and then picks the act with the highest average payoff. The "average payoff" is really the prior expected payoff, when no sample is taken. The act with the highest average payoff, or lowest average loss, is called the *optimal act*.

The procedures for calculating prior expected payoffs and prior expected losses can be expressed algebraically:

$$EP_0(a_i) = E_0[m(a_j, \theta_j)] = \sum_j m_{ij} f_0(\theta_j), \qquad (24.3)$$

and

$$EL_0(a_i) = E_0[l(a_i, \theta_j)] = \sum_j l_{ij} f_0(\theta_j). \qquad (24.4)$$

where E_0 is a "prior expectation" and $f_0(\theta_j)$ is a "prior probability for θ_j." The subscript 0 is used consistently in Bayesian analysis to mean "prior," which is itself an abbreviation of "prior to taking a sample." We use f_0 for a prior probability instead of P_0 because the letter P already has several other meanings in Bayesian analysis, such as "payoff."

Our factory manager decided on act a_1, buying the high-capacity machine, from a *prior analysis,* which is an analysis that *chooses the optimal act without taking a sample.* If the manager has no opportunity to gather additional information—perhaps because there is no time left—she should go ahead and buy the high-capacity machine. On the other hand, if there *is* an opportunity to gather additional information, the manager should consider doing so. The decision about whether to gather additional information can itself be analyzed, as we shall see in the next chapter, via a "preposterior analysis", which shows how many additional sample observations should be made and which can come out 0, meaning no more observations should be gathered for the final decision. Crucial to posterior analysis and preposterior analysis is the notion of "expected value of perfect information," which we introduce next.

24.5 EXPECTED VALUE OF PERFECT INFORMATION

The notion of "prior expected value of perfect information," $EVPI_0$, is related to a measure called "prior expected payoff with perfect information," $EPPI_0$. The calculation of $EPPI_0$ is based on the expected payoff obtained under the assumption that the decision maker has access to a *perfect predictor*. This implies that, if the decision maker could obtain perfect information on the state random variable, he would select a^* each time—the act that would yield the highest payoff for the state value that is forecast by the perfect predictor.

In the new-machine example, we work with the payoffs of Table 24.1 and with the prior probabilities of 4/7, 2/7, and 1/7 for the state variable. The only new idea is that of the perfect predictor. If the manager knew in advance that θ_1 would occur, she would pick a_1, which has a payoff of \$2.5 million and a probability of 4/7. If she knew in advance that θ_2 would occur, she would pick a_2, which has a payoff of \$2.0 million and a probability of 2/7. If she knew in advance that θ_3 would occur, she would pick a_3, which has a payoff of \$0.8 million and a probability of 1/7. Therefore, the prior expected payoff with perfect information is

$$EPPI_0 = 2.5(4/7) + 2.0(2/7) + 0.8(1/7) \doteq 2.1143,$$

We compare this with the expected payoff of the optimal act, from a prior analysis, to get the *prior expected value of perfect information*:

$$EVPI_0 = EPPI_0 - EP_0(a_1^*) = 2.1143 - 1.7143 = 0.4000, \text{ or } \$400,000.$$

We can calculate $EVPI_0$ from prior expected losses instead of from prior expected payoffs. The prior expected loss with perfect information is always 0, because the best act for each state of nature would always be selected. The prior expected loss for the optimal act is $EL_0(a_1^*) = 0.4000$. This loss of 0.4000 would be eliminated with perfect information; the prior expected value of perfect information is therefore

$$EVPI_0 = EL_0(a_1^*) - 0.0000 = 0.4000, \text{ or } \$400,000$$

It can be proved that $EVPI_0$ must be the same, whether it is calculated from prior expected payoffs or prior expected losses.

The general formulas for calculating $EVPI_0$ are

$$EPPI_0 = \sum_j m_{\dagger j} f_0(\theta_j); \qquad (24.5)$$

$$EVPI_0 = EPPI_0 - EP_0(a_i^*), \qquad (24.6)$$

where $m_{\dagger j}$ is the same as in Equation 24.2 and where a_i^* is the optimal act based on a prior analysis, such as a_1^* in the new-machine example. Another way of calculating $EVPI_0$ is

$$EVPI_0 = EL_0(a_i^*) \qquad (24.7)$$

In Section 24.3, we say that opportunity losses are a measure of the cost of imperfect information about the state of nature. We now make this notion precise. $EL_0(a_i^*)$, the prior expected (opportunity) loss of the *optimal act*, is the *cost of uncertainty* to decision makers. If they were certain which state of nature would occur—if they had perfect information—they could eliminate $EL_0(a_i^*)$. This implies that $EL_0(a_i^*)$, or $EVPI_0$, is the highest price that a decision maker should ever consider paying for additional information after running a prior analysis. In the new-machine example, the manager should reject immediately any additional information costing over \$400,000 on the grounds that it costs more than it is worth.

The additional information that could be gathered is usually less than perfect, so it is usually worth less than $EVPI_0$. Under suitable conditions, a preposterior analysis can be run to determine whether the cost of some additional information is low enough to justify gathering it, even though it is less than perfect. If there is no additional information whose cost is low enough to justify gathering it, the decision maker should make the final decision on the basis of the prior analysis.

24.6 BAYESIAN POSTERIOR ANALYSIS

The decision maker who gathers additional information after running a prior analysis uses the additional information to revise his probability distribution for the state variable. The payoffs remain the same and so do the (opportunity) losses. The purpose of the additional information, then, is to make possible a better forecast of which state of nature will eventually occur.

The decision maker then performs a *posterior analysis* by using Bayesian measure on the payoffs and posterior probabilities, or on the losses and posterior probabilities, to pick the act with the highest expected payoff (which is the same act as the one with the lowest expected loss).

The formulas for calculating the posterior expected payoff of each act, or the posterior expected loss of each act, are the same as (24.3) and (24.4) except for the subscript 0. This is changed from 0 to 1, indicating that a posterior analysis is being performed instead of a prior analysis. The formulas for posterior analysis are

$$EP_1(a_i) = E_1[m(a_i, \theta_j)] = \sum_j m_{ij} f_1(\theta_j), \qquad (24.8)$$

and

$$EL_1(a_i) = E_1[l(a_i, \theta_j)] = \sum_j l_{ij} f_1(\theta_j), \qquad (24.9)$$

Continuing the new-machine example, suppose the Humble Economic Research Institute specializes in forecasting general economic conditions and has offered its services to our decision maker, the manager of the manufacturing firm. Humble's forecasting procedure is based on the expansion plans of major business firms. It mails detailed questionnaires to all industrial firms with assets in excess of \$100 million. The questionnaires inquire into the firms' capital investment plans. It then makes projections for capital investment for the whole nation based on the completed questionnaires. Next it determines, assuming that the investment plans will be actually realized, whether (1) there will be a definite increase in national capital investment for the coming year, compared with the current year; (2) there will be no change or only a slight change in national capital investment for the coming year, compared with the current year; or (3) there will be a definite decline in national capital investment for the coming year, compared with the current year. Humble identifies these three possible sample results as follows: x_1, indicating prosperity; x_2, indicating stability; and x_3, indicating recession.

On the basis of previous surveys of this type, Humble assesses the reliability of the sample evidence in the following probabilistic terms:

$$f(x_1 \mid \theta_1) = 0.6; \qquad f(x_2 \mid \theta_1) = 0.3; \qquad f(x_3 \mid \theta_1) = 0.1;$$

$$f(x_1 \mid \theta_2) = 0.2; \qquad f(x_2 \mid \theta_2) = 0.7; \qquad f(x_3 \mid \theta_2) = 0.1;$$

$$f(x_1 \mid \theta_3) = 0.1; \qquad f(x_2 \mid \theta_3) = 0.3; \qquad f(x_3 \mid \theta_3) = 0.6.$$

Each row of probabilities sums to 1, because one of three sample results must occur for any given state of the economy. Each column of probabilities does not add up to 1, because the sum here is not a meaningful concept. However, the individual probabilities in each column are meaningful and are the likelihoods employed in Bayes' theorem. They measure the reliability of each sample result. For example, referring to the first column, when the state was prosperity in the past, Humble's forecasts correctly indicated prosperity 60% of the time. When the state was stability, however, 20% of Humble's forecasts incorrectly indicated prosperity. When the state was recession, 10% of Humble's forecasts incorrectly indicated prosperity.

Now suppose Humble's current forecast is for stability, x_2, and suppose the manager in the new-machine example has just received a copy of Humble's forecast after paying a fee to Humble. (The fee for such economic consulting might be of the order of $5,000, especially if Humble adds some material to its report dealing with the manager's special problems. This fee is so much smaller than $EVPI_0$ = $400,000 that common sense suggests strongly that Humble's report is worth the fee even if the report is not perfectly accurate.) Now the maneger should revise her prior probabilities for $\bar{\theta}$ by means of Bayes' theorem, in view of Humble's forecast of stability. The revision is accomplished via the calculations shown in Table 24.3.

If we use payoffs instead of losses to pick the best act, we apply Bayes' theorem to the payoffs of Table 24.1 and the posterior probabilities of Table 24.3. We get

$$EP_1(a_1) \doteq 2.5(0.4137931) + 1.5(0.4827586) + (-1.0)(0.1034483)$$

$$\doteq 1.6552$$

$$EP_1(a_2) \doteq 1.6(0.4137931) + 2.0(0.4827586) + 0.0(0.1034483) \doteq 1.6276$$

$$EP_1(a_3) \doteq 1.2(0.4137931) + 1.2(0.4827586) + 0.8(0.1034483) \doteq 1.1586,$$

TABLE 24.3 Revising the Prior Probabilities in the New-machine Example[a]

State of Nature θ_j	Prior Probability $f_0(\theta_j)$	Likelihood $f(x_2 \mid \theta_j)$	Joint Probability $f_0(\theta_j)f(x_2 \mid \theta_j)$	Posterior Probability $f_1(\theta_j)$
θ_1	4/7 ≐ 0.5714286	0.3	0.1714286	0.4137931
θ_2	2/7 ≐ 0.2857143	0.7	0.2000000	0.4827586
θ_3	1/7 ≐ 0.1428571	0.3	0.0428571	0.1034483
Total	7/7 = 1.0000000	—	$f(x_2)$ = 0.4142857	1.0000000

[a] All entries were calculated to more than 7 decimal places to ensure accuracy in the last column. If intermediate results are rounded back to 7 decimal places before the last column is calculated, slight discrepancies due to rounding error will result.

The best act remains a_1; it has the highest posterior expected payoff. If we wish, we can use the symbol ** to indicate the optimal act revealed by a posterior analysis. Then the symbol a_1^{**} automatically shows that a_1 is optimal on the basis of a posterior analysis.

If you compare the prior expected payoffs with the posterior expected payoffs, you will see that the spread between $EP_1(a_1^{**})$ and the second-highest expected payoff, $EP_1(a_2)$, has narrowed to a great extent compared with the spread between $EP_0(a_1^*)$ and $EP_0(a_2)$. We comment on this shortly.

If we use losses instead of payoffs to pick the best act, we apply Equation (24.9) to the losses of Table 24.2 and the posterior probabilities of Table 24.3. We get

$$EL_1(a_1^{**}) \doteq 0.0(0.4137931) + 0.5(0.4827586) + 1.8(0.1034483)$$

$$\doteq 0.4276;$$

$$EL_1(a_2) \doteq 0.9(0.4137931) + 0.0(0.4827586) + 0.8(0.1034483)$$

$$\doteq 0.4552;$$

$$EL_1(a_3) \doteq 1.3(0.4137931) + 0.8(0.4827586) + 0.0(0.1034483)$$

$$\doteq 0.9241.$$

As must always happen, the act with the smallest expected loss is the act with the largest expected payoff. The optimal act is a_1, on the basis of posterior expected losses.

We can calculate the expected value of perfect information as part of a posterior analysis. Equations (24.5), (24.6), and (24.7) apply only to a prior analysis, but, by changing the subscript 0 to the subscript 1, we obtain equations applying to a posterior analysis:

$$EPPI_1 = \sum_j m_{\gamma j} f_1(\theta_j); \tag{24.10}$$

$$EVPI_1 = EPPI_1 - EP_1(a_i^{**}); \tag{24.11}$$

$$EVPI_1 = EL_1(a_i^{**}). \tag{24.12}$$

Having already calculated $EL_1(a_1^{**})$ for the new-machine example, we see that $EVPI_1 \doteq \$427{,}600$ because of Equation (24.11). This is now the cost of uncertainty, after using the new information. Note that, from the prior analysis alone, the cost of uncertainty was $EVPI_0 = \$400{,}000$. The cost of uncertainty has risen due to our using the new information!

There are several noteworthy features in the posterior analysis for the new-machine example. First, the optimal act is the same—buying the high-capacity machine—in the posterior analysis as it was in the prior analysis; the new information from the economic forecasting service did not change the optimal act. This is not especially unusual because of the way prior probabilities are assigned and the particular sample result obtained.

Second, the difference in the expected payoffs between the best act and the second-best act in the posterior analysis is $\$1{,}655{,}200 - \$1{,}627{,}600 = \$27{,}600$; a_1 and a_2 are almost tied for being the optimal act. This is unusual, although it is mathematically possible, as this example demonstrates.

Third, the $\$27{,}600$ difference in posterior expected payoffs between the best act and the second-best act is much smaller than the difference in prior expected payoffs between the best act and the second-best act, which was $\$1{,}714{,}300 - \$1{,}485{,}700 = \$228{,}600$. The prior analysis clearly chose a_1 as the optimal act. After getting the additional economic information, the posterior analysis shows a_1 to be only slightly better than a_2. This is unusual. Ordinarily, the additional information used in a posterior analysis makes it more clear what the optimal act is rather than less clear.

Fourth, the expected value of perfect information is $\$427{,}600$ in the posterior analysis, and this figure is an increase over the $\$400{,}000$ figure in the prior analysis. This, too, is unusual. The additional information has increased the cost of uncertainty here, whereas it usually decreases the cost of uncertainty.

The posterior analysis uses the same information as the prior analysis except for the revised probabilities for the states of nature. Therefore, when trying to account for the differences between the results in the posterior analysis and the results in the prior analysis, we should start by looking at the probabilities of prosperity, stability, and recession. The key fact is that the manager used to be quite confident of prosperity, giving it a probability of about 0.57 compared to 0.29 for the probability of stability and 0.14 for the probability of recession. The economic consulting service contradicted this estimate by forecasting stability, not prosperity. The unusual results in our new-machine example flow, essentially, from this contradiction between the manager's initial forecast of prosperity and the consultant's forecast of stability.

The next question is what the manager should do, now that the results of the posterior analysis have been calculated. We offer no firm solution, but we do offer some suggestions. Perhaps an econometrician can find some new information that is statistically independent of Humble's information. If so, and if the new information is cheap enough, the manager should get some more information, re-revise her probabilities for $\tilde{\theta}$, and recalculate the optimal act. As another possibility, the manager can review the "track record" for Humble: the conditional probabilities that produced the entries in the column for $f(x_2 \mid \theta_j)$ in Table 24.3. A "track record" is merely a statement of how well the forecaster's past forecasts predicted what actually happened. The nine conditional probabilities preceding Table 24.3 constitute Humble's track record. We used three of these probabilities as the likelihoods called for by Bayes' theorem, in the calculations of Table 24.3.

It is not clear, though, that this is the proper procedure. For example, if this forecast by Humble is more difficult than most forecasts, the conditional probability of correctly predicting stability in Table 24.3 should be lowered from 0.7 to something less. If this forecast is easier than most, the conditional probability of correctly predicting stability should be increased to something greater than 0.7. Even raising this issue—the correctness of the likelihoods—is unusual. Ordinarily the likelihoods in a Bayesian posterior analysis come from a random sample, and there is very little doubt that the numbers from the random sample are appropriate and should be used as they are given.

As yet another possibility, the manager can conclude that the posterior probabilities for the states of nature in Table 24.3 are correct (or at least approximately correct), in view of her own prior probabilities and Humble's track record, and make the final decision now. Because a_1 and a_2 are almost equally attractive, the manager should choose between them on the basis of factors not considered in the Bayesian analysis. For example, if the firm has surplus cash, go with a_1; if it is short of cash, go with a_2. If the firm's president is market-oriented, go with a_1 so that customers will be satisfied; if the firm's president is cost-oriented, go with a_2 so that investment costs will be reduced. Or use any other factors that will break the tie between a_1 and a_2. The fact that a_1 and a_2 are tied (or almost tied) should not be viewed as a failure of the analysis. True, the analysis failed to show which act is clearly best, but that result is itself valuable. It means that, for the costs and revenues and probabilities that were included in the analysis, either a_1 or a_2 is a good decision. The final choice between them can be based on factors that were not included in the analysis.

24.7   A COMPREHENSIVE EXAMPLE

We shall now illustrate all the material presented in this chapter up to now by a comprehensive example. This should help to pull all the material together and make it more understandable. The example will also illustrate a case wherein simple random sampling from a virtually infinite population can be used to gather as much new information as is desired for a terminal decision.

Before each new product is marketed nationally, a certain cosmetics firm always has a panel of executives to evaluate its potential market shares, to decide on the possible acts, to estimate the payoff and

TABLE 24.4 Payoff Table for the Black Jade Example

Act	State of Nature		
	$\pi_1 = 0.15$	$\pi_2 = 0.10$	$\pi_3 = 0.05$
a_1: market	$1,000,000	$0	−$200,000
a_2: do not market	$0	$0	$0

loss functions, and to assign prior probabilities to the states of nature. The firm's research staff has just perfected a new perfume with Oriental ingredients, called "Black Jade." The panel, assigned by the President of the firm to evaluate this new product, has decided the following as a first approximation to a complete analysis.

1. To consider only three states of nature: Its potential shares of the market are $\pi_1 = 0.15$, $\pi_2 = 0.10$, and $\pi_3 = 0.05$.

2. To consider only two acts: a_1 = market the new perfume and a_2 = do not market the new perfume.

3. According to these states and acts, the payoff and loss functions are estimated as shown by Table 24.4 and Table 24.5, respectively.

   While a decision can be made by either expected payoff or expected loss, we usually work with latter, since the expected loss for the optimal act is also the $EVPI_0$. Convert Table 24.4 into a loss table, Table 24.5.
   From either Table 24.4 or Table 24.5, we see that neither of the two acts, a_1 and a_2, is dominated by the other: both acts are admissible.

4. The prior probabilities of the states are:

$$f_0(\pi_1) = 0.6, f_0(\pi_2) = 0.3, \text{ and } f_0(\pi_3) = 0.10.$$

(These prior probabilities reveal that the panel is very enthusiastic about the new product.)

In any event, with the conclusions of the panel so far, the prior analysis leads to

$$EL_0(a_1^*) = \$0(0.6) + \$0(0.3) + \$200,000(0.10)$$
$$= \$20,000;$$

$$EL_0(a_2) = \$1,000,000(0.6) + \$0(0.3) + \$0(0.10)$$
$$= \$600,000.$$

TABLE 24.5 Loss Table for the Black Jade Example

Act	State of Nature		
	$\pi_1 = 0.15$	$\pi_2 = 0.10$	$\pi_3 = 0.05$
a_1: market	$0	$0	$200,000
a_2: do not market	$1,000,000	$0	$0

Naturally, we had to compute the two prior expected losses before we knew that the * belongs to a_1 instead of a_2.

It may be noted that there is a large difference between the two prior expected losses. However, this is not the crucial factor in deciding whether to choose an act now or to make the terminal decision after first gathering more information. The key factor is the expected value of perfect information. In our example, $EVPI_0 = EL_0(a_1^*) = \$20,000$. This is a rather large value and it might be very wise to spend a few hundred or a even a few thousand dollars on additional information. Suppose that \$1,000 will buy a carefully and properly conducted survey of ten women. This is not a very large sample, but a small pilot survey is a reasonable way of starting any kind of market research. Suppose the sample is randomly selected, suppose the survey accurately predicts the future behavior of each woman in the sample, and suppose that none of the ten women in sample liked the new perfume. We can summarize this sample result by saying that, in the first survey F, the sample size is $n_F = 10$ and the sample result was $x_F = 0$. Here, x_F is the x called for by Bayes' theorem.

Having obtained the sample result, we move on to revise the prior probabilities for the state random variable. This is done in Table 24.6.

Next, we calculate posterior expected losses with results in the last column of Table 24.6. They are

$$EL_1(a_1^{**}) \doteq \$0(0.417) + \$0(0.371) + \$200,000(0.212)$$
$$\doteq \$21,200;$$

$$EL_1(a_2) \doteq \$1,000,000(0.417) + \$0(0.371) + \$0(0.212)$$
$$\doteq \$417,000.$$

We see that the optimal act has not changed from the prior analysis despite the highly unfavorable additional sample information. However, $EVPI_1 = EL_1(a_1^{**}) > EVPI_0$. The sample information has increased the cost of uncertainty; the panel is less certain of the optimal act now than before the availability of sample information. The expected value of perfect information is now worth \$21,200 and, hence, it is reasonable to gather more sample information before the terminal decision. Suppose \$5,000 would buy another 90 observations; suppose that this has been done, and suppose that none of the 90 extra women liked the new perfume. We can summarize this sample result by saying that, in the

TABLE 24.6 Revising Prior Probabilities for the Black Jade Example

State of Nature π_j	Prior Probability $f_0(\pi_j)$	Likelihood $f(x_F = 0 \mid \pi_j)$	Joint Probability $f_0(\pi_j)f(x_F = 0 \mid \pi_j)$	Posterior Probability $f_1(\pi_j)$
$\pi_1 = 0.15$	0.6	$(0.85)^{10}$	$(0.6)(0.85)^{10} \doteq 0.118$	0.417
$\pi_2 = 0.10$	0.3	$(0.90)^{10}$	$(0.3)(0.90)^{10} \doteq 0.105$	0.371
$\pi_3 = 0.5$	0.1	$(0.95)^{10}$	$(0.1)(0.95)^{10} \doteq 0.060$	0.212
Total	1.0	—	$f(x_F = 0) \doteq 0.283$	1.000

TABLE 24.7 Re-Revising Probabilities for the Black Jade Example

π_j	$f_0(\pi_j)$	$f(x_S = 0 \mid \pi_j)$	$f_0(\pi_j)f(x_S = 0 \mid \pi_j)$	$f_1(\pi_j)$
0.15	0.417	$(0.85)^{90}$	$0.417(0.85)^{90} \doteq 0.0000002$	0.0001
0.10	0.371	$(0.90)^{90}$	$0.371(0.90)^{90} \doteq 0.0000282$	0.0133
0.05	0.212	$(0.95)^{90}$	$0.212(0.95)^{90} \doteq 0.0020950$	0.9866
Total	1.000	—	$f(x_S = 0) \doteq 0.0021233$	1.0000

second sample, S, the sample size was $n_S = 90$ and the sample result was $x_S = 0$. Now, x_S is the x called for by Bayes' theorem. Treating the posterior probabilities revised by the first sample as prior probabilities, we can re-revise these probabilities by the information provided by the second sample, as shown in Table 24.7.

The posterior expected losses (posterior to the second sample) become

$$EL_1(a_1) \doteq \$0(0.0001) + \$0(0.0133) + \$200,000(0.9866)$$
$$\doteq \$197,320;$$

$$EL_1(a_2^{**}) \doteq \$1,000,000(0.0001) + \$0(0.0133) + \$0(0.9866)$$
$$\doteq \$100.$$

Thus, with the information provided by the first and second samples together, the optimal act has changed from a_1 to a_2. Now, $EVPI_1 = \$100$. No further information of any value could be bought with only $100 for problems of this kind. It is time to stop gathering further information and the terminal decision should be made: Do not market the new perfume. Earlier uncertainties about the states of nature have been resolved by gathering enough sample information to drive $EVPI$ down to nearly zero.

24.8 BAYESIAN DECISION THEORY AND POINT ESTIMATION

As was pointed out, the Bayesian procedure for estimation, just as the classical method, is informal because it does not include a payoff or loss function in the analysis. To have a formal approach to estimation, we may think of the choice of an estimate as a problem in decision making under uncertainty. In this context, there is a one-to-one correspondence between the action set and the set of state values. Now, if a payoff or loss function can be established to give the payoff or loss associated with an erroneous estimate (act), then the problem of point estimation can be treated in the general framework of Bayesian decision theory, as considered in the previous sections of this chapter. To clarify the decision-theoretic approach to point estimation, let us consider an example in detail.

The manager of a food store agrees to accept a certain make of perishable fancy French cakes for sale each day under the condition that the bakery picks up all unsold units the next morning when delivery of the fresh stock is made. Each cake costs the food store $6 and it can be sold at a price of $10. Any unsold unit at the end of each day can be returned for a credit of $3. Under these conditions, how many units of this perishable cake should the manager order for each day? This is mainly an estimation problem, since she must estimate the demand—the state random variable D. That is, she must estimate the number of customers that will come in each day and want to purchase a cake.

Now, for the sake of simplicity, we shall assume that unsatisfied demand due to understock will not affect future sales, and we shall also ignore fixed costs in handling. From previous statements of the problem, we see that a profit of $4 will be made on each cake sold and a loss of $3 will be suffered on each cake stocked but unsold by the end of each business day. Thus, the payoff function in this case can be stated simply as follows:

$$M(a_i, d_j) = \begin{cases} \$4 - \$(a_i - d_j), & \text{if } a_i > d_j; \\ \$4a_i, & \text{if } a_i \leq d_j. \end{cases}$$

In this payoff function, d_j stands for the various demand levels—the values of the state random variable D.

Since it is more convenient and fruitful to work with the loss function than with the payoff function in the Bayesian decision framework, we shall now give the loss function for this problem. To do this, we note that if the stock is less than the demand, there will be an "opportunity loss" of $4 per cake; if the stock is greater than the demand, there will be a loss of $3 per cake. Hence, the loss function for this case becomes

$$L(a_i, d_j) = \begin{cases} \$3(a_i - d_j), & \text{if } a_i \geq d_j; \\ \$4(d_j - a_i), & \text{if } a_i < d_j. \end{cases}$$

Next, suppose that, according to the judgment and past experience of the manager for products of this kind, the demand for the fancy French cakes should be at least three units and at most eight units per day; then the state random variable D, should range in values from 3

TABLE 24.8 Payoff Table for the French Cake Example

Act: a_i	State (demand): d_j					
	3	4	5	6	7	8
a_1: 3	$12	$12	$12	$12	$12	$12
a_2: 4	9	16	16	16	16	16
a_3: 5	6	13	20	20	20	20
a_4: 6	3	10	17	24	24	24
a_5: 7	0	7	14	21	28	28
a_6: 8	−3	4	11	18	25	32

TABLE 24.9 Loss Table for French Cake Example

Act: a_i	State (demand): d_j					
	3	4	5	6	7	8
a_1: 3	$ 0	$ 4	$8	$12	$16	$20
a_2: 4	3	0	4	8	12	16
a_3: 5	6	3	0	4	8	12
a_4: 6	9	6	3	0	4	8
a_5: 7	12	9	6	3	0	4
a_6: 8	15	12	9	6	3	0

consecutively to 8 cakes. Furthermore, it is easy to see that there is a stock action corresponding to each of the state values: a_1 = stock 3, ..., and a_6 = stock 8. With the state and act sets and the payoff and loss functions previously determined, the payoff and loss tables for our example would be as shown by Tables 24.8 and 24.9, respectively.

Now, suppose the manager, in view of her experience of food items of similar nature in the past, is able to specify a prior probability distribution for the state random variable D as follows:

$$f_0(d_1 = 3) = 0.05; \quad f_0(d_4 = 6) = 0.40;$$

$$f_0(d_2 = 4) = 0.10, \quad f_0(d_5 = 7) = 0.10;$$

$$f_0(d_3 = 5) = 0.30, \quad f_0(d_6 = 8) = 0.05.$$

With the loss table and prior probabilities, for any act, a_i, the expected loss is computed by

$$EL_0(a_i) = \sum_j l_{ij} f_0(d_j).$$

Thus, for example, for a_1, we have

$$EL_0(a_1) = \sum_j l_{ij} f_0(d_j)$$

$$= 0(0.5) + 4(0.10) + \ldots + 20(0.05)$$

$$= \$10.20.$$

The expected losses for the remaining five acts are computed in the same way and are recorded in the first two columns in Table 24.10.

TABLE 24.10 Prior and Posterior Expected Losses for the French Cake Example

Act	$EL_0(a_i)$	$EL_1(a_i)$
$a_1 = 3$	$10.20	$12.10
$a_2 = 4$	6.55	8.10
$a_3 = 5$	3.60	4.30
$a_4 = 6$	2.75	1.99
$a_5 = 7$	4.70	3.40
$a_6 = 8$	7.35	5.93

From the column for $EL_0(a_i)$ in Table 24.10, we see that the optimal act in the prior analysis is $a_4^* = 6$, with the lowest expected loss of \$2.75. The manager should order 6 cakes per day with the information she has available now. Alternatively, in the decision-theoretic sense, her prior optimal estimate of the daily demand is 6. Such an estimate is considered as "optimal" because it either minimizes the expected loss (or maximizes the expected payoff). If the manager is satisfied with the prior analysis, the problem is solved.

It is also interesting to note, in this example, any act other than those specified is inadmissible. Consider, for instance, the order action $a_7 = 9$. For a_7, the row of values in the loss table would be 18, 15, 12, 9, 6, and 3. However, in all the six columns for $a_6 = 8$, the corresponding losses are less; hence a_7 is dominated by a_6 and the former is inadmissible. The same is true for any act $a_i < a_1 = 3$. This is the reason why in stock or inventory decision situations, there is always a one-to-one correspondence between the number of acts and the number of state values, especially in the discrete case.

To continue our example, we see that $EL_0(a_4^*) = EVPI_0 = \$2.75$. This is a very small amount of money. One may think that a posterior analysis is at once impossible and unnecessary. However, it may also be pointed out that in problems such as our current example, the cost of obtaining additional information may be very low and the decision maker may be willing to pay more than $EVPI_0$ for a perfect predictor if the same perfect predictor can be used to forecast the demand for each day.

In any event, just for purpose of illustrating the mechanism of determining the posterior optimal estimate (act) for problems of this kind, suppose the manager would like to obtain more information for a terminal decision on the daily order. For this purpose, suppose the manager decided to stock the cake on a 2-day trial basis and suppose in this period 50 customers patronized her store each day and a total of 14 cakes were sold. In view of this additional information, what would be her regular optimal order-decision now? Of course, to answer this question, the first thing she should so is to revise her prior probability distribution for the daily demand. This is done in Table 24.11.

TABLE 24.11 Revising Prior Probabilities for the French Cake Example

State		Prior Probability (3)	Likelihood (4)	Joint Probabilities (Prior probability) times (likelihood) (5) = (3)(4)	Posterior Probability (6)
d_j (1)	$d_j/50$ (2)				
3	0.06	0.05	17	0.85	0.001
4	0.08	0.10	149	19.40	0.027
5	0.10	0.30	513	153.90	0.214
6	0.12	0.40	954	381.60	0.531
7	0.14	0.10	1143	114.30	0.159
8	0.16	0.05	979	48.95	0.068
Total		1.00	—	719.00	1.000

There are a number of points that must be noted in the procedure of revising the probabilities in Table 24.11. First of all, since the sampling is binomial, the computations of the conditional probabilities given the sample result, likelihoods, require that the state values be proportions. Thus, the daily demand in units of cakes have been converted into proportions of the number of customers per day, as $d_j/50$. These state values are as given in column (2) in the table. Second, the prior probability mass function remains as before because it applies to d_j as well as to $d_j/50$. Third, the conditional probabilities of the sample with $n = 100$ and $x = 14$, are binomial probabilities. Furthermore, these probabilities, as likelihoods, are multiplied by 10,000 each in order to make calculations more compact by reducing the possible large number of decimal points in the joint probabilities as in the Black Jade example. This procedure is quite legitimate since, in the application of Bayes' theorem, the likelihoods are determined from the conditional distribution of the sample result given the possible values of the state random variable. Once a sample result is observed, the likelihoods, as functions of the state random variable, with x fixed, can be taken to be any positive multiples of the conditional probabilities, $f(x \mid \theta_j)$ without affecting the final results—the posterior probabilities. Thus, the values in column (4) of Table 24.11 are computed by using

$$f_{b(x \mid n, \pi_j)(10,000)} = \binom{100}{14}(\pi_j)^{10}(1 - \pi_j)^{90}(10,000).$$

For example, given $\pi_4 = 0.12$, we have

$$f_{b(14 \mid 100, 0.12)(10,000)} = \binom{100}{14}(0.12)^{10}(0.88)^{90}(10,000)$$

$$\doteq 0.0954(10,000) = 954.$$

[In actual work, probabilities (or likelihoods) such as this should be computed by computers.]

The resulting $f_1(\pi_j)$, just as $f_0(\pi_j)$, can be applied to both d_j and $d_j/50$. The posterior expected losses for the various acts are computed in the usual fashion by

$$EL_1(a_i) = \sum_j l_{ij} f_1(\pi_j).$$

The computed expected losses are entered in the third column of Table 24.10. From these results we see that the manager's optimal estimate (act) of the daily demand is still $a_4^{**} = 6$. Namely, in this example, $a_4^* = a_4^{**}$ despite the fact that a relatively large sample has been used and that the sample result corresponds to the order-action of $a_5 = 7$. This is, however, not a surprising conclusion if we take notice of the fact that $f_0(\pi_4)$ is four times as large as $f_0(\pi_5)$. Moreover, even though $f_0(\pi_5)$ has been revised upward by more than 60%, $f_0(\pi_4)$ has also been revised upward by more than 33%. As a consequence, $f_1(\pi_4)$ is still more than 3.3 times as large as $f_1(\pi_5)$. It is interesting to observe, though, that the sample results in probabilities becoming more concentrated about the posterior optimal estimate—the expected value of perfect information has thereby been reduced from \$2.75 to \$1.99. You must be reminded also that this reduction in the expected loss from prior to posterior analysis is not always the case. As previously observed, if the sample information is strongly contrary to the prior information, there are situations in which the revised probabilities lead to larger expected losses for the optimal act.

The procedure of employing the Bayesian measure to find the optimal act presented so far is quite general and can be applied in any situation. However, the calculations involved are often extensive and at times complex. Mathematical drudgery is compounded when the set of actions is large or when the state random variable can assume a large number, or even an infinite number of values as in the continuous case. However, you should not be worried about such possibilities since, in certain frequently encountered situations, the Bayesian decision criterion simplifies to *equivalent special forms* that greatly reduce computational labor. It turns out that such special forms depend upon particular types of loss functions. Furthermore, when a special Bayesian decision criterion can be applied, the expected value of perfect information, prior or posterior, can also be computed from a simple formula if the prior mass or density function of the state random variable is a natural conjugate distribution. In the next few sections of this chapter we are concerned with the equivalent special forms of the Bayesian measure with two important and frequently employed loss functions: the piecewise-linear and the quadratic loss functions.

24.9 PIECEWISE-LINEAR LOSS FUNCTIONS

The inventory model of the French cake example just evaluated, as in many other decision problems of the same kind, is called an *equivalent state-action problem* because there is a different "best" action for each state value. Furthermore, this example also possesses a piecewise-linear loss function, since, as shown by Figure 24.1, the payoff function for each act is piecewise-linear in two segments. As a result, as shown by Figure 24.2, the corresponding loss function for each act is also piecewise-linear in two segments. Under these conditions, as shown by Theorem 24.1 introduced below, the use of Bayesian measure leads to a special form that is very simple to apply compared with the usual procedure.

THEOREM 24.1 SPECIAL FORM OF THE BAYESIAN DECISION CRITERION FOR EQUIVALENT-ACTION PROBLEMS INVOLVING PIECEWISE-LINEAR LOSS FUNCTIONS *In any decision situation where there is a different "best" action for each state value and where the loss function is piecewise-linear, with b_u as the cost per unit of underestimating and b_0 as the cost per unit of overestimating the state*

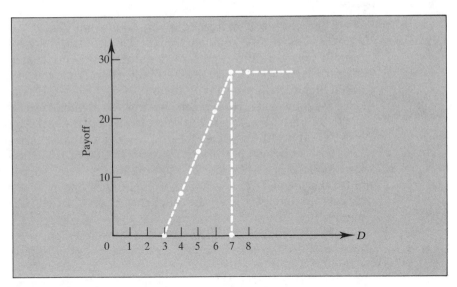

FIGURE 24.1 Payoff function for $a_5 = 7$ for the French cake problem. (*Source:* Table 24.8.)

random variable, $\tilde{\theta}$, as defined by

$$L(a, \tilde{\theta}) = \begin{cases} b_u(\theta - a), & if\ a < \theta, \\ 0, & if\ a = \theta, \\ b_0(a - \theta), & if\ a > \theta; \end{cases} \tag{24.13}$$

then the use of the Bayesian measure leads to a special form which directs the decision maker to select

$$P(\tilde{\theta} \le a) = F_\theta(a_i^*) = \frac{b_u}{b_u + b_0} \tag{24.14}$$

as the optimal estimate (act) for $\tilde{\theta}$.

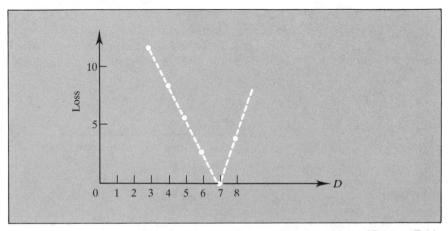

FIGURE 24.2 Loss function for $a_5 = 7$ for the inventory problem. (*Source:* Table 24.9.)

Theorem 24.1 states that in equivalent-action problems with piecewise-linear loss functions, the probability law for the state random variable whose values represent the state values can be replaced by the ratio $b_u/(b_u + b_0)$. This ratio is simply the $b_u/(b_u + b_0)$ fractile of the probability distribution for $\tilde{\theta}$, denoted as f^*. It can be used instead of the Bayesian measure to select among the available actions. Furthermore, (24.14) can be applied to discrete as well as continuous probability laws. To apply this special form, one only needs to form the CMF or CDF for $\tilde{\theta}$, prior or posterior. The application of this special form to a continuous probability law of the states of nature, as we shall see, is quite simple and always leads to a unique optimal estimate. For a discrete probability law, the application of (24.14) is slightly more involved.

For illustration, consider the French cake example once more. For this example, the loss function, as has been stated, is piecewise linear with $b_u = 4$ and $b_0 = 3$. Thus,

$$f^* = \frac{4}{4 + 3} \doteq 0.57.$$

From Table 24.12, we see that this result leads to the selection of a_4 as the optimal prior as well as the optimal posterior estimate as before, since $F_0(\theta_4) = 0.85 > 0.57$ and $F_1(\theta_4) = 0.773 > 0.57$. In this case, we have a unique optimal estimate in the prior as well as posterior analyses because, as shown by Figure 24.3, f^* (=0.57) hits the *riser* for $\theta_4 = 6$. However, if f^* is equal to, say, 0.45, it would then hit the graph for $F_0(\theta_j)$ at a *step*, corresponding to $F_0(\theta_3) = 5$. In this case, every θ such that $5 \leq \theta < 6$ is a 0.45 fractile of $F_0(\theta_j)$. This means that any θ such that $5 \leq \theta < 6$ is an optimal estimate (act). Generally, when f^* hits a step, every θ below the step is an optimal act. Care must be taken to ensure that when an endpoint of a step is excluded, the value of θ is excluded from the set of optimal estimates. (See Figure 24.3).

In the continuous case, the optimal estimate of $\tilde{\theta}$ always assumes a unique solution once the CDF is given. This is shown by Figure 24.4. In this figure, a^* stands for the optimal value of a and f^* stands for the desired fractile of the distribution for $\tilde{\theta}$.

Now, it is interesting to note that for problems involving piecewise-linear loss functions and a different "best" action for each state with a

TABLE 24.12 CDFs for the French Cake Example

a_i	θ_j	$F_0(\theta_j)$	$F_1(\theta_j)$
a_1	$\theta_1 = 3$	0.05	0.001
a_2	$\theta_2 = 4$	0.15	0.028
a_3	$\theta_3 = 5$	0.45	0.242
a_4	$\theta_4 = 6$	0.85	0.773
a_5	$\theta_5 = 7$	0.95	0.932
a_6	$\theta_6 = 8$	1.00	1.000

Source: Table 24.11.

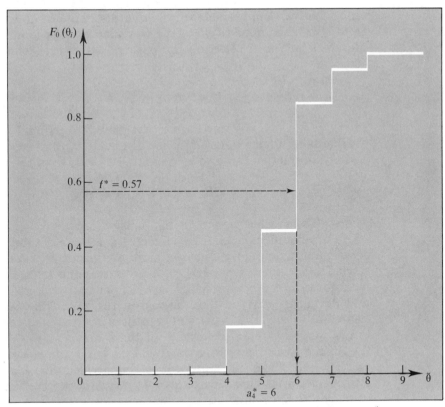

FIGURE 24.3 Graphic solution for locating the optimal act for the French cake problem. (*Source:* Table 24.12.)

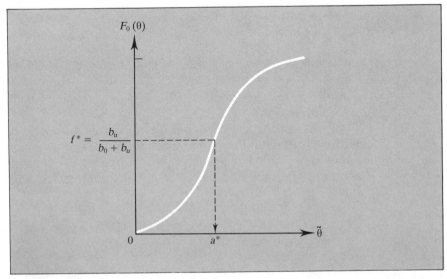

FIGURE 24.4 Locating the optimal act a^* from a continuous CDF of the state random variable.

continuous random variable whose prior distribution can be assumed to be $n(\tilde{\mu}_0, \tilde{\sigma}_0)$, the application of the Bayesian decision criterion leads to the special form of selecting the optimal act by the following simple equation:

$$a^* = \tilde{\mu}_0 + z_{f^*}(\tilde{\sigma}_0), \qquad (24.15)$$

where z_{f^*} is the f^* fractile for the standard normal distribution. Furthermore, under a normal prior distribution, the expected value of perfect information can also be computed directly from the formula

$$EVPI_0 = (b_u + b_0)[n(z_{f^*})](\tilde{\sigma}_0), \qquad (24.16)$$

where $n(z_{f^*})$ denotes the probability density for z_{f^*}.

Consider an example. The manager of a men's clothing store has to determine the optimal number of suits of a particular size and type to stock for the coming season. Suppose such suits made by a certain manufacturer can be purchased at $110 per unit and sold at $165 per unit during the season. Suits unsold at the end of the season can be cleared at a price of $75 per suit. Furthermore, the manager, according to his past experience, believes that the demand for such clothing for the coming season is approximately normally distributed with $\mu_0 = 250$ and $\sigma_0 = 45$. From the statement of this problem, his loss function is clearly piecewise-linear with $b_u = \$55$ and $b_0 = \$35$. Thus, for this example, we have, first,

$$f^* = \frac{55}{55 + 35} \doteq 0.6111.$$

Next, from the table of values for $N(0, 1)$, we find that $z_{0.6111} \doteq 0.28$. This means that the 0.6111 fractile of $n(250,45)$ is 0.28 standard deviations to the right of the mean. Namely, $\mu_0 + 0.28(\sigma_0)$. Hence, by (24.15), we have

$$a^* = 250 + 0.28(45) \doteq 263.$$

To minimize his expected loss, the manager should order 263 suits for the coming season.

If the manager would like to make his terminal decision with additional sample information, what is the maximum amount of money he should be willing to spend for this purpose? The answer is given by computing the expected value of perfect information with (24.16) as follows:

$$EVPI_0 = (55 + 35)[n(+0.28)](45)$$

$$= 90(0.3836)(45) = \$1,553.58.$$

The value $n(z_{f^*}) = (z_{0.28}) = 0.3836$ is obtained from the table for $n(0, 1)$ the density function for the standard normal variable, Table V.

It should be noted that with piecewise-linear loss functions and normal prior distribution, $a*$ is the optimal action given by (24.15) which is nothing but an alternative expression of (24.14). Here, $z = (a* - \tilde{\mu}_0)/\tilde{\sigma}_0$ is the corresponding standardized state random variable. It is important to observe, though, that $a*$ depends merely on the relative magnitudes of b_u and b_0 via the ratio as defined by (24.14), the *EVPI* depends on the absolute magnitudes via the sum of b_u and b_0 as revealed by (24.16).

Finally, the piecewise-linear loss function is quite realistic and, therefore, Theorem 24.1 has wide applicability, especially in those problems involving inventories. Although Theorem 24.1 has been given without proof, it is intuitively meaningful and reasonable. For instance, if $b_u = b_0$, $a*$ corresponds to the 0.50 fractile, or the median, of the decision maker's probability law. One may ask here: When the costs of overestimation and underestimation are equal, why does the Bayesian special form of decision criterion leads to the selection of the median instead of the mean as the optimal act? The answer is that if the median is chosen, the probability of overestimation is equal to that of underestimation. In the same train of thought, if $b_u > b_0$, then $f* > 0.50$ and the cost of underestimation is greater than the cost of overestimation, the optimal act should be higher than the median; that is, the decision maker should "hedge" his estimate upward to avoid the greater cost of underestimation. In the extreme, when b_0 becomes very small relative to b_u, the optimal estimate moves further and further to the right of the decision maker's probability distribution in order to avoid high cost of underestimation. From the same kind of reasoning, when $b_u < b_0$, just the opposite is true. Namely, the optimal estimate is on the left of the median. In general, the greater the relative difference between b_u and b_0, the further from the median the optimal estimate will be.

24.10 QUADRATIC LOSS FUNCTIONS

While the piecewise-linear loss function is often quite realistic and has wide applicability, there may be situations in which it cannot be applied. For example, we may often find decision problems for which the costs of overestimation and underestimation are equal, $b_0 = b_u = b$, but for which an error in estimation of two units is much greater than twice as costly as an error of just one unit. In general, we may find that the loss associated with an error in estimation is proportional to the *square* of the error. The loss function for such a situation is called a *quadratic loss function* or a *squared-error loss function*. Fortunately, when this kind of loss function is encountered, the application of the Bayesian decision criterion also leads to a very simple special form, as Theorem 24.2 indicates.

THEOREM 24.2 SPECIAL FORM OF THE BAYESIAN DECISION CRITERION FOR EQUIVALENT STATE–ACTION PROBLEMS WITH QUADRATIC LOSS FUNCTIONS *When the loss function for any act a_i is quadratic in an equivalent state-action* *problem as defined by*

$$L(a, \tilde{\theta}) = b(a - \theta)^2, \tag{24.17}$$

where b is a nonnegative constant not necessarily equal to unity, the optimal estimate (act) is the expected value of the state random variable; that is,

$$a^* = E(\tilde{\theta}). \tag{24.18}$$

Furthermore, the expected value of perfect information is given by the expectation of the loss function defined by (24.17). Namely,

$$EVPI = E[b(a - \theta)^2]$$
$$= bV(\tilde{\theta}). \tag{24.19}$$

There are a number of additional comments and explanations that must be made about the foregoing theorem. First of all, in the three equations given in the theorem, the subscripts for "prior" and "posterior" quantities are not given, because Theorem 24.2, as Theorem 24.1, can be applied to both prior and posterior analyses. Second, the constant b attached to the loss function can be determined from the problem or indirectly. Indirectly, the value of b can be determined if the decision maker can specify the amount he would be willing to pay for perfect information on the state, if he knew for sure that the true state of nature differs by only one unit from a given value of the state random variable. For example, the decision maker may be asked what is amount he is willing to pay for perfect information on the state, given that it is either only 99 or only 101 (thus one unit away from a state value of $\tilde{\theta} = 100$.) If he states that this information is worth \$50, then b is \$50. It must be observed that b is assumed to be independent of $\tilde{\theta}$. Finally, the application of (24.19) is quite general and depends upon the prior probability law. For example, if the prior density of $\tilde{\theta}$ is assumed to be a beta distribution, then we have $EVPI_0 = bV_0(\tilde{\pi}) = b[\tilde{r}_0(\tilde{n}_0 - \tilde{r}_0)]/\tilde{n}_0^2(\tilde{n}_0 + 1)$. Likewise, if the prior density for $\tilde{\theta}$ is $n(\tilde{\mu}_0, \tilde{\sigma}_0)$, then (24.19) is written as $EVPI_0 = b\tilde{\sigma}_0^2$.

The special form of the Bayesian decision criterion given by (24.18) is a consequence of the fact that the expected squared deviation, or the mean-square error, is a minimum if it is calculated from the mean of the state random variable. Thus, it is only necessary to know $E_0(\tilde{\theta})$ in order to determine a^*. Here, the decision maker behaves as if the mean of the state were the true value of the state variable. He knows from (24.18) that he does not have to go through a long, complicated analysis using the complete loss table and the full distribution of the state variable in order to choose his optimum act. The summary measure of the distribution of the state variable given in (24.18), the expectation, leads him to exactly the same act as the full analysis would have. The expectation in (24.18) is called a *certainty equivalent*. In general, a summary measure of a distribution of a state variable is a certainty equivalent when it is treated as if it were the true value of the state

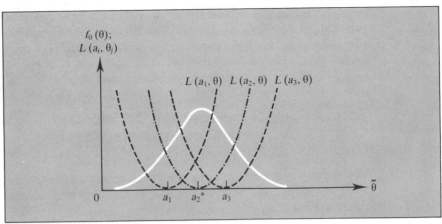

FIGURE 24.5 Graphic illustration of $a^* = E_0(\tilde{\theta})$ with quadratic loss functions.

variable and leads to the same optimum act as the one resulting from an analysis using the full distribution of the state variable. When a piecewise-linear loss function is employed, the f^* fractile of the distribution of the state is also a certainty equivalent. Indeed, the sample mean is considered as a good estimator by classicists because it minimizes the mean-square error. Also note that estimation with a quadratic loss function is a rough Bayesian counterpart of the classical notion of efficient estimators.

Figure 24.5 is designed to give an intuitive understanding of the desirable features of selecting $E_0(\tilde{\theta})$ as the optimal act with a quadratic loss function. In this figure, loss functions for three acts are given along with the prior density curve for the state. Note that when the expected loss of an act is computed, the loss function is weighted by the density function. From the graph we see that a_2, which is numerically equal to $E_0(\tilde{\theta})$, is optimal, since its loss function is low when the density is high, and vice versa. However, for a_1 and a_3, the loss functions are quite high when the density is high and, therefore, the expected loss for either act would be higher than that for a_2.

24.11 TWO-ACTION PROBLEMS WITH LINEAR PAYOFF OR LOSS FUNCTIONS

The special forms of Bayesian decision criteria covered by Theorems 24.1 and 24.2 are concerned with problems in which there is a one-to-one correspondence between the number of acts and the number of state values. In such cases, the act a can take on any real value and thus these are often called *infinite-action problems*. In many decision problems, the actions may be optimal over more than one state. With problems of this kind, typically, the number of states exceeds the number of available actions. As a result, Theorems 24.1 and 24.2 are not appropriate. In general, with *nonequivalent state-action problems* of this kind, the procedure is to evaluate the expected losses for the various possible actions. Fortunately again, if the payoff functions are linear over the state random variable, the Bayesian decision criterion can be simplified into special forms as before. The relatively simple but quite useful case involves only two actions and a continuous state random variable. This is the only case we shall introduce in this section.

Special Form of the Bayesian Decision Criterion for Two-Action Problems with Linear Payoffs

When the payoffs for the outcomes for a given action can be represented by linear functions over the states in two-action problems, the payoff functions can be written as follows:

$$M(a_1, \tilde{\theta}) = c_1 + b_1\theta;$$
$$M(a_2, \tilde{\theta}) = c_2 + b_2\theta.$$

It is assumed here that for the constants in these functions, we have $c_1 < c_2$ and $b_1 > b_2$, as illustrated by Figure 24.6. These inequalities ensure that the two payoff functions intersect for some $\theta > 0$. For these functions, the expected payoffs for a_1 and a_2 are simply

$$E_0[M(a_1, \tilde{\theta})] = EP_0(a_1) = c_1 + b_1E_0(\tilde{\theta}),$$

and

$$E_0[M(a_2, \tilde{\theta})] = EP_0(a_2) = c_2 + b_2E_0(\tilde{\theta}).$$

Clearly, if $EP_0(a_1) > EP_0(a_2)$, a_1 is a better act than a_2 and vice versa. To simplify the decision still further, we may introduce the concept of

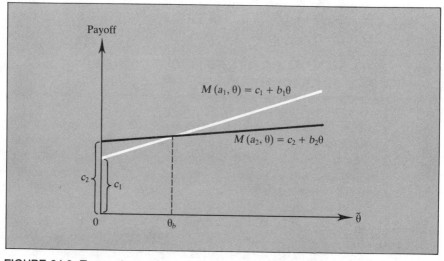

FIGURE 24.6 Two-action problem with linear payoff functions.

"break-even value" of the state variable, denoted as θ_b, which is the value of $\tilde{\theta}$ at which the decision maker would be indifferent between the two acts, and which is obtained by equating the two payoff functions defined previously:

$$c_1 + b_1\theta_b = c_2 + b_2\theta_b.$$

Solving for θ_b yields

$$\theta_b = \frac{c_2 - c_1}{b_1 - b_2}. \qquad (24.20)$$

With θ_b determined, we see that as long as the expected value of the state is greater than θ_b, $EP_0(a_1) > EP_0(a_2)$. This is quite easy to verify. Given

$$E_0(\tilde{\theta}) > \frac{c_2 - c_1}{b_1 - b_2},$$

we must have

$$E_0(\tilde{\theta})(b_1 - b_2) > (c_2 - c_1),$$

since $(b_1 - b_2) > 0$. This result can be rearranged to obtain

$$c_1 + b_1 E_0(\tilde{\theta}) > c_2 + b_2 E_0(\tilde{\theta})$$

which is the same as to say that

$$EP_0(a_1) > EP_0(a_2).$$

Using an analogous procedure, we would conclude that when $E_0(\tilde{\theta}) < \theta_b$, $EP_0(a_1) < EP_0(a_2)$, and a_2 would be the optimal act over a_1.

Previous discussion leads to the obvious conclusion: If $E_0(\tilde{\theta}) > \theta_b$, select a_1; otherwise, select a_2. This special form of the Bayesian criterion can also be expressed in terms of loss functions. If the payoff functions are linear, the corresponding loss functions must also be linear. Since the opportunity loss for each combination of act and state value is the difference between the payoff for that act and the payoff obtainable for the optimal act, the loss functions corresponding to the payoff functions stated before would be

$$L(a_1, \tilde{\theta}) = \begin{cases} (b_1 - b_2)(\theta_b - \theta), & \text{if } \theta \leq \theta_b, \\ 0, & \text{if } \theta \geq \theta_b; \end{cases}$$

$$L(a_2, \tilde{\theta}) = \begin{cases} 0, & \text{if } \theta \leq \theta_b, \\ (b_1 - b_2)(\theta - \theta_b), & \text{if } \theta \geq \theta_b. \end{cases}$$

The optimal act is then chosen by substituting $E_0(\tilde{\theta})$ for θ and choosing the act for which $L[a_i, E_0(\tilde{\theta})]$ is the lesser. More precisely, we state: The

Bayesian decision criterion for nonequivalent state-action problems with two actions and linear payoffs directs the decision maker to select the action for which the loss is a minimum for the expected value of the state random variable; that is, $\min_{a} [L(a, E(\tilde{\theta}))]$.

It is important to note that the special form of the Bayesian decision criterion just established is independent of the pattern of the prior density function; the decision depends upon the comparison between $E_0(\tilde{\theta})$ and θ_b. However, if the prior density for the state is assumed to follow some special probability distribution, such as the beta or normal probability law, then the expected value of perfect information can be determined directly from established formulas.

Linear Payoff Functions and the Normal Probability Law

We now consider the case of problems with two-action and normal states. In general, when the loss functions are linear, as stated at the end of the previous subsection, the expected losses for a_1 and a_2 can be evaluated by

$$EL(a_1) = (b_1 - b_2) \int_{\theta_b}^{\infty} (\theta - \theta_b) f(\theta) \, d\theta$$

and

$$EL(a_2) = (b_1 - b_2) \int_{-\infty}^{\theta_b} (\theta_b - \theta) f(\theta) \, d\theta.$$

Under the assumption that $f(\theta)$ obeys the normal probability law, we can obtain the previous two values from the table for the "unit normal linear loss integral," which is defined as

$$L_N(D) = \int_{D}^{\infty} (\theta - D) n(\theta) \, d\theta,$$

where $n(\theta)$ stands for the standard normal density function. The table for $L_N(D)$ is presented in Table XII in Appendix C of this text. This table facilitates the computation of the expected value of perfect information, when the loss functions are linear and when the prior distribution is assumed to be normal with μ_0 and σ_0, as defined below:

$$EVPI_0 = |b_1 - b_2|(\tilde{\sigma}_0)[L_N(D_0)], \tag{24.21}$$

where

$$D_0 = \left| \frac{\mu_b - \tilde{\mu}_0}{\tilde{\sigma}_0} \right|. \tag{24.22}$$

In (24.22), μ_b clearly stands for the breakeven value of the state random variable $\tilde{\mu}$.

Let us consider an example. A manufacturer has to decide whether to introduce, a_1, or not to introduce, a_2, a new product. The total fixed costs of introducing the product are estimated to be \$8.1 million. The *variable profit contribution rate*—that is, the selling price minus the unit variable costs—is calculated to be \$3 per unit of sales. According to past sales records the manufacturing firm has 50,000 potential customers for the new product. Of interest in this decision situation are the manufacturer's distribution of the mean number of sales per customer $\tilde{\mu}$ and the payoff functions of the two acts. In terms of information available the payoff functions are as follows:

$$M(a_1, \tilde{\mu}) = -\$8,100,000 + \$3(50,000)\mu$$
$$= -\$8,100,000 + \$150,000\mu;$$

$$M(a_2, \tilde{\mu}) = 0.$$

With these payoff functions, we have the breakeven mean number of sales as

$$\mu_b = \frac{0 - (-8,100,000)}{150,000 - 0} = 54.$$

Thus, if the expected value for the decision maker's prior distribution of $\tilde{\mu}$ is greater than 54, then act a_1, introduce the new product, would be optimal.

In this case the loss functions are

$$L(a_1, \tilde{\mu}) = \begin{cases} \$150,000(54 - \mu), & \text{if } \mu \leqslant 54, \\ 0, & \text{if } \mu \geqslant 54; \end{cases}$$

$$L(a_2, \tilde{\mu}) = \begin{cases} \$150,000(\mu - 54), & \text{if } \mu \geqslant 54, \\ 0, & \text{if } \mu \leqslant 54. \end{cases}$$

Graphs for the payoff and loss functions for this new-product problem are given in Figure 24.7 and Figure 24.8, respectively. From these

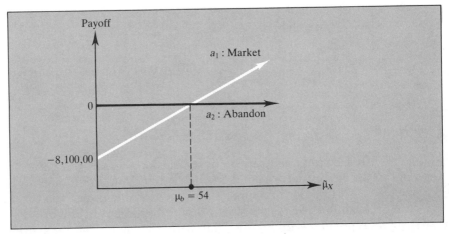

FIGURE 24.7 Payoff functions: New-product example.

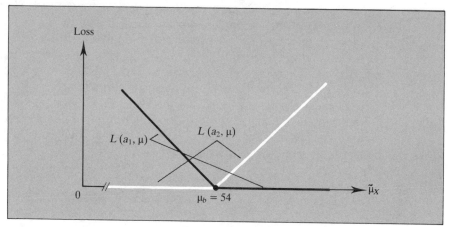

FIGURE 24.8 Loss functions: New-product example.

figures we see that if a_1 is selected, a loss occurs only when the mean demand turns out to be less than 54 units per customer. If a_2 is selected and the actual mean demand exceeds 54 units, then an opportunity loss will result and the more the demand exceeds 54, the greater the loss becomes. Also notice that the nonzero portion of the loss function here is symmetric about μ_b, implying that equal differences between μ and μ_b, regardless of sign, will produce equal opportunity losses—assuming a nonoptimal act is already chosen.

Now suppose the manufacturer is able to establish a normal prior density function for the mean number of sales with $\mu_0 = 60$ and $\sigma_0 = 4$; then clearly a_1 is the optimal act and, for this act, we have

$$EP_0(a_1^*) = -8{,}100{,}000 + 150{,}000(60)$$
$$= \$900{,}000.$$

To determine the expected value of perfect information for a_1^*, we first note that

$$|b_1 - b_2| = \$150{,}000;$$

$$\sigma_0 = 4;$$

$$D_0 = \left| \frac{\mu_b - \mu_0}{\sigma_0} \right| = \left| \frac{54 - 60}{4} \right| = 1.50;$$

$$L_N(D_0) = L_N(1.50) = 0.02931, \qquad \text{from Table XII.}$$

Thus,

$$EVPI = |b_1 - b_2|\sigma_0[L_N(D_0)]$$
$$= 150{,}000(4)(0.02931) = \$17{,}586.$$

If the manufacturer can delay his decision and if a perfect predictor can be obtained, he should be willing to pay up to $17,586 for it.

In order to appreciate the reasonableness of the conclusion for the manufacturer's problem, the information in Figure 24.8 has been reproduced in Figure 24.9 with the manufacturer's prior probability density superimposed over the state. From this diagram it can be seen

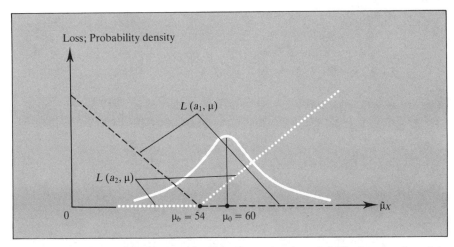

FIGURE 24.9 Loss functions and subjective normal probability law for the state variable $\tilde{\mu}_x$.

that the expected loss for a_1 is $L(a_1, \tilde{\mu})$ weighted by the density for the state. However, when $L(a_1, \tilde{\mu})$ is positive and high for the state value below μ_b, the density is very low; and when the density is high for the state above $\tilde{\mu}_b$, $L(a_1, \tilde{\mu})$ is zero. On the other hand, when $L(a_2, \tilde{\mu})$ is zero, the density is low for the state value less than μ_b, and the density is high for the state value in excess of μ_b when $L(a_2, \tilde{\mu})$ is positive and increasing. As a result, when $\mu_0 > \mu_b$, $EL_0(a_1) < EL_0(a_2)$; when $\mu_0 < \mu_b$, $EL_0(a_1) > EL_0(a_2)$.

Now, returning to the example on hand, we note that the expected value of perfect information in the prior analysis is rather large and the terminal decision can obviously be delayed for a while for problems of this kind. That is, the manufacturer should conduct a posterior analysis with additional information. Suppose, in doing this, the manufacturer has made and sent some sample units of the new product to 80 of his 50,000 potential customers at random, resulting a sample mean of $\bar{x} = 57$ units. Furthermore, assume the manufacturer, because of his past experience and observations of similar products sold by his competitors, is certain that the variance of the distribution of the state random variable $\tilde{\mu}$ is $\sigma^2 = 320$, then we would have $\sigma_{\bar{X}}^2 = 320/80 = 4$. With these information, the parameters of the posterior distribution of $\tilde{\mu}$ become

$$\mu_1 = \frac{\mu_0 \sigma_{\bar{X}}^2 + \bar{x}\sigma_0^2}{\sigma_0^2 + \sigma_{\bar{X}}^2}$$

$$= \frac{(60)(4) + (57)(16)}{16 + 4} = 57.6;$$

$$\sigma_1^2 = \frac{(\sigma_0^2)(\sigma_{\bar{X}}^2)}{\sigma_0^2 + \sigma_{\bar{X}}^2}$$

$$= \frac{(16)(4)}{16 + 4} = 3.2;$$

$$\sigma_1 = \sqrt{3.2} \doteq 1.7889.$$

Since $\mu_1 = 57.6 > \mu_b = 54$, the posterior optimal act is still a_1. The expected payoff for the optimal act and the expected value of perfect information in the posterior analysis are computed in the same way as in the prior analysis. They are, respectively,

$$EP_1(a_1^{**}) = -8{,}100{,}000 + 150{,}000(57.6)$$

$$= \$540{,}000;$$

$$EVPI_1 = |b_1 - b_2|\sigma_1[L_N(D_1)] \qquad (24.23)$$

$$= 150{,}000(1.7889)(0.008266)$$

$$\doteq \$2218.$$

Note the similarity between the formulas for $EVPI_0$ and $EVPI_1$. Also note that in (24.23), the value of D_1 in the loss integral L_N is defined as

$$D_1 = \left| \frac{\mu_b - \tilde{\mu}_1}{\tilde{\sigma}_1} \right| \qquad (24.24)$$

for our example,

$$= \left| \frac{54 - 57.6}{1.7889} \right|$$

$$\doteq 2.01$$

and

$$L_N(D_1) = L_N(2.01) = 0.008266,$$

which is obtained from the same "unit normal linear loss integral" table, (Table XII) mentioned before.

It is interesting to note that both the posterior expected payoff for the optimal act and the expected value of perfect information for our example are smaller than those obtained in the prior analysis. The reduction in EP_1 from EP_0 clearly reflects the fact that, owing to the sample result, the posterior mean μ_1 is smaller than the prior mean μ_0. In general, for most sample results, the expected loss after sampling should be smaller because of the additional information, which tends to produce a smaller posterior variance and thus reduces uncertainty. Our example agrees with this generalization. an exception to this rule is when μ_1 is much closer to μ_b than μ_0, hence making D_1 smaller than D_0 and producing a larger $L_N(D_1)$ relative to $L_N(D_0)$.

Linear Payoffs and the Beta Probability Law

In a two-action problem with linear payoffs, if the state random variable is $\tilde{\pi}$, the Bernoulli parameter, the payoff functions can be written as

$$M(a_1, \tilde{\pi}) = c_1 + b_1\pi;$$

$$M(a_2, \tilde{\pi}) = b_1 + b_2\pi.$$

As before, it is assumed here that $c_1 < c_2$ and that $b_1 > b_2$. With these payoff functions, the breakeven value of $\tilde{\pi}$ is

$$\pi_b = \frac{c_2 - c_1}{b_1 - b_2}. \tag{24.25}$$

If the decision maker wishes to make the terminal decision with prior information only, then a_1 is the optimal estimate for $\tilde{\pi}$ when $E_0(\tilde{\pi}) > \pi_b$ and a_2 is the optimal estimate of $\tilde{\pi}$ if $E_0(\tilde{\pi}) < \pi_b$. Furthermore, if the prior density function of the state random variable $\tilde{\pi}$ is assumed to obey the beta probability law with parameters $\tilde{r}_0$ and $\tilde{n}_0$, then, as can be verified, the expected value of perfect information can be computed by the following formulas:

$$EVPI_0 = |b_1 - b_2|[E_0(\tilde{\pi})P_\beta(\tilde{\pi} > \pi_b \mid \tilde{r}_0 + 1, \tilde{n}_0 + 1)$$
$$- \pi_b P_\beta(\tilde{\pi} > \pi_b \mid \tilde{r}_0, \tilde{n}_0)], \qquad \text{if } E_0(\tilde{\pi}) \leq \pi_b; \tag{24.6a}$$

$$EVPI_0 = |b_1 - b_2|[\pi_b P_\beta(\tilde{\pi} < \pi_b) \mid \tilde{r}_0, \tilde{n}_0)$$
$$- E_0(\tilde{\pi})P_\beta(\tilde{\pi} < \pi_b \mid \tilde{r}_0 + 1, \tilde{n}_0 + 1)], \qquad \text{if } E_0(\tilde{\pi}) > \pi_b. \tag{24.26b}$$

Consider this example. A small manufacturing firm produces 1,000 units of a certain product each day. The total net profit for selling each day's product is $1,000. Each defective unit produced and sold will cost the firm $3 for reworking and handling. Before each day's production run, the process can be adjusted and the fraction defective can be reduced by 50%. The adjustment cost is $300. Under these conditions the total expected cost with adjustment, for action a_1, is

$$\$3(1000)(0.5\pi) + \$300 = \$1500\pi + \$300,$$

and the total expected cost without adjustment, for action a_2, is

$$\$3(1000\pi) = \$3000\pi.$$

Thus, we have for this decision problem the payoff functions as given below:

$$M(a_1, \tilde{\pi}) = \$100 - \$300 - \$1500\pi$$
$$= \$700 - \$1500\pi;$$
$$M(a_2, \tilde{\pi}) = \$1000 - \$3000\pi.$$

These functions yield a breakeven value of

$$\pi_b = \frac{1000 - 700}{-1500 - (-3000)} = 0.20.$$

Now, suppose the production manager, in terms of his knowledge of the past performance of the production process, believes that the prior density for $\tilde{\pi}$ is beta with $r_0 = 1$ and $n_0 = 8$; then we have

$E_0(\tilde{\pi}) = 1/8 = 0.125$, which is less than $\pi_b = 0.20$. Hence, the optimal act on the basis of prior information alone is a_2^*—no adjustment before the production run.

Also, for the prior optimal act here, by (24.26a), we have

$$EVPI_0 = [-1500 - (-3000)][0.125P_\beta(\tilde{\pi} > 0.2 \mid 2, 9)$$
$$- 0.20P_\beta(\tilde{\pi} > 0.20 \mid 1, 8)].$$

As you may recall that the beta probabilities can be evaluated by binomial probabilities. For our problem, we see that

$$P_\beta(\tilde{\pi} > 0.20 \mid 2, 9) = 1 - P_\beta(\tilde{\pi} < 0.20 \mid 2, 9)$$
$$= 1 - P_B(r \geq 2 \mid 8, 0.20)$$
$$= 1 - 0.4967$$
$$= 0.5033;$$
$$P_\beta(\tilde{\pi} > 0.20 \mid 1, 8) = 1 - P_\beta(\tilde{\pi} < 0.20 \mid 1, 8)$$
$$= 1 - P_B(r \geq 1 \mid 7, 0.20)$$
$$= 1 - 0.7903$$
$$= 0.2097.$$

With these results,

$$EVPI_0 = \$1500[(0.125)(0.5033) - 0.20(0.2097)]$$
$$\doteq 31.46.$$

Thus, the production manager should be willing to pay up to \$31.46 to know $\tilde{\pi}$ for certain. Now, suppose he is somewhat doubtful one day that the process is in control. He decides to produce only 50 units first and a random sample of 5 units is selected from units produced for inspection. Suppose two defective units are found; what is his decision now in view of this additional information?

Now, with the sample information, we have

$$E_1(\tilde{\pi}) = \frac{1 + 2}{8 + 5} = 0.25,$$

which is greater than $\pi_b = 0.20$. Consequently, the posterior optimal act is a_1^{**}—make adjustment before additional units are produced. You may be advised at this point that the posterior expected value of perfect information can also be computed by equations (24.26). All you have to do is replace $E_0(\tilde{\pi})$, $\tilde{r}_0$, and $\tilde{n}_0$ by $E_1(\tilde{\pi})$, $\tilde{r}_1$ and $\tilde{n}_1$ in the appropriate expression. This is left to you as an exercise.

GLOSSARY OF FORMULAS

(24.1) $L(a_i, \theta_j) = M(a_+, \theta_j) - M(a_i, \theta_j)$;

(24.2) $l_{ij} = m_{+j} - m_{ij}$.

We use either one of these two equations to obtain (opportunity) losses from monetary payoffs. In these expressions $M(a_+, \theta_j) = m_{+j}$, the highest payoff for the state θ_j.

(24.3) $EP_0(a_i) = \sum_j m_{ij} f_0(\theta_j)$;

(24.4) $EL_0(a_i) = \sum_j l_{ij}(f_0(\theta_j)$.

The Bayesian decision criterion is called the Bayesian measure. It may be defined either as the expected payoffs (24.3) or as expected losses (24.4). Of course, both measures would lead to the same optimal act in a given decision situation. Here, the subscript 0, as in other instances, denotes prior quantities (in prior analysis).

(24.5) $EPPI_0 = \sum_j m_{+j} f_0(\theta_j)$.

The expected payoff with perfect information, *EPPI*, defined here, means that if the decision maker has a perfect predictor, informing him in advance which state of nature is going to prevail, he will always select the act with highest payoff for that state, m_{+j}. The expected loss would always be zero with such a perfect predictor, because the best act would always be chosen.

(24.6) $EVPI_0 = EPPI_0 - EP_0(a_i^*)$;

(24.7) $EVPI_0 = EL_0(a_i^*)$.

The expected value of perfect information is the maximum amount of money a decision maker is willing to spend in obtaining additional information for a terminal decision. It is defined either as the difference between expected payoff with perfect information, *EPPI*, and the expected payoff for the optimal act as defined by (24.6), or as the expected loss of the optimal act. Note that $EL_0(a_i^*)$ is the cost of uncertainty to the decision maker. When he has perfect information $EL_0(a_i^*)$ is zero, implying $EL_0(a_i^*)$ or $EVPI_0$ is the highest price that he should ever consider paying for additional information after completing a prior analysis.

(24.8) $EP_1(a_i) = \sum_j m_{ij} f_1(\theta_j)$;

(24.9) $EL_1(a_i) = \sum_j l_{ij} f_1(\theta_j)$.

The computation of posterior expected payoffs and posterior expected losses are made by these two equations, respectively. The subscript 1 here, as in other places, indicates posterior quantities.

(24.10) $EPPI_1 = \sum_j m_{+j} f_1(\theta_j)$;

(24.11) $EVPI_1 = EP_1(a_i^{**})$;

(24.12) $EVPI_1 = EL_1(a_i^{**})$.

These posterior measures correspond to the respective prior measures as given by (24.5), (24.6), and (24.7). These two sets of equations are identical in interpretation and logic.

(24.13) $L(a, \tilde{\theta}) = \begin{cases} b_u(\theta - a), & \text{if } a < \theta; \\ 0, & \text{if } a = \theta; \\ b_0(a - \theta), & \text{if } a > \theta; \end{cases}$

(24.14) $P(\tilde{\theta} \leq a) = F_\theta(a_i^*) = \dfrac{b_u}{b_u + b_0}$.

Equation (24.13) is the general expression for a piecewise-linear loss function. In this expression as well as in (24.14), b_u = cost per unit for underestimating $\tilde{\theta}$ and b_0 = cost per unit of overestimating $\tilde{\theta}$. For equivalent-action problems involving piecewise-linear loss functions, the application of the Bayesian decision criterion leads to the special form as defined by (24.14), which turns out to be the $b_u/(b_u + b_0)$ fractile of the decision maker's probability law for the state variable. This fractile is denoted as f^* in general.

(24.15) $a^* = \tilde{\mu}_0 + z_{f^*}(\tilde{\sigma}_0)$;

(24.16) $EVPI_0 = (b_u + b_0)[(n(z_{f^*})](\tilde{\sigma}_0)$.

The first equation here states that the optimal act is so determined for problems involving piecewise-linear loss functions, equivalent-action, and prior normal distribution for $\tilde{\theta}$. In this expression z_{f^*} is the f^* fractile for the standard normal distribution. Furthermore, under the three conditions specified, the prior expected value of perfect information is defined by (24.16), where $n(z_{f^*})$ denotes the probability density for z_{f^*}.

(24.17) $L(a, \tilde{\theta}) = b(a - \theta)^2$;

(24.18) $a^* = E(\tilde{\theta})$;

(24.19) $EVPI = bV(\tilde{\theta})$.

With equivalent-action problems involving quadratic loss functions as defined by (24.17), the application of the Bayesian decision criterion leads the decision maker to select as the optimal act (estimate) the expectation of the state random variable, as shown by (24.18). Furthermore, for this special form of the Bayesian measure, the expected value of perfect information is simply the product of b (the nonnegative constant in the loss function, and the variance of the state random variable. Equations (24.18) and (24.19) are applicable for both prior and posterior analyses.

(24.20) $\theta_b = \dfrac{c_2 - c_1}{b_1 - b_2}$.

In a two-action decision problem with linear payoffs, the payoff functions can be given as $M(a_1, \tilde{\theta}) = c_1 + b_1\theta$ and $M(a_2, \tilde{\theta}) = c_2 + b_2\theta$. Assuming $c_1 < c_2$ and $b_1 > b_2$, we have the breakeven value of the state for the two acts as defined by (24.20). The application of Bayesian measure in this case leads to the following special form: The optimal act is a_1 is $E(\tilde{\theta}) > \theta_b$; if $E(\tilde{\theta}) < \theta_b$, a_2 is the optimal act.

(24.21) $EVPI_0 = |b_1 - b_2|\tilde{\sigma}_0[L_N(D_0)]$;

(24.22) $D_0 = \left| \dfrac{\mu_b - \tilde{\mu}_0}{\tilde{\sigma}_0} \right|$.

In a two-action decision problem with linear payoff functions, the expected value of perfect information can computed by (20.21) if a normal prior function is assumed for the state random variable $\tilde{\mu}$. In this expression $L_N(D_0)$ stands for the prior "unit normal linear loss integral." The D_0 in $L_N(D_0)$ is defined by (20.22). The value of $L_N(D)$, irrespective of the subscript of D is given in Table XII for "unit normal linear loss integral" in Appendix C.

(24.23) $EVPI_1 = |b_1 - b_2|\tilde{\sigma}_1[L_N(D_1)]$

(24.24) $D_1 = \left| \dfrac{\mu_b - \tilde{\mu}_1}{\tilde{\sigma}_1} \right|$.

These two equations correspond to the previous two equations just summarized, except that the posterior quantities are used.

(24.25) $\pi_b = \dfrac{c_2 - c_1}{b_1 - b_2}$.

When the state random variable is $\tilde{\pi}$ in the two-action problems with linear payoffs, the payoff functions are given as $M(a_1, \tilde{\pi}) = c_1 + b_1\pi$ and $M(a_2, \tilde{\pi}) = b_1 + b_2\pi$. As explained in (24.20), a_1 is optimal if $E(\tilde{\pi}) > \pi_b$ and a_2 is optimal if $E(\tilde{\pi}) < \pi_b$.

(24.26a) $EVPI_0 = |b_1 - b_2| \, [E_0(\tilde{\pi})P_\beta(\tilde{\pi} > \pi_b \,|\, \tilde{r}_0 + 1, \tilde{n}_0 + 1)$
$\qquad\qquad -p_bP_\beta(\tilde{\pi} > \pi_b\tilde{r}_0, \tilde{n}_0)]$, $\qquad\qquad$ if $E_0(\tilde{\pi}) \leqslant \pi_b$;

(24.26b) $EVPI_0 = |b_1 - b_2| \, [\pi_bP_\beta(\tilde{\pi} < \pi_b \,|\, \tilde{r}_0, \tilde{n}_0)$
$\qquad\qquad - E_0(\tilde{\pi})P_\beta(\tilde{\pi} < \pi_b \,|\, \tilde{r}_0 + 1, \tilde{n}_0 + 1)$, $\qquad\qquad$ if $E_0(\tilde{\pi}) > \pi_b$.

These two equations define the prior expected value of perfect information in the two-action problems involving linear payoff functions where the state random variable is $\tilde{\pi}$, which has beta prior. Note that the beta probabilities can be obtained via the binomial probabilities and that these equations can also be used to compute $EVPI_1$, by replacing prior values by posterior values.

REVIEW QUESTIONS

24.1 Explain why both the classical and Bayesian theories of estimation and testing are informal in nature.

24.2 What are the four implications of decision making in general? List them and explain each in detail.

24.3 What is a payoff matrix? Why do we consider it as the "economics" of a decision problem?

24.4 How do we differentiate an admissible act from an inadmissible act with a payoff table?

24.5 What is an opportunity loss? How is a loss matrix derived from a payoff matrix?

24.6 What is the difference between an opportunity loss and an accounting loss? Give an example of your own.

24.7 What is the Bayesian decision rule called? How is it defined?

24.8 How is the "optimal act" defined within the Bayesian decision framework?

24.9 What does $EPPI_0$ stand for? What does it mean? How is it determined?

24.10 Explain why $EVPI_0$ is identical with $EL_0(a_i^*)$.

24.11 Explain why a decision maker would never spend more than $EVPI_0$ in a decision situation to obtain additional information?

24.12 Within the Bayesian decision framework, there is no room for any consideration other than the Bayesian measure for making the terminal decision. Is this statement true? Explain your answer.

24.13 Explain in your own words how the Bayesian measure can be considered as the "optimal act," as well as "the optimal estimate", of the state random variable.

24.14 What do we mean by equivalent-action problems?

24.15 How is the special form of Bayesian decision criterion stated with the equivalent-action problems involving piecewise-linear loss functions? Provide an intuitive explanation for the plausibility of this special form.

24.16 How is a quadratic loss function stated? What does it mean? How is the constant b in such a loss function detremined?

24.17 What is the special form of the Bayesian decision criterion for equivalent-action problems involving quadratic loss functions? Give an intuitive explanation for the reasonableness of this special form.

24.18 What do we mean by nonequivalent-action problems? Can you give a few examples of your own for such problems?

24.19 What is the special form of the Bayesian decision criterion for two-action problems with linear payoff functions? Do you think it is a reasonable decision rule? Why?

24.20 Under what conditions can the $EVPI_0$ and $EVPI_1$ be calculated directly by specially designed formulas when the Bayesian special forms are used to determine the optimal estimates (acts)? Can you explain why?

PROBLEMS

Instructions: Computations for the solutions of the problems in this chapter are quite simple except for the revision of prior probabilities in some instances. Such being the case, you should use computer programs. Also, to simplify the computations, posterior probabilities can be calculated by first converting the likelihoods into whole numbers by applying an appropriate multiple in order to avoid too many decimal points in the joint probabilities, as was illustrated in the French Cake example.

24.1 To explore the influence of different priors in the new-machine example, recalculate the optimal act and $EVPI_0$ in the prior analysis of Section 24.4, assuming that the respective prior probabilities for prosperity, stability, and recession are:
   a. 0.8, 0.1, 0.1;
   b. 0.5, 0.3, 0.2;
   c. 1/3, 1/3, 1/3;
   d. 2/7, 4/7, 1/7;
   e. 1/7, 2/7, 4/7.

24.2 To explore the influence of different priors in the Black Jade example, recalculate the optimal act and $EVPI_0$ in the prior analysis of Section 24.7, assuming that the respective prior probabilities for the three studies are:
   a. 0.80, 0.15, 0.05;
   b. 0.45, 0.45, 0.10;
   c. 1/3, 1/3, 1/3;
   d. 0.3, 0.6, 0.1;
   e. 0.1, 0.3, 0.6.

24.3 Continue Problem 24.1 by recalculating the optimal act and $EVPI_1$ in the posterior analysis of Section 24.6, for each of the priors in Problems 24.1(a) through 24.1(e).

24.4 Continue Problem 24.2 by recalculating the optimal act and $EVPI_1$ in both of the posterior analyses of Section 24.7, for each of the priors in Problems 24.2(a) through 24.2(e).

24.5 To explore the influence of different likelihoods in the new-machine example, recalculate the optimal act and $EVPI_1$ in the posterior analysis of Section 24.6, using the prior probabilities of Table 24.3 and assuming that the respective entries in the column for $f(x \mid \theta_j)$ in Table 24.3 are not 0.3, 0.7, 0.3 but
   a. 0.01, 0.99, 0.01;
   b. 0.1, 0.9, 0.1;
   c. 0.30, 0.35, 0.30;
   d. 0.7, 0.3, 0.3;
   e. 0.3, 0.3, 0.7.

We are assuming that Humble forecasts stability in parts (a), (b) and (c), prosperity in part (d), and recession in part (e).

24.6 To explore the influence of different likelihoods in the Black Jade example, recalculate the optimal act and $EVPI_1$ in both the posterior analyses of Section 24.7, using the prior probabilities of 0.6, 0.3, and 0.1, and assuming that the sample surveys came out as tabulated below.

	Survey F	Survey S
a.	0 in 10 liked it	5 in 90 liked it
b.	1 in 10 liked it	4 in 90 liked it
c.	0 in 10 liked it	10 in 90 liked it
d.	1 in 10 liked it	9 in 90 liked it
e.	0 in 10 liked it	15 in 90 liked it
f.	1 in 10 liked it	14 in 90 liked it
g.	2 in 10 liked it	13 in 90 liked it

24.7 A newstand at a certain subway station in Chicago sells for 35 cents a daily newspaper for which it pays 20 cents. Unsold newspapers are returned for a refund of 15 cents a copy. Without bothering to go through thousands of purchase tickets and refund tickets, the owner judges his daily sales to have had the following relative frequencies:

Daily sales:	1000	1500	2000	2500	3000	3500	4000
Relative frequency:	0.20	0.25	0.15	0.15	0.10	0.10	0.05

Let the possible acts be a_1 = buy 1,000 papers, a_2 = buy 1,500 papers, ... , a_7 = buy 4,000 papers.
a. State the payoff and loss functions mathematically.
b. Give the payoff and loss matrices.
c. Using the owner's judgments of the relative frequencies of past sales as the prior probabilities for the states of nature, calculate the optimal act and $EVPI_0$.

24.8 An ice-cream bar vendor must decide in advance how many deluxe ice cream bars to order each day. He makes a profit of 50 cents on each bar sold and suffers a loss of 30 cents on each unsold bar during the same day. He estimates the probabilities of various levels of demand to be $f_0(175) = 0.2$, $f_0(225) = 0.2$, $f_0(250) = 0.2$, $f_0(275) = 0.2$, and $f_0(325) = 0.2$. Let the possible acts be a_1 = buy 175 bars, a_2 = buy 225 bars, ... , a_5 = buy 325 bars. Do the same as for the preceding problem.

24.9 A firm manufacturing goods that are affected by styles and fashions must decide now how many of the newest fashion to make for the next season. It has estimated an (opportunity) loss of $20 for each unit of overstock, because it must reduce selling prices sharply after the end of the season in order to sell the remaining inventory. It has also estimated an (opportunity) loss of $10 for each unit of understock, because inability to fill customers' orders means lost profit and unhappy customers. The firm estimates it has a probability of 0.1 of selling

60,000 units during the season; 0.1 of selling 75,000 units; 0.2 of selling 90,000 units, 0.2 of selling 100,000 units; 0.2 of selling 110,000 units; 0.1 of selling 125,000 units; and 0.1 of selling 140,000 units. Let the possible acts be a_1 = make 60,000 units, a_2 = 75,000 units, . . . , a_7 = make 140,000 units. Do the same as for Problem 24.7.

24.10 Referring to Problems 24.7 and 24.9, discuss briefly whether it is reasonable to use the same prior probability distribution for every time period. Are there some obvious facts, or easily available sources of information, that should be used each time some newspapers are purchased or some goods are manufactured?

24.11 Mr. Jones has $1,000,000 available to invest. He can either put the money in the bank at 6% interest or he can start a new business. For the second act, he expects a 12% return if the business is successful or a 50% loss if the business is unsuccessful. Using a 1-year time period, what probability must be assign to the occurrence of a success (of the business venture) to make the expected monetary payoffs of the two possible acts equally attractive? (Note: a problem like this is called *sensitivity analysis*. In many decision problems, we find that the optimal act is insensitive to prior probabilities; that is, the optimal act remains the same unless the prior probability changes radically.)

24.12 Suppose a decision maker is facing a problem with the following payoff matrix:

	State of Nature		
Act	θ_1	θ_2	θ_3
a_1	100	60	20
a_2	60	100	32
a_3	40	60	80

With what values of the prior probabilities $f_0(\theta_1)$, $f_0(\theta_2)$, and $f_0(\theta_3)$ will the decision maker be indifferent among the three acts?

24.13 Suppose a manufacturer has perfected a new home-kitchen food mill that sells for about the same price as its competition but is easier to use and to clean. The problem is whether these features are enough to make it attractive to the market. The prior probability distribution for sales is as follows: $f_0(\theta_1) = 0.4$, where θ_1 is a high level of sales; $f_0(\theta_2) = 0.4$, where θ_2 is a medium level of sales; $f_0(\theta_3) = 0.2$, where θ_3 is a low level of sales. The possible acts are a_1 = introduce the food mill nationally and a_2 = abandon the new product. Payoffs in millions of dollars are estimated to be as tabulated below.

	State of Nature		
Act	θ_1	θ_2	θ_3
a_1	4.0	1.0	−1.6
a_2	0.0	0.0	0.0

If desired, additional information can be obtained by running a market test costing roughly $25,000. The possible test results are x_1 = high levels of sales during the test, x_2 = medium level of sales during the test, and x_3 = low level of sales during the test. The likelihoods, or value of $f(x_k \mid \theta_j)$, are as tabulated below.

| Test Result, or | State of Nature | | |
Value of x_k	θ_1	θ_2	θ_3
x_1	0.7	0.3	0.1
x_2	0.2	0.5	0.1
x_3	0.1	0.2	0.8

a. Calculate the loss table.
b. Run a prior analysis.
c. In view of $EVPI_0$, should the market test be run?
d. Assuming that a market test is run and a low level of sales occurs during the test, run a posterior analysis.
e. Comment briefly on what your value of $EVPI_1$ means.

24.14 Repeat Problem 24.13, except that now a medium level of sales occurs during the market test.

24.15 Repeat Problem 24.14, except that now a high level of sales occurs during the market test.

24.16 A factory uses "acceptance sampling" to decide whether to accept each lot of incoming components from suppliers or to reject the lot and return it to the supplier. For one kind of component from a particular supplier, past experience suggest the following prior distribution for the fraction defective:

θ_j:	θ_1:0.02	θ_2:0.04	θ_3:0.06	θ_4:0.08
$f_0(\theta_j)$:	0.4	0.3	0.2	0.1

The payoff table for the two possible acts is:

| Act | State of Nature | | | |
	θ_1	θ_2	θ_3	θ_4
a_1: accept the lot	$12,000	$2,000	−$4,000	−$30,000
a_2: reject the lot	−$1,000	−$1,000	−$1,000	−$1,000

The inspection done during sampling costs $5 per item drawn into the sample, and the "overhead" costs of drawing the sample and reporting its results total $250 for one sample. For administrative convenience, a sampling plan of SRS without replacement and $n = 50$ is used for every sample. N varies from lot to lot but is always at least 2,500.

a. Calculate the loss table.
b. Run a prior analysis.
c. In view of $EVPI_0$, should a sample be taken?

    d. Assuming that a sample is taken and no defectives appear in the sample, run a posterior analysis.

    e. Comment briefly on what your value of $EVPI_1$ means.

24.17 Repeat Problem 24.16 except that now 1 defective appears in the sample.

24.18 Repeat Problem 24.16 except that now 2 defectives appear in the sample.

24.19 Repeat Problem 24.16 except that now 3 defectives appear in the sample.

24.20 Repeat Problem 24.16 except that now 4 defectives appear in the sample.

24.21 Repeat Problem 24.16 except that now 8 defectives appear in the sample.

24.22 Repeat Problem 24.16 except that now 12 defectives appear in the sample.

24.23 A contractor wishes to submit a competitive bid for the modernization of an office building. Having studied the specifications, he estimates that the cost of the project can be represented by the probability distribution tabulated below.

Cost (c_i)	Probability of cost $[P(c_i)]$
$25,000	0.25
30,000	0.65
35,000	0.10

The contractor is now considering three possible bids. The probability of his getting the contract depends upon his bid, and according to his judgment the data tabulated below seen reasonable.

Bid (a_i)	Probability of Being Awarded the Contract $[P(a_i)]$
$33,000	0.60
36,000	0.35
40,000	0.05

    a. If the contractor is willing to use expected monetary returns as his decision rule, which of these three bids should he submit? (*Hint*: Whatever bid the contractor submits, he may or may not be awarded the contract. If he does not get it, his payoff will be zero. If he does get it, his profits depend upon the difference between his bid amount and the possible construction costs. Therefore, three more possible payoffs are associated with each bid. For instance, if he takes a_1 and the actual cost turns out to be c_1, his payoff will be $33,000 - 25,000 = \$8,000$. The probability for this conditional profit to occur is the joint probability

$$P[M(a_1, c_1)] = P(a_1)P(c_1) = 0.60(0.25) = 0.15.$$

In the same manner, all the possible conditional profits and their associated probabilities can be calculated for each possible amount bid, and then the Bayesian measure for each bid can be determined.

b. What is his optimal act?

c. What is the expected value for $a*$?

24.24 A toy-store manager must decide how many units of a certain make of electric train to stock for the coming Christmas season. The probability distribution for demand levels is estimated as tabulated below.

Demand	Probability
10	0.05
15	0.05
20	0.15
25	0.20
30	0.25
35	0.20
40	0.10
Total	1.00

Each train set costs the store $60, and the retail price during the season is $100. Those not sold during the season must be marked down to $40 per set.

a. Select the optimal act by using the special form of Bayesian strategy with a piecewise-linear loss function.

b. What is the expected payoff for the optimal act?

24.25 An ice-cream bar vendor must decide in advance how many ice cream bars to order each day. He makes a profit of 25 cents on each bar sold and suffers a loss of 12 cents on each unsold bar during the same day. Suppose he has a normal prior distribution for his daily demand with $\mu_0 = 350$ and $\sigma_0 = 50$. What is his optimal order each day? For this optimal order, what is the $EVPI_0$?

24.26 The marketing research department of a firm assumes a normal distribution for the firm's sales for the next year with $\mu_0 = 100,000$ and $\sigma_0 = 20,000$. Furthermore, according to past experience, losses are piecewise-linear and the error of an overstock is twice as costly as the error of an understock. Under these circumstances, what is the optimal estimate for the amount that should be manufactured, assuming no carryover inventory? What is the expected value of perfect information for this optimal estimate?

24.27 Suppose that in estimating the potential share of the market for his output, a decision maker believes a beta prior with $r_0 = 1$ and $n_0 = 8$ and a loss function of $L(a, \tilde{\pi}) = \$1500(a - \pi)^2$ are appropriate. What is his optimal estimate for $\tilde{\pi}$? and, for this estimate, what is the value of $EVPI_0$?

24.28 For the preceding problem, if the prior probability law is $\beta_0(1, 7)$, and the loss function is $L(a, \tilde{\pi}) = \$2500(a - \pi)^2$, what are the optimal estimates of $\tilde{\pi}$ and $EVPI_0$ now?

24.29 To continue with Problem 24.28, with a random sample with $n = 20$ yielding $r = 3$, what are the posterior optimal act and expected value of perfect information?

24.30 A department store is considering whether to build a branch store in a new suburb where there are about 100,000 families. Fixed costs required are estimated to be $20 million, which management plans to recover completely in the first five years on a straight-line basis—that is, to recover one-fifth of the total fixed cost each of the first five years. Furthermore, the average profit of all items to be carried by the new branch is estimated to be $5.00 per unit of sales. After considerable study of the population composition, family income, and so on, the management believes the mean number of sales per family each year is normal with $\mu_0 = 10$ and $\sigma_0 = 3$. With the information given, determine $EP_0(a^*)$ and $EVPI_0$.

24.31 To continue with the preceding problem, suppose a random sample with $n = 50$ families results in a mean number of sales per family of 12 and, furthermore, that the variance for state random variable μ_x is known to be 2. What are the expected payoffs for the posterior optimal act? What is the posterior expected value of perfect information?

24.32 Suppose you retail women's clothing and you are told that an inventory of 7,000 different items is up for sale for $250,000. You hire a women's clothing expert to evaluate this proposition, and he informs you that, in his prior judgment, the mean value of the inventories is normally distributed with an expectation of $45.00 per item and a standard deviation of $10.00. How should you decide *a priori*? What is the expected value of perfect information for your optimal decision?

24.33 Suppose you authorize the expert to conduct a posterior analysis in the preceding problem. He does this by assuming the variance of state random variable to be 8 and selecting a random sample with $n = 64$ items, which yields a sample mean of $48. In view of this additional information, find the posterior expected payoffs and expected value of perfection for the optimal act. Comment on the results of this and the previous problems.

24.34 The management of a firm has already decided to market a new product. However, this product can be produced by two types of machines, I and II; both produce the same amount of output of identical quality per hour. Machine I requires a fixed investment of $600,000 with a variable operating cost of $10 per hour. Machine II costs only $300,000 to purchase and has a variable operating cost of $16 per hour. Owing to uncertainty of the demand for the new product, there is a great deal of uncertainty attached to the number of hours of operating time during the next few years. The management expresses this uncertainty in terms of a prior normal distribution with $\mu_0 = 54,000$ hours and $\sigma_0^2 = 16,000$ hours^2. Under these circumstances, what are the breakeven value μ_b and the expected cost of the optimal act $EVPI_0$, respectively?

24.35 In a decision situation concerning the Bernoulli process, a prior beta density has been assumed with $r_0 = 1$ and $n_0 = 20$. The payoff functions are given as

$$M(a_1, \tilde{\pi}) = \$4000 - 10,000\pi;$$
$$M(a_2, \tilde{\pi}) = \$5000 - 20,000\pi.$$

What are the expected payoffs and the expected value of perfect information in the prior analysis?

24.36 For the preceding problem, with random sample with $n = 15$ and $r = 1$, what are the posterior expected act and expected value of perfect information, respectively?

24.37 A manufacturer must decide between the following two acts:

a_1: Buy a new lot of 1,000 units of a certain machine part which contains no defective units at a cost of $500.00;

a_2: Use an old lot of the same kind of machine parts that contains an unknown proportion of defectives at no cost except that each defective unit requires a rework cost of $2.50.

a. What is the breakeven value of $\tilde{\pi}$ in this case?

b. Given a beta prior of $n_0 = 10$ and $r_0 = 3$, what are the $a*$ and $EVPI_0$?

Appendix to Chapter 24
Decision Making with
Expected Utility

The use of money as a measure of the consequence of an act can be questioned on the grounds that different decision makers can place different valuations on the same amount of money, owing to their different financial circumstances and reactions to risk. Consider, for example, the following three decision situations:

I. a_1 = having a gain of $1,000 with certainty,

   a_2 = having a gain of $3,200 or a loss of $1,000 with equal probabilities;

II. a_1 = having a loss of $100 with certainty;

   a_2 = having a gain of zero with probability of 0.995 or a loss of $10,000 with probability of 0.05;

III. a_1 = having a gain of $100,000 with certainty;

   a_2 = having a gain of $2,000,000 if the toss of a die comes up with a number 5 or less and a loss of $8,000,000 if the die turns up 6.

In each of these three situations, if the expected monetary value is used, then a_2 should be preferred over a_1—yet many people would select a_1. Why?

In case I, if one can gain $1,000 for sure, why risk losing $1,000 to gain only $100 more in expected value (the expected value of a_2 is $1,100)?

In case II, while a sure loss of $100 is painful, it may be a reasonable price to pay to avoid risking the huge loss of $10,000, however slight the probability. This is indeed why any prudent man would buy fire insurance on his house, even though the expected monetary value of such an act is negative.

In case III, the expected value of a_1 is less than one-third of the expected value of a_2; if the decision maker is financially strong and ambitious, he may prefer a_2 over a_1. However, to many others, the sure gain of $100,000 is more attractive than the possible windfall gain of $2,000,000 at the risk of a fantastic loss of $8,000,000, which they can never afford. This illustrates clearly the famous St. Petersburg paradox, in which rational men often refrain from games with favorable odds when the stakes are too high.

The St. Petersburg paradox led Daniel Bernoulli, more than a century ago, to investigate utility rather than money as a basis of rational choice among alternatives. Utility theory was fully developed and applied by Von Neumann and Morgenstern in the 1940s.

In current usage, a *utility index* is a real number that gives a subjective preference measure of the decision maker to an outcome, or payoff, of an action. Here, an outcome may be given in terms of many different things, such a marbles, money, or even death or life. The utility of a payoff O_i may be denoted as $U(O_i)$, which is usually given an arbitrary unit called *utile*.

A utility function of a decision maker can be thought of as a preference relationship that is based on a set of psychological axioms—axioms established to test the consistency of the decision maker's reactions to varying degrees of risk. Among these axioms, the two states below are of basic importance.

AXIOM 1 *If an individual considers payoff O_1 preferable to payoff O_2, then $U(O_1) > U(O_2)$. In this connection we see that if he prefers O_1 to O_2 and if he also prefers O_2 to O_3, then he should prefer O_1 to O_3 and $U(O_1) > U(O_3)$.*

This is the axiom of *transitivity,* a principle that can also be extended to cover *indifference* relationships. Thus, if a decision maker is indifferent between O_1 and O_2 and if he is also indifferent between O_2 and O_3, then he should be indifferent between O_1 and O_3. This says that if a decision maker finds $U(O_1) = U(O_2)$ and $U(O_2) = U(O_3)$, then he must also find $U(O_1) = U(O_3)$.

AXIOM 2 *If the decision maker is indifferent between two alternatives, a_1—receiving a payoff O_1 for certain and a_2—taking a bet, gamble, or lottery chance in which he receives a payoff O_2 with probability p and a payoff O_3 with probability $(1 - p)$, then $U(O_1) = U(O_2)p + U(O_3)(1 - p)$.*

Now, if we have available a payoff matrix for a decision situation, we may select the most preferable payoff O^* and the least preferable payoff O_* and arbitrarily let $U(O^*) = 1$ and $U(O_*) = 0$. The selection of 1 and 0 is entirely arbitrary; any other numerical scale can be employed as long as $U(O^*) > U(O_*)$. With utility indices for O^* and O_* determined, the utility index for any other intermediate payoff O must satisfy

$$U(O_*) \leqslant U(O) \leqslant U(O^*)$$

or

$$0 \leqslant U(O) \leqslant 1.$$

The value of $U(O)$ can be determined more precisely by employing the second axiom; that is, $U(O)$ can be determined by considering the following pair of gambles:

GAMBLE a_1 Receive O for certain;

GAMBLE a_2: Receive O^* with probability p and receive O_* with probability $(1 - p)$.

Next, we have

$$E_0[U(a_1)] = [U(O)](1) = U(O);$$
$$E_0[U(a_2)] = [U(O^*)](p) + [U(O_*)](1 - p)$$
$$= 1(p) + 0(1 - p)$$
$$= p.$$

Obviously, if $U(0) > p$, then gamble a_1 is preferred; if $U(0) < p$, then a_2 is preferred; if $U(0) = p$, then one should feel indifferent between a_1 and a_2. If this last result turns out to be the case for a particular value of p for the decision maker, his utility for O is p. That is, if this last result turns out to be the case, $U(O) = p$. If the decision maker preferred a_1 over a_2, or a_2 over a_1, he changes the numerical value of p in a_2 and asks himself again whether he likes a_1 and a_2 equally well or not. He continues doing this until he finds a value of p for which he likes a_1 and a_2 equally well. At this point his utility for O has been measured and is equal to p. Here, p is sometimes called the *indifference probability*. It turns out then that the determination of $U(O)$ is the same as the determination of p, the probability at which a decision maker would be indifferent between the two gambles. Alternatively, we may say that if we let $U(O^*) = 1$ and $U(O_*) = 0$, we are interpreting the utility of an intermediate payoff as an indifference probability—a subjective probability established such that a decision maker would be equally satisfied with either the a_1 or the a_2 shown above.

While utility indices can be constructed for payoffs expressed in anything, our chief concern is with the utility function for money. Generally, in business and economic decision situations, payoffs are first determined in terms of monetary units; then the monetary payoffs are converted into utility indices if the decision is to be made on the basis of utility. A *utility function for money*, also called the *cash-equivalent function*, can still be based upon indifference probabilities for various amounts of cash determined in various gambling propositions. To simplify our discussion still further, however, we shall introduce the notion of "reference contract," a device of taking into account the unique cash values that a decision maker places on different gambles, or contracts.

To establish a *reference contract* in a given decision situation, the decision maker must determine the amount of cash he would be willing to accept to give up the advantage of a contract or the amount of cash he would pay to be relieved of its obligations. Consider for example, a decision situation in which the payoffs in monetary units are as given in Table 24.A1. A reference contract always contains only two payoffs, the maximum payoff occurring in the payoff matrix and the minimum payoff occurring in the payoff matrix. Here, the reference contract would have the payoffs of $1,000 and $-$1,000. The reference contract specifies a probability of p of receiving the maximum payoff and a probability of $1 - p$ of receiving the minimum payoff. The value of p varies to suit

TABLE 24.A1 Payoff Matrix in Dollars for the Reference Contract Example

	θ_i:	θ_1	θ_2	θ_3	θ_4
a_i	$f_0(\theta_i)$:	0.3	0.4	0.2	0.1
a_1		$ 600	$ 600	$ 300	$-$300
a_2		750	900	$-$600	350
a_3		1000	1000	$-$1000	0

particular circumstances, as explained below. The payment an individual is willing to make for this contract will evidently depend upon two things: (1) the probability of winning, p; (2) the psychological impact on the individual of such a gain or loss.

We notice that the expected gain for the reference contract under consideration is

$$E(G) = 1000p + (-1000)(1 - p)$$
$$= 2000p - 1000.$$

Now, if $p = 1$—that is, if winning \$1,000 is a certainty and there is no chance of losing \$1,000—then $E(G) = \$1,000$. Evidently any rational person will be indifferent between \$1,000 and the contract, since the gain is the same whether he has the cash or the contract in hand. It is therefore reasonable to assign a utility index of 1 to the maximum payoff of a given decision situation. In our example, $U(\$1,000) = 1$. With similar reasoning, we see that if $p = 0$, any rational individual would be willing to pay up to \$1,000 in order to be relieved of the obligation of losing \$1,000 with certainty. Thus, $U(-\$1,000) = 0$.

However, how much would a person accept to give up the benefits (or pay to be removed from the obligations) of the contract under consideration if p were equal to, say, 0.7? First we note that the expected monetary value for the contract becomes

$$E(G) = 2000(0.7) - 1000$$
$$= \$400.$$

The answer now depends upon the psychological impacts of a possible \$1,000 gain and a possible \$1,000 loss. Within this context we classify decision makers in accordance with their psychological reactions to risk into the three categories of risk takers, risk evaders, and risk neutrals. A *risk taker* is a person who demands an amount of cash-certain in excess of the expected monetary payoff before yielding the contract. Thus, if X is a risk taker, he would gain more satisfaction from a \$1,000 win (and there is a 70% chance of winning it) than he would lose by incurring a \$1,000 loss (and there is a 30% chance of losing it). He might demand, say, \$650 in cash-certain before giving up the contract with 7:3 odds of a \$1,000 gain. For X, the risk taker, or the gambler, $U(\$650) = 0.7$ utiles, since he is indifferent between a gain of \$650 for certain and a gamble involving a 70% chance of winning \$1,000 and a 30% chance of losing \$1,000. In general, a risk taker would be willing to pay something to participate in a fair game—a game having an expected monetary value of zero.

A *risk evader* is a person who would yield the contract for an amount of cash-certain that is less than the expected monetary gain of the contract. If Y is a risk evader, his suffering over a \$1,000 loss (with a probability of 0.3 for its occurrence) would outweigh the joy over a \$1,000 gain (with a probability of 0.7 for its occurrence). He might then be willing to accept nothing ($0 cash-certain), in order to be freed from the possibility of losing $1,000, even though the expected value of the contract is $400. Such a person as Y willingly pays to avoid making a fair bet. For Y in our example, $U(\$0) = 0.7$ utiles.

A person is said to be *risk neutral* if he is indifferent between the contract and the amount of cash equal to its expected value. Thus, if Z is risk neutral, he seeks neither to avoid nor to encourage risk. For Z, $U(\$400) = 0.7$ utiles.

The maximum amount of cash-certain that an individual would willingly exchange for a specified reference contract at each probability level p is the individual's *cash-equivalent function,* or his *utility function for money.* Since p can take on any value between 0 and 1, it would be impossible to determine the cash-certain equivalent for each possible value of p. In practice this function is derived by selecting about ten values of p, determining the cash equivalent of the reference contract at these values, and interpolating the intervening values. This amounts to plotting the values obtained through direct inquiries and drawing a freehand curve through these points. If the individual is consistent in his preferences, the curve will be monotonic and more or less smooth.

Table 24.A2 presents the utility functions of three individuals derived from asking them to determine the cash equivalent of a contract promising a $1,000 gain with probability p and a $1,000 loss with probability $1 - p$. Data in this table are plotted and connected in Figure 24.A1. From either Table 24.A2 or its corresponding graph, we see that X is the risk taker who prefers to gamble and always demands a cash-certain amount greater than the expected value of the contract. Individual Y is the risk evader who is always willing to accept a smaller cash-certain amount than the expected value of the contract. In the case of Z, the utility function of money is linear, reflecting his indifference between the contract and its expected value; he is risk neutral. It is important to observe that while risk-neutral decision makers would always have the same linear utility function for money, the cash-equivalent functions for risk takers or risk evaders may differ in curvature from one decision maker to another.

TABLE 24.A2 Utility Functions for Money

Probability of $1000 Gain, p	Reference Contract		
	X	Y	Z
1.0	$1000	$1000	$1000
0.9	850	500	800
0.8	750	250	600
0.7	650	0	400
0.6	500	−200	200
0.5	350	−325	0
0.4	200	−450	−200
0.3	0	−600	−400
0.2	−250	−750	−600
0.1	−600	−875	−800
0.0	−1000	−1000	−1000

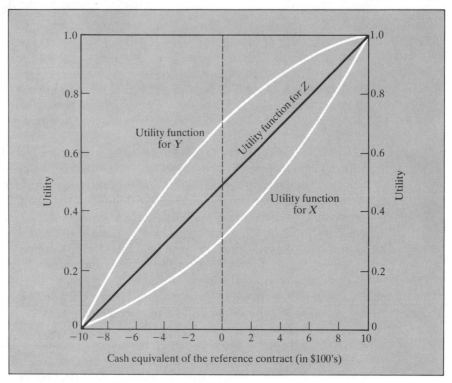

FIGURE 24.A1. Utility functions for the illustrative example in Table 24.A2.

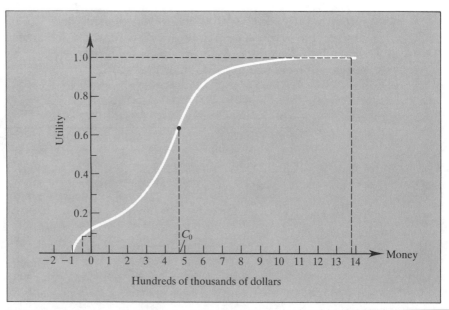

FIGURE 24.A2. A typical utility function for money.

Returning to the payoff functions in Table 24.A1, we note that $EP_0(a_1) = \$450$ and that $EP_0(a_2) = EP_0(a_3) = \$500$. If the expected-monetary-value criterion is used, any decision maker will be indifferent between a_2 and a_3, and either is preferred over a_1. However, if we take into consideration a decision maker's reaction toward risk—that is, if utility indices are employed—then a different optimal act may result for a different decision maker. Now suppose both X and Y in our illustration would like to make their decisions on the basis of expected utility, which is defined as

$$EU_0(a_i) = \sum_j u_{ij} f_0(\theta_j), \qquad (24.A1)$$

where u_{ij} stands for the utility index for the ith act and the jth state, and $f_0(\theta_j)$ stands for the prior probability that $\tilde{\theta} = \theta_j$. We first convert the monetary payoffs in Table 24.A1 into utility payoffs by interpolating from the graphs of their respective utility functions for money in Figure 24.A2. The results are given in Table 24.A3.

Now, applying the Bayesian decision criterion to utility payoffs, for X we have

$$EU_0(a_1) = \sum_j u_{1j} f_0(\theta_j)$$
$$= 0.66(0.3) + 0.66(0.4) + 0.46(0.2) + 0.19(0.10)$$
$$= 0.573 \text{ utiles};$$

$$EU_0(a_2) = \sum_j u_{2j} f_0(\theta_j) = 0.678 \text{ utiles};$$

$$EU_0(a_3^*) = \sum_j u_{3j} f_0(\theta_j) = 0.730 \text{ utiles}.$$

For Y we have

$$EU_0(a_1^*) = 0.860 \text{ utiles};$$
$$EU_0(a_2) = 0.821 \text{ utiles}$$
$$EU_0(a_3) = 0.770 \text{ utiles}$$

Thus, in terms of utility indices, a_3 is the optimal act for X and a_1 is the optimal act for Y, since each has the highest expected utility for the respective decision maker.

TABLE 24.A3 Payoff Matrix in Utiles for X and Y

Act	X				Y			
	θ_1	θ_2	θ_3	θ_4	θ_1	θ_2	θ_3	θ_4
a_1	0.66	0.66	0.46	0.19	0.92	0.92	0.82	0.52
a_2	0.80	0.92	0.10	0.50	0.95	0.98	0.30	0.84
a_3	1.00	1.00	0.00	0.30	1.00	1.00	0.00	0.70

We can gain additional insights into the properties of utility functions by studying their graphs, such as Figure 24.A1. We see in this figure that the shape of the curve for the risk-taker shows an increasing marginal utility for money. It means that when his cash position increases, he places more value on each additional dollar to be gained. The curve for the risk-averse Y, however, shows just the reverse—a decreasing marginal utility of money. If one's utility function is linear over the whole range, it appears as a straight line such as the diagonal line in Figure 24.A1. Such a function shows the utility in proportion to the monetary value; in this case, expected value computed directly from monetary payoffs would indicate the expected utility of each alternative.

In fact, none of these three types of utility functions is very realistic. Recent literature suggests that, typically, the utility function of an individual or organization may follow a pattern such as shown by Figure 24.A2. Here, the utility function has an inflection point associated with a cash asset position, C_0, called the *level of aspiration*. With a lower cash position, a decision maker will search for opportunitites to increase his income and is willing to be a risk-taker. If gambles are available to him in this range, equal to or greater than C_0, however, he becomes risk averse and would be willing to sacrifice some income to be relieved of the obligations of some risk alternatives.

Utility indices assigned to payoffs, or outcomes, are such, then, that the rank order of the expected utility reflects the decision maker's action preferences. Utility indices are attractive and easy to manipulate but very difficult and time-consuming to construct. Another problem is that individuals are often inconsistent in stating their preferences for specified combinations of risk and associated consequences. Thus, it may be questioned at times how accurately the resulting utility functions represent the decision maker's true preferences. Perhaps, too, different responses would have been obtained at different times because of changes in the decision maker's moods or outlook. It is equally apparent that a person's utility function may change from one decision situation to another. The same individual might not have the same reaction to risk in the stock market as at the poker table. When we attempt to determine a utility function representing organizational policy, the difficulty may be compounded by the multitude of organization objectives. Thus, utility indices should always be used with some caution.

We observe, too, that when the range of payoffs is relatively small, the expected monetary value can be used directly without introducing serious errors. However, the question, "How small is small?" is a subjective matter. A range of $1,000 may be quite large for this author, for example, but trivial for a large business firm.

25* Bayesian Decision Theory: Preposterior and Sequential Analyses

25.1 INTRODUCTION

In the last chapter the prior and posterior analyses of the Bayesian decision theory were presented. In general, within the Bayesian decision framework, one tries to select the optimal act from the set of all possible acts given the payoff or loss functions in a problem situation with all the available information relevant to the states of nature. The decision maker may make his terminal decision with prior information alone or do it with additional information provided by a sample, experiment, or test of some sort.

It must be observed now that, when it is judged to be desirable and feasible to integrate additional information into a decision process, the Bayesian decision theory typically takes on the form of what is called *preposterior analysis*. This is a paper study that, among other things, attempts to evaluate the possible effects on the actions of all possible sample results of every feasible sample size in order to determine the "optimal decision function". Precisely, a *preposterior analysis* is designed to answer, before any fresh information is gathered, three basic questions.

1. From the results of a prior analysis, should the decision maker attempt to conduct a posterior analysis?

2. If the answer to (1) is positive, what is the feasible maximum sample size for the decision situation?

3. Among all the feasible sample sizes, which is the *optimal sample size*? That is, what is the sample size that can give the decision maker the highest "expected net gain from sampling"?

Answers to the foregoing questions center around the relationships among three quantities: the expected value of perfect information, the cost of sampling, and the expected net gain from sampling. From these relationships, one can readily determine the size of optimal amount of information before any additional information is actually gathered. This procedure is thus one of the most important contributions to decision making by Bayesian statistics.

To conduct a preposterior analysis, one may concentrate on the evaluation of the expected net gain from sampling with a particular *single-stage sampling plan* or with a *multiple-stage sampling plan*. The latter is a method in which the decision maker attempts to revise his probabilities after each trial and to decide whether to continue sampling or whether to stop sampling and make a terminal decision. The choice here involves the study of an entire stream of potential future sample results, together with the possibility of stopping after any trial and make a terminal decision. It is, therefore, often called *sequential analysis*.

The objectives and mechanisms of both types of preposterior analyses are identical. The multiple-stage sampling plan is simply an extension of the single-stage sampling plan. It must be noted here, though, that the motivation of a sequential analysis, as has already been explained in the chapter on statistical quality control, is to obtain the same level of efficiency as the single-stage sampling plan but with lower costs. It is also interesting to point out that, so far as the cost-saving objective is concerned, the Bayesian preposterior sequential analysis in principle has a greater "expected net gain from sampling" than the single-stage sampling plan with a fixed sample size. However, this is only true if there is involved no fixed cost of sampling for each and every fresh sample. Otherwise, each sampling plan may be better or worse, depending upon the exact nature of the decision situation. Because of this, we give a more detailed presentation of the single-stage sampling plan than of a multiple-sampling plan in the discussion that follows. Furthermore, when we speak of preposterior analysis without any particular identification we always refer to the single-stage sampling plan.

You must also be informed that throughout this chapter, we shall assume, as we did in the last one, that the decision maker is "risk neutral" in the sense that his utility function for money is linear. That is, the maximization of monetary payoffs or the minimization of monetary opportunity losses, is a suitable decision criterion.

25.2 THE MECHANISM OF PREPOSTERIOR ANALYSIS

It has been pointed out a number of times previously that it would have been worthwhile for the decision maker to pay up to the value of $EVPI_0$

for perfect information to eliminate his uncertainty concerning the state of nature. However, since no sample or experiment could be expected to yield perfect information, the decision maker does not yet have a clear guide as to the worth of gathering further information. To enable him to calculate the worth of additional information from any source, the notion of the "expected value of sample information" is crucial. This notion will aid the decision maker in determining the best sample size in a given decision situation; it is, therefore, the central core in a preposterior analysis.

Procedures of preposterior analyses for decision problems with any number of acts or any number of states are the same. However, for the purpose of simplifying the arithmetic work, when the various aspects of preposterior analysis are first introduced, we will commence our discussion with a simple illustrative problem for which there are only two acts and a small number of states.

The Gamma Excavation Company is offered a contract to excavate sites for three radar towers to be constructed by the U.S. Air Force along the coast of Maine at a fee of $10,000. The management of Gamma Company estimates that it will cost $2,200 to excavate each site where no rock layer is encountered in the work and $4,000 to excavate each site where a rock layer is encountered. In this case, Gamma clearly has the following two courses of action:

a_1: accept the offer;

a_2: reject the offer.

Payoff functions for these two acts can be determined easily from the statement of the problem and are given in the last two columns of Table 25.1.

Gamma is not completely certain whether a rock layer will be encountered in any of the three sites but is able to assign prior probabilities to the four possible states on the basis of knowledge of the general region of the excavation sites, as shown in the first two columns of Table 25.1.

It may be noted that in preposterior analysis the selection of the optimal act with the current state of information is equivalent to a decision process with a sample size of 0. That is, the prior analysis can

TABLE 25.1 Prior Distribution and Payoffs For the Excavation Problem

State: No. of Sites Containing a Rock Layer θ_j	$f_0(\theta_j)$	Payoff	
		a_1: accept	a_2: reject
θ_1: 0	0.30	$3400	$0
θ_2: 1	0.35	1600	0
θ_3: 2	0.20	−200	0
θ_4: 3	0.15	−2000	0

now be appropriately called the *decision function* with $n = 0$. For our current example, given $n = 0$, we have

$$EP_0(a_1^*) = 3400(0.30) + 1600(0.35) + (-200)(0.20) + (-2000)(0.15)$$

$$= \$1240;$$

and

$$EP_0(a_2) = 0.$$

Thus, the decision function with $n = 0$ leads to the selection of a_1 as the optimal act. For this act,

$$EVPI_0 = EPPI_0 - EP_0(a_1^*)$$

$$= [3400(0.30) + 1600(0.35) + (0)(0.20) + 0(0.15)] - 1240$$

$$= 1580 - 1240 = \$340,$$

which sets the upper limit for the worth of obtaining additional information.

Proceeding to the possibility of obtaining further information before a terminal decision is made, let us assume that Gamma can determine whether or not a given site has rock layer by experimental drilling at a cost of \$150 per site. Given this cost information, we see that the optimal sample size can never exceed 2.

Having determined the feasible sample sizes, Gamma should evaluate the outcomes of every possible sample size up through two. For $n = 1$—that is, if Gamma selects one site at random and drills experimentally—there are two possible sample outcomes:

x_1: the drilling indicates no rock layer;

x_2: the drilling indicates a rock layer.

We assume that the sample information is absolutely correct (unlike the Black Jade example). Prior probabilities can now be revised for each these two possible results. These revisions are made in Table 25.2.

TABLE 25.2 Revising Probabilities for $n = 1$ for the Excavation Problem

x_k	θ_j	$f_0(\theta_j)$	$f(x_k \mid \theta_j)$	$f_0(\theta_j)f(x_k \mid \theta_j)$	$f_1(\theta_j)$
x_1	θ_1	0.30	1	0.30	0.50
	θ_2	0.35	2/3	0.23	0.38
	θ_3	0.20	1/3	0.07	0.12
	θ_4	0.15	0	0.00	0.00
		1.00	—	$f(x_1) = 0.60$	1.00
x_2	θ_1	0.30	0	0.00	0.00
	θ_2	0.35	1/3	0.12	0.30
	θ_3	0.20	2/3	0.13	0.32
	θ_4	0.15	1	0.15	0.38
		1.00	—	$f(x_2) = 0.40$	1.00

Two observations must be made about the computations contained in Table 25.2. First, the likelihoods are conditional to the true state. For example, $f(x_1 \mid \theta_1) = 1$, since if none of the sites has a rock layer, the probability that a drilling result indicates no rock layer must be 1, and so on. Next, the values of $f(x_1)$ and $f(x_2)$ form what is called a *predictive probability distribution*, since $f(x_k)$ is employed in making predictions about sample results before they are actually observed.

Continuing our analysis for $n = 1$, we note that in terms of the revised probabilities, we have

$$EP_1(a_1^{**} \mid x_1) = 3400(0.50) + 1600(0.38) + (-200)(0.12) + (-2000)(0)$$

$$= \$2284,$$

$$EP_1(a_2 \mid x_1) = 0;$$

$$EP_1(a_1 \mid x_2) = 3400(0) + 1600(0.30) + (-200)(0.32) + (-2000)(0.38)$$

$$= \$344,$$

$$EP_1(a_2^{**} \mid x_2) = 0.$$

These computations indicate that if x_1 occurs, then a_1 is the posterior optimal act; if x_2 occurs, then a_2 is the posterior optimal act. Note carefully that the expected values for the posterior optimal acts are *conditional* on the same results, and the probabilities that the sample will indicate x_1 and x_2 are the predictive probabilities, $f(x_1) = 0.60$ and $f(x_2) = 0.40$, respectively. Therefore, the *unconditional expected payoff*, which we shall call the *expected payoff for the decision function with* $n = 1$, denoted as $EP(1)$, must be the weighted expected payoffs of the posterior optimal acts with predictive probabilities as weights. For our example,

$$EP(1) = EP_1(a_1^{**} \mid x_1)f(x_1) + EP_1(a_2^{**} \mid x_2)f(x_2)$$

$$= 2284(0.60) + 0(0.40)$$

$$= \$1370.40.$$

We take note now that, in our example, $EP(1) > EP(0)$, the latter being the expected payoff for the prior optimal act. This result indicates that experimentally drilling one site selected at random might be worthwhile. The increase in expected payoff from $n = 0$ to $n = 1$ here is $\$130.40$. The increase in the expected payoff of a decision function with sample size n from the expected payoff of the prior optimal act is defined as the *expected value of sample information, EVSI(n)*. For our example,

$$EVSI(1) = EP(1) - EP_0(a_1^*)$$

$$= 1370.40 - 1240.00$$

$$= \$130.40.$$

While sample information works to reduce uncertainty attached to the state variable and, therefore, to increase the expected payoff of the optimal act, there will still be no net gain from sampling unless $EVSI(n)$ is greater than the sampling cost, $C(n)$. The difference between $EVSI(n)$ and $C(n)$ is called the *expected net gain from sampling, ENGS(n)*, and, for our current illustration,

$$ENGS(1) = 130.40 - 150.00$$

$$= -\$19.60$$

which is negative, indicating that a sample with $n = 1$ is noneconomical and it should not be undertaken. It is important to note here that the negative value of $ENGS(1)$ does not preclude the possibility that larger samples may still be worthwhile. Thus, we should proceed to evaluate the decision function with $n = 2$.

For $n = 2$, we simply repeat the procedure for $n = 1$. If Gamma selects two sites at random for experimental drilling, then there would be the following three possible sample results:

x_1: neither of the two sites contains a rock layer;

x_2: exactly one of the two sites contains a rock layer;

x_3: both of the sites contain rock layers.

Should the sample be with replacement or without replacement? Sometimes, samples should be taken with replacement, but here the sample should be taken without replacement. Once Gamma knows for sure whether a particular site has a rock layer, it is clearly a waste of $150 to drill on the same site again.

Thus the likelihoods are hypergeometric probabilities. Precisely, the $f(x_k \mid \theta_j)$ values in Table 25.3 are obtained as follows:

$$f(x_1 \mid \theta_1) = \binom{3}{2} \Big/ \binom{3}{2} = 1,$$

$$f(x_1 \mid \theta_2) = \binom{1}{0}\binom{2}{2} \Big/ \binom{3}{2} = \frac{1}{3},$$

$$f(x_1 \mid \theta_3) = f(x_1 \mid \theta_4) = 0;$$
$$f(x_2 \mid \theta_1) = f(x_2 \mid \theta_4) = 0,$$

$$f(x_2 \mid \theta_2) = \binom{1}{1}\binom{2}{1} \Big/ \binom{3}{2} = \frac{2}{3},$$

$$f(x_2 \mid \theta_3) = \binom{2}{1}\binom{1}{1} \Big/ \binom{3}{2} = \frac{2}{3};$$

$$f(x_3 \mid \theta_1) = f(x_3 \mid \theta_2) = 0,$$

$$f(x_3 \mid \theta_3) = \binom{2}{2}\binom{1}{0} \Big/ \binom{3}{2} = \frac{1}{3},$$

$$f(x_3 \mid \theta_4) = \binom{3}{2} \Big/ \binom{3}{2} = 1.$$

TABLE 25.3 Revising Probabilities for $n = 2$ for the Excavation Problem

x_k	θ_j	$f_0(\theta_j)$	$f(x_k \mid \theta_j)$	$f_0(\theta_j)f(x_k \mid \theta_j)$	$f_1(\theta_j)$
x_1	θ_1	0.30	1	0.30	0.71
	θ_2	0.35	1/3	0.12	0.29
	θ_3	0.20	0	0.00	0.00
	θ_4	0.15	0	0.00	0.00
		1.00	—	$f(x_1) = 0.42$	1.00
x_2	θ_1	0.30	0	0.00	0.00
	θ_2	0.35	2/3	0.23	0.64
	θ_3	0.20	2/3	0.13	0.36
	θ_4	0.15	0	0.00	0.00
		1.00	—	$f(x_2) = 0.36$	1.00
x_3	θ_1	0.30	0	0.00	0.00
	θ_2	0.35	0	0.00	0.00
	θ_3	0.20	1/3	0.07	0.32
	θ_4	0.15	1	0.15	0.68
		1.00	—	$f(x_3) = 0.22$	1.00

From the posterior probabilities in Table 25.3, we have the following conditional expected payoffs for various acts given each sample result:

$$EP_1(a_1^{**} \mid x_1) = 3400(0.71) + 1600(0.29) + (-200)(0) + (-2000)(0)$$

$$= \$2878,$$

$$EP_1(a_2 \mid x_1) = 0;$$

$$EP_1(a_1^{**} \mid x_2) = 3400(0) + 1600(0.64) + (-200)(0.36) + (-2000)(0)$$

$$= \$952,$$

$$EP_1(a_2 \mid x_2) = 0;$$

$$EP_1(a_1 \mid x_3) = 3400(0) + 1600(0) + (-200)(0.32) + (-2000)(0.68)$$

$$= -\$1424,$$

$$EP_1(a_2^{**} \mid x_3) = 0.$$

Thus, if x_1, no rock layer, or x_2, one rock layer, is observed in a sample of 2, a_1 is optimal; if x_3, two rock layers, is observed, a_2 is optimal. With the conditional expected payoffs for the posterior optimal acts, the unconditional expected payoff for the decision function with $n = 2$ becomes

$$EP(2) = \sum_k EP_1(a_i^{**} \mid x_k)f(x_k)$$

$$= 2878(0.42) + 952(0.36) + 0(0.22)$$

$$= \$1551.48.$$

Also, for this decision function,

$$EVSI(2) = EP(2) - EP(0)$$
$$= 1551.48 - 1240.00$$
$$= \$311.48;$$

and

$$ENGS(2) = EVSI(2) - C(2)$$
$$= 311.48 - 300.00$$
$$= \$11.48,$$

which is positive, and $n = 2$ is economically worthwhile.

The calculations above reveal that the decision function with $n = 2$ is better than that with $n = 1$ because $ENGS(2) > ENGS(1)$. But is it possible to increase the expected net gain from sampling still more with $n = 3$? The answer in our example is no, since it has already been established that the optimal samples size cannot exceed 2 in terms of $EVPI_0$ and $C(n)$. Thus, we can state the optimal decision rule for the Gamma problem as follows: Drill experimentally two sites selected at random; take a_1, accept the offer, if none or one of the sites contains a rock layer; take a_2, reject the offer, if both sites contain rock layers.

25.3 PREPOSTERIOR ANALYSIS GENERALIZED

The mechanism of preposterior analysis introduced in the preceding section is quite general and can be applied to any decision problem with any number of acts and any number of states. However, in order to gain a more systematic understanding of this procedure, we now restate, extend, and generalize what has been presented before.

A preposterior analysis is a paper study that attempts to determine the optimal decision function before the actual gathering of further information takes place. It begins with the establishment of a prior probability distribution for the state random variable and an estimate of the cost of sampling. Next, the expected value of perfect information, or the expected opportunity loss, for the prior optimal act is determined. If $EVPI_0 = EL_0(a_i^*) < C(n)$, for all $n \geq 1$, a terminal decision should be made now with the current state of information. Otherwise, it might be worthwhile to obtain additional information before a terminal decision is made.

When sampling is judged to be possibly worthwhile, we start with the decision function with $n = 1$ and increase the size of n consecutively until the optimal sample size, denoted as n^*, has been found. For each n the analysis is the same, and involves the following steps.

1. Revise the prior probabilities for each and every possible sample result for a sample of size $n = 1$.

2. Identify the posterior optimal act, a_i^{**}, for each particular sample result and compute its conditional expected payoff as

$$EP_1(a_i^{**} \mid x_k) = \sum_j m_{ij} f_1(\theta_j \mid x_k) \qquad (25.1)$$

or its conditional expected (opportunity) loss as

$$EL_1(a_i^{**} \mid x_k) = \sum_j l_{ij} f_1(\theta_j \mid x_k). \qquad (25.2)$$

3. With conditional expected payoffs (or losses) of posterior optimal acts for various sample results obtained, the unconditional expected payoff (or loss) for the decision function with a particular sample size is determined. This expectation is a weighted average of the conditional expected payoffs (or losses) of the posterior optimal acts with the predictive probabilities as weights. Thus, we have

$$EP(n) = \sum_k EP_1(a_i^{**} \mid x_k) f(x_k) \qquad (25.3)$$

in terms of payoffs, or

$$EL(n) = \sum_k EL_1(a_i^{**} \mid x_k) f(x_k) \qquad (25.4)$$

in terms of opportunity losses, where $n = 1, 2, 3, \ldots$.

4. The increase in expected payoff or reduction in expected loss as the result of sampling, compared with decision making without sampling, is called the expected value of sampling information, which is defined as

$$EVSI(n) = EP(n) - EP_0(a_i^*) \qquad (25.5)$$

in terms of payoffs or

$$EVSI(n) = EL_0(a_i^*) - EL(n) \qquad (25.6)$$

in terms of opportunity losses. Note, also, that prior analysis here is called the decision function for $n = 0$; thus, $EP_0(a_i^*)$ may be written as $EP(0)$ and $EL(a_i^*)$ may be written as $EL(0)$.

5. Unless the expected value of sampling exceeds the cost of obtaining the sample, sampling is a waste of time and money. The expected net gain from sampling is simply

$$ENGS(n) = EVSI(n) - C(n). \qquad (25.7)$$

If $ENGS$ of a proposed sample is zero or negative, then the sample should not be taken.

6. This process is repeated for increasing values of n until the optimal size of the sample is found. The *optimal sample size* n^* is that n for which the expected net gain from sampling is maximized. That is,

$$ENGS(n^*) \geq ENGS(n) \qquad \text{for all possible } n. \qquad (25.8)$$

In the case where $n^* = 0$, the decision maker should make his terminal decision without further sampling.

It may be noted that the determination of n^* hinges on $ENGS$ which, in turn, depends upon $EVSI$ and $C(n)$. In order to gain some additional insights about preposterior analysis, let us make a few observations on the behavior of these functions and their relationships.

25.4 THE NATURE OF *ENGS*

Two commonly encountered types of $ENGS$ curves are shown in Figures 25.1 and 25.2. The former is drawn under the assumption that $C(n) = v(n)$ and the latter that $C(n) = F + v(n)$. In these expressions, F represents the total fixed cost of sampling (designing, administering, analyzing, reporting, and so on) that will be incurred if a sample of any size at all is taken, and v stands for the unit variable cost of sampling under the assumption that the incremental cost of each additional sample observation is identical.

Note that the behaviors of $EVSI$, $C(n)$, $ENGS$, and their relationships, in both cases, are nearly identical. In each case we see that $EVSI$ increases continuously with increasing sample size, but it increases with a decreasing rate of increase with $EVPI_0$ as its limit. Note also that

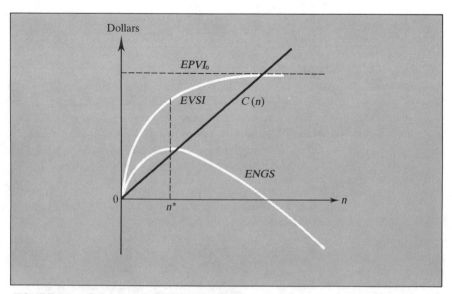

FIGURE 25.1 Behavior of *ENGS* with $C(n) = v(n)$.

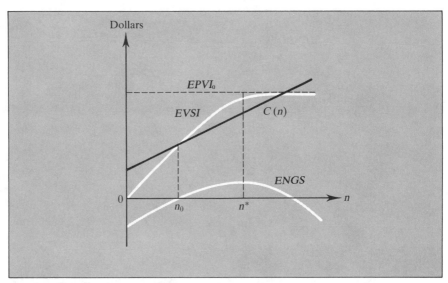

FIGURE 25.2 Behavior of *ENGS* with $C(n) = F + v(n)$.

$C(n)$ is a linear function. Owing to the behaviors of these two functions, the *ENGS*, being a difference between *EVSI* and $C(n)$, increases at the beginning, reaches a maximum, then declines, and eventually becomes negative. The sample size that corresponds to the maximum of the *ENGS* curve in either diagram is the optimal sample size. Also, with reference to Figure 25.2, we see that when there is a large element of fixed cost in $C(n)$, for n that is smaller than n_0, *ENGS* is negative. This implies that when a sample of small size is noneconomical, a larger sample may still be worthwhile.

   Curves for *ENGS* as presented in Figures 25.1 and 25.2 are by no means the only types of *ENGS* curves. We next discuss three other

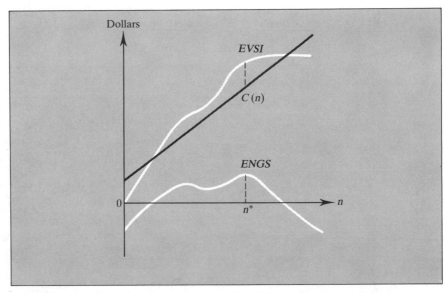

FIGURE 25.3 Illustrating the case where *ENGS* has more than one peak.

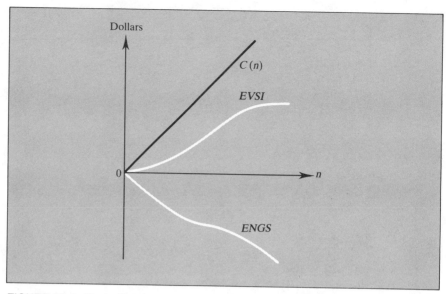

FIGURE 25.4 Illustrating the case of negative *ENGS* for all *n*.

forms of *ENGS* curves that might be encountered from time to time. First, as revealed by Figure 25.3, an *ENGS* curve may decline from a peak and then peak again. We see that in this particular case n^* corresponds to the second peak of the *ENGS* curve. The second case is a situation in which, shown by Figure 25.4, the expected value of sample information cannot meet its cost of sampling, irrespective of the sample size. In this case, *ENGS* is negative for all sample sizes and, as a result, the decision maker should select his optimal act with the current information. Figure 25.5 illustrates yet another possibility, in which any sample size in the interval between n_1 and n_3 would be worthwhile; *ENGS* has a single peak, and $n^* = n_2$. However, if circumstances are

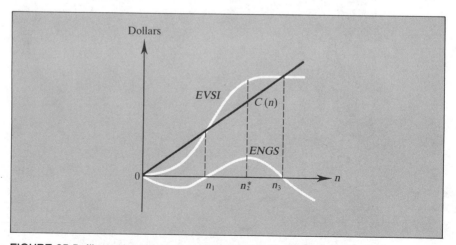

FIGURE 25.5 Illustrating the case where *ENGS* is negative for small *n*.

such that the decision maker cannot observe a sample greater than size n_1, further sampling should be rejected and the terminal decision made on the basis of the information available. This could happen, for instance, if there were an externally imposed time restriction on the final decision.

Given that additional information is worthwhile and possible, the optimal sample size for decision problems with finite acts and finite states is usually determined by trial and error—by the so-called iterative procedure. The problem with this procedure is that it may require so much computational time and labor to find *EVSI* (hence *ENGS*) when n is at all large that it would scare and frustrate the most patient of us. In practice, fortunately, whenever a preposterior analysis is called for, the problem is usually programmed for a computer. Indeed, the recent growing acceptance of Bayesian statistics by theoretical and applied statisticians is largely due to the availability of computers.

In this connection, it may also be observed that, just as in the case of prior analysis, when the state is continuous and when the prior density is a natural conjugate distribution, very often rather simple mathematical expressions can be formulated for the determination of *EVSI* and n^* directly. We shall now turn to consider the simplified procedures for posterior analysis and optimal information gathering for two special but frequently encountered decision situations: the cases of binomial and normal sampling.

25.5 PREPOSTERIOR ANALYSIS WITH BINOMIAL SAMPLING

In the case of binomial sampling, the state random variable is often assumed to be continuous with a beta prior density function. Then the solution to the decision problem hinges on the number of acts and the type of loss function. Recall that when the number of acts is infinite and the loss function is of the form $L(a, \tilde{\pi}) = b(a - \pi)^2$, the optimal act is the one whose numerical value is equal to the expected value of the state random variable $\tilde{\pi}$. Again, with an infinite number of acts but where the loss function is piecewise-linear, the optimal act (or estimate) corresponds to the $f^* = b_u/(b_u + b_0)$ fractile of the decision maker's distribution of the state. Finally, when there are two actions and when the loss function is linear, the optimal act is selected with reference to the breakeven value π_b of $\tilde{\pi}$. For the first case, a single formula can be derived to determine the optimal sample size. Unfortunately, this cannot be done for the last two cases. What we can do for the second case is to find approximate answers with methods which are appropriate under sampling from the normal distribution, and, for the third case, to obtain answers with the aid of a computer. Thus, in this section we will be concerned with the first case only.

Recall that if the prior probability law of a state random variable $\tilde{\pi}$ is a beta density with parameters $\tilde{r}_0$ and $\tilde{n}_0$ and that if the loss function is of the quadratic form, then

$$EVPI_0 = bV_0(\tilde{\pi})$$

$$= \frac{b[\tilde{r}_0(\tilde{n}_0 - \tilde{r}_0)]}{n_0^2(\tilde{n}_0 + 1)}.$$

It can be shown that if a simple random sample of size n is selected from a binomial population whose unknown $\tilde{\pi}$ is assumed to have a beta prior, then the expected value of sample information is given by

$$EVSI(\tilde{n}) = bV_0(\tilde{\pi})\left(\frac{n}{\tilde{n}_0 + n}\right)$$

$$= EVPI_0\left(\frac{n}{\tilde{n}_0 + n}\right). \qquad (25.9)$$

This equation is quite easy to apply once $EVPI_0$ is obtained. It is also an obvious demonstration of the fact that $EVSI$ has $EVPI_0$ as its upper limit. We see here that as n increases, $n/(\tilde{n}_0 + n)$ approaches 1 and $EVSI(n)$ approaches $EVPI_0$.

Turning to the problem of determining the optimal sample size, we assume that $C(n) = F + (v)(n)$ and, thus, the expected net gain from sampling in this case must be as follows:

$$ENGS(n) = EVSI(n) - [F + (v)(n)]. \qquad (25.10)$$

The maximum value of this function, or the optimal sample size n^*, as can be verified, is given by the following expression:

$$n^* = \sqrt{\frac{b[V_0(\tilde{\pi})]\tilde{n}_0}{v}} - \tilde{n}_0. \qquad (25.11)$$

This formula yields the optimal sample size provided that the n^* it gives is such that $n^* > 0$ and $ENGS(n^*) > 0$; if either condition is not met, the optimal sample size is 0.

As an illustration, let us consider the problem in which the executives of a national TV network attempt to estimate the potential audience share for a new series with a criminal family as the background. Crucial to this problem is the determination of the time spot for scheduling the series. The executives have tentatively decided on this point in following way: If the estimated audience is

1. less than 20%, the series will be scheduled at 11:30 p.m.;

2. between 20 and 22%, the series will be scheduled at 7:00 p.m.;

3. greater than 22%, the series will be scheduled at 8:00 or 9:00 p.m.

Next, after considerable deliberation, the executives are able to assume a beta prior for the state random variable $\tilde{\pi}$ with $n_0 = 10$ and $r_0 = 2$.

Furthermore, according to their judgment, the loss function is quadratic and they are willing to pay up to \$250,000 in order to be sure that the percentage of audience is 1% below or above the state value of 20%. Thus, the loss function here becomes

$$L(a, \tilde{\pi}) = \$250,000(a - \pi)^2.$$

Now, from the prior beta function for the state, we see that

$$V_0(\tilde{\pi}) = \frac{2(10 - 2)}{10^2(10 + 1)} \doteq 0.014555.$$

Next, suppose the cost of sampling is given by the function

$$C(n) = \$100 + \$3(n),$$

then, by (25.11), we have

$$n^* = \sqrt{\frac{250,000(0.014555)(10)}{3}} - 10$$

$$\doteq 100.$$

Finally, for this optimal decision function, and by (25.10),

$$ENGS(100) = 250,000(0.014555)\left(\frac{100}{10 + 100}\right)$$

$$- [100 + 3(100)]$$

$$\doteq \$2908.$$

With these results, the complete optimal decision rule for the TV problem becomes: Take a random sample with $n^* = 100$ and determine the posterior expected value of the state, $E_1(\tilde{\pi})$; on the basis of $E_1(\tilde{\pi})$, decide at what time the series should scheduled in accordance with the criteria already established.

25.6 PREPOSTERIOR ANALYSIS WITH NORMAL SAMPLING

Whenever normal sampling is possible, it is always preferred over binomial sampling, since more relevant information can be obtained for the decision problem on hand. For example, in quality control, the study of dimensional values, such as diameters of steel pipes, or breaking strength of iron bars, is clearly more revealing of the quality of the output than the classification of products into defective and non-defective categories. Our discussion on preposterior analysis for normal sampling will be confined to two-action decision problems involving linear payoffs and known variances of the population. Our concern here, as in any preposterior analysis, is of course with optimal information gathering.

We shall illustrate the procedure of preposterior analysis with normal sampling by the same example of the problem of introducing, a_1, or not introducing, a_2, a new product that was evaluated in the previous chapter. Recall that this problem was evaluated by assuming a prior normal density function $n_0(\mu_0 = 60, \sigma_0^2 = 16)$ with the estimated payoff functions

$$M(a_1, \tilde{\mu}) = -\$8,100,000 + \$15,000\mu,$$

$$M(a_2, \tilde{\mu}) = 0.$$

From these payoff functions, we obtain $\mu_b = 54$ which is less than $\mu_0 = 60$. Thus,

$$EP_0(a_1^*) = \$900,000$$

with

$$EVPI_0 = \$17,586.$$

Next, a simple random sample of $n = 80$ customers was selected and a sample mean of $\bar{x} = 57$ was found. Thus, the posterior analysis here yielded $\mu_1 = 57.6$, $\sigma_1^2 = 3.2$. With these results,

$$EP_1(a_1^{**}) = \$540,000,$$

for which

$$EVPI_1 = \$2218.$$

We see that, for this problem, both prior and posterior analyses led to the same optimal action, a_1—introducing the new product. However, we note also that both the expected value of posterior optimal act and the expected value of perfect information are smaller than the corresponding prior quantities. These results, as explained before, were due to the relationships among $\tilde{\mu}_1$, $\tilde{\mu}_0$, μ_b, D_1, and D_0.

However, conclusions previously made about the differences between prior and posterior analyses are not at issue in the case of preposterior analysis. Now, it is the knowledge of the optimal sample size before sampling that is desired. Once again the expected value of a decision function, or a sampling plan, depends on the loss it avoids, which in turn depends on the reduction in the degree of uncertainty attached to the state random variable. Specifically, to determine the expected value of sample information we need a measure that will indicate the amount of reduction in the variance from the prior to the posterior distribution of the state. Such a measure obviously can be thought to be the difference between the prior and posterior variances. That is, denoting this measure by $\tilde{\sigma}^{2*}$, we have

$$\tilde{\sigma}^{2*} = \tilde{\sigma}_0^2 - \tilde{\sigma}_1^2$$

$$= \tilde{\sigma}_0^2 - \frac{(\tilde{\sigma}_0^2)(\tilde{\sigma}_{\bar{X}}^2)}{\tilde{\sigma}_0^2 + \tilde{\sigma}_{\bar{X}}^2}$$

$$= \frac{(\tilde{\sigma}_0^2)^2}{\tilde{\sigma}_0^2 + \tilde{\sigma}_{\bar{X}}^2}. \tag{25.12}$$

This is the variance of the *prior density function for the posterior mean*, $\tilde{\mu}_1$, which is established before actual sampling. Furthermore, this prior density has as its expectation $E_0(\tilde{\mu}_1) = \mu_0$. This density function is a *prerevised*, or *preposterior*, *density* for $\tilde{\mu}_1$ which is not to be confused with the posterior density for $\tilde{\mu}_X$. The solution for n^* now hinges on the prior density function for the posterior mean, for which we can calculate $E_0(\tilde{\mu}_1)$ and $\tilde{\sigma}^{2*}$, and on how $\tilde{\mu}_1$ is distributed prior to actual sampling. We state here without further explanation that this density is normal if the prior probability law is normal. In addition, the procedure of obtaining the expected value of sample information is analogous to that of obtaining the expected value of perfect information. That is,

$$EVSI(n) = |b_1 - b_2| \, \tilde{\sigma}^*[L_N(D^*)], \qquad (25.13)$$

where

$$D^* = \left| \frac{\mu_b - \tilde{\mu}_0}{\tilde{\sigma}^*} \right|. \qquad (25.14)$$

Some facts about (25.14) are worth noting. First, the smaller the difference between μ_b and $\tilde{\mu}_0$, the more difficult it will be to make the correct decision and, therefore, the greater will be the expected value of sample information. Next, other things being equal, if $\tilde{\sigma}_0^2$ is large, then there is a high degree of uncertainty. Thus, the larger $\tilde{\sigma}_0^2$ is, the more likely a wrong decision is to be made—or the more valuable sample information becomes. Third, the smaller the population variance, σ^2, the greater would be the value of *EVSI*. One reason for this is that $\tilde{\sigma}_{\bar{X}}^2$ would be smaller, so a more compact sampling distribution would result from a less dispersed population; another is that D^* would decrease, increasing $L_N(D^*)$. Finally, *EVSI* increases with increases in n, with $EVPI_0$ as its limit when n gets to infinity.

Let us now have a look at the decision function with $n = 80$ for the new-product example. From the prior and preposterior analyses conducted before, we have

$$\sigma^{2*} = \frac{(16)^2}{16 + 4} = 12.8;$$

$$\sigma^* = \sqrt{12.8} \doteq 3.58;$$

$$D^* = \left| \frac{54 - 60}{3.58} \right| \doteq 1.68;$$

$$L_N(D^*) = L_N(1.68) = 0.01920;$$

$$EVSI(80) = 150,000(3.58)(0.01920)$$

$$\doteq \$10,310.$$

Assuming that the cost of sampling in this case is given as

$$C(n) = \$1,000 + \$20n,$$

then the expected net gain from sampling for this decision function becomes

$$ENGS(80) = 10{,}310 - [1{,}000 + 20(80)]$$

$$= \$7{,}710.$$

This rather large positive value of $ENGS$ indicates that the proposed sample of size 80 is worthwhile; but is $n = 80$ the optimal sample size?

To answer the foregoing question, and assuming that no sample had been taken yet but $\sigma^2 = 320$, we note that, in general, with normal sampling,

$$ENGS(n) = |b_1 - b_2|\, \sigma^*[L_N(D^*)] - [F + v(n)].$$

This expression, however, is rather difficult to manipulate for the purpose of yielding the optimal sample size. Thus, in practice, we resort to an equivalent method of obtaining n^* as given below:

$$n^* = \text{antilog}(T + \log \tilde{\sigma}_X^2 - \log \tilde{\sigma}_0^2), \qquad (25.15)$$

where

$$T = f(D_0, \log G)$$

with

$$D_0 = \left| \frac{\mu_b - \tilde{\mu}_0}{\tilde{\sigma}_0} \right|$$

and

$$\log G = \log\left[\frac{b(\tilde{\sigma}_0^2)^{3/2}}{v\sigma_X^2} \right]$$

$$= \log b + \tfrac{3}{2}\log \tilde{\sigma}_0^2 - (\log v + \log \sigma_X^2).$$

Values of the function T are given in Table XIII of Appendix C. To use this table, we shall adopt the practice of rounding the values of D_0 and G to one decimal place and then employing linear interpolation. Also, in the expression for $\log G$, $b = |b_1 - b_2|$.

Employing (25.15) to determine n^* for the new-product example, we have

$$D_0 = \left| \frac{54 - 60}{4} \right| = 1.5;$$

$$\log G = \log 150{,}000 + \tfrac{3}{2}\log 16 - (\log 20 + \log 320)$$

$$\doteq 3.2;$$

$$T = f(1.5; 3.2) = 0.94 \qquad \text{[from Table XIII]};$$

$$n^* = \text{antilog}(0.94 + \log 320 - \log 16)$$

$$\doteq \text{antilog}(2.2410)$$

$$\doteq 174.$$

If n^* were not at least 1, we would conclude here that sampling should not be engaged in, and that the decision should be made now using only the prior distribution for the state variable. Since our n^* is at least one, we must make one more calculation. We have to calculate $ENGS(n^*)$. If $ENGS(n^*)$ is negative, we conclude that sampling should not be engaged in at all, since even the most useful sample is not worth its cost, and that the decision should be made now using only the prior distribution for the state variable. If $ENGS(n^*)$ is positive, we conclude that taking a sample of size n^* and then making our decision is the best course of action. Actually, if the fixed costs of sampling are zero (if $F = 0$), we can omit the step of calculating $ENGS(n^*)$, since it will never change the decision concerning sampling. In our example, the fixed costs of sampling are greater than zero, so we must calculate $ENGS(n^*)$.

$$\sigma_{\bar{X}}^2 = \frac{320}{174} \doteq 1.8391;$$

$$\sigma^{2*} = \frac{(16)^2}{16 + 1.8391} \doteq 14.3505;$$

$$\sigma^* = \sqrt{14.3505} \doteq 3.7882;$$

$$D^* = \left| \frac{54 - 60}{3.7882} \right| \doteq 1.58;$$

$$L_N(D^*) = L_N(1.58) = 0.02436;$$

$$EVSI(174) = 150{,}000(3.7882)(0.02436)$$

$$\doteq \$13{,}842;$$

$$C(174) = 1{,}000 + 20(174) = \$4{,}480;$$

$$ENGS(174) = 13{,}842 - 4{,}480 = \$9{,}362.$$

Since the resulting $ENGS > 0$, the proposed sample is justified. It must be noted here that n^* determined by (25.15) is only an approximation because of roundings of the values of D_0 and $\log G$, and of interpolations. This does not matter, in practice. Mathematical analysis of the effects of using an $n \neq n^*$ suggests the following: If n is within 20% of n^*, that is, between $0.8n^*$ and $1.2n^*$, the prior expectation of the posterior optimal loss using n will be at most 2.5% above the prior expectation of the posterior optimal loss using n^*. Thus a calculated n^* that does not quite agree with the true n^* because of roundings and interpolations is ordinarily accurate enough. It should be pointed out, though, that once the actual n being used departs enough from the n^* that should be used, the effects can be severe. It is only in the neighborhood of n^* that using an $n \neq n^*$ scarcely affects anything.

To specify an optimal decision function completely in the case of normal sampling, we still need a critical value of the sample mean, denoted as $\bar{X}_c$, in order to determine whether a_1 or a_2 is the optimal act. In general, a_1 should be selected if $\bar{X} > \bar{X}_c$, and a_2 should be selected if $\bar{X} \leq \bar{X}_c$. To derive a formula for $\bar{X}_c$, we note that a decision for problems with two actions and linear payoffs can be made by comparing the expectation of the state with the breakeven value of the state. The prior and posterior optimal acts can be reversed only if the prior and posterior expectations are on the opposite sides of μ_b. Furthermore, the posterior mean is a weighted average of the prior and sample means; that is,

$$\tilde{\mu}_1 = \frac{\tilde{\mu}_0 \tilde{\sigma}_{\bar{X}}^2 + \bar{X} \tilde{\sigma}_0^2}{\tilde{\sigma}_0^2 + \tilde{\sigma}_{\bar{X}}^2}.$$

Consequently, the value of a sample mean that is just small enough (when $\mu_b < \tilde{\mu}_0$), or just large enough (when $\mu_b > \tilde{\mu}_0$), to make $\tilde{\mu}_1 = \mu_b$ can be derived from the expression for $\tilde{\mu}_1$ by setting $\tilde{\mu}_1 = \mu_b$. The value of a sample mean that is smaller than the one that equates μ_b with the right side of the above equation will produce a $\tilde{\mu}_1$ that is less than μ_b, and vice versa. In either case, the prior and posterior decisions would be altered. Hence, $\bar{X}_c$ can be found by solving

$$\mu_b = \frac{\tilde{\mu}_0 \tilde{\sigma}_{\bar{X}}^2 + \bar{X}_c \tilde{\sigma}_0^2}{\tilde{\sigma}_0^2 + \tilde{\sigma}_{\bar{X}}^2}$$

for $\bar{X}$. Rearranging yields

$$\bar{X}_c = \frac{\tilde{\sigma}_{\bar{X}}^2}{\tilde{\sigma}_0^2}(\mu_b - \tilde{\mu}_0) + \mu_b. \qquad (25.16)$$

Applying the foregoing expression to the new-product example, we have

$$\bar{x}_c = \frac{1.8391}{16}(54 - 60) + 54$$

$$\doteq 53.31.$$

With this result, the complete decision rule for the new-product example may be stated as follows: Take a simple random sample with $n = 174$ and compute the sample mean; select a_1—introduce the new product—if $\bar{x} > 53.31$; select a_2—abandon the product—if $\bar{x} \leq 53.31$.

25.7 MULTIPLE-STAGE DECISION PROCEDURES

So far we have been concerned exclusively with what are called *single-stage decision problems* in which the decision maker selects the optimal act with whatever information is available at a single point of time. Occasions may arise when multiple decisions must be made before a problem is resolved. In a *multiple-stage decision problem* a choice is made after some information has been obtained between making a terminal decision or gathering further information; if further information is gathered, a choice has to be made again between making a terminal decision or gathering even more information. These decisions progress sequentially until a terminal decision is made. The sequential acceptance sampling plan mentioned in Chapter 14 is an important illustration of multiple-stage decision procedures. This procedure is applicable in any business problem when a delay in decision is allowable. When an immediate decision can be made only after considering the outcomes and decisions that may follow, it is necessary to start at the final stage of the problem and work backward through each stage to determine the optimal act. In other words, a multiple-stage problem is resolved by treating each stage as a single-stage problem and working back from the last problem stage.

As implied earlier, a multiple-stage decision procedure corresponds to a sequential sampling plan. At each stage, additional sample information is obtained and prior probabilities are revised accordingly. Then a decision is made whether to continue sampling or to make a terminal decision. This choice is made with due consideration of a complete flow of potential sample outcomes. It is in this sense that the process of "backward induction" is required in a sequential analysis. Other than this, a sequential decision procedure uses the same principles and concepts as have already been covered for single-stage decision problems. A brief introduction to sequential analysis is presented in this section.

To illustrate, let us consider a simple sequential decision situation in which there are only two acts, two states, and two stages. The management of Beta Manufacturing Company, in anticipation of an increase in demand for its product, is contemplating building an additional plant. The cost of construction is estimated to be $2 million. If the anticipated increase in demand occurs, a net profit of $3 million will be realized. Accordingly to the best knowledge of management at present, there is a 50% chance of the increase in demand. Since the decision can be delayed, management decides to have at least one sample survey of the market conditions among Beta's current customers at a cost of $60,000. Management is undecided whether a second sample should also be taken among Beta's current and potential customers at a cost of $120,000. The first sample is 65% reliable in the sense that if there will be an increase in demand, the probability is 0.65 that the sample will indicate an increase in demand. Also, if there will be no increase in demand, the sample has a 0.35 probability of indicating that. The information of the second sample is 70% reliable in the same sense.

First, let us conduct a prior analysis for this decision problem in order to assess whether it is feasible and reasonable to resort to an information gathering process for a sequential decision rule. The payoffs are as displayed in Table 25.4. From this table, we see that a_1 is the prior optimal act and that

$$EP_0(a_1^*) = 3(0.5) + (-2)(0.5) = \$0.5 \text{ million};$$

$$EVPI_0 = [3(0.5) + 0(0.5)] - 0.5 = \$1.0 \text{ million}.$$

This rather large value of $EVPI_0$ relative to the cost of the proposed first

TABLE 25.4 Payoffs for the New-plant Example (in millions of dollars)

Act	State	
	θ_1: increase	θ_2: no increase
a_1: build	3	-2
a_2: don't build	0	0

sample clearly justifies management's decision to proceed with the first sample. We turn next to the question of whether Beta should proceed with the two-stage sampling process.

As was mentioned earlier, in a multiple-stage problem we should evaluate the decision backward by evaluating the best moves at the later stages in order to determine the best moves at earlier stages. For clarity in exposition of such backward induction, we find a graphic tool, called the *decision-flow diagram*, or the *decision tree*, to be most valuable. The decision tree for our current illustrative example is as shown by Figure 25.6. In a decision tree, a square represents a *decision fork* at which the decision maker must decide either to continue sampling or to stop sampling, or to make a terminal selection of the optimal act; a circle represents a *chance fork* at which either the chance events of sample results are branched out or the states of nature are branched out.

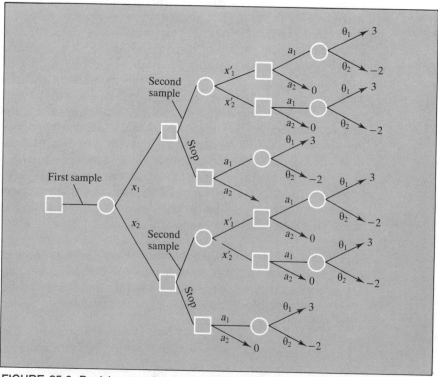

FIGURE 25.6 Decision tree for evaluating the new-plant example with two stages and payoffs in millions of dollars.

Let us study Figure 25.6 carefully. This figure starts with a decision fork where management has already decided to take the first sample. This sample leads to a chance fork where two possible sample results may be obtained:

x_1: indication of an increase in the demand;

x_2: indication of no increase in the demand.

Given that x_1 and x_2 results, management must decide either to continue sampling (take the second sample) or to stop sampling. The decision to continue sampling leads to another chance fork where two possible sample results of the second sample may occur:

x_1': indication of an increase in the demand;

x_2': indication of no increase in the demand.

For each of these two sample results, management must choose between a_1 and a_2, each of which, in turn, leads to specific payoffs. If a_2 is selected, the payoff is zero. If a_1 is selected, the payoffs are conditional upon the chance events—that is, the states of nature. These payoffs are given in millions of dollars and are entered at the end branches of the tree. If management decides to stop sampling after the first sample, it must decide immediately on the selection of the optimal act. Again, if a_2 is selected, the payoff is zero, and if a_1 is selected, the payoff is $3 million given that θ_1 emerges and −$2 million given that θ_2 occurs.

Next, we must determine the expected payoffs for each stage. To do this, we first revise the prior probabilities given the sample results of the first and the second sample, respectively. Posterior probabilities obtained with the first sample are given in Table 25.5 and those obtained from the first and the second samples are given in Table 25.6. Note that the prior probabilities used in Table 25.6 are the posterior probabilities obtained in Table 25.5.

Two things about the computations in Tables 25.5 and 25.6 may be mentioned before we proceed with our analysis. First, identical posterior probabilities in Table 25.6 can be obtained by revising the original prior probabilities with the combined information of the two samples. In

TABLE 25.5 Revision of Probabilities with Results from the First Sample, for the New-plant Example

x_k	θ_j	$f_0(\theta_j)$	$f(x_k \mid \theta_j)$	$f_0(\theta_j)f(x_k \mid \theta_j)$	$f_1(\theta_j \mid x_k)$
x_1:	θ_1	0.50	0.65	0.325	0.65
	θ_2	0.50	0.35	0.175	0.35
		1.00	—	$f(x_1) = 0.500$	1.00
x_2:	θ_1	0.50	0.35	0.175	0.35
	θ_2	0.50	0.65	0.325	0.65
		1.00	—	$f(x_2) = 0.500$	1.00

TABLE 25.6 Revision of Probabilities with Results from First and Second Samples, for the New-plant Example

x_k and x_k'	θ_j	$f_0(\theta_j)$	$f(x_k' \mid \theta_j)$	$f_0(\theta_j)f(x_k' \mid \theta_j)$	$f_1(\theta_j \mid x_k')$
x_1 and x_1':	θ_1	0.65	0.70	0.455	0.8125
	θ_2	0.35	0.30	0.105	0.1875
		1.00	—	$f(x_1') = 0.560$	1.0000
x_1 and x_2':	θ_1	0.65	0.30	0.195	0.4432
	θ_2	0.35	0.70	0.245	0.5568
		1.00	—	$f(x_2') = 0.440$	1.0000
x_2 and x_1':	θ_1	0.35	0.70	0.245	0.5568
	θ_2	0.65	0.30	0.195	0.4432
		1.00	—	$f(x_1') = 0.440$	1.0000
x_2 and x_2':	θ_1	0.35	0.30	0.105	0.1875
	θ_2	0.65	0.70	0.455	0.8125
		1.00	—	$f(x_2') = 0.560$	1.0000

doing this, the likelihoods are simply the product of the separate "reliabilities" of the two samples. For example, $f(x_1, x_1' \mid \theta_1) = 0.65(0.70) = 0.455$, $f(x_2, x_1' \mid \theta_1) = 0.35(0.70) = 0.245$, and so on. Second, the first $f(x_1') = 0.455$ in Table 25.6 should be interpreted as the probability that predicts that both the first and the second sample results will indicate an increase in demand; the second $f(x_1') = 0.105$ refers to the probability that predicts the first sample will indicate no increase in demand and the second sample will indicate an increase in demand; and so on.

To continue with our analysis, Figure 25.6 is included in Figure 25.7 with the predictive probabilities, $f(x_k \mid \theta_j)$ and $f(x_k' \mid \theta_j)$, and posterior probabilities, $f_1(\theta_j \mid x_k)$ and $f_1(\theta_j \mid x_k')$, entered at the appropriate branches of the new decision tree. The analysis of the tree begins with end branches on the right inward to the left. Expected payoffs for each act and for each decision function at each stage are computed with the proper posterior and predictive probabilities, respectively. These expected payoffs are entered into the decision or chance forks for easy identifications. From these expected payoffs, optimal acts are selected at each stage until we arrive at the first decision fork at the beginning of the tree. Note that whenever appropriate, sampling costs must be deducted from the expected payoffs of the optimal decision functions in order to ascertain whether to continue or stop additional sampling. Note also that the wavy double bar on any branch indicates an act or decision whose expected payoff is less than that of the other in a given stage and it is thus eliminated from further consideration.

For example, the entry in the extreme upper right circle is 2.0625 because $3(0.8125) + (-2)(0.1875) = 2.0625$. The square to the left also shows this expected payoff, for the following reason. From that square, one could achieve expected payoffs of either 2.0625 or 0, depending on

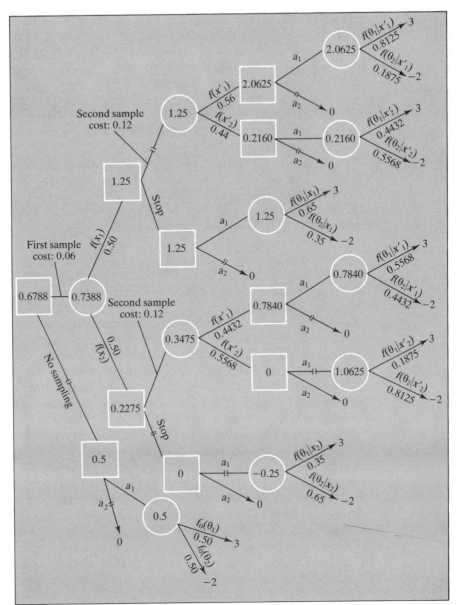

FIGURE 25.7 Evaluation of the new-plant example decision tree with payoffs and expected payoffs in millions of dollars.

whether one chose act a_1 or a_2. Of course, one chooses the higher payoff, so the entry in the square reflects that fact. Also, the branch leading to the lower payoff is barred off, showing it should never be taken. The circle just below the extreme upper right circle shows 0.2160 because $3(0.4432) + (-2)(0.5568) = 0.2160$. The square to its left also shows this expected payoff, and the branch from that square leading to a lower expected payoff is barred off. The circle to the left of both of these squares shows 1.25 because $2.0625(0.56) + 0.2160(0.44) = 1.2500$. Neither of the branches from this circle can be barred off, though, because a circle represents a chance outcome not subject to the control of the decision maker, rather than an act the decision maker can choose. Now, going left from the circle with 1.25, one notes a sample cost of 0.12 en route to the square. If one got to this square by this branch, the expected payoff would be $1.25 - 0.12 = 1.13$. The other branch from this same square produces a payoff of 1.25 in this square, though. Since 1.25 is greater than 1.13, the branch producing the 1.13 is barred off. Similar calculations are done for the rest of the decision tree, entering appropriate expected payoffs in the circles and squares and barring off unwise branches.

We can now confirm or deny our tentative decision to take the first sample. The decision tree shows that "no sampling" has an expected payoff of 0.5000, while the branch involving at least some sampling has an expected payoff of 0.6788. Naturally, we go ahead and confirm our decision to do at least some sampling.

Having computed the expected payoffs for each decision or chance fork, the decision maker (the management of Beta Co.) would proceed to evaluate the decision via the decision tree from left to right in the following manner. If x_1 (indication of an increase in demand) results from the first sample, the decision maker should stop further sampling and select a_1 as the terminal optimal act with an expected payoff of $1.25 million. However, if x_2 (indication of no increase in demand) occurs, he should decide to proceed with the second sample. If x_1' is observed, he should select a_1 as optimal with an expected payoff of $0.784 million; but if x_2' is observed, he should select a_2 as optimal with an expected payoff of $0. For these optimal decisions, based on the second sample, the expected payoff is $0.3475 million and the expected net gain from the second sample is $0.3475 - 0.1200 = \$0.2275$ million.

Thus, the expected payoffs of taking the best acts after observing x_1 and x_2 are $1.25 and $0.2275 million, respectively. Weighting these expected values by the predictive probabilities of the results of the first sample, we obtain $0.7388 million as the gross expected payoff of proceeding into the first stage of the decision process. Deducting the sampling cost of $0.06 million from this, we get a value of $0.6788 million for entering the first stage and selecting optimal courses of action thereafter. Comparing this payoff to $EP_0(a_1^*) = \$0.5$ million, we see that the increase is expected payoff in this case is $0.6788 - 0.5000 = 0.1788$ or $178,800.

A few additional remarks on the sequential decision rule are now in order. First, this rule can be appropriate whenever a delay in the decision is a definite alternative course of action. Second, it provides a decision framework for determining what decisions should be made and when they should be made. Namely, it presents an overall strategy for the decision maker that informs him what decision or action to take at each decision fork in the decision tree. Third, in general, a sequential decision plan with a maximum sample size n will yield a higher expected net gain from sampling than a single-stage sampling plan with sample size n, provided there is no new fixed cost of sampling for each additional sample. Finally, whenever a sequential sampling plan is appropriate, there are usually more than two stages. In the extreme, for example, one may evaluate an item-by-item sequential sampling plan in quality control or acceptance sampling in which the sampling is ended whenever the cost of the additional observation exceeds the expected opportunity loss of the optimal terminal act. In such a case, the decision tree could become extremely large and computation very lengthy and boring. Again, computers must be used as our aid, and sometimes even they cannot cope with all the complexities, in which case approximations to the full analysis are used.

25.8 CLASSICAL AND BAYESIAN STATISTICS CONTRASTED

The branch of statistics called inferential statistics has the main objective of making inferences, and thus decisions, about unknown population parameters or whole probability distributions. The two main approaches to this field of investigation are the classical and the Bayesian, between which the borderline is by no means clear. However, three major differences do stand out. The first is that the classical statisticians only accept the relative frequency theory of probability, while the Bayesians insist on the subjective interpretation of probability. The second is that the classical estimation and testing procedures are based on sample information alone because of the classical statisticians' insistence on objectivity, in contrast to the use of all available information—subjective judgment and empirical evidence—by the Bayesians. Third, the classical theory treats a population parameter as an unknown constant, whereas the Bayesian approach considers it as a random variable.

Granted the foregoing differences, it must be observed that the Bayesians also accept the assumptions of normal populations, known variances, and so on, from which sampling distributions are derived. In this sense, Bayesian inferential procedures can actually be considered as an extension from those of the classical. As an extension, Bayesian methods are more flexible and sometimes intuitively more appealing.

In estimation, an advantage of the Bayesian over the classical method is that the posterior variance is often smaller than the variance of the likelihood function. This implies that Bayesian interval estimates are often shorter than the classical owing to the Bayesians' use of prior probability laws.

In classical inferences, the likelihood function is employed to develop likelihood ratio tests. In Bayesian inferences, the likelihood function and the prior distribution are the two inputs to Bayes' theorem. In contrast to the classical method, the Bayesian considers the posterior odds ratio, which is the product of the prior odds ratio and the likelihood ratio, instead of just looking at the likelihood ratio. This means that the classical and the Bayesian results will be identical in numerical values, with different interpretations, if the prior odds ratio is one which amounts to the assumption of a diffuse prior state of information. Also, for large samples, the likelihood ratio goes (ordinarily) to zero or infinity, making classical and Bayesian results virtually identical.

Although the Bayesian procedure seems to compare favorably with the classical, the classical method is still useful in a number of special situations. First is the circumstance in which a large amount of sample information can be made available rather inexpensively. Next is the case in which only a diffuse prior state of information can be established. In both cases so far, the classical and the Bayesian conclusions might be the same, but the former often has the advantage of being easier to apply. At times, too, the prior probability law may be extremely difficult to establish and manipulate, especially when the prior distribution is multivariate in nature. In such a situation, if the difference in the results produced by the two methods is not enough to change the final conclusion, the classical procedure is clearly preferred, to avoid mathematical complexities. Indeed, in our discussion of association analyses, for example, we were exclusively concerned with classical inferences. Finally, in scientific or experimental work where it is difficult to measure the consequences of a decision, the classical method is also useful. Thus, in experimental design and the analysis of variance discussed in Chapter 16, the procedures of inference used were classical. In this connection, it may also be noted that in many scientific investigations, such as medical research, the decision should be made on the basis of empirical data alone in order to avoid the use of prior belief which may often represent the prejudices or biases of interested parties.

In general, inferential statistics, classical as well as Bayesian, embodies decision-making procedures under uncertainty in an informal way—informal in the sense that it does not explicitly evaluate the losses or payoffs of the consequences of wrong or correct decisions. The inclusion of loss or payoff functions in decision analysis takes us into the scope of decision theory, where one is required to take some action rather than to make some inference about some uncertain quanity. In decision theory, we speak of the optimizing behavior of a decision maker in the sense of maximizing expected payoff or minimizing expected loss.

Informal inferential methods may be adequate and even preferred when the consequences of wrong decisions are not serious or when the relevant payoffs or losses cannot be clearly determined. The formal decision-theoretic approach assumes importance when the consequences of potential decisions are important and can be at least approximately measured, as in many business decision situations.

Not only is the Bayesian approach more difficult conceptually than the classical, it is also more time-consuming to apply, especially with the formal decision-theoretic analysis. To avoid some of the difficulty involved with the application of Bayes' theorem, the Bayesians have developed the concept of natural conjugate prior distributions, which are families of special probability models that simplify the computational burden when they are used as prior distributions.

Owing to limited space and the elementary nature of this text, only two special conjugate families of distributions, with reference to normal and binomial sampling, have been presented. Similar procedures have been developed for other processes involving sampling from univariate or from multivariate populations. The underlying logic of employing these special mass or density functions as prior probability laws, and the procedure of using Bayes' theorem to produce posterior distributions with sample results, is identical with binomial and normal sampling; however, increasing mathematical complexities are usually encountered. In this connection, it must also be noted that the extra computational labor with Bayesian methods is usually no longer a drawback because of the wide availability of computers.

GLOSSARY OF FORMULAS

(25.1) $EP_1(a_i^{**} \mid x_k) = \sum_j m_{ij} f_1(\theta_j \mid x_k);$

(25.2) $EL_1(a_i^{**} \mid x_k) = \sum_j l_{ij} f_1(\theta_j \mid x_k);$

(25.3) $EP(n) = \sum_k EP_1(a_i^{**} \mid x_k) f(x_k);$

(25.4) $EL(n) = \sum_k EL_1(a_i^{**} \mid x_k) f(x_k);$

(25.5) $EVSI(n) = EP(n) - EP_0(a_i^*);$

(25.6) $EVSI(n) = EL_0(a_i^*) - EL(n);$

(25.7) $ENGS(n) = EVSI(n) - C(n);$

(25.8) $ENGS(n^*) \geq ENGS(n)$, for all possible n.

This group of equations provides an outline and a summary of the preposterior analysis of the Bayesian decision theory with the single-stage sampling plan. You should have no trouble understanding these equations once you can identify the meaning of each notation in these formulas. Section 25.3 contains the explanations of these equations. You are advised, therefore, to review that section if you feel unfamiliar with any of these expressions.

(25.9) $EVSI(n) = EVPI_0\left(\dfrac{n}{\tilde{n}_0 + n}\right);$

(25.10) $ENGS(n) = EVSI(n) - [F + (v)(n)];$

(25.11) $n^* = \sqrt{\dfrac{bV_0(\tilde{\pi})\tilde{n}_0}{v}} - \tilde{n}_0.$

These three equations define $EVSI(n)$, $ENGS(n)$, and n^*, respectively, in the case of preposterior analysis with binomial sampling when the state random variable is $\tilde{\pi}$ with a quadratic loss function of the form

$L(a, \tilde{\pi}) = b(a - \pi)^2.$ In (25.9) $EVPI_0 = b[\tilde{r}_0(\tilde{n}_0 - \tilde{r}_0)]/n_0^2(\tilde{n}_0 + 1),$ where b is a nonnegative constant. The definition of the expected value of sample information for the decision function of size n, (25.9), shows clearly that $EVSI$ has $EVPI_0$ as its upper limit, since as n increases, the ratio $n/(\tilde{n}_0 + n)$ approaches 1. Equation (25.10) defines the expected net gain from sampling as the difference $EVSI - C(n)$, where, for $C(n)$, F stands for the total fixed cost and $(v)(n)$ denotes the total variable cost of sampling. You may be reminded that to determine the optimal sample size in this case by (25.11), n^* and $ENGS(n^*)$ must both be greater than zero.

(25.12) $\sigma^{2*} = \dfrac{(\tilde{\sigma}_0^2)^2}{\tilde{\sigma}_0^2 + \tilde{\sigma}_{\bar{X}}^2};$

(25.13) $EVSI(n) = |b_1 - b_2| \, \tilde{\sigma}^*[L_n(D^*)];$

(25.14) $D^* = \left| \dfrac{\mu_b - \tilde{\mu}_0}{\tilde{\sigma}^*} \right|.$

These formulas are concerned with preposterior analysis with normal sampling. Equation (25.12) defines the variance of the prior density function for the posterior mean. It measures the reduction in variance from the prior to the posterior distribution of the state random variable $\tilde{\mu}_X$. Having defined $\tilde{\sigma}^{2*}$, the expected value of sample information in normal sampling for the decision function n can be computed by (25.13). In this expression the D^* value in $L_n(D^*)$ is defined by (25.14) which, as usual, is found in the table for the "unit normal linear loss integral" (Table XII in Appendix C).

(25.15) $n^* = \text{antilog}(T + \log \sigma_X^2 - \log \tilde{\sigma}_0^2).$

This equation is used to determine the optimal size of sample in normal sampling. For this equation, $T = f(D_0, \log G)$, where $D_0 = |(\mu_b - \tilde{\mu}_0)/\tilde{\sigma}_0|$ and $\log G = \log[b((\tilde{\sigma}_0^2)^{3/2})/v\sigma_X^2] = \log b + 3/2(\log \tilde{\sigma}_0^2) - (\log v + \log \sigma_X^2).$ Also, in the expression for $\log G$, $b = |b_1 - b_2|.$

(25.16) $\bar{X} = \dfrac{\tilde{\sigma}_{\bar{X}}^2}{\tilde{\sigma}_0^2}(\mu_b - \tilde{\mu}_0) + \mu_b.$

With normal sampling, the complete decision rule in preposterior analysis requires a critical value of the sample mean after n^* is found. In general, if $\bar{X} > \bar{X}_c$, a_1 is optimal; and if $\bar{X} \leq \bar{X}_c$, a_2 is optimal. This critical value of the sample mean is defined by (25.16). Note that this expression is derived from $\mu_b = (\tilde{\mu}_0\tilde{\sigma}_{\bar{X}}^2 + \bar{X}_c\tilde{\sigma}_0^2)/(\tilde{\sigma}_0^2 + \tilde{\sigma}_{\bar{X}}^2).$

REVIEW QUESTIONS

25.1 How is "preposterior analysis" defined? Why do we consider it an important contribution to statistical analysis by the Bayesians?

25.2 What is the difference between single-stage and multiple-stage sampling plans in Bayesian preposterior analysis?

25.3 Differentiate the three concepts *EVPI, EVSI,* and *ENGS* from each other.

25.4 Why is it impossible to obtain perfect information from sampling? What is the implication of this observation?

25.5 What is a decision function? In particular, what do we mean by the decision function with $n = 0$?

25.6 What constitutes a predictive probability distribution? How is it obtained?

25.7 What are the two general forms of the cost functions of sampling?

25.8 The expected net gain from sampling plays a central role in preposterior analysis. What is this role?

25.9 How do we go about determining the feasible maximum sample size in a given decision situation?

25.10 How would you define the notion of optimal sample size in a given decision situation? Can we always determine the exact optimal size of the sample? Why or why not?

25.11 Give an outline of the steps involved in a preposterior analysis. Be specific.

25.12 Interpret the diagrams in Figures 25.1 to 25.5 inclusive.

25.13 In the example of scheduling a TV series, the network executives assign a value of $250,000 to b in the quadratic loss function. Do you think this value is too big, or too small, or just about right? Explain your answer fully.

25.14 It has been said that whenever normal sampling is feasible it is always preferred over binomial sampling. Explain, with examples.

25.15 The optimal sample size determined by (25.15) is at best an approximation; yet we insist that such an approximation is quite adequate for all practical purposes. Why?

25.16 For the case of normal sampling in preposterior analysis, how is the "prior density function for the posterior mean" derived; What are its expectation and variance?

25.17 The main objective of a sequential sampling plan is cost saving for the gathering of optimal information. Can this objective be achieved all the time, compared with the single-stage sampling plan? Explain why or why not?

25.18 In what sense do we consider the multiple-stage sampling plan a preposterior analysis in the Bayesian decision framework?

25.19 What do we mean by decision and chance forks in a decision tree for sequential analysis? Is a decision tree always an efficient device in aiding us to conduct a multiple-stage sampling plan? Explain your answer.

25.20 What do we mean by "backward induction" in a sequential analysis? Explain as fully as your can.

25.21 What are the similarities and differences between classical and Bayesian inferential procedures?

25.22 In view of your answer to the preceding question, do you consider the classical and Bayesian approaches to decision making as substitutes for each other or as complementary methods to each other? Be thorough and specific in your answer.

PROBLEMS

25.1 The agent of a manufacturing firm has agreed to receive, periodically, shipments of four machines. The machines must be moved from the railroad station upon arrival and installed in good working order in the customers' plants. The moving costs are paid by the customer. Each time the machines arrive, the agent faces a decision problem with the following two acts:

a_1: accept responsibility for the shipment;

a_2: reject responsibility for the shipment.

If he selects a_1, he receives a flat fee of \$1,000 from the manufacturer but he must reset, at his own cost, any machine that is not in good order. The cost of resetting is estimated to be \$400. If the selects a_2, he receives no fee but is reimbursed by the manufacturer for any resetting costs. According to his past experience with this kind of machine, the probability distribution of the number of machines requiring resetting together with the payoffs is as shown in Table 25.P1.

TABLE 25.P1

No. of Machines Requiring Resetting θ_j	$f_0(\theta_j)$	Payoff	
		a_1	a_2
θ_1: 0	0.35	\$1,000	0
θ_2: 1	0.20	600	0
θ_3: 2	0.20	200	0
θ_4: 3	0.15	−200	0
θ_4: 4	0.10	−600	0

Suppose that the agent decides to conduct a preposterior analysis and suppose that the cost of sampling is \$25 per machine. If $n = 1$, $x_1 =$ the observed machine does not require resetting and $x_2 =$ the observed machine requires resetting; if $n = 2$, $x_1 =$ neither observed machine requires resetting, $x_2 =$ exactly one observed machine requires resetting, and $x_3 =$ both observed machines require resetting; and so on. For any machine drawn into the sample, the observational process produces absolutely correct information. Under these conditions, what is the complete preposterior analysis for the agent?

25.2 A wildcatter must decide whether to drill, a_1, or not to drill, a_2, for oil at a certain location. According to his careful calculations, he finally establishes a loss function for this venture in thousands of dollars as shown in Table 25.P2. The wildcatter is, however, unable to have a more precise judgment on the prior probabilities of the state values other than the assumption that both of the states are equally likely; that is, $f_0(\theta_1) = f_0(\theta_2) = 0.5$. He can, of course, revise these prior probabilities by the results of geological tests in form of seismic information. Each such test costs \$25,000. All such tests are independent of each other and provide absolutely accurate information. Conduct a complete preposterior analysis for the wildcatter's decision problem.

TABLE 25.P2

	State	
a_i	θ_1: oil	θ_2: no oil
a_1: drill	0	500
a_2: don't drill	1,000	0

25.3 A manufacturer who attempts to estimate the potential market of a new product has a beta prior with $r_0 = 1$ and $n_0 = 9$. His acts are infinitely numerous here, since they consist of all possible values for his market share, from $a = 0$ to $a = 1$. He also estimates the loss function to be $L(a, \tilde{\pi}) = \$150,000 \, (a - \pi)^2$ and the sampling-cost function to be $C(n) = \$200 + \$3n$. In this decision situation, what are n^* and $ENGS(n^*)$, respectively?

25.4 For the preceding problem, the manufacturer would like to introduce the product only if his market share is 0.2 or more. Suppose, in a sample of 58, 11 have indicated that they would like to buy his product. What would his decision be? Why?

25.5 A bank is considering establishing a new branch in a suburb. According to a feasibility study made by an economist, the proportion of the population in the area who may become customers of the proposed branch is characterized by a beta distribution with $r_0 = 2$ and $n_0 = 15$. The economist also hypothesized a loss function in the form of $L(a, \tilde{\pi}) = \$500,000 \, (a - \tilde{\pi})^2$. Suppose $C(n) = \$500 + \$6n$. What is the optimal sample size if the bank would like to base its decision on the basis of a preposterior analysis? What are the $EVSI$ and $ENGS$, respectively, for the optimal decision rule?

25.6 A retailer has an opportunity to buy a lot of 100,000 novelty items at a total cost of \$15,000, which he can sell at \$0.30 each. The retailer believes that he can sell most of the lot but any unsold items will become worthless. He judges that the sales have a prior normal density with $\mu_0 = 54,000$ and $\sigma_0 = 11,250$ units. He has 1,800 regular customers and, therefore, the prior analysis in terms of mean sales per customer would be defined by $\mu_0 = 54,000/1,800 = 30$ and $\sigma_0 = 11,250/1,800 = 6.25$. With these data, determine the payoff functions for $a_1 =$ buy the lot and $a_2 =$ don't buy the lot, respectively. Conduct a prior analysis.

Suppose the population variance is known to be 160 and suppose the retailer wishes to make a terminal decision with a posterior analysis by taking a sample with $n = 40$, which yields a sample mean of 32.5. What are the expected payoff and *EVSI* now? Compare the results of the prior and posterior analysis so far.

Now, suppose, for this problem, $C(n) = \$100 + \$3(n)$, what is the complete preposterior analysis? That is, what is his optimal decision rule?

25.7 The Goldstein Finance Company is offered a half interest in a newly formed manufacturing firm for electronic calculators for $4 million. Thus, Goldstein is confronted with a_1: invest in the firm and a_2: don't invest in firm. If the new firm is a success, θ_1, Goldstein will make a net profit of $8 million; if it is a failure, θ_2, Goldstein will lose all the original investment. In order to appraise the situation, Goldstein feels some research must be carried out. The research project will yield one of the following two indications:

x_1: the new firm will be a success;

x_2: the new firm will be a failure.

The research project will cost $350,000 and each of its possible indications is 65% reliable. Furthermore, prior probabilities for the two states are 0.4 and 0.6, respectively. Goldstein also believes that a more extensive research project should be undertaken after the results of the earlier research are known. This extra extensive research will cost $600,000 and each of its possible indications is 85% reliable. This project will yield x_1' (indication of success) or x_2' (indication of failure).
a. Draw a decision tree for this decision problem.
b. Conduct a prior analysis and verify that $EVPI_0 = \$2.4$ million.
c. Revise the prior probabilities with the results from the first research project and verify that $f(x_1) = 0.47$ and $f(x_2) = 0.53$.
d. Revise the prior probabilities with the results from the first and second projects and verify that given x_1, $f(x_1') = 0.5372$, and $f(x_2') = 0.4628$; and that given x_2, $f(x_1') = 0.3350$, and $f(x_2') = 0.6650$.
e. Redraw the decision tree with predictive and posterior probabilities entered at the appropriate branches. Compute the expected payoffs for various decision forks from the end of the tree inward.
f. State the overall optimal strategy for Goldstein's investment problem and verify that the net expected payoff for the sequential decision rule is approximately $1.41 million.

25.8 ABC, Inc., has to decide between

a_1: market the new product, and

a_2: don't market the new product,

whose opportunity losses, conditional upon the two states of nature

θ_1: the new product is a success,

θ_2: the new product is a failure,

are estimated (in units of $100,000) to be as in Table 25.P3.

TABLE 25.P3

	θ_1: success	θ_2: failure
a_1: market	$ 0	12
a_2: don't market	15	0

The prior probabilities of success and failure are estimated as 0.30 and 0.70, respectively. ABC is contemplating making this decision with a two-stage sequential sampling plan. Each market survey costs $80,000. Survey results are to be classified as favorable, indifferent, and unfavorable. The likelihoods of these results for each survey are estimated as below. For the first survey:

$$f(x_1 \mid \theta_1) = 0.70, \qquad f(x_2 \mid \theta_1) = 0.18, \qquad f(x_3 \mid \theta_1) = 0.12;$$

$$f(x_1 \mid \theta_2) = 0.10, \qquad f(x_2 \mid \theta_2) = 0.10, \qquad f(x_3 \mid \theta_2) = 0.80.$$

For the second survey:

$$f(x_1' \mid \theta_1) = 0.80, \qquad f(x_2' \mid \theta_1) = 0.10, \qquad f(x_3' \mid \theta_1) = 0.10;$$

$$f(x_1' \mid \theta_2) = 0.05, \qquad f(x_2' \mid \theta_2) = 0.08, \qquad f(x_3' \mid \theta_2) = 0.87.$$

Give a complete evaluation of the sequential decision procedure with the aid of decision trees.

26 Nonparametric Statistics

26.1 INTRODUCTION

In our previous discussions on classical and Bayesian inferential procedures, we have often assumed that the population distributions are somehow known. The assumption most frequently employed is that the populations are normally distributed. Such an assumption is often unjustified in reality. Sometimes the data show conclusively that the population is nonnormal, as in the case of family income of a given nation. Sometimes the data do not show conclusively whether the population is normal or nonnormal, as in the case of reactions to an experimental arthritis drug, where a dozen people took the experimental drug and a dozen people took a conventional pain reliever. Here, the sample sizes are too small for us to judge whether the populations are normal, or anything reasonably close to normal.

There is, fortunately, a third approach to inferences that does not require any assumption about normality or, for that matter, any assumption at all about the distribution patterns of the elements in the population—except, occasionally, very mild assumptions concerning continuity, symmetry, or unimodality. Inferential procedures by this approach are called *nonparametric statistics*. This name, however, is quite unfortunate, because it suggests that values of population parameters are not involved. Nothing could be further from the truth. With this approach, as with the classical or Bayesian, the purpose of taking a sample is, as always, the estimation of a parameter. A better name for nonparametric statistics is *distribution-free statistics,* which suggests appropriately that the methods are free from any assumption about the distribution of the elements in the population.

Distribution-free statistics can be used to study a sample selected at random from virtually any kind of population, and thus nonparametric statistics are almost universally applicable. This universality carries a price, however—a price so high that it should not be paid unless we have no choice in the matter. Essentially, this price is the probability of committing type II error. In general, a nonparametric test has a substantially greater value of β, for the same value of α, than a similar parametric test has. Therefore, if a choice is available, the parametric test should always be used. Very often, a choice is not available, so that nonparametric tests become our only avenue in statistical analysis.

Unquestionably, nonparametric methods are very useful. Many have been designed and widely used in the recent past; it seems fitting then that we should have at least a brief survey of nonparametric theory in a text on modern statistical analysis.

Actually, the reader is not completely ignorant of nonparametric statistics. The Durbin–Watson test on serial correlation is a nonparametric technique. Chebyshev's theorem is also a nonparametric result. In the pages that follow, we present a number of nonparametric tests that have been found to be useful and reasonably efficient.

26.2 TESTS ON RANDOMNESS

Two questions frequently encountered in statistical applications are: (1) Is this sample a random sample? and (2) Is this process a random process? The first question can be answered only by examining the selection method—not the sample results themselves. If serial numbers were assigned to members of the frame and random digits were then used to select serial numbers, the sample is a random sample, provided of course that no mistakes were made during this procedure. The second question arises when we want to know whether a sample known to be nonrandomly selected can, nevertheless, be treated as if it were a random sample. An example of such data would be the number of defective items produced each day by a newly installed machine. Assuming the total number of items produced each day is a constant, we can then work either with the number of defective items or the proportion of defective items, for quality control. Suppose, in the judgment of the foreman and the supervising engineers, the machine has been properly installed and adjusted and should be producing in the way it is going to produce for the rest of its useful life. We can then gather a few weeks' data on the numbers of defective items and see whether these data behave like a random series. We are asking whether this process is random. We cannot hope to answer this question fully, since there is no limit to the aspects of randomness that must be tested before the data have been "completely" tested for randomness. We can, though, test for some aspects of randomness. Our null hypothesis is that the data are random, independent drawings from a stable population.

In this section, we shall introduce two simple nonparametric tests for randomness based on the concept of "runs": (1) runs above and below the median, and (2) runs up and down.

Runs Above and Below the Median

Suppose that we have a sample of, say, 26 observations gathered as listed in the order below:

$$97, 89, 25, 81, 11, 83, 16, 96, 44, 32, 98, 19, 68,$$

$$33, 25, 54, 74, 82, 17, 49, 33, 22, 62, 20, 92, 80$$

The median is $(54 + 49)/2 = 51.5$. We proceed to observe now whether each observation is above or below this median value. If above the median, we mark it as an a, and if below the median, we mark it as a b. For the sample above, we have the following sequence of a's and b's:

$$aa-b-a-b-a-b-a-bb-a-b-a-bb-aaa-bbbb-a-b-aa.$$

Each sequence of a's or b's, uninterrupted by the other letter, is a *run* and we have, therefore, 17 runs for our data.

Now, the number of runs above and below the median is a random variable. Under the null hypothesis that the sample is randomly selected, R is approximately normally distributed for $n \geq 25$ with

$$E(R) = \frac{n + 2}{2} \qquad (26.1)$$

and

$$V(R) = \frac{n(n - 2)}{4(n - 1)}. \qquad (26.2)$$

The alternative hypothesis is often of the left-tail variety. This is especially appropriate if we suspect clustering of like observations, that is, too few runs, since such a situation often indicates a shifting population mean. We may occasionally wish to conduct a right-tail test to look for systematic swings above and below the median from one observation to another. When we have no specific ideas, except that H_1 should be the opposite of H_0, we may then proceed to make a two-sided test. In any event, the test statistic is

$$Z = \frac{R - E(R)}{\sqrt{V(R)}}. \qquad (26.3)$$

Suppose that we wish to have a two-sided test for our illustrative data at $\alpha = 0.01$; we would have

$$E(R) = \frac{26 + 2}{2} = 14;$$

$$V(R) = \frac{26(26 - 2)}{4(26 - 1)} = 6.24;$$

$$Z = \frac{17 - 14}{\sqrt{6.24}} \doteq 1.20.$$

Since the observed value of Z falls between -2.58 and $+2.58$, H_0 cannot be rejected at the 1% level of significance. Our sample is selected randomly, independently, and at a stable rate, as far as this test can tell.

When there are sample values that are tied with (equal to) the median value, either they may be disregarded so that the number of runs and sample size are reduced, or they may be assigned a's or b's by a random process such as the toss of a coin. Notice that nothing at all was said about the form of the population distribution.

Runs Up and Down

A test for runs up and down is similar to the preceding test. Given a sample of n observations recorded in the order obtained, we place either a plus sign (+) or a minus sign (−) between each pair of successive observations, depending on whether the latter observation is greater or less than the preceding observation. Now, each string of + 's or − 's, uninterrupted by the other sign, is counted as a run. For example, using the same sample data, we have

$$- - + - + - + - - + - + - - + + + - + - - + - + -,$$

a total of 19 runs. Be sure to note these signs are determined between two successive observations, and that there are $(n - 1)$ such signs for a sample of size n. Again, ties may be broken by a chance process.

Under the null hypothesis as stated before, R is approximately normally distributed for $n \geq 20$ with

$$E(R) = (1/3)(2n - 1) \tag{26.4}$$

and

$$V(R) = (1/90)(16n - 29). \tag{26.5}$$

The test statistic is

$$Z = \frac{R - E(R)}{\sqrt{V(R)}}. \tag{26.6}$$

Suppose we wish to test against a left-tail alternative, with our illustrative data, at $\alpha = 0.01$; we have then

$$R = 19;$$
$$E(R) = (1/3)(2(26) - 1) = 17;$$
$$V(R) = (1/90)(16(26) - 29) = 4.3;$$
$$Z = \frac{19 - 17}{\sqrt{43}} \doteq 0.96.$$

Note that $0.96 > -2.33$, and randomness is accepted at $\alpha = 0.01$.

26.3 VON NEUMANN RATIO TEST ON INDEPENDENCE

Tests for independence are the same as the tests for randomness. We have here distinguished these two types of tests merely for the purpose of convenience in presentation. Now, in this section, we shall introduce a procedure called the *Von Neumann ratio* for testing randomness (independence) in time-series data. The D–W test for serial correlation discussed in Chapter 19 is a generalized Von Neumann ratio test.

Business and economic data ordered in time sequences are known to be nonrandom samples. Often, an observation in price, production, national income, or the like, for a month or year is statistically dependent to some extent upon the value of that variable in the previous time period. This dependence or "lag" relationship between successive terms of a time series is called *serial correlation*. Sometimes, the terms *autocorrelation* and *lag correlation* are also employed for this dependence relationship. When a distinction is made, one often takes *autocorrelation* to mean the lag relationship in the population, *serial correlation* to mean the lag relationship in a sample, and *lag correlation* to mean the lag relationship between two different time series. However, these terms are often used interchangeably, and this is the practice we shall adopt in this text.

A key question, always, in testing for independence is whether $P(x_{i+1} = a \mid x_i = b) = P(x_{i-1} = a)$. If the probabilities are equal for all values of i, there is no serial correlation, as far as this test is concerned. The key question asks whether knowledge of the value of the ith observation helps in predicting the value of the $(i + 1)$th observation. If it does, serial correlation is definitely present. If it does not, serial correlation is absent as far as this test is concerned. For example, in repeatedly rolling a fair die, the knowledge that the 64th roll was a five is no help at all in predicting the outcome of the 65th roll. $P(x_{65} = a \mid x_{64} = 5) = P(x_{65} = a) = 1/6$ for each value of a. As another example, suppose you had never looked at the temperature data for Minneapolis for 1905, but were asked to give right now the daily low temperature for April Fool's Day (April 1, 1905). If you are generally familiar with weather patterns in the United States Midwest, you know that this is early spring in Minneapolis and quite changeable—the weather can be very cold, or rather cool with a howling blizzard, or gorgeously sunny and very mild. Would it help you "predict" the April Fool's Day low if you knew the preceding day's low? Of course it would. If March 31st's low was 0°F., it was a cold snap and April 1st was quite likely to be cold, also. If March 31st's low was 45°F., it was a warm spell, and April 1st was quite likely to be warm, also. Serial correlation is definitely present.

The general version of the key question does not restrict the lag to just one observation. That is, the general version asks whether $P(x_{i+j} = a \mid x_i = b) = P(x_{i+j} = a)$ for all i and j, $j \geqslant 1$. If so, serial correlation is absent. If, for any values of i and j, the probabilities are unequal, serial correlation is present.

If serial correlation is present, it can be either "positive" or "negative." Speaking intuitively, positive serial correlation means that a high observation is likely to be followed by another high observation and a low observation is likely to be followed by another low observation. The Minneapolis temperature example had positive serial correlation. Many sets of data exhibit positive serial correlation. Negative serial correlation means that an unusually high observation is likely to be followed by an unusually low observation and an unusually low observation is likely to be followed by an unusually high observation. It might be thought that such sets of data are rare, but in any event they do exist. There can be an obvious explanation for such data, often involving a corrective process that is not properly adjusted. For example, on a cold winter day in Minneapolis, the thermostat in a house could let the house get quite cold, say 60°F., before turning on the furnace, and then let the house get quite warm, say 80°F., before turning off the furnace. The average temperature would be about 70°F., but temperature observations taken every 15 minutes would show an obvious and systematic tendency for a high reading to be immediately (that is, in 15 minutes) followed by a low reading, and vice versa. The readings for a whole day would show many more cycles above and below the average than, say, readings taken at random from a population that is normal with a mean of 70°F. and a standard deviation of 5°F.

The Von Neumann ratio test of independence is based on the *mean-square-successive difference*, defined as follows:

$$K = \frac{\delta^2}{S_Y^2},\qquad(26.7)$$

where

$$\delta^2 = \frac{1}{n-1}\sum_i (y_{i+1} - y_i)^2$$

and

$$S_Y^2 = \frac{1}{n}\sum_i (y_i - \bar{Y})^2.$$

As implied by the definition of δ^2, the ratio K is closely related to the variance of the differences between successive observations. When these differences are small, a small K will result and positive serial correlation in the population is indicated. When these differences are large, a large K will result and negative serial correlation is revealed. Thus, very large and very small values of K would lead us to the rejection of randomness or independence.

To effect the test of independence by the Von Neumann ratio, a table worked out by B. I. Hart, presented in Appendix C as Table XIV may be used. This table gives the 5% and 1% points of the distribution of K. It gives two critical values, k and k', for each level of significance and each sample size. For instance, if $n = 10$ and $\alpha = 0.05$, $k = 1.1803$ and $k' = 3.2642$. If $K < k$, K is considered as significant and we reject H_0 and conclude that there exists positive serial correlation. If $K > k'$, we would reject H_0 and conclude that negative serial correlation exists. H_0 is accepted when $k < K < k'$.

Using the hypothetical data in Table 26.1 as an illustration, we have the following results:

$$\bar{y} = \frac{70}{8} = 8.75;$$

$$s_Y^2 = \frac{43.5}{8} \doteq 5.44;$$

$$\delta^2 = \frac{27}{(8-1)} \doteq 3.86;$$

$$K = \frac{3.86}{5.44} \doteq 0.71,$$

We see from Table XIV that $0.71 < 0.7575 = k$ for $n = 8$; H_0 is rejected at $\alpha = 0.01$. Positive serial correlation exists in the population.

TABLE 26.1 Data Illustrating the Von Neumann Ratio Test

Year	y_i	$(y_i - \bar{y})^2$	$(y_{i+1} - y_i)^2$
1	5	14.0625	4
2	7	3.0625	1
3	6	7.5625	16
4	10	1.5625	0
5	10	1.5625	1
6	9	0.0625	4
7	11	5.0625	1
8	12	10.5625	—
Total	70	43.5000	27

Source: Hypothetical.

26.4 SIGN TEST ON POPULATION MEDIAN

A nonparametric method frequently used to test hypotheses on the population median $\tilde{x}_{.5}$, is the *one-sample sign test*. This test, though not all that powerful, is highly useful on three accounts. First, it may be applied even if the data are measured on the ordinal scale. Second, it requires no assumption of any kind about the population distribution. Third, it is applicable even if the sample is small.

The procedure for conducting a test on the median by the sign test is as follows.

1. Specify the value of the population median in H_0. This value may be denoted as $\tilde{x}_{.5(0)}$.

2. List the observations of the sample values and give each of these values a "sign". A plus sign is assigned to a sample value if it is greater than $\tilde{x}_{.5(0)}$; a minus sign is assigned to a sample value if it less than $\tilde{x}_{.5(0)}$. When the sample value is equal to $\tilde{x}_{.5(0)}$ it is marked "0" and is eliminated from the analysis; the sample size is reduced accordingly.

3. The test statistic in this sign test is denoted as S, which may be the sum of the plus signs or the sum of minus signs, depending upon the type of test that is to be conducted, as described next.

4. Finally, the decision rule is to compare S with critical values of S that are the fractiles of the distribution of S, which, in turn, as shown in Table 26.2, depend upon the values of n and α. We note

TABLE 26.2 Fractiles of the Distribution of S for the Sign Test on Population Median

n	α 0.005	0.025	0.05	0.125	n	α 0.005	0.025	0.05	0.125
1	—	—	—	—	16	2	3	4	5
2	—	—	—	—	17	2	4	4	5
3	—	—	—	0	18	3	4	5	6
4	—	—	—	0	19	3	4	5	6
5	—	—	0	0	20	3	5	5	6
6	—	0	0	1	21	4	5	6	7
7	—	0	0	1	22	4	5	6	7
8	0	0	1	1	23	4	6	7	8
9	0	1	1	2	24	5	6	7	8
10	0	1	1	2	25	5	7	7	9
11	0	1	2	3	26	6	7	8	9
12	1	2	2	3	27	6	7	8	10
13	1	2	3	3	28	6	8	9	10
14	1	2	3	4	29	7	8	9	10
15	2	3	3	4	30	7	9	10	11

Source: Adopted from Table 1 in W. J. Mockinnon, "Table for Both Sign Test and Distribution-Free Confidence Intervals of the Median for Sizes to 1,000," *Journal of the American Statistical Association*, **59** (1964), 935–56.

TABLE 26.3 Sign Test for Supermarket Data (in Thousands of Dollars with $\bar{x}_{.5(0)} = 145$)

Sample Value	Sign	Sample Value	Sign	Sample Value	Sign
146	+	148	+	139	−
107	−	145	0	150	+
145	0	102	−	122	−
125	−	115	−	110	−
143	−	149	+	119	−
109	−	150	+	123	−

the following three types of tests:

a. For a lower-tail test, S = the number of (+) signs and H_0 is rejected if and only if $S \leqslant S_{n;\alpha}$.

b. For an upper-tail test, S = the number of (−) signs and H_0 is rejected if and only if $S \leqslant S_{n;\alpha}$.

c. For a double-tail test, S = the number of (+) signs or number of (−) signs, whichever is smaller, and H_0 is rejected if and only if $S \leqslant S_{n;\alpha/2}$.

Table 26.2 gives the critical values of S for a few selected fractiles for S with sample sizes from 1 to 30 inclusive.

Let us consider an example for the illustration of the one-sample sign test on population median. The President of a new national supermarket chain, which has just finished its first year of business, wishes to find out whether the median volume of average monthly sales of the stores is greater than $145 thousand dollars, as initially projected by his consultants. For this problem, he decides to obtain the answer by testing $H_0: \tilde{x}_{.5} \geqslant 145$ against $H_1: \tilde{x}_{.5} < 145$. A random sample of 18 stores has been selected for observation and the results, together with their signs, are as recorded in Table 26.3. In this table we find that two sample values are equal to the hypothesized value of $145. These two values are discarded and the sample size is reduced to 16. Also, for a lower-tail test, the value of S is the number of plus signs and is 5. Now, suppose the President sets $\alpha = 0.05$, H_0 will be rejected if and only if $S \leqslant S_{16;0.05}$. From Table 26.2, we find this critical value to be 4. Since the computed value of S is greater than the critical value, H_0 cannot be rejected. Evidently, the initial projection seems adequate.

26.5 THEOREM OF CHI-SQUARE TESTS ON GOODNESS-OF-FIT

Chi-square is an amazingly versatile statistic. In addition to its use for inference with variances, it can also be used to test any hypothesis concerning categorical data, of which the binomial form is but a special case. We are concerned here with categorical data consisting of absolute frequencies occurring in the various classes or compartments of a table of simple or multiple classifications. Owing to the differences in classification and in reasons for testing, chi-square tests can themselves be classified as tests for goodness-of-fit, the independence of cross-classification (or contingency) tables, and homogeneity. These chi-square tests constitute a part of nonparametric statistics. In general, the chi-square tests on frequencies are called *chi-square tests on goodness-of-fit*.

We begin here with some general comments on such tests. *Goodness-of-fit tests* constitute a way of deciding whether a population has some specific distribution when only sample data are available and due allowances are made for sampling error. Precisely, we wish to test the null hypothesis that the population has exactly the distribution as specified against the alternative that the population does not have the distribution as specified. We proceed to inquire what should be the *expected*, or *theoretical*, *frequencies* if the null hypothesis is true. We denote such frequencies as e_i. Next, we investigate sample data for the purpose of establishing what are called *observed frequencies* o_i. Finally, we compare these two sets of frequencies and, on the basis of their differences, form an appropriate decision criterion to judge whether these differences are due to chance variations in random sampling. If so, H_0 is not rejected; otherwise, it is rejected.

There are a number of ways of measuring the amount of disagreement between observed and expected frequencies. The following expression is most frequently used:

$$\sum_{i}^{k} \frac{(o_i - e_i)^2}{e_i},$$

where the summation is over the k classes of the frequencies. Furthermore, the distribution of this sum is given by Theorem 26.1.

THEOREM 26.1 SAMPLING DISTRIBUTION OF $\sum_{i=1}^{k} [(o_i - e_i)^2/e_i]$ *If a population has k classes, $k \geq 2$, if the proportions of the population in various categories are $\pi_1, \pi_2, \ldots, \pi_k$, and if an SRS with size n is selected from the population with replacement, then as n approaches infinity, the statistic*

$$\chi_\delta^2 = \sum_{i=1}^{k} \frac{(o_i - e_i)}{e_i} \tag{26.8}$$

has a χ^2 distribution with δ equal to the number of classes or categories compared, less the number of restrictions imposed on the comparison, where $e_i = n\pi_i$ = the expected number of sample observations in one category $(i = 1, 2, \ldots, k)$, o_i = the observed number of sample observations in the same category as e_i.

This theorem is often called the χ^2 *goodness-of-fit, test*.

In the application of Theorem 26.1, there are a number of important points to be observed.

1. No assumption is made about the population distribution. It does not matter whether the individual values of the population are normally, uniformly, exponentially, or in any other way distributed. The statistic, in other words, is distribution-free.

2. Although the theorem calls for simple random sampling with replacement, it is applicable without change if sampling without replacement is used, unless the population is very small relative to the sample size.

3. In the determination of the number of degrees of freedom for (26.8), $\delta = k - 1$ if the expected frequencies are computed without having to estimate population parameters from sample statistics. When $\delta = k - 1$, if we know $k - 1$ of the expected frequencies, the remaining expected frequency is uniquely determined because we must satisfy the condition $\sum o_i = \sum e_i = n$. However, for (26.8), $\delta = k - 1 - m$ if we can compute the expected frequencies only after estimating m parameters by sample statistics.

4. The sample size does not have to be anywhere near infinity to have close approximation to the chi-square distribution. As rule of thumb, if $e_i \geq 5$ for each class, Theorem 26.1 applies. Even this rule is sometimes relaxed, permitting one or two categories have expected frequencies as low as 2. However, if quite a few classes have expected frequencies substantially below 5, Theorem 26.1 does not apply, because the measure of disagreement between observed and expected frequencies no longer obeys the χ^2 probability law.

5. Classes, or categories, can be combined, when necessary, to satisfy the rule that $e_i \geq 5$ for all categories in the final calculations. In doing this, it must be remembered that the number of degrees of freedom is determined by the number of classes after the regrouping.

6. The values of o_i must be whole numbers or 0. In addition, the o_i must be absolute frequencies, not relative frequencies or any kind of density. The values of e_i however, need not be whole numbers, as our later examples show.

7. Whenever $\delta = 1$, especially when the total frequency is small, say, less than 50, it is advisable to introduce a continuity correction factor of $\frac{1}{2}$ in calculating the chi-square values. That is, when $\delta = 1$, we modify (26.8) in the following way:

$$\chi_\delta^2 = \sum_{i=1}^{k} \frac{(|o_i - e_i| - \frac{1}{2})^2}{e_i}, \qquad |o_i - e_i| \geq \frac{1}{2}. \qquad (26.9)$$

Whenever $|o_i - e_i| < \frac{1}{2}$, we take $|o_i - e_i| = 0$. With this practice, (26.9) applies to all o_i and e_i.

With this much background, we move now to some specific χ^2 tests of goodness-of-fit.

26.6 χ^2 TEST ON GOODNESS-OF-FIT OF A TRIANGLE DISTRIBUTION

Suppose we are interested in finding out whether a particular pair of backgammon dice used in a casino game is fair, we may test H_0: the dice are fair, against H_1: the dice are not fair. We can also test H_0: the sum of the two dice is distributed as a triangle, against H_1: the sum of the two dice is not distributed as a triangle. These two sets of hypotheses are identical, since if the dice are fair, then the distribution of the sum, which ranges in value from 2 to 12 inclusive, must be distributed as a triangle. In any event, whichever way the hypotheses are formulated, the problem can be analyzed by employing Theorem 26.1.

Suppose we have tossed the said pair of dice 200 times and the numbers of each possible sum from the trials are given in columns (1) and (2) in Table 26.4. Obviously, the numbers entered in the second column of Table 26.4 are the observed frequencies for the sums. Under the assumption that the dice are fair, the probability that the sum will be 2 in a single toss of a toss is 1/36. Therefore, the expected number of occcurrences of a sum of 2 in one toss of the dice is 1/36 and in 200 tosses it is (1/36)(200). The expected frequencies for each of the other possible sums can be computed in exactly the same manner. (Note that the probability distribution of the sum in tossing two fair dice is a triangle.) The values are given in column (3) of Table 26.4. From values of o_i and e_i and by (26.8), we obtain the χ^2 value via the computations made in the last column of Table 26.4.

Usually, the χ^2 test on goodness-of-fit is of the upper-tail variety. Hence, for our current example, if we set $\alpha = 0.01$, with $\delta = k - 1 =$

TABLE 26.4 The χ^2 Test on the Fairness of Two Dice

Sum (1)	o_i (2)	e_i (3)	$(o_i - e_i)^2/e_i$ (4)
2	6	$(1/36)(200) \doteq 5.56$	$(6 - 5.56)^2/5.56 = 0.035$
3	12	$(2/36)(200) \doteq 11.11$	$(12 - 11.11)^2/11.11 \doteq 0.071$
4	17	$(3/36)(200) \doteq 16.67$	$(17 - 16.67)^2/16.67 \doteq 0.007$
5	25	$(4/36)(200) \doteq 22.22$	$(25 - 22.22)^2/22.22 \doteq 0.143$
6	23	$(5/36)(200) \doteq 27.78$	$(23 - 27.78)^2/27.78 = 0.514$
7	33	$(6/36)(200) \doteq 33.33$	$(33 - 33.33)^2/33.33 \doteq 0.003$
8	28	$(5/36)(200) \doteq 27.78$	$(28 - 27.78)^2/27.78 = 0.017$
9	18	$(4/36)(200) \doteq 22.22$	$(18 - 22.22)^2/22.22 \doteq 0.801$
10	21	$(3/36)(200) \doteq 16.67$	$(21 - 16.67)^2/16.67 \doteq 1.125$
11	13	$(2/36)(200) \doteq 11.11$	$(13 - 11.11)^2/11.11 = 0.322$
12	4	$(1/36)(200) \doteq 5.56$	$(4 - 5.56)^2/5.56 = 0.438$
Total	200	$\sum e_i \doteq 200.00$	$\chi_{10}^2 \doteq 3.989$

Source: Experimental results of tossing two dice two hundred times, conducted by this author's assistant, Ming Yang Wang, June, 1987.

$11 - 1 = 10$, the critical value of χ^2_{10} is 21.67, which is much larger than the computed value of approximately 3.989. H_0 cannot be rejected. We may take this conclusion either to mean that the dice are fair or to mean that the fit of a triangle distribution to the sum of tossing two dice is very close or very good.

26.7 THE χ^2 TEST OF GOODNESS-OF-FIT OF NORMALITY

As mentioned before, many parametric tests require that the population be normally distributed or at least approximately normally distributed, or that the CLT holds. It seems proper that when we encounter a new situation in which the assumption of normality for the population is required, we should conduct a test first to see whether such an assumption is plausible. A χ^2 test of goodness-of-fit can be run on sample data for this purpose. Here, we would like to know whether the sample drawn from the population under investigation is consistent with some normal distribution for which both the mean and standard deviation are unknown. One way to find out is to test the null hypothesis that the population is exactly normal against the alternative hypothesis that the population is not normally distributed. Then we proceed to take a sample of n observations and use the sample mean and sample standard deviation as estimates for the corresponding parameters to calculate π_i. Next, we compute the theoretical or expected frequencies which are subject to three constraints: $\sum e_i = n$, $\mu = \bar{X}$, and $\sigma = S$. Thus, in the application of (26.8) to fit a normal distribution to sample data, we have $\delta = k - 1 - m = k - 1 - 2 = k - 3$—three degrees of freedom are lost.

As an example of the χ^2 test on normality, suppose a sample of 360 observations consists of measurements of electrical resistance in each of 360 electronic components selected at random from a day's production, resulting in the frequency distribution shown in the first three columns of Table 26.5.

TABLE 26.5 A χ^2 Test on Normality

| Resistance | | o_i | π_i | e_i | $(o_i - e_i)^2/e_i$ |
Over (1)	Through (2)	(3)	(4)	(5)	(6)
3.3	3.4	10	0.0307[a]	11.052[a]	0.10
3.4	3.5	37	0.1007	36.252	0.02
3.5	3.6	73	0.2243	80.748	0.74
3.6	3.7	114	0.2886	103.896	0.98
3.7	3.8	81	0.2243	80.748	0.00
3.8	3.9	31	0.1007	36.252	0.76
3.9	4.0	14	0.0307[b]	11.052[b]	0.79
Total		360	1.0000	360.000	3.39

[a] For the interval from $-\infty$ to 3.4.
[b] For the interval from 3.9 to ∞.
Source: Hypothetical.

As you can easily verify, with the grouped data in columns (1) through (3), we find that

$$\bar{x} \doteq 3.65 \text{ ohms} \qquad \text{and} \qquad s \doteq 0.1337 \text{ ohm.}$$

From these results, we wish to know whether the electrical resistance of the day's production is normally distributed. By using 3.65 and 0.1337 as μ and σ for the random variable X—(electrical resistance), it is quite simple to compute the π_i and e_i for the categories (classes) in Table 26.5. For instance, π_2 is calculated as follows:

$$\pi_2 \doteq P(3.4 < X \leqslant 3.5)$$
$$\doteq N\left(\frac{3.5 - 3.65}{0.1337}\right) - N\left(\frac{3.4 - 3.65}{0.1337}\right)$$
$$\doteq N(-1.12) - N(-1.87)$$
$$\doteq 0.1314 - 0.0307$$
$$= 0.1007.$$

This result is entered into the fourth column of Table 26.5. For this class, $e_2 = (0.1007)(360) = 36.252$ and this appears in the fifth column of Table 26.5.

It is important to note that in the first three columns of Table 26.5 the categories are not collectively exhaustive. This problem arises because we have no data at or below 3.3 ohms or above 4.0 ohms, but a normal curve still allocates some probability in both tails beyond these two values. A practical and reasonable solution to this problem is to redefine the first category so that it runs from $-\infty$ to 3.4 and to redefine the last category so that it runs from 4.0 to ∞. With these designations, no part of the normal distribution's area is ignored, and the π_i still add to 1 as they should.

For our example, the computed value of χ^2 is 3.39, with $\delta = 7 - 1 - 2 = 4$. If we set $\alpha = 0.05$, the region of rejection is from 9.49 to ∞. Our calculated value is nowhere near this region. The fit of a normal distribution is good as far as this test can discover. H_0 is not rejected.

Had we summarized the data using 14 categories (classes) instead of 7, the fit with a normal distribution would have been poor and H_0 would have been rejected with the same set of sample data. This implies that the consequence of applying the χ^2 test on frequencies with class intervals is somewhat dependent on the choice of class intervals.

26.8 THE χ^2 TEST ON INDEPENDENCE

As the previous two sections reveal, the χ^2 test on goodness-of-fit is in essence the test on frequencies of two or more categories. As such, χ^2 tests are concerned with populations as well as samples classified in accordance with a single attribute distributed as the multinomial probability law. We shall now see that the same technique of chi-square tests can be applied to many other types of data. We are, for instance, often interested in whether two or more factors are statistically independent. The factors can be called "treatments" or "attributes" or "random variables."

When the population and the sample are classified according to two or more attributes, we may use *tests of independence* to determine whether the attributes are statistically independent. For instance, a random sample of n retail stores may be cross-classified by size of capitalization and by type of ownership. The proportion of each of the classes in the population is unknown. Our interest would be to establish whether there is any dependency relationship between a store's capitalization and its type of ownership. Clearly, in a case such as this, we would want to test the hypothesis that the size of capitalization is independent of the type of ownership against the hypothesis that they are related or dependent.

Tests of independence are also called *contingency-table tests*. So far, we have been concerned with only *one-way classification tables* since, in each case, the observed frequencies have occupied a single row or a single column. Also, because the observed frequencies are distributed in k classes (columns or rows), one-way classification tables are called $1 \times k$ (read 1 *by k*) or $k \times 1$ *tables*. Extending these ideas, we can arrive at tables in which the observed frequencies occupy r rows and c columns. Such tables are often called *contingency tables*. Corresponding to each observed frequency in an $r \times c$ table, there is an expected frequency computed under the specified null hypothesis. Frequencies, observed or expected, that occupy the cells of a contingency table are called *cell frequencies*. The total frequency in each row or each column is called a *marginal frequency*.

To evaluate differences between observed and expected frequencies contained in contingency tables, we employ the same statistic as that for the tests discussed in the previous section, i.e. Equation (26.8). However, this equation is now written in a slightly different way:

$$\chi_\delta^2 = \sum_{i=1}^{rc} \frac{(o_i - e_i)^2}{e_i}.$$

The sum is taken over all the rc cells in a contingency table; in general,

$$\delta = (r - 1)(c - 1).$$

In testing independence with a 2×2 contingency table, we have $\delta = (2 - 1)(2 - 1) = 1$. As recommended before, the continuity correction factor of 1/2 should be then used to compute the chi-square value. For large samples, corrected and uncorrected chi-square values may be practically the same, and so the continuity correction factor may be ignored. Moreover, to test two or more factors for statistical independence, we may compute an expected cell frequency by

$$e = \frac{\text{column total}}{\text{grand total}} (\text{row total}). \tag{26.10}$$

Finally, since the expected frequencies must agree with the marginal total of the observed frequencies, and since there are only four cells in a 2×2 contingency table, once a single cell expected frequency is computed all the rest can be filled in automatically. Consider an example as follows.

There is reason to believe that high-income families usually send their children to private colleges and low-income families often send their children to city or state colleges. To verify this, 1,600 families are selected at random from California and the following results are obtained.

Observed data

| Income | College | | Total |
	Private	Public	
Low	506	494	1,000
High	438	162	600
Total	944	656	1,600

Here, we have two classifications: income, and type of college. We see at a glance that, relatively, a greater number of high-income families send their children to private colleges than do low-income families. But is such a difference in proportions significant or is it merely the result of chance variations in random sampling? The chi-square test of independence can be used to answer questions such as this by comparing the set of observed frequencies with that of expected frequencies.

The null hypothesis here is, essentially, that family income and type of college are independent. Tentatively assuming that this H_0 is true, we are then justified to use (26.10) to compute the expected cell frequencies. For example, the expected number of low-income families that send their children to private colleges is

$$e = \frac{944}{1600} (1000) = 590.$$

With this result, all other expected frequencies can be filled in as shown by the following display.

Expected Data

| Income | College | | Total |
	Private	Public	
Low	590	410	1,000
High	354	246	600
Total	944	656	1,600

From the observed and expected frequencies determined, by the modified version of (26.8), we have

$$\chi_1^2 = \sum_{i=1}^{rc} \frac{(o_i - e_i)^2}{e_i}$$

$$= \frac{(506 - 590)^2}{590} + \frac{(494 - 410)^2}{410} + \frac{(438 - 354)^2}{354} + \frac{(162 - 246)^2}{246}$$

$$\doteq 77.78.$$

(*Note:* The computation is made here without the continuity correction, because the sample is large.)

Since $P(\chi_1^2 \geq 3.84) = 0.05$ and $P(\chi_1^2 \geq 6.63) = 0.01$, the null hypothesis of statistical independence is rejected at $\alpha = 0.05$ as well as at $\alpha = 0.01$. Family income and type of college are dependent.

As a second example, let us consider this: Are men different from women with respect to their concept of a successful life defined in terms of material well-being M, spiritual well-being S, and fame F? Suppose that a random sample of 430 people has been selected across the United States and the following results have been obtained:

Observed Data

Sex	Successful Life			Total
	M	S	F	
Men	80	95	60	235
Women	60	70	65	195
Total	140	165	125	430

In this case, we are interested in testing the hypothesis that one's concept of a successful life is independent of one's sex against the hypothesis that one's sex is related to one's idea of a successful life. The null hypothesis here says that men and women are of the same opinion insofar as the meaning of a successful life is concerned. Under this assumption, we would expect by (26.10), for example, 140/430 of the 430 people interviewed to define a successful life as material well-being. The expected numbers of men and of women who consider this a criterion for a successful life, respectively, are

$$(140/430)(235) = 76.51;$$

$$(140/430)(195) = 63.49.$$

Expected frequencies for other cells can be obtained in the same manner; they are recorded below.

Expected Data

Sex	Successful Life			Total
	M	S	F	
Men	76.51	90.17	68.32	235
Women	63.49	74.83	56.68	195
Total	140.00	165.00	125.00	430

There are six cells for a 2×3 contingency table. The requirement that cell frequencies must agree with marginal frequencies, however, gives us but 2 degrees of freedom. We are free to place one number in one of the three columns and to place another number in any one of the four cells of the remaining two columns. After these two numbers are given, all numbers in the empty cells are uniquely determined from the indicated marginal frequencies. This conclusion is in agreement with the fact that $\delta = (r - 1)(c - 1) = (2 - 1)(3 - 1) = 2$.

For the data given before, we find that

$$\chi_2^2 = \frac{(80 - 76.51)^2}{76.51} + \frac{(95 - 90.17)^2}{90.17} + \frac{(60 - 68.32)^2}{68.32}$$
$$+ \frac{(60 - 63.49)^2}{63.49} + \frac{(70 - 74.83)^2}{74.83} + \frac{(65 - 56.68)^2}{56.68} = 3.16.$$

Since $P(\chi_2^2 > 5.99) = 0.05$ and $P(\chi_2^2 > 9.21) = 0.01$, we accept the null hypothesis that the concept of a successful life is independent of a person's sex at both $\alpha = 0.05$ and 0.01. Men and women interpret a successful life in the same way with respect to the three principles.

26.9 EFFICIENT FORMULAS FOR COMPUTING χ^2

There are available efficient formulas for computing chi-square values from 2×2 and 2×3 contingency tables which involve only observed frequencies.

Denote cell frequencies as A, B, C, and D, marginal frequencies as m_1, m_2, m_3, and m_4, and total number of observations as n, for a 2×2 contingency table as given below; then it can be shown that

Observed Data

A	B	m_3
C	D	m_4
m_1	m_2	n

$$\chi_1^2 = \frac{n(AD - BC)^2}{m_1 m_2 m_3 m_4}. \tag{26.11}$$

For instance, applying the above formula to our first example for test of independence, we have

$$\chi_1^2 = \frac{1600((506)(162) - (494)(438))^2}{(944)(656)(1000)(600)} = 77.78,$$

which is as obtained before.

When the sample is small, say, less than 50, and when some or all cell frequencies are less than 5, it is desirable to compute χ_1^2 with a continuity correction factor. In this case, the efficient formula becomes

$$\chi_1^2 = \frac{n(AD - BC - \frac{1}{2}n)^2}{m_1 m_2 m_3 m_4}. \tag{26.12}$$

For a 2×3 contingency table, given the following notations,

Observed Data

A	B	C	m_4
D	E	F	m_5
m_1	m_2	m_3	n

it can be shown that

$$\chi_2^2 = \frac{n}{m_4}\left(\frac{A^2}{m_1} + \frac{B^2}{m_2} + \frac{C^2}{m_3}\right) + \frac{n}{m_5}\left(\frac{D^2}{m_1} + \frac{E^2}{m_2} + \frac{F^2}{m_3}\right) - n. \tag{26.13}$$

Applying (26.13) to the data in our second earlier example of test on independence we have

$$\chi_2^2 = \frac{430}{235}\left(\frac{80^2}{140} + \frac{95^2}{165} + \frac{60^2}{125}\right) + \frac{430}{195}\left(\frac{60^2}{140} + \frac{70^2}{165} + \frac{65^2}{125}\right) - 430 = 3.16$$

as before.

In general, we note that

$$\chi_\delta^2 = \sum_{i=1}^{rc} \frac{(o_i - e_i)^2}{e_i} = \sum_{i=1}^{rc} \frac{o_i^2}{e_i} - n. \tag{26.14}$$

This formula is valid for contingency tables of any dimension. However, its use requires expected frequencies. hence it is recommended for only 3×3 or greater dimension tables. To see the generality of this expression, we may apply it to the data in our 2×3 contingency table test on successful life and find that

$$\chi_2^2 = \sum \frac{o_i^2}{e_i} - n = \frac{80^2}{76.51} + \frac{95^2}{90.17} + \frac{60^2}{68.32} + \frac{60^2}{63.49} + \frac{70^2}{74.83} + \frac{65^2}{56.68} - 430$$

$$= 3.16$$

as before.

26.10 THE χ^2 TEST ON HOMOGENEITY

Tests of homogeneity are designed to determine whether two or more independent random samples are drawn from the same population or from different populations.

The chi-square test of homogeneity is an extension of the chi-square test of independence. In both cases we are concerned with cross-classified data. As we shall immediately see, too, the same test statistic used for tests of independence is used for tests of homogeneity. These two types of test are, however, different in a number of ways. First, they are associated with different kinds of problems. Tests of independence are concerned with the problem of whether one attribute is independent of another, while tests of homogeneity are concerned with whether different samples comes from the same population. Second, the former involve a single sample taken from one population; but the latter involve two or more independent samples, one from each of the populations in question. This second point also implies that, in the case of independence, all marginal frequencies are chance quantities while, in the case of homogeneity, row totals are sample sizes that are chosen numbers.

To illustrate this type of test, let us suppose that three samples are taken: one consists of 115 professional people, one of 110 businessmen, and one of 125 farmers. Each individual chosen is asked to select, say, one of the three categories that best represents his feeling toward a certain national policy. Suppose these three categories are (1) in favor of the policy F; (2) against the policy A; (3) indifferent toward the policy I. Assume that the results of the interviews are distributed as follows.

Observed Data

Occupation	Reaction			Total
	F	A	I	
Professionals	80	21	14	115
Businessmen	72	15	23	110
Farmers	69	31	25	125
Total	221	67	62	350

From the way the problem is posed, an appropriate null hypothesis to be tested seems to be: The three samples come from the same population; that is, the three classifications are homogeneous insofar as the opinion of the three different groups of people about the national policy under consideration is concerned. This also means there exists no difference in opinion among the three classes of people on the issue. From the alternative expression of the null hypothesis for this problem, we can see why it is called a test of homogeneity. (When we say things are homogeneous we mean that they have something in common or that they are the same or that they are equal.)

We note that if the null hypothesis stated before is true, then the best estimates for proportions specifying "in favor of the policy," "against the policy," and "indifferent toward the policy," respectively, should be 221/350, 67/350, and 62/350. Thus, of the 115 professional people, by (26.10) expected frequencies for the three categories become

$$(221/350)(115) = 72.61 \text{ in favor,}$$

$$(67/350)(115) \doteq 22.01 \text{ against,}$$

and

$$(62/350)(115) \doteq 20.37 \text{ indifferent.}$$

Expected frequencies for the other two groups of people can be computed in the same way. Expected data for the whole problem are as follows.

Expected Data

Occupation	Reaction			Total
	F	A	I	
Professionals	72.61	22.01	20.37	115^a
Businessmen	69.46	21.06	19.49	110^a
Farmers	78.93	23.93	22.14	125
Total	221.00	67.00	62.00	350

^{a} Disagrees with sum of row entries because of rounding.

Now, we are ready to compute the test statistic. By the efficient formula, (26.14), we have

$$\chi_4^2 = \sum_i^{rc} \frac{o_i^2}{e_i} - n$$

$$= \frac{80^2}{72.61} + \frac{21^2}{22.01} + \frac{14^2}{20.37} + \frac{72^2}{69.46} + \frac{15^2}{21.06}$$

$$+ \frac{23^2}{19.49} + \frac{69^2}{78.93} + \frac{31^2}{23.93} + \frac{25^2}{22.14} - 350$$

$$\doteq 8.96.$$

This computed value falls in the region of nonrejection for $\alpha = 0.05$ since $P(\chi_4^2 \geq 9.49) = 0.05$. The views of the three types of professional people are homogeneous so far as the national policy under discussion is concerned.

26.11 THE MANN–WHITNEY TEST FOR TWO INDEPENDENT SAMPLES

When the simple random sampling procedure has been used to draw two independent samples, the *Mann–Whitney test,* often called the *rank-sum test,* can be employed to test the null hypothesis that the CDF of the population from which the first sample is selected is the same as the CDF of the population from which the second sample is selected. This is a substitute for the parametric t test on equality between two population means on the basis of two independent samples. The rank-sum test introduced here is used when the required normal-population assumptions are not justified.

To apply the Mann–Whitney test, we let the subscript 1 refer to either sample, and we let the subscript 2 refer to the other sample. The sample sizes, then, are n_1 and n_2. We rank all $(n_1 + n_2)$ observations in a single array, from smallest to largest, *keeping track* of which sample furnished each observation. Then we assign the ranks from 1 to $(n_1 + n_2)$ to the arrayed observations, again keeping track of which sample furnished which observation. (If there are ties during the ranking process, we give each tied observation the mean of the ranks for which it is tied, but the method presented here should not be used if more than one-fourth of all the observations are involved in ties.) Table 26.6 shows an easy way of assigning ranks. The data in column (1) of Table 26.6 could arise from market values of homes in two townships of

TABLE 26.6   Worksheet for a Mann–Whitney Test

	Observations (in thousands of dollars) (1)	Ranked Observations from Sample 1 (2)	Ranked Observations from Sample 2 (3)	Ranks for Observations in Sample 1 (4)	Ranks for Observations in Sample 2 (5)
First sample $(n_1 = 12)$	70	65	—	1	—
	77	67	—	2	—
	125	68	—	3	—
	65	70	—	4	—
	130	—	73	—	5
	67	—	75	—	6
	68	77	—	7	—
	132	103	—	8	—
	135	—	106	—	9
	103	—	110	—	10
	137	—	121	—	11
	136	—	123	—	12
Second sample $(n_2 = 13)$	75	125	—	13	—
	164	—	128	—	14
	73	—	129	—	15
	106	130	—	16	—
	128	132	—	17	—
	129	—	134	—	18
	110	135	—	19	—
	123	136	—	20	—
	121	137	—	21	—
	150	—	150	—	22
	134	—	151	—	23
	160	—	160	—	24
	151	—	164	—	25
Total				$R_1 = 131$	$R_2 = 194$

Source: Hypothetical.

the same county, where the underlying question is the fairness of the taxes imposed on the homes. Let us suppose that the data in column (1) are very carefully determined market values of homes in each of two independent random samples, one sample from each township.

Next, we compute either R_1, which is the sum of the ranks of sample 1, or R_2, which is the sum of the ranks of sample 2. Ordinarily, it is easier to compute the sum of ranks for the sample having fewer observations in it. Let R_j be the sum of ranks actually computed. In Table 26.6, we let $R_j = R_1 = 131$, because sample 1 has fewer observations in it. (We could, correctly, let $R_j = R_2 = 194$, if we wanted to.)

If the null hypothesis (of identical CDFs in the two populations) is true, and if $n_1 > 8$ and $n_2 > 8$, the sampling distribution of R_j is approximately normal with mean

$$E(R_j) = \frac{n_j(n_1 + n_2 + 1)}{2}, \qquad (26.15)$$

and variance

$$V(R_j) = \frac{n_1 n_2(n_1 + n_2 + 1)}{12}, \qquad (26.16)$$

The test statistic is

$$Z = \frac{R_j - E(R_j)}{\sqrt{V(R_j)}} \qquad (26.17)$$

although a better test statistic, which includes a continuity correction factor is

$$Z = \frac{R_j + C - E(R_j)}{\sqrt{V(R_j)}} \quad \text{where} \quad \begin{cases} C = +1/2 & \text{if } R_j < E(R_j), \\ C = -1/2 & \text{if } R_j > E(R_j), \\ C = 0 & \text{if } R_J = E(R_j). \end{cases} \qquad (26.18)$$

This is a two-tailed test, so the region of rejection is $Z < -1.96$ or $Z > +1.96$ for $\alpha = 0.05$, or $Z < -2.58$ or $Z > +2.58$ for $\alpha = 0.01$.

For Table 26.6, letting $R_j = R_1 = 131$ and noting that then $n_j = n_1 = 12$, we apply (26.17) as follows:

$$R_j = 131;$$

$$E(R_j) = \frac{12(12 + 13 + 1)}{2} = 156;$$

$$V(R_j) = \frac{12(13)(12 + 13 + 1)}{12} = 338;$$

$$z = \frac{131 - 156}{\sqrt{338}} \doteq -1.36.$$

For this value of z, we do not reject the null hypothesis of equal CDFs.

To apply (26.18) to the same data, we note that $C = +1/2$ because R_j is less than $E(R_j)$. Then

$$z = \frac{131 + 1/2 - 156}{\sqrt{338}} \doteq -1.33$$

for which we do not reject the null hypothesis.

If we had let $R_j = R_2 = 194$ in Table 26.5 n_j would have equalled n_2, which is 13, and we would have applied (26.17) as follows:

$$R_j = 194;$$

$$E(R_j) = \frac{13(12 + 13 + 1)}{2} = 169;$$

$$V(R_j) = \frac{12(13)(12 + 13 + 1)}{12} = 338;$$

$$z = \frac{194 - 169}{\sqrt{338}} \doteq +1.36.$$

We would not reject the null hypothesis. Applying (26.18) to these data would produce $z = (194 - 1/2 - 169)/\sqrt{338} \doteq +1.33$, for which we would not reject the null hypothesis. The CDF of the market values of homes in one township is the same as the CDF of the market values of homes in the other township, as far as this test can discover from these data.

We have presented the Mann–Whitney test as a two-tailed test. It can be used as an upper-tail test or as a lower-tail test, but the continuity correction in Equation (26.18) requires modification in such cases.

26.12 THE WILCOXON TEST FOR TWO MATCHED SAMPLES

When we have selected two SRSs that are matched, or dependent, samples, the *Wilcoxon test,* also called the *signed-rank test,* can be used to test the null hypothesis that CDF of the population from which the first sample is drawn is the same as the CDF of the population from which the second sample is drawn. The alternative hypothesis is that there is some difference between the two CDFs.

Suppose, for example, that two auditing procedures are to be compared, using 10 pairs of auditors matched by sex and years of experience. We are interested in whether the distributions of auditing speeds are the same under the two procedures or whether they are different. We can examine this issue by running a signed-rank test to determine whether the CDFs of the two populations are identical (no difference in the distributions of auditing speeds) or not (same difference in the distributions of auditing speeds).

Random selection enters this context in the following way. A large staff of auditors is partitioned into pairs, where each person in a pair has the same sex and approximately the same number of years of experience. (This way of matching auditors is reasonable because women are often better than men at detailed tasks and because experience permits faster speeds.) Each person in a pair, then, has about the same auditing speed as the other person in the same pair. Finally, 10 pairs of auditors are chosen at random from the entire staff of paired auditors. Then randomness should be used again within each pair to see which person uses procedure 1 and which person uses procedure 2. The actual data consist of average numbers of accounts audited per hour, for each person in the experiment. These averages are paired, of course, corresponding to the pairing of the people.

Now, if the null hypothesis is rejected, it is reasonable to attribute the difference between the CDFs to the auditing procedures rather than to sex or years of experience. If the auditors had not been assigned into matched pairs, the slower auditing procedure (for example) might produce faster actual speeds because experienced women predominated in the sample using that auditing procedure, in which case attributing the speed difference to the auditing procedure would be a serious mistake. This kind of matched-sample experimental design is a helpful and common approach to "keeping other things equal" when one wants to examine any effect that is said to exist provided other things are equal.

It is important to realize that, for the signed-rank test, the null hypothesis asserts the identity of the entire CDFs of the two populations. Not only will the population means be equal if the null hypothesis is true, but so will the population standard deviations, population medians, population modes, and so on. There are other nonparametric tests that do not test entire CDFs. It is, for example, possible to look into the equality of central tendencies by using a nonparametric test that is sensitive largely to differences in location and nearly insensitive to differences in shape.

Suppose the raw data are as presented in the first three columns of Table 26.7. The next step, as always for matched samples, is computing the difference for each pair of observations. These differences appear in column (4) of Table 26.7. Next rank the differences from lowest to highest, ignoring the signs of the differences. These ranks are in column (5) of Table 26.7. (The ranking can be from highest to lowest, if desired; the final statistical computations are the same for either ranking.) Then attach the sign of the difference in column (4) to the rank in column (5), producing the signed ranks in column (6).

Now get two sums of signed ranks. One is the sum of the positive signed ranks; this is 48 in the table. The other is the absolute value of the sum of the negative signed ranks; this is $|(-1) + (-6)| = 7$. Call the smaller of these sums T. Here, of course, $T = 7$.

The interpretation of T depends on the sample size. If n, which is the number of pairs in the sample data, is between 7 and 15, use Table 26.8.

For the auditor data, $n = 10$ and $T = 7$. Therefore, for $\alpha = 0.05$,

TABLE 26.7 Auditor Data for the Signed-Rank Test

(1) Pair i	(2) Procedure 1 x_i	(3) Procedure 2 y_i	(4) $d_i = x_i - y_i$	(5) Rank of $|d_i|$	(6) Signed Rank of $|d_i|$
1	109	61	48	10	10
2	100	78	22	9	9
3	77	57	20	8	8
4	69	64	5	5	5
5	59	60	−1	1	−1
6	69	75	−6	6	−6
7	87	85	2	2	2
8	88	84	4	4	4
9	88	85	3	3	3
10	91	83	8	7	7

Source: Hypothetical.

we reject H_0 and conclude that the CDFs are different. For $\alpha = 0.01$, we do not reject H_0.

If n is 16 or more and the null hypothesis is true, the sampling distribution of T is approximately normal, with

$$E(T) = \frac{n(n + 1)}{4} \qquad (26.19)$$

and

$$V(T) = \frac{n(n + 1)(2n + 1)}{24}. \qquad (26.20)$$

The test statistic for samples with $n \geqslant 16$ is

$$Z = \frac{T - E(T)}{\sqrt{V(T)}}, \qquad (26.21)$$

TABLE 26.8 Critical Values of T When $n < 16$ in the Wilcoxon Signed-rank Test

n = Number of Pairs	Reject H_0 if T Is Less Than or Equal to	
	$\alpha \doteq 0.05$	$\alpha \doteq 0.01$
7	2	0
8	2	0
9	6	2
10	8	3
11	11	5
12	14	7
13	17	10
14	21	13
15	25	16

Source: George W. Snedecor and William G. Cochran, *Statistical Methods,* 6th ed. (Ames, Iowa). The Iowa State University Press, 1967, p. 555.

although a better test statistic, which includes a continuity correction, is

$$Z = \frac{T + 1/2 - E(T)}{\sqrt{V(T)}}. \qquad (26.22)$$

The rejection region for Z is established in the usual way for a two-tailed test. If $\alpha = 0.05$, for example, $Z < -1.96$ or $Z > +1.96$ leads to rejecting H_0.

Two kinds of ties can occur in a table like Table 26.7. One kind of tie involves equal raw data in a pair of data, so that $d = 0$ for that pair of data. Whenever $d = 0$, that pair of data is ignored completely and n is reduced by 1 for each ignored pair of data. The other kind of tie involves d's that are not 0 but are equal to each other in absolute value, so that it is not clear what entries should go into columns (5) and (6). The basic procedure is to enter an average rank in column (5) and then to attach the sign in the usual way in column (6). For example, suppose $d_{23} = 6$ and $d_{38} = -6$ in a set of data, and all the other differences are either more positive than 6 or more negative than -6. Then ranks 1 and 2 are involved for d_{23} and d_{38}. Each of them is assigned the rank $(1 + 2)/2 = 1\frac{1}{2}$, and $1\frac{1}{2}$ is the entry in column (5) for both d_{23} and d_{38}. The entry in column (6) for d_{23} is $1\frac{1}{2}$, and the entry in column (6) for d_{38} is $-1\frac{1}{2}$.

As another example, suppose $d_6 = 71$, $d_{12} = 71$, and $d_{25} = -71$ in a set of data, and ranks 7, 8, and 9 are involved. Now there are three d's that are equal in absolute value. The entry in column (5) for each of these d's is the average of the ranks 7, 8, and 9, or $(7 + 8 + 9)/3 = 8$. The entry in column (6) for d_6 is 8, the entry in column (6) for d_{12} is 8, and the entry in column (6) for d_{25} is -8. If more than one-fourth of the nonzero d's are involved in ties, however, the methods of this section do not apply (although there is a special adjustment that can be made).

The signed-rank test is always a two-tailed test, the way we have presented it, even though picking the smaller sum as T ensures that we always work with the lower tail. Modifications of the signed-rank test exist that allow one-tailed alternative hypotheses.

The Wilcoxon signed-rank test is a nonparametric substitute for the t test on the difference between two population means for paired observations (dependent samples). However, this t test requires the assumption that the underlying population differences are normally distributed, whereas the Wilcoxon signed-rank test requires no such assumption.

26.13 THE MEDIAN TEST FOR TWO SAMPLES

The *median test* is designed to evaluate the null hypothesis that two SRSs have been selected from populations whose distributions are identical. The only assumption needed to apply this test is that the population must be continuous. This test is less efficient than either the rank-sum test or the signed-rank test presented in the two previous two sections. However, it does possess two desirable properties over the two nonparametric tests mentioned. First, the median test can be applied to both independent and dependent samples. Second, it can be easily generalized to evaluate three or more populations that are assumed to be identically distributed.

The median test is again of the upper-tail variety. To apply it to test $H_0: f(x) = g(x)$ against $H_1: f(x) = g(x + c)$, the procedure may be summarized as follows.

1. Combine observations in the two samples into a single series and arrange them in an array of descending order. Then find the grand median, denoted as $\bar{m}_{.5}$ for the combined data.

2. Count the number of observations in the first sample which are greater than $\bar{m}_{.5}$ and those which are smaller than $\bar{m}_{.5}$. Denote these numbers as a_1 and b_1, respectively. Do the same for the second sample and denote the resulting numbers as a_2 and b_2, respectively.

3. The a_i and b_i are cell frequencies in a 2×2 contingency table. Let n_1 and n_2 be the respective sample sizes, m_1 and m_2 be the respective marginal frequencies for the rows, and n be the grand sample size; sample data now may be presented as follows.

	Sample 1	Sample 2	Total
Above $\bar{m}_{.5}$	a_1	a_2	m_1
Below $\bar{m}_{.5}$	b_1	b_2	m_2
Total	n_1	n_2	n

Clearly, from this table, we see that,

$$\chi_1^2 = \frac{n(a_1 b_2 - a_2 b_1)^2}{n_1 n_2 m_1 m_2} \qquad (26.23)$$

can be used as the test statistic for the set of hypotheses mentioned before. It is interesting to note that this chi-square with $\delta = 1$ is sensitive only to the location of the median and is insensitive to the differences in the pattern of distributions. Also, when $n_1 < 10$ and $n_2 < 10$, a correction factor should be introduced to compute the chi-square value as discussed before.

Two different makes of machines are adjusted to produce a given product. Defective units produced daily by both machines are observed at random and recorded as in the first two columns of Table 26.9. Do these results indicate that the distributions of defective items of the two machines are identical at $\alpha = 0.05$?

TABLE 26.9 Defectives Data for the Median Test

Machine I	Machine II	Array of I and II	
69	98	109	
109	56	105	
63	62	98	73
90	75	93	71
73	68	91	70
76	80	90	70
85	70	88	69
78	87	87	68
77	59	85	66
91	66	81	63
61	70	80	63
88	63	78	62
105	<u>81</u>	77	61
93		76	59
<u>71</u>		<u>75</u>	<u>56</u>

From Table 26.9, we have

$$n_1 = 15, \quad n_2 = 13, \quad n = 28;$$

$$\bar{m}_{.5} = (76 + 75)/2 = 75.5;$$

$$a_1 = 10, \quad a_2 = 5.$$

These data are presented by the contingency table below.

	I	II	Total
Above 75.5	10	4	14
Below 75.5	5	9	14
Total	15	13	28

$$\chi_1^2 = \frac{(28)(90 - 20)^2}{(15)(13)(14)(14)} = 3.59.$$

Since $P(\chi_1^2 \geq 3.84) = 0.05$, the reserved value of $\chi_1^2 = 3.59$ falls in the region of nonrejection. We conclude that the two samples came from populations with identical distributions of defective units produced daily.

26.14 THE MEDIAN TEST FOR MORE THAN TWO INDEPENDENT SAMPLES

The median test for two samples can easily be extended to compare several populations. We first consider independent samples. As before, we assume that the populations are continuously distributed.

The null hypothesis to be tested now is: The c populations are identical with respect to their distribution functions. The alternative is simply the opposite of H_0.

The testing procedure here is the same as in the two-sample case. The c independent random samples, with $n_1, n_2, \ldots, n_c$, are combined into a single distribution and the grand median is found. Then each sample observation in each sample is compared with $\bar{m}_{.5}$. Denote those observations in the ith sample which are above $\bar{m}_{.5}$ as a_i; the sample data may then be presented as a $2 \times c$ contingency table as below.

	Sample 1	Sample 2	...	Sample c	Total
Above $\bar{m}_{.5}$	a_1	a_2	...	a_c	m_1
Below $\bar{m}_{.5}$	b_1	b_2	...	b_c	m_2
Total	n_1	n_2	...	n_c	n

It can be shown that if $n \geqslant 20$ and $n_i \geqslant 5$ a satisfactory approximation to the exact significance level can be found by the expression

$$\chi_\delta^2 = \frac{(n-1)}{m_1 m_2} \sum_{i=1}^c \frac{(na_i - n_i m_1)^2}{nn_i} \tag{26.24}$$

which has an approximate chi-square distribution with $\delta = c - 1$.

In using this test, we may note that ties often occur with observed data either because of rounding or because of lack of precision in measurements. A safe way to deal with ties here is to assign ties either as a or as b in a way that makes a_i as close as possible to b_i in the ith sample. This procedure has at least the merit of being conservative.

Let us consider an example. A random sample of ten is drawn from the senior students who have taken the graduate record examination, based on a total of 20 points, from each of the three colleges. Observations on the grades of those students sampled are given in Table 26.10. In view of these data, can we conclude that the distributions of grades are identical for all three colleges at $\alpha = 0.05$?

TABLE 26.10 Score Data

Sample 1	Sample 2	Sample 3
10	11	9
13	13	10
17	15	11
15	18	14
15	15	10
13	14	10
12	16	8
10	20	9
10	13	8
10	17	10

For the above data, the grand sample median is found to $\bar{m}_{.5} = 12.5$. Comparing each observation in the three samples with $\bar{m}_{.5}$, we obtain the following results:

	1	2	3	Total
Above 12.5	5	9	1	15
Below 12.5	5	1	9	15
Total	10	10	10	30

$$\chi_2^2 = \frac{(30-1)}{(15)(15)} \left\{ \frac{[(30)(5) - (10)(15)]^2}{(30)(10)} \right.$$

$$\left. + \frac{[(30)(9) - (10)(15)]^2}{(30)(10)} + \frac{[(30)(1) - (10)(15)]^2}{(30)(10)} \right\} = 12.48.$$

Thus we conclude that the population distributions are not identical, since $P(\chi_2^2 > 5.99) = 0.05$. The departure from identity may be inferred from this significant result: effects of experimental treatments are associated with the different colleges.

26.15 THE MEDIAN TEST FOR MORE THAN TWO DEPENDENT SAMPLES

When there are three or more experimental treatments to be compared and these groups are matched in terms of one or more factors or levels, the median test for several independent samples introduced in the previous section can be adjusted to test the identity of population distributions with c matched groups. The procedure is outlined as follows.

First, sample data are arranged into c columns representing treatments and r rows representing blocks of experimental materials. Next, the median of each row is found. Third, each observation in each row is given a sign of (+) or (−), depending upon whether or not its value is greater than or less than the median for that row. Finally, the number of plus signs occurring in the ith column, a_i, is determined. After this is done, sample data are then reduced into a $2 \times c$ contingency table as follows:

Sign	Sample				Total
	I	II	...	c	
+	a_1	a_2	...	a_c	$m_1 = ra$
−	b_1	b_2	...	b_c	$m_2 = n - ra$
Total	n_1	n_2	...	n_c	n

where r is the number of rows in the original data table and

$$a = c/2, \qquad \text{for } c \text{ even};$$
$$a = (c + 1)/2, \qquad \text{for } c \text{ odd}.$$

If we assume that the distributions of the row populations are identical, we can test the hypothesis that the distributions of populations represented by the columns are identical. The testing statistic in this case is

$$\chi_\delta^2 = \left[\frac{c - 1}{ra(c - a)} \right] \frac{\sum\limits_{i=1}^{c} (ca_i - ra)^2}{c} \tag{26.25}$$

which is approximately distributed as chi-square with $\delta = c - 1$.

Suppose that we wish to determine the relative yields of four varieties of corn. Moreover, let us suppose that there are six blocks of land available for this experiment. Each block of land is divided into four plots of equal size. Plots of each block of land are then assigned to the four types of corn at random. Suppose that the data in Table 26.11, are obtained.

Be sure to note that ratings of observations in each row are compared with the median of that row. From these ratings, can we conclude that the distributions underlying the four different types of corn are identical at $\alpha = 0.05$?

To answer this question, we note that in terms of the ratings above we have the following contingency table.

Sign	I	II	III	IV	
+	1	2	6	3	$12 = ra$
−	5	4	0	3	$12 = n - ra$
	6	6	6	6	24

$$\chi_3^2 = \frac{3}{12(2)} \left[\frac{((4)(1) - 6(2))^2}{4} + \frac{((4)(2) - (6)(2))^2}{4} \right.$$
$$\left. + \frac{((4)(6) - (6)(2))^2}{4} + \frac{((4)(3) - (6)(2))^2}{4} \right] = 7.00.$$

TABLE 26.11 Median Test on Corn Data

r: Block	I	II	III	IV	Row Median
1	4(−)	9(+)	10(+)	5(−)	7.0
2	3(−)	4(−)	9(+)	8(+)	6.0
3	4(−)	6(−)	11(+)	8(+)	7.0
4	5(−)	3(−)	10(+)	10(+)	7.5
5	7(+)	5(−)	8(+)	6(−)	6.5
6	6(−)	8(+)	9(+)	7(−)	7.5
a_i	1	2	6	3	—

For $\delta = 3$, this value is less than the critical chi-square value of 7.81 for the 5% level of significance. H_0 cannot be rejected.

We should note that what we have done in this section is similar to the test of treatment effects against interaction in the analysis of variance. If we are interested not only in the fact that the treatment populations are identically distributed but also in the fact that the treatment means are equal, we should be prepared to assume that either the joint effects are nil or the data should be analyzed by the random effects or mixed models. It may be pointed out, too, that the procedure just introduced can also be extended to a two-variable classification-with-replication analysis where both the treatment and interaction effects are tested. However, such an extension requires many more assumptions and is quite time-consuming and laborious.

26.16 THE KRUSKAL–WALLIS TEST FOR THREE OR MORE INDEPENDENT SAMPLES

W. M. Kruskal and W. A. Wallis have extended the Wilcoxon test for two samples to cover $c \geq 3$ independent samples by constructing the model on the basis of ranked data. This extension is called the *H test*, designed to test the null hypothesis that the CDFs of the three or more populations are identical against the alternative that they are not all identical. This test is the nonparametric analog for the one-variable classification ANOVA model, which is designed to test the H_0 that all populations means are equal against the H_1 that at least some of the population means are unequal.

It is assumed that there are c populations and that a simple random sample has been drawn from each population. The sample sizes are $n_1, n_2, \ldots, n_c$, and the overall sample size is n, where $n = n_1 + n_2 + \ldots + n_c$. The H test begins by ranking all n observations. Then the sum of these ranks for each sample is found. Call this sum T_j for the jth sample. It can be proved that the overall sum of ranks, which is $\sum_{j=1}^{c} T_j$, must also be equal to

$$T = \frac{n(n+1)}{2}. \tag{26.26}$$

Provided each sample size is at least 3 (that is, $n_j \geq 3$ for all j), the test statistic H defined as

$$H = \left[\frac{12}{n(n+1)} \left(\sum_{j=1}^{c} \frac{T_j^2}{n_j} \right) \right] - 3(n+1) \tag{26.27}$$

is approximately distributed as χ^2 with $\delta = c - 1$.

When ties occur in ranking the n observations, each of the tied observations is assigned an average rank. For example, if two observations are tied and the ranks for them would be 5 and 6, each is assigned the rank of 5.5. As another example, if three observations are tied and the ranks for them would be 10, 11, and 12, each is assigned the rank of 11.

An adjusted value of H, denoted as H', should be computed when there are ties. We define H' as follows:

$$H' = \frac{H}{C},$$

(26.28)

where C, the correction factor, is

$$C = 1 - \frac{\sum\limits_{k=1}^{m} (t_k^3 - t_k)}{n^3 - n}.$$

(26.29)

In (26.29), m is the number of ties and t_k is the number of observations in the kth tie.

As a numerical example, suppose that a random sample has been taken from each of three sources of high-tension steel wires and that their tensile strengths in hundreds of pounds have been measured. We wish to test whether these observations indicate that the parent populations are identically distributed. The observed data are presented in Table 26.12, together with the overall rank of each datum (given in parentheses).

For these data, $n = 33$. Applying (26.26) yields

$$T = \frac{33(34)}{2} = 561.$$

TABLE 26.12 Tensile Strengths of Three Samples of Steel Wires

	Sample 1	Sample 2	Sample 3
	29 (17.5)	36 (26.5)	24 (11.5)
	36 (26.5)	17 (2)	18 (3)
	37 (29.5)	19 (4)	20 (5)
	36 (26.5)	21 (7)	24 (11.5)
	36 (26.5)	26 (14)	25 (13)
	35 (24)	29 (17.5)	28 (16)
	39 (32)	27 (15)	31 (20)
	38 (31)	21 (7)	34 (23)
	40 (33)	32 (21)	30 (19)
	23 (10)	33 (22)	22 (9)
		37 (29.5)	21 (7)
			16 (1)
T_j	256.5	165.5	139.0
n_j	10	11	12

Source: Hypothetical.

Applying (26.27) yields

$$H = \frac{12}{33(34)} \left[\frac{256.5^2}{10} + \frac{165.5^2}{11} + \frac{139^2}{12} \right] - 3(34) \doteq 12.22.$$

Table 26.12, however, shows that there are 3 two-way ties, 1 three-way tie, and 1 four-way tie, so H' should be computed.

$$C = 1 - \frac{(2^3 - 2) + (2^3 - 2) + (2^3 - 2) + (3^3 - 3) + (4^3 - 4)}{33^3 - 33} \doteq 0.997$$

and

$$H' = \frac{12.22}{0.997} \doteq 12.26.$$

The values of H and H' are practically the same in this example because the samples are rather large and there are not too many ties.

For $\alpha = 0.01$ and $\delta = c - 1 = 2$, the upper-tail critical value of χ^2 is 9.21. Because the observed value of H' is larger than this, the null hypothesis of identical population distributions is rejected.

The H test compares reasonably well with the F test in the analysis of variance. When samples are large, however, it is difficult to rank the observations correctly without using the computer.

26.17 RANK CORRELATION COEFFICIENT

When a random sample of n pairs is drawn from a bivariate population, and the *observations are ranks instead of measurements*, the covariability or lack of it between X and Y is established by the *rank correlation coefficient*, a nonparametric method developed by C. Spearman in 1904. The original data can be ranks, as when each of two judges ranks the same group of people for leadership ability or any other quality. The original data can be measurements that do not even approximately meet the assumptions of the bivariate normal population model (in which case Chapter 17's methods should not be used), but it is valid to convert the data from measurements to ranks and then use the rank correlation coefficient.

The data, then, are in the form (x, y), where x is the rank of individual i according to criterion X, and y is the rank of the same individual according to criterion Y. Then we define $d = y - x$. The Spearman rank correlation coefficient, r_s, is now defined as

$$r_s = 1 - \frac{6 \sum d^2}{n(n^2 - 1)}. \qquad (26.30)$$

If the ranks agree perfectly, $d = 0$ for every individual and $r_s = 1$. If the ranks disagree as much as is mathematically possible, it can be proved that $r_s = -1$. Therefore $-1 \leqslant r \leqslant +1$. If $r_s = 0$, there is no relationship between the two sets of ranks.

If there are ties in the ranks under criterion X or in the ranks under criterion Y, mean ranks are assigned to the tied individuals. That is, when two or more individuals are tied, each is assigned the mean of the ranks they would otherwise have.

When no ties in rank exist, the exact sampling distribution of r_s can be worked out. Tables for the distribution of r_s are available for small n. When $n \geqslant 20$, we can test the hypothesis $\rho_s = 0$ against the alternative $\rho_s \neq 0$ (or $\rho_s \leqslant 0$ against $\rho_s > 0$, or $\rho_s \geqslant 0$ against $\rho_s < 0$) by using the statistic

$$t = \frac{r_s\sqrt{n-2}}{\sqrt{1-r^2}}, \qquad \text{with } \delta = n - 2. \tag{26.31}$$

When $8 \leqslant n < 20$, the r_s in Equation (26.30) should be replaced by $\bar{r}_s$, where $\bar{r}_s$ includes a continuity correction and is calculated as

$$\bar{r}_s = 1 - \frac{\sum d^2}{(1/6)[n(n^2 - 1)] + 1}. \tag{26.32}$$

Let us consider an example. In a diving contest, two judges each ranked ten divers in the order of their diving ability. The data are shown in the first three columns of Table 26.13.

Is there a relationship between the two judges' rankings? To find out, we test H_0: $\rho_s = 0$ against H_1: $\rho_s \neq 0$. Applying Equation (26.32) to the data yields

$$\bar{r}_s = 1 - \frac{24}{[1/6][10(10^2 - 1)] + 1} \doteq 0.8554.$$

TABLE 26.13   Diving-meet Data with Rank Correlation Computations

Contestant	Judge I	Judge II	d	d^2
1	8	9	1	1
2	3	5	2	4
3	9	10	1	1
4	2	1	−1	1
5	7	8	1	1
6	10	7	−3	9
7	4	3	−1	1
8	6	4	−2	4
9	1	2	1	1
10	5	6	1	1
Totals			0	24

Source: Hypothetical.

Applying Equation (26.31) yields

$$t = \frac{0.8554\sqrt{10 - 2}}{\sqrt{1 - 0.8554^2}} \doteq 4.67, \quad \text{with } \delta = 10 - 2 = 8.$$

The upper critical value of t for $\alpha = 0.05$ in this situation is 2.306. The observed value of t is well beyond this value, so H_0 is rejected. There is a relationship between the judges' rankings that cannot easily be explained by chance alone. Because $\bar{r}_s$ is positive, the relationship is one of agreement, not disagreement.

26.18 PARAMETRIC VERSUS NONPARAMETRIC STATISTICS

In this chapter we have introduced a number of the most frequently used nonparametric methods. While nonparametric theory arose as early as the middle of the nineteenth century, the well-known nonparametric method of testing independence and goodness-of-fit by the chi-square test was formulated by Karl Pearson in 1900. The true beginning of this theory, however, was Spearman's rank-correlation coefficient test for covariability, popularized by Harold Hotelling and Margaret R. Pabst in 1936. Even then there was little interest in nonparametric statistics until 1945, when Wilcoxon proposed a test for the two-sample case that was distinguished by both its simplicity and its excellent results, even in cases where the population distribution is known to be normal.

There are many reasons for the wide adoption and the continuous growth of nonparametric theory since 1945. Both theoretical and practical necessities are concerned with nonparametric problems. Theoretically, it is always desirable to discover procedures of statistical inference that have the minimum number of restrictions imposed by the underlying assumptions. Practically, it is important for scientific investigators to have at their disposal simple and widely applicable techniques.

Nonparametric statistics, being primarily concerned with order relations, provides us with two important motives for its study and development. In the first place, data may occur naturally in the form of ranks. When this is the case, direct ordinal analysis would then suffice for reaching a judgment about the underlying variable or variables. Moreover, when the order relations in data are considered alone, the reasoning behind each nonparametric method requires relatively simple probability theory, so that the sampling distributions of test statistics can easily be found.

The basic importance of nonparametric theory from a theoretical viewpoint is perhaps that it requires only the simple assumption that the population distribution under investigation be continuous but does not require the specific form of the distribution, as is often required by parametric theory. Even the assumption of continuity is not vital and can be relaxed. Thus, when data are gathered from populations whose distributions are unknown or cannot be assumed, we have little choice but to employ the nonparametric tests.

The foregoing remarks, however, are not meant to mislead the reader into believing that nonparametric methods are usually superior to the parametric decision procedures. As a matter of fact, in most situations where both the parametric and nonparametric techniques apply, the former are distinctly more desirable than the latter on at least two counts.

First, in general, the nonparametric tests have less than 100% *power efficiency* as compared to the parametric tests. The concept of "power efficiency" may be explained by a simple example. Suppose that we have two alternative testing procedures A and B for a given H_0. If A requires $n = 25$ but B requires $n = 50$ in order to reach a power of, say, 0.95 for a given true alternative at $\alpha = 0.05$, then we say that the power efficiency of B is only 50% of that of A. It can be shown, for normal populations, that the sign test, for example, requires 40 to 50% more observations than the t test, and the Wilcoxon signed-rank test requires about 5% more scores than the t test in order to be equally powerful.

Second, the null hypothesis tested by a nonparametric method is seldom equivalent to that tested by a parametric procedure. In general, with nonparametric tests, hypotheses are less precise and yield less information in conclusions. For example, when the usual assumptions for the analysis of variance are met, we test the hypothesis that the treatment means are equal by the F ratio. In accepting this H_0, we have not only accepted the statement of equal means, but we have also implicitly accepted the conclusion that the treatment populations are identically distributed. When this H_0 is rejected, we know precisely that the populations are not all identical with respect to their central tendencies. The order method of comparing several samples, on the other hand, is concerned with the null hypothesis that the population distributions are the same. When this H_0 is rejected, we have a rather vague conclusion that the population distributions are not all identical. But are they different in terms of central tendency or in terms of variability? This question is left unanswered by the nonparametric tests we have presented. Thus, the lack of identity does not tell us very much. To be sure, this problem can be reduced or even eliminated if we are willing to make some mild assumptions about population distributions. Such assumptions, however, may be just as offensive as those the order statistics have been designed to avoid.

GLOSSARY OF FORMULAS

26.1) $E(R) = \dfrac{n + 2}{2};$

(26.2) $V(R) = \dfrac{n(n - 2)}{4(n - 1)};$

(26.3) $Z = [R - E(R)]/\sqrt{V(R)}$.

When we conduct a test on randomness by the "runs above or below the median" procedure and when $n \geq 25$, the number of runs above and below the median is asymptotically normally distributed with expectation and variance as defined by (26.1) and (26.2), respectively. Thus, when the sample is large, this test on randomness can be conducted by the standard normal deviate as defined by (26.3).

(26.4) $E(R) = (1/3)(2n - 1)$;

(26.5) $V(R) = (1/90)(16n - 29)$;

(26.6) $Z = [R - E(R)]/\sqrt{V(R)}$.

To test randomness by the "runs-up-and-down" procedure, the number of runs would be approximately normally distributed with expectation and variance as defined by (26.4) and (26.5), respectively. The test statistic is defined by (26.6)—a standard normal deviate. For use of this test, n must be 20 or greater.

(26.7) $K = \delta^2/S_Y^2$.

This quantity is used to test the independence of time series data. It is called the Von Neumann ratio. In this test statistic, S_Y^2 is simply the variance of the series and $\delta^2 = [\sum (y_{i+1} - y_i)^2]/(n - 1)$—the mean-square—successive differences. When a positive serial correlation (trend) exists, the value of K tends to be very small. When a negative serial correlation (trend) exists, K tends to be very large. The critical values of K are denoted as k and k', respectively. When $K < k$, independence is rejected in favor of the existence of positive serial correlation. When $K > k'$, independence is rejected in favor of the existence of negative serial correlation. The values of k and k' for $\alpha = 0.05$ and $\alpha = 0.01$ are given in the table entitled "Significant Points for the Ratio of the Mean Square Successive Difference to the Variance" Table XII in Appendix C.

(26.8) $\chi_\delta^2 = \sum_{i=1}^{k} \frac{(o_i - e_i)^2}{e_i}$;

(26.9) $\chi_\delta^2 = \sum_{i=1}^{k} \frac{(|o_i - e_i| - 1/2)^2}{e_i}$; $|o_i - e_i| \geq \frac{1}{2}$.

Here, χ^2 is defined as the ratio of the sum of squared differences between observed and expected (theoretical) frequencies. It is used as the test statistic for a number of nonparametric tests. Here, too, δ varies from one case to another. When it is used to test on frequencies or goodness-of-fit, $\delta = k - 1$ or $\delta = k - 1 - m$. The former is used when the expected frequencies are computed without having to estimate population parameters with sample statistics, since then we only have to satisfy the condition that $\sum o_i = \sum e_i = n$. The latter is employed if the expected frequencies can only be computed by using m, $m = 1, 2, \ldots$, statistics to estimate the m population parameters. Note, here k is the number of classes or categories. When (26.8) is used to test independence (or contingency tables), and homogeneity, $\delta = (r - 1)(c - 1)$, where r stands for the number of rows and c stands for the number of columns of a contingency table. Finally, when $\delta = 1$ and $n \leqslant 50$, a continuity correction factor of $1/2$ should be used to compute the chi-square value as (26.9) suggests.

(26.10) $\quad e = \dfrac{\text{column total}}{\text{grand total}} (\text{row total}).$

This equation is used to compute the expected cell frequencies from the contingency tables of observed data.

(26.11) $\quad \chi_1^2 = \dfrac{n(AD - BC)^2}{m_1 m_2 m_3 m_4};$

(26.12) $\quad \chi_1^2 = \dfrac{n(AD - BC - \frac{1}{2}n)^2}{m_1 m_2 m_3 m_4}.$

These are the efficient formulas for the computations of χ^2 values from a 2×2 contingency table without, (26.11), and with, (26.12), the continuity correction factor, respectively. Here, n is sample size, A, B, C, and D are the cell frequencies, and m_i are the marginal total frequencies for the observed data.

(26.13) $\quad \chi_2^2 = \dfrac{n}{m_4}\left(\dfrac{A^2}{m_1} + \dfrac{B^2}{m_2} + \dfrac{C^2}{m_3}\right) + \dfrac{n}{m_3}\left(\dfrac{D^2}{m_1} + \dfrac{E^2}{m_2} + \dfrac{F^2}{m_3}\right) - n.$

This is the efficient formula for computing the χ^2 value from observed frequencies directly in a 2×3 contingency table. In this expression, m_4 and m_5 are the marginal total frequencies for the two rows; m_1, m_2, and m_3 are the total marginal frequencies for the three columns, $A, \ldots, F$ are the cell frequencies, and n is the sample size.

(26.14) $\quad \chi_\delta^2 = \displaystyle\sum_{i=1}^{rc} \dfrac{(o_i - e_i)^2}{e_i} = \sum_{i=1}^{rc} \dfrac{o_i^2}{e_i} - n.$

This is the generalized efficient formula for the computation of χ^2 values from contingency tables of any dimension. The usefulness of this formula lies in the fact that we need not calculate the differences between observed and expected frequencies. In this formula, n may stand for the sample size for contingency table tests, or for the sum of sizes of the independent samples for test of homogeneity.

(26.15) $\quad E(R_j) = n_j(n_1 + n_2 + 1)/2;$

$\quad\quad\quad V(R_j) = n_1 n_2(n_1 + n_2 + 1)/12;$

$\quad\quad\quad Z = [R_j - E(R_j)]/\sqrt{V(R_j)};$

$\quad\quad\quad Z = [R_j + C - E(R_j)]/\sqrt{V(R_j)};$

where

$$C = \begin{cases} +1/2 & \text{if } R_j < E(R_j), \\ -1/2 & \text{if } R_j > E(R_j), \\ 0 & \text{if } R_j = E(R_j). \end{cases}$$

This group of equations concerns the Mann–Whitney test, or rank-sum test on the identity between the CDFs of two populations with two independent samples. In these expressions, R_j usually stands for the sum of the ranks for the sample having fewer observations merely to reduce the amount of labor. When $n_1 > 8$ and $n_2 > 8$, the sampling distribution of R_j is approximately normally distributed with expectation and variance defined by (26.15) and (26.16), respectively. The test statistic is defined either as (26.17) or as (26.18). The latter, with the incorporation of a continuity correction factor, is considered to be better in application.

(26.19) $E(T) = \dfrac{n(n + 1)}{4};$

(26.20) $V(T) = n(n + 1)(2n + 1)/24;$

(26.21) $Z = [T - E(T)]/\sqrt{V(T)};$

(26.22) $Z = [T + 1/2 - E(T)]/\sqrt{V(T)}.$

This group of expressions are related to the Wilcoxon test, or the signed-rank test for the identity of the CDFs of two populations with matched pairs. In these formulas, T is the absolute value of the smaller sum of the signed ranks. When $n \geqslant 16$, the statistic T is approximately normal with $E(T)$ and $V(T)$ as defined by the first two equations, respectively. The test statistic Z may or may not contain a continuity correction.

(26.23) $\chi_1^2 = n(a_1 b_2 - a_2 b_1)^2/n_1 n_2 m_1 m_2.$

This is the test statistic in the median test on the identity between two population distributions. It can be used whether the samples are independent or dependent. Here, a_i refers to the number of observations in the ith sample that are greater than the grand sample median; $b_i = n - a_i$; $n = n_1 + n_2$; m_i refers to the row total marginal frequencies in a 2×2 contingency table.

(26.24) $\chi_\delta^2 = \dfrac{(n - 1)}{m_1 m_2} \sum_{i=1}^{c} \dfrac{(na_i - n_i m_1)^2}{nn_i}.$

This is the test statistic for the null hypothesis that c, $c \geqslant 3$, populations are identically distributed with independent samples. For this statistic, $\delta = c - 1$. Other symbols in the expression represent quantities as in (26.23).

(26.25) $\chi_\delta^2 = \left[\dfrac{c-1}{ra(c-a)}\right]\left[\sum\limits_{i=1}^{c} (ca_i - ra)^2/c\right].$

To employ the median test on the identity of c population distributions with dependent samples, this expression is used as the test statistic. Here, r stands for the number of rows—the experimental material; $a = c/2$ for c even; $a = (c+1)/2$ for c odd; a_i is the number of observations that exceed the grand sample median in value in the ith sample.

(26.26) $T = n(n+1)/2;$

(26.27) $H = \left[\dfrac{12}{n(n+1)} \left(\sum\limits_{j=1}^{c} \dfrac{T_j^2}{n_j}\right)\right] - 3(n+1);$

(26.28) $H' = H/C;$

(26.29) $C = 1 - \dfrac{\sum\limits_{k=1}^{m} (t_k^3 - t_k)}{n^3 - n}.$

This set of formulas is related to what is called the H test on the identity among three or more population distributions in the independent-sample case. Ranks for observations in all the c samples are assigned in this case by considering them as a single series. The sum of the ranks for the jth sample is denoted as T_j and $\sum T_j = T$ which is defined by (26.26). The test statistic H, (26.27) is distributed as a χ^2 with $\delta = c - 1$. Also, $n = \sum n_j$, where n is the grand sample size. For this test, when ties occur, tied observations are assigned mean ranks. When samples are rather small and when many sets of ties appear, H', (26.28), should be used as the test statistic. In H', C is defined by (26.29), where m is the number ties and t_k is the number of observations in the kth tie.

(26.30) $r_s = 1 - [6\sum d^2/n(n^2 - 1)];$

(26.31) $t = \dfrac{r_s\sqrt{n-2}}{\sqrt{1 - r_s^2}};$

(26.32) $\bar{r}_s = 1 - \dfrac{\sum d^2}{(1/6)[n(n^2-1)] + 1}.$

Equations in this group are concerned with measuring and testing the strength between two variables when the bivariate population distribution is unspecified or when data are originally given in ranks. The first equation, (26.30), defines what is called the *rank-correlation coefficient* in which d stands for differences between pairs of differences of ranks. Equation (26.31) is the test statistic for the null hypothesis that $\rho_s = 0$ against some appropriate alternative. It is a t variable with $\delta = n - 2$. We use this test statistic only when $n > 20$. The third equation in this group is the rank-correlation coefficient with a continuity correction. Its significance also be tested by (26.32), provided $8 \leqslant n \leqslant 20$.

REVIEW QUESTIONS

26.1 How are parametric and nonparametric statistics differentiated from each other?

26.2 What difference is there, if any, between "nonparametric statistics" and "distribution-free statistics"? In your judgment, which name seems more appropriate for this branch of statistics?

26.3 What is the most important from a theoretical point of view for the development and use of nonparametric theory?

26.4 Why do we say that when sample data can be validly analyzed by both parametric and nonparametric methods we should always use the former?

26.5 "Runs" in different nonparametric tests are obtained in different ways. Can you give a generalized definition of your own of this notion?

26.6 Of what use are the tests on randomness?

26.7 Within the framework of the Von Neumann ratio test, are independence, randomness, and nonautauregression identical terms? Explain.

26.8 Do you think the procedure used to test on population median can also be used to test on population mean? If so, do we need any additional assumption of continuity? If not, why not?

26.9 In connection with the χ^2 tests on goodness-of-fit, answer the following questions.
   a. What are the null and alternative hypotheses?
   b. Why is the test ordinarily an upper-tail test?
   c. Are there any restrictions on the expected frequencies? If, what are they?
   d. Are there any restrictions on the observed frequencies? If so, what are they?

26.10 If we conduct the χ^2 goodness-of-fit of a binomial distribution or Poisson distribution to appropriate sample data, how should the number of degrees of freedom be determined? Explain.

26.11 What is the Yates continuity correction for χ^2? When should it be used? What can it achieve?

26.12 What is the difference between the χ^2 tests on independence and homogeneity?

26.13 Explain the rationale of using Equation (26.10) to determine the expected frequencies for the cells of a contingency table. Use some examples of your own.

26.14 What is the difference between Wilcoxon signed-rank test and Mann–Whitney rank-sum test? How are the ranks determined in each case?

26.15 How are the null and alternative hypotheses stated in the signed-rank and rank-sum tests?

26.16 Compared to the signed-rank and rank-sum tests, what are the advantages and disadvantages of the median test on the identity between two population distributions?

26.17 To which parametric test does the median test for three or more dependent samples correspond?

26.18 What is the H test used for? How are the null and alternative hypotheses stated for this test? To which parametric test does this test correspond?

26.19 In comparing two or more populations with nonparametric methods, the null hypothesis is usually stated in terms of the identity between or among the population distributions. However, with parametric tests, the null hypothesis is usually concerned with a specific property of the populations, such as central tendency, variability, and so on. In view of this difference in practice, can you conclude that the nonparametric tests provide us with more information than the corresponding parametric tests and, therefore, that the former is better than the latter? Explain fully.

26.20 What is the difference between r and r_s in terms of assumptions? In terms of the types of data to which they can be applied?

26.21 Can r_s be computed from samples for which the data are measurements or magnitudes? If so, how? If not, why not?

PROBLEMS

Note: A number of computer programs for nonparametric tests are available in many software packages. You may apply such programs to the more involved problems for this chapter.

26.1 A sample of 30 observations is listed in the order in which they were observed:

80, 34, 10, 20, 40, 64, 50, 47, 44, 25, 86, 66, 49, 53, 65,
77, 28, 28, 55, 74, 81, 90, 67, 53, 38, 71, 72, 73, 75, 78.

In view of these data, can we accept randomness of the sample by the runs-up-and-down test at $\alpha = 0.01$? By the above-and-below-the-median test at $\alpha = 0.01$?

26.2 Suppose a sample has the following values, which are listed in the order in which they were selected:

97, 89, 81, 11, 83, 16, 96, 44, 32, 98, 19, 68, 33,
25, 54, 74, 82, 17, 49, 33, 22, 62, 20, 92, and 80.

What is the proper conclusion concerning the null hypothesis that the sample is random at $\alpha = 0.01$ by the sums-above-and-below-the-median test?

26.3 The following figures represent the number of days per month on which a secretary was late, over a recent period of months:

1, 0, 1, 4, 5, 1, 1, 3, 3, 5, 0, 0, 2, 0, 4, 1, 4, 4, 0, 3, 5, and 5.

Do you think this sequence is random, at $\alpha = 0.05$ by the sums-up-and-down test?

26.4 Suppose that a sample of time-series data consists of 30 observations and suppose that from this set of data we have obtained $s_Y^2 = 8$ and $\delta^2 = 5.508$. Do these results indicate independence among the successive terms in the sample by the Von Neumann ratio test?

26.5 For the data in Table 21.1, test the null hypothesis that there is positive trend in the series at $\alpha = 0.05$ by the Von Neumann ratio test.

26.6 By applying the Von Neumann ratio test to data in Table 21.2 for testing the existence of independence in the series, what conclusion can you reach at $\alpha = 0.05$ and $\alpha = 0.01$?

26.7 Testing H_0: $\tilde{x}_5 = 55$ against H_1: $\tilde{x}_5 \neq 55$ at $\alpha = 0.05$ by the sign test applied to the sample data in Problem 26.1, what conclusion can you reach?

26.8 Would you reach the same conclusion as in the preceding problem if we were testing H_0: $\tilde{x}_5 \leq 55$ against H_1: $\tilde{x}_5 > 55$?

26.9 Applying the sign test to the sample data in Problem 26.2 to test $\tilde{x}_5 \geq 60$ against $\tilde{x}_5 < 60$ at $\alpha = 0.01$, what conclusion can you reach?

26.10 The probability distribution of the number of machine breakdowns per day in a large factory has been established in the past, prior to the most recent 100 days, and is given in the first two columns of Table 26.P1. Machine breakdowns for the most recent 100 days are shown in the third column of the same table. Can we conclude from these data that the probability distribution of machine breakdowns has not changed from the one previously established? That is, would chance alone reasonably account for the disagreements between the second and third columns, if the third column were a random sample from a large population? Answer for $\alpha = 0.05$ and also for $\alpha = 0.01$.

TABLE 26.P1   Machine Breakdown Data

Number of Breakdowns	Past Probability	Number of Days in the Last 100 Days
0	0.06	10
1	0.18	16
2	0.20	20
3	0.20	26
4	0.18	14
5	0.10	8
6	0.08	6
Totals	1.00	100

26.11 The number of sales made by a salesman is usually closely related to the number of sales calls he makes, so salesmen are encouraged to make as many calls as they can. If salesmen are equally ambitious, energetic, resourceful, and so on, and if they face the same sales problems, they should all make the same number of calls during the same period of time. The sales manager of a certain company wants to test the hypothesis that all six of her salesmen make the same number of calls per period of time. She randomly selects 250 individual sales-call records from the last 12 months of records. Their distribution by salesman is as follows.

Salesman:	A	B	C	D	E	F
Number of calls:	40	25	57	37	56	35

If H_0 is true, what are the expected frequencies in this situation? Are the observed frequencies consistent with the expected frequencies at $\alpha = 0.01$?

26.12 Table 26.P2 contains the probability distribution of a random variable Y and also the observed frequencies from a random sample of 200. Test whether the sample data in the third column came from the probability distribution in the first and second columns.

TABLE 26.P2

y	$P(Y = y)$	Observed Frequency
0	0.25	33
1	0.25	40
2	0.20	56
3	0.15	33
4	0.10	22
5	0.05	16
Totals	1.00	200

26.13 The number of defectives has been recorded for each random sample of 4 items drawn from each of 150 large shipments, resulting in the following frequency distribution.

Number of defectives:	0	1	2	3	4
Number of samples:	55	75	10	5	5

If every large shipment has 10% defectives, what are the expected numbers of samples in this situation? Are the observed numbers of samples consistent with these expected numbers at $\alpha = 0.05$? at $\alpha = 0.01$?

26.14 The χ^2 goodness-of-fit tests presented in this chapter are all upper-tail tests, which means that improbably high values of χ^2 lead to rejecting H_0. Should improbably low values of χ^2 also lead to rejecting H_0? Explain your answer as fully as you can. For example, if a die is tossed 60,000 times and produces

10,000 ones, 10,000 twos, and so on, then a χ^2 test of fairness would produce $\chi^2 = 0$. Is this strong evidence that the die is fair? If not, what conclusion should be drawn?

26.15 It has been hypothesized that there are three times as many automobile accidents on Saturdays and Sundays as on any other day of the week in a certain state. If this is the null hypothesis and if it is true, what is the probability distribution of auto accidents throughout a week? From the records of the state, 100 accidents are chosen independently of one another. The distribution of accidents according to the days of the week is found to be as follows.

Mon.	Tue.	Wed.	Thu.	Fri.	Sat.	Sun.
5	9	10	8	11	30	27

Test this null hypothesis at $\alpha = 0.05$ and at $\alpha = 0.01$.

26.16 A survey of 200 families, all with 3 children each, selected at random from a large population, gave the following results:

Male children:	0	1	2	3
Number of families:	40	58	62	40

Determine whether these data are consistent with the hypothesis that male children and female children are equally likely, at $\alpha = 0.05$, and at $\alpha = 0.01$.

26.17 It is often stated that instructors tend to grade their students according to the "normal curve." Grades of 162 students in freshman mathematics classes during a certain year are found to be distributed as shown in Table 26.P3. In the raw data underlying Table 26.P3, $\sum x = 11,030$ and $\sum x^2 = 783,762$. Assuming that these grades constitute a random sample, determine whether we can conclude that this sample has been drawn from a population of grades that are normally distributed, at $\alpha = 0.01$. If $2 < e < 5$ for exactly one class, you are close enough to meeting the rule of thumb $e \geqslant 5$; do not combine classes. Let the class limits be exactly 40, exactly 50, and so on.

TABLE 26.P3

Numerical Grade		Frequency
Over	Through	
30	40	5
40	50	10
50	60	28
60	70	52
70	80	31
80	90	26
90	100	10
Total	—	162

26.18 Repeat Problem 16.17, except that now the frequency 52 is 32 and the last frequency of 10 is 30, representing some "grade inflation"; $\sum x$ increases by 600 and $\sum x^2$ increases by 96,000.

26.19 Four hundred independent samples, each with 200 observations, are drawn from a population and the sample means are computed. This experiment gives the information in the Table 26.P4. From these results, can we conclude that the sample means are normally distributed? If not, what might explain the nonnormality? (The Central Limit Theorem should work well for $n = 200$.) Let the class limits be exactly 105, exactly 110, and son, as in Table 26.P4.

TABLE 26.P4

Class for $\bar{x}$	f
100–105	21
105–110	56
110–115	74
115–120	112
120–125	70
125–130	47
130–135	20
Total	400

26.20 Repeat Problem 26.19, except that now the frequency 74 is decreased by 13 to 61 and the frequency 112 is increased by 13 to 125.

26.21 An educator is interested in the relationship between levels of wages and levels of education. He has randomly selected 250 employees in a large California bank from those who have been with the bank for at least 5 years. His observations are shown in Table 26.P5.

TABLE 26.P5 Observed Data on Education and Income, in Numbers of Employees

	College Degree	No College Degree	Totals
Wages of $30,000 or more	100	45	145
Wages below $30,000	80	25	105
Totals	180	70	250

a. State the null and alternative hypotheses.
b. Compute the expected frequencies.
c. Calculate χ^2 and decide whether to reject H_0 at $\alpha = 0.05$ and also at $\alpha = 0.01$.

26.22 Table 26.P6 presents the number of workers in a random sample from a large insurance company, cross-classified by sex and by the presence or absence of a raise in wages last year.

TABLE 26.P6

	Number of Workers		
	Men	Women	Totals
Raise	607	306	913
No raise	110	57	167
Totals	717	363	1080

In view of these data, are the company's wage increases independent of sex at $\alpha = 0.05$? at $\alpha = 0.01$?

26.23 A random sample of 550 New York registered voters is selected, and their opinions on legalized gambling are obtained. The results, cross-classified by occupation, are as in Table 26.P7:

TABLE 26.P7

	Numbers of Registered Voters			
	For	Against	Indifferent	Totals
Businesspeople	152	52	26	230
Others	85	168	67	320
Totals	237	220	93	550

Do you think the opinions on legalized gambling are independent of occupation? Comment on why such a conclusion is quite understandable.

26.24 A random sample consisting of 100 men and 100 women gave the results in Table 26.P8 in connection with their attitudes toward President Reagan's suggested policy on early retirement, which was introduced in 1981.

TABLE 26.P8

Sex	For	Against	Total
Men	25	75	100
Women	45	55	100
Totals	70	130	200

In view of this information, can you conclude that the American people's attitude toward the suggestion was independent of sex at $\alpha = 0.05$?

26.25 A marketing research firm wants to determine whether the inclusion of a dollar bill in a questionnaire would increase the number of responses. Accordingly, 300 questionnaires, half with dollar bills and half without, are sent to 300 persons selected at random. The following results are shown in Table 26.P9.

TABLE 26.P9

	Responded	Did Not Respond	Total
Dollar bill included	97	53	150
Dollar bill not included	80	70	150
Total	177	123	300

Is there significant evidence to indicate that the inclusion of a dollar bill is related to the number of responses to the questionnaire?

26.26 A sample of 100 small machine parts was taken from products produced by three different operators to determine whether they tended to produce the same distribution of output quality as defined by two quality classes. The results are given in Table 26.P10.

TABLE 26.P10

Quality	Operator		
	1	2	3
Good	30	27	23
Average	8	6	6

a. State the null and alternative hypotheses.
b. What conclusion can you reach?

26.27 A firm selling four products wishes to determine whether sales are distributed similarly among four general classes of customers. A random sample of 1,000 sales records provides the information in Table 26.P11.

TABLE 26.P11

Customer Group	Product			
	1	2	3	4
Professionals	85	23	56	36
Businesspeople	153	44	128	75
Factory workers	128	26	101	45
Farmers	34	7	15	44

a. State the null and alternative hypotheses.
b. What conclusion can you reach?

26.28 Fifteen pairs of plots are planted with two varieties of soybeans, and the observed yields are recorded in Table 26.P12. What conclusion can you reach using the signed-rank test?

TABLE 26.P12

Pair	Variety I	Variety II
1	135	134
2	129	137
3	130	151
4	146	142
5	127	138
6	128	142
7	125	140
8	151	122
9	151	121
10	128	138
11	134	122
12	132	119
13	121	130
14	136	139
15	121	128

26.29 A motion study is designed to test the efficiency of two procedures, I and II, for assembling a certain mechanism. The workers are paired on the basis of intelligence quotients and number of years of education. Members of each pair are assigned by lot to one of the two procedures. Time in seconds for completing the assemblage is recorded in Table 26.P13. Apply the signed-rank test, indicating the appropriate rejection region.

TABLE 26.P13

Pair	I	II
1	44	41
2	40	44
3	50	22
4	56	30
5	64	35
6	51	26
7	26	25
8	26	30
9	32	34
10	53	23
11	56	29
12	29	25
13	29	29
14	20	20

26.30 The data in Table 26.P14 are the results of planting corn with two different types of fertilizer on eight pairs of plots.

TABLE 26.P14

Pair	1	2	3	4	5	6	7	8
A	164	165	158	149	170	155	154	162
B	150	143	152	160	151	151	148	134

a. What are the populations whose distributions are tested if the Wilcoxon signed-rank test is applied here?
b. State H_0.
c. Should H_0 be rejected?

26.31 In a paired experiment, speeds (in number of items packed per hour by a worker) by two different systems are given in Table 26.P15. How should H_0 be stated here? Can we reject this H_0 using the signed-rank test at $\alpha = 0.05$? 0.01?

TABLE 26.P15

Pair	System I	System II	Pair	System I	System II
1	10.4	7.3	10	10.3	11.5
2	11.6	6.2	11	13.6	9.4
3	9.3	12.3	12	12.7	8.5
4	8.0	9.1	13	14.3	13.3
5	15.5	13.4	14	13.9	10.1
6	12.1	7.0	15	14.8	8.7
7	11.8	13.8	16	12.3	7.2
8	13.4	9.0	17	14.9	7.0
9	15.3	8.1	18	12.4	12.4

26.32 Repeat Problem 26.31, but reverse the results for pair 16 (being now 7.2 for system I and 12.3 for System II) and also for pair 17 (being now 7.0 for System I and 14.9 for System II). Suppose these reversals were required because someone spotted several errors in the way Table 26.P15 was constructed from the raw data. Do these errors seriously affect the conclusion about which is the better system?

26.33 Suppose every observation in column (1) of Table 26.6 pertaining to the Mann–Whitney test, is multiplied by 10. What changes, if any, would there be in R_1, R_2, $E(R_j)$, $V(R_j)$, Z, and the final conclusion?

26.34 Suppose several recording errors were discovered in column (1) of Table 26.6, and the corrections require shifting the last three observations of the first sample (which are 103, 137, and 136) to the second sample, and shifting the last three observations of the second sample (which are 134, 160, and 151) to the first sample. What conclusion should now be reached? Were the recording serious?

26.35 Apply the Mann–Whitney test to the data of Problem 26.29, assuming now that the workers are not paired and that the two samples are independent.

26.36 Apply the median test for the identity of the population distributions to data in Table 26.P12. Comment on the conclusion reached here as compared to that in Problem 26.28.

26.37 Apply the median test for the identity of population distributions to data in Table 26.P13. Compare the conclusion reached here to that reached in Problem 26.29.

26.38 Measurements of height (in inches) of five adult males of each of four different nationalities are given below.

I:	61	65	62	67	64
II:	63	67	66	68	70
III:	60	69	68	71	72
IV:	64	68	70	74	71

Use the median test for independent samples to determine whether the underlying populations are identical at $\alpha = 0.05$.

26.39 Suppose that in an experiment evaluating four different methods of teaching statistics, 10 matched groups of 4 students each had been used. The students were matched in terms of their intelligence quotients and freshman mathematics grades. At the end of the course, final grades were rated with respective row medians, and the overall table of frequencies of plus and minus categories within columns is shown below.

	I	II	III	IV	
+	9	7	2	2	$20 = ra$
−	1	3	8	8	$20 = n - ra$

Are the above results consistent with the hypothesis that the population distributions (populations being grades of the four methods of teaching) are identical at $\alpha = 0.01$?

26.40 Three methods of making concrete are available. Eight sample blocks are made by each method. The compressive strength in pounds per square inch is measured and the following data result.

Method I:	147	140	149	146	152	143	150	155
Method II:	146	138	148	131	140	125	127	130
Method III:	158	150	160	165	158	171	140	165

Use the median test for independent samples to test the identity among the population distributions at $\alpha = 0.01$.

26.41 The data in Table 26.P16 represent differences in heights between husband and wife for three different nationalities. Do they come from identical populations, judging from the H test?

TABLE 26.P16

	French	Japanese	American
	2.1 (13.5)	3.4 (26)	5.1 (33)
	0.8 (2)	1.5 (6.5)	2.7 (22)
	2.5 (18)	1.7 (9)	4.2 (32)
	0.7 (1)	1.9 (11.5)	2.7 (22)
	2.4 (16)	2.5 (18)	4.1 (31)
	2.6 (20)	3.1 (25)	2.9 (24)
	1.1 (4)	1.5 (6.5)	2.7 (22)
	1.3 (4)	1.9 (11.5)	2.3 (15)
	1.3 (5)	1.6 (8)	2.5 (18)
	1.8 (10)	3.6 (28)	3.5 (27)
	0.9 (3)		2.1 (13.5)
			3.7 (29.5)
			3.7 (29.5)
n_j	10	10	13
T_j	92.5	150	318.5

26.42 To determine whether the distributions of three brands of computers are identical in terms of number of breakdowns per 50 working days, the data in Table 26.P17 are obtained.

TABLE 26.P17

I:	7.7	6.8	8.5	9.0	11.0	8.9	10.1	9.5
II:	8.7	9.2	10.5	9.8	11.4	12.6	10.9	9.9
III:	10.7	9.8	12.5	11.4	10.8	13.5	14.1	12.7

What conclusion can be drawn using the H test?

26.43 The data in Table 26.P18 are two sets of ranks, each set is assigned by a professor of management to the same ten characteristics of business leadership.

TABLE 26.P18

Characteristic	Professor I	Professor II
A	10	6
B	1	9
C	2	3
D	9	10
E	8	2
F	6	7
G	7	5
H	5	1
I	4	8
J	3	4

Compute $\bar{r}_s$. From this result, can we conclude that there is some relationship between the two sets of ranks? If so, what is the relationship? Is r_s significant at $\alpha = 0.05$ and at $\alpha = 0.01$?

26.44 The data in Table 26.P19 are costs and sales, in thousands of dollars, for twelve drug stores.

TABLE 26.P19

Store	Costs	Sales
1	11	19
2	10	15
3	14	20
4	13	14
5	12	16
6	20	33
7	21	32
8	15	18
9	22	29
10	18	22
11	19	23
12	16	20

a. Compute the rank correlation coefficient r_s for these data. Is the result significant at $\alpha = 0.05$?
b. Compute r by Equation (17.27). Is r significant at $\alpha = 0.05$?
c. Comment on the results in (a) and (b).

Appendix A
Summation Algebra

Rather complicated additions occur quite often in statistics, so precise notation is needed. This appendix on summation algebra constitutes a brief discussion of the sigma notation for addition employed throughout this text.

A.1 SINGLE SUMMATION

The Greek capital letter sigma, Σ, is a shorthand notation for designating a sum. For example, the sum

$$x_1 + x_2 + \cdots + x_n$$

may be conveniently written with the single summation sign as

$$\sum_{i=1}^{n} x_i, \tag{A.1}$$

which is read as "the summation of x_i from $i = 1$ to $i = n$." Here, i is called the *index of summation* and is a variable ranging over the integers $1, 2, \ldots, n$. The expression $i = 1$ below the Σ sign indicates that 1 is the initial value taken on by i, and the n above the Σ sign indicates the terminal value of i. The symbol x_i is called the *summand*; it is a function of i that takes on values of $x_1, x_2, \ldots, x_n$, respectively, as i takes on values $1, 2, \ldots, n$. The Σ sign says that the values taken by the summand are to be added.

The symbol used for the index of summation is sometimes called a *dummy index,* because it is completely arbitrary. For example,

$$x_1 + x_2 + \cdots + x_n = \sum_{i=1}^{n} x_i = \sum_{j=1}^{n} x_j = \sum_{k=1}^{n} x_k = \cdots.$$

As illustrations, we see that

$$\sum_{i=1}^{3} i = 1 + 2 + 3 = 6,$$

$$\sum_{i=1}^{3} i^2 = 1^2 + 2^2 + 3^2 = 14,$$

$$\sum_{i=0}^{r} \frac{1}{2^i} = \frac{1}{2^0} + \frac{1}{2^1} + \frac{1}{2^2} + \cdots + \frac{1}{2^r},$$

$$\sum_{i=1}^{5} x_i = x_1 + x_2 + \cdots + x_5,$$

$$\sum_{i=6}^{9} x_i = x_6 + x_7 + x_8 + x_9.$$

From the last two examples we can readily appreciate that

$$x_1 + x_2 + \cdots + x_9 = \sum_{i=1}^{5} x_i + \sum_{i=6}^{9} x_i = \sum_{i=1}^{9} x_i.$$

A familiar function of n values $x_1, x_2, \ldots, x_n$ is their arithmetic mean (their sum divided by n), denoted by $\bar{x}$. Using the Σ notation, we can write

$$\bar{x} = \frac{x_1 + x_2 + \cdots + x_n}{n}$$

$$= \frac{1}{n} \sum_{i=1}^{n} x_i.$$

If the range of summation is completely clear from the context, the index of summation can be omitted. Thus, we use

$$\sum x \quad \text{to replace} \quad \sum_{i=1}^{n} x_i;$$

$$\frac{1}{n} \sum x \quad \text{to replace} \quad \frac{1}{n} \sum_{i=1}^{n} x_i;$$

$$\sum x^2 - \left(\sum x\right)^2 \quad \text{to replace} \quad \sum_{i=1}^{n} x_i^2 - \left(\sum_{i=1}^{n} x_i\right)^2;$$

and so on.

A.2 THEOREMS FOR SINGLE SUMMATION

THEOREM 1 *If a is some constant value over the n different values of i, then*

$$\sum_{i=1}^{n} a = na. \tag{A.2}$$

The reason is that each of the x's is equal to a constant quantity a, and thus

$$\sum_{i=1}^{n} a = a + a + \cdots + a = na.$$

THEOREM II *Given the value a, which is a constant over all individual values entering into the summation, then*

$$\sum_{i=1}^{n} ax_i = a \sum_{i=1}^{n} x_i, \tag{A.3}$$

since

$$\sum_{i=1}^{n} ax_i = ax_1 + ax_2 + \cdots + ax_n$$

$$= a(x_1 + x_2 + \cdots + x_n)$$

$$= a \sum_{i=1}^{n} x_i = a \sum x.$$

THEOREM III *If the only operation to be carried out before a sum is taken is itself a sum (or a difference), then the summation may be distributed; namely,*

$$\sum_{i} (x_i + y_i - z_i) = \sum_{i} x_i + \sum_{i} y_i - \sum_{i} z_i. \tag{A.4}$$

This is true because

$$\sum_{i} (x_i + y_i - z_i) = (x_1 + y_1 - z_1) + (x_2 + y_2 - z_2)$$

$$+ \cdots + (x_n + y_n - z_n)$$

$$= (x_1 + \cdots + x_n) + (y_1 + \cdots + y_n)$$

$$- (z_1 + \cdots + z_n)$$

$$= \sum_{i} x_i + \sum_{i} y_i - \sum_{i} z_i$$

$$= \sum x + \sum y - \sum z.$$

THEOREM IV *If some operation is to be carried out on the individual values of X before the summation, this is indicated by the mathematical* *notation. Unless the summation sign is included within this notation, the summation is to be made after the other operation.*

For example,

$$\sum_i x_i^2 = x_1^2 + x_2^2 + \cdots + x_n^2,$$

whereas

$$\left(\sum_i x_i\right)^2 = (x_1 + x_2 + \cdots + x_n)^2.$$

Thus,

$$\sum_i x_i^2 \neq \left(\sum_i x_i\right)^2,$$

for all possible x_i, although there are some sets of x_i's for which

$$\sum_i x_i^2 = \left(\sum_i x_i\right)^2.$$

Also,

$$\sum \sqrt{x_i} = \sqrt{x_1} + \sqrt{x_2} + \cdots + \sqrt{x_n},$$

whereas

$$\sqrt{\sum x} = \sqrt{x_1 + x_2 + \cdots + x_n}.$$

A.3 FINITE DOUBLE AND TRIPLE SUMS

The values of a variable X, the summand, are sometimes arranged as a two-way table as follows:

$$
\begin{matrix}
x_{11} & x_{12} & \cdots & x_{1m} \\
x_{21} & x_{22} & \cdots & x_{2m} \\
\vdots & \vdots & \vdots & \vdots \\
x_{n1} & x_{n2} & \cdots & x_{nm}
\end{matrix}
$$

where the individual values may be denoted as x_{ij}, $i = 1, 2, \ldots, n$ and $j = 1, 2, \ldots, m$. The sum of x_{ij} can be obtained by first adding the various rows and then adding the row totals to get the desired results. Of course, we would obtain the same result by adding first the column values and then the column totals. This is simply the application of the single summation twice to get a double summation as shown below:

$$
\begin{aligned}
\sum_{i=1}^{n} \sum_{j=1}^{m} x_{ij} &= \sum_{i=1}^{n} (x_{i1} + x_{i2} + \cdots + x_{im}) \\
&= (x_{11} + x_{12} + \cdots + x_{1n}) \\
&\quad + (x_{21} + x_{22} + \cdots + x_{2m}) \\
&\quad + \cdots + (x_{n1} + x_{n2} + \cdots + x_{nm}).
\end{aligned}
\tag{A.5}
$$

Consider now the case of a triple summation sign, the largest one used in this text. If the values of variables are arranged in a table that consists of n rows and m columns—that is, nm cells, where each individual value belongs to exactly one cell in the table, then the kth observation in the ijth cell is denoted as x_{ijk}. Also, we denote the number of observations in cell ij as n_{ij}. The notation for the sum of the observations in such a table can be written by employing the single summation sign three times as below:

$$\sum_{i=1}^{n} \sum_{j=1}^{m} \sum_{k=1}^{n_{ij}} x_{ijk},$$

or,

$$\sum_{i} \sum_{j} \sum_{k} x_{ijk}.$$

This notation says: "Take a particular cell, ij, and add up all the n_{ij} values in that cell; then, holding row i constant, sum the results of each cell sum over all the columns; finally, sum the results of each row i over all the rows." A little reflection will reveal that this is simply the sum of the individual values in the table.

A.4 THEOREMS FOR DOUBLE SUMMATION

Let us now observe some of the theorems governing double sums that are of special interest and that can also be applied to triple or even higher summations.

THEOREM I *If a is a constant, then*

$$\sum_{i=1}^{n} \sum_{j=1}^{m} a = \sum_{i=1}^{n} ma = nma \qquad (A.6)$$

and

$$\sum_{i=1}^{n} \sum_{j=1}^{m} ax_{ij} = a \sum_{i=1}^{n} \sum_{j=1}^{m} x_{ij}. \qquad (A.7)$$

THEOREM II *If both limits on the summation signs are constants, then the order of summation may be interchanged.*

$$\sum_{i=1}^{n} \sum_{j=1}^{m} x_{ij} = \sum_{j=1}^{m} \sum_{i=1}^{n} x_{ij}. \qquad (A.8)$$

THEOREM III

$$\sum_{i=1}^{n} \sum_{j=1}^{m} (x_{ij} + y_{ij}) = \sum_{i=1}^{n} \sum_{j=1}^{m} x_{ij} + \sum_{i=1}^{n} \sum_{j=1}^{m} y_{ij}, \qquad (A.9)$$

since

$$\sum_{i}^{n} \sum_{j}^{m} (x_{ij} + y_{ij}) = \sum_{i}^{n} (x_{i1} + y_{i1}) + \sum_{i}^{n} (x_{i2} + y_{i2})$$

$$+ \cdots + \sum_{i}^{n} (x_{im} + y_{im})$$

$$= \sum_{i}^{n} (x_{i1} + x_{i2} + \cdots + x_{im})$$

$$+ \sum_{i}^{n} (y_{i1} + y_{i2} + \cdots + y_{im})$$

$$= \sum_{i}^{n} \sum_{j}^{m} x_{ij} + \sum_{i}^{n} \sum_{j}^{m} y_{ij}.$$

THEOREM IV

$$\sum_{i=1}^{n} \sum_{j=1}^{m} x_i = \sum_{i}^{n} \left(\sum_{j}^{m} x_i \right) = m \sum_{i=1}^{n} x_i. \qquad (A.10)$$

THEOREM V

$$\sum_{i=1}^{n} \sum_{j=1}^{m} x_i y_j = \left(\sum_{i=1}^{n} x_i \right) \left(\sum_{j=1}^{m} y_j \right), \qquad (A.11)$$

since

$$\sum_{i}^{n} \sum_{j}^{m} x_i y_j = \sum_{i}^{n} (x_i y_1 + x_i y_2 + \cdots + x_i y_m)$$

$$= y_1 \sum_{i}^{n} x_i + y_2 \sum_{i}^{n} x_i + \cdots + y_m \sum_{i}^{n} x_i$$

$$= \left(\sum_{i}^{n} x_i \right) \left(\sum_{j}^{m} y_j \right).$$

Note that V does not say that

$$\sum_{i=1}^{n} x_i y_i = \left(\sum_{i=1}^{n} x_i \right) \left(\sum_{i=1}^{n} y_i \right).$$

This so-called equality is false except in special cases. Theorem V refers to double summation with two different indices of summation.

THEOREM VI

$$\left(\sum_{i=1}^{n} x_i \right)^2 = \sum_{i=1}^{n} x_i^2 + 2 \sum_{i<j} x_i x_j, \qquad (A.12)$$

since

$$\left(\sum_{i}^{n} x_i \right)^2 = (x_1 + x_2 + \cdots + x_n)^2$$

$$= x_1^2 + x_2^2 + \cdots + x_n^2 + 2(x_1 x_2 + x_1 x_3 + \cdots$$

$$+ x_1 x_n + x_2 x_3 + \cdots + x_{n-1} x_n)$$

$$= \sum_{i}^{n} x_i^2 + 2 \sum_{i<j} x_i x_j.$$

Note that $\sum_{i<j}$ has not been explicitly defined; its meaning should be obvious from the explanation of Theorem VI.

Appendix B
A Note on Further Reading

B.1 THE END OF A BEGINNING

We now have come to the end of a beginning. This text has presented many standard statistical methods that have been widely and successfully used for many years. The obvious limitations of an introductory course, however, have prevented our covering many other topics, elementary as well as advanced, that are important. It seems appropriate, therefore, that we now introduce the reader to some references for further study in the hope that we have not closed but have rather opened up the subject of statistical reasoning.

As readers explore statistical analysis, they may encounter technical difficulties from time to time without a basic knowledge of calculus and matrix algebra. There are many good texts covering these topics, such as the programmed basic text by E. W. Martin, Jr., entitled *Mathematics for Decision Making* (Irwin, 1969). Volume I of this text covers linear mathematics and Volume II covers calculus. The reader may also benefit by consulting Serge Lang's *First Course in Calculus*, Fourth Edition (Addison-Wesley, 1978). A text by Clopper Almon, Jr., presents a uniform, connected exposition of linear algebra: *Matrix Methods in Economics* (Addison-Wesley, 1967).

B.2 STATISTICAL ENCYCLOPEDIA

The *International Encyclopedia of Statistics* (Free Press, 1978), edited by William H. Kruskal and Judith M. Tanur, is a comprehensive work of more than 1,200 pages, and it covers a very wide variety of topics ranging from basic issues to detailed statistical procedures. Many articles are easy to read; some are difficult because they cover advanced material. There is also much material on history, biography, and bibliography. This work is a good starting point for further reading on any statistical topic.

B.3   INTRODUCTORY STATISTICS

Textbooks on business and economic statistics fall into three categories: (1) those that stress descriptive measures and classical inferential procedures, paying little or no attention to Bayesian statistics; (2) those that are oriented almost exclusively toward Bayesian methods at the expense of classical analysis and time-series studies; and (3) those that attempt a "balanced" presentation of all elementary statistical methods useful in the study of quantitative economics and management science. Texts of the first two kinds seem to view classical and Bayesian theories as substitutes for each other; those of the third kind seem to suggest that they complement each other. In terms of the third approach, methods of one school or the other may be more appropriate or useful in certain circumstances and, although both may lead to identical conclusions from the same set of data, the interpretations of results may differ. We have subscribed to this approach in preparing this book.

Basic texts with an orientation similar to ours include Morris Hamburg, *Statistical Analysis for Decision Making,* 4th Edition (Harcourt Brace Jovanovich, 1987); Peters and Summers, *Statistical Analysis for Business Decisions* (Prentice-Hall, 1968); Stephen P. Shao, *Statistics for Business and Economics,* 3d Edition (Charles E. Merrill, 1976); and Spurr and Bonini, *Statistical Analysis for Business Decisions,* 2d Edition (Irwin, 1973). A more advanced text that treats both the classical and Bayesian methods rather extensively is *Statistics: Probability, Inference and Decision* by Hayes and Winkler, 2d Edition (Holt, Rinehart & Winston, 1975).

There are numerous introductory textbooks that stress classical analysis. Two deserving special mention are E. C. Bryant's *Statistical Analysis,* 2d Edition (McGraw-Hill, 1966), and Taro Yamane's *Statistics,* 3d Edition (Harper & Row, 1973). Bryant's book is recommended for its lucid presentation and Yamane's book for its broad coverage. Two more books deserving special metnion are W. Allen Wallis and Harry V. Roberts, *Statistics: A New Approach* (Free Press, 1956), and William G. Cochran and George W. Snedecor, *Statistical Methods,* 7th Edition (Iowa State University Press, 1980) Wallis and Roberts write clearly and give a wealth of illustrations from real life. Cochran and Snedecor cover many topics including some more advanced material, with many detailed numerical examples drawn from actual research data. Both books stress interpreting numerical results, not merely calculating them.

Texts with a Bayesian orientation at the elementary level include

Howard Raiffa, *Decision Analysis* (Addison-Wesley, 1968); R. Schlaifer, *Probability and Statistics for Business Decisions* (McGraw-Hill, 1959); K. Sasaki, *Statistics for Modern Decision Making* (Wadsworth, 1968); Dyckman, Smidt, and McAdams, *Management Decision Making Under Uncertainty* (Macmillan, 1969); and R. Schlaifer, *Analysis of Decisions Under Uncertainty* (McGraw-Hill, 1965). A more advanced text is Pratt, Raiffa, and Schlaifer, *Introduction to Statistical Decision Theory* (McGraw-Hill, 1965). An advanced and standard text on Bayesian statistics is *Applied Statistical Decision Theory* under the joint authorship of H. Raiffa and R. Schlaifer (Harvard University Press, 1961). Two additional rather advanced texts in this group which may benefit the reader, are G. Hadly, *Introduction to Probability and Statistical Decision Theory* (Holden-Day, 1967), and D. V. Lindley, *Introduction to Probability and Statistics from a Bayesian View Point* (Cambridge University Press, 1980).

Some of the more recent books on introductory statistics are Stockton and Clark, *Introduction to Business and Economics Statistics,* 6th Edition (Southwestern Publishing Co., 1980); Lawrence Lapin, *Statistics for Modern Business Decisions,* 3d Edition (Harcourt Brace Jovanovich, 1982); William R. Heitzman and Frederich W. Mueller, *Statistics for Business and Economics* (Allyn & Bacon, 1980); D. V. Huntsberger, D. J. Croft, and P. Billingsley, *Statistical Inference for Management and Economics,* 2d Edition (Allyn & Bacon, 1980); and R. C. Gulezian, *Statistics for Decision Making* (Holt, Reinhart & Winston, 1979).

Additional recent books on introductory statistics are Robert E. Mason, *Statistical Techniques in Business and Economics,* 5th Edition (Irwin, 1982); Plane and Opperman, *Statistics for Management Decisions,* Revised Edition (Business Publications, Inc., 1981); Anderson, Sweeney, and Williams, *Introduction to Statistics: An Applications Approach* (West); Hoel and Jessen, *Basic Statistics for Business and Economics,* 2d Edition (Wiley, 1977); Groebner and Shannon, *Business Statistics: A Decision-Making Approach* (Merrill, 1981); Miller, *Introductory Statistics for Business and Economics* (St. Martin's, 1980); Sanders, Murphy, and Eng, *Statistics: A Fresh Approach,* 2d Edition (McGraw-Hill, 1979); Ullman, *Elementary Statistics: An Applied Approach* (Wiley, 1978); McClave and Besnon, *Statistics for Business and Economics,* 2d Edition (Dellen Publishing Co., 1982); Wonnacott and Wonnacott, *Introductory Statistics for Business and Economics,* 3d Edition (Wiley, 1984); and Lawrence Lapin, *Statistics for Modern Business Decisions,* 4th Edition (Harcourt Brace Jovanovich, 1987).

B.4 MATHEMATICAL STATISTICS

Mathematical statistics is concerned with the underlying axioms for statistical inference and decision making, and with the discovery and proof of theorems in probability and statistics. Knowledge in this area also has practical use in clarifying the strengths and limitations of statistical methods in actual applications.

Books on mathematical statistics and probability theory suitable for the reader with a background in elementary calculus include: E. Borel, *Elements of the Theory of Probability* (Prentice-Hall, 1965); J. E. Freund, *Mathematical Statistics* (Prentice-Hall, 1962); P. Hoel, *Introduction to Mathematical Statistics,* 4th Edition (Wiley, 1971); W. B. Lindgren, *Statistical Theory,* 3d Edition (Macmillan, 1976); and J. Neymen, *First Course in Probability and Statistics* (Holt, Rinehart & Winston, 1950). Some more advanced well-known texts in this field are W. Feller, *An Introduction to Probability and Its Applications,* Vols. 1 and 2 (Wiley, 1968, 1971); and E. Parzen, *Modern Probability Theory and Its Applications* (Wiley, 1960).

B.5 SAMPLING AND SAMPLING DESIGNS

For detailed presentations of the sampling plans frequently used in practice and for discussions of when to use each of these sampling plans, see W. G. Cochran, *Sampling Techniques,* 3d Edition (Wiley, 1977); W. E. Deming, *Sample Design in Business Research* (Wiley, 1960); Hanson, Hurwitz, and Madow, *Sample Survey Methods and Theory,* Vols. 1 and 2 (Wiley, 1953); and A. Stuart, *Basic Ideas of Scientific Sampling,* 2d Edition (Hafner, 1976).

B.6 EXPERIMENTAL DESIGN AND THE ANALYSIS OF VARIANCE

Our introduction to these versatile and useful topics is very brief. If the reader is interested in these techniques of statistical investigation, he may consult the following references. C. C. Li presents a simple and quite readable *Introduction to Experimental Statistics* (McGraw-Hill, 1964). Charles R. Hicks offers simple and realistic numerical examples in *Fundamental Concepts in the Design of Experiments,* 2d Edition (Holt, Rinehart & Winston, 1973). A readable text on ANOVA as well as on regression studies at the intermediate level is *Applied Linear Statistical Models* by John Neter and William Wasserman (Irwin, 1974). A systematic account of the methods from the viewpoint of the user and the consultant is given by O. Kempthorne's *The Design and Analysis of Experiments* (Wiley, 1952). Comprehensive treatments of the underlying principles of experimental design for behavioral scientists can be found in B. J. Winer's *Statistical Principles in Experimental Design,* 2d Edition (McGraw-Hill, 1971).

B.7 STATISTICAL QUALITY CONTROL

Statistical quality control uses samples to determine whether the output of a production process meets specified quality standards. In this text we have undertaken a systematic but brief discussion of statistical quality control. For detailed discussions on this topic the reader may consult some of the following references: Dudley J. Cowden, *Statistical Methods in Quality Control* (Prentice-Hall, 1957); Acheson J. Duncan, *Quality Control and Industrial Statistics*, 4th Edition (Irwin, 1974); Eugene L. Grant, *Statistical Quality Control*, 4th Edition (McGraw-Hill, 1972); W. A. Shewhart, *Economic Control of Quality of Manufactured Product* (Van Nostrand, 1931); Statistical Research Group, Columbia University, *Sampling Inspection* (McGraw-Hill, 1948); and United States Department of Defense, *Sampling Procedures and Tables for Inspection by Attributes* (*MIL-STD-105D*) (Washington, D.C., 1963).

B.8 NONPARAMETRIC STATISTICS

This text has presented only the simplest nonparametric tests. Nonparametric methods exist also for confidence intervals, the analysis of variance, and so forth. These and other more advanced nonparametric techniques can be found in *A Nonparametric Introduction to Statistics* (Macmillan, 1968) by Kraft and Van Eeden; *Elements of Nonparametric Statistics* (Wiley, 1967) by E. G. Noether; *Nonparametric Statistics for the Behavioral Sciences* (McGraw-Hill, 1956) by S. Siegel; and *Practical Nonparametric Statistics*, 2d Edition, by W. J. Conover (Wiley, 1980).

B.9 REGRESSION AND CORRELATION ANALYSIS

A lucid discussion on the important topics of linear as well as nonlinear association analysis can be found in J. Johnston's *Econometric Methods*, 3d Edition (McGraw-Hill, 1980), Chapters 1–4. For more comprehensive coverage, the reader may consult Draper and Smith, *Applied Regression Analysis*, 2d Edition (Wiley, 1981), and Ezekiel and Fox, *Methods of Correlation and Regression Analysis*, 3d Edition (Wiley, 1959). At the intermediate level, you may consult *Data Analysis and Regression: A Second Course in Statistics*, by F. Mosteller and J. W. Tukey (Addison-Wesley, 1977), and *A Second Course in Business Statistics: Regression Analysis*, by W. Mendenhall and J. T. McClave (Dellen Publishing Co., 1981). For very advanced treatments of regression and correlation, the reader is referred to E. J. Williams, *Regression Analysis* (Wiley, 1959), and S. James Press, *Applied Multivariate Analysis* (Holt, Rinehart & Winston, 1972).

B.10 INDEX NUMBERS, TIME SERIES, AND FORECASTING

A short but highly instructive book on the method of constructing index numbers is W. M. Persons, *The Construction of Index Numbers*

(Houghton Mifflin, 1928). This volume gives special attention to the problems of bias resulting from the type of average used and from correlation between quantities and prices. The definitive work on index numbers is Irving Fisher, *The Making of Index Numbers* (Houghton Mifflin, 1927), which discusses tests of reliability for many different formulas for computing index numbers. A more recent text is B. D. Mudgett, *Index Numbers* (Wiley, 1951). A good discussion on the difficulties and limitations of constructing price indices can be found in Joint Economic Committee, 87th Congress, 1st Session, *Government Price Statistics: Hearings before the Subcommittee on Economic Statistics* (U.S. Government Printing Office, 1961).

A comprehensive, clear presentation of the classical approach to time-series analysis can be found in Croxton, Cowden, and Klein, *Applied General Statistics*, 3d Edition (Prentice-Hall, 1967). Chapter 22 in this volume also discusses correlation in time series. An excellent but rather advanced treatment of some topics in time-series analysis is given in Part 3 of Gerhard Tintner, *Econometrics* (Wiley, 1952). Up-to-date methods in analyzing time-series data can be found in *Spectral Analysis of Economic Time Series* (Princeton University Press, 1964) under the joint authorship of C. W. J. Granger and M. Hatanaka; *Statistical Analysis of Stationary Time Series* (Wiley, 1957) by W. F. Grenander and M. Rosenblatt; and *Symposium on Time Series Analysis* (Wiley, 1963), edited by M. Rosenblatt; M. B. Priestley, *Spectral Analysis and Time Series* (Academic Press, 1981). Systematic inferential methods for time-series parameters and procedures of forecasting with time-series data can be found in two rather advanced volumes: *Time Series Analysis: Forecasting and Control*, Revised Edition (Holden-Day, 1976) by George E. P. Box and Gwilym M. Jenkins; and *Applied Time Series Analysis for Managerial Forecasting* (Holden-Day, 1973) by Charles R. Nelson.

On forecasting, the reader may consult R. D. Brown, *Smoothing, Forecasting, and Prediction* (Prentice-Hall, 1963), and Spencer, Clark, and Hoguet, *Business and Economic Forecasting* (Irwin, 1961). Additional references can be found in these two volumes.

B.11   ADDITIONAL REFERENCES

To complete our list of references we might cite some sources for operations research, game theory, journals, bibliography, and tables.

Operations research is concerned with the application of mathematical and statistical methods to the study of the operations of large, complex organizations or activities. Its objective is to provide top-level administrators with a quantitative basis for decisions that will increase the effectiveness of such organizations in carrying out their basic objectives. A book recommended for its rigor and comprehensive coverage is H. M. Wagner, *Principles of Operations Research*, 2d Edition (Prentice-Hall, 1975). This volume requires a considerable knowledge of mathematics. Wagner also lists further references in this field.

Methods for dealing with decision situations involving the competitive actions of rational opponents are part of game theory. There are several good texts on game theory. One that surveys the central ideas and results of game theory and related decision-making models without using excessive mathematical detail is *Games and Decisions*, co-authored by R. D. Luce and H. Raiffa (Wiley, 1957).

To keep up with current developments, the reader may wish to study regularly some journals of statistics, such as the *Journal of the American Statistical Association, Econometrica, Journal of Time Series Analysis,* and *Review of Economics and Statistics.*

The reader may also find the following set of general reference works and tables a valuable addition to his personal library: Buckland and Fox, *Bibliography of Basic Texts on Statistical Methods* (Hafner, 1963); Hauser and Leonard, *Government Statistics for Business Use,* 2d Edition (Wiley, 1956); E. B. Cox, *Basic Tables in Business and Economics* (McGraw-Hill, 1966); Freund and Williams, *Dictionary/Outline of Basic Statistics* (McGraw-Hill, 1966); RAND Corporation, *A Million Random Digits with 100,000 Normal Deviates* (Macmillan, 1955); and U.S. Department of Commerce, *Handbook of Mathematical Functions,* 9th printing with corrections (U.S. Government Printing Office, 1970), especially Chapter 1 on mathematical constants, Chapter 24 on combinatorial analysis, and Chapter 26 on probability functions.

Appendix C
Statistical Tables

TABLE I Equidistributed Random Numbers

03	47	43	73	86	36	96	47	36	61	46	98	63	71	62	33	26	16	80	45	60	11	14	10	95
97	74	24	67	62	42	81	14	57	20	42	53	32	37	32	27	07	36	07	51	24	51	79	89	73
16	76	62	27	66	56	50	26	71	07	32	90	79	78	53	13	55	38	58	59	88	97	54	14	10
12	56	85	99	26	96	96	68	27	31	05	03	72	93	15	57	12	10	14	21	88	26	49	81	76
55	59	56	35	64	38	54	82	46	22	31	62	43	09	90	06	18	44	32	53	23	83	01	30	30
16	22	77	94	39	49	54	43	54	82	17	37	93	23	78	87	35	20	96	43	84	26	34	91	64
84	42	17	53	31	57	24	55	06	88	77	04	74	47	67	21	76	33	50	25	83	92	12	96	76
63	01	63	78	59	16	95	55	67	19	98	10	50	71	75	12	86	73	58	07	44	39	52	38	79
33	21	12	34	29	78	64	56	07	82	52	42	07	44	38	15	51	00	13	42	99	66	02	79	54
57	60	86	32	44	09	47	27	96	54	49	17	46	09	62	90	52	84	77	27	08	02	73	43	28
18	18	07	92	46	44	17	16	58	09	79	83	86	19	62	06	76	50	03	10	55	23	64	05	05
25	62	38	97	75	84	16	07	44	99	83	11	46	32	24	20	14	85	88	45	10	93	72	88	71
23	42	40	64	74	82	97	77	77	81	07	45	32	14	08	32	98	94	07	72	93	85	79	10	75
52	36	28	19	95	50	92	26	11	97	00	56	76	31	38	80	22	02	53	53	86	60	42	04	53
37	85	94	35	12	83	39	50	08	30	42	34	07	96	88	54	42	06	87	98	35	85	29	48	39
70	29	17	12	13	40	33	20	38	26	13	89	51	03	74	17	76	37	13	04	07	74	21	19	30
56	62	18	37	35	96	83	50	87	75	97	12	25	93	47	70	33	24	03	54	97	77	46	44	80
99	49	55	22	77	88	42	95	45	72	16	64	36	16	00	04	43	18	66	79	94	77	24	21	90
16	08	15	04	72	33	27	14	34	09	45	59	34	68	49	12	72	07	34	45	99	27	72	95	14
31	16	93	32	43	50	27	89	87	19	20	15	37	00	49	52	85	66	60	44	38	68	88	11	80
68	34	30	13	70	55	74	30	77	40	44	22	78	84	26	04	33	46	09	52	68	07	97	06	57
74	57	25	65	76	59	29	97	68	60	71	91	38	67	54	13	58	18	24	76	15	54	55	95	52
27	42	37	86	53	48	55	90	65	72	96	57	69	36	10	96	46	92	42	45	97	60	49	04	91
00	39	68	29	61	66	37	32	20	30	77	84	57	03	29	10	45	65	04	26	11	04	96	67	24
29	94	98	94	24	68	49	69	10	82	53	75	91	93	30	34	25	20	57	27	40	48	73	51	92
16	90	82	66	59	83	62	64	11	12	67	19	00	71	74	60	47	21	29	68	02	02	37	03	31
11	27	94	75	06	06	09	19	74	66	02	94	37	34	02	76	70	90	30	86	38	45	94	30	38
35	24	10	16	20	33	32	51	26	38	79	78	45	04	91	16	92	53	56	16	02	75	50	95	98
38	23	16	86	38	42	38	97	01	50	87	75	66	81	41	40	01	74	91	62	48	51	84	08	32
31	96	25	91	47	96	44	33	49	13	34	86	82	53	91	00	52	43	48	85	27	55	26	89	62
66	67	40	67	14	64	05	71	95	86	11	05	65	09	68	76	83	20	37	90	57	16	00	11	66
14	90	84	45	11	75	73	88	05	90	52	27	41	14	86	22	98	12	22	08	07	52	74	95	80
68	05	51	18	00	33	96	02	75	19	07	60	62	93	55	59	33	82	43	90	49	37	38	44	59
20	46	78	73	90	97	51	40	14	02	04	02	33	31	08	39	54	16	49	36	47	95	93	13	30
64	19	58	97	79	15	06	15	93	20	01	90	10	75	06	40	78	78	89	62	02	67	74	17	33
05	26	93	70	60	22	35	85	15	13	92	03	51	59	77	59	56	78	06	83	52	91	05	70	74
07	97	10	88	23	09	98	42	99	64	61	71	62	99	15	06	51	29	16	93	58	05	77	09	51
68	71	86	85	85	54	87	66	47	54	73	32	08	11	12	44	95	92	63	16	29	56	24	29	48
26	99	61	65	53	58	37	78	80	70	42	10	50	67	42	32	17	55	85	74	94	44	67	16	94
14	65	52	68	75	87	59	36	22	41	26	78	63	06	55	13	08	27	01	50	15	29	39	39	43

Source: This table is taken from Table XXXIII of Fisher and Yates: *Statistical Tables for Biological, Agricultural, and Medical Research,* published by Longman Group Ltd., London (previously published by Oliver & Boyd, Ltd., Edinburgh), and by permission of the authors and publishers.

TABLE II The Cumulative Binomial Distribution

n	r	$\pi = .10$	$\pi = .20$	$\pi = .25$	$\pi = .30$	$\pi = .40$	$\pi = .50$
5	0	.59049	.32768	.23730	.16807	.07776	.03125
	1	.91854	.73728	.63281	.52822	.33696	.18750
	2	.99144	.94208	.89648	.83692	.68256	.50000
	3	.99954	.99328	.98437	.96922	.91296	.81250
	4	.99999	.99968	.99902	.99757	.98976	.96875
	5	1.00000	1.00000	1.00000	1.00000	1.00000	1.00000
10	0	.34868	.10737	.05631	.02825	.00605	.00098
	1	.73610	.37581	.24403	.14931	.04636	.01074
	2	.92981	.67780	.52559	.38278	.16729	.05469
	3	.98720	.87913	.77588	.64961	.38228	.17187
	4	.99837	.96721	.92187	.84973	.63310	.37695
	5	.99985	.99363	.98027	.95265	.83376	.62305
	6	.99999	.99914	.99649	.98941	.94524	.82812
	7	1.00000	.99992	.99958	.99841	.98771	.94531
	8		1.00000	.99997	.99986	.99832	.98926
	9			1.00000	.99999	.99990	.99902
	10				1.00000	1.00000	1.00000
15	0	.20589	.03518	.01336	.00475	.00047	.00003
	1	.54904	.16713	.08018	.03527	.00517	.00049
	2	.81594	.39802	.23609	.12683	.02711	.00369
	3	.94444	.64816	.46129	.29687	.09050	.01758
	4	.98728	.83577	.68649	.51549	.21728	0.5923
	5	.99775	.93895	.85163	.72162	.40322	.15088
	6	.99969	.98194	.94338	.86886	.60981	.30362
	7	.99997	.99576	.98270	.94999	.78690	.50000
	8	1.00000	.99921	.99581	.98476	.90495	.69638
	9		.99989	.99921	.99635	.96617	.84912
	10		.99999	.99988	.99933	.99065	.94077
	11		1.00000	.99999	.99991	.99807	.98242
	12			1.00000	.99999	.99972	.99631
	13				1.00000	.99997	.99951
	14					1.00000	.99997
	15						1.00000
20	0	.12158	.01153	.00317	.00080	.00004	.00000
	1	.39175	.06918	.02431	.00764	.00052	.00002
	2	.67693	.20608	.09126	.03548	.00361	.00020
	3	.86705	.41145	.22516	.10709	.01596	.00129
	4	.95683	.62965	.41484	.23751	.05095	.00591
	5	.98875	.80421	.61717	.41637	.12560	.02069
	6	.99761	.91331	.78578	.60801	.25001	.05766
	7	.99958	.96786	.89819	.77227	.41589	.13159
	8	.99994	.99002	.95907	.88667	.59560	.25172
	9	.99999	.99741	.98614	.95204	.75534	.41190
	10	1.00000	.99944	.99606	.98286	.87248	.58810
	11		.99990	.99906	.99486	.94347	.74828
	12		.99998	.99982	.99872	.97897	.86841
	13		1.00000	.99997	.99974	.99353	.94234
	14			1.00000	.99996	.99839	.97931
	15				.99999	.99968	.99409
	16				1.00000	.99995	.99871
	17					.99999	.99980
	18					1.00000	.99998
	19						1.00000

TABLE II The Cumulative Binomial Distribution (*Continued*)

n	r	$\pi = .10$	$\pi = .20$	$\pi = .25$	$\pi = .30$	$\pi = .40$	$\pi = .50$
25	0	.07179	.00378	.00075	.00013	.00000	.00000
	1	.27121	.02739	.00702	.00157	.00005	.00000
	2	.53709	.09823	.03211	.00896	.00043	.00001
	3	.76359	.23399	.09621	.03324	.00237	.00008
	4	.90201	.42067	.21374	.09047	.00947	.00046
	5	.96660	.61669	.37828	.19349	.02936	.00204
	6	.99052	.78004	.56110	.34065	.07357	.00732
	7	.99774	.89088	.72651	.51185	.15355	.02164
	8	.99954	.95323	.85056	.67693	.27353	.05388
	9	.99992	.98267	.92867	.81056	.42462	.11476
	10	.99999	.99445	.97033	.90220	.58577	.21218
	11	1.00000	.99846	.98027	.95575	.73228	.34502
	12		.99963	.99663	.98253	.84623	.50000
	13		.99992	.99908	.99401	.92220	.65498
	14		.99999	.99979	.99822	.96561	.78782
	15		1.00000	.99996	.99955	.98683	.88524
	16			.99999	.99990	.99567	.94612
	17			1.00000	.99998	.99879	.97836
	18				1.00000	.99972	.99268
	19					.99995	.99796
	20					.99999	.99954
	21					1.00000	.99992
	22						.99999
	23						1.00000
50	0	.00515	.00001	.00000	.00000		
	1	.03379	.00019	.00001	.00000		
	2	.11173	.00129	.00009	.00000		
	3	.25029	.00566	.00050	.00003		
	4	.43120	.01850	.00211	.00017		
	5	.61612	.04803	.00705	.00072	.00000	
	6	.77023	.10340	.01939	.00249	.00001	
	7	.87785	.19041	.04526	.00726	.00006	
	8	.94213	.30733	.09160	.01825	.00023	
	9	.97546	.44374	.16368	.04023	.00076	.00000
	10	.99065	.58356	.26220	.07885	.00220	.00001
	11	.99678	.71067	.38162	.13904	.00569	.00005
	12	.99900	.81394	.51099	.22287	.01325	.00015
	13	.99971	.88941	.63704	.32788	.02799	.00047
	14	.99993	.93928	.74808	.44683	.05396	.00130
	15	.99998	.96920	.83692	.56918	.09550	.00330
	16	1.00000	.98556	.90169	.68388	.15609	.00767
	17		.99374	.94488	.78219	.23688	.01642
	18		.99749	.97127	.85944	.33561	.03245
	19		.99907	.98608	.91520	.44648	.05946
	20		.99968	.99374	.95224	.56103	.10132
	21		.99990	.99738	.97491	.67014	.16112
	22		.99997	.99898	.98772	.76602	.23994
	23		.99999	.99963	.99441	.84383	.33591
	24		1.00000	.99988	.99763	.90219	.44386
	25			.99996	.99907	.94266	.55614
	26			.99999	.99966	.96859	.66409
	27			1.00000	.99988	.98397	.76006
	28				.99996	.99238	.83888
	29				.99999	.99664	.89868
	30				1.00000	.99863	.94054

TABLE II The Cumulative Binomial Distribution (*Continued*)

n	r	$\pi = .10$	$\pi = .20$	$\pi = .25$	$\pi = .30$	$\pi = .40$	$\pi = .50$
50	31					.99948	.96755
	32					.99982	.98358
	33					.99994	.99233
	34					.99998	.99670
	35					1.00000	.99870
	36						.99953
	37						.99985
	38						.99995
	39						.99999
	40						1.00000
100	0	.00003					
	1	.00032					
	2	.00194					
	3	.00784					
	4	.02371	.00000				
	5	.05758	.00002				
	6	.11716	.00008				
	7	.20605	.00028	.00000			
	8	.32087	.00086	.00001			
	9	.45129	.00233	.00004			
	10	.58316	.00570	.00014	.00000		
	11	.70303	.01257	.00039	.00001		
	12	.80182	.02533	.00103	.00002		
	13	.87612	.04691	.00246	.00006		
	14	.92743	.08044	.00542	.00016		
	15	.96011	.12851	.01108	.00040		
	16	.97940	.19234	.02111	.00097		
	17	.98999	.27119	.03763	.00216		
	18	.99542	.36209	.06301	.00452	.00000	
	19	.99802	.46016	.09953	.00889	.00001	
	20	.99919	.55946	.14883	.01646	.00002	
	21	.99969	.65403	.21144	.02883	.00004	
	22	.99989	.73893	.28637	.04787	.00011	
	23	.99996	.81091	.37018	.07553	.00025	
	24	.99999	.86865	.46167	.11357	.00056	
	25	1.00000	.91252	.55347	.16313	.00119	
	26		.94417	.64174	.22440	.00240	.00000
	27		.96585	.72238	.29637	.00460	.00001
	28		.97998	.79246	.37678	.00843	.00002
	29		.98875	.85046	.46234	.01478	.00004
	30		.99394	.89621	.54912	.02478	.00009
	31		.99687	.93065	.63311	.03985	.00020
	32		.99845	.95540	.71072	.06150	.00044
	33		.99926	.97241	.77926	.09125	.00089
	34		.99966	.98357	.83714	.13034	.00176
	35		.99985	.99059	.88392	.17947	.00332
	36		.99994	.99482	.92012	.23861	.00602
	37		.99998	.99725	.94695	.30681	.01049
	38		.99999	.99860	.96602	.38219	.01760
	39		1.00000	.99931	.97901	.46208	.02844
	40			.99968	.98750	.54329	.04431
	41			.99985	.99283	.62253	.06661
	42			.99994	.99603	.69674	.09667
	43			.99997	.99789	.76347	.13563
	44			.99999	.99891	.82110	.13563

TABLE II The Cumulative Binomial Distribution (*Continued*)

n	r	$\pi = .10$	$\pi = .20$	$\pi = .25$	$\pi = .30$	$\pi = .40$	$\pi = .50$
100	45			1.00000	.99946	.86891	.18410
	46				.99974	.90702	.24206
	47				.99988	.93621	.30865
	48				.99995	.95770	.38218
	49				.99998	.97290	.46021
	50				.99999	.98324	.53979
	51				1.00000	.98999	.61782
	52					.99424	.69135
	53					.99680	.79794
	54					.99829	.81590
	55					.99912	.86437
	56					.99956	.90333
	57					.99979	.93339
	58					.99990	.95569
	59					.99996	.97156
	60					.99998	.98240
	61					.99999	.98951
	62					1.00000	.99398
	63						.99668
	64						.99824
	65						.99911
	66						.99956
	67						.99980
	68						.99991
	69						.99996
	70						.99998
	71						.99999
	72						1.00000

Source: From *Poisson's Binomial Exponential Limit* by E. C. Molina (Van Nostrand, 1942). Reprinted by permission of Van Nostrand Company.

TABLE III The Hypergeometric Distribution

N	n	k	r or x	P(r)	p(x)	N	n	k	r or x	P(r)	p(x)
10	1	1	0	0.900000	0.900000	10	5	3	0	0.083333	0.083333
10	1	1	1	1.000000	0.100000	10	5	3	1	0.500000	0.416667
10	2	1	0	0.800000	0.800000	10	5	3	2	0.916667	0.416667
10	2	1	1	1.000000	0.200000	10	5	3	3	1.000000	0.083333
10	2	2	0	0.622222	0.622222	10	5	4	0	0.023810	0.023810
10	2	2	1	0.977778	0.355556	10	5	4	1	0.261905	0.238095
10	2	2	2	1.000000	0.022222	10	5	4	2	0.738095	0.476190
10	3	1	0	0.700000	0.700000	10	5	4	3	0.976190	0.238095
10	3	2	1	1.000000	0.300000	10	5	4	4	1.000000	0.023810
10	3	2	0	0.466667	0.466667	10	5	5	0	0.003968	0.003968
10	3	2	1	0.933333	0.466667	10	5	5	1	0.103175	0.099206
10	3	2	2	1.000000	0.066667	10	5	5	2	0.500000	0.396825
10	3	3	0	0.291667	0.291667	10	5	5	3	0.896825	0.396825
10	3	3	1	0.816667	0.525000	10	5	5	4	0.996032	0.099206
10	3	3	2	0.991667	0.175000	10	5	5	5	1.000000	0.003968
10	3	3	3	1.000000	0.008333	10	6	1	0	0.400000	0.400000
10	4	1	0	0.600000	0.600000	10	6	1	1	1.000000	0.600000
10	4	1	1	1.000000	0.400000	10	6	2	0	0.133333	0.133333
10	4	2	0	0.333333	0.333333	10	6	2	1	0.666667	0.533333
10	4	2	1	0.866667	0.533333	10	6	2	2	1.000000	0.333333
10	4	2	2	1.000000	0.133333	10	6	3	0	0.033333	0.033333
10	4	3	0	0.166667	0.166667	10	6	3	1	0.333333	0.300000
10	4	3	1	0.666667	0.500000	10	6	3	2	0.833333	0.500000
10	4	3	2	0.966667	0.300000	10	6	3	3	1.000000	0.166667
10	4	3	3	1.000000	0.033333	10	6	4	0	0.004762	0.004762
10	4	4	0	0.071429	0.071429	10	6	4	1	0.119048	0.114286
10	4	4	1	0.452381	0.380952	10	6	4	2	0.547619	0.428571
10	4	4	2	0.880952	0.428571	10	6	4	3	0.928571	0.380952
10	4	4	3	0.995238	0.114286	10	6	4	4	1.000000	0.071429
10	4	4	4	1.000000	0.004762	10	6	5	1	0.023810	0.023810
10	5	1	0	0.500000	0.500000	10	6	5	2	0.261905	0.238095
10	5	1	1	1.000000	0.500000	10	6	5	3	0.738095	0.476190
10	5	2	0	0.222222	0.222222	10	6	5	4	0.976190	0.238095
10	5	2	1	0.777778	0.555556	10	6	5	5	1.000000	0.023810
10	5	2	2	1.000000	0.222222	10	6	6	2	0.071429	0.071429
10	6	6	3	0.452381	0.380952	10	8	3	2	0.533333	0.466667
10	6	6	4	0.880952	0.428571	10	8	3	3	1.000000	0.466667
10	6	6	5	0.995238	0.114286	10	8	4	2	0.133333	0.133333
10	6	6	6	1.000000	0.004762	10	8	4	3	0.666667	0.533333
10	7	1	0	0.300000	0.300000	10	8	4	4	1.000000	0.333333
10	7	1	1	1.000000	0.700000	10	8	5	3	0.222222	0.222222
10	7	2	0	0.066667	0.066667	10	8	5	4	0.777778	0.555556
10	7	2	1	0.533333	0.466667	10	8	5	5	1.000000	0.222222
10	7	2	2	1.000000	0.466667	10	8	6	4	0.333333	0.333333
10	7	3	0	0.008333	0.008333	10	8	6	5	0.866667	0.533333

(*Continued*)

TABLE III The Hypergeometric Distribution (*Continued*)

N	n	k	r or x	P(r)	p(x)	N	n	k	r or x	P(r)	p(x)
10	7	3	1	0.183333	0.175000	10	8	6	6	1.000000	0.133333
10	7	3	2	0.708333	0.525000	10	8	7	5	0.466667	0.466667
10	7	3	3	1.000000	0.291667	10	8	7	6	0.933333	0.466667
10	7	4	1	0.033333	0.033333	10	8	7	7	1.000000	0.066667
10	7	4	2	0.333333	0.300000	10	8	8	6	0.622222	0.622222
10	7	4	3	0.833333	0.500000	10	8	8	7	0.977778	0.355556
10	7	4	4	1.000000	0.166667	10	8	8	8	1.000000	0.022222
10	7	5	2	0.083333	0.083333	10	9	1	0	0.100000	0.100000
10	7	5	3	0.500000	0.416667	10	9	1	1	1.000000	0.900000
10	7	5	4	0.916667	0.416667	10	9	2	1	0.200000	0.200000
10	7	5	5	1.000000	0.083333	10	9	2	2	1.000000	0.800000
10	7	6	3	0.166667	0.166667	10	9	3	2	0.300000	0.300000
10	7	6	4	0.666667	0.500000	10	9	3	3	1.000000	0.700000
10	7	6	5	0.966667	0.300000	10	9	4	3	0.400000	0.400000
10	7	6	6	1.000000	0.033333	10	9	4	4	1.000000	0.600000
10	7	7	4	0.291667	0.291667	10	9	5	4	0.500000	0.500000
10	7	7	5	0.816667	0.525000	10	9	5	5	1.000000	0.500000
10	7	7	6	0.991667	0.175000	10	9	6	5	0.600000	0.600000
10	7	7	7	1.000000	0.008333	10	9	6	6	1.000000	0.400000
10	8	1	0	0.200000	0.200000	10	9	7	6	0.700000	0.700000
10	8	1	1	1.000000	0.800000	10	9	7	7	1.000000	0.300000
10	8	2	0	0.022222	0.022222	10	9	8	7	0.800000	0.800000
10	8	2	1	0.377778	0.355556	10	9	8	8	1.000000	0.200000
10	8	2	2	1.000000	0.622222	10	9	9	8	0.900000	0.900000
10	8	3	1	0.066667	0.066667	10	9	9	9	1.000000	0.100000

Source: Extracted with permission from Gerald J. Lieberman and Donald B. Owen, *Tables of the Hypergeometric Probability Distribution,* (Stanford University Press, Stanford, Calif., 1961).

TABLE IV The Cumulative Poisson Distribution

r	$\lambda = .1$	$\lambda = .2$	$\lambda = .3$	$\lambda = .4$	$\lambda = .5$
0	.90484	.81873	.74082	.67032	.60653
1	.99532	.98248	.96306	.93845	.90980
2	.99985	.99885	.99973	.99207	.98561
3	1.00000	.99994	.99998	.99994	.99825
4		1.00000	1.00000	1.00000	.99983
5					.99999
6					1.00000

r	$\lambda = .6$	$\lambda = .7$	$\lambda = .8$	$\lambda = .9$	$\lambda = 1.0$
0	.54881	.49658	.44933	.40657	.36788
1	.87810	.84419	.80879	.77248	.73576
2	.97688	.96586	.95258	.93714	.91970
3	.99664	.99425	.99092	.98654	.98101
4	.99961	.99921	.99859	.99766	.99634
5	.99996	.99991	.99982	.99966	.99941
6	1.00000	.99999	.99998	.99996	.99992
7		1.00000	1.00000	1.00000	.99999
8					1.00000

r	$\lambda = 2$	$\lambda = 3$	$\lambda = 4$	$\lambda = 5$	$\lambda = 6$
0	.13534	.04979	.01832	.00674	.00248
1	.40601	.19915	.09158	.04043	.01735
2	.67668	.42319	.23810	.12465	.06197
3	.85712	.64723	.43347	.26503	.15120
4	.94735	.81526	.62884	.44049	.28506
5	.98344	.91608	.78513	.61596	.44568
6	.99547	.96649	.88933	.76218	.60630
7	.99890	.98810	.94887	.86663	.74398
8	.99976	.99620	.97864	.93191	.84724
9	.99995	.99890	.99187	.96817	.91608
10	.99999	.99971	.99716	.98630	.95738
11	1.00000	.99993	.99908	.99455	.97991
12		.99998	.99973	.99798	.99117
13		1.00000	.99992	.99930	.99637
14			.99998	.99977	.99860
15			1.00000	.99993	.99949
16				.99998	.99982
17				1.00000	.99994
18					.99998
19					1.00000

(*Continued*)

TABLE IV The Cumulative Poisson Distribution (*Continued*)

r	$\lambda = 7$	$\lambda = 8$	$\lambda = 9$	$\lambda = 10$
0	.00091	.00033	.00012	.00004
1	.00730	.00302	.00123	.00050
2	.02964	.01375	.00623	.00277
3	.08176	.04238	.02123	.01034
4	.17299	.09963	.05496	.02925
5	.30071	.19124	.11569	.06709
6	.44971	.31337	.20678	.13014
7	.59871	.45296	.32390	.22022
8	.72909	.59255	.45565	.33282
9	.83050	.71662	.58741	.45793
10	.90148	.81589	.70599	.58304
11	.94665	.88808	.80301	.69678
12	.97300	.93620	.87577	.79156
13	.98719	.96582	.92615	.86446
14	.99428	.98274	.95853	.91654
15	.99759	.99177	.97796	.95126
16	.99904	.99628	.98889	.97296
17	.99964	.99841	.99468	.98572
18	.99987	.99935	.99757	.99281
19	.99996	.99975	.99894	.99655
20	.99999	.99991	.99956	.99841
21	1.00000	.99997	.99982	.99930
22		.99999	.99993	.99970
23		1.00000	.99998	.99988
24			.99999	.99995
25			1.00000	.99998
26				.99999
27				1.00000

Source: From *Poisson's Binomial Exponential Limit* by E. C. Molina (Van Nostrand, 1942). Reprinted by permission of Van Nostrand Reinhold Company.

TABLE V Ordinates of the Standard Normal Distribution

z	$f(z)$	z	$f(z)$	z	$f(z)$
.00	.39894	1.50	.12952	3.00	.00443
.05	.39844	1.55	.12001	3.05	.00381
.10	.39695	1.60	.11092	3.10	.00327
.15	.39448	1.65	.10226	3.15	.00279
.20	.39104	1.70	.09405	3.20	.00238
.25	.38667	1.75	.08628	3.25	.00203
.30	.38139	1.80	.07895	3.30	.00172
.35	.37524	1.85	.07206	3.35	.00146
.40	.36827	1.90	.06562	3.40	.00123
.45	.36053	1.95	.05959	3.45	.00104
.50	.35207	2.00	.05399	3.50	.00087
.55	.34294	2.05	.04879	3.55	.00073
.60	.33322	2.10	.04398	3.60	.00061
.65	.32297	2.15	.03955	3.65	.00051
.70	.31225	2.20	.03547	3.70	.00042
.75	.30114	2.25	.03174	3.75	.00035
.80	.28969	2.30	.02833	3.80	.00029
.85	.27798	2.35	.02522	3.85	.00024
.90	.26609	2.40	.02239	3.90	.00020
.95	.25406	2.45	.01984	3.95	.00016
1.00	.24197	2.50	.01753	4.00	.00014
1.05	.22988	2.55	.01545		
1.10	.21785	2.60	.01358		
1.15	.20594	2.65	.01191		
1.20	.19419	2.70	.01042		
1.25	.18265	2.75	.00909		
1.30	.17137	2.80	.00792		
1.35	.16038	2.85	.00687		
1.40	.14973	2.90	.00595		
1.45	.13943	2.95	.00514		

Note 1. $Z = N[(x - \mu)/\sigma]$.
Note 2. $f(z)$ = ordinate at $Z = z$.
Note 3. $f(z) = f(-z)$. For example, $f(0) = 0.39894$ and $f(1.25) = f(-1.25) = 0.18265$.

TABLE VI Values of the Standard Normal Distribution Function

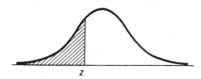

z	−.09	−.08	−.07	−.06	−.05	−.04	−.03	−.02	−.01	.00	z
−3.8	.0001	.0001	.0001	.0001	.0001	.0001	.0001	.0001	.0001	.0001	−3.8
−3.7	.0001	.0001	.0001	.0001	.0001	.0001	.0001	.0001	.0001	.0001	−3.7
−3.6	.0001	.0001	.0001	.0001	.0001	.0001	.0001	.0001	.0002	.0002	−3.6
−3.5	.0002	.0002	.0002	.0002	.0002	.0002	.0002	.0002	.0002	.0002	−3.5
−3.4	.0002	.0003	.0003	.0003	.0003	.0003	.0003	.0003	.0003	.0003	−3.4
−3.3	.0003	.0004	.0004	.0004	.0004	.0004	.0004	.0005	.0005	.0005	−3.3
−3.2	.0005	.0005	.0005	.0006	.0006	.0006	.0006	.0006	.0007	.0007	−3.2
−3.1	.0007	.0007	.0008	.0008	.0008	.0008	.0009	.0009	.0009	.0010	−3.1
−3.0	.0010	.0010	.0011	.0011	.0011	.0012	.0012	.0013	.0013	.0014	−3.0
−2.9	.0014	.0014	.0015	.0015	.0016	.0016	.0017	.0018	.0018	.0019	−2.9
−2.8	.0019	.0020	.0021	.0021	.0022	.0023	.0023	.0024	.0025	.0026	−2.8
−2.7	.0026	.0027	.0028	.0029	.0030	.0031	.0032	.0033	.0034	.0035	−2.7
−2.6	.0036	.0037	.0038	.0039	.0040	.0041	.0043	.0044	.0045	.0047	−2.6
−2.5	.0048	.0049	.0051	.0052	.0054	.0055	.0057	.0059	.0060	.0062	−2.5
−2.4	.0064	.0066	.0068	.0069	.0071	.0073	.0076	.0078	.0080	.0082	−2.4
−2.3	.0084	.0087	.0089	.0091	.0094	.0096	.0099	.0102	.0104	.0107	−2.3
−2.2	.0110	.0113	.0116	.0119	.0122	.0125	.0129	.0132	.0136	.0139	−2.2
−2.1	.0143	.0146	.0150	.0154	.0158	.0162	.0166	.0170	.0174	.0179	−2.1
−2.0	.0183	.0188	.0192	.0197	.0202	.0207	.0212	.0217	.0222	.0228	−2.0
−1.9	.0233	.0239	.0244	.0250	.0256	.0262	.0268	.0274	.0281	.0287	−1.9
−1.8	.0294	.0301	.0307	.0314	.0322	.0329	.0336	.0344	.0352	.0359	−1.8
−1.7	.0367	.0375	.0384	.0392	.0401	.0409	.0418	.0427	.0436	.0446	−1.7
−1.6	.0455	.0465	.0475	.0485	.0495	.0505	.0516	.0526	.0537	.0548	−1.6
−1.5	.0559	.0571	.0582	.0594	.0606	.0618	.0630	.0643	.0655	.0668	−1.5
−1.4	.0681	.0694	.0708	.0721	.0735	.0749	.0764	.0778	.0793	.0808	−1.4
−1.3	.0823	.0838	.0853	.0869	.0885	.0901	.0918	.0934	.0951	.0968	−1.3
−1.2	.0985	.1003	.1020	.1038	.1057	.1075	.1094	.1112	.1131	.1151	−1.2
−1.1	.1170	.1190	.1210	.1230	.1251	.1271	.1292	.1314	.1335	.1357	−1.1
−1.0	.1379	.1401	.1423	.1446	.1469	.1492	.1515	.1539	.1562	.1587	−1.0
−.9	.1611	.1635	.1660	.1685	.1711	.1736	.1762	.1788	.1814	.1841	−.9
−.8	.1867	.1894	.1922	.1949	.1977	.2005	.2033	.2061	.2090	.2119	−.8
−.7	.2148	.2177	.2206	.2236	.2266	.2296	.2327	.2358	.2389	.2420	−.7
−.6	.2451	.2483	.2514	.2546	.2578	.2611	.2643	.2676	.2709	.2743	−.6
−.5	.2776	.2810	.2843	.2877	.2912	.2946	.2981	.3015	.3050	.3085	−.5
−.4	.3121	.3156	.3192	.3228	.3264	.3300	.3336	.3372	.3409	.3446	−.4
−.3	.3483	.3520	.3557	.3594	.3632	.3669	.3707	.3745	.3783	.3821	−.3
−.2	.3859	.3897	.3936	.3974	.4013	.4052	.4090	.4129	.4168	.4207	−.2
−.1	.4247	.4286	.4325	.4364	.4404	.4443	.4483	.4522	.4562	.4602	−.1
.0	.4641	.4681	.4721	.4761	.4801	.4840	.4880	.4920	.4960	.5000	.0

TABLE VI Values of the Standard Normal Distribution Function (*Continued*)

z	.00	.01	.02	.03	.04	.05	.06	.07	.08	.09	z
.0	.5000	.5040	.5080	.5120	.5160	.5199	.5239	.5279	.5319	.5359	.0
.1	.5398	.5438	.5478	.5517	.5557	.5596	.5636	.5675	.5714	.5753	.1
.2	.5793	.5832	.5871	.5910	.5948	.5987	.6026	.6064	.6103	.6141	.2
.3	.6179	.6217	.6255	.6293	.6331	.6368	.6406	.6443	.6480	.6517	.3
.4	.6554	.6591	.6628	.6664	.6700	.6736	.6772	.6808	.6844	.6879	.4
.5	.6915	.6950	.6985	.7019	.7054	.7088	.7123	.7157	.7190	.7224	.5
.6	.7257	.7291	.7324	.7357	.7389	.7422	.7454	.7486	.7517	.7549	.6
.7	.7580	.7651	.7642	.7673	.7704	.7734	.7764	.7794	.7823	.7852	.7
.8	.7881	.7900	.7939	.7967	.7995	.8023	.8051	.8078	.8106	.8133	.8
.9	.8159	.8186	.8212	.8238	.8264	.8289	.8315	.8340	.8365	.8389	.9
1.0	.8413	.8438	.8461	.8485	.8508	.8531	.8554	.8577	.8599	.8621	1.0
1.1	.8643	.8665	.8686	.8708	.8729	.8749	.8770	.8790	.8810	.8830	1.1
1.2	.8849	.8869	.8888	.8906	.8925	.8943	.8962	.8980	.8897	.9015	1.2
1.3	.9032	.9049	.9066	.9082	.9099	.9115	.9131	.9147	.9162	.9177	1.3
1.4	.9192	.9207	.9222	.9236	.9251	.9265	.9279	.9292	.9306	.9319	1.4
1.5	.9332	.9345	.9357	.9370	.9382	.9394	.9406	.9418	.9429	.9441	1.5
1.6	.9452	.9463	.9474	.9484	.9495	.9505	.9515	.9525	.9535	.9545	1.6
1.7	.9554	.9564	.9573	.9582	.9591	.9599	.9608	.9616	.9625	.9633	1.7
1.8	.9641	.9648	.9656	.9664	.9671	.9678	.9686	.9693	.9699	.9706	1.8
1.9	.9713	.9719	.9726	.9732	.9738	.9744	.9750	.9756	.9761	.9767	1.9
2.0	.9772	.9778	.9783	.9788	.9793	.9798	.9803	.9808	.9812	.9812	2.0
2.1	.9821	.9826	.9830	.9834	.9838	.9842	.9846	.9850	.9854	.9857	2.1
2.2	.9861	.9864	.9868	.9871	.9875	.9878	.9881	.9884	.9887	.9890	2.2
2.3	.9893	.9896	.9898	.9901	.9904	.9906	.9909	.9911	.9913	.9916	2.3
2.4	.9918	.9920	.9922	.9924	.9927	.9929	.9931	.9932	.9934	.9936	2.4
2.5	.9938	.9940	.9941	.9943	.9945	.9946	.9948	.9949	.9951	.9952	2.5
2.6	.9953	.9955	.9956	.9957	.9959	.9960	.9961	.9962	.9963	.9964	2.6
2.7	.9965	.9966	.9967	.9968	.9969	.9970	.9971	.9972	.9973	.9974	2.7
2.8	.9974	.9975	.9976	.9977	.9977	.9978	.9979	.9979	.9980	.9981	2.8
2.9	.9981	.9982	.9982	.9983	.9984	.9984	.9985	.9985	.9986	.9986	2.9
3.0	.9986	.9987	.9987	.9988	.9988	.9989	.9989	.9989	.9990	.9990	3.0
3.1	.9990	.9991	.9991	.9991	.9992	.9992	.9992	.9992	.9993	.9993	3.1
3.2	.9993	.9993	.9994	.9994	.9994	.9994	.9994	.9995	.9995	.9995	3.2
3.3	.9995	.9995	.9995	.9996	.9996	.9996	.9996	.9996	.9996	.9997	3.3
3.4	.9997	.9997	.9997	.9997	.9997	.9997	.9997	.9997	.9997	.9998	3.4
3.5	.9998	.9998	.9998	.9998	.9998	.9998	.9998	.9998	.9998	.9998	3.5
3.6	.9998	.9998	.9999	.9999	.9999	.9999	.9999	.9999	.9999	.9999	3.6
3.7	.9999	.9999	.9999	.9999	.9999	.9999	.9999	.9999	.9999	.9999	3.7
3.8	.9999	.9999	.9999	.9999	.9999	.9999	.9999	.9999	.9999	.9999	3.8

Note 1. If a random variable X is not "standard," its values must be "standardized": $Z = (x - \mu)/\sigma$. That is,

$$P(X \leq x) = N\left(\frac{x - \mu}{\sigma}\right).$$

Note 2. For $Z \geq 4$, $N(z) = 1$ to four decimal places; for $Z \leq -4$, $N(z) = 0$ to four decimal places.

TABLE VII Table of the "Student's" Distribution: Values of t

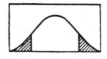

Degrees of Freedom	Probability												
	0.9	0.8	0.7	0.6	0.5	0.4	0.3	0.2	0.1	0.05	0.02	0.01	0.001
1	0.158	0.325	0.510	0.727	1.000	1.376	1.963	3.078	6.314	12.706	31.821	63.657	636.619
2	0.142	0.289	0.445	0.617	0.816	1.061	1.386	1.886	2.920	4.303	6.965	9.925	31.598
3	0.137	0.277	0.424	0.584	0.765	0.978	1.250	1.638	2.353	3.182	4.541	5.841	12.924
4	0.134	0.271	0.414	0.569	0.741	0.941	1.190	1.533	2.132	2.776	3.747	4.604	8.610
5	0.132	0.267	0.408	0.559	0.727	0.920	1.156	1.476	2.015	2.571	3.365	4.032	6.869
6	0.131	0.265	0.404	0.553	0.718	0.906	1.134	1.440	1.943	2.447	3.143	3.707	5.959
7	1.130	0.263	0.402	0.549	0.711	0.896	1.119	1.415	1.895	2.365	2.998	3.499	5.408
8	0.130	0.262	0.399	0.546	0.706	0.889	1.108	1.397	1.860	2.306	2.896	3.355	5.041
9	0.129	0.261	0.398	0.543	0.703	0.883	1.100	1.383	1.833	2.262	2.821	3.250	4.781
10	0.129	0.260	0.397	0.542	0.700	0.879	1.093	1.372	1.812	2.228	2.764	3.169	4.587
11	0.129	0.260	0.396	0.540	0.697	0.876	1.088	1.363	1.796	2.201	2.718	3.106	4.437
12	0.128	0.259	0.395	0.539	0.695	0.873	1.083	1.356	1.782	2.179	2.681	3.055	4.318
13	0.128	0.259	0.394	0.538	0.694	0.870	1.079	1.350	1.771	2.160	2.650	3.012	4.221
14	0.128	0.258	0.393	0.537	0.692	0.868	1.076	1.345	1.761	2.145	2.624	2.977	4.140
15	0.128	0.258	0.393	0.536	0.691	0.866	1.074	1.341	1.753	2.131	2.602	2.947	4.073
16	0.128	0.258	0.392	0.535	0.690	0.865	1.071	1.337	1.746	2.120	2.583	2.921	4.015
17	0.128	0.257	0.392	0.534	0.689	0.863	1.069	1.333	1.740	2.110	2.567	2.898	3.965
18	0.127	0.257	0.392	0.534	0.688	0.862	1.067	1.330	1.734	2.101	2.552	2.878	3.922
19	0.127	0.257	0.391	0.533	0.688	0.861	1.066	1.328	1.729	2.093	2.539	2.861	3.883
20	0.127	0.257	0.391	0.533	0.687	0.860	1.064	1.325	1.725	2.086	2.528	2.845	3.850
21	0.127	0.257	0.391	0.532	0.686	0.859	1.063	1.323	1.721	2.080	2.518	2.831	3.819
22	0.127	0.256	0.390	0.532	0.686	0.858	1.061	1.321	1.717	2.074	2.508	2.819	3.792
23	0.127	0.256	0.390	0.532	0.685	0.858	1.060	1.319	1.714	2.069	2.500	2.807	3.767
24	0.127	0.256	0.390	0.531	0.685	0.857	1.059	1.318	1.711	2.064	2.492	2.797	3.745
25	0.127	0.256	0.390	0.531	0.684	0.856	1.058	1.316	1.708	2.060	2.485	2.787	3.725
26	0.127	0.256	0.390	0.531	0.684	0.856	1.058	1.315	1.706	2.056	2.479	2.779	3.707
27	0.127	0.256	0.389	0.531	0.684	0.855	1.057	1.314	1.703	2.052	2.473	2.771	3.690
28	0.127	0.256	0.389	0.530	0.683	0.855	1.056	1.313	1.701	2.048	2.467	2.763	3.674
29	0.127	0.256	0.389	0.530	0.683	0.854	1.055	1.311	1.699	2.045	2.462	2.756	3.659
30	0.127	0.256	0.389	0.530	0.683	0.854	1.055	1.310	1.697	2.042	2.457	2.750	3.646
40	0.126	0.255	0.388	0.529	0.681	0.851	1.050	1.303	1.684	2.021	2.423	2.704	3.551
60	0.126	0.254	0.387	0.527	0.679	0.848	1.046	1.296	1.671	2.000	2.390	2.660	3.460
100	0.126	0.254	0.386	0.526	0.677	0.845	1.041	1.289	1.658	1.980	2.358	2.617	3.373
∞	0.126	0.253	0.385	0.524	0.674	0.842	1.036	1.282	1.645	1.960	2.326	2.576	3.291

Source: This table is abridged from Table II of Fisher and Yates: *Statistical Tables for Biological, Agricultural and Medical Research,* published by Longman Group Ltd., London (previously published by Oliver & Boyd Ltd., Edinburgh) and by permission of the authors and publishers.

TABLE VIII The Chi-Square Distribution

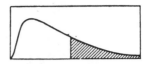

	Probability that chi-square value will be exceeded							
df	.995	.990	.975	.950	.050	.025	.010	.005
1	—	—	—	.004	3.84	5.02	6.63	7.88
2	.01	.02	.05	.10	5.99	7.38	9.21	10.60
3	.07	.11	.22	.35	7.81	9.35	11.34	12.84
4	.21	.30	.48	.71	9.49	11.14	13.28	14.86
5	.41	.55	.83	1.15	11.07	12.83	15.09	16.75
6	.68	.87	1.24	1.64	12.59	14.45	16.81	18.55
7	.99	1.24	1.69	2.17	14.07	16.01	18.48	20.28
8	1.34	1.65	2.18	2.73	15.51	17.53	20.09	21.96
9	1.73	2.09	2.70	3.33	16.92	19.02	21.67	23.59
10	2.16	2.56	3.25	3.94	18.31	20.48	23.21	25.19
11	2.60	3.05	3.82	4.57	19.68	21.92	24.72	26.76
12	3.07	3.57	4.40	5.23	21.03	23.34	26.22	28.30
13	3.57	4.11	5.01	5.89	22.36	24.74	27.69	29.82
14	4.07	4.66	5.63	6.57	23.68	26.12	29.14	31.32
15	4.60	5.23	6.26	7.26	25.00	27.49	30.58	32.80
16	5.14	5.81	6.91	7.96	26.30	28.85	32.00	34.27
17	5.70	6.41	7.56	8.67	27.59	30.19	33.41	35.72
18	6.26	7.01	8.23	9.39	28.87	31.53	34.81	37.16
19	6.84	7.63	8.91	10.12	30.14	32.85	36.19	38.58
20	7.43	8.26	9.59	10.85	31.41	34.17	37.57	40.00
21	8.03	8.90	10.28	11.59	32.67	35.48	38.93	41.40
22	8.64	9.54	10.98	12.34	33.92	36.78	40.29	42.80
23	9.26	10.20	11.69	13.09	35.17	38.08	41.64	44.18
24	9.89	10.86	12.40	13.85	36.42	39.36	42.98	45.56
25	10.52	11.52	13.12	14.61	37.65	40.65	44.31	46.93
26	11.16	12.20	13.84	15.38	38.89	41.92	45.64	48.29
27	11.81	12.88	14.57	16.15	40.11	43.19	46.96	49.64
28	12.46	13.56	15.31	16.93	41.34	44.46	48.28	50.99
29	13.12	14.26	16.05	17.71	42.56	45.72	49.59	52.34
30	13.79	14.95	16.79	18.49	43.77	46.98	50.89	53.67
40	20.71	22.16	24.43	26.51	55.76	59.34	63.69	66.77
50	27.99	29.71	32.36	34.76	67.50	71.42	76.15	79.49
60	35.53	37.48	40.48	43.19	79.08	83.30	88.38	91.95
70	43.28	45.44	48.76	51.74	90.53	95.02	100.43	104.22
80	51.17	53.54	57.15	60.39	101.88	106.63	112.33	116.32
90	59.20	61.75	65.65	69.13	113.14	118.14	124.12	128.30
100	67.33	70.06	74.22	77.93	124.34	129.56	135.81	140.17

TABLE IX The F Distribution

Upper 10% Points

δ_2 \ δ_1	1	2	3	4	5	6	8	12	15	20	30	60	∞
1	39.86	49.50	53.59	55.83	57.24	58.20	59.44	60.71	61.22	61.74	62.26	62.79	63.33
2	8.53	9.00	9.16	9.24	9.29	9.33	9.37	9.41	9.42	9.44	9.46	9.47	9.49
3	5.54	5.46	5.39	5.34	5.31	5.28	5.25	5.22	5.20	5.18	5.17	5.15	5.13
4	4.54	4.32	4.19	4.11	4.05	4.01	3.95	3.90	3.87	3.84	3.82	3.79	3.76
5	4.06	3.78	3.62	3.52	3.45	3.40	3.34	3.27	3.24	3.21	3.17	3.14	3.10
6	3.78	3.46	3.29	3.18	3.11	3.05	2.98	2.90	2.87	2.84	2.80	2.76	2.72
7	3.59	3.26	3.07	2.96	2.88	2.83	2.75	2.67	2.63	2.59	2.56	2.51	2.47
8	3.46	3.11	2.92	2.81	2.73	2.67	2.59	2.50	2.46	2.42	2.38	2.34	2.29
9	3.36	3.01	2.81	2.69	2.61	2.55	2.47	2.38	2.34	2.30	2.25	2.21	2.16
10	3.29	2.92	2.73	2.61	2.52	2.46	2.38	2.28	2.24	2.20	2.16	2.11	2.06
11	3.23	2.86	2.66	2.54	2.45	2.39	2.30	2.21	2.17	2.12	2.08	2.03	1.97
12	3.18	2.81	2.61	2.48	2.39	2.33	2.24	2.15	2.10	2.06	2.01	1.96	1.90
13	3.14	2.76	2.56	2.43	2.35	2.28	2.20	2.10	2.05	2.01	1.96	1.90	1.85
14	3.10	2.73	2.52	2.39	2.31	2.24	2.15	2.05	2.01	1.96	1.91	1.86	1.80
15	3.07	2.70	2.49	2.36	2.27	2.21	2.12	2.02	1.97	1.92	1.87	1.82	1.76
16	3.05	2.67	2.46	2.33	2.24	2.18	2.09	1.99	1.94	1.89	1.84	1.78	1.72
17	3.03	2.64	2.44	2.31	2.22	2.15	2.06	1.96	1.91	1.86	1.81	1.75	1.69
18	3.01	2.62	2.42	2.29	2.20	2.13	2.04	1.93	1.89	1.84	1.78	1.72	1.66
19	2.99	2.61	2.40	2.27	2.18	2.11	2.02	1.91	1.86	1.81	1.76	1.70	1.63
20	2.97	2.59	2.38	2.25	2.16	2.09	2.00	1.89	1.84	1.79	1.74	1.68	1.61
21	2.96	2.57	2.36	2.23	2.14	2.08	1.98	1.87	1.83	1.78	1.72	1.66	1.59
22	2.95	2.56	2.35	2.22	2.13	2.06	1.97	1.86	1.81	1.76	1.70	1.64	1.57
23	2.94	2.55	2.34	2.21	2.11	2.05	1.95	1.84	1.80	1.74	1.69	1.62	1.55
24	2.93	2.54	2.33	2.19	2.10	2.04	1.94	1.83	1.78	1.73	1.67	1.61	1.53
25	2.92	2.53	2.32	2.18	2.09	2.02	1.93	1.82	1.77	1.72	1.66	1.59	1.52
26	2.91	2.52	2.31	2.17	2.08	2.01	1.92	1.81	1.76	1.71	1.65	1.58	1.50
27	2.90	2.51	2.30	2.17	2.07	2.00	1.91	1.80	1.75	1.70	1.64	1.57	1.49
28	2.89	2.50	2.29	2.16	2.06	2.00	1.90	1.79	1.74	1.69	1.63	1.56	1.48
29	2.89	2.50	2.28	2.15	2.06	1.99	1.89	1.78	1.73	1.68	1.62	1.55	1.47
30	2.88	2.49	2.28	2.14	2.05	1.98	1.88	1.77	1.72	1.67	1.61	1.54	1.46
40	2.84	2.44	2.23	2.09	2.00	1.93	1.83	1.71	1.66	1.61	1.54	1.47	1.38
60	2.79	2.39	2.18	2.04	1.95	1.87	1.77	1.66	1.60	1.54	1.48	1.40	1.29
120	2.75	2.35	2.13	1.99	1.90	1.82	1.72	1.60	1.55	1.48	1.41	1.32	1.19
∞	2.71	2.30	2.08	1.94	1.85	1.77	1.67	1.55	1.49	1.42	1.34	1.24	1.00

TABLE IX The *F* Distribution (*Continued*)

δ_2 \ δ_1	1	2	3	4	5	6	8	12	15	20	30	60	∞
1	161.4	199.5	215.7	224.6	230.2	234.0	238.9	243.9	245.9	248.0	250.1	252.2	254.3
2	18.51	19.00	19.16	19.25	19.30	19.33	19.37	19.41	19.43	19.45	19.46	19.48	19.50
3	10.13	9.55	9.28	9.12	9.01	8.94	8.85	8.74	8.70	8.66	8.62	8.57	8.53
4	7.71	6.94	6.59	6.39	6.26	6.16	6.04	5.91	5.86	5.80	5.75	5.69	5.63
5	6.61	5.79	5.41	5.19	5.05	4.95	4.82	4.68	4.62	4.56	4.50	4.43	4.36
6	5.99	5.14	4.76	4.53	4.39	4.28	4.15	4.00	3.94	3.87	3.81	3.74	3.67
7	5.59	4.74	4.35	4.12	3.97	3.87	3.73	3.57	3.51	3.44	3.38	3.30	3.23
8	5.32	4.46	4.07	3.84	3.69	3.58	3.44	3.28	3.22	3.15	3.08	3.01	2.93
9	5.12	4.26	3.86	3.63	3.48	3.37	3.23	3.07	3.01	2.94	2.86	2.79	2.71
10	4.96	4.10	3.71	3.48	3.33	3.22	3.07	2.91	2.85	2.77	2.70	2.62	2.54
11	4.84	3.98	3.59	3.36	3.20	3.09	2.95	2.79	2.72	2.65	2.57	2.49	2.40
12	4.75	3.89	3.49	3.26	3.11	3.00	2.85	2.69	2.62	2.54	2.47	2.38	2.30
13	4.67	3.81	3.41	3.18	3.03	2.92	2.77	2.60	2.53	2.46	2.38	2.30	2.21
14	4.60	3.74	3.34	3.11	2.96	2.85	2.70	2.53	2.46	2.39	2.31	2.22	2.13
15	4.54	3.68	3.29	3.06	2.90	2.79	2.64	2.48	2.40	2.33	2.25	2.16	2.07
16	4.49	3.63	3.24	3.01	2.85	2.74	2.59	2.42	2.35	2.28	2.19	2.11	2.01
17	4.45	3.59	3.20	2.96	2.81	2.70	2.55	2.38	2.31	2.23	2.15	2.06	1.96
18	4.41	3.55	3.16	2.93	2.77	2.66	2.51	2.34	2.27	2.19	2.11	2.02	1.92
19	4.38	3.52	3.13	2.90	2.74	2.63	2.48	2.31	2.23	2.16	2.07	1.98	1.88
20	4.35	3.49	3.10	2.87	2.71	2.60	2.45	2.28	2.20	2.12	2.04	1.95	1.84
21	4.32	3.47	3.07	2.84	2.68	2.57	2.42	2.25	2.18	2.10	2.01	1.92	1.81
22	4.30	3.44	3.05	2.82	2.66	2.55	2.40	2.23	2.15	2.07	1.98	1.89	1.78
23	4.28	3.42	3.03	2.80	2.64	2.53	2.37	2.20	2.13	2.05	1.96	1.86	1.76
24	4.26	3.40	3.01	2.78	2.62	2.51	2.36	2.18	2.11	2.03	1.94	1.84	1.73
25	4.24	3.39	2.99	2.76	2.60	2.49	2.34	2.16	2.09	2.01	1.92	1.82	1.71
26	4.23	3.37	2.98	2.74	2.59	2.47	2.32	2.15	2.07	1.99	1.90	1.80	1.69
27	4.21	3.35	2.96	2.73	2.57	2.46	2.31	2.13	2.06	1.97	1.88	1.79	1.67
28	4.20	3.34	2.95	2.71	2.56	2.45	2.29	2.12	2.04	1.96	1.87	1.77	1.65
29	4.18	3.33	2.93	2.70	2.55	2.43	2.28	2.10	2.03	1.94	1.85	1.75	1.64
30	4.17	3.32	2.92	2.69	2.53	2.42	2.27	2.09	2.01	1.93	1.84	1.74	1.62
40	4.08	3.23	2.84	2.61	2.45	2.34	2.18	2.00	1.92	1.84	1.74	1.64	1.51
60	4.00	3.15	2.76	2.53	2.37	2.25	2.10	1.92	1.84	1.75	1.65	1.53	1.39
120	3.92	3.07	2.68	2.45	2.29	2.17	2.02	1.83	1.75	1.66	1.55	1.43	1.25
∞	3.84	3.00	2.60	2.37	2.21	2.10	1.94	1.75	1.67	1.57	1.46	1.32	1.00

Upper 5% Points

TABLE IX The F Distribution (Continued)

Upper $2\frac{1}{2}$% Points

δ_2 \ δ_1	1	2	3	4	5	6	8	12	15	20	30	60	∞
1	647.8	799.5	864.2	899.6	921.8	937.1	956.7	976.7	984.9	993.1	1001	1010	1018
2	38.51	39.00	39.17	39.25	39.30	39.33	39.37	39.41	39.43	39.45	39.46	39.48	39.50
3	17.44	16.04	15.44	15.10	14.88	14.73	14.54	14.34	14.25	14.17	14.08	13.99	13.90
4	12.22	10.65	9.98	9.60	9.36	9.20	8.98	8.75	8.66	8.56	8.46	8.36	8.26
5	10.01	8.43	7.76	7.39	7.15	6.98	6.76	6.52	6.43	6.33	6.23	6.12	6.02
6	8.81	7.26	6.60	6.23	5.99	5.82	5.60	5.37	5.27	5.17	5.07	4.96	4.85
7	8.07	6.54	5.89	5.52	5.29	5.12	4.90	4.67	4.57	4.47	4.36	4.25	4.14
8	7.57	6.06	5.42	5.05	4.82	4.65	4.43	4.20	4.10	4.00	3.89	3.78	3.67
9	7.21	5.71	5.08	4.72	4.48	4.32	4.10	3.87	3.77	3.67	3.56	3.45	3.33
10	6.94	5.46	4.83	4.47	4.24	4.07	3.85	3.62	3.52	3.42	3.31	3.20	3.08
11	6.72	5.26	4.63	4.23	4.04	3.88	3.66	3.43	3.33	3.23	3.12	3.00	2.80
12	6.55	5.10	4.47	4.12	3.89	3.73	3.51	3.28	3.18	3.07	2.96	2.85	2.72
13	6.41	4.97	4.35	4.00	3.77	3.60	3.39	3.15	3.05	2.95	2.84	2.72	2.60
14	6.30	4.86	4.24	3.89	3.66	3.50	3.29	3.05	2.95	2.84	2.73	2.61	2.49
15	6.20	4.77	4.15	3.80	3.58	3.41	3.20	2.96	2.86	2.76	2.64	2.52	2.40
16	6.12	4.69	4.08	3.73	3.50	3.34	3.12	2.89	2.79	2.68	2.57	2.45	2.32
17	6.04	4.62	4.01	3.66	3.44	3.28	3.06	2.82	2.72	2.62	2.50	2.38	2.25
18	5.98	4.56	3.95	3.61	3.38	3.22	3.01	2.77	2.67	2.56	2.44	2.32	2.19
19	5.92	4.51	3.90	3.56	3.33	3.17	2.96	2.72	2.62	2.51	2.39	2.27	2.13
20	5.87	4.46	3.86	3.51	3.29	3.13	2.91	2.68	2.57	2.46	2.35	2.22	2.09
21	5.83	4.42	3.82	3.48	3.25	3.09	2.87	2.64	2.53	2.42	2.31	2.18	2.04
22	5.79	4.38	3.78	3.44	3.22	3.05	2.84	2.60	2.50	2.39	2.27	2.14	2.00
23	5.75	4.35	3.75	3.41	3.18	3.02	2.81	2.57	2.47	2.36	2.24	2.11	1.97
24	5.72	4.32	3.72	3.38	3.15	2.99	2.78	2.54	2.44	2.33	2.21	2.08	1.94
25	5.69	4.29	3.69	3.35	3.13	2.97	2.75	2.51	2.41	2.30	2.16	2.05	1.91
26	5.66	4.27	3.67	3.33	3.10	2.94	2.73	2.49	2.39	2.28	2.16	2.03	1.88
27	5.63	4.24	3.65	3.31	3.08	2.92	2.71	2.47	2.36	2.25	2.13	2.00	1.85
28	5.61	4.22	3.63	3.29	3.06	2.90	2.69	2.45	2.34	2.23	2.11	1.98	1.83
29	5.59	4.20	3.61	3.27	3.04	2.88	2.67	2.43	2.32	2.21	2.09	1.96	1.81
30	5.57	4.18	3.59	3.25	3.03	2.87	2.65	2.41	2.31	2.20	2.07	1.94	1.79
40	5.42	4.05	3.46	3.13	2.90	2.74	2.53	2.29	2.18	2.07	1.94	1.80	1.64
60	5.29	3.93	3.34	3.01	2.79	2.63	2.41	2.17	2.06	1.94	1.82	1.67	1.48
120	5.15	3.80	3.23	2.89	2.67	2.52	2.30	2.05	1.94	1.82	1.69	1.53	1.31
∞	5.02	3.69	3.12	2.79	2.57	2.41	2.19	1.94	1.83	1.71	1.57	1.39	1.00

TABLE IX The F Distribution (*Continued*)

Upper 1% Points

δ_2 \ δ_1	1	2	3	4	5	6	8	12	15	20	30	60	∞
1	4052	4999.5	5403	5625	5764	5859	5982	6106	6157	6209	6261	6315	6366
2	98.50	99.00	99.17	99.25	99.30	99.33	99.37	99.42	99.43	99.45	99.47	99.48	99.50
3	34.12	30.82	29.46	28.71	28.24	27.91	27.49	27.05	26.87	26.69	26.50	26.32	26.13
4	21.20	18.00	16.69	15.98	15.52	15.21	14.80	14.37	14.20	14.02	13.84	13.65	13.46
5	16.26	13.27	12.06	11.39	10.97	10.67	10.29	9.89	9.72	9.55	9.38	9.20	9.02
6	13.75	10.92	9.78	9.15	8.75	8.47	8.10	7.72	7.56	7.40	7.23	7.06	6.88
7	12.25	9.55	8.45	7.85	7.46	7.19	6.84	6.47	6.31	6.16	5.99	5.82	5.65
8	11.26	8.65	7.59	7.01	6.63	6.37	6.03	5.67	5.52	5.36	5.20	5.03	4.86
9	10.56	8.02	6.99	6.42	6.06	5.80	5.47	5.11	4.96	4.81	4.65	4.48	4.31
10	10.04	7.56	6.55	5.99	5.64	5.39	5.06	4.71	4.56	4.41	4.25	4.08	3.91
11	9.65	7.21	6.22	5.67	5.32	5.07	4.74	4.40	4.25	4.10	3.94	3.78	3.60
12	9.33	6.93	5.95	5.41	5.06	4.82	4.50	4.16	4.01	3.86	3.70	3.54	3.36
13	9.07	6.70	5.74	5.21	4.86	4.62	4.30	3.96	3.82	3.66	3.51	3.34	3.17
14	8.86	6.51	5.56	5.04	4.69	4.46	4.14	3.80	3.66	3.51	3.35	3.18	3.00
15	8.68	6.36	5.42	4.89	4.56	4.32	4.00	3.67	3.52	3.37	3.21	3.05	2.87
16	8.53	6.23	5.29	4.77	4.44	4.20	3.89	3.55	3.41	3.26	3.10	2.93	2.75
17	8.40	6.11	5.18	4.67	4.34	4.10	3.79	3.46	3.31	3.16	3.00	2.83	2.65
18	8.29	6.01	5.09	4.58	4.25	4.01	3.71	3.37	3.23	3.08	2.92	2.75	2.57
19	8.18	5.93	5.01	4.50	4.17	3.94	3.63	3.30	3.15	3.00	2.84	2.67	2.49
20	8.10	5.85	4.94	4.43	4.10	3.87	3.56	3.23	3.09	2.94	2.78	2.61	2.42
21	8.02	5.78	4.87	4.37	4.04	3.81	3.51	3.17	3.03	2.88	2.72	2.55	2.36
22	7.95	5.72	4.82	4.31	3.99	3.76	3.45	3.12	2.98	2.83	2.67	2.50	2.31
23	7.88	5.66	4.76	4.26	3.94	3.71	3.41	3.07	2.93	2.78	2.62	2.45	2.26
24	7.82	5.61	4.72	4.22	3.90	3.67	3.36	3.03	2.89	2.74	2.58	2.40	2.21
25	7.77	5.57	4.68	4.18	3.85	3.63	3.32	2.99	2.85	2.70	2.54	2.36	2.17
26	7.72	5.53	4.64	4.14	3.82	3.59	3.29	2.96	2.81	2.66	2.50	2.33	2.13
27	7.68	5.49	4.60	4.11	3.78	3.56	3.26	2.93	2.78	2.63	2.47	2.29	2.10
28	7.64	5.45	4.57	4.07	3.75	3.53	3.23	2.90	2.75	2.60	2.44	2.26	2.06
29	7.60	5.42	4.54	4.04	3.73	3.50	3.20	2.87	2.73	2.57	2.41	2.23	2.03
30	7.56	5.39	4.51	4.02	3.70	3.47	3.17	2.84	2.70	2.55	2.39	2.21	2.01
40	7.31	5.18	4.31	3.83	3.51	3.29	2.99	2.66	2.52	2.37	2.20	2.02	1.80
60	7.08	4.98	4.13	3.65	3.34	3.12	2.82	2.50	2.35	2.20	2.03	1.84	1.60
120	6.85	4.79	3.95	3.48	3.17	2.96	2.66	2.34	2.19	2.03	1.86	1.66	1.38
∞	6.63	4.61	3.78	3.32	3.02	2.80	2.51	2.18	2.04	1.88	1.70	1.47	1.00

TABLE IX The F Distribution (Continued)

Upper ½% Points

δ_2 \ δ_1	1	2	3	4	5	6	8	12	15	20	30	60	∞
1	16211	20000	21615	22500	23056	23437	23925	24426	24630	24836	25044	25253	25465
2	198.5	199.0	199.2	199.2	199.3	199.3	199.4	199.4	199.4	199.4	199.5	199.5	199.5
3	55.55	49.80	47.47	46.19	45.39	44.84	44.13	43.39	43.08	42.78	42.47	42.15	41.83
4	31.33	26.28	24.26	23.15	22.46	21.97	21.35	20.70	20.44	20.17	19.89	19.61	19.32
5	22.78	18.31	16.53	15.56	14.94	14.51	13.96	13.38	13.15	12.90	12.66	12.40	12.14
6	18.63	14.54	12.92	12.03	11.46	11.07	10.57	10.03	9.81	9.59	9.36	9.12	8.88
7	16.24	12.40	10.88	10.05	9.52	9.16	8.68	8.18	7.97	7.75	7.53	7.31	7.08
8	14.69	11.04	9.60	8.81	8.30	7.95	7.50	7.01	6.81	6.61	6.40	6.18	5.95
9	13.61	10.11	8.72	7.96	7.47	7.13	6.69	6.23	6.03	5.83	5.62	5.41	5.19
10	12.83	9.43	8.08	7.34	6.87	6.54	6.12	5.66	5.47	5.27	5.07	4.86	4.64
11	12.23	8.91	7.60	6.88	6.42	6.10	5.68	5.24	5.05	4.86	4.65	4.44	4.23
12	11.75	8.51	7.23	6.52	6.07	5.76	5.35	4.91	4.72	4.53	4.33	4.12	3.90
13	11.37	8.19	6.93	6.23	5.79	5.48	5.08	4.64	4.46	4.27	4.07	3.87	3.65
14	11.06	7.92	6.68	6.00	5.56	5.26	4.86	4.43	4.25	4.06	3.86	3.66	3.44
15	10.80	7.70	6.48	5.80	5.37	5.07	4.67	4.25	4.07	3.88	3.69	3.48	3.26
16	10.58	7.51	6.30	5.64	5.21	4.91	4.52	4.10	3.92	3.73	3.54	3.33	3.11
17	10.38	7.35	6.16	5.50	5.07	4.78	4.39	3.97	3.79	3.61	3.41	3.21	2.98
18	10.22	7.21	6.03	5.37	4.96	4.66	4.28	3.86	3.68	3.50	3.30	3.10	2.87
19	10.07	7.09	5.92	5.27	4.85	4.56	4.18	3.76	3.59	3.40	3.21	3.00	2.78
20	9.94	6.99	5.82	5.17	4.76	4.47	4.09	3.68	3.50	3.32	3.12	2.92	2.69
21	9.83	6.89	5.73	5.09	4.68	4.39	4.01	3.60	3.43	3.24	3.05	2.84	2.61
22	9.73	6.81	5.65	5.02	4.61	4.32	3.94	3.54	3.36	3.18	2.98	2.77	2.55
23	9.63	6.73	5.58	4.95	4.54	4.26	3.88	3.47	3.30	3.12	2.92	2.71	2.48
24	9.55	6.66	5.52	4.89	4.49	4.20	3.83	3.42	3.25	3.06	2.87	2.66	2.43
25	9.48	6.60	5.46	4.84	4.43	4.15	3.78	3.37	3.20	3.01	2.82	2.61	2.38
26	9.41	6.54	5.41	4.79	4.38	4.10	3.73	3.33	3.15	2.97	2.77	2.56	2.33
27	9.34	6.49	5.36	4.74	4.34	4.06	3.69	3.28	3.11	2.93	2.73	2.52	2.29
28	9.28	6.44	5.32	4.70	4.30	4.02	3.65	3.25	3.07	2.89	2.69	2.48	2.25
29	9.23	6.40	5.28	4.66	4.26	3.98	3.61	3.21	3.04	2.86	2.66	2.45	2.21
30	9.18	6.35	5.24	4.62	4.23	3.95	3.58	3.18	3.01	2.82	2.63	2.42	2.18
40	8.83	6.07	4.98	4.37	3.99	3.71	3.35	2.95	2.78	2.60	2.40	2.18	1.93
60	8.49	5.79	4.73	4.14	3.76	3.49	3.13	2.74	2.57	2.39	2.19	1.96	1.69
120	8.18	5.54	4.50	3.92	3.55	3.28	2.93	2.54	2.37	2.19	1.98	1.75	1.43
∞	7.88	5.30	4.28	3.72	3.35	3.09	2.74	2.36	2.19	2.00	1.79	1.53	1.00

Source: From U.S. Department of Commerce, National Bureau of Standards, *Handbook of Mathematical Functions* (Applied Mathematics Series, 55) (November

TABLE X Values of $Z = \left(\frac{1}{2}\right) \ln\left(\frac{1 + r}{1 - r}\right)$

	r (3d decimal)						r (3d decimal)				
r	.000	.002	.004	.006	.008	r	.000	.002	.004	.006	.008
.00	.0000	.0020	.0040	.0060	.0080	.50	.5493	.5520	.5547	.5573	.5600
1	.0100	.0120	.0140	.0160	.0180	1	.5627	.5654	.5682	.5709	.5736
2	.0200	.0220	.0240	.0260	.0280	2	.5763	.5791	.5818	.5846	.5874
3	.0300	.0320	.0340	.0360	.0380	3	.5901	.5929	.5957	.5985	.6013
4	.0400	.0420	.0440	.0460	.0480	4	.6042	.6070	.6098	.6127	.6155
.05	.0500	.0520	.0541	.0561	.0581	.55	.6194	.6213	.6241	.6270	.6299
6	.0601	.0621	.0641	.0661	.0681	6	.6328	.6358	.6387	.6416	.6446
7	.0701	.0721	.0741	.0761	.0782	7	.6475	.6505	.6535	.6565	.6595
8	.0802	.0822	.0842	.0862	.0882	8	.6625	.6655	.6685	.6716	.6746
9	.0902	.0923	.0943	.0963	.0983	9	.6777	.6807	.6838	.6869	.6900
.10	.1003	.1024	.1044	.1064	.1084	.60	.6931	.6963	.6994	.7026	.7057
1	.1104	.1125	.1145	.1165	.1186	1	.7089	.7121	.7153	.7185	.7218
2	.1206	.1226	.1246	.1267	.1287	2	.7250	.7283	.7315	.7348	.7381
3	.1307	.1328	.1348	.1368	.1389	3	.7414	.7447	.7481	.7514	.7548
4	.1409	.1430	.1450	.1471	.1491	4	.7582	.7616	.7650	.7684	.7718
.15	.1511	.1532	.1552	.1573	.1593	.65	.7753	.7788	.7823	.7858	.7893
6	.1614	.1634	.1655	.1676	.1696	6	.7928	.7964	.7999	.8035	.8071
7	.1717	.1737	.1758	.1779	.1799	7	.8107	.8144	.8180	.8217	.8254
8	.1820	.1841	.1861	.1882	.1903	8	.8291	.8328	.8366	.8404	.8441
9	.1923	.1944	.1965	.1986	.2007	9	.8480	.8518	.8556	.8595	.8634
.20	.2027	.2048	.2069	.2090	.2111	.70	.8673	.8712	.8752	.8792	.8832
1	.2132	.2153	.2174	.2195	.2216	1	.8872	.8912	.8953	.8994	.9035
2	.2237	.2258	.2279	.2300	.2321	2	.9076	.9118	.9160	.9202	.9245
3	.2342	.2363	.2384	.2405	.2427	3	.9287	.9330	.9373	.9417	.9461
4	.2448	.2469	.2490	.2512	.2533	4	.9505	.9549	.9549	.9639	.9684
.25	.2554	.2575	.2597	.2618	.2640	.75	0.973	0.978	0.982	0.987	0.991
6	.2661	.2683	.2704	.2726	.2747	6	0.996	1.001	1.006	1.011	1.015
7	.2769	.2790	.2812	.2833	.2855	7	1.020	1.025	1.030	1.035	1.040
8	.2877	.2899	.2920	.2942	.2964	8	1.045	1.050	1.056	1.061	1.066
9	.2986	.3008	.3029	.3051	.3073	9	1.071	1.077	1.082	1.088	1.093
.30	.3095	.3117	.3139	.3161	.3183	.80	1.099	1.104	1.110	1.116	1.121
1	.3205	.3228	.3250	.3272	.3294	1	1.127	1.133	1.139	1.145	1.151
2	.3316	.3339	.3361	.3383	.3406	2	1.157	1.163	1.169	1.175	1.182
3	.3428	.3451	.3473	.3496	.3518	3	1.188	1.195	1.201	1.208	1.214
4	.3541	.3564	.3586	.3609	.3632	4	1.221	1.228	1.235	1.242	1.249
.35	.3654	.3677	.3700	.3723	.3746	.85	1.256	1.263	1.271	1.278	1.286
6	.3769	.3792	.3815	.3838	.3861	6	1.293	1.301	1.309	1.317	1.325
7	.3884	.3907	.3931	.3954	.3977	7	1.333	1.341	1.350	1.358	1.367
8	.4001	.4024	.4047	.4071	.4094	8	1.376	1.385	1.394	1.403	1.412
9	.4118	.4142	.4165	.4189	.4213	9	1.422	1.432	1.442	1.452	1.462
.40	.4236	.4260	.4284	.4308	.4332	.90	1.472	1.483	1.494	1.505	1.516
1	.4356	.4380	.4404	.4428	.4453	1	1.528	1.539	1.551	1.564	1.576
2	.4477	.4501	.4526	.4550	.4574	2	1.589	1.602	1.616	1.630	1.644
3	.4599	.4624	.4648	.4673	.4698	3	1.658	1.673	1.689	1.705	1.721
4	.4722	.4747	.4772	.4797	.4822	4	1.738	1.756	1.774	1.792	1.812
.45	.4847	.4872	.4897	.4922	.4948	.95	1.832	1.853	1.874	1.897	1.921
6	.4973	.4999	.5024	.5049	.4075	6	1.946	1.972	2.000	2.029	2.060
7	.5101	.5126	.5152	.5178	.5204	7	2.092	2.127	2.165	2.205	2.249
8	.5230	.5256	.5282	.5308	.5334	8	2.298	2.351	2.410	2.477	2.555
9	.5361	.5387	.5413	.5440	.5466	9	2.647	2.759	2.903	3.106	3.453

TABLE XI The Durbin–Watson d Statistic

	Significance points of d_L and d_U: 5%									
	$k' = 1$		$k' = 2$		$k' = 3$		$k' = 4$		$k' = 5$	
n	d_L	d_U	d_L	d_U	d_L	d_U	d_L	d_U	d_L	d_U
15	1.08	1.36	0.95	1.54	0.82	1.75	0.69	1.97	0.56	2.21
16	1.10	1.37	0.98	1.54	0.86	1.73	0.74	1.93	0.62	2.15
17	1.13	1.38	1.02	1.54	0.90	1.71	0.78	1.90	0.67	2.10
18	1.16	1.39	1.05	1.53	0.93	1.69	0.82	1.87	0.71	2.06
19	1.18	1.40	1.08	1.53	0.97	1.68	0.86	1.85	0.75	2.02
20	1.20	1.41	1.10	1.54	1.00	1.68	0.90	1.83	0.79	1.99
21	1.22	1.42	1.13	1.54	1.03	1.67	0.93	1.81	0.83	1.96
22	1.24	1.43	1.15	1.54	1.05	1.66	0.96	1.80	0.86	1.94
23	1.26	1.44	1.17	1.54	1.08	1.66	0.99	1.79	0.90	1.92
24	1.27	1.45	1.19	1.55	1.10	1.66	1.01	1.78	0.93	1.90
25	1.29	1.45	1.21	1.55	1.12	1.66	1.04	1.77	0.95	1.89
26	1.30	1.46	1.22	1.55	1.14	1.65	1.06	1.76	0.98	1.88
27	1.32	1.47	1.24	1.56	1.16	1.65	1.08	1.76	1.01	1.86
28	1.33	1.48	1.26	1.56	1.18	1.65	1.10	1.75	1.03	1.85
29	1.34	1.48	1.27	1.56	1.20	1.65	1.12	1.74	1.05	1.84
30	1.35	1.49	1.28	1.57	1.21	1.65	1.14	1.74	1.07	1.83
31	1.36	1.50	1.30	1.57	1.23	1.65	1.16	1.74	1.09	1.83
32	1.37	1.50	1.31	1.57	1.24	1.65	1.18	1.73	1.11	1.82
33	1.38	1.51	1.32	1.58	1.26	1.65	1.19	1.73	1.13	1.81
34	1.39	1.51	1.33	1.58	1.27	1.65	1.21	1.73	1.15	1.81
35	1.40	1.52	1.34	1.58	1.28	1.65	1.22	1.73	1.16	1.80
36	1.41	1.52	1.35	1.59	1.29	1.65	1.24	1.73	1.18	1.80
37	1.42	1.53	1.36	1.59	1.31	1.66	1.25	1.72	1.19	1.80
38	1.43	1.54	1.37	1.59	1.32	1.66	1.26	1.72	1.21	1.79
39	1.43	1.54	1.38	1.60	1.33	1.66	1.27	1.72	1.22	1.79
40	1.44	1.54	1.39	1.60	1.34	1.66	1.29	1.72	1.23	1.79
45	1.48	1.57	1.43	1.62	1.38	1.67	1.34	1.72	1.29	1.78
50	1.50	1.59	1.46	1.63	1.42	1.67	1.38	1.72	1.34	1.77
55	1.53	1.60	1.49	1.64	1.45	1.68	1.41	1.72	1.38	1.77
60	1.55	1.62	1.51	1.65	1.48	1.69	1.44	1.73	1.41	1.77
65	1.57	1.63	1.54	1.66	1.50	1.70	1.47	1.73	1.44	1.77
70	1.58	1.64	1.55	1.67	1.52	1.70	1.49	1.74	1.46	1.77
75	1.60	1.65	1.57	1.68	1.54	1.71	1.51	1.74	1.49	1.77
80	1.61	1.66	1.59	1.69	1.56	1.72	1.53	1.74	1.51	1.77
85	1.62	1.67	1.60	1.70	1.57	1.72	1.55	1.75	1.52	1.77
90	1.63	1.68	1.61	1.70	1.59	1.73	1.57	1.75	1.54	1.78
95	1.64	1.69	1.62	1.71	1.60	1.73	1.58	1.75	1.56	1.78
100	1.65	1.69	1.63	1.72	1.61	1.74	1.59	1.76	1.57	1.78

TABLE XI The Durbin–Watson *d* Statistic (*Continued*)

| | **Significance points of d_L and d_U: 2.5%** | | | | | | | | | |
| | $k'=1$ | | $k'=2$ | | $k'=3$ | | $k'=4$ | | $k'=5$ | |
n	d_L	d_U	d_L	d_U	d_L	d_U	d_L	d_U	d_L	d_U
15	0.95	1.23	0.83	1.40	0.71	1.61	0.59	1.84	0.48	2.09
16	0.98	1.24	0.86	1.40	0.75	1.59	0.64	1.80	0.53	2.03
17	1.01	1.25	0.90	1.40	0.79	1.58	0.68	1.77	0.57	1.98
18	1.03	1.26	0.93	1.40	0.82	1.56	0.72	1.74	0.62	1.93
19	1.06	1.28	0.96	1.41	0.86	1.55	0.76	1.72	0.66	1.90
20	1.08	1.28	0.99	1.41	0.89	1.55	0.79	1.70	0.70	1.87
21	1.10	1.30	1.01	1.41	0.92	1.54	0.83	1.69	0.73	1.84
22	1.12	1.31	1.04	1.42	0.95	1.54	0.86	1.68	0.77	1.82
23	1.14	1.32	1.06	1.42	0.97	1.54	0.89	1.67	0.80	1.80
24	1.16	1.33	1.08	1.43	1.00	1.54	0.91	1.66	0.83	1.79
25	1.18	1.34	1.10	1.43	1.02	1.54	0.94	1.65	0.86	1.77
26	1.19	1.35	1.12	1.44	1.04	1.54	0.96	1.65	0.88	1.76
27	1.21	1.36	1.13	1.44	1.06	1.54	0.99	1.64	0.91	1.75
28	1.22	1.37	1.15	1.45	1.08	1.54	1.01	1.64	0.93	1.74
29	1.24	1.38	1.17	1.45	1.10	1.54	1.03	1.63	0.96	1.73
30	1.25	1.38	1.18	1.46	1.12	1.54	1.05	1.63	0.98	1.73
31	1.26	1.39	1.20	1.47	1.13	1.55	1.07	1.63	1.00	1.72
32	1.27	1.40	1.21	1.47	1.15	1.55	1.08	1.63	1.02	1.71
33	1.28	1.41	1.22	1.48	1.16	1.55	1.10	1.63	1.04	1.71
34	1.29	1.41	1.24	1.48	1.17	1.55	1.12	1.63	1.06	1.70
35	1.30	1.42	1.25	1.48	1.19	1.55	1.13	1.63	1.07	1.70
36	1.31	1.43	1.26	1.49	1.20	1.56	1.15	1.63	1.09	1.70
37	1.32	1.43	1.27	1.49	1.21	1.56	1.16	1.62	1.10	1.70
38	1.33	1.44	1.28	1.50	1.23	1.56	1.17	1.62	1.12	1.70
39	1.34	1.44	1.29	1.50	1.24	1.56	1.19	1.63	1.13	1.69
40	1.35	1.45	1.30	1.51	1.25	1.57	1.20	1.63	1.15	1.69
45	1.39	1.48	1.34	1.53	1.30	1.58	1.25	1.63	1.21	1.69
50	1.42	1.50	1.38	1.54	1.34	1.59	1.30	1.64	1.26	1.69
55	1.45	1.52	1.41	1.56	1.37	1.60	1.33	1.64	1.30	1.69
60	1.47	1.54	1.44	1.57	1.40	1.61	1.37	1.65	1.33	1.69
65	1.49	1.55	1.46	1.59	1.43	1.62	1.40	1.66	1.36	1.69
70	1.51	1.57	1.48	1.60	1.45	1.63	1.42	1.66	1.39	1.70
75	1.53	1.58	1.50	1.61	1.47	1.64	1.45	1.67	1.42	1.70
80	1.54	1.59	1.52	1.62	1.49	1.65	1.47	1.67	1.44	1.70
85	1.56	1.60	1.53	1.63	1.51	1.65	1.49	1.68	1.46	1.71
90	1.57	1.61	1.55	1.64	1.53	1.66	1.50	1.69	1.48	1.71
95	1.58	1.62	1.56	1.65	1.54	1.67	1.52	1.69	1.50	1.71
100	1.59	1.63	1.57	1.65	1.55	1.67	1.53	1.70	1.51	1.72

Source: Reproduced by permission of the editor and authors, from J. Durbin and G. S. Watson, "Testing for serial correlation in least squares regression (II)," *Biometrika,* **38,** 1951, pp. 159–178.

TABLE XII The Unit Normal Linear Loss Function[a]

D	.00	.01	.02	.03	.04	.05	.06	.07	.08	.09
.0	.3989	.3940	.3890	.3841	.3793	.3744	.3697	.3649	.3602	.3556
.1	.3509	.3464	.3418	.3373	.3328	.3284	.3240	.3197	.3154	.3111
.2	.3069	.3027	.2986	.2944	.2904	.2863	.2824	.2784	.2745	.2706
.3	.2668	.2630	.2592	.2555	.2518	.2481	.2445	.2409	.2374	.2339
.4	.2304	.2270	.2236	.2203	.2169	.2137	.2104	.2072	.2040	.2009
.5	.1978	.1947	.1917	.1887	.1857	.1828	.1799	.1771	.1742	.1714
.6	.1687	.1659	.1633	.1606	.1580	.1554	.1528	.1503	.1478	.1453
.7	.1429	.1405	.1381	.1358	.1334	.1312	.1289	.1267	.1245	.1223
.8	.1202	.1181	.1160	.1140	.1120	.1100	.1080	.1061	.1042	.1023
.9	.1004	.09860	.09680	.09503	.09328	.09156	.08986	.08819	.08654	.08491
1.0	.08332	.08174	.08019	.07866	.07716	.07568	.07422	.07279	.07138	.06999
1.1	.06862	.06727	.06595	.06465	.06336	.06210	.06086	.05964	.05844	.05726
1.2	.05610	.05496	.05384	.05274	.05165	.05059	.04954	.04851	.04750	.04650
1.3	.04553	.04457	.04363	.04270	.04179	.04090	.04002	.03916	.03831	.03748
1.4	.03667	.03587	.03508	.03431	.03356	.03281	.03208	.03137	.03067	.02998
1.5	.02931	.02865	.02800	.02736	.02674	.02612	.02552	.02494	.02436	.02380
1.6	.02324	.02270	.02217	.02165	.02114	.02064	.02015	.01967	.01920	.01874
1.7	.01829	.01785	.01742	.01699	.01658	.01617	.01578	.01539	.01501	.01464
1.8	.01428	.01392	.01357	.01323	.01290	.01257	.01226	.01195	.01164	.01134
1.9	.01105	.01077	.01049	.01022	$.0^{2}9957$	$.0^{2}9698$	$.0^{2}9445$	$.0^{2}9198$	$.0^{2}8957$	$.0^{2}8721$
2.0	$.0^{2}8491$	$.0^{2}8266$	$.0^{2}8046$	$.0^{2}7832$	$.0^{2}7623$	$.0^{2}7418$	$.0^{2}7219$	$.0^{2}7024$	$.0^{2}6835$	$.0^{2}6649$
2.1	$.0^{2}6468$	$.0^{2}6292$	$.0^{2}6120$	$.0^{2}5952$	$.0^{2}5788$	$.0^{2}5628$	$.0^{2}5472$	$.0^{2}5320$	$.0^{2}5172$	$.0^{2}5028$
2.2	$.0^{2}4887$	$.0^{2}4750$	$.0^{2}4616$	$.0^{2}4486$	$.0^{2}4358$	$.0^{2}4235$	$.0^{2}4114$	$.0^{2}3996$	$.0^{2}3882$	$.0^{2}3770$
2.3	$.0^{2}3662$	$.0^{2}3556$	$.0^{2}3453$	$.0^{2}3352$	$.0^{2}3255$	$.0^{2}3159$	$.0^{2}3067$	$.0^{2}2977$	$.0^{2}2889$	$.0^{2}2804$
2.4	$.0^{2}2720$	$.0^{2}2640$	$.0^{2}2561$	$.0^{2}2484$	$.0^{2}2410$	$.0^{2}2337$	$.0^{2}2267$	$.0^{2}2199$	$.0^{2}2132$	$.0^{2}2067$
2.5	$.0^{2}2005$	$.0^{2}1943$	$.0^{2}1883$	$.0^{2}1826$	$.0^{2}1769$	$.0^{2}1715$	$.0^{2}1662$	$.0^{2}1610$	$.0^{2}1560$	$.0^{2}1511$
3.0	$.0^{3}3822$	$.0^{3}3689$	$.0^{3}3560$	$.0^{3}3436$	$.0^{3}3316$	$.0^{3}3199$	$.0^{3}3087$	$.0^{3}2978$	$.0^{3}2873$	$.0^{3}2771$
3.5	$.0^{4}5848$	$.0^{4}5620$	$.0^{4}5400$	$.0^{4}5188$	$.0^{4}4984$	$.0^{4}4788$	$.0^{4}4599$	$.0^{4}4417$	$.0^{4}4242$	$.0^{4}4073$
4.0	$.0^{5}7145$	$.0^{5}6835$	$.0^{5}6538$	$.0^{5}6253$	$.0^{5}5980$	$.0^{5}5718$	$.0^{5}5468$	$.0^{5}5227$	$.0^{5}4997$	$.0^{5}4777$

[a] The value $L_N(D)$ is the expected opportunity loss (or EVPI) for a linear loss function with slope one and a unit normal distribution. The value D represents the relative position of the break-even point.

When using $L_N(D)$ for a general normal distribution, the value D represents the deviation of the break-even point X_b from the mean μ, expressed in standard deviation, σ, units.

Source: These tables of "Unit Normal Loss Function" appear in Introduction to Statistics for Business Decisions, by Robert Schlaifer (McGraw-Hill, 1961). They are reproduced here by specific permission of the copyright holder, The President and Fellows of Harvard College.

TABLE XIII Table for $T = f(D_0, \log G)$: Normal Sampling

$\log G$	$D_0 = .0$	.2	.4	.6	.8	1.0	1.2	1.4	1.6	1.8	2.0
.3	-.9414										
.4	-.7943	-.9100									
.5	-.6587	-.7327									
.6	-.5343	-.5854									
.7	-.4200	-.4573									
.8	-.3148	-.3433	-.4585								
.9	-.2175	-.2400	-.3227								
1.0	-.1269	-.1452	-.2091								
1.1	-.0419	-.0573	-.1089	-.2269							
1.2	.0382	.0249	-.0182	-.1081							
1.3	.1142	.1026	.0655	-.0075							
1.4	.1867	.1764	.1438	.0820	-.0328						
1.5	.2563	.2470	.2178	.1640	.0714						
1.6	.3234	.3148	.2884	.2405	.1619	.0183					
1.7	.3883	.3804	.3560	.3126	.2438	.1304					
1.8	.4513	.4439	.4213	.3814	.3197	.2241					
1.9	.5127	.5058	.4846	.4475	.3912	.3074	.1693				
2.0	.5727	.5662	.5461	.5113	.4592	.3839	.2693				
2.1	.6316	.6253	.6062	.5733	.5245	.4555	.3557				
2.2	.6893	.6833	.6650	.6337	.5876	.5235	.4339	.2963			
2.3	.7462	.7404	.7228	.6928	.6489	.5887	.5066	.3885			
2.4	.8023	.7966	.7796	.7507	.7087	.6516	.5752	.4700			
2.5	.8576	.8521	.8356	.8076	.7672	.7126	.6408	.5447	.4041		
2.6	.9123	.9070	.8909	.8637	.8246	.7722	.7039	.6146	.4912		
2.7	.9665	.9613	.9456	.9191	.8811	.8304	.7651	.6811	.5693	.3978	
2.8	1.0202	1.0151	.9998	.9738	.9368	.8876	.8247	.7450	.6416	.4954	
2.9	1.0735	1.0685	1.0534	1.0280	.9918	.9439	.8831	.8067	.7097	.5793	
3.0	1.1265	1.1215	1.1067	1.0817	1.0462	.9994	.9403	.8667	.7747	.6553	.4772

TABLE XIII Table for $T = f(D_0, \log G)$: Normal Sampling (Continued)

log G	$D_0 = .0$	.2	.4	.6	.8	1.0	1.2	1.4	1.6	1.8	2.0
3.1	1.1791	1.1742	1.1596	1.1350	1.1000	1.0542	.9966	.9253	.8373	.7259	.5720
3.2	1.2314	1.2266	1.2121	1.1878	1.1535	1.1085	1.0520	.9828	.8981	.7928	.6541
3.3	1.2834	1.2787	1.2644	1.2404	1.2065	1.1622	1.1068	1.0392	.9572	.8568	.7288
3.4	1.3352	1.3305	1.3164	1.2927	1.2592	1.2155	1.1611	1.0948	1.0151	.9186	.7985
3.5	1.3868	1.3822	1.3682	1.3447	1.3115	1.2684	1.2148	1.1498	1.0719	.9787	.8646
3.6	1.4383	1.4337	1.4197	1.3965	1.3636	1.3210	1.2680	1.2041	1.1279	1.0373	.9281
3.7	1.4896	1.4850	1.4712	1.4481	1.4155	1.3733	1.3209	1.2579	1.1831	1.0947	.9894
3.8	1.5407	1.5361	1.5224	1.4995	1.4672	1.4253	1.3735	1.3112	1.2376	1.1511	1.0490
3.9	1.5917	1.5872	1.5735	1.5507	1.5186	1.4771	1.4257	1.3641	1.2916	1.2067	1.1072
4.0	1.6426	1.6381	1.6245	1.6018	1.5699	1.5286	1.4777	1.4167	1.3450	1.2615	1.1643
4.1	1.6934	1.6889	1.6754	1.6528	1.6211	1.5801	1.5295	1.4690	1.3981	1.3158	1.2205
4.2	1.7441	1.7396	1.7262	1.7037	1.6721	1.6313	1.5811	1.5211	1.4508	1.3695	1.2758
4.3	1.7948	1.7903	1.7769	1.7545	1.7230	1.6824	1.6324	1.5729	1.5032	1.4228	1.3305
4.4	1.8453	1.8409	1.8275	1.8052	1.7738	1.7334	1.6837	1.6244	1.5553	1.4757	1.3846
4.5	1.8958	1.8914	1.8781	1.8558	1.8246	1.7843	1.7348	1.6758	1.6072	1.5282	1.4381
4.6	1.9463	1.9418	1.9285	1.9064	1.8752	1.8351	1.7857	1.7271	1.6588	1.5805	1.4913
4.7	1.9967	1.9923	1.9790	1.9568	1.9258	1.8857	1.8366	1.7782	1.7103	1.6325	1.5441
4.8	2.0470	2.0426	2.0294	2.0073	1.9763	1.9364	1.8874	1.8292	1.7616	1.6842	1.5965
4.9	2.0973	2.0929	2.0797	2.0577	2.0268	1.9869	1.9381	1.8801	1.8127	1.7358	1.6487
5.0	2.1476	2.1432	2.1300	2.1080	2.0772	2.0374	1.9887	1.9308	1.8638	1.7871	1.7006
5.1	2.1979	2.1935	2.1803	2.1583	2.1275	2.0878	2.0392	1.9815	1.9147	1.8384	1.7523
5.2	2.2481	2.2437	2.2306	2.2086	2.1778	2.1382	2.0897	2.0321	1.9655	1.8894	1.8037
5.3	2.2983	2.2939	2.2808	2.2588	2.2281	2.1886	2.1401	2.0827	2.0162	1.9404	1.8551
5.4	2.3485	2.3441	2.3310	2.3091	2.2784	2.2389	2.1905	2.1332	2.0668	1.9913	1.9062
5.5	2.3986	2.3943	2.3811	2.3593	2.3286	2.2891	2.2408	2.1836	2.1174	2.0420	1.9573
5.6	2.4488	2.4444	2.4313	2.4094	2.3788	2.3394	2.2911	2.2340	2.1679	2.0927	2.0082
5.7	2.4989	2.4945	2.4814	2.4596	2.4290	2.3896	2.3414	2.2843	2.2183	2.1433	2.0590
5.8	2.5490	2.5447	2.5316	2.5097	2.4791	2.4398	2.3916	2.3346	2.2687	2.1938	2.1098
5.9	2.5991	2.5948	2.5817	2.5598	2.5293	2.4900	2.4419	2.3849	2.3191	2.2443	2.1604
6.0	2.6492	2.6449	2.6318	2.6100	2.5794	2.5401	2.4920	2.4352	2.3694	2.2947	2.2110

6.1	2.6993	2.6949	2.6819	2.6601	2.6295	2.5903	2.5422	2.4854	2.4197	2.3451	2.2615
6.2	2.7494	2.7450	2.7319	2.7101	2.6796	2.6404	2.5924	2.5356	2.4699	2.3954	2.3119
6.3	2.7994	2.7951	2.7820	2.7602	2.7297	2.6905	2.6425	2.5857	2.5202	2.4457	2.3623
6.4	2.8495	2.8451	2.8321	2.8103	2.7798	2.7406	2.6926	2.6359	2.5704	2.4960	2.4127
6.5	2.8995	2.8952	2.8821	2.8604	2.8299	2.7907	2.7427	2.6860	2.6205	2.5462	2.4630
6.6	2.9496	2.9452	2.9322	2.9104	2.8799	2.8407	2.7928	2.7361	2.6707	2.5964	2.5133
6.7	2.9996	2.9953	2.9822	2.9605	2.9300	2.8908	2.8429	2.7863	2.7208	2.6466	2.5636
6.8	3.0496	3.0453	3.0322	3.0105	2.9800	2.9409	2.8930	2.8364	2.7710	2.6968	2.6138
6.9	3.0997	3.0953	3.0823	3.0605	3.0301	2.9909	2.9430	2.8864	2.8211	2.7469	2.6640
7.0	3.1497	3.1454	3.1323	3.1106	3.0801	3.0410	2.9931	2.9365	2.8712	2.7971	2.7142
7.1	3.1997	3.1954	3.1823	3.1606	3.1302	3.0910	3.0432	2.9866	2.9213	2.8472	2.7643
7.2	3.2498	3.2454	3.2324	3.2106	3.1802	3.1411	3.0932	3.0366	2.9713	2.8973	2.8145
7.3	3.2998	3.2954	3.2824	3.2607	3.2302	3.1911	3.1432	3.0867	3.0214	2.9474	2.8646
7.4	3.3498	3.3454	3.3324	3.3107	3.2802	3.2411	3.1933	3.1467	3.0715	2.9975	2.9147
7.5	3.3998	3.3955	3.3824	3.3607	3.3303	3.2911	3.2433	3.1868	3.1215	3.0476	2.9648
7.6	3.4498	3.4455	3.4324	3.4107	3.3803	3.3412	3.2933	3.2368	3.1716	3.0976	3.0149
7.7	3.4998	3.4995	3.4825	3.4607	3.4303	3.3912	3.3434	3.2869	3.2216	3.1477	3.0650
7.8	3.5498	3.5455	3.5325	3.5107	3.4803	3.4412	3.3934	3.3369	3.2717	3.1977	3.1151
7.9	3.5999	3.5955	3.5828	3.5608	3.5303	3.4912	3.4434	3.3869	3.3217	3.2478	3.1651
8.0	3.6499	3.6455	3.6325	3.6108	3.5803	3.5412	3.4934	3.4369	3.3717	3.2978	3.2152
φ	−.3501	−.3544	−.3674	−.3891	−.4195	−.4586	−.5064	−.5629	−.6280	−.7018	−.7844
3.0	.4772										
3.1	.5720										
3.2	.6541										
3.3	.7288	.5407									
3.4	.7985	.6346									
3.5	.8646	.7161									
3.6	.9231	.7904	.6837								
3.7	.9894	.8597	.7658								
3.8	1.0490	.9255	.8403								
3.9	1.1072	.9887	.9098								
4.0	1.1643	1.0498		.7188							

TABLE XIII Table for $T = f(D_0, \log G)$: Normal Sampling (Continued)

log G	$D_0 = .0$	.2	.4	.6	.8	1.0	1.2	1.4	1.6	1.8	2.0
4.1	1.2205	1.1092	.9757	.8028							
4.2	1.2758	1.1673	1.0389	.8784							
4.3	1.3305	1.2242	1.1000	.9486	.7388						
4.4	1.3846	1.2802	1.1594	1.0151	.8265						
4.5	1.4381	1.3355	1.2175	1.0786	.9044						
4.6	1.4913	1.3900	1.2744	1.1400	.9761						
4.7	1.5441	1.4440	1.3305	1.1997	1.0435	.8358					
4.8	1.5965	1.4975	1.3857	1.2580	1.1079	.9174					
4.9	1.6487	1.5506	1.4403	1.3151	1.1698	.9915					
5.0	1.7006	1.6033	1.4942	1.3712	1.2300	1.0606					
5.1	1.7523	1.6557	1.5477	1.4265	1.2886	1.1262	.9159				
5.2	1.8037	1.7078	1.6008	1.4812	1.3460	1.1891	.9939				
5.3	1.8551	1.7597	1.6535	1.5352	1.4024	1.2500	1.0657				
5.4	1.9062	1.8113	1.7059	1.5888	1.4579	1.3092	1.1332	.8967			
5.5	1.9573	1.8628	1.7580	1.6419	1.5127	1.3671	1.1976	.9815			
5.6	2.0082	1.9141	1.8099	1.6946	1.5669	1.4239	1.2595	1.0575			
5.7	2.0590	1.9652	1.8615	1.7471	1.6206	1.4798	1.3196	1.1279			
5.8	2.1098	2.0163	1.9130	1.7992	1.6739	1.5349	1.3783	1.1944	.9505		
5.9	2.1604	2.0672	1.9642	1.8511	1.7267	1.5893	1.4356	1.2580	1.0338		
6.0	2.2110	2.1180	2.0154	1.9028	1.7792	1.6432	1.4920	1.3194	1.1089		
6.1	2.2615	2.1687	2.0664	1.9542	1.8314	1.6966	1.5475	1.3791	1.1787		
6.2	2.3119	2.2193	2.1173	2.0055	1.8834	1.7496	1.6023	1.4373	1.2447		
6.3	2.3623	2.2699	2.1681	2.0567	1.9351	1.8023	1.6565	1.4943	1.3079	1.0733	
6.4	2.4127	2.3204	2.2188	2.1077	1.9866	1.8546	1.7102	1.5504	1.3690	1.1484	
6.5	2.4630	2.3708	2.2694	2.1586	2.0380	1.9066	1.7634	1.6057	1.4284	1.2181	
6.6	2.5133	2.4212	2.3200	2.2094	2.0891	1.9585	1.8162	1.6603	1.4865	1.2841	1.0148
6.7	2.5636	2.4716	2.3705	2.2602	2.1402	2.0101	1.8687	1.7144	1.5434	1.3474	1.0998
6.8	2.6138	2.5219	2.4210	2.3108	2.1912	2.0615	1.9209	1.7679	1.5993	1.4084	1.1759
6.9	2.6640	2.5722	2.4713	2.3614	2.2420	2.1127	1.9729	1.8210	1.6545	1.4678	1.2463
7.0	2.7142	2.6224	2.5217	2.4119	2.2927	2.1639	2.0246	1.8737	1.7090	1.5259	1.3127

7.1	1.3763	1.5828	1.7630	1.9261	2.0761	2.2148	2.3434	2.4623	2.5720	2.6726	2.7643
7.2	1.4377	1.6387	1.8164	1.9782	2.1274	2.2657	2.3940	2.5127	2.6223	2.7228	2.8145
7.3	1.4973	1.6939	1.8695	2.0301	2.1786	2.3165	2.4445	2.5631	2.6725	2.7730	2.8646
7.4	1.5555	1.7484	1.9221	2.0817	2.2297	2.3672	2.4950	2.6134	2.7228	2.8232	2.9147
7.5	1.6125	1.8023	1.9745	2.1332	2.2806	2.4178	2.5454	2.6637	2.7730	2.8733	2.9648
7.6	1.6686	1.8558	2.0265	2.1845	2.3314	2.4683	2.5957	2.7139	2.8231	2.9234	3.0149
7.7	1.7239	1.9088	2.0784	2.2356	2.3822	2.5188	2.6461	2.7642	2.8733	2.9735	3.0650
7.8	1.7784	1.9615	2.1300	2.2867	2.4328	2.5693	2.6964	2.8144	2.9234	3.0236	3.1151
7.9	1.8325	2.0138	2.1814	2.3376	2.4834	2.6197	2.7466	2.8645	2.9735	3.0737	3.1651
8.0	1.8860	2.0659	2.2327	2.3884	2.5339	2.6700	2.7968	2.9147	3.0237	3.1238	3.2152
8.1	1.9390	2.1177	2.2838	2.4391	2.5844	2.7203	2.8470	2.9648	3.0738	3.1739	3.2652
8.2	1.9918	2.1693	2.3348	2.4897	2.6348	2.7706	2.8972	3.0150	3.1238	3.2239	3.3153
8.3	2.0441	2.2208	2.3857	2.5403	2.6852	2.8208	2.9474	3.0651	3.1739	3.2740	3.3653
8.4	2.0962	2.2720	2.4365	2.5908	2.7355	2.8710	2.9975	3.1152	3.2240	3.3240	3.4154
8.5	2.1481	2.3231	2.4872	2.6412	2.7858	2.9212	3.0477	3.1653	3.2740	3.3741	3.4654
8.6	2.1997	2.3741	2.5378	2.6916	2.8360	2.9714	3.0978	3.2153	3.3241	3.4241	3.5154
8.7	2.2512	2.4250	2.5884	2.7420	2.8863	3.0215	3.1479	3.2654	3.3742	3.4742	3.5654
8.8	2.3025	2.4758	2.6388	2.7923	2.9365	3.0717	3.1980	3.3155	3.4242	3.5242	3.6155
8.9	2.3536	2.5265	2.6893	2.8426	2.9867	3.1218	3.2481	3.3655	3.4742	3.5742	3.6655
9.0	2.4046	2.5771	2.7397	2.8928	3.0368	3.1719	3.2981	3.4156	3.5243	3.6242	3.7155
9.1	2.4555	2.6277	2.7900	2.9430	3.0870	3.2220	3.3482	3.4656	3.5743	3.6743	3.7655
9.2	2.5063	2.6782	2.8403	2.9932	3.1371	3.2721	3.3983	3.5157	3.6243	3.7243	3.8155
9.3	2.5570	2.7286	2.8906	3.0434	3.1872	3.3222	3.4483	3.5657	3.6744	3.7743	3.8655
9.4	2.6077	2.7790	2.9408	3.0936	3.2373	3.3722	3.4983	3.6157	3.7244	3.8243	3.9156
9.5	2.6582	2.8293	2.9911	3.1437	3.2874	3.4223	3.5484	3.6658	3.7744	3.8743	3.9656
9.6	2.7087	2.8796	3.0413	3.1938	3.3375	3.4723	3.5984	3.7158	3.8244	3.9243	4.0156
9.7	2.7592	2.9299	3.0914	3.2439	3.3876	3.5224	3.6485	3.7658	3.8744	3.9744	4.0656
9.8	2.8096	2.9802	3.1416	3.2940	3.4376	3.5724	3.6985	3.8158	3.9244	4.0244	4.1156
9.9	2.8599	3.0304	3.1917	3.3441	3.4877	3.6225	3.7485	3.8658	3.9745	4.0744	4.1656
10.0	2.9102	3.0806	3.2418	3.3942	3.5377	3.6725	3.7985	3.9159	4.0245	4.1244	4.2156
φ	−2.0872	−1.9179	−1.7572	−1.6052	−1.4619	−1.3272	−2.2013	−1.0840	−.9754	−.8756	−.7844

A minus sign in front of any tabular entry applies to the entire entry. Thus −.9414 = 9.0586 − 10.
If log G > 8.0, use the approximation $T = \tfrac{1}{2}(\log G) + \varphi(D_0)$, where $\varphi(D_0)$ is the last entry in each column for D_0.

Source: These tables for $T = f(D_0, \log G)$: Normal Sampling appear in *Introduction to Statistical Decision Making*, by Pratt, Raiffa and Schlaiffer (McGraw-Hill, 1965). They are reproduced by specific permission of the copyright holder, The President and Fellows of Harvard College.

TABLE XIV 5% and 1% Significance Points for the Ratio of the Mean Square Successive Difference of the Variance: Values of δ^2/s^2 for Different Levels of Significance

	Values of k		Values of k'			Values of k		Values of k'	
n	$P = .01$	$P = .05$	$P = .95$	$P = .99$	n	$P = .01$	$P = .05$	$P = .95$	$P = .99$
4	.8341	1.0406	4.2927	4.4992	33	1.2667	1.4885	2.6365	2.8583
5	.6724	1.0255	3.9745	4.3276	34	1.2761	1.4951	2.6262	2.8451
6	.6738	1.0682	3.7318	4.1262	35	1.2852	1.5014	2.6163	2.8324
7	.7163	1.0919	3.5748	3.9504	36	1.2940	1.5075	2.6068	2.8202
8	.7575	1.1228	3.4486	3.8139	37	1.3025	1.5135	2.5977	2.8085
9	.7974	1.1524	3.3476	3.7025	38	1.3108	1.5193	2.5889	2.7973
10	.8353	1.1803	3.2642	3.6091	39	1.3188	1.5249	2.5804	2.7865
11	.8706	1.2062	3.1938	3.5294	40	1.3266	1.5304	2.5722	2.7760
12	.9033	1.2301	3.1335	3.4603	41	1.3342	1.5357	2.5643	2.7658
13	.9336	1.2521	3.0812	3.3996	42	1.3415	1.5408	2.5567	2.7560
14	.9618	1.2725	3.0352	3.3458	43	1.3486	1.5458	2.5494	2.7466
15	.9880	1.2914	2.9943	3.2977	44	1.3554	1.5506	2.5424	2.7376
16	1.0124	1.3090	2.9577	3.2543	45	1.3620	1.5552	2.5357	2.7289
17	1.0352	1.3253	2.9247	3.2148	46	1.3684	1.5596	2.5293	2.7205
18	1.0566	1.3405	2.8948	3.1787	47	1.3745	1.5638	2.5232	2.7125
19	1.0766	1.3547	2.8675	3.1456	48	1.3802	1.5678	2.5173	2.7049
20	1.0954	1.3680	2.8425	3.1151	49	1.3856	1.5716	2.5117	2.6977
21	1.1131	1.3805	2.8195	3.0869	50	1.3907	1.5752	2.5064	2.6908
22	1.1298	1.3923	2.7982	3.0607	51	1.3957	1.5787	2.5013	2.6842
23	1.1456	1.4035	2.7784	3.0362	52	1.4007	1.5822	2.4963	2.6777
24	1.1606	1.4141	2.7599	3.0133	53	1.4057	1.5856	2.4914	2.6712
25	1.1748	1.4241	2.7426	2.9919	54	1.4107	1.5890	2.4866	2.6648
26	1.1883	1.4336	2.7264	2.9718	55	1.4156	1.5923	2.4819	2.6585
27	1.2012	1.4426	2.7112	2.9528	56	1.4203	1.5955	2.4773	2.6524
28	1.2135	1.4512	2.6969	2.9348	57	1.4249	1.5987	2.4728	2.6465
29	1.2252	1.4594	2.6834	2.9177	58	1.4294	1.6019	2.4684	2.6407
30	1.2363	1.4672	2.6707	2.9016	59	1.4339	1.6051	2.4640	2.6350
31	1.2469	1.4746	2.6587	2.8864	60	1.4384	1.6082	2.4596	2.6294
32	1.2570	1.4817	2.6473	2.8720					

Source: Frieda S. Swed and C. Eisenhart, "Tables for testing randomness of grouping in a sequence of alternatives," *Annals of Mathematical Statistics,* Vol. XIV, March 1943, pp. 70–87. Reproduced by permission.

Index